JANE'S
WORLD COMBAT AIRCRAFT

JANE'S

WORLD COMBAT AIRCRAFT

Michael J. H. Taylor

JANE'S INFORMATION GROUP

Copyright © 1988 Michael J. H. Taylor

First published in the United Kingdom in 1988 by
Jane's Information Group
163 Brighton Road, Coulsdon, Surrey, CR3 2NX

Distributed in the Philippines and the USA and its dependencies by
Jane's Information Group Inc
1340 Braddock Place, Suite 300, PO Box 1436
Alexandria, Virginia 22313-2036

Typeset by Tameside Filmsetting Ltd.
Printed and bound in Great Britain by
Butler & Tanner Ltd, Frome and London

Contents

Introduction

When *Jane's All the World's Aircraft* first appeared nearly 80 years ago, its many near-blank pages attested to the fact that heavier-than-air flight was still very much in its infancy. But the gaps soon disappeared as aircraft manufacture began to expand spectacularly and *Jane's* came to be accepted as *the* aviation reference. Book and industry grew apace over the succeeding decades, so that today's *All the World's Aircraft* is a 1½-million-word behemoth retailing at more than £70. Such a price tag has until now meant that the wealth of facts in *Jane's* has been denied to the aviation book buyer in the street. *World Combat Aircraft* is the result of a decision to bring some of the information contained in the mighty *Jane's All the World's Aircraft* to the general reader at a price he/she can afford.

This new book offers the detail synonymous with *Jane's* but also goes one step further. While *All the World's Aircraft* has to confine itself mainly to those aircraft currently under development, in production or undergoing modification, *World Combat Aircraft* details every type of fighting aircraft which is in service in significant numbers or likely to be in the future, from the Hawker Hunter and early MiGs to the Mi-28 'Havoc' and Lockheed RF-19 stealth aircraft.

1

Argentina

FAMA
FÁBRICA ARGENTINA DE MATERIALES AEROSPACIALES

The original Fábrica Militar de Aviones (Military Aircraft Factory) came into operation on 10 October 1927 as a central organisation for aeronautical research and production in Argentina. Its name was changed to Instituto Aerotécnico in 1943 and then to Industrias Aeronáuticas y Mecánicas del Estado (IAME) in 1952. In 1957 it became a State enterprise under the title of Dirección Nacional de Fabricaciónes e Investigaciónes Aeronáuticas (DINFIA), but reverted to its original title in 1968 as a component of the Area de Material Córdoba (AMC) division of the Argentine Air Force. The new title FAMA, a consequence of the joint agreement with Brazil for co-development of the CBA-123 transport aircraft, was expected to come into effect in late 1987.

FAMA comprises two large divisions. The Instituto de Investigaciónes Aeronáuticas y Espacial (IIAE) is responsible for the design of aircraft, and the design, manufacture and testing of rockets, sounding equipment and other equipment. FAMA itself controls the aircraft manufacturing facilities (Grupo Fabricación) situated in Córdoba, as well as the Centro de Ensayos en Vuelo (Flight Test Centre), to which all aircraft produced in Argentina are sent for certification tests. The laboratories, factories and other aeronautical division buildings occupy a total covered area of approx 253,000 m² (2,723,265 sq ft); the Area de Material Córdoba employs more than 3,500 persons, of whom about 2,300 are in the Grupo Fabricación.

In current production is the nationally designed Pucará counter-insurgency aircraft.

FAMA IA 58 and IA 66 Pucará

This twin-turboprop light-attack aircraft, named after a type of stone fortress built by the early South American Indians, flew for the first time on 20 August 1969 with 674 kW (904 ehp) Garrett TPE331-U-303 turboprop engines. It was followed on 6 September 1970 by a second prototype, powered by 761 kW (1,022 ehp) Turboméca Astazou XVI G turboprops, which were adopted as standard for the initial production version.

Four versions of the Pucará have been built, as follows:

IA 58A. Initial (two-seat) production version, of which the first example (A-501) made its first flight on 8 November 1974. Total of 60 ordered originally for the Fuerza Aérea Argentina (FAA), which later ordered 48 more, partly to replace about 24 aircraft lost during the fighting in the South Atlantic in 1982. Deliveries to the FAA began in the Spring of 1976, and the last example was due to be completed in 1986. Currently in service with the FAA's III Brigada Aérea at Reconquista (2° and 3° Escuadrons) and the IX Brigada (4° Escuadron) at Comodoro Rivadavia. Some early production aircraft have been converted to single-seat configuration, with extra fuselage fuel tank in place of rear seat; further similar conversions may be planned. Six IA 58As were delivered to the Fuerza Aérea Uruguaya, and a further 40 were offered for export in 1986.

IA 58B. As early IA 58A, but with more powerful built-in armament, in a deeper front fuselage, and updated avionics.

FAMA IA 58A Pucará combat aircraft of the Argentine Air Force.

The single-seat FAMA IA 58C Pucará Charlie, with additional nose gun and external ordnance.

Prototype only (AX-05), which first flew on 15 May 1979. Forty ordered for FAA in 1980, but cancelled in favour of continued production of IA 58A.

IA 58C Pucará Charlie. First details of this single-seat Pucará variant, which was flown for the first time on 30 December 1985, became available in the Autumn of 1984. Its development, based on experience gained during the Falklands/Malvinas campaign of 1982, is intended to extend its attack capability against such targets as helicopters and surface vessels, and to enable it also to carry out a low-level air-defence role.

Unlike the single-seat IA 58A conversions, it is the front cockpit which is deleted in the IA 58C. This enables the existing built-in armament of two 20 mm and four 7.62 mm guns to be supplemented by a 30 mm DEFA 553 cannon in the upper nose with, initially, 270 rounds of ammunition. Externally, provision is made to carry two CITEFA Martin Pescador (Kingfisher) supersonic tactical missiles underwing, or a pair of Matra R.550 Magic air-to-air missiles for self-defence underwing or on two additional Alkan launchers mounted under the tips of strengthened outer wings.

The remaining cockpit has been enlarged, and given added armour protection against hits from light-calibre weapons. Improvements and additions to the avionics include an Omega/VLF system with radar altimeter for nap-of-the-earth navigation; a radar warning receiver; new HF and VHF-FM/AM communications; HSI; and ADI with gyro platform. Options include IFF, a Saab RGS-2 or similar lead-computing predictor sight, head-up display, and internal or pod mounted flares, chaff or jamming equipment. Provision is made for wing and tail unit anti-icing.

The IA 58C retains the same powerplant as the A version, except that the Astazou XVIG engines now have self-start capability and modified nozzles to reduce their infra-red signature. Maximum take-off and landing weights remain unchanged. Cruising speed at sea level (presumably at max T-O weight) is estimated at 250 knots (463 km/h; 288 mph), and payload/range capability is expected to be increased by up to 20 per cent.

Fixed armament is the same as for the IA 58A, plus a nose-mounted 30 mm DEFA 553 cannon with 270 rds. It has two underwing pylon attachments, plus air-to-air missile launchers under each wingtip. Typical weapon combinations can include twelve 125 kg bombs or 250 lb napalm containers; six 125 kg bombs with eight 5 in rockets; three 500 kg retarded bombs; three 220 kg napalm tanks with four launchers each containing forty 74 mm grenades; seven launchers each for nineteen 2.75 in rockets; four such launchers with a 300 litre drop-tank, or three launchers with two 300 litre drop-tanks; three such rocket launchers with a pair of Matra Magic air-to-air missiles; two Magics and a 1,100 litre drop-tank; or two 300 litre drop-tanks plus an ECM pod linked automatically with the radar warning receiver.

Some Argentine Air Force officials have been quoted as saying that the FAA plans to retrofit its IA 58As to IA 58C standard, but whether this will be so, whether a production order will be placed for new-build aircraft, or whether re-equipment will involve a mixture of both appears still to be undecided. As a result, Pucará Charlie could well remain a prototype. The FAMA's Grupo Fabricación is said to be capable of producing up to three and a half Pucarás per month.

IA 66. Prototype (AX-06), first flown in late 1980 with 746 kW (1,000 shp) Garrett TPE331-11-601W turboprops. Further development unlikely following development of IA 58C.

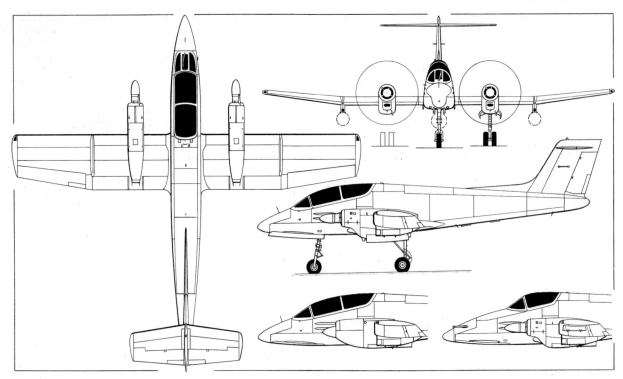

FAMA IA 58A Pucará. Scrap views: IA 66 (left), IA 58C (right). *(Pilot Press)*

The following description applies to the IA 58A in its final production form:

TYPE: Twin-turboprop close-support, reconnaissance and counter-insurgency aircraft.

WINGS: Cantilever low-wing monoplane. Wing section NACA 62_2A215 at root, NACA 64_1A212 at tip. Dihedral 7° on outer panels. Incidence 2°. No sweepback. Electrically controlled hydraulically actuated trailing-edge slotted flaps, inboard and outboard of each engine nacelle. Modified Frise ailerons. No slats. Balance tab in starboard aileron, electrically operated trim tab in port aileron.

FUSELAGE: Conventional semi-monocoque fail-safe structure, built in forward, central and rear main sections. Upper part of nosecone opens upward for access to avionics and equipment.

TAIL UNIT: Cantilever semi-monocoque structure. Fixed-incidence tailplane and elevators mounted near top of fin. Curved dorsal fin. Rudder and elevators, each fitted with electrically operated inset trim tab.

LANDING GEAR: Hydraulically retractable tricycle type, with emergency mechanical backup. All units retract forward, steerable nose unit (33° left and right) into fuselage, main units into engine nacelles. Single Dunlop wheel on nose unit, twin wheels on main units, all with Dunlop Type III tubeless tyres size 7.50-10. Dunlop Hydraulic disc brakes on mainwheels only. Parking and emergency brake. No anti-skid units. Landing gear suitable for grass strip operation. Provision for 80 m (262 ft) take-off run using three JATO bottles attached to underfuselage pylon.

POWERPLANT: Two 729 kW (978 shp) Turboméca Astazou XVIG turboprop engines, each driving a Ratier-Forest 23LF-379 three-blade variable-pitch fully-feathering metal propeller with spinner. Water injection system. Electric de-icing of engine air intakes. Fuel in two AMC (Area de Material Córdoba) fuselage tanks (combined capacity 772 litres; 204 US gallons; 170 Imp gallons) and one AMC self-sealing tank in each wing (combined capacity 508 litres; 134 US gallons; 111 Imp gallons). Overall usable internal capacity 1,280 litres (338 US gallons; 281 Imp gallons). Gravity refuelling point for all tanks on top of fuselage aft of cockpit. Fuel system includes two accumulator tanks, permitting up to 30 s of inverted flight. A long-range auxiliary tank, usable capacity 318 or 1,100 litres (84–291 US gallon; 70 or 242 Imp gallon) can be attached to the fuselage centreline pylon, and a 318 litre (84 US gallon; 70 Imp gallon) auxiliary tank on each underwing pylon. Possible external fuel loads are therefore 318, 636, 954, 1,100 or 1,736 litres (84, 168, 252, 291 or 459 US gallons; 70, 140, 210, 242 or 382 Imp gallons); max internal and external usable fuel capacity is 3,016 litres (797 US gallons; 663 Imp gallons).

ACCOMMODATION: Pilot and co-pilot in tandem on Martin-Baker AP06A zero/zero ejection seats beneath single AMC moulded Plexiglas canopy which is hinged at rear and opens upward. Rear (co-pilot) seat elevated 25 cm (10 in) above front seat. Rearview mirror for each crew member. Teleflex heated and bullet-proof windscreen, with wiper. Armour plating in cockpit floor, resistant to 7.62 mm ground fire from 150 m (500 ft). Dual controls and blind-flying instrumentation standard.

AVIONICS AND EQUIPMENT: Standard avionics include Delta VOR/LOR/ILS, Smiths magnetic compass, Sperry gyro compass and dual artificial horizons, Bendix DFA-73A-1 ADF receiver, Bendix RTA-42A VHF com transceiver, SunAir RE-800 HF com transceiver, Bendix RNA-34 VOR/LOC/glideslope receiver, SunAir ACU-810 HF coupler/amplifier, Delta audio amplifier, and intercom. Optional avionics include ECM, weather radar, IFF, inertial navigation system, Machmeter, and VHF-FM tactical communications system. Standard equipment includes dual Pioneer airspeed and vertical speed indicators, dual Kollsman altimeters, dual Air Precision turn and bank indicators, dual Bendix accelerometers, dual attitude indicators (plus standby), dual bearing/distance/heading indicators, flap position indicator, dual landing gear position indicators, Air Precision chronometer, dual Jaeger engine rpm and AMC torque indicators, dual Brion Leroux propeller pitch indicators, dual Jaeger fuel and oil temperature indicators, dual Faure Herman fuel flow and AMC fuel quantity indicators, heated pitot intake, three pitot static ports, GE landing light in leading edge of each underwing pylon, AMC taxying light on nosewheel strut, fin-tip anti-collision light, wingtip navigation lights, instrument panel lights and warning lights.

ARMAMENT: Two 20 mm Hispano DCA-804 cannon, each with 270 rds, in underside of forward fuselage; and four 7.62 mm FN-Browning M2-30 machine-guns, each with 900 rds, in sides of fuselage abreast of cockpit. Alkan 115E ejector pylon on centreline beneath fuselage, capacity 1,000 kg (2,205 lb); Alkan 105E pylon, capacity 500 kg (1,102 lb), beneath each wing outboard of engine nacelle. Max external stores load with full internal fuel is 1,500 kg (3,307 lb), including gun and rocket pods, bombs, cluster bombs, incendiaries, mines, torpedoes, air-to-surface missiles, camera pod(s) or auxiliary fuel tank(s). Max external weapons load when carrying drop tanks on the fuselage or wing stations is 1,000 kg (2,205 lb). Typical loads can include twelve 125 kg bombs; seven launchers each with nineteen 2.75 in rockets; a 12.7, 20 or 30 mm gun pod and two 318 litre drop tanks; six 125 kg bombs and sixteen 5 in rockets; six launchers each with forty 74 mm cartridges, plus onboard ECM; twelve 250 lb napalm bombs; three 500 kg delayed-action bombs; or two twin-7.62 mm machine-gun pods, plus three launchers each containing nineteen 2.75 in rockets. SFOM 83A3 reflector sight permits weapon release at any desired firing angle; optional Bendix AWE-1 programmer allows release in step or ripple modes of single weapons, pairs or salvos.

DIMENSIONS, EXTERNAL:

Wing span	14.50 m (47 ft 6$\frac{7}{8}$ in)
Length overall	14.253 m (46 ft 9$\frac{1}{8}$ in)
Length of fuselage	13.675 m (44 ft 10$\frac{1}{2}$ in)
Fuselage: Max width	1.32 m (4 ft 4 in)
Max depth	1.95 m (6 ft 4$\frac{3}{4}$ in)
Height overall	5.362 m (17 ft 7$\frac{1}{8}$ in)
Wheel track (c/l of shock absorbers)	4.20 m (13 ft 9$\frac{1}{4}$ in)
Wheelbase	3.885 m (12 ft 9 in)
Propeller diameter	2.59 m (8 ft 6 in)

AREA:

Wings, gross	30.30 m² (326.1 sq ft)

WEIGHTS:

Weight empty, equipped	4,020 kg (8.862 lb)
Max fuel load: internal	1,000 kg (2,205 lb)
external	1,359 kg (2,997 lb)
Max external stores load	1,500 kg (3,307 lb)
Max T-O weight	6,800 kg (14,991 lb)

PERFORMANCE (at AUW of 5,500 kg; 12,125 lb except where indicated):

Max critical Mach number at max T-O weight	0.77
Never-exceed speed at max T-O weight	Mach 0.63 (405 knots; 750 km/h; 466 mph)
Max level speed at 3,000 m (9,840 ft)	270 knots (500 km/h; 310 mph)
Max cruising speed at 6,000 m (19,680 ft)	259 knots (480 km/h; 298 mph)
Econ cruising speed	232 knots (430 km/h; 267 mph)

Stalling speed, flaps and landing gear down, AUW of 4,790 kg (10,560 lb)	78 knots (143 km/h; 89 mph)
Max rate of climb at S/L	1,080 m (3,543 ft)/min
Service ceiling	10,000 m (32,800 ft)
Min ground turning radius	6.50 m (21 ft 4 in)
T-O run	300 m (985 ft)
T-O to 15 m (50 ft)	705 m (2,313 ft)
Landing from 15 m (50 ft), landing weight of 5,100 kg (11,243 lb)	603 m (1,978 ft)
Landing run, landing weight as above	200 m (656 ft)

Attack radius at T-O weight of 6,500 kg (14,330 lb), 10% reserves of initial fuel:

with 1,500 kg (3,307 lb) of external weapons:

lo-lo-lo	121 nm (225 km; 140 miles)
lo-lo-lo	175 nm (325 km; 202 miles)
hi-lo-hi	189 nm (350 km; 217 miles)

with 1,200 kg (2,645 lb) of external weapons:

lo-lo-lo	216 nm (400 km; 248 miles)
lo-lo-hi	310 nm (575 km; 357 miles)
hi-lo-hi	350 nm (650 km; 404 miles)

with 800 kg (1,764 lb) of ordnance and 450 litres (119 US gallons; 99 Imp gallons) of external fuel:

lo-lo-lo	310 nm (575 km; 357 miles)
lo-lo-hi	445 nm (825 km; 512 miles)
hi-lo-hi	526 nm (975 km; 606 miles)

Ferry range at 5,485 m (18,000 ft) with max internal and external fuel	2,002 nm (3,710 km; 2,305 miles)
g limits	+6/ −3

Brazil

Embraer
EMPRESA BRASILEIRA DE AERONÁUTICA SA

Embraer was created on 19 August 1969, and came into operation on 2 January 1970 to promote the development of the Brazilian aircraft industry. The Brazilian government owns 54.41% of the voting shares, 94.79% of the subscribed capital being held by private shareholders. Embraer has a workforce of 8,431 persons and a factory area of 293,000 m² (3,153,825 sq ft).

Embraer EMB-111

Brazilian Air Force designation: P-95

This land-based maritime surveillance aircraft, based on the EMB-110 Bandeirante twin-turboprop general-purpose transport, was designed to meet specifications issued by the Comando Costeiro, the Brazilian Air Force's Coastal Command, which has 10 in service with Nos 1 and 2 Squadrons of the 7° Grupo de Aviação based at Salvador, Bahia, and Florianopolis, Santa Catarina. The main external differences in this version are the large nose radome, housing search radar, and the addition of wingtip fuel tanks.

The first EMB-111 flew for the first time on 15 August 1977, and deliveries to the Brazilian Air Force began on 11 April 1978. A further ten were ordered for the Brazilian Air Force in December 1987.

Six were also delivered to the Chilean Navy in 1978–79. These aircraft have some mission equipment changes,

Embraer EMB-111 maritime surveillance aircraft of the Brazilian Air Force.

including full de-icing system, and passive ECM antennae under the nose and at the tail. One EMB-111 was delivered in August 1981 to the Gabonese Air Force.

Embraer EMB-111. *(Pilot Press)*

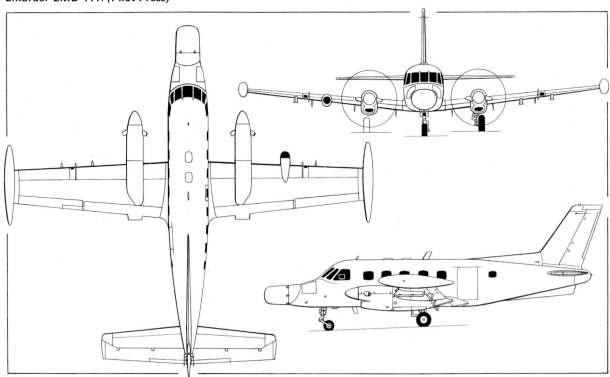

6

TYPE: Twin-turboprop maritime surveillance aircraft.

WINGS: Cantilever low-wing monoplane. Wing section NACA 23016 (modified) at root, NACA 23012 (modified) at tip. Sweepback 0° 19' 48" at quarter chord. Dihedral 7° at 28 per cent chord. Incidence 3°. Compared with EMB-110P2, has reinforced wing leading edges and is fitted with tip tanks. Statically balanced Frise ailerons and double-slotted flaps. Trim tab in port aileron. De-icing system optional.

FUSELAGE: Semi-monocoque structure. Nose radome. Two upward hinged doors, one on each side of nose, provide access to avionics.

TAIL UNIT: Cantilever structure, with sweptback vertical surfaces and 10° tailplane dihedral. Glassfibre dorsal fin. Ventral fin. Trim tabs in rudder and port elevator; mass balance on elevator tab and duplicated control rods to elevator. De-icing system optional.

LANDING GEAR: Hydraulically retractable tricycle type, with single wheel on each unit. Mainwheel tyre size 670 × 270-12 (10 ply rating). Steerable, forward retracting nosewheel unit has tyre size 6.50-8.

POWERPLANT: Two 559 kW (750 shp) Pratt & Whitney Canada PT6A-34 turboprop engines, each driving a Hartzell three-blade reversible-pitch propeller with spinner. Four integral fuel tanks in wings (total capacity 1,914 litres; 506 US gallons; 421 Imp gallons), and two permanent wingtip tanks (total capacity 636 litres; 168 US gallons; 140 Imp gallons). Overall total fuel capacity 2,550 litres (674 US gallons; 561 Imp gallons), of which 2,454 litres (648 US gallons; 540 Imp gallons) are usable.

ACCOMMODATION: Pilot and co-pilot side by side on flight deck. Main cabin can accommodate search radar/radio operator, ECM operator, one or two observers, and second radar or ECM operator. Port side door at rear, for crew and cargo, opens inwards and can be used for airdrop of paratroops and survival equipment. Galley and toilet in main cabin.

AVIONICS AND EQUIPMENT: One Collins 618T-3B or 718U-5 AM/SSB/CW transceiver, two Collins 618M-3 VHF transceivers, one Collins AN/ARC-159 UHF transceiver, Collins audio interphone, two Sperry C-14 gyromagnetic compasses, two Bendix DFA-74A or Collins DF-206 ADF receivers, two Collins VIR-30A or VIR-31A VOR/ILS/marker beacon receivers, one Collins AN/APX-92 IFF transponder, one Collins DF-301E VHF/DF or UHF/DF, one Collins DME-40 DME, one Bendix ALA-51 or Collins ALT-50 radio altimeter, one Litton LN-33 inertial navigation system, Thomson-CSF passive ECM, and one AIL AN/APS-128 (SPAR-1) sea patrol radar. Optional avionics include Bendix M4-D autopilot and ONS-25 Omega, single or dual Sperry STARS IVB or IVC flight directors, entertainment radio, tape deck, PA system, and complete de-icing and anti-icing system.

ARMAMENT AND OPERATIONAL EQUIPMENT: Four under-wing pylons for eight 5 in HVAR air-to-surface rockets (two per pylon), or four launchers each with seven 2.75 in FFAR rockets; or three stores pylons, plus a 50 million candlepower searchlight on the starboard wing leading edge. For target marking, six Brazilian built Mk 6 smoke grenades are carried, as well as a Motorola SST-121 transponder. Flares of 200,000 candlepower also available for illumination of targets at night. Ventral chute for smoke marker buoys, high-intensity flares or chaff dispensing. Provision for 1.4 kW loudhailer system.

DIMENSIONS, EXTERNAL:

Wing span over tip tanks	15.95 m (52 ft 4 in)
Length overall	14.91 m (48 ft 11 in)
Length of fuselage	14.38 m (47 ft 2¼ in)
Height overall	4.91 m (16 ft 1¼ in)
Wheelbase	4.26 m (13 ft 11¾ in)

AREA:

Wings, gross	29.10 m² (313.23 sq ft)

WEIGHTS:

Weight empty, equipped	3,900 kg (8,598 lb)
Max T-O weight	7,000 kg (15,432 lb)

PERFORMANCE (at max T-O weight, ISA + 15°C, except where indicated):

Max cruising speed at 3,050 m (10,000 ft)	194 knots (360 km/h; 223 mph)
Econ cruising speed at 3,050 m (10,000 ft)	187 knots (347 km/h; 215 mph)
Stalling speed at max landing weight	73 knots (135 km/h; 84 mph) CAS
Max rate of climb at S/L	362 m (1,190 ft)/min
Time to 3,050 m (10,000 ft)	13 min
Time to 4,575 m (15,000 ft)	28 min
Service ceiling, at AUW of 5,300 kg (11,684 lb)	7,770 m (25,500 ft)
T-O run	650 m (2,135 ft)
T-O to 15 m (50 ft)	1,050 m (3,445 ft)
Landing from 15 m (50 ft), short-field technique	640 m (2,100 ft)
Landing run, short-field technique	450 m (1,475 ft)
Min ground turning radius	12.80 m (42 ft 0 in)
Range at 3,050 m (10,000 ft), max fuel, 45 min reserves	1,590 nm (2,945 km; 1,830 miles)

Chile

Cardoen
INDUSTRIAS CARDOEN LTDA

Cardoen Attack Helicopter

Reports that Chile was developing an armed helicopter began to circulate in 1984, and at the FIDA air show at El Bosque in March 1986 Cardoen displayed a mockup of such an aircraft: a twin-turboshaft helicopter apparently based on the MBB BO 105.

The most recent reports now suggest that the attack helicopter will be based on the Bell Model 206 helicopter. A metal mockup of this AH was due to be completed in the Autumn of 1987, with a flying prototype available about a year later.

Artist's impression of the proposed Cardoen attack helicopter. *(Jane's/Mike Keep)*

China (PEOPLE'S REPUBLIC)

National Aircraft Factories

Shenyang, Liaoning Province; Xian (Sian), Shaanxi (Shensi) Province; Harbin, Heilongjiang (Heilungkiang) Province; Shanghai Municipality; Beijing (Peking) Municipality; Nanchang, Jiangxi (Kiangsi) Province; Hanzhong (Hanchung), Shaanxi Province; Tianjin (Tientsin) Municipality; Shijiazhuang (Shihchiachuang), Hebei (Hopei) Province; Chengdu, Sichuan Province; and elsewhere.

The longest established of the Chinese national aircraft factories are those at Shenyang and Harbin. The latter had its origin in the plant of the Manshu Aeroplane Manufacturing Company, one of several aircraft and aero engine manufacturing facilities established in Manchukuo (Manchuria) by the Japanese invaders in 1938. A large flying training school was established by the Japanese at Shenyang (then known as Mukden) in 1940. After the Communist regime came to power in mainland China in 1949 the Manchurian factories were re-established and re-equipped with Soviet assistance. Shenyang and Harbin are still major centres of Chinese aircraft and aero engine production, under the jurisdiction of the Ministry of Aviation Industry. There are design and development centres at Shenyang, Beijing, Harbin and elsewhere. Total workforce of the Chinese aerospace industry was estimated at 350,000 in 1984, although several aircraft factories are engaged also in manufacturing non-aerospace products. Xian, Harbin and other Chinese factories also carry out subcontract work on the ATR 42, BAe 146 (landing gear doors), Boeing 737-300 (fins and cabin doors), McDonnell Douglas MD-80 (landing gear doors) and Shorts 360 (wing centre-sections and cabin doors).

First jet aircraft built in China were the single-seat MiG-15*bis* and two-seat MiG-15UTI. These were not given Chinese designations. They were followed by the MiG-17F (Chinese designation J-5) and MiG-17PF (J-5 Jia or J-5A). A 'UTI' tandem two-seat conversion of the J-5, known as the JJ-5, was developed by the Chinese. These types were followed by Soviet and Chinese versions of the MiG-19 (J-6), and a more recent fighter designated J-8 is being developed at Shenyang.

Harbin is responsible for the Soviet Ilyushin Il-28 jet bomber (Chinese H-5), and the nationally designed SH-5 patrol and anti-submarine bomber amphibian. It is also the chief centre for helicopter production.

Aircraft built at Xian (Sian) include the Soviet Tupolev Tu-16 bomber (Chinese designation H-6), and Chinese versions of the MiG-21 (J-7). Xian also produces Wopen-8 (RD-3M) jet engines for the Tu-16/H-6.

Nanchang, previously responsible for licence production of the Yak-18A (Chinese designation CJ-5), is currently manufacturing a Chinese attack aircraft (the Q-5) developed from the J-6/MiG-19. Nanchang has also been suggested as the likely production centre for the Changhe Z-8 helicopter.

Output of older fighters and bombers is now diminishing, with increasing emphasis being placed on the development of new aircraft making use of China's growing technological capability. The reduction of 1 million personnel in China's armed forces manpower is intended to make more funds available during the seventh Five-Year Plan (1986–90) for the purchase of modern weapons and technology, while at the same time shifting emphasis in the aviation industry towards a target of a 60–40 per cent bias in favour of civil aircraft production. As a further step in this direction, increased effort is being made to export Chinese-built aircraft (including the F-7M and A-5C) through the newly established, Hong Kong based Aircraft Technology Ltd, in which the Chinese import/export organisation CATIC is a partner with Lucas Aerospace of the UK (40% each) and a Hong Kong businessman (20%).

The Chinese language is gradually being simplified to a new Latinised or Westernised form of spelling known as Pinyin. Under this system, the transliterated spellings with which Western readers have been familiar for years have, in many cases, undergone some change. For example, Peking is written as Beijing, which conforms more closely with the Chinese pronunciation. Place names in this section are shown first in the current Pinyin spelling, followed where applicable by the 'old' spelling.

On the military side of priority programmes for the period 1986–90, design studies have been initiated at Xian for a 1990s twin-engined supersonic bomber (H-7?), and this factory is also developing another new tandem two-seat military aircraft of which a mockup or prototype was under construction in mid-1985. The latter may be the reported Q-6 attack aircraft, said to be equipped with a 30 mm anti-tank gun system, or (perhaps less likely) a twin-turbofan advanced trainer (CJ-8?). (Designation CJ-7 is believed to apply to a new turboprop trainer programme.) Details of new fighter programmes are much more speculative. Reports continue to persist, without supporting evidence, of a delta-winged J-10 and swept (or swing) winged J-12 under development, with designation 'gaps' explained by a fighter version of 'Fantan-A' (J-9 'Fantan-B'), and possible Chinese production of the MiG-23 (as J-11). While all of these would be logical and credible areas of present/future activity, positive evidence of their factual existence is still awaited. However, China's Aviation Minister did confirm in 1986 that a new type of fighter would be developed during the seventh Five-Year Plan.

The Air Force of the People's Liberation Army has an operational home defence fighter force of about 4,000 J-5s, J-6s and J-7s, and a tactical air force of more than 1,000 J-5s, H-5s and Q-5s. The PLA Air Force currently deploys a medium-bomber force of about 120 Tu-16/H-6s, which are nuclear capable. More than 100 CSS-1 (Dongfeng 2) MRBMs and CSS-2 and CSS-3 (Dongfeng 3 and 4) IRBMs are also deployed in a mobile strategic role, supplemented by a few CSS-4 (Dongfeng 5) KBMs ICBMs able to deliver a 5 mT warhead over a range of 7,000 nm (13,000 km; 8,075 miles).

Changhe
CHANGHE AIRCRAFT MANUFACTURING CORPORATION

Changhe Z-8

Chinese name: Zhishengji-8 (Vertical take-off aircraft 8) or Zhi-8

Chinese sources recently confirmed the existence of this 13,000 kg (28,660 lb) helicopter, which is based on the Aérospatiale SA 321JA Super Frelon and flew for the first time on 11 December 1985. It was developed jointly by the Changhe Aircraft Manufacturing Corporation and the China Helicopter Research and Design Bureau, both located at Jingdezhen in Jiangxi Province. It is planned to complete a batch of ten Zhi-8s by 1990.

First prototype of the Changhe Zhi-8 Chinese version of the Aérospatiale Super Frelon.

Harbin
HARBIN AIRCRAFT MANUFACTURING CORPORATION

Ilyushin Il-28 and Harbin H-5

NATO reporting names: Beagle (Il-28/H-5) and Mascot (Il-28U/HJ-5)
Chinese name: Hongzhaji-5 (Bomber aircraft 5) or Hong-5

Designed in the USSR by the Ilyushin bureau, the Il-28 was developed to meet a 1946 requirement for which Sukhoi Su-10 and various Tupolev prototypes were also built. The clear leader among the competing designs was the Il-28, which was given a high development priority following a personal order from the Soviet leader, Josef Stalin, in the Spring of 1947.

Three Il-28 prototypes were completed, the first of these making its initial flight on 8 August 1948, powered by two 22.3 kN (5,004 lb st) RD-45 centrifugal-flow turbojet engines, a Soviet derivative of the Rolls-Royce Nene. State acceptance trials were completed in the Spring of 1949, and, again under direct order from Stalin, 25 Il-28s were available in time to take part in the 1950 May Day flypast. Most or all of these are believed to have been pre-production aircraft, possibly powered by RD-45FA engines, an improved version of the RD-45 rated at 26.9 kN (6,040 lb st).

V-VS (Soviet tactical aviation) units began working-up with the Il-28 in the late Summer of 1950, although major deliveries did not begin until the following year. From then

Egyptian Air Force Ilyushin Il-28, currently used for maritime reconnaissance. (Denis Hughes)

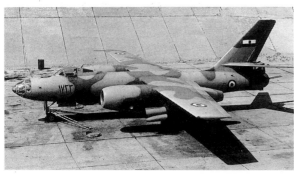

until about 1960, several thousand Il-28s were built, in a number of Soviet factories and also for a time in Czechoslovakia, where the aircraft was known by the Czechoslovak designation B-228. Production aircraft have VK-1A engines, an improved development of the RD-45 produced by the Klimov design bureau.

About 500 Il-28s were supplied to other Communist and Socialist states, including Afghanistan, Algeria, Bulgaria, Cuba, Czechoslovakia, Egypt, Finland, Germany (Democratic Republic), Hungary, Indonesia, Korea (People's Republic), Nigeria, Poland, Romania, Somalia, South Yemen, Syria, North Viet-Nam and Yemen Arab Republic. A similar number was supplied to the People's Republic of China, where the Il-28 entered production in 1966 after the political break with the Soviet Union, in H-5 form. Production at Harbin ended about 1982; about 500 H-5s are believed still to equip the air force of the People's Liberation Army, with about 130 more in service with the PLA Navy. Some may be configured for nuclear weapon delivery.

Soviet versions were:

Il-28. Standard three-seat tactical light bomber. Detailed description applies to this version except where indicated.

Il-28U (Uchebny: instruction). Two-seat operational and pilot training version, which appeared in 1951. NATO reporting name 'Mascot'. Armament and ventral ground-mapping radar fairing deleted; 'solid' nose; second, 'stepped' cockpit (with full dual controls) ahead of and below pilot's cockpit. Two or three supplied to each operational Il-28 unit.

Il-20. 'Demilitarised' version, with armament and some military equipment deleted, used by Aeroflot in the mid-1950s for the high-speed transportation of newspaper matrices. Cargo loaded via navigator's hatch in forward fuselage.

Il-28R (Razvedchik: reconnaissance). Three-seat tactical reconnaissance version. Wingtip auxiliary fuel tanks standard; weapons bay occupied by alternative packs containing cameras or electronic sensors. Some examples fitted with second radome under centre of fuselage.

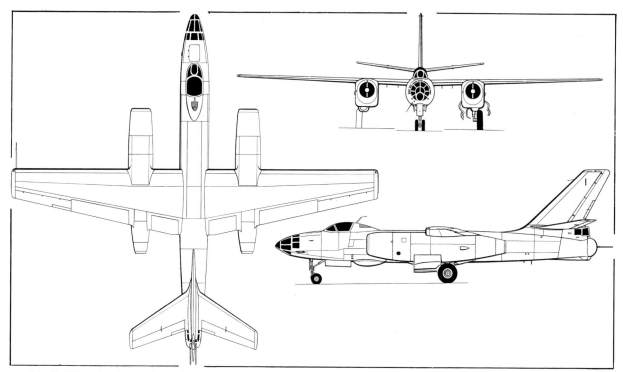

Harbin H-5/Ilyushin Il-28. *(Pilot Press)*

Il-28T (Torpedonosets: torpedo carrier). Three-seat torpedo-bomber version for AV-MF (Soviet Naval Aviation), contemporary with Il-28R. Modified avionics; one large or two smaller torpedoes, or mines or depth charges, in weapons bay.

In addition to the above, many Il-28s when obsolescent in their original roles were converted for target towing (with hook attachment under tailcone), meteorological reconnaissance, ECM and other electronic duties.

Chinese versions were:

H-5 (Hongzhaji-5 or Hong-5). Standard three-seat tactical light bomber, similar to basic Il-28. Some early examples were exported to Albania. Production also included torpedo-bomber version similar to Soviet Il-28T.

HJ-5 (Hongzhaji Jiaolianji-5 or Hongjiao-5). Two-seat operational and pilot training version, similar to Soviet Il-28U (NATO reporting name 'Mascot'). Armament and ventral ground mapping radar fairing deleted; 'solid' nose; second, 'stepped' cockpit (with full dual controls) ahead of and below pilot's cockpit. Two or three supplied to each operational H-5 unit.

HZ-5 (Hongzhaji Zhenchaji-5 or Hongzhen-5). Three-seat tactical reconnaissance version, similar to Soviet Il-28R. Wingtip auxiliary fuel tanks standard; weapons bay occupied by alternative packs containing cameras or electronic sensors.

In 1985 China ordered modified Rushton low level towed targets from the FR Group in the UK. These are for use with H-5s of the PLA Navy, to simulate sea-skimming anti-ship missiles.

Current operators of the Il-28 and/or H-5 series are Afghanistan, China, Egypt, North Korea, Poland (Navy) and Romania.

The description which follows applies primarily to the standard Il-28 bomber, but is modified where possible to apply to other models, including the Chinese-built H-5:

TYPE: Three-seat tactical light bomber.

WINGS: Cantilever shoulder-wing monoplane, with non-swept leading edges and tapered trailing edges. TsAGI SR-5S wing section, with max thickness/chord ratio of 12%. Incidence 0° 38'. Dihedral 3° from roots. Hydraulically-actuated trailing-edge slotted flaps, inboard and outboard of each engine nacelle, with settings of 0°, 20° and 50°. Plain ailerons, which deflect 15° up and 20° down. Trim tab in each aileron. Hot-air de-icing of leading edges.

FUSELAGE: Conventional semi-monocoque structure, of circular cross-section. Glazed nose, with optically-flat bomb-aiming panel. 'Solid' fairing aft of pilot's cockpit incorporates a dielectric panel. Single ventral radome standard, forward of weapons bay; some aircraft have two such radomes, others none. Compartment in rear of fuselage for radio, batteries, air-conditioning and other equipment.

TAIL UNIT: All-swept cruciform structure. Fin, on root platform built integrally with fuselage, has leading-edge sweep of 45°. Fixed-incidence tailplane has 33° sweepback on leading edges and 7° dihedral. Trim tabs in rudder and each elevator. Hot-air de-icing of fin and tailplane leading edges; de-icing air vents in fin and tailplane tips.

LANDING GEAR: Hydraulically-actuated retractable tricycle type, with pneumatic emergency extension. Twin-wheel nose unit, with shimmy damper, retracts rearward into fuselage. Single-wheel main units retract forward and upward into engine nacelles, the legs rotating through 90° during retraction to enable the wheels to lie flat behind doors which form a bulge under the nacelle. Mainwheel tyres size 1,150 × 355 mm; nosewheel tyres size 600 × 180 mm.

11

POWERPLANT: Two Klimov VK-1A non-afterburning turbojet engines, each rated at 26.5 kN (5,952 lb st) and mounted in an underwing pod. Fuel in five flexible fuselage tanks (three foward and two aft of weapons bay), integral wing tanks, and (standard on Il-28R, optional on other models) wingtip auxiliary tanks. Total fuel capacity, including tip-tanks, 7,908 litres (2,090 US gallons; 1,740 Imp gallons). Bifurcated intakes, each with central 'bullet' fairing to facilitate distribution of airflow. Provision for assisted take-off using JATO rocket under fuselage on each side.

ACCOMMODATION: Flight crew of three (instructor and pupil only in Il-28U), all in pressurised and airconditioned accommodation. Pilot on ejection seat in single 'fighter' type cockpit, under jettisonable canopy which opens sideways to starboard. Navigator/bomb-aimer, also on ejection seat, occupies a position forward, below and to starboard of pilot, access to which is via an upward-opening jettisonable hatch above the nose and offset to starboard. (In Il-28U, roof hatch of forward cockpit hinges sideways to starboard.) Access to radio operator/rear gunner's position is via a power-operated downward-opening hatch in underside of rear fuselage, which also serves as escape hatch for this member of the crew. Dual controls in Il-28U.

AVIONICS AND EQUIPMENT: HF and UHF radio (HF antenna on fairing aft of pilot's cockpit); radio compass; radio altimeter; IFF; PSB-N ground-mapping radar in underfuselage fairing forward of weapons bay; tail warning radar in fairing beneath tailcone; landing light in nosewheel leg door.

ARMAMENT AND OPERATIONAL EQUIPMENT: Two fixed, forward-firing Nudelman-Richter 23 mm NR-23 cannon (each with 100 rds) in lower forward fuselage, one each side of nosewheel bay; associated gyro gunsight in pilot's cockpit. Two similar guns, each with 225 rds, on Il-K6 ball-type movable mounting in tail turret. Internal weapons bay in mid-fuselage, with normal and max capacities of 1,000 kg (2,205 lb) and 3,000 kg (6,614 lb) respectively. Typical loads may include four 500 kg or eight 250 kg bombs or (Il-28T) one large or two smaller torpedoes, mines or depth charges. Some H-5s may be configured for nuclear weapon delivery. FAB-3000 primary bombsight is a modification of the US Norden M-9 of the Second World War. Provision in standard Il-28 for single AFA 33/20, 33/75-50 or 33/100 vertical camera, installed beneath rearmost forward-fuselage fuel tank. Il-28R can carry from three to five cameras in the weapons bay, plus 12 to 18 flares or photoflash bombs.

DIMENSIONS, EXTERNAL:			
Wing span (excl tip-tanks)	21.45 m (70 ft 4½ in)	at 8,000 m (26,250 ft)	473 knots (876 km/h; 544 mph)
Length of fuselage (excl tail guns)	17.65 m (57 ft 11 in)	at 10,000 m (32,800 ft)	461 knots (855 km/h; 531 mph)
Fuselage: Max diameter	1.80 m (5 ft 10¾ in)	at 12,000 m (39,370 ft)	434 knots (805 km/h; 500 mph)
Height overall	6.70 m (21 ft 11¾ in)	Typical cruising speed	415 knots (770 km/h; 478 mph)
Wheel track	7.40 m (24 ft 3½ in)	Rate of climb:	
Wheelbase	approx 8.10 m (26 ft 7 in)	max, at S/L	900 m (2,952 ft)/min
AREA:		at 5,000 m (16,400 ft)	630 m (2,067 ft)/min
Wings, gross	60.80 m² (654.5 sq ft)	at 8,000 m (26,250 ft)	420 m (1,378 ft)/min
WEIGHTS:		at 12,000 m (39,370 ft)	72 m (236 ft)/min
Weight empty, equipped	12,890 kg (28,417 lb)	Time to 5,000 m (16,400 ft)	6 min 30 s
Fuel load: normal	3,800 kg (8,377 lb)	Time to 10,000 m (32,800 ft)	18 min 0 s
max (incl 200 kg; 441 lb in tip-tanks)		Service ceiling	12,300 m (40,350 ft)
	6,600 kg (14,550 lb)	T-O run: at normal T-O weight	875 m (2,870 ft)
Internal weapon load: normal	1,000 kg (2,205 lb)	at max T-O weight	1,150 m (3,773 ft)
max	3,000 kg (6,614 lb)	Landing run at landing weight of	
Normal T-O weight	18,400 kg (40,565 lb)	14,690 kg (32,385 lb)	1,170 m (3,838 ft)
Max T-O weight	21,200 kg (46,738 lb)	Range with max fuel, at max T-O weight:	
PERFORMANCE (at normal T-O weight except where indicated):		at 410 knots (760 km/h; 472 mph) at 1,000 m	
Max level speed:		(3,280 ft)	612 nm (1,135 km; 705 miles)
at S/L	432 knots (800 km/h; 497 mph)	at 415 knots (770 km/h; 478 mph) at 10,000 m	
at 1,750 m (5,740 ft)	473 knots (876 km/h; 544 mph)	(32,800 ft)	1,176 nm (2,180 km; 1,355 miles)
at 4,500 m (14,760 ft)	487 knots (902 km/h; 560 mph)	at 232 knots (430 km/h; 267 mph) at 10,000 m	
		(32,800 ft)	1,295 nm (2,400 km; 1,490 miles)

Harbin SH-5

Chinese name: Shuishang Hongzhaji 5 (Maritime bomber 5) or Shuihong-5
Westernised designation: PS-5

The SH-5 was designed by the Seaplane Research and Design Bureau (No. 605) of the Ministry of Aviation Industry in Jingmen City, Hubei Province, but its development has been somewhat protracted. Design work began in 1969, the first prototype was rolled out in 1971, and the first flight was made on 3 April 1976. It is believed that three prototypes were completed, production not starting until about 1984.

The *Liberation Army Daily* reported on 3 September 1986 that a new flying-boat had entered service with the naval air force of the PLA, following a demonstration to Premier

Zhao Zhiyang on 30 August. At least four were then in service with a senior seaplane unit at Qingdao naval air station, and by Autumn 1987 the SH-5 was operational also at Tuandao naval air base in Shandong. It is a very large aircraft, comparable in size to Japan's Shin Meiwa US-1A.

The Chinese are reportedly seeking an ASW and avionics upgrade for the SH-5, possibly similar to that now under way for the Dassault-Breguet Atlantique 2.

TYPE: Maritime patrol and anti-submarine bomber, surveillance, SAR and transport amphibian.

WINGS: All-metal cantilever high-wing monoplane. Anhedral outboard of outer engine nacelles. Spoiler forward of each outer flap segment. Trim tab in each aileron.

Harbin SH-5 (PS-5) patrol and anti-submarine bomber amphibian, now in service with the Chinese Navy. *(CATIC)*

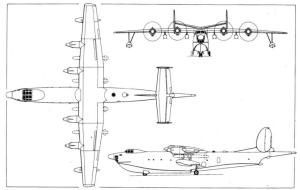

Harbin SH-5 (PS-5). *(Pilot Press)*

FUSELAGE: Unpressurised semi-monocoque hull, with high length/beam ratio and single-step planing bottom. Curved spray suppression strakes along sides of nose; spray suppression slots in lower sides, aft of inboard propeller plane. Small water rudder at rear of hull. 'Thimble' radome on nose; MAD in extended tail 'sting'.

TAIL UNIT: High mounted dihedral tailplane, with oval endplate fins and rudders, mounted on fairing above rear fuselage. Trim tabs in each rudder and each elevator.

LANDING GEAR: Retractable tricycle type, with single mainwheels and twin-wheel nose unit.

POWERPLANT: Four 2,349 kW (3,150 ehp) Shanghai WJ-5A-1 turboprops, each driving a four-blade propeller with spinner.

ACCOMMODATION: Standard eight-person crew includes a flight crew of five (pilot, co-pilot, navigator, flight engineer and radio operator), plus systems/equipment operators according to mission. Three freight compartments in front portion of hull. Mission crew cabin amidships, aft of which are two further compartments, one for communications and other electronic equipment and the rear one for specialised mission equipment. All compartments connected by corridor, with watertight doors aft of flight deck and between each compartment.

AVIONICS AND EQUIPMENT: Include inertial navigation system, air data computer, radio altimeter, and radio compass.

ARMAMENT AND OPERATIONAL EQUIPMENT: Doppler search radar in 'thimble' radome forward of nose transparencies. Magnetic anomaly detector (MAD) in extended tail 'sting'. Four underwing hardpoints for C-101 sea skimming supersonic anti-shipping or other missiles (one on each inboard pylon), lightweight torpedoes (up to three on each outer pylon), or other stores. Depth charges, mines, bombs, sonobuoys, SAR gear or other mission equipment and stores in rear of hull, as required.

DIMENSIONS, EXTERNAL:			
Wing span			36.00 m (118 ft 1¼ in)
Length overall			38.90 m (127 ft 7½ in)
Height overall			9.79 m (32 ft 1½ in)
Propeller diameter (estimated)			3.80 m (12 ft 5½ in)
AREA:			
Wings, gross			144.0 m² (1,550.0 sq ft)
WEIGHTS AND LOADINGS:			
Weight empty, equipped:			
SAR and transport		less than	25,000 kg (55,115 lb)
ASW			26,500 kg (58,422 lb)
Fuel load (max)			16,500 kg (36,376 lb)
Max internal weapons load			6,000 kg (13,228 lb)
Max payload (bulk cargo)			10,000 kg (22,045 lb)
Normal T-O weight			36,000 kg (79,366 lb)
Max T-O weight			45,000 kg (99,208 lb)
PERFORMANCE:			
Max level speed			299 knots (555 km/h; 345 mph)
Max cruising speed			243 knots (450 km/h; 280 mph)
Min patrol speed			124 knots (230 km/h; 143 mph)
T-O speed (water)			87 knots (160 km/h; 100 mph)
Service ceiling			7,000 m (22,965 ft)
T-O run (water)			548 m (1,798 ft)
Landing run (water)			240 m (788 ft)
Range with max fuel			2,563 nm (4,750 km; 2,951 miles)
Endurance (2 engines)			12 to 15 h

Nanchang
NANCHANG AIRCRAFT MANUFACTURING COMPANY

Nanchang Q-5

NATO reporting name: Fantan
Chinese name: Qiangjiji-5 (Attack aircraft 5) or Qiang-5

Design of this twin-jet attack aircraft, derived from the J-6/MiG-19 produced in China, began in 1958, and the first flight was made on 5 June 1965. Misidentified first as F-6bis and then as F-9 by Western reports, its correct designation was first indicated by Chinese officials in 1980. By that time the Q-5 had been in service for some ten years, production having peaked in about 1971 with nearly 100 being manufactured. By 1978 production had almost ended, apart from making good attrition losses, but it was stepped up in about 1981 to meet export orders from North Korea and Pakistan. This important Chinese aircraft continues in production, both for domestic use (**Q-5III**) and, as the **A-**

13

Nanchang A-5C of No 26 TAS, 36 TAW the Pakistan Air Force. *(Denis Hughes)*

5C, for export. Current manufacture is said to be by the Hongdu Aircraft Corporation.

The total number in Chinese service is thought to be in the region of 600, including up to 100 serving in an air-defence role with the air arm of the PLA Navy. The latter version has a small 'teardrop' fairing on the starboard side of the nose, probably housing a gun ranging radar of the 'High Fix' type.

Deliveries of an initial batch of 52 export **A-5B**s (= **Q-5II**) to the Pakistan Air Force began in February 1983 and have been completed. Further deliveries of A-5Cs are under way and may eventually provide a total of 140 A-5s to equip eight attack squadrons and an OCU. The first PAF units are No. 16 Squadron at Rafiqui Shorkot, No. 26 at Peshawar and No. 7 at Masroor.

The airframe of the Q-5 is based substantially on that of the J-6, but with a number of significant changes. The main wing structure is basically unchanged and retains the four (now 6) attachment points and large boundary-layer fences, but the underwing spoilers are omitted and the flaps have undergone some redesign. There are more extensive changes

to the centre and front of the fuselage, which is nearly 25 per cent longer than that of the J-6. The purpose of these changes in the original **Q-5I** was to make room for an internal weapons bay, but this area is no longer used for carrying weapons. Instead, fuselage fuel tank capacity has been increased by approx 70 per cent compared with that carried internally by the J-6. Cockpit canopy opening differs from that on the J-6, and the spine fairing behind it leads to a smaller dorsal fin and larger main fin. The 'solid' ogival nose provides sufficient room for an attack radar, although aircraft in service so far have metal skinned noses and clearly do not carry this equipment, which would also require relocation of the nose mounted pitot tube. It is, however, expected to be a feature of the improved **Q-5M/A-5M** now under study (see following entry).

The J-6 powerplant is retained, but with twin lateral intakes instead of the single divided nose intake of the Soviet design. Early production Q-5Is retained also the various louvres and airscoops associated with this installation, but many of these have disappeared from the cleaner looking Q-5

Nanchang Q-5III/A-5C. *(Pilot Press)*

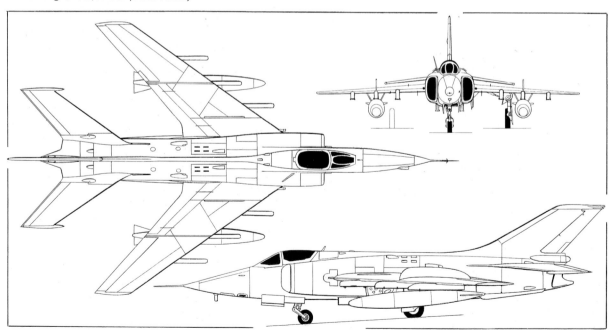

Pakistani Nanchang A-5C armed with Sidewinder missiles. *(Denis Hughes)*

III current production version, referred to in some reports as 'Fantan-C', which also has a relocated tail braking parachute installation similar to that on later production versions of the J-6. Like the J-6, the Q-5 has two wing mounted cannon (23 mm instead of 30 mm); these occupy the revised wing-root position outboard of the engine air intake trunks.

A design study has been carried out by the FR Group in the UK to equip the Q-5 as a receiver for in-flight refuelling, with a Xian H-6 bomber adapted to act as the tanker aircraft.

TYPE: Single-seat close air support and ground attack aircraft, with capability also for air-to-air combat.

WINGS: Cantilever mid-wing monoplane, of low aspect ratio, with 4° anhedral from roots. Sweepback at quarter-chord 52° 30′. Construction essentially similar to that of J-6/MiG-19, with three-point attachment to fuselage. Deep, full-chord boundary-layer fence on each upper surface at mid span. Inboard of each fence is a hydraulically actuated Gouge flap, the inner end of which is angled to give a trailing edge at right angles to side of fuselage. Hydraulically actuated internally balanced aileron outboard of each fence. Electrically operated inset trim tab at inboard end of each aileron.

FUSELAGE: Conventional structure, built in forward and rear portions which are detachable aft of wing trailing edge to provide access to engines. Air intake on each side of fuselage, abreast of cockpit; twin jetpipes side-by-side at rear. Top and bottom 'pen nib' fairings aft of nozzles. Centre fuselage is 'waisted' in accordance with area rule. Dorsal spine fairing between rear of cockpit and leading edge of fin. Forward hinged, hydraulically actuated door type airbrake under centre of fuselage, forward of bomb attachment points. Shallow ventral strake under each jetpipe.

TAIL UNIT: Cantilever structure, with sweepback on all surfaces; of generally similar configuration to that of J-6, but with taller main fin and smaller dorsal fin. Mechanically actuated mass balanced rudder, with electrically operated inset trim tab. One-piece hydraulically actuated all-moving tailplane, with anti-flutter weight projecting forward from each tip. Tail warning antenna in tip of fin.

LANDING GEAR: Hydraulically retractable wide-track tricycle type, with single wheel on each unit. Main units retract inward into wings, non-steerable nosewheel forward into fuselage, rotating through 90° to lie flat in gear bay. Mainwheels have size 830 × 205-1 tyres and pneumatic drum brakes. Tail braking parachute, deployable also in flight, in bullet fairing at root of vertical tail trailing edge beneath rudder (or in tailcone of early production Q-5I).

POWERPLANT: Two Shenyang Wopen-6 (WP-6) turbojet engines (Chinese version of Tumansky/Mikulin R-9BF-811), each rated at 25.50 kN (5,732 lb st) dry and 31.87 kN (7,165 lb st) with afterburning, mounted side-by-side in rear of fuselage. Lateral air intake, with small splitter plate, for each engine. Hydraulically actuated nozzles. Internal fuel in three forward and two rear fuselage tanks with combined capacity of 3,720 litres (983 US gallons; 818.5 Imp gallons). Provision for carrying a 760 litre (201 US gallon; 167 Imp gallon) drop-tank on each inboard underwing pylon, to give max internal/external fuel capacity of 5,240 litres (1,384 US gallons; 1,153 Imp gallons). When inboard wing stations are occupied by bombs, a 400 litre (106 US gallon; 88 Imp gallon) drop-tank can be carried instead on each outboard underwing pylon.

ACCOMMODATION: Pilot only, in pressurised cockpit under one-piece jettisonable canopy which is hinged at rear and opens upward. Low-speed seat allows for safe ejection within speed range of 135–458 knots (250–850 km/h; 155–528 mph) at zero height or above. Aircraft in Pakistani service have been refitted with Martin-Baker PKD10 zero/zero seats. Armour plating in some areas of cockpit to protect pilot from anti-aircraft gunfire.

AVIONICS AND EQUIPMENT: Include CT-3 VHF com transceiver, WL-7 radio compass, WG-4 low-altitude radio altimeter, LTC-2 horizon gyro, YII-3 IFF, Type 932 radar warning receiver and XS-6 marker beacon receiver. 'High Fix' type gun ranging radar on air-defence version. 'Odd Rods' type IFF aerials under nose on Q-5I/A-5A replaced on Q-5III/A-5C by a single blade antenna. Space provision in nose and centre fuselage for additional or updated avionics, including an attack radar. Landing light under fuselage, forward of nosewheel bay and offset to port; taxying light on nosewheel leg.

ARMAMENT AND OPERATIONAL EQUIPMENT: Internal armament consists of one 23 mm cannon (Chinese 23-2), with 100 rds, in each wing root. Ten attachment points normally for external stores: two pairs in tandem under centre of fuselage, and three under each wing (inboard and outboard of mainwheel leg). Fuselage stations can each carry a 250 kg bomb (Chinese 250-2, US Mk 82 or Snakeye, French Durandal, or similar). Inboard wing stations can carry any of these; a 500 or 750 lb bomb; a BL755 600 lb cluster bomb; or 6 kg or 25 lb practice bombs. Normal bomb carrying capacity is 1,000 kg (2,205 lb), max capacity 2,000 kg (4,410 lb). Instead of bombs, the inboard wing stations can each carry a 760 litre drop-tank (see 'Powerplant' paragraph) or a launcher for 57 mm (eight Chinese 57-1), 68 mm, or 90 mm (nine Chinese 90-1) rockets. The outboard wing stations can each by occupied by a 400 litre drop-tank (when the larger tank is not carried inboard) or, with suitable modification, by air-to-air missiles such as the Chinese PL-2 ('Atoll' derivative), PL-2B, PL-7, Sidewinder and Matra R.550 Magic. Recent photographs have shown the Q-5 with what appear to be two ECM pods, mounted on the middle pylon just outboard of the inner stores station under each wing. Within the overall max T-O weight, all stores mentioned can be carried provided that CG shift remains within the allowable operating range of 31.5 to 38 per cent of mean aerodynamic chord, and more than 22 external stores configurations are possible. The aircraft carries an SH-1J or ABSIA optical sight for level and dive bombing, or for air-to-ground rocket launching. Aircraft in Chinese service can carry a single 5-20 kT nuclear bomb.

DIMENSIONS, EXTERNAL (Q-5III):	
Wing span	9.70 m (31 ft 10 in)
Length overall:	
incl nose probe	16.255 m (53 ft 4 in)
excl nose probe	15.415 m (50 ft 7 in)
Height overall	4.516 m (14 ft 9¾ in)
Wheel track	approx 4.70 m (15 ft 5 in)
Wheelbase	approx 4.00 m (13 ft 1½ in)
AREA:	
Wings, gross	27.95 m² (300.85 sq ft)
WEIGHTS:	
Weight empty	6,494 kg (14,317 lb)
Fuel: max internal	2,883 kg (6,356 lb)
two 400 litre drop-tanks	620 kg (1,367 lb)
two 760 litre drop-tanks	1,178 kg (2,597 lb)
max internal/external	4,061 kg (8,953 lb)
Max external stores load	2,000 kg (4,410 lb)
Max T-O weight: 'clean'	9,530 kg (21,010 lb)
with max external stores	12,000 kg (26,455 lb)
PERFORMANCE (at max 'clean' T-O weight, with afterburning, except where indicated):	
Max limiting Mach number (VNE)	Mach 1.5

Max level speed: at 11,000 m (36,000 ft)
              Mach 1.12 (643 knots; 1,190 km/h; 740 mph)
  at S/L   653 knots (1,210 km/h; 752 mph)
*Max rate of climb at 5,000 m (16,400 ft)
          4,980–6,180 m (16,340–20,275 ft)/min
Service ceiling   15,850 m (52,000 ft)
T-O run:
  *'clean', 15° flap   700–750 m (2,300–2,460 ft)
  with max external stores, 25° flap   1,250 m (4,100 ft)
Landing run:
  25° flap, brake-chute deployed   1,060 m (3,480 ft)
Combat radius with max external stores, afterburners off:
  lo-lo-lo (500 m; 1,640 ft)   216 nm (400 km; 248 miles)
  hi-lo-hi (8,000/500/8,000 m; 26,250/1,640/26,250 ft)
          324 nm (600 km; 373 miles)
Range at 11,000 m (36,000 ft) with max internal and external fuel,
  afterburners off   nearly 1,080 nm (2,000 km; 1,243 miles)
g limits:
  with full load of bombs and/or drop-tanks   5
  with drop-tanks empty   6.5
  'clean'   7.5
*Depending upon airfield altitude and temperature

Nanchang Q-5M/A-5M

This improved version of the Q-5/A-5 is the subject of a collaborative programme begun in July 1986 between CATIC and Aeritalia to upgrade the aircraft's avionics by incorporating a new nav/attack system similar to that used in the AMX aircraft. This would incorporate a ranging radar, inertial navigation system, head-up display, air data computer, two central computers and MIL-STD-1553B data bus. M (for Modified) version of the Q-5 would also have improved WP-6A turbojets with dry and afterburning ratings of 29.42 kN (6,614 lb st) and 36.78 kN (8,267 lb st) respectively. The changes are expected to increase empty weight to 6,634 kg (14,625 lb); max T-O weight remains unchanged. Twelve external stores stations will offer 22 configurations.

PERFORMANCE (estimated):
Max level speed:
  at 11,000 m (36,000 ft)
        Mach 1.2 (688 knots; 1,275 km/h; 792 mph)
  at S/L   661 knots (1,225 km/h; 761 mph)
Service ceiling   16,000 m (52,500 ft)
T-O run with max external stores, 25° flap
        1,200 m (3,937 ft)
Combat radius with max external stores, ISA, 10% reserves:
  lo-lo-lo   more than 162 nm (300 km; 186 miles)
  hi-lo-hi   more than 216 nm (400 km; 248 miles)

Shenyang
SHENYANG AIRCRAFT COMPANY

Shenyang and Mikoyan-Gurevich MiG-15
NATO reporting name: Fagot

The Soviet MiG-15 flew for the first time in I-310 prototype single-seat fighter form on 30 December 1947. The powerplant for this flight was one of 25 British Rolls-Royce Nene turbojets supplied to the Soviet Union alongside 30 Derwent engines.

Production of the MiG-15 began with the Soviet-built RD-45 engine (a Nene development), later superseded by the 26.5 kN (5,952 lb st) Klimov VK-1 on the improved MiG-15*bis*. In addition to Soviet production, MiG-15s were built in China, Czechoslovakia and Poland. The single-seat MiG-15*bis* and tandem two-seat MiG-15UTI trainer were the first jet aircraft to be built in China, and were identical in all important respects to their Soviet counterparts.

Today, not many MiG-15s of Soviet or Chinese origin remain operational in a fighter-bomber role, although the MiG-15UTI (NATO Midget) trainer is still flown by some 24

Air Force of the People's Liberation Army MiG-15.
(Mark Wagner)

nations. It is believed that only Albania, the Congo Republic, and perhaps China and North Korea retain any for combat, the numbers being too small to warrant detailing of the aircraft.

Egyptian Air Force Mikoyan-Gurevich MiG-15UTI two-seat trainer. *(Denis Hughes)*

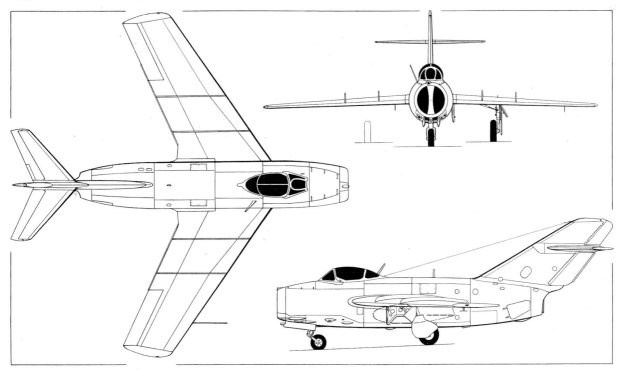

Mikoyan-Gurevich MiG-15*bis*. *(Pilot Press)*

Shenyang J-5 and JJ-5

In addition to the Chinese-built versions of the Soviet Mikoyan-Gurevich MiG-17 fighter, designated J-5 and detailed with the MiG-17 in the USSR section of this book, a two-seat advanced training version was also built as the JJ-5, representing a unique Chinese development of the basic MiG-17 fighter. The following details refer specifically to this.

NATO reporting name: Fresco
Chinese name: Jianjiji Jiaolianji-5 (Fighter training aircraft 5) or Jianjiao-5
Export designations: FT-5 and F-5T

In essence, the JJ-5 appears to combine the tandem cockpits and forward fuselage of the MiG-15UTI with the rest of the airframe of the MiG-17PF (Shenyang J-5A), though retaining the latter's lipped intake, the small radome

Examples of the JJ-5 two-seat training version of the Shenyang J-5/MiG-17.

17

indicating provision for a radar-ranging gunsight in the front cockpit.

An instructor's cockpit, with dual controls and raised seat, is installed to the rear of the standard pilot's cockpit. The canopy over the front seat is sidways-hinged, opening to starboard. The rear seat is enclosed by a rearward-sliding canopy. Other changes by comparison with the single-seat fighter include use of a non-afterburning Wopen-5D or WP-5D (Klimov VK-1A) turbojet engine, rated at 26.48 kN (5,952 lb st); and reduction of the armament to a single 23 mm gun, carried in a removable belly pack, with the barrel to the starboard side of the nosewheel doors.

Max internal fuel capacity is 1,500 litres (396 US gallons; 330 Imp gallons), and there is provision to carry two 400 litre (106 US gallon; 88 Imp gallon) underwing drop-tanks as standard. Two additional hardpoints can be fitted outboard of the drop-tanks. The ailerons have hydraulic servo assistance, with manual reversion; tailplane is fixed-incidence, with manually-operated elevators. Pneumatic wheel brakes are hand-operated by a lever on the control column, with differential actuation by rudder-pedal movement. Chinese semi-automatic ejection seats are fitted; their safe use is not guaranteed below 260 m (853 ft) at speeds up to 188 knots (350 km/h; 217 mph), or below 2,000 m (6,560 ft) at higher speeds.

The JJ-5 is the standard advanced trainer of the Chinese air forces, to which pupil pilots graduate after basic training on the CJ-6. It was first seen outside China when a number were delivered to the Pakistan Air Force in early 1975; these aircraft are designated FT-5. The other known recipient was Sudan (designation F-5T).

DIMENSIONS, EXTERNAL:	
Wing span	9.628 m (31 ft 7 in)
Length overall	11.50 m (37 ft 9 in)
Height overall	3.80 m (12 ft 5¾ in)
Wheel track	3.85 m (12 ft 7½ in)
WEIGHTS:	
Weight empty, equipped	4,080 kg (8,995 lb)
Normal T-O weight	5,401 kg (11,907 lb)
Max T-O weight	6,215 kg (13,700 lb)
PERFORMANCE:	
Never-exceed speed:	
at 5,000 m (16,400 ft)	
	Mach 0.932 (565 knots; 1,048 km/h; 651 mph)
at 9,750 m (32,000 ft)	
	Mach 0.92 (486 knots; 902 km/h; 562 mph)
Normal operating speed	418 knots (775 km/h; 482 mph)
Rate of climb at S/L	1,620 m (5,315 ft)/min
Service ceiling	14,300 m (46,900 ft)
T-O run	760 m (2,493 ft)
Landing run	780–830 m (2,559–2,723 ft)
Range with max fuel at 12,000 m (39,370 ft)	
	664 nm (1,230 km; 764 miles)
Max endurance at 13,700 m (45,000 ft) with two 400 litre (106 US gallon; 88 Imp gallon) drop-tanks	2 h 38 min

Shenyang/Tianjin J-6

NATO reporting names: Farmer-C (MiG-19SF) and Farmer-D (MiG-19PF)
Chinese name: Jianjiji-6 (Fighter aircraft 6) or Jian-6
Export designation: F-6

The J-6 is basically a MiG-19 fighter built in China. Many MiG-19s had been delivered to China in knocked-down form before the deterioration of Moscow–Beijing relations. The designation J-6 was given to the Chinese version of the MiG-19S fighter, which first flew in December 1961 and from mid-1962 became standard equipment in the Air Force of the People's Liberation Army.

Seven versions are known to have been produced at Shenyang, and more recently also at Tianjin (Tientsin):

J-6 (Jianjiji-6 or Jian-6). Chinese equivalent of single-seat MiG-19S/SF day fighter ('Farmer-C'). Superseded by J-6C.

Shenyang/Tianjin Jian-6C/F-6 day fighters supplied by China to the Pakistan Air Force. *(John Fricker)*

J-6A (Jianjiji-6 Jia or Jian-6A). Chinese version of MiG-19PF limited all-weather fighter ('Farmer-D') with gun and rocket armament.

Jian-6/FT-6 two-seat fighter-trainer of the Pakistan Air Force. *(Denis Hughes)*

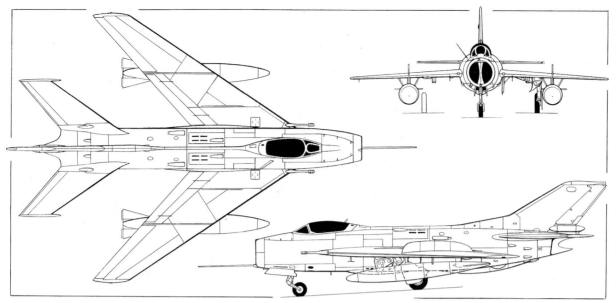

Shenyang/Tianjin Jian-6C. *(Pilot Press)*

J-6B (Jianjiji-6 Yi or Jian-6B). Equivalent to limited all-weather MiG-19PM ('Farmer-D'), armed with radar homing missiles (NATO 'Alkali').

J-6C (Jianjiji-6 Bing or Jian-6C). Day fighter development of MiG-19SF/J-6, distinguished externally by relocated brake chute in bullet fairing at base of rudder.

J-6Xin (Jianjiji-6Xin or Jian-6Xin). Version of Jian-6A/MiG-19PF with Soviet Izumrud (Emerald) intake mounted radar replaced by a Chinese developed airborne interception radar in a needle shaped radome mounted centrally on the intake splitter plate.

JJ-6 (Jianjiji Jiaolianji-6 or Jianjiao-6). Tandem two-seat fighter-trainer version, developed in China.

JZ-6 (Jianjiji Zhenchaji-6 or Jianzhen-6). Single-seat fighter-reconnaissance version, generally similar to Soviet MiG-19R, with cameras mounted in lower forward fuselage instead of the third 30 mm cannon which occupies this position in the fighter-bomber versions.

Production of the J-6 was stepped up from about 1966, and several thousand were built subsequently, including export versions designated **F-6** (fighters) and **FT-6** (two-seat trainers) for Pakistan, Albania, Bangladesh, Egypt, Iran (via North Korea), Iraq (via Egypt and Jordan), Kampuchea, Tanzania (one squadron), and Viet-Nam.

In the PLA Air Force J-6 variants are still the dominant type, with about 3,000 believed to be in service for air-to-air interception, battlefield interdiction, close support, counter-air and tactical reconnaissance. The J-6 also serves in smaller numbers (about 500) with the air force of the PLA Navy.

Chinese sources have recently stated that aircraft production at Shenyang had been substantially reduced, and much manufacturing effort diverted to non-aerospace products. This, plus the lack of mention of the F-6 in current export campaigns, suggests that the aircraft is probably no longer in full-scale production, though it may continue for a time to meet attrition requirements, any outstanding export orders, and manufacture of components common with the Nanchang Q-5.

The details below refer to the MiG-19SF, modified where possible to apply to Chinese versions of the J-6.

TYPE: Single-seat day fighter, attack and tactical recon-naissance aircraft.

WINGS: Cantilever all-metal mid-wing monoplane. Wing section TsAGI S-12S at root, SR-7S at tip. Thickness/chord ratio 8.74% (root), 8.00% (tip). Anhedral 4° 30′. Sweepback at quarter-chord 55°. Entire trailing edge of each wing formed by aerodynamically balanced aileron (outboard) and large Fowler-type TsAGI slotted flap, both hydraulically powered. Compressed-air em-ergency extension system for flaps. Ailerons have provision for reversion to manual control. Electrically actuated trim tab in port aileron. Large full-chord boundary-layer fence, 320 mm ($12\frac{1}{2}$ in) deep, above each wing at mid-span to enhance aileron effectiveness. Plate-type spoiler beneath each wing, forward of aileron, to improve lateral control and rate of roll, especially at supersonic speeds. Spoiler actuation is coupled with that of aileron, and takes place only when aileron is deflected downward.

FUSELAGE: Conventional semi-monocoque structure of circular section, with divided air intake in nose and side-by-side twin orifices at rear. Top and bottom 'pen-nib' fairings aft of nozzles. Entire rear fuselage detaches at wing trailing edge for engine servicing. Forward-hinged door-type airbrake, operated hydraulically, on each side of fuselage aft of wing trailing edge. Forward-hinged perforated door-type airbrake under centre of fuselage. Shallow ventral strake on centreline under rear of fuselage. Upward-hinged pitot boom mounted on lower lip of nose intake.

TAIL UNIT: Conventional structure. Hydraulically-actuated one-piece horizontal surfaces, with electrical emergency actuation in the event of hydraulic failure. Anti-flutter weight projecting forward from each tailplane tip. Stick-to-tailplane gearing, via electro-mechanical linkage, reduces required stick forces during high-*g* manoeuvres. Sweepback on fin leading-edge 57° 37′. Mass-balanced rudder, with electrically-actuated trim tab. Large dorsal fin between fin and dorsal spine enclosing actuating rods for tail control surfaces. Fin-tip incorporates antenna for tail warning radar.

LANDING GEAR: Wide-track retractable tricycle type, with single wheel on each unit. Hydraulic actuation, nosewheel retracting forward, main units inward into wing roots. Pneumatic emergency extension system. Nose unit is steerable, self-centering, and fitted with hydraulic shimmy damper. Main units have 660 × 220 mm tyres; nosewheel tyre size 500 × 180. Low-pressure tubeless tyres on all units. Pneumatically-operated disc brakes on main wheels, with pneumatic emergency backup. Separate nosewheel brake, with independent hydraulic actuation. Pneumatically-deployed brake parachute housed in bullet fairing on top of rear fuselage, at base of rudder. Small tail bumper.

POWERPLANT: Two Shenyang-built Wopen-6 or WP-6 developments of Tumansky (Mikulin bureau) R-9BF-811 turbojet, each rated at 25.50 kN (5,732 lb st) dry and 31.87 kN (7,165 lb st) with afterburning. Hydraulically-actuated nozzles. Two main fuel tanks in tandem between cockpit and engines, and two smaller tanks under forward end of engine tailpipes, total capacity 2,170 litres (573 US gallons; 477 Imp gallons). Provision for two 760 or 1,140 litre (201 or 301 US gallon; 167 or 251 Imp gallon) underwing drop-tanks, raising max total fuel capacity to 3,690 litres (975 US gallons; 811 Imp gallons) or 4,450 litres (1,175 US gallons; 979 Imp gallons) respectively; provision on Pakistan Air Force aircraft for underfuselage tank.

ACCOMMODATION: Pilot only, on Martin-Baker PKD10 zero-zero ejection seat, under rearward-sliding jettison-able blister canopy. Fluid anti-icing system for wind-screen. Cockpit pressurised.

AVIONICS AND EQUIPMENT: Standard avionics include VHF transceiver, blind-flying equipment, radio compass, radio altimeter, tail-warning system, navigation lights, taxying light on nosewheel leg, and landing light in bottom of front fuselage.

ARMAMENT: Two or three 30 mm NR-30 belt fed cannon, one in each wing root and (not on J-6A or JZ-6) one under starboard side of nose. Aircraft supplied to Pakistan have an attachment under each wing for a Harbin built AIM-9B Sidewinder air-to-air missile, outboard of drop-tank. More usual is the provision of one or two attachments inboard of each tank. Packs of eight air-to-air rockets can be carried on these inboard points, or on the drop-tank attachments. Alternative underwing loads can include four air-to-air guided weapons, two 250 kg (or 500 lb) bombs, or single rockets of up to 212 mm calibre. Optical gunsight. Gun camera in top lip of air intake of J-6. Izumrud airborne interception radar in centre of nose intake of J-6A, with ranging unit in top of intake, the former being replaced in J-6Xin by a Chinese developed radar in a 'spike' fairing.

DIMENSIONS, EXTERNAL:

Wing span	9.20 m (30 ft 2¼ in)
Length overall:	
incl nose probe	14.90 m (48 ft 10½ in)
excl nose probe	12.60 m (41 ft 4 in)
Length of fuselage	11.82 m (38 ft 9½ in)
Fuselage: Max diameter	1.45 m (4 ft 9 in)
Height overall	3.88 m (12 ft 8¾ in)
Wheel track	4.15 m (13 ft 7½ in)

AREA:

Wings, gross	25.00 m² (269 sq ft)

WEIGHTS (F-6):

Weight empty, nominal	5,760 kg (12,700 lb)
Max external fuel load	approx 907 kg (2,000 lb)
T-O weight 'clean'	7,545 kg (16,634 lb)
Combat T-O weight (two 760 litre drop-tanks and two Sidewinders)	8,965 kg (19,764 lb)
Max T-O weight with external stores	approx 10,000 kg (22,045 lb)

PERFORMANCE:

Max level speed, 'clean':	
at 11,000 m (36,000 ft)	Mach 1.45 (831 knots; 1,540 km/h; 957 mph)
at low level	Mach 1.09 (723 knots; 1,340 km/h; 832 mph)
Stalling speed, no external stores:	
flaps and landing gear up	126 knots (234 km/h; 145 mph)
flaps and landing gear down	120 knots (222 km/h; 138 mph)
Max rate of climb at S/L, with afterburning	more than 9,145 m (30,000 ft)/min
Service ceiling	17,900 m (58,725 ft)
Absolute ceiling	19,870 m (65,190 ft)
T-O run: with afterburning	approx 670 m (2,200 ft)
with underwing tanks, no afterburning	900 m (2,953 ft)
Landing run: with brake-chute	600 m (1,970 ft)
without brake-chute	890 m (2,920 ft)
Combat radius with two 760 litre external tanks	370 nm (685 km; 426 miles)
Normal range at 14,000 m (46,000 ft)	750 nm (1,390 km; 863 miles)
Max range with two 760 litre external tanks	1,187 nm (2,200 km; 1,366 miles)
Max endurance at 14,000 m (46,000 ft)	2 h 38 min

Shenyang J-8

NATO reporting name: Finback
Chinese name: Jianjiji-8 (Fighter aircraft 8) or Jian-8
Export designation: F-8

Development of the J-8 began in the mid-1960s, the first example being completed in about 1969. Initially, it appeared to follow closely the same design philosophy as the Soviet Mikoyan Ye-152A 'Flipper'.

According to Chinese official sources, only limited production of the J-8 I (about 50 aircraft) was undertaken. An improved version was expected, however, and the possible existence of a J-8 with twin lateral air intakes was reported as long ago as 1979. Confirmation that such a version had been developed came in January 1985, when the Xinhua news agency announced that a J-8 with wingroot intakes had made a successful first flight in early May 1984. Initial flight testing was said to have been very successful, showing a considerable improvement in performance compared with the earlier model. The test programme continued into 1987. The new version is designated **J-8 II** in China, or **F-8 II** in Westernised form.

The main purpose of the configuration change was twofold, the first being to provide a 'solid' nose with adequate accommodation for a modern AI radar, and the second to provide increased airflow for a more powerful

Prototype Shenyang J-8 II single-seat multi-role fighter. *(CATIC)*

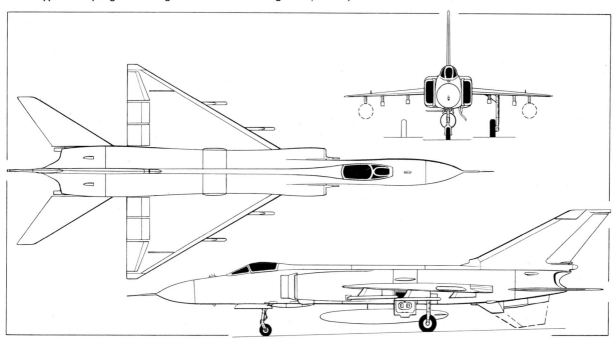

Shenyang J-8 II version of Finback. *(Pilot Press)*

engine installation, it being generally conceded that, with its original 59.82 kN (13,448 lb st) WP-7B engines, the J-8 I was underpowered. The powerplant problem seems to have been overcome, at least for the time being, by fitting the J-8 II with twin engines designated WP-13A II, a Chinese derivative of the Tumansky R-13-300.

In early 1986, US government approval was given for American avionics companies to bid for the avionics upgrade under FMS (foreign military sales) regulations. The requirement was reported to be for 50 shipsets, plus five spare kits, of an avionics suite comprising an AI radar, inertial navigation system, HUD, mission and air data computers, and a data bus. The first contract awarded, for the fire control system, went to Grumman Corporation on 5 August 1987. Two J-8 IIs are to be delivered to the USA in early 1989 for flight test and certification of the upgrade package, with kit deliveries scheduled for 1991–95. The improved version is

intended for service in Manchuria and along China's northern border with the USSR. Most US avionics, however, would be approved only for J-8 IIs for use within China, and other Western alternatives are being sought to enable the aircraft to be exported.

TYPE: Single-seat twin-engined air superiority fighter, with secondary ground attack capability.

WINGS: Cantilever mid-wing monoplane. Thin-section delta wings, with slight anhedral and 60° sweepback on leading edges. Small fence on each upper surface near tip. Two-segment single-slotted trailing-edge flaps on each wing inboard of aileron. Control surfaces have hydraulically boosted actuation.

FUSELAGE: Conventional semi-monocoque structure, 'waisted' between air intakes and tail section in accordance with area rule. Dielectric nosecone. Four door-type under-fuselage airbrakes, one under each engine air intake trunk

21

and one immediately aft of each mainwheel well. Spine fairing along top of fuselage from cockpit to fin, with small airscoop at foot of fin leading edge. Additional airscoop at top of rear fuselage on each side, above tailplane.

TAIL UNIT: Cantilever sweptback surface, comprising broad chord fin and rudder and low-set all-moving tailplane; 60° sweepback on tailplane leading edges. (Tailplane anti-flutter weights of J-8 I deleted). Ventral fin similar to that of MiG-23, main portion of which folds sideways to starboard during take-off and landing, to provide additional directional stability. Rudder and tailplane actuation is hydraulically boosted. Dielectric panels at tip of main fin and on non-folding portion of ventral fin leading edge.

LANDING GEAR: Hydraulically retractable tricycle type, with single wheel on each unit. Nose unit retracts forward, main units inward into centre fuselage; mainwheels turn to stow vertically inside fuselage, resulting in a slight overwing bulge. Brake-chute in bullet fairing at base of rudder.

POWERPLANT: Two Wopen-13A II turbojet engines (Chinese development of Tumansky R-13-300), each rated at 65.9 kN (14,815 lb st) with afterburning, mounted side-by-side in rear fuselage with 'pen nib' fairing above and between exhaust nozzles. Lateral, non-swept air intakes, with large splitter plates similar in shape to those of MiG-23. Internal

fuel capacity (four wing plus fuselage tanks) estimated at approx 5,400 litres (1,426 US gallons; 1,188 Imp gallons). Provision for auxiliary fuel tanks on fuselage centreline and each outboard underwing pylon.

ACCOMMODATION: Pilot only, on ejection seat under one-piece canopy hinged at rear and opening upward. Cockpit pressurised.

AVIONICS AND OPERATIONAL EQUIPMENT: VHF/UHF and HF/SSB com radio, Tacan, radio compass, radar altimeter, marker beacon receiver, 'Odd Rods' type IFF, radar warning receiver and ECM. Autopilot for attitude and heading hold, altitude hold and stability augmentation. Existing fire control system comprises a monopulse radar, optical gyro gunsight and gun camera. Enlarged avionics bays in nose and fuselage provide room for modernised fire control system.

ARMAMENT: One 23 mm Type 23-3 twin-barrel cannon, with 200 rds, in underfuselage pack immediately aft of nose-wheel doors. Seven external stations (one under fuselage and three under each wing) for a variety of stores which can include PL-2B infra-red air-to-air missiles, PL-7 medium-range semi-active radar homing air-to-air missiles, 18-round pods of 57 mm Type 57-2 unguided air-to-air rockets, launchers for 90 mm air-to-surface rockets, bombs, or (centreline and outboard underwing stations only) auxiliary fuel tanks.

DIMENSIONS, EXTERNAL:	
Wing span	9.344 m (30 ft 7⅞ in)
Length overall, incl nose probe	21.59 m (70 ft 10 in)
Height overall	5.41 m (17 ft 9 in)
Wheel track	approx 3.80 m (12 ft 7 in)
Wheelbase	approx 7.25 m (23 ft 9½ in)
AREA:	
Wings, gross	42.2 m² (454.2 sq ft)
WEIGHTS:	
Weight empty	9,820 kg (21,649 lb)
Normal T-O weight	14,300 kg (31,526 lb)
Max T-O weight	17,800 kg (39,242 lb)
PERFORMANCE:	
Design max operating Mach number	2.2

Design max level speed	701 knots (1,300 km/h; 808 mph) IAS
Max rate of climb at S/L	12,000 m (39,370 ft)/min
Acceleration from Mach 0.6 to 1.25 at	
5,000 m (16,400 ft)	54 s
Service ceiling	20,000 m (65,620 ft)
T-O run, with afterburning	670 m (2,198 ft)
Landing run, brake-chute deployed	1,000 m (3,280 ft)
Combat radius	432 nm (800 km; 497 miles)
Max range	1,187 nm (2,200 km; 1,367 miles)
g limit in sustained turn at Mach 0.9 at	
5,000 m (16,400 ft)	+ 4.83

Xian
XIAN AIRCRAFT COMPANY

Xian (Tupolev) H-6

NATO reporting name: Badger
Chinese name: Hongzhaji-6 (Bomber aircraft 6) or Hong-6

First steps to assemble the Tupolev Tu-16 bomber (see USSR section) under licence in China were taken in 1958, but work

was suspended in 1960 after the political break with the USSR. A production programme was reinstated some two years later, and the formidable task was undertaken of copying the design without Soviet assistance. Deliveries of the Chinese-built H-6 version began in about 1968, and seven of the 26 nuclear devices tested at Lop Nur (Lop Nor) up to 1980 were airdropped from Tu-16/H-6s. Other weapons that can be carried by the H-6 include the C-ASM cruise missile and the C-601 air-launched derivative of the Soviet 'Styx'.

Production of this aircraft has been relatively slow, but it continues at a low rate, and the number in service is now believed to be about 120, the current version being designated **H-6IV** or **B-6D**. Mikulin RD-3M engines for the H-6 are built at Xian as the Wopen-8 or WP-8. China is supplying spares for the Tu-16 bombers of the Egyptian Air Force, and the possibility remains that ECM, reconnaissance or other variants may be developed in the future. An aerial tanker design study for the H-6 has been carried out by the FR Group of the UK. This version would serve primarily as a refuelling tanker for the Q-5/A-5 attack aircraft; there are no plans at present for a receiver version of the H-6.

Xian H-6 strategic bomber of the Chinese Air Force.

As with other Chinese developments of original Soviet designs, some local modifications have been noted: aircraft carrying C-601 missiles, for example, have a bigger and cylindrical 'chin' fairing, presumably housing a Chinese variation of the original radar antenna. One Tu-16/H-6 has been seen with fully circular air intakes, made possible by greater engine/fuselage clearance, apparently to overcome intake boundary layer airflow problems. There have also been unconfirmed reports of a four-engined version.

Chinese data for the B-6D are as follows:

POWERPLANT: Two 93.17 kN (20,944 lb st) Xian Wopen-8 turbojets, derived from Mikulin RD-3M.

DIMENSIONS, EXTERNAL:

Wing span	34.189 m (112 ft 2 in)
Length overall	34.800 m (114 ft 2 in)
Height overall	10.355 m (33 ft 11¾ in)

WEIGHTS:

Weight empty	38,530 kg (84,944 lb)
Internal bomb load: normal	3,000 kg (6,614 lb)
max	9,000 kg (19,841 lb)
Two C-601 missiles	4,880 kg (10,758 lb)
Max T-O weight	75,800 kg (167,110 lb)

PERFORMANCE (with two underwing C-601 anti-shipping missiles):

Max cruising speed	424 knots (786 km/h; 488 mph)
T-O speed with full load	163 knots (302 km/h; 188 mph)
Max rate of climb at S/L	1,140 m (3,740 ft)/min
Service ceiling	12,000 m (39,370 ft)
T-O run with full load	2,100 m (6,890 ft)
Normal landing run	1,540 m (5,050 ft)
Combat radius	971 nm (1,800 km; 1,118 miles)
Max range	2,320 nm (4,300 km; 2,672 miles)
Max endurance	5 h 41 min

Xian J-7 Chinese-built counterpart of the MiG-21F ('Fishbed-C').

Xian (Mikoyan) J-7

NATO reporting name: Fishbed
Chinese name: Jianjiji-7 (Fighter aircraft 7) or Jian-7
Export designations: F-7 and F-7M

The Chinese version of the Mikoyan MiG-21 day fighter was based originally on a number of Soviet built MiG-21Fs ('Fishbed-Cs') delivered to China before the political break with the USSR in 1960. The task of copying the airframe, the Tumansky R-11 afterburning turbojet engine (built at Chengdu as the Wopen-7 or WP-7) and equipment was accomplished quickly, and the first J-7 made its initial flight in December 1964. The type began to enter service with the air force of the People's Liberation Army in 1965.

Between 60 and 80 J-7s had been completed before production was halted in 1966 by the onset of the Cultural Revolution, but it was resumed subsequently with a number of modifications. An early priority was to extend the very short TBO life (said to be only about 100 hours) of the original powerplant, and this was at least doubled in the improved Wopen-7A, which develops 43.1 kN (4,400 kg; 9,700 lb st) dry and 50.0 kN (5,100 kg; 11,243 lb st) with afterburning. Exports of early production J-7/F-7s were made to Albania and Tanzania.

The early model J-7 suffered from the same operational shortcomings as the MiG-21F, namely short endurance and a lack of adequate air-to-air firepower. At the beginning of the 1980s Chinese engineers undertook a further series of modifications aimed at upgrading both handling qualities and combat performance of the aircraft. Major improvements in this version, designated **J-7 II** in China, include use of a Wopen-7B engine, in which the afterburning thrust is increased by 9.8 kN (1,000 kg; 2,205 lb), the addition on the port side of a second 30 mm gun, and the ability to carry an 800 litre (211 US gallon; 176 Imp gallon) drop-tank under the fuselage. The three-position, mechanically movable shock cone in the MiG-21F's nose intake, housing the range-only radar, has been replaced by a more efficient no-step system permitting continuously variable positioning of the centrebody, similar to that introduced on the Soviet-built 'Fishbed-E' in the mid-1960s. Introduction of a new zero-height/low-speed ejection seat is accompanied by a new cockpit canopy, hinged at the rear and opening upward, in place of the early-pattern MiG-21 canopy which was hinged at the base of the windscreen. The tail braking parachute has been transferred from under the rear fuselage to a 'bullet' fairing beneath the rudder, as on late-production Chinese J-6s and Q-5s. Current export examples of this version, designated **F-7B**, are to this standard.

Components and engines for the F-7 have been exported in some numbers to Egypt, which also ordered up to 160

23

complete aircraft for its own use (as advanced trainers) and for supply to Iraq. Some of these aircraft, and Egypt's Soviet supplied MiG-21MFs, are being retrofitted with an advanced head-up display and launchers for AIM-9P3/4 Sidewinder air-to-air missiles.

In 1984 China released details of an improved version now known as the **F-7M Airguard**, differing mainly in having more modern Western avionics which include a HUDWACS (head-up display and weapon aiming computer system) instead of the optical sighting system, a more effective ranging radar, new air data computer and radar altimeter, new IFF, and more secure com radio. Other changes include a more efficient electrical power system to cater for the new avionics; two additional underwing stores points; ability to carry the newer and longer-range PL-7 air-to-air missile, which outwardly resembles the Matra Magic; a slightly different version of the Wopen-7B engine; and a relocated nose probe. The F-7M, which is already in service with the PLA Air Force, is being marketed for export by Aircraft Technology Ltd of Hong Kong. According to ATL, one export order for the F-7M had been fulfilled by CATIC before becoming a partner in ATL, and total exports of the F-7 (all models) have exceeded 500. Customer nations have included Egypt, Pakistan, Somalia and Sudan, with reportedly Iran and Zimbabwe.

Guizhou Aviation Industry Group JJ-7/FT-7 two-seat trainer version of the Xian J-7/F-7. *(J. M. G. Gradige)*

Current Soviet versions of the MiG-21 are fully described and illustrated in the USSR section of this edition. China has also developed its own two-seat training version, known as the **JJ-7** or **FT-7**; this is described separately. The following description applies to the current standard F-7B and F-7M Chinese models:

TYPE: Single-seat day fighter and close-support aircraft.

WINGS: As for standard MiG-21, with 57° sweepback on leading edges, 2° anhedral, slotted flaps and balanced ailerons.

FUSELAGE: Generally as MiG-21F except for automatically operated, continuously adjustable shock cone in centre of nose intake, instead of three-step mechanically adjustable centrebody of earlier J-7s. Brake chute relocated from under rear fuselage to 'bullet' fairing at base of vertical tail. In F-7M, nose probe is relocated above intake, offset to starboard, as on Soviet built MiG-21PFM 'Fishbed-J'.

TAIL UNIT: All-swept surfaces, with all-moving tailplane, as for MiG-21.

LANDING GEAR: Inward retracting mainwheels, with 660 × 220 tyres and LS-16 disc brakes; forward retracting nosewheel, with 500 × 180 tyre and LS-15 double-acting brake. Tail braking parachute at base of vertical tail.

POWERPLANT: One Chengdu Wopen-7B turbojet engine in F-7B (43.1 kN/4,400 kg; 9,700 lb st dry, 59.8 kN/6,100 kg; 13,448 lb st with afterburning). Wopen-7B(BM) in F-7M has same ratings, but kerosene (instead of gasoline) starting. Total internal fuel capacity of 2,385 litres (630 US gallons; 524.5 Imp gallons), in six tanks in fuselage and two integral tanks in each wing. Provision for carrying a 500 or 800 litre (132 or 211 US gallon; 110 or 176 Imp gallon) centreline drop-tank, and/or a 500 litre drop-tank on each outboard underwing pylon. Max possible internal/external fuel capacity 4,185 litres (1,106 US gallons; 920.5 Imp gallons).

ACCOMMODATION: Pilot only, on Chengdu Aircraft Corporation zero-height/low-speed ejection seat operable between 70 and 459 knots (130–850 km/h; 81–528 mph) IAS. One-piece canopy, hinged at rear to open upward.

AVIONICS: *(F-7B)* Include CT-3 VHF com radio, WL-7 radio compass, Type 262 radio altimeter, XS-5A marker beacon receiver, Type 222 ranging radar, and Type 602 (Soviet 'Odd Rods' type) IFF transponder. *(F-7M)* GEC

Xian F-7M Airguard Chinese-built export version of the MiG-21 ('Fishbed'). *(ATL)*

Avionics suite includes Type 956 HUDWAC, AD 3400 two-band UHF/VHF multi-function com system, Type 226 Skyranger ranging radar with ECCM, and an air data computer. Other avionics include Type 602 IFF transponder, Type 0101 HR A/2 radar altimeter, WL-7 radio compass, and XS-6A marker beacon receiver. The HUDWAC (head-up display and weapon aiming computer) provides the pilot with displays for instrument flying, with air-to-air and air-to-ground weapon delivery superimposed on the same area of view as the target. It can store 32 weapon parameter functions, allowing both current and future weapon variants to be accommodated. In air-to-air combat its four modes (missiles, conventional gunnery, snapshoot gunnery, or dogfight status) allow for all eventualities. There are also two navigation functions: approach mode, and a standby aiming reticle provided by the HUD.

ARMAMENT: *(F-7B)* Two 30 mm Type 30-1 belt-fed cannon, with 60 rds/gun, in fairings under front fuselage just forward of wing-root leading edges. One hardpoint under each wing, each capable of carrying a PL-2 ('Atoll' type), PL-2A or similar infra-red homing air-to-air missile, a pod of eighteen 57 mm unguided rockets, or a bomb of up to 250 kg size (500 kg in max overload condition). SM-3A optical or AFS3A computing gunsight interfaced with ranging radar and angle-of-attack sideslip transmitter, with gun camera mounted on sighting head. *(F-7M)* Gunsight replaced by a GEC Avionics Type 956 head-up display (also showing navigational data) and weapon aiming computer. Outboard underwing pylons are 'wet' for the carriage of drop-tanks. The centreline pylon is used for a drop-tank only. Each inboard pylon is capable of carrying a PL-2, -2A, -5B or -7 air-to-air missile or, at customer's option, a Matra R.550 Magic; one pod of eighteen Type 57-2 (57 mm) air-to-air and air-to-ground rockets; one pod of seven Type 90-1 (90 mm) air-to-ground rockets; or a 50, 150, 250, or 500 kg bomb. Each outboard pylon can carry one of the above rocket pods, a 50 or 150 kg bomb, or a 500 litre drop-tank.

DIMENSIONS, EXTERNAL:	
Wing span	7.154 m (23 ft 5⅝ in)
Length overall:	
excl nose probe	13.945 m (45 ft 9 in)
incl nose probe	14.885 m (48 ft 10 in)
Height overall	4.103 m (13 ft 5½ in)
Wheel track	2.692 m (8 ft 10 in)
Wheelbase	4.807 m (15 ft 9¼ in)
AREA:	
Wings, gross	23.00 m² (247.6 sq ft)
WEIGHTS:	
Weight empty: F-7B	5,145 kg (11,343 lb)
F-7M	5,275 kg (11,629 lb)
Normal max T-O weight with two PL-2 or PL-7 air-to-air missiles:	
F-7B	7,372 kg (16,252 lb)
F-7M	7,531 kg (16,603 lb)

PERFORMANCE (at normal max T-O weight with two PL-2 or PL-7 air-to-air missiles, except where indicated):

Max level speed between 12,500 and 18,500 m (41,010–60,700 ft); F-7B, F-7M	Mach 2.05
	(1,175 knots; 2,175 km/h; 1,350 mph)
Max rate of climb at S/L:	
F-7B	9,000 m (29,527 ft)/min
F-7M	10,800 m (35,435 ft)/min
Acceleration from Mach 0.9 to 1.2 at 5,000 m (16,400 ft):	
F-7M	35 s
Max sustained turn rate:	
F-7M (Mach 0.7 at S/L)	14.7°/s
F-7M (Mach 0.8 at 5,000 m; 16,400 ft)	9.5°/s
Service ceiling: F-7B	18,800 m (61,680 ft)
F-7M	18,200 m (59,710 ft)

Absolute ceiling: F-7B	19,200 m (62,990 ft)
F-7M	18,700 m (61,350 ft)
T-O run: F-7B	800–1,000 m (2,625–3,280 ft)
F-7M	700–950 m (2,297–3,117 ft)
Landing run with brake-chute:	
F-7B	800–1,000 m (2,625–3,280 ft)
F-7M	600–900 m (1,969–2,953 ft)

Typical mission profiles (F-7M):
Combat air patrol at 11,000 m (36,000 ft) with two air-to-air missiles and three 500 litre drop-tanks, incl 5 min combat 45 min
Long-range interception at 11,000 m (36,000 ft) at 351 nm (650 km; 404 miles) from base, incl Mach 1.5 dash and 5 min combat, stores as above
Hi-lo-hi interdiction radius, out and back at 11,000 m (36,000 ft), with three 500 litre drop-tanks and two 150 kg bombs 324 nm (600 km; 373 miles)
Lo-lo-lo close air support radius with four rocket pods, no external tanks 200 nm (370 km; 230 miles)

Range:
F-7B, two PL-2 missiles only	
	647 nm (1,200 km; 745 miles)
F-7B, two PL-2s and one 800 litre drop-tank	
	804 nm (1,490 km; 926 miles)
F-7M, two PL-7 missiles and three 500 litre drop-tanks	
	939 nm (1,740 km; 1,081 miles)
F-7M, self-ferry with one 800 litre and two 500 litre drop-tanks, no missiles	1,203 nm (2,230 km; 1,385 miles)
g limits: F-7B	+ 7
F-7M	+ 8

GUIZHOU JJ-7

Chinese name: Jianjiji Jiaolianji-7 or Jianjiao-7 (Fighter training aircraft 7)
Export designation: FT-7

The JJ-7 or FT-7 is a Xian two-seat trainer version of the J-7/F-7, generally similar outwardly to its Soviet counterpart, the MiG-21U (NATO 'Mongol-A'), and is said to be capable of providing most of the training necessary for the Shenyang J-8/F-8 fighter as well as the full syllabus for all versions of the J-7/F-7. Avionics are generally as described for the single-seat F-7M.

Differences from the single-seat J-7 include sideways opening (to starboard) twin canopies, the rear one fitted with a retractable periscope, twin ventral strakes of modified shape, and a removable saddleback fuel tank aft of the second cockpit. A 480 or 800 litre (127 or 211 US gallon, 105.5 or 176 Imp gallon) drop-tank can be carried under the centre fuselage, and there is a single underwing pylon each side for such stores as PL-2/-2B air-to-air missiles, 18-round pods of 57 mm rockets, or bombs of up to 250 kg size. If required, the JJ-7 can also be fitted with a Type 23-3 twin-barrel 23 mm gun in an underbelly pack.

DIMENSIONS, EXTERNAL: As J-7 except:	
Length overall, incl probe	14.874 m (48 ft 9½ in)

Czechoslovakia

Aero
AERO VODOCHODY NÁRODNI PODNIK
(Aero Vodochody National Corporation)

This factory perpetuates the name of one of the three founder companies of the Czechoslovak aircraft industry, which began activities in 1919 with the manufacture of Austrian Phönix fighters. Subsequent well known products included the A 11 military general-purpose biplane and its derivatives, and licence manufacture of the French Bloch 200 twin-engined bomber. The present works was established on 1 July 1953.

Aero L-39ZA Albatros

The L-39 basic and advanced jet trainer was developed by a team led by Dipl Ing Jan Vlcek, working in close co-operation with the USSR. The first flight, on 4 November 1968, was made by the second prototype.

A pre-production batch of ten aircraft began to join the flight test programme in 1971, and series production started in late 1972, following official selection of the L-39 to succeed the L-29 Delfin as the standard jet trainer for the air forces of the Soviet Union, Czechoslovakia and the German Democratic Republic. Service trials took place in 1973 in Czechoslovakia and the USSR, and by the Spring of 1974 the L-39 had begun to enter service with the Czechoslovak Air Force.

The number of recipient air forces has since increased, and there are five versions of the Albatros. Of these, the L-39 ZA is a ground-attack and reconnaissance version of the L-39 ZO armed trainer, with an underfuselage gun pod and four underwing weapons stations, and reinforced wings and landing gear. It is in service with the Czechoslovak and Romanian air forces.

Aero L-39ZA in Czechoslovak Air Force insignia. This photograph shows clearly the underfuselage gun pod housing a 23 mm GSh-23 cannon. *(Vaclav Jukl)*

The details below apply to the L39-ZA specifically.

TYPE: Two-seat ground-attack and reconnaissance aircraft, based on L-39 ZO trainer.

POWERPLANT: One 16.87 kN (3,792 lb st) Ivchenko AI-25 TL turbofan engine mounted in rear fuselage, with semi-circular lateral air intake, fitted with splitter plate, on each side of fuselage above wing centre-section.

ACCOMMODATION: Crew of two in tandem, on Czechoslovak VS-1-BRI rocket assisted ejection seats, operable at zero height and at speeds down to 81 knots (150 km/h; 94 mph), beneath individual transparent canopies which hinge sideways to starboard and are jettisonable. Rear seat elevated. One-piece windscreen hinges forward to provide

Aero L-39ZA Albatros. *(Pilot Press)*

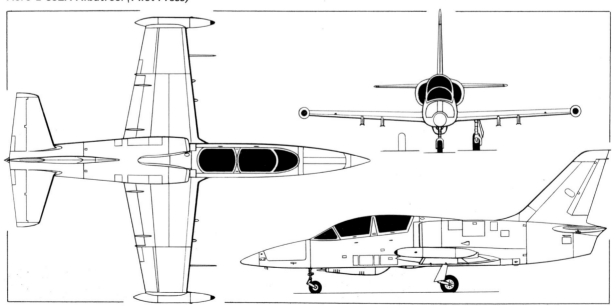

access to front instrument panel. Internal transparency between front and rear cockpits.

ARMAMENT: Underfuselage pod below front cockpit, housing a single 23 mm Soviet GSh-23 two-barrelled cannon; ammunition for this gun (max 150 rds) is housed in fuselage, above gun pod. Gun/rocket firing and weapon release controls, including electrically controlled ASP-3 NMU-39 Z gyroscopic gunsight and FKP-2-2 gun camera, in front cockpit only. Four underwing hardpoints, the inboard pair each stressed for loads of up to 500 kg (1,102 lb) and the outer pair for loads of up to 250 kg (551 lb) each; max underwing stores load 1,100 kg (2,425 lb). Non-jettisonable pylons, each comprising a D3-57D stores rack. Typical underwing stores can include various combinations of bombs (two 500 kg, four 250 kg or six 100 kg); four UB-16-57 M pods each containing sixteen S-5 57 mm air-to-surface rockets; infra-red air-to-air missiles (outer pylons only); a five-camera day reconnaissance pod (port inboard pylon only); or (on inboard stations only) two 350 litre (92.5 US gallons; 77 Imp gallon) drop-tanks.

DIMENSIONS, EXTERNAL:	
Wing span	9.46 m (31 ft $0\frac{1}{2}$ in)
Length overall	12.13 m (39 ft $9\frac{1}{2}$ in)
Height overall	4.77 m (15 ft $7\frac{3}{4}$ in)
Wheel track	2.44 m (8 ft 0 in)
Wheelbase	4.39 m (14 ft $4\frac{3}{4}$ in)
AREA:	
Wings, gross	18.80 m² (202.36 sq ft)
WEIGHTS:	
Weight empty, equipped	3,656 kg (8,060 lb)
Fuel load: fuselage tanks	824 kg (1,816 lb)
wingtip tanks	156 kg (344 lb)
Max external stores load	1,100 kg (2,425 lb)
T-O weight 'clean'	4,549 kg (10,029 lb)
Max T-O weight	5,600 kg (12,346 lb)

PERFORMANCE (at max T-O weight except where indicated):

Max limiting Mach number	Mach 0.80
Max level speed at 5,000 m (16,400 ft)	
	407 knots (755 km/h; 469 mph)
Max rate of climb at S/L	1,260 m (4,130 ft)/min
Service ceiling	11,000 m (36,100 ft)
T-O run (concrete)	480 m (1,575 ft)
g limits:	
operational, at 4,200 kg (9,259 lb) AUW	+ 8/ − 4
ultimate, at 4,200 kg (9,259 lb) AUW	+ 12
operational, at 5,500 kg (12,125 lb) AUW	+ 5.2/ − 2.6

Egypt

AOI
ARAB ORGANISATION FOR INDUSTRIALISATION

The AOI was set up in November 1975 by Egypt, Saudi Arabia, Qatar and the United Arab Emirates, with a capital of more than $1,000 million, to provide the basis for an Arab military industry. The main centres of production were to be in the Cairo area, using and building upon the extensive facilities already existing. Initial plans to manufacture the Westland Lynx and its Rolls-Royce Gem engine under licence were terminated in 1979 when Saudi Arabia, Qatar and the UAE withdrew from the partnership following the Camp David agreement between Egypt and Israel.

Since then, however, the AOI has gained strength as a purely Egyptian based organisation, and is now engaged in several important aircraft, aero engine and other military programmes. It is organised into five divisions, which between them have a workforce of about 20,000 people, including approximately 3,000 employed in its four subsidiaries. Rockets, missiles and other weapons are produced by the SAKR Factory near Cairo (except for the Swingfire programme, which is managed by ABDCo); armoured and other military vehicles are manufactured by the Kader Factory, at Heliopolis, and the AAVCo.

Egypt's long-term intention is to become completely self-sufficient in the manufacture of arms and other military equipment. It is absorbing a gradual transfer of technology from Western manufacturers, beginning with licence production of aircraft main components, subassemblies and complete systems.

The main centre for this resurgence is Helwan, south of Cairo. Helwan air base is the Egyptian Air Force centre for all major aircraft overhaul and maintenance, as well as its headquarters for maintenance and repair training. Nearby is a large industrial complex, the chief elements of which are an aircraft factory (No 36) and an aero-engine factory (No. 135), with 3,000 and 3,500 employees respectively. Helwan also accommodates the Arab British Helicopter Company and Arab British Engine Company. By 'reverse engineering', ABECo has also manufactured components for, and overhauled, Soviet TV2-117A turboshaft engines for Egypt's Mil Mi-8 helicopter fleet.

The principal aircraft and engine programmes currently or recently undertaken by the AOI are as follows:

Aérospatiale Gazelle. Fifty-four French-built Gazelles supplied earlier now retrofitted to SA 342L standard. December 1981 follow-on contract for 36 aircraft (also SA 342Ls), of which all except six assembled under licence at ABHCo factory at Helwan. Egyptian programme began in June 1983, with first Helwan assembled Gazelle making initial flight at end of September and being handed over to Egyptian Air Force on 1 December 1983. Production completed, including 18 spare Astazou XIVH engines.

Aérospatiale Super Puma. Protocol signed on 10 November 1983, providing for component manufacture (now in progress) and possible ultimate assembly.

Egyptian-built Alpha Jet MS2 ground-attack aircraft.

Dassault-Breguet Falcon 50. Component manufacture.

Dassault-Breguet Mirage 2000. Egyptian Air Force has ordered 20 (French-built), with further 20 on option. Some components for first batch are of Egyptian manufacture; first deliveries were scheduled for 1986. Egyptian assembly (possibly from 27th aircraft onward) may be undertaken in second batch.

Dassault-Breguet/Dornier Alpha Jet. Total of 45 ordered by Egypt, comprising 30 (designated **MS1**) to replace Czech L-29 Delfin and MiG-15UTI in the training role and 15 **MS2** ground-attack versions to replace the MiG-17. First four in each batch delivered in flyaway condition by France (1982 and 1983 respectively); remaining 26 MS1s and 11 MS2s assembled from French kits by AOI Aircraft Factory. First flight of Egyptian assembled MS1 made on 1 September 1982; first delivery to Egyptian Air Force 4 November 1982. Production completed in 1985. Programme also included manufacture of components (flaps, ailerons, rudders, rear fuselages, exhaust shrouds and 310 litre; 82 US gallon; 68 Imp gallon drop-tanks), as well as licence assembly of 80 Larzac engines by Factory 135.

Embraer EMB-312 Tucano. October 1983 contract for 120 Tucanos (80 for Iraq, 40 for Egypt), of which first ten were delivered complete by Embraer. Remainder being assembled from Brazilian-built kits by Kader Factory at Heliopolis; PT6A-25 engines for these aircraft also being assembled in Egypt. Deliveries of Egyptian assembled Tucanos to the Egyptian Air Force began in November 1985, when three of the 12 aircraft completed by that time were officially accepted. Deliveries to Egyptian Air Force totalled 42 by 1 January 1987. Contract includes option on further 60 aircraft (Egypt 40, Iraq 20).

France

Aérospatiale
AÉROSPATIALE SNI

Aérospatiale was formed on 1 January 1970, by decision of the French government, as a result of the merger of the former Sud-Aviation, Nord-Aviation and SEREB companies. It had a registered capital of 1,016,490,000 francs, facilities extending over a total area of 8,498,465 m² (91,477,475 sq ft), of which 2,005,674 m² (21,589,075 sq ft) are covered, and a staff (including subsidiary companies) of 38,800 persons on 1 January 1987.

In addition to the helicopters which follow, other Aérospatiale utility and general-purpose types are combat capable. These include the Alouette III, AS 350L$_1$ Ecureuil and AS 355M$_2$ Ecureuil 2. The decision whether or not to detail a particular helicopter has been based on the main uses to which it is put.

Aérospatiale SA 321 Super Frelon

The Super Frelon is a three-engined multi-purpose helicopter derived from the smaller SA 3200 Frelon. Under a technical co-operation contract, Sikorsky Aircraft, USA, provided assistance in the development of the Super Frelon, in particular with the detail specifications, design, construction and testing of the main and tail rotor systems. Under a further agreement, the main gearcase and transmission box were produced in Italy by Fiat.

The first prototype of the Super Frelon (originally designated SA 3210-01) flew on 7 December 1962, powered by three 985 kW (1,320 shp) Turmo IIIC$_2$ engines, and represented the troop transport version. The second prototype, flown on 28 May 1963, was representative of the naval version, with stabilising floats on the main landing gear supports. Four pre-production aircraft followed, and the French government ordered an initial production series of 17, designated SA 321G, in October 1965. A total of 99 Super Frelons was sold for civil and military operation in eight countries. The SA 321G is the only combat version as designed, although details are also provided of the SA 321H which Iraq has adopted for anti-ship duties, using Exocet missiles.

SA 321G. Anti-submarine helicopter. First version of the SA 321 to enter production. The first SA 321G flew on 30 November 1965 and deliveries began in early 1966. Twenty-

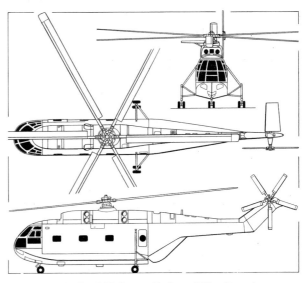

Aérospatiale SA 321 Super Frelon. *(Pilot Press)*

four built. In service with Flottille 32F of Aéronavale, which was commissioned at Lanvéoc-Poulmic on 5 May 1970. Duties of this squadron include patrols in support of *Redoutable* class nuclear submarines entering and leaving their base on the Île Longue. The SA 321G can also be operated from the French helicopter carrier *Jeanne d'Arc*. Under a contract placed in late 1979, the original ORB 31 Héraclès I radar fitted to these aircraft was replaced by ORB 32 Héraclès II of doubled performance in terms of power (80 kW) and scan (360°).

SA 321H. Version for air force and army service, without stabilising floats or external fairings on each side of lower fuselage. Turmo IIIE$_6$ engines instead of Turmo IIIC$_6$ in other versions. No de-icing equipment fitted.

TYPE: Three-engined heavy-duty helicopter.

ROTOR SYSTEM: Six-blade main rotor and five-blade anti-torque tail rotor. Main rotorhead consists basically of two six-armed star plates carrying the drag and flapping hinges for each blade. The root of each blade carries a fitting for pitch control and each blade has an individual hydraulic damper to govern movement in the drag plane. Each main blade is 8.60 m (28 ft 2½ in) long, with constant chord and NACA 0012 section. Tail rotor has blades 1.60 m (5 ft 3 in) long. Rearward folding of all six main rotor blades of SA 321G is accomplished automatically by hydraulic jacks, simultaneously with automatic folding of the tail-rotor pylon.

FUSELAGE: Boat-hull fuselage of conventional semi-monocoque construction, with watertight compartments inside planing bottom. On the SA 321G there is a small stabilising float attached to the rear landing gear support structure on each side. The tail section of the SA 321G folds for stowage. Small fixed stabiliser on starboard side of tail rotor pylon on all versions.

LANDING GEAR: Non-retractable tricycle type, by Messier-Hispano-Bugatti. Twin wheels on each unit. Oleo-

Aérospatiale SA 321G Super Frelon, used by *Flottille* 32F of the *Aéronavale*. (J. M. G. Gradidge)

pneumatic shock absorbers can be shortened on the SA 321G to reduce height of aircraft for stowage. Hydraulic disc brakes on main wheels. Nosewheel unit is steerable and self-centering.

POWERPLANT: Three 1,170 kW (1,570 shp) Turboméca Turmo $IIIC_6$ turboshaft engines ($IIIE_6$ in SA 321H); two mounted side-by-side forward of main rotor shaft and one aft of rotor shaft. Fuel in flexible tanks under floor of centre fuselage, with total standard capacity of 3,975 litres (1,050 US gallons; 874 Imp gallons). Optional auxiliary fuel tankage comprises two 500 litre (132 US gallon; 110 Imp gallon) internal tanks in the SA 321G, and three 666 litre (176 US gallon; 146.5 Imp gallon) internal tanks in the SA 321H.

ACCOMMODATION (military versions): Crew of two on flight deck, with dual controls and advanced all-weather equipment. SA 321G carries three other flight crew, and has provision for 27 passengers. SA 321H transport accommodates 27–30 troops, 5,000 kg (11,023 lb) of internal or external cargo, or 15 stretchers and two medical attendants. Rear loading ramp is actuated hydraulically and can be opened in flight.

ARMAMENT AND OPERATIONAL EQUIPMENT: The ASW SA 321G operates normally in tactical formations of three or four aircraft, each helicopter carrying the full range of detection, tracking and attack equipment, including a self-contained navigation system associated with a Doppler radar, a 360° radar with transponder and display console, and dipping sonar. Four homing torpedoes can be carried in pairs on each side of the main cabin. Both the SA 321G and H can be fitted with an anti-surface-vessel weapon system, consisting of two Exocet missiles and launch installation, associated with an Omera-Segid Héraclès ORB 31D or ORB 32 radar for target designation. Other equipment is provided for secondary duties such as towing and minesweeping. Rescue hoist of 275 kg (606 lb) capacity standard.

DIMENSIONS, EXTERNAL:	
Diameter of main rotor	18.90 m (62 ft 0 in)
Diameter of tail rotor	4.00 m (13 ft 1½ in)
Length overall, rotors turning	23.03 m (75 ft 6⅝ in)
Length of fuselage, tail rotor turning	20.08 m (65 ft 10¾ in)
Length of fuselage	19.40 m (63 ft 7¾ in)
Length overall: SA 321G, blades and tail folded	
	17.07 m (56 ft 0 in)
Width overall:	
SA 321G, blades and tail folded	5.20 m (17 ft 0¾ in)
Width of fuselage	2.24 m (7 ft 4¼ in)
Height over tail rotor (normal)	6.76 m (22 ft 2¼ in)
Height overall: SA 321G, blades and tail folded	
	4.94 m (16 ft 2½ in)
Wheel track	4.30 m (14 ft 1 in)
Wheelbase	6.56 m (21 ft 6¼ in)
Rear loading ramp: Length	1.90 m (6 ft 2¾ in)

Width	1.90 m (6 ft 2¾ in)
WEIGHTS:	
Weight empty, standard aircraft:	
SA 321G	6,863 kg (15,130 lb)
SA 321H	6,702 kg (14,775 lb)
Max T-O weight	13,000 kg (28,660 lb)
PERFORMANCE (at max T-O weight):	
Never-exceed speed at S/L	148 knots (275 km/h; 171 mph)
Cruising speed at S/L	134 knots (248 km/h; 154 mph)
Max rate of climb at S/L	300 m (985 ft)/min
Service ceiling	3,100 m (10,170 ft)
Hovering ceiling IGE	1,950 m (6,400 ft)
Normal range at S/L	440 nm (815 km; 506 miles)
Range at S/L with 3,500 kg (7,716 lb) payload	
	549 nm (1,020 km; 633 miles)
Endurance in ASW role	4 h

Aérospatiale SA 330 Puma and AS 332 Super Puma

The twin-engined SA 330 Puma was developed initially to meet a French Army requirement for a medium sized *hélicoptère de manoeuvre*, able to operate by day or night in all weathers and all climates. In 1967 the SA 330 was selected for the RAF Tactical Transport Programme, and was included in a three-type joint production agreement between Aérospatiale and Westland in the UK.

The first of two SA 330 prototypes flew on 15 April 1965, and the last of six pre-production models on 30 July 1968, followed in September 1968 by the first production aircraft.

Military versions of the Puma have been as follows:

SA 330B. For French Army (ALAT) and French Air Force. First flown January 1969; deliveries began Spring 1969; became operational with the Groupe de l'Aviation Légère of the 7th French Division at Habsheim Base, Mulhouse, France, in June 1970. Turmo $IIIC_4$ engines, each of 990 kW (1,328 shp) for T-O and 884 kW (1,185 shp) max continuous rating.

SA 330C/H. Military export versions. First flown September 1968. Initially with Turmo IVB engines (each 1,400 shp). No air intake anti-icing. From end of 1973 H models delivered with Turmo IVC engines (each 1,575 shp) and intake anti-icing.

SA 330E. For Royal Air Force, by whom it is designated Puma HC. Mk 1. Forty built, with Turmo $IIIC_4$ engines. First production example flown on 25 November 1970. First

Royal Air Force Aérospatiale Puma HC.Mk 1, based on the SA 330E version. *(Crown Copyright)*

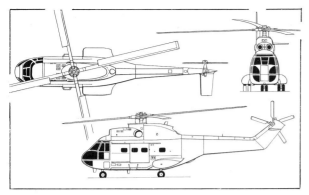

Aérospatiale SA 330E Puma. *(Pilot Press)*

ASW version of the Aérospatiale AS 332F₁ Super Puma armed with torpedoes.

RAF squadron (No. 33) formed in 1971, followed by No. 230 in 1972.

SA 330L. Military version introduced in 1976 with main rotor blades of composite materials. Increased max T-O weight, including certification at 7,500 kg (16,535 lb) for cargo-sling mission.

A total of 697 SA 330 Pumas had been sold by 1 February 1987, in 46 countries. ICA of Brasov, Romania, began manufacture of 100 SA 330H Pumas under licence in 1977, as IAR-330s, and is now the sole producer of this helicopter. Nurtanio of Indonesia completed the assembly of 11 from knocked-down components in the second quarter of 1983 but, like the parent company, is now concentrating on manufacture of the Super Puma.

Design of the AS 332 Super Puma derivative of the Puma was started in 1974, and the programme received a formal go-ahead from the French government in June 1975. As a first stage, Aérospatiale retrofitted a Puma airframe with two Turboméca Makila turboshaft engines and an uprated transmission. This experimental helicopter, designated AS 331, flew for the first time on 5 September 1977. It was followed, on 13 September 1978, by the first flight of the first prototype AS 332 Super Puma, embodying more extensive changes to provide increased payload and performance, simplified maintenance, reduced cabin noise level, reduced vulnerability to hostile fire in combat areas, and better crew and passenger survivability in a crash. Original plans to fit a 'fenestron' ducted tail rotor were dropped after evaluation of a 'fenestron' on the SA 330Z testbed indicated no worthwhile performance gains.

Externally evident airframe changes compared with the SA 330 Puma include a lengthened nose; increased wheelbase and wheel track; a new high energy absorption landing gear with a single wheel on each of the main units, which offer an optional 'kneeling' capability to reduce overall dimensions for shipboard stowage; and an added ventral fin. The main and tail rotor blades have a new and more efficient profile. The current versions of the Super Puma, introduced in 1986, have uprated Makila IA1 engines.

Current military versions of the Super Puma are:

AS 332B₁. Military version. Introduced in 1986, with uprated Turboméca Makila IA1 engines and 40 kVA instead of 20 kVA alternators. Standard fuselage, seating up to 23 troops and two crew. Cabin floor reinforced for loads of 1,500 kg/m² (307 lb/sq ft).

AS 332F₁. Naval version, with folding tail-rotor pylon, deck landing assist device and anti-corrosion treatment.

Makila IA1 engines. Suitable for search and rescue, ASW and anti-ship roles.

AS 332M₁. As 332B₁, but with cabin lengthened by 0.76 m (2 ft 6 in) to provide two more seats and two additional windows. Fuel capacity increased.

In early 1986, a Super Puma began flight evaluation of the Orchidée (Observatoire Radar Cohérent Héliporté d'Investigation Des Eléments Ennemis) battlefield surveillance system, intended as a key system for co-ordinating the actions of all French ground forces by the mid-1990s. The Orchidée scanner is carried on a rotating mount under the rear of the helicopter's cabin. When not in use it is retracted upward to stow transversely under the junction of the rear fuselage and tailboom. It is a high-performance Doppler radar, capable of detecting and pinpointing troops and vehicles up to 54 nm (100 km; 62 miles) behind enemy lines while the Super Puma is 27 nm (50 km; 31 miles) inside friendly territory at an altitude of around 3,000 m (9,850 ft). Aérospatiale is industrial prime contractor for Orchidée, in conjunction with Laboratoire Central des Télécommunications, which supplies the radar and is responsible for the surveillance system. This is able to transmit data in real time to mobile ground stations built by Electronique Serge Dassault. Thomson-CSF and Matra are responsible for associated countermeasures.

All Super Puma variants are certificated for IFR category A and B operation, to FAR Pt 29 standards. The first Super Puma (a civil AS 332L) equipped for operation to IFR Cat II standards was certificated by the DGAC on 7 July 1983 and

Orchidée battlefield surveillance radar extended in operational position under Puma test aircraft.

31

Aérospatiale AS 332M₁ Super Puma, similar to AS 332B₁ but with lengthened cabin for 25 troops.

delivered to Lufttransport of Norway in September 1983. Certification of this version for flight into known icing conditions was granted on 29 June 1983. Corresponding FAA certifications cover Cat II automatic approach, using a SFIM CDV 85 P4 four-axis flight director coupler, and flight into known icing conditions under FAR Pt 25 Appendix C.

Orders for 254 Super Pumas, including six prototypes, for service in 30 countries, had been received by February 1987. They include three for operation by the French Air Force on support duties at nuclear firing ranges in the Pacific; 22 military models for transport duties with the Singapore Air Force; 30 for maritime search and rescue (10), VIP transportation (2) and tactical transport duties (18) with the Spanish armed forces; six naval models, each armed with two

Exocet missiles, for Kuwait; and other military models for Abu Dhabi (8, incl 2 VIP), Argentina (up to 24), Brazil (8), Chile (3) and Oman (2 for Royal Flight).

Deliveries of the Super Puma from French production began in mid-1981. IPTN of Indonesia is manufacturing several versions under licence, and 12 of the Spanish tactical transports will be assembled in Spain by CASA.

The following details refer to the Super Puma:

TYPE: Twin-turbine multi-role helicopter.

ROTOR SYSTEM: Four-blade main rotor, with a fully articulated hub and integral rotor brake. Each drag hinge is fitted with an elastomeric frequency adaptor. The blade cuffs, equipped with horns, are connected by link rods to the swashplate, which is actuated by three hydraulic twin-

Aérospatiale AS 332M₁ Super Puma. *(Pilot Press)*

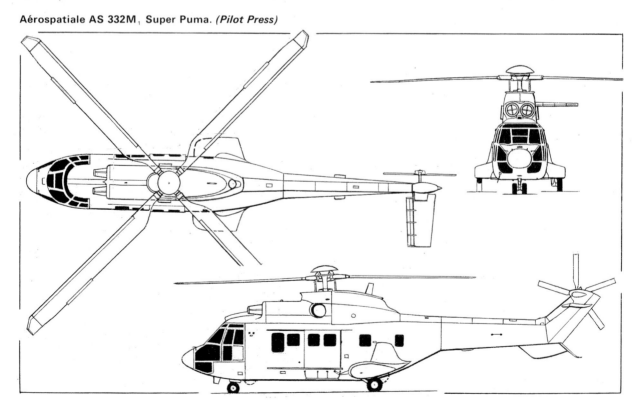

cylinder servo control units. The tips are swept. Attachment of each blade to its sleeve by means of two quick-disconnect pins enables the blades to be folded back quickly by manual methods. The five-blade tail rotor has flapping hinges only, and is located on the starboard side of the tailboom. Optional de-icing system, with heating mat on leading edge of each main and tail rotor blade.

FUSELAGE: Conventional semi-monocoque structure, embodying anti-crash features. Monocoque tailboom supports the tail rotor on the starboard side and a horizontal stabiliser with fixed leading-edge slat (and optional pneumatic de-icing) on the port side. Large ventral fin. Optional folding tailboom for aircraft that serve on ships such as frigates.

LANDING GEAR: Retractable tricycle type, of Messier-Hispano-Bugatti high energy absorbing design. All units retract rearward hydraulically, mainwheels into fairings on sides of fuselage. Optional 'kneeling' capability for main units. Twin-wheel self-centering nose unit, tyre size 466 × 176. Single wheel on each main unit with tyre size 615 × 225-10. Hydraulic differential disc brakes, controlled by foot pedals. Lever operated parking brake. Emergency pop-out flotation units can be mounted on main landing gear fairings and forward fuselage.

POWERPLANT: Two Turboméca Makila IA1 turboshaft engines, each with max contingency rating of 1,400 kW (1,877 shp) and max continuous rating of 1,184 kW (1,588 shp). Air intakes protected by a grille against ingestion of ice, snow and foreign objects; but multi-purpose intake is necessary for flight into sandy areas. AS 332B$_1$ has five flexible fuel tanks under cabin floor, with total capacity of 1,560 litres (412 US gallons; 343 Imp gallons). AS 332M$_1$ has a basic fuel system of six flexible tanks with total capacity of 2,060 litres (544 US gallons; 453 Imp gallons). Provision for additional 1,900 litres (502 US gallons; 418 Imp gallons) in four auxiliary ferry tanks installed in cabin. Two external auxiliary tanks are available, with total capacity of 700 litres (185 US gallons; 154 Imp gallons). Fuel system is designed to avoid fuel leakage following a crash, with flexible fuel lines and interconnections between tanks, self-sealing valves and automatic fuel pump shutdown in a crash. Options include a fuel dumping system, pressure refuelling, and crash-resistant or self-sealing tanks.

ACCOMMODATION: One pilot (VFR) or two pilots side-by-side (IFR) on flight deck, with jump seat for third crew member or paratroop dispatcher. Provision for composite light alloy/Kevlar armour for crew protection on military models. Dual controls, co-pilot instrumentation and anti-crash flight deck/cabin floors. Max accommodation for 21 passengers in AS 332B$_1$/F$_1$, and 25 in AS 332M$_1$. Variety of interiors available for VIP use, or for air ambulance duty carrying six stretchers and eleven seated casualties/attendants, or nine stretchers and three seated. Strengthened floor for cargo carrying, with lashing points. A hatch in the floor below the centreline of the main rotor is provided for carrying loads of up to 4,500 kg (9,920 lb) on an internally mounted cargo sling. A fixed or retractable rescue hoist (capacity 275 kg; 606 lb) can be mounted externally on the starboard side of the fuselage.

AVIONICS AND EQUIPMENT: Optional communications equipment includes VHF, UHF, tactical HF and HF/SSB radio installations and intercom system. Navigational equipment includes radio compass, radio altimeter, VLF Omega, Decca navigator and flight log, Doppler, and VOR/ILS with glidepath. SFIM 155 autopilot, with provision for coupling to self contained navigation and microwave landing systems. Full IFR instrumentation available optionally. The search and rescue version has nose mounted Bendix RDR 1400 or RCA Primus 500 search radar, Doppler, and Crouzet Nadir or Decca self-contained navigation system, including navigation computer, polar indicator, roller map display, hover indicator, route mileage indicator and ground speed and drift indicator. For naval ASW and ASV missions, aircraft can be fitted with nose mounted Omera type ORB 3214 360° radar, linked to a tactical table in the cabin, and an Alcatel/Thompson-Sintra HS 12 sonar station in the cabin.

ARMAMENT AND OPERATIONAL EQUIPMENT (optional): Typical alternatives for army/air force missions are one 20 mm gun, two 7.62 mm machine-guns, or two pods each containing thirty-six 68 mm rockets or nineteen 2.75 in rockets. Armament and equipment for naval missions includes two AM39 Exocet, six AS.15TT, or one Exocet and 3 AS.15TT missiles, or two torpedoes and sonar, or MAD and sonobuoys.

DIMENSIONS, EXTERNAL:	
Main rotor diameter	15.60 m (51 ft 2¼ in)
Tail rotor diameter	3.05 m (10 ft 0 in)
Length overall, rotors turning	18.70 m (61 ft 4¼ in)
Length of fuselage, incl tail rotor:	
AS 332B$_1$/F$_1$	15.53 m (50 ft 11½ in)
AS 332M$_1$	16.29 m (53 ft 5½ in)
Height overall	4.92 m (16 ft 1¾ in)
Height, blades and tail pylon folded:	
AS 332F$_1$	4.80 m (15 ft 9 in)
Height to top of rotorhead	4.60 m (15 ft 1¼ in)
Width overall, excl rotors	3.79 m (12 ft 5¼ in)
Wheel track	3.00 m (9 ft 10 in)
Wheelbase: AS 332B$_1$/F$_1$	4.49 m (14 ft 8¾ in)
AS 322M$_1$	5.28 m (17 ft 4 in)
AREA:	
Main rotor disc	191.1 m² (2,057.4 sq ft)
WEIGHTS:	
Weight empty: AS 332B$_1$	4,290 kg (9,458 lb)
AS 332F$_1$	4,475 kg (9,866 lb)
AS 332M$_1$	4,420 kg (9,744 lb)
Max T-O weight:	
AS 332B$_1$/F$_1$/M$_1$ internal load	9,000 kg (19,841 lb)
all versions, with slung load	9,350 kg (20,615 lb)
PERFORMANCE (at max T-O weight):	
Never-exceed speed	150 knots (278 km/h; 172 mph)
Econ cruising speed at S/L:	
AS 332B$_1$/M$_1$	136 knots (251 km/h; 156 mph)
AS 332F$_1$	130 knots (240 km/h; 149 mph)
Max rate of climb at S/L:	
AS 332B$_1$/M$_1$	426 m (1,397 ft)/min
AS 332F$_1$	372 m (1,220 ft)/min
Service ceiling:	
AS 332B$_1$/F$_1$/M$_1$	3,500 m (11,480 ft)
Hovering ceiling IGE:	
AS 332B$_1$/F$_1$/M$_1$	2,800 m (9,180 ft)
Hovering ceiling OGE:	
AS 332B$_1$/F$_1$/M$_1$	1,650 m (5,410 ft)
Range at S/L, standard tanks, no reserves:	
AS 332B$_1$	334 nm (618 km; 384 miles)
AS 332F$_1$	460 nm (850 km; 528 miles)
AS 332M$_1$	455 nm (842 km; 523 miles)
Range at S/L with external (2 × 338 litre) and auxiliary (320 litre) tanks, no reserves:	
AS 332M$_1$	672 nm (1,245 km; 773 miles)

Aérospatiale Super Puma Mk II

This developed version of the Super Puma introduces a new main rotor which offers improved performance and economy without changes to the standard powerplant of two Makila IA1 turboshafts, although the main transmission is upgraded to transmit increased power. Slightly longer main rotor blades with parabolic tips are fitted to a Spheriflex head, which is lighter and simpler than the current type. The rear fuselage is lengthened by 45 cm (1 ft 5¾ in), to provide adequate clearance between the new main rotor and the tail rotor. Range can be increased by installing two 250 litre (66 US gallon; 55 Imp gallon) optional fuel tanks in the main landing gear sponsons. A four-tube EFIS cockpit display and digital autopilot will be included in an eventual upgrading of the avionics.

Following testing of the Spheriflex head on a Puma, the prototype Super Puma Mk II flew for the first time on 6 February 1987. A second prototype was expected to begin flight tests before the end of 1987, with deliveries of the Super Puma Mk II scheduled to start in 1990.

DIMENSIONS, EXTERNAL:	
Main rotor diameter	16.20 m (53 ft 1¾ in)
WEIGHT:	
Max T-O weight: civil	9,000 kg (19,841 lb)
military	9,500 kg (20,945 lb)

Aérospatiale SA 342L₁ Gazelle armed with four Hot missile launchers.

Aérospatiale SA 341 and SA 342 Gazelle

The first prototype of the Gazelle five-seat lightweight helicopter (designated SA 340) made its first flight on 7 April 1967, powered by an Astazou III engine. It was followed by a second prototype on 12 April 1968, and then by four pre-production SA 341 Gazelles.

The first production SA 341 Gazelle flew for the first time on 6 August 1971, with a longer cabin than its predecessors, enlarged tail unit, additional door on the starboard side at rear (optional on production aircraft) and uprated Astazou IIIA engine.

The following military versions of the Gazelle have been built:

SA 341B. British Army version, with Astazou IIIN engine. Designated Gazelle AH. Mk 1.

SA 341C. British Navy version. Designated Gazelle HT. Mk 2.

SA 341D. Royal Air Force training version. Designated Gazelle HT. Mk 3.

SA 341E. Royal Air Force communications version. Designated Gazelle HCC. Mk 4.

SA 341F. Original French Army version, with Astazou IIIC engine; 166 procured.

SA 341H. Military export version, with Astazou IIIB engine.

SA 342K. Military version, first flown on 11 May 1973 and supplied to Kuwait. 650 kW (870 shp) Astazou XIVH engine, with momentum-separation shrouds over intakes.

SA 342L. Military counterpart of SA 342J, with improved 'fenestron' tail rotor.

SA 342L₁. Current basic military version, with higher max T-O weight than earlier models. Powered by Astazou XIVM turboshaft with max rating of 640 kW (858 shp) and max continuous rating of 441 kW (592 shp).

SA 342M. For ALAT (French Army Light Aviation Corps). Differs from SA 342L₁ in having an ALAT instrument panel. Optional equipment specified as standard

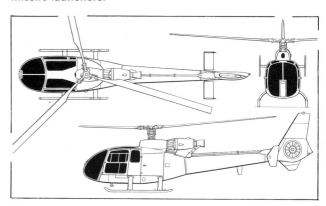

Aérospatiale SA 341D Gazelle. *(Pilot Press)*

by ALAT includes SFIM PA 85G autopilot, Crouzet Nadir self-contained navigation system, Decca 80 Doppler and night flying equipment. An exhaust deflector remains optional. Order for first increment of planned total of 158 announced in December 1978, each armed with four Hot missiles and gyro stabilised sight for anti-tank warfare. Deliveries to the ALAT trials unit (GALSTA) began on 1 February 1980, and to an operational unit on 9 June 1980.

A two-stretcher ambulance configuration has received FAA supplemental type certification. No major modification is necessary to convert the aircraft to carry two patients longitudinally on the port side of the cabin, one above the other, leaving room for the pilot and a medical attendant in tandem on the starboard side. The dual spineboard arrangement weighs 27 kg (60 lb) and stows into the baggage compartment when not in use.

Under an Anglo-French agreement signed in 1967, Gazelles are produced jointly with Westland Helicopters Ltd; they have also been built under licence in Egypt and Yugoslavia. A total of 1,185 had been delivered for civil and military operation in 39 countries by 1 February 1987. Yugoslavia had built a further 222 by that date.

Three Class Elc records were set by the SA 341-01 at Istres on 13 and 14 May 1971, and were unbeaten by mid-1986.

These were: 167.28 knots (310.00 km/h; 192.62 mph) in a straight line over a 3 km course; 168.36 knots (312.00 km/h; 193.87 mph) in a straight line over a 15/25 km course; and 159.72 knots (296.00 km/h; 183.93 mph) over a 100 km closed circuit.

The following details apply to the SA 342, except where indicated:

TYPE: Five-seat light utility helicopter.

ROTOR SYSTEM. Three-blade semi-articulated main rotor and 13-blade shrouded fan anti-torque tail rotor (known as a 'fenestron' or 'fan-in-fin'). Rotorhead and rotor mast form a single unit. The main rotor blades are of NACA 0012 section, attached to NAT hub by flapping hinges. There are no drag hinges. Tail-rotor blades have articulation for pitch change only. Main rotor blades can be folded manually for stowage. Rotor brake standard.

FUSELAGE: Cockpit structure is based on a welded light alloy frame which carries the windows and doors. This is mounted on a conventional semi-monocoque lower structure consisting of two longitudinal box sections connected by frames and bulkheads. Central section encloses the baggage hold and main fuel tank and supports the main reduction gearbox. Rear section supports the engine and tailboom.

TAIL UNIT: Small horizontal stabiliser on tailboom, ahead of tail-rotor fin.

LANDING GEAR: Steel-tube skid type. Wheel can be fitted at rear of each skid for ground handling. Provision for alternative float or ski landing gear.

POWERPLANT: One Turboméca Astazou XIVM turboshaft engine, installed above fuselage aft of cabin and rated at 640 kW (858 shp). Two standard fuel tanks in fuselage (one beneath baggage compartment) with total usable capacity of 545 litres (144 US gallons; 120 Imp gallons). Provision for 200 litre (53 US gallon; 44 Imp gallon) ferry tank inside rear cabin. Total possible usable fuel capacity 745 litres (197 US gallons; 164 Imp gallons).

ACCOMMODATION: Crew of one or two side-by-side in front of cabin, with bench seat to the rear for a further three persons. The bench seat can be folded into floor wells to leave a completely flat cargo floor. Access to baggage compartment via rear cabin bulkhead, or via optional door on starboard side. Cargo tiedown points in cabin floor. Baggage compartment at rear of cabin. Dual controls optional.

AVIONICS AND EQUIPMENT: Optional communications equipment includes UHF, VHF, HF, intercom systems and homing aids. Optional navigation equipment includes radio compass, radio altimeter and VOR. Blind-flying instrumentation and autopilot optional. A variety of operational equipment can be fitted, according to role, including a 700 kg (1,540 lb) cargo sling, 135 kg (300 lb) rescue hoist, one or two stretchers (internally), or photographic and survey equipment.

ARMAMENT: Military loads can include two pods of Brandt 68 mm or FZ 2.75 in rockets, two AS.12 wire guided missiles with APX-Bézu 334 gyro stabilised sight, four or six Hot wire-guided missiles with APX 397 gyro stabilised sight, two forward firing 7.62 mm machine-guns, or one GIAT axial 20 mm gun.

DIMENSIONS, EXTERNAL:	
Main rotor diameter	10.50 m (34 ft 5½ in)
Tail rotor diameter	0.695 m (2 ft 3⅜ in)
Length overall	11.97 m (39 ft 3 5/16 in)
Length of fuselage, incl tail rotor	9.53 m (31 ft 3 3/16 in)
Width, rotors folded	2.04 m (6 ft 8½ in)
Height to top of rotorhead	2.72 m (8 ft 11⅛ in)
Height overall	3.19 m (10 ft 5½ in)
Skid track	2.015 m (6 ft 7 5/16 in)
AREA:	
Main rotor blades, each	1.57 m² (16.9 sq ft)
WEIGHTS:	
Weight empty: 342L₁	997 kg (2,198 lb)

Max T-O and landing weight:	
342L₁	2,000 kg (4,410 lb)
342M	1,900 kg (4,188 lb)
PERFORMANCE (SA 342L₁ at max T-O weight):	
Never-exceed speed at S/L	151 knots (280 km/h; 174 mph)
Max cruising speed at S/L	140 knots (260 km/h; 161 mph)
Max rate of climb at S/L	468 m (1,535 ft)/min
Service ceiling	4,100 m (13,450 ft)
Hovering ceiling: IGE	3,040 m (9,975 ft)
OGE	2,370 m (7,775 ft)
Range at S/L with standard fuel	
	383 nm (710 km; 440 miles)

Aérospatiale SA 365F/AS.15TT Dauphin 2

On 13 October 1980, the government of Saudi Arabia placed in France orders for military equipment valued at 14,400 million francs. Known as the Sawari contract, it included the supply of 24 SA 365F Dauphin 2 helicopters, based on the SA 365N. The first four of these are equipped with an Omera ORB 32 radar for search and rescue duties. The remaining 20 are anti-ship helicopters, equipped with Thomson-CSF Agrion 15 radar, Aérospatiale AS.15TT all-weather air-to-surface missiles and Crouzet MAD, for operation both from shore bases and frigates. Subsequent orders include five for Ireland, equiped with Bendix RDR L500 search radar, SFIM L55 autopilot, CDV L55 four-axis flight director/coupler, Crouzet Nadir Mk II nav computer, ESD Cina B Doppler, Crouzet ONS 200A long-distance nav system and five-screen EFIS instrumentation, for fishery surveillance and SAR from ship and shore bases.

An SA 365N was modified to flight-test the equipment and weapon systems of the SA 365F, and made its first flight in the new configuration on 22 February 1982. It was followed by the first production SA 365F on 2 July 1982, equipped as a search and rescue helicopter with arrester hook, search radar, searchlight, self-contained navigation system, auto-

Aérospatiale SA 365F/AS.15TT Dauphin 2 anti-ship helicopter firing one of its missiles.

matic hover/transition coupler and rescue winch. This aircraft completed deck landing trials on the French Navy missile frigate *De Grasse* and destroyer *Duperré* in the Summer of 1983, landing in headwinds of up to 90 km/h (56 mph), crosswinds up to 56 km/h (35 mph), tailwinds of 10 km/h (6 mph) and with the ships rolling up to 12°.

The anti-ship version carries the Agrion 15 radar on a roll-stabilised pivot mounting under its nose to ensure a 360° field of sweep, a total of four AS.15TT missiles in pairs on an outrigger on each side of the fuselage, and the MAD 'bird' on the port side of the rear fuselage. Agrion 15 is derived from the Iguane radar fitted to the Atlantique ATL2 maritime patrol aircraft, and possesses a track-while-scan capability that enables it to detect threats over long ranges while tracking ten targets simultaneously. Range of the AS.15TT missile is greater than 8 nm (15 km; 9.3 miles). In addition to locating and attacking hostile warships, the SA 365F/AS.15TT can be utilised for coastal surveillance and ship escort duties, and to provide over-the-horizon target designation for long-range anti-ship missiles launched from ship or shore. An anti-submarine version is available, initially with MAD, sonobuoys and homing torpedoes, but with provision for Alcatel HS 12 sonar.

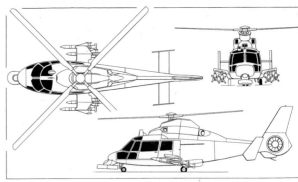

Aérospatiale SA 365F Dauphin 2. *(Pilot Press)*

The SA 365F carries a normal crew of two, has provision for 10 passengers and is powered by two Turboméca Arriel IM turboshaft engines, each rated at 522 kW (700 shp) for take-off and with a max continuous rating of 465 kW (624 shp). Compared with the SA 365N, it has a larger, carbonfibre 11-blade 'fenestron' to improve hovering performance, particularly in the most severe condition of hovering with the wind from threequarters aft.

DIMENSIONS, EXTERNAL:		PERFORMANCE (at max T-O weight):	
Main rotor diameter	11.93 m (39 ft 1¾ in)	Never-exceed speed	160 knots (296 km/h; 184 mph)
Diameter of 'fenestron'	1.10 m (3 ft 7⁵⁄₁₆ in)	Max cruising speed at S/L	
Length overall, rotor turning	13.74 m (45 ft 1 in)		154 knots (285 km/h; 177 mph)
Length of fuselage	12.11 m (39 ft 8¾ in)	Max rate of climb at S/L	390 m (1,280 ft)/min
Width over missiles	4.20 m (13 ft 9½ in)	Hovering ceiling: IGE	2,150 m (7,050 ft)
Height to top of tail fin	3.99 m (13 ft 1 in)	OGE	1,200 m (3,935 ft)
WEIGHTS:		Range with max standard fuel at S/L	
Weight empty	2,172 kg (4,788 lb)		467 nm (865 km; 537 miles)
Max slung load	1,600 kg (3,527 lb)		
Max T-O weight, internal or external load			
	4,100 kg (9,039 lb)		

Aérospatiale SA 365M Panther

This multi-role military development of the Dauphin 2 was first flown in prototype form on 29 February 1984. It has since undergone considerable refinement, and was first shown in production form, as the Panther, on 30 April 1986. The Panther will be available for delivery in 1988.

The airframe of the Panther is basically similar to that of the SA 365N, but with greater emphasis on survivability in combat areas. Composite materials are used exclusively for the dynamic components and for an increased (15 per cent) proportion of the fuselage structure. The crew seats are armoured, and similar protection will be extended to the flying control servos and engine controls of production Panthers. Other features include a cable cutter, self-sealing fuel tanks and redundant hydraulic circuits. Further development is expected to permit continued operation of the main transmission after total loss of lubricating oil.

Similar attention has been paid to crashworthiness. The crew seats will tolerate 15*g*. The entire basic airframe is designed to withstand an impact at a vertical speed of 7 m (23 ft)/s at max T-O weight; the fuel system is capable of withstanding a 14 m (46 ft)/s crash.

The Panther is powered by two Turboméca TM 333-1M turboshaft engines, each rated at 681 kW (913 shp), and utilises the larger carbonfibre 'fenestron' of the SA 365F. To reduce IR signature, the airframe is finished in low IR reflecting paint, and the engine efflux is first mixed with cool

ambient air and then ejected upward. Noise level is low, and radar signature is minimised by the aircraft's composite structure and special paints. Night operations are made practicable by adaptation of the cockpit to nap-of-the-earth flight using night vision goggles. Equipment can include a Sherloc radar warning receiver, IR jammer and chaff dispenser.

As a high-speed assault transport, the Panther will carry a crew of two and eight to ten troops over a radius of action of

Second prototype SA 365M Panther carrying two 20 mm gun pods. *(Brian M. Service)*

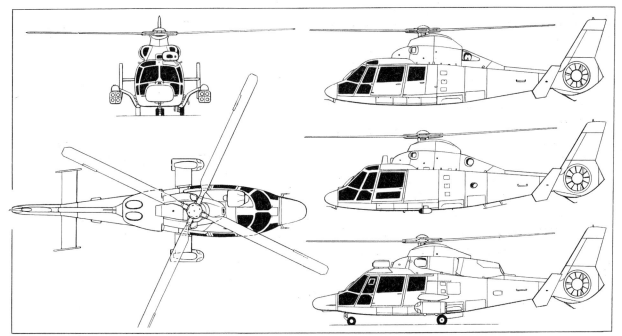

Aérospatiale SA 365M Panther. Additional side views: SA 365N₁ Dauphin 2 (top), SA 366G-1 Dolphin (centre)
The Dolphin is the version developed for the US Coast Guard and is US designated HH-65A. *(Pilot Press)*

215 nm (400 km; 248 miles), or 60 troops per hour over 11 nm (20 km; 12 miles). For close support missions of three-hour duration, the fuselage-side outriggers can each carry a pack of 22 Brandt 68 mm rockets, a launcher for 19 Forges de Zeebrugge 2.75 in rockets or a 20 mm GIAT gun pod with 180 rounds. Three-hour day or night anti-tank missions are possible, carrying four two-round packs of Hot anti-tank missiles with an associated Viviane roof mounted stabilised sight. Operations against fixed-wing aircraft or other helicopters are envisaged, using either 20 mm guns or four two-round packs of Matra Mistral infra-red homing air-to-air missiles. Secondary roles could include armed or unarmed reconnaissance, electronic warfare, target designation, aerial command post, search and rescue, casualty evacuation (four stretchers) and transport of up to 1,600 kg (3,525 lb) of external freight.

DIMENSIONS, EXTERNAL: As for SA 365F Dauphin 2
WEIGHTS:
Basic operating weight, incl 2 crew	2,690 kg (5,930 lb)
Max slung load	1,600 kg (3,527 lb)
Max T-O weight, internal or external load	
	4,100 kg (9,039 lb)

PERFORMANCE (at max T-O weight):
Never-exceed speed	160 knots (296 km/h; 184 mph)
Max cruising speed at S/L	
	150 knots (278 km/h; 172 mph)
Max rate of climb at S/L	276 m (905 ft)/min
Hovering ceiling: IGE	3,000 m (9,840 ft)
OGE	2,300 m (7,545 ft)
Range with max standard fuel at S/L	
	400 nm (740 km; 460 miles)

Breguet Alizé

The Breguet Type 1050 Alizé (Tradewind) three-seat carrier-based anti-submarine 'hunter-killer' was derived from the Type 960 Vultur of 1951, which had an unusual mixed powerplant arrangement comprising a Hispano-Suiza built Nene turbojet engine in the rear fuselage and an Armstrong Siddeley Mamba turboprop in the nose. The first prototype Alizé made its initial flight on 6 October 1956, and was followed by five pre-production aircraft. These had logged a total of 2,300 flying hours by the end of 1958, including catapulting and deck landing trials on the carrier *Arromanches*.

Orders for 75 Alizés were placed by the French Navy for use from both light and fleet-type aircraft carriers. The first was delivered on 20 May 1959. A further 12, ordered by the Indian Navy, were delivered from 1961, and the force took surplus French aircraft to raise its total to 17. Of these, five or six are still available, although they have now been withdrawn from carrier use. Until final phase-out in 1989, Indian Alizés will undertake coastal protection from land bases.

Modernised French Navy Breguet Alizé carrier-based anti-submarine aircraft.

37

The French Navy modernised 28 of its remaining 34 Alizé carrier based anti-submarine aircraft, to extend their effectiveness through the 1990s. The work included installation of new Thomson-CSF Iguane radar in the retractable underfuselage radome, as fitted to the Atlantique 2, a Crouzet Oméga Equinox navigation system, and ESM equipment. All 28 updated aircraft were back in service with 6F Flottille at Nimes-Garons by 1986. Since 1959, the French Navy Alizés have accumulated about 270,000 flying hours.

TYPE: Three-seat carrier-based anti-submarine aircraft.

WINGS: Cantilever low-wing monoplane, with hydraulically folding outer panels. Thickness/chord ratio 15% at root, 10% at tip. Double-slotted flaps in inboard and outboard sections on each wing.

FUSELAGE: Semi-monocoque structure.

TAIL UNIT: Conventional cantilever type, with tailplane and balanced elevators, tall fin with horn-balanced rudder.

LANDING GEAR: Retractable tricycle type, the main wheels retracting forward into combined landing gear/armament nacelles on the wing leading edges. Twin wheels on each main unit, size 6.5 × 10. Steerable nosewheel. Hydraulic brakes and landing gear retraction. Retractable arrester hook under rear fuselage.

POWERPLANT: One 2,100 ehp Rolls-Royce Dart RDa 7 Mk 21 turboprop engine, driving a Rotol four-blade variable-pitch metal propeller with spinner. Five fuel tanks, comprising one 114 litre (30 US gallon; 25 Imp gallon) tank and one 232 litre (61.3 US gallon; 51 Imp gallon) tank in each inner wing section and one 1,409 litre (372 US gallon; 310 Imp gallon) fuselage tank.

ACCOMMODATION: Enclosed cabin with side-by-side seating for the pilot and forward radar operator at front and sideways-facing seat for rear operator behind on starboard side.

AVIONICS: See introductory notes.

WEAPONS: Weapons bay in fuselage accommodates a torpedo or three 160 kg depth charges. Racks for two 160 kg or 175 kg depth charges under inner sections of wings, and for six 5 in rockets or two AS.12 missiles under outer sections. Sonobuoys in front of wheel fairing.

DIMENSIONS, EXTERNAL		PERFORMANCE:	
Wing span	15.60 m (51 ft 2 in)	Max level speed at 3,050 m (10,000 ft)	
Length overall	13.86 m (45 ft 5¾ in)		280 knots (518 km/h; 322 mph)
Width folded	7.00 m (22 ft 11½ in)	Max level speed at S/L	248 knots (460 km/h; 286 mph)
Height overall	5.00 m (16 ft 5 in)	Patrol speed 130–200 knots (240–370 km/h; 149–230 mph)	
Wheel track	4.87 m (15 ft 11¾ in)	Max rate of climb at S/L	420 m (1,380 m)/min
Wheelbase	5.67 m (18 ft 7¼ in)	Service ceiling	8,000 m (26,250 ft)
AREA:		T-O run from land	575 m (1,886 ft)
Wings, gross	36.00 m² (387.5 sq ft)	Landing run from land	470 m (1,542 ft)
WEIGHTS:		Range	1,349 nm (2,500 km; 1,553 miles)
Weight empty, equipped	5,700 kg (12,566 lb)	Max endurance with 475 litre auxiliary tank	7 h 40 min
Max T-O weight	8,200 kg (18,078 lb)	Normal endurance	5 h 10 min

Dassault-Breguet
AVIONS MARCEL DASSAULT–BREGUET AVIATION

Avions Marcel Dassault–Breguet Aviation resulted from the merger in December 1971 of Avions Marcel Dassault with Breguet Aviation. In January 1979, 20 per cent of its stock was assigned to the French State, and in November 1981 the State shareholding was raised to 46 per cent. Due to a double voting right of some of its shares, the French State holds a majority control of the company.

Dassault-Breguet is engaged in the development and production of military and civil aircraft, and servo control equipment. Series production of its aircraft is undertaken under a widespread subcontracting programme, with final assembly and flight testing handled by the company. Its 18 separate works and facilities cover about 653,335 m² (7,032,500 sq ft), with a total of about 15,000 employees.

Dassault-Breguet has established close links with the industries of other countries. The programme for the Atlantique maritime patrol aircraft associates manufacturers in Belgium, France, West Germany, Italy and the Netherlands under the overall responsibility of their respective governments. In the same way the British and French governments are associated in the SEPECAT concern, formed to control the Dassault-Breguet/BAe Jaguar programme; and the West German and French governments are associated in the Dassault-Breguet/Dornier Alpha Jet programme. Purchase of Mirage fighters by Belgium and Spain led to Belgian and Spanish participation in Mirage III/5 and Mirage F1 production. Similarly, purchase of Mirage 2000 fighters by Greece has led to co-production of components for this aircraft by the Hellenic Aerospace Industry. Dassault-Breguet's Biarritz-Parme factory manufactures fuselages for Fokker.

Dassault-Breguet Mirage III

The Mirage III was designed initially as a Mach 2 high-altitude all-weather interceptor, capable of performing ground support missions and requiring only small airstrips. Developed versions include a two-seat trainer, long-range fighter-bomber and reconnaissance aircraft. A total of 1,412 Mirage III/5/50s of all types (incl 870 Mirage IIIs) was ordered and delivered for service in 20 countries, including licence production abroad. Current users of the Mirage III are Abu Dhabi, Argentina, Australia, Brazil, Chile, France, Lebanon, Pakistan, South Africa, Spain, Switzerland and Venezuela.

The experimental prototype flew for the first time on 17 November 1956, powered by a SNECMA Atar 101G turbojet with afterburner (44.1 kN; 9,900 lb st).

Since 1977, Dassault has been involved in programmes to update the navigation and attack systems, flight aids, radio com/nav, powerplant and other features of in-service Mirage III/5/50 aircraft. In particular, several air forces have awarded Dassault contracts to install an inertial platform, digital computer, CRT head-up display, air-to-ground laser rangefinder and other equipment for improved navigational accuracy, easier target acquisition, and high bombing precision in the various CCIP (continuous computation of the impact point) or CCRP (continuous computation of the release point) modes, including standoff capability through the introduction of CCRP with initial point. Combat efficiency in the air-to-air gunnery mode is improved considerably by display of a highly accurate hot-line on the HUD.

All of these improvements are designed to decrease the pilot's task, so enhancing efficiency and survivability, in parallel with improved reliability.

Another major improvement available for the Mirage III/5/50 series is a flight refuelling kit able to offer an increase of 30 to more than 100 per cent in radius of action. This system was demonstrated in flight before becoming generally available to Mirage operators in 1986. It involves lengthening the nose of the aircraft by 90 mm (3½ in) to accommodate system changes associated with a non-retractable probe on the starboard side, forward of the windscreen, and a single-point pressure refuelling port for both internal and external tanks. Overall refuelling can be accomplished at a rate of 1,000 litres (264 US gallons; 220 Imp gallons)/min. Turnaround time between missions can be greatly reduced, at no cost in Mach 2 performance.

Versions of the Mirage III currently in service are as follows:

Mirage III-B. Two-seat version of the III-A pre-series 'production' version, with tandem seating under one-piece canopy; radar deleted, but fitted with radio beacon equipment. Fuselage 0.6 m (23.6 in) longer than that of III-A. Intended primarily as a trainer, but suitable for strike sorties, carrying same air-to-surface armament as Mirage III-C. Prototype flew for first time on 20 October 1959, and first production model on 19 July 1962. Total of 174 two-seaters ordered, including III-B and III-D variants for 19 countries.

Mirage III-BE. Two-seat version of the III-E for French Air Force. Similar model also supplied to foreign air forces.

Mirage III-C. All-weather interceptor and day ground-attack fighter. Full production version of III-A with SNECMA Atar 9B turbojet engine, optional SEPR 841

Mirage III-BS two-seat trainer in Swiss Air Force service.

rocket engine and CSF Cyrano I*bis* air-to-air radar. Initial series of 95 for French Air Force, of which the first flew on 9 October 1960. One supplied to Swiss Air Force. Total of 244 built, including III-CJ for Israel and III-CZ for South Africa.

Mirage III-D. Two-seat version, built initially in Australia for the RAAF. Similar, French-built models ordered by 12 countries, including six more for Australia. Atar 9C afterburning turbojet engine. Tandem seating under one-piece canopy; radar deleted, but fitted with radio beacon equipment. Intended primarily as a trainer, but suitable for strike sorties, carrying air-to-surface armament. Total of 186 Mirage III-B/III-D/5 two-seaters sold to 20 countries.

Mirage III-D2Z. For South Africa. Generally similar to III-D but with SNECMA Atar 9K-50 turbojet. Delivered 1974–75. (See also Atlas Cheetah.)

Mirage III-E. Long-range fighter-bomber/intruder version, with Atar 9C afterburning turbojet engine, of which 532 were built for 13 air forces. First of three prototypes flew on 5 April 1961, and the first delivery of a production III-E was made in January 1964. Thirty III-Es of the 4e Escadre of the French Air Force, equipping two squadrons at Luxeuil, were made carriers of the 15 kt AN 52 tactical nuclear weapon.

Mirage III-O. Version of the Mirage III-E manufactured under licence in Australia. Main differences compared with the standard III-E are fitment of a Sperry twin gyro platform and PHI 5CI navigation unit. First two III-Os assembled in

South African Air Force Dassault-Breguet Mirage III-EZ at Waterkloof. *(Aviation Picture Library)*

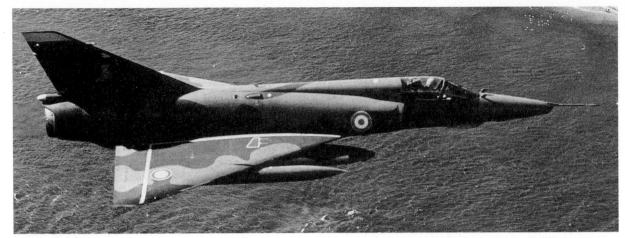

Mirage III-RD, with improved Doppler navigation system and Omera 40 and 33 cameras in the modified nose.

France; first of these handed over on 9 April 1963. Further 98 built in Australia.

Mirage III-R. Reconnaissance version of III-E. Set of five Omera type 31 cameras, in place of radar in nose, can be focused in four different arrangements for very-low-altitude, medium-altitude, high-altitude and night-reconnaissance missions. Self contained navigation system. Provision for air-to-surface armament. Two prototypes, of which the first flew in November 1961. Total of 159 production models ordered, including Mirage 5-Rs, for nine air forces.

Mirage III-R2Z. For South Africa. Generally similar to III-R but with SNECMA Atar 9K-50 turbojet. Delivered 1974–75.

Mirage III-RD. Similar to III-R but with improved Doppler navigation system in fairing under front fuselage, gyro gunsight and nose pack containing Omera 40 and 33 cameras. Twenty built for French Air Force; others, with avionics changes, for Pakistan. An unspecified variant related to the French Air Force version has provision for carrying SAT Cyclope infra-red tracking equipment in a modified nosecone.

Mirage III-S. Developed from the Mirage III-E, with a Hughes TARAN electronics fire-control system and armament of HM-55 Falcon missiles. Thirty-six supplied to Swiss Air Force, of which the first two were built in France and the remainder by the Federal Aircraft Factory in Switzerland (see also Switzerland).

The following description refers to the Mirage III-E, but is generally applicable to all versions:

TYPE: Single-seat fighter-bomber/intruder aircraft.

WINGS: Cantilever low-wing monoplane of delta planform, with conical camber. Thickness/chord ratio 4% to 3.5%.

Dassault-Breguet Mirage III-E. *(Pilot Press)*

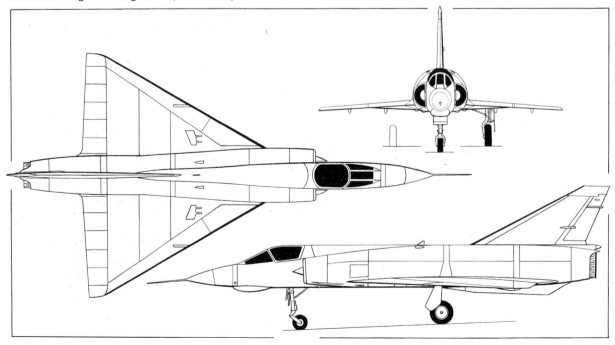

Anhedral 1°. No incidence. Sweepback on leading edge 60° 34'. Trailing edge of each wing comprises two elevons for pitch and roll control, and an inboard flap which also has an elevator function. All control surfaces hydraulically powered by Dassault twin-cylinder actuators with artificial feel. Air-brakes, comprising small panels hinged to upper and lower wing surfaces, near leading edge.

FUSELAGE: 'Waisted' structure in accordance with area rule.

TAIL UNIT: Sweptback fin and hydraulically actuated powered rudder only. Dassault twin-cylinder actuators with artificial feel.

LANDING GEAR: Retractable tricycle type, with single wheel on each unit. Hydraulic retraction, nosewheel rearward main units inward. Messier-Hispano-Bugatti disc brakes. Mainwheel tyres size 750 × 230-15/1. Nosewheel tyre size 450 × 390-05. Braking parachute.

POWERPLANT: One SNECMA Atar 9C turbojet engine (60.8 kN; 13,670 lb st with afterburning), fitted with an overspeed system which is engaged automatically from Mach 1.4 and permits a thrust increase of approx 8 per cent in the high supersonic speed range. Movable half-cone centrebody in each air intake. Optional and jettisonable SEPR 844 single-chamber rocket motor (14.7 kN; 3,300 lb st) under engine bay. Space for structural fuel tank, capacity 550 litres (145 US gallons; 121 Imp gallons), when rocket motor is not fitted. Four flexible fuel tanks around engine air inlet ducts, combined capacity 1,020 litres (269 US gallons; 224 Imp gallons). Two integral fuel tanks in each wing, combined capacity 1,370 litres (362 US gallons; 301 Imp gallons). Total available internal fuel (without rocket motor) 2,940 litres (777 US gallons; 646 Imp gallons). Provision for this to be augmented by two 625, 1,100, 1,300 or 1,700 litre (165, 291, 343, or 449 US gallon; 137, 242, 285 or 374 Imp gallon) underwing drop-tanks; 500 litre (132 US gallon; 110 Imp gallon) non-jettisonable supersonic tanks; JL-100 jettisonable tanks each housing both 250 litres (66 US gallons; 55 Imp gallons) fuel and air-to-surface rockets; Bidon Cyclope jettisonable tanks each housing 1,100 litres (291 US gallons; 242 Imp gallons) fuel and electronic equipment; or Bidon Homing jettisonable tanks housing 850 litres (225 US gallons; 187 Imp gallons) fuel and electronic equipment.

ACCOMMODATION: Single seat under rearward-hinged canopy. Hispano-built Martin-Baker RM4 zero-altitude/90 knots (167 km/h; 104 mph) ejection seat.

AVIONICS AND EQUIPMENT: Duplicated UHF, Tacan, Doppler, CSF Cyrano II fire-control radar in nose, navigation computer, bombing computer and automatic gunsight. Central gyro and other avionics provide accurate and stabilised heading information. CSF 97 sighting system gives air-to-air facility for cannon and missiles, air-to-ground facility for dive bombing or LABS, and navigation facility for horizon and heading.

ARMAMENT: Ground attack armament consists normally of two 30 mm DEFA 552A guns in fuselage, each with 125 rounds of incendiary, high-explosive or armour piercing ammunition, and two 1,000 lb bombs, or an AS.30 air-to-surface missile under the fuselage and 1,000 lb bombs under the wings. Total external load, on five hardpoints, 4,000 kg (8,818 lb). Alternative underwing stores include combined tank/bomb carriers, each with 500 litres (110 Imp gallons) of fuel and 907 kg (2,000 lb) of bombs; JL-100 pods, each with 250 litres (66 US gallons; 55 Imp gallons)

of fuel and 18 rockets; and jettisonable underwing fuel tanks. For interception duties, one Matra R:530 air-to-air missile can be carried under fuselage, with optional guns and two Matra Magic missiles.

DIMENSIONS, EXTERNAL:	
Wing span	8.22 m (26 ft 11½ in)
Length overall: III-E	15.03 m (49 ft 3½ in)
III-R	15.50 m (50 ft 10¼ in)
Height overall	4.50 m (14 ft 9 in)
Wheel track	3.15 m (10 ft 4 in)
Wheelbase: III-E	4.87 m (15 ft 11¾ in)
AREA:	
Wings, gross	35.00 m² (376.7 sq ft)
WEIGHTS:	
Weight empty: III-E	7,050 kg (15,540 lb)
III-R	6,600 kg (14,550 lb)
T-O weight 'clean': III-E	9,600 kg (21,165 lb)
Max T-O weight: III-E, R	13,700 kg (30,200 lb)

PERFORMANCE (Mirage III-E, in 'clean' condition with guns installed, except where indicated):

Max level speed at 12,000 m (39,375 ft)	
Mach 2.2 (1,268 knots; 2,350 km/h; 1,460 mph)	
Max level speed at S/L	750 knots (1,390 km/h; 863 mph)
Cruising speed at 11,000 m (36,000 ft)	Mach 0.9
Time to 11,000 (36,000 ft), Mach 0.9	3 min
Time to 15,000 m (49,200 ft), Mach 1.8	6 min 50 s
Service ceiling at Mach 1.8	17,000 m (55,775 ft)
Ceiling, using rocket motor	23,000 m (75,450 ft)
T-O run, according to mission (up to max T-O weight)	
700–1,600 m (2,295–5,250 ft)	
Landing run, using brake parachute	
700 m (2,295 ft)	
Combat radius, ground attack	
647 nm (1,200 km; 745 miles)	

Dassault-Breguet Mirage 3 NG

This new-generation (Nouvelle Génération) development of the Mirage III/5/50 series is based on the same well-proven airframe, but introduces features which give it much improved air combat performance and survivability in air-to-ground operations. It is powered, like the Mirage 50 and F1, by a SNECMA Atar 9K-50 turbojet engine, rated at 70.6 kN (15,873 lb st) with afterburning. New aerodynamic advances are evident in the added non-retractable swept-back foreplanes and highly-swept wing root leading-edge

Prototype of the Dassault-Breguet Mirage 3 NG.

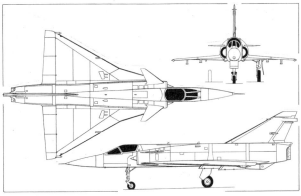

Dassault-Breguet Mirage 3 NG. *(Pilot Press)*

DIMENSIONS, EXTERNAL
Wing span	8.22 m (26 ft 11½ in)
Length overall	15.65 m (51 ft 4¼ in)
Height overall	4.50 m (14 ft 9 in)
Wheel track	3.15 m (10 ft 4 in)
Wheelbase	4.87 m (15 ft 11¾ in)

AREAS:
Wings, gross	35.00 m² (376.7 sq ft)
Foreplanes	1.00 m² (10.8 sq ft)

WEIGHTS:
T-O weight 'clean'	10,000 kg (22,050 lb)
Max T-O weight	14,700 kg (32,400 lb)

PERFORMANCE:
Max authorised Mach number in level flight	2.2
Max authorised speed in level flight	
750 knots (1,390 km/h; 863 mph) IAS	
Service ceiling at Mach 2	16,460 m (54,000 ft)

extensions. It also features a fully fly-by-wire control system derived from that of the Mirage 2000, and can be equipped for in-flight refuelling.

The navigation/attack system of the Mirage 3 NG is an up-to-date and highly reliable system composed basically of an inertial platform, CRT head-up display, and optional forward looking sensors such as modernised Cyrano IV radar, a laser rangefinder or Agave air-to-air/air-to-surface radar.

Maximum take-off weight is increased significantly by comparison with the Mirage III. This enables the external load carrying capability to be increased, notably by the addition of four lateral stores stations on the fuselage. Provision is made for adapting the Mirage 3 NG to advanced weapons, and for its use as either a specialised reconnaissance aircraft or a vehicle for mission-adapted reconnaissance packs.

The prototype Mirage 3 NG flew for the first time on 21 December 1982. No orders have yet been announced.

Dassault-Breguet Mirage 5

The Mirage 5 is a ground-attack aircraft using the same airframe and engine as the Mirage III-E. The basic VFR version has simplified avionics, 470 litres (124 US gallons; 103 Imp gallons) greater fuel capacity than the III-E, in a tank between the engine air intakes, and considerably extended stores carrying capability. It combines the full Mach 2+ capability of the Mirage III, and its ability to operate from semi-prepared airfields, with simpler maintenance. In ground-attack configuration, up to 4,000 kg (8,818 lb) of weapons and 1,000 litres (264 US gallons; 220 Imp gallons) of fuel can be carried externally on seven wing and fuselage attachment points. The Mirage 5 can also be flown as an interceptor, with two Magic or Sidewinder air-to-air missiles and 4,700 litres (1,242 US gallons; 1,034 Imp gallons) of external fuel. At customer's option, any degree of IFR/all-weather operation can be provided for, with reduced

Dassault-Breguet Mirage 5 ground-attack aircraft, based on the Mirage III-E. *(Dr Alan Beaumont)*

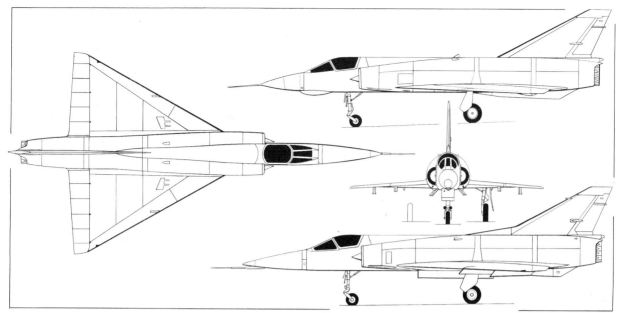

Dassault-Breguet Mirage 5. Upper side view: Mirage III-E. *(Pilot Press)*

fuel or weapons load. The Mirage 5 was flown for the first time on 19 May 1967.

A total of 525 Mirage 5s was ordered for eleven air forces, including Mirage 5-R reconnaissance variants and two-seat Mirage 5-Ds. Customers were the air forces of Abu Dhabi, Argentina, Belgium, Colombia, Egypt, France, Gabon, Libya, Pakistan, Peru and Zaire.

Since 1977, a Mirage Advanced Technology Update Programme has encompassed the Mirage 5. Details can be found under the Mirage III entry. The flight refuelling kit has already been ordered by one air force for its Mirage 5s. Current modernisation programmes, involving the Peruvian Mirage 5 inventory and part of the Egyptian inventory, are in progress in the respective home countries. They are intended, primarily, to add an inertial platform, digital computer and CRT head-up display.

Dassault-Breguet Mirage 50

The Mirage 50 multi-mission fighter retains the basic airframe of the Mirage III/5 series, but is powered by the SNECMA Atar 9K-50 turbojet, as fitted in the Mirage F1s of the French Air Force and ten other air forces. This gives 70.6 kN (15,873 lb st) with afterburning, representing a thrust increase of between 17 and 23 per cent compared with standard Mirage III/5s.

The prototype Mirage 50 flew for the first time on 15 April 1979. First and only announced customer was the air force of Chile, which ordered a total of sixteen.

The Mirage 50 was designed to be suitable for air superiority duties with guns and dogfight missiles, air patrol and supersonic interception, and ground attack combined with self-defence capability. It can carry the full range of operational stores, armament and equipment developed for the Mirage III/5 series, and was offered with Agave or Cyrano IVM multi function radar (with Matra Magic or 530

DIMENSIONS, EXTERNAL: As Mirage III-E, except:

Length overall	15.56 m (51 ft $0\frac{1}{2}$ in)

WEIGHTS:

Weight empty, equipped	7,150 kg (15,765 lb)
T-O weight, 'clean'	9,900 kg (21,825 lb)
Max T-O weight	13,700 kg (30,200 lb)

PERFORMANCE:

Max level speed at altitude	Mach 2.2
	(750 knots; 1,390 km/h; 863 mph IAS)
Max rate of climb at S/L	11,160 m (36,600 ft)/min
Time to 17,700 m (58,000 ft) at Mach 2, with two Magic missiles	6 min 48 s
Service ceiling at Mach 2	18,000 m (59,055 ft)
T-O run with two Magic missiles	915 m (3,000 ft)
T-O run at max T-O weight	1,830 m (6,000 ft)

Combat radius with two 400 kg bombs and max external fuel, with reserves:

lo-lo-lo at Mach 0.6	370 nm (685 km; 425 miles)
hi-lo-hi at Mach 0.85/0.9	675 nm (1,250 km; 775 miles)

ENAER-modified Dassault-Breguet Mirage 50 CN, with fixed foreplanes and upgraded avionics.

air-to-air missiles respectively), an inertial nav/attack system, and head-up display. It was also made available in reconnaissance and two-seat training versions. Improvements compared with other delta-wing Mirages include a 15–20 per cent shorter take-off run, improved armament/fuel load, higher rate of climb, faster acceleration and better manoeuvrability. Maximum internal fuel capacity is 3,475 litres (918 US gallons; 764 Imp gallons). Underwing and underfuselage tanks can increase total capacity to 4,700 litres (1,242 US gallons; 1,034 Imp gallons).

DIMENSIONS, EXTERNAL: As Mirage III-E, except:	
Length overall	15.56 m (51 ft 0½ in)
WEIGHTS:	
Weight empty, equipped	7,150 kg (15,765 lb)
T-O weight, 'clean'	9,900 kg (21,825 lb)
Max T-O weight	13,700 kg (30,200 lb)
PERFORMANCE:	
Max level speed at altitude	Mach 2.2
	(750 knots; 1,390 km/h; 863 mph IAS)
Max rate of climb at S/L	11,160 m (36,600 ft)/min
Time to 9,150 m (30,000 ft) at Mach 0.9	2 min 36 s
Time to 13,715 m (45,000 ft) at Mach 1.8	4 min 42 s
Service ceiling at Mach 2	18,000 m (59,055 ft)
T-O run with two Magic missiles	800 m (2,625 ft)
T-O run at max T-O weight	1,830 m (6,000 ft)
Combat radius at low altitude with two 400 kg bombs	
	340 nm (630 km: 391 miles)

Dassault-Breguet Mirage 2000

Indian Air Force name: Vajra

The Mirage 2000 was selected on 18 December 1975 as the primary combat aircraft of the French Air Force from the mid-1980s. Under French government contract, it was developed initially as an interceptor and air superiority fighter, powered by a single SNECMA M53 turbofan engine and with Thomson-CSF RDM multi-mode Doppler radar. The Mirage 2000 is equally suitable for reconnaissance, close support, and low-altitude attack missions in areas to the rear of a battlefield.

Five prototypes were built, of which four single-seat multi-

Dassault-Breguet Mirage 2000B of the French Air Force.

role models were funded by the French Air Force and one two-seater by the manufacturers. The first single-seater made its first flight, at Istres, on 10 March 1978, only 27 months after programme launch in December 1975. The second flew on 18 September 1978, the third on 26 April 1979 and the fourth on 12 May 1980. The **Mirage 2000B** two-seat trainer version flew on 11 October 1980 and, like its four predecessors, achieved supersonic speed (between Mach 1.3 and 1.5) during its first flight. On the basis of structural testing, the Mirage 2000 airframe was approved for a load factor of + 9g and rate of roll of 270°/s in subsonic and supersonic flight, clean or with four air-to-air missiles.

A SNECMA M53-2 engine, rated at 83.4 kN (18,740 lb st), was fitted for early prototype testing, and was replaced in 1980 by the uprated M53-5 which also powers initial production aircraft. The first prototype was re-engined subsequently with a more powerful M53-P2, as intended for later production aircraft, and made its first flight in this revised form on 1 July 1983. Meanwhile, the manufacturers' prototype is being used to develop equipment and other changes proposed for future variants and for export models of the Mirage 2000. Further airframes were built for static and fatigue testing.

The first production **Mirage 2000C** made its first flight on 20 November 1982, and deliveries began in 1983. The first production Mirage 2000B flew on 7 October 1983. Escadron de Chasse (EC) 1/2 'Cigognes' was the first French Air Force unit to become operational, at Dijon on 2 July 1984, and has twelve Mirage 2000Cs and three 2000Bs. EC 3/2 'Alsace'

Dassault-Breguet Mirage 2000C armed with Super 530 and Magic air-to-air missiles.

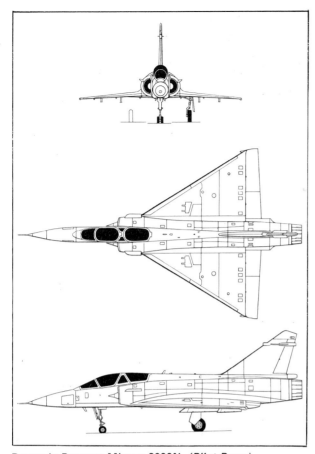

Dassault-Breguet Mirage 2000N. *(Pilot Press)*

First production Dassault-Breguet Mirage 2000N carrying an ASMP nuclear missile.

are planned to increase to 139 Cs, 19 Bs and 85 Ns, out of an eventual requirement of 300 to 400 Mirage 2000s of various versions for the French Air Force. Production is being increased progressively to ten aircraft a month in 1988, to satisfy the present level of domestic and export orders. Wings are manufactured at Martignas, fuselages at Argenteuil; final assembly and flight testing take place at Mérignac.

Export customers for the Mirage 2000 include Abu Dhabi, Egypt, India, Jordan, Peru and Greece. Egypt gave an initial firm contract for 20 (16 2000 EM and 4 BM, all with M53-P2 engines) in January 1982. India placed an initial order for 40 in October 1982 (36 2000H and 4 TH), all of which had been

Dassault-Breguet Mirage 2000C. *(Pilot Press)*

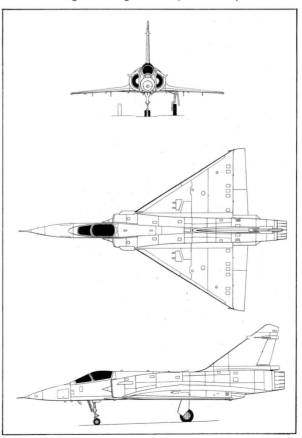

followed and Escadron de Chasse et de Transformation (ECT) 2/2 'Côte d'Or' (OCU) became operational in 1987. Eventually, these aircraft will equip four wings (escadres), each with three interceptor squadrons. More than 100 of Thomson-CSF's new RDI pulse-Doppler radars are being delivered, to replace the RDM in Mirage 2000Cs of the French Air Force.

Following a mid-1979 go-ahead, the first of two prototypes of the **Mirage 2000N** two-seat low-altitude penetration version made its first flight on 2 February 1983; the second flew on 21 September 1983. Strengthened for flight at a typical 600 knots (1,110 km/h; 690 mph) at 60 m (200 ft) above the terrain, this version is intended as a vehicle for the ASMP medium-range air-to-surface nuclear missile, and has ESD Antilope V terrain following radar, two Sagem inertial platforms, improved TRT AHV-12 radio altimeter, Thomson-CSF colour CRT, an Omera vertical camera, special ECM, and two Magic AAMs. Production deliveries began on 19 February 1987, and 36 of the planned total of 112 will be in service by 1988, when the 2000N will become operational as a replacement for Mirage III-E and Jaguar nuclear attack aircraft. Two wings with a total of five tactical squadrons will receive this version, beginning with the 4th Escadre at Luxeuil, followed by the 7th at Toul.

Funding approved under the 1986 defence budget brought the total number of aircraft ordered to 169 (84 Cs, 22 Bs and 63 Ns, of which more than 38 Cs and Bs had been completed by the beginning of 1986), excluding the seven prototypes. By the end of the current 1984–88 defence programme, the totals delivered by 1986. The four THs and 26 of the Hs have M53-5 engines temporarily; the final 10 Hs will be powered from the start by the M53-P2. First flight by a 2000H (KF-101) was made on 21 September 1984, followed in early 1985 by the first TH (KT-201). The first of two Indian squadrons (No. 7 *Battle Axe*) was formed at Gwalior AB on 29 June 1985, when the Mirage 2000 received the Indian name Vajra (Divine Thunder). A follow-on order for nine aircraft was signed in March 1986. Peru ordered 26 aircraft in December 1982 (24 2000P and 2 DP), but has since reduced the total to 12. Abu Dhabi has ordered 36 (22 2000EAD, 8 RAD and 6 DAD); deliveries began in 1986. The RAD reconnaissance versions for this customer will be able to carry a COR 2 or Harold surveillance equipment pod; the second 18 for Abu Dhabi will be fitted with Elettronica (Italy) ECM, comprising threat warning receivers and self-protection jammers. A recent customer is Greece, which in July 1985 signed a contract for 40 (36 2000EGM and 4 BGM), while Jordan has agreed in principle to buy 20.

The following description applies to the single-seat Mirage 2000C, except where indicated:

TYPE: Single-seat interceptor, air superiority and multi-role fighter.

WINGS: Cantilever multi-spar low-wing monoplane of delta planform, with cambered profile. Leading-edge sweepback 58°. Large radius root fairings. Full span two-segment automatic leading-edge slats provide variable camber in combat, but are retracted during all phases of acceleration and low-altitude cruise, to reduce drag. Two-section elevons, forming entire trailing edge of each wing, have carbonfibre skin, with light alloy honeycomb core. Fly-by-wire control system for elevons and slats, with surfaces actuated by hydraulic servo units. No tabs. Retractable airbrake above and below each wing.

FUSELAGE: Conventional semi-monocoque structure, 'waisted' in accordance with area rule; of conventional construction except for glassfibre radome and carbonfibre/light alloy honeycomb panel over avionics compartment, immediately aft of canopy. Small fixed strake, with marked dihedral, near leading edge of each air intake trunk.

TAIL UNIT: Cantilever fin and inset rudder only; latter actuated by fly-by-wire control system via hydraulic servo units. Much of fin skin and all rudder skin of boron/epoxy/carbon composites with light alloy structure for fin and light alloy honeycomb core for rudder. Sweepback on fin leading edge 53°. No tab.

LANDING GEAR: Retractable tricycle type by Messier-Hispano-Bugatti, with twin nosewheels, and single wheel on each main unit. Hydraulic retraction, nosewheels rearward, main units inward. Electro-hydraulic nosewheel steering, through 45° to each side. Manual disconnect permits nosewheel unit to castor through 360° for ground towing. Light alloy wheels and tubeless tyres, size 360 × 135-6 on nosewheels, 750 × 230-15 on mainwheels. Messier-Hispano-Bugatti hydraulically actuated carbon composite disc brakes on mainwheels, with anti-skid units. Runway arrester gear standard. Brake chute in canister above jet nozzle.

POWERPLANT: One SNECMA M53-P2 turbofan engine, rated at 64.3 kN (14,462 lb st) dry and 95.1 kN (21,385 lb st) with afterburning. Movable half-cone centrebody in each air intake. Internal fuel capacity 4,000 litres (1,057 US gallons; 880 Imp gallons) in 2000C, 3,920 litres (1,035 US gallons; 862 Imp gallons) in 2000B. Provision for one jettisonable 1,300 litre (343 US gallon; 286 Imp gallon) fuel tank under centre of fuselage and a 1,700 litre (449 US gallon; 374 Imp gallon) drop-tank under each wing. Total internal/external fuel capacity 8,700 litres (2,298 US gallons; 1,914 Imp gallons) in 2000C, 8,620 litres (2,276 US gallons; 1,896 Imp gallons) in 2000B. Detachable flight refuelling probe forward of cockpit on starboard side.

ACCOMMODATION: Pilot only in 2000C, on Martin-Baker F10Q zero/zero ejection seat, under transparent canopy, in pressurised cockpit. Canopy hinged at rear to open upward.

AVIONICS AND EQUIPMENT: Thomson-CSF RDM multi-mode radar or RDI pulse-Doppler radar, each with operating range of 54 nm (100 km; 62 miles). (Mirage 2000N will have ESD/Thomson-CSF Antilope V ground-scan radar.) Sagem Uliss 52 inertial platform, ESD Type 2084 central digital computer and Digibus digital data bus, Thomson-CSF TMV-980 data display system (VE-130 head-up and VMC-180 head-down) (two head-down in 2000N), Sfena 605 autopilot, Thomson-CSF/ESD ECM with VCM-65 display, Matra Spirale passive counter-measures, LMT Deltac Tacan, LMT NRAI-7A IFF transponder, Socrat 8900 solid state VOR/ILS and IO-300-A marker beacon receiver, TRT radio altimeter (AHV-6 in 2000B and C, AHV-9 in export aircraft, AHV-12 in 2000N), TRT ERA 7000 V/UHF com transceiver, TRT ERA 7200 UHF or EAS secure voice com, Thomson-CSF Serval radar warning receiver, Crouzet type 90 air data computer, and Thomson-CSF Atlis laser designator and marked target seeker (in pod on forward starboard underfuselage station). Omera vertical camera in 2000N.

ARMAMENT: Two 30 mm DEFA 554 cannon in 2000C (not fitted in B or N), with 125 rds/gun. Nine attachments for external stores, five under fuselage and two under each wing. Fuselage centreline and inboard wing stations each stressed for 1,800 kg (3,968 lb) loads; other four fuselage points for 400 kg (882 lb) each, and outboard wing points for 300 kg (661 lb) each. Typical interception weapons comprise two Matra Super 530 or 530D missiles (inboard) and two Matra 550 Magic or Magic 2 missiles (outboard) under wings. Alternatively, each of the four underwing hardpoints can carry a Magic. Primary weapon for 2000N is ASMP tactical nuclear missile. In an air-to-surface role, the Mirage 2000 can carry up to 6,300 kg (13,890 lb) of external stores, including eighteen Matra 250 kg retarded bombs or Thomson-Brandt BAP 100 anti-runway bombs; sixteen Durandal penetration bombs; one or two Matra BGL 1,000 kg laser guided bombs; five or six Matra Belouga cluster bombs or Thomson-Brandt BM 400 400 kg modular bombs; one Rafaut F2 practice bomb launcher; two Aérospatiale AS 30L, Matra Armat anti-radar, or Aérospatiale AM39 Exocet anti-ship, air-to-surface missiles; four Matra LR F4 rocket launchers, each with eighteen 68 mm rockets; two packs of 100 mm rockets; a Dassault-Breguet CC630 gun pod, containing two 30 mm cannon and ammunition; a Dassault-Breguet COR 2 multi-camera pod or Dassault-Breguet AA-3-38 Harold long-range oblique photographic (Lorop) pod; a Thomson-CSF Atlis laser designator/marked target seeker pod; two Thomson-CSF DB 3141/3163 self-defence ECM pods; one Thomson-CSF Caiman offensive or intelligence ECM pod; or an Intertechnique 231-300 'buddy' type in-flight refuelling pod. Fuselage centreline and inboard underwing stations are 'wet' for carriage of jettisonable fuel tanks (see 'Powerplant' paragraph for details). For air defence weapon training, a Cubic Corpn AIS (airborne instrumentation subsystem) pod, externally resembling a Magic missile, can replace the Magic on its launch rail, enabling pilot to simulate a firing without carrying the actual missile.

Dassault-Breguet Mirage 4000 (foreground) flying alongside Rafale A.

DIMENSIONS, EXTERNAL:
Wing span	9.13 m (29 ft 11½ in)
Length overall: 2000C	14.36 m (47 ft 1¼ in)
2000B	14.55 m (47 ft 9 in)
Height overall: 2000C	5.20 m (17 ft 0¾ in)
2000B	5.15 m (16 ft 10¾ in)
Wheel track	3.40 m (11 ft 1¾ in)
Wheelbase	5.00 m (16 ft 4¾ in)

AREA:
Wings, gross	41.0 m² (441.3 sq ft)

WEIGHTS:
Weight empty: 2000C	7,500 kg (16,534 lb)
2000B	7,600 kg (16,755 lb)
Max internal fuel: 2000C	3,160 kg (6,967 lb)
2000B	3,095 kg (6,823 lb)
Max external fuel: 2000C	3,720 kg (8,201 lb)
2000B	3,715 kg (8,190 lb)
Max external stores load	6,300 kg (13,890 lb)
T-O weight 'clean': 2000C	10,860 kg (23,940 lb)
2000B	10,960 kg (24,165 lb)
Max T-O weight: 2000C and B	17,000 kg (37,480 lb)

PERFORMANCE (Mirage 2000C):
Max level speed	over Mach 2.2
Max continuous speed	Mach 2.2
	(800 knots; 1,482 km/h; 921 mph IAS)

Max speed at low altitude without afterburning, carrying eight 250 kg bombs and two Magic missiles
over 600 knots (1,110 km/h; 690 mph)
Min speed in stable flight	100 knots (185 km/h; 115 mph)
Max rate of climb at S/L	17,060 m (56,000 ft)/min
Time to 15,000 m (49,200 ft) and Mach 2	4 min

Time from brake release to intercept target flying at Mach 3 at 24,400 m (80,000 ft) less than 5 min
Service ceiling	18,000 m (59,000 ft)

Range: with four 250 kg bombs
more than 800 nm (1,480 km; 920 miles)
with two 1,700 litre drop-tanks
more than 1,000 nm (1,850 km; 1,150 miles)
with one 1,300 litre and two 1,700 litre drop-tanks
1,800 nm (3,335 km; 2,073 miles)
g limits:	+ 9 normal
	+ 13.5 ultimate

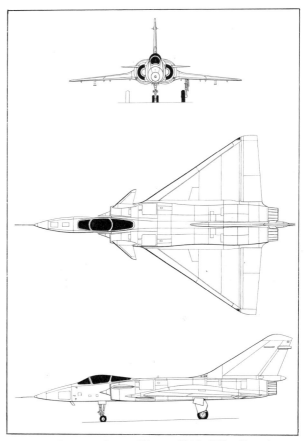

Dassault-Breguet Super Mirage 4000. *(Pilot Press)*

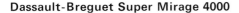

Dassault-Breguet Super Mirage 4000

The Super Mirage 4000 prototype is a twin-turbofan scale-up of the Mirage 2000 that was designed to be suitable for interception as well as low-altitude penetration attack at a considerable distance from its base. It flew for the first time on 9 March 1979.

In 1986 the Super Mirage 4000 resumed flying in support of the Rafale programme, with particular emphasis on evaluating the behaviour of a delta-canard aircraft in turbulent conditions.

Dassault Mirage IV-A and IV-P

The Mirage IV tandem two-seat supersonic delta-wing bomber was designed specifically to deliver a nuclear weapon. Its development and production were undertaken in association with many other companies. In particular, Sud-Aviation took responsibility for the wing and rear fuselage, and Breguet for the tail surfaces.

The original prototype Mirage IV, which flew for the first time on 17 June 1959, was a scaled-up derivative of the Mirage III fighter, powered by two SNECMA Atar 09 turbojets (each 58.8 kN; 13,225 lb st with afterburner) and with a take-off weight of approximately 25,000 kg (55,115

Dassault Mirage IV-P strategic bomber carrying an ASMP test vehicle.

lb). It reached a speed of Mach 1.9 during its 14th test flight in July 1959, and exceeded Mach 2 during its 33rd flight.

The prototype was followed by three pre-production Mirage IVs, of which the first flew on 12 October 1961. Powered by two 62.76 kN (14,110 lb st) Atar 09Cs, this aircraft was slightly larger than the first and was more representative of the production Mirage IV-A, with a large circular radome under its centre fuselage, ahead of the semi-submerged nuclear free-fall bomb. This first pre-production aircraft was used for bombing trials and development at Colomb-Béchar. The second pre-production Mirage IV was similar, and was used to develop the navigation system and for flight refuelling trials with a Boeing KC-135F Stratotanker.

The last of the three pre-production aircraft flew on 23 January 1963, and was a completely operational model with Atar 09Ks, full equipment, including flight refuelling nose-probe, and armament.

The French Air Force ordered a total of 50 production Mirage IV-As for delivery during the period 1964–65. A follow-on order for 12 more was placed subsequently, and the Mirage IV-A became operational with the French Air Force's 91e Escadre de Bombardement at Mont-de-Marsan, the 93e Escadre at Istres, and with a third unit at St Dizier, east of Paris.

The production Mirage IV-A was given advanced electronic navigation and bombing equipment. However, a two-year study of the problems of low-altitude penetration showed that the Mirage IV-A could be adapted for a low-level role with minor modifications. These were subsequently introduced on the assembly line and incorporated retrospectively into aircraft already delivered.

Following the deployment of new ballistic forces (MSBS missiles on *Le Redoutable* class submarines and SSBS land-based missiles), Mirage IV-As took on a tactical strike role with nuclear and conventional weapons. Of the 43 IVs remaining in 1987, some have been assigned to the IV-P programme (see below), while others had been previously modified into strategic reconnaissance aircraft. The reconnaissance models can still undertake a strike role, and are believed to be held in reserve.

Eighteen of the Mirage IV bombers operated by the Commandement des Forces Aériennes Stratégiques (CFAS) of the French Air Force were assigned to be modified to carry the ASMP medium-range air-to-surface nuclear missile. Navigation and targeting capabilities are improved by installation of a Thomson-CSF Arcana pulse-Doppler radar and dual inertial systems. Uprated EW equipment includes, typically, a Thomson-CSF TMV 015 Barem jamming pod and a Philips BOZ-100 chaff/flare pod on the two outboard underwing hardpoints, with external fuel tanks (each 2,000 litres; 528 US gallons; 440 Imp gallons) on the inboard hardpoints. Radar warning receivers are also fitted.

Modified aircraft, redesignated Mirage IV-P (for pénétration), attained initial operational capability with Escadron de Bombardement 1/91 'Gascogne' at Mont-de-Marsan on 1 May 1986, followed by Escadron de Bombardement 2/91 'Marne' at St Dizier on 1 December 1986. A few aircraft are allocated to the OCU; CIFAS 328 'Aquitaire' at Bordeaux.

The following details refer mainly to the Mirage IV-A, although the major differences between this model and the IV-P are detailed above.

TYPE: Two-seat supersonic bomber.

Dassault Mirage IV-P. *(Pilot Press)*

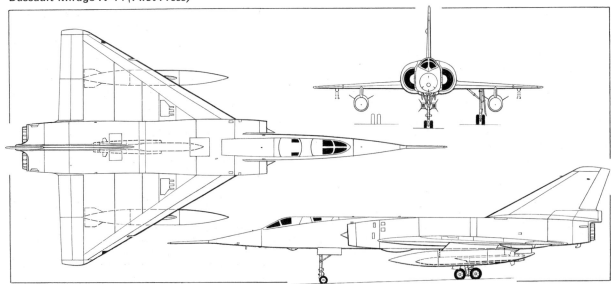

WINGS: Cantilever mid-wing monoplane. Thickness/chord ratio varies from 3.8 to 3.2%. Sweepback on leading edge 60°. Entire trailing edge of each wing made up of two elevons, operated independently by Dassault electro-hydraulic twin-cylinder servo control units, with signals from auto-stabiliser fed into the system. Hydraulically-actuated air-brakes above and below each wing near wing-root leading edge. No high-lift devices, conical camber, spoilers or tabs. Single notch in leading edge of each wing at about 66% span. No de-icing system.

FUSELAGE: All-metal semi-monocoque structure. Rear portion comprises two circular ducts housing turbojets. Underside of rear fuselage recessed to accommodate weapon.

TAIL UNIT: Sweptback fin and rudder only, of multi-spar metal construction. Rudder actuated in same way as elevons. Housing for Aerazur brake parachute, with clamshell doors, at base of rudder. No tabs or de-icing system.

LANDING GEAR: Hydraulically retractable tricycle type. Twin-wheel steerable nose unit retracts rearward. Four-wheel bogie main units retract inward into fuselage. Messier oleo-pneumatic shock absorbers, wheels and brakes.

POWERPLANT: Two SNECMA Atar 9K-50 turbojet engines, each rated at 70.61 kN (15,873 lb st) with afterburning. Movable half-cone centrebodies in air intakes. Integral fuel tanks between main and rear spars in each wing and in leading edge forward of landing-gear bay. Fuel tanks occupy most of centre fuselage between rear cockpit and engine bay. Further tanks between double skins outboard of each engine air-duct, under air-ducts and engines, and in leading edge of tail-fin. Provision for carrying a large jettisonable fuel tank of 2,000 litres (528 US gallons; 440 Imp gallons) capacity under each wing. For ferrying, an external tank can be carried in the underfuselage weapon recess. Flight refuelling nose-probe. Two groups of six JATO units can be attached under the wings for short-field take-off.

ACCOMMODATION: Crew of two in tandem on Martin-Baker (Hispano-built) Mk BM.4 ejection seats. Rearward-hinged canopy over pilot's seat. Rearward-hinged cover over navigator's position.

AVIONICS AND EQUIPMENT: Includes Thomson-CSF Cyrano IV radar under centre fuselage, Marconi Doppler, Dassault computer and countermeasures equipment, SFENA autopilot and Omera-Robot cameras. Mirage IV-P uses Arcana pulse-Doppler radar and dual inertial systems, Thomson-CSF jamming pod, Philips BOZ-100 chaff/flare pod, and radar warning receivers.

ARMAMENT: One 60 kT nuclear weapon semi-recessed under fuselage, or 16 × 1,000 lb conventional bombs, or four Martel air-to-surface missiles under the wings and fuselage. Mirage IV-P carries the ASMP (Air-Sol Moyenne Portée) supersonic nuclear air-to-surface missile, with a yield and range of 150 kT and 40–54 nm (75–100 km; 46–62 miles) respectively. ASMP is intended for standoff attacks against heavily defended targets, such as airfields and command and communications centres.

DIMENSIONS, EXTERNAL			
Wing span	11.85 m (38 ft 10$\frac{1}{2}$ in)	Average T-O weight	31,600 kg (69,665 lb)
Length overall	23.50 m (77 ft 1 in)	Max T-O weight	33,475 kg (73,800 lb)
Height overall	5.65 m (18 ft 6$\frac{1}{2}$ in)	PERFORMANCE:	
AREA:		Max level speed at 11,000 m (36,000 ft)	Mach 2.2
Wings, gross	78.00 m² (840.0 sq ft)	Combat speed at high altitude	Mach 1.8
WEIGHTS:		Service ceiling	20,000 m (65,615 ft)
Weight empty	14,500 kg (31,965 lb)	Tactical radius	668 nm (1,240 km; 771 miles)
		Ferry range	2,158 nm (4,000 km; 2,485 miles)

Dassault-Breguet Mirage F1

In early 1964 Dassault was awarded a French government contract to develop a replacement for the Mirage III, followed shortly afterwards by an order for a prototype aircraft which was designated Mirage F2. This was a two-seat fighter, powered by a SNECMA (Pratt & Whitney) TF 306 turbofan engine. It first flew on 12 June 1966.

Concurrently with work on the Mirage F2, Dassault also developed, as a private venture, a much smaller single-seat aircraft, the Mirage F1, with a SNECMA Atar 9K turbojet engine. The prototype Mirage F1-01 flew for the first time on 23 December 1966, and exceeded Mach 2 during its fourth flight on 7 January 1967.

In September 1967, three pre-series F1 aircraft and a structural test airframe were ordered by the French government. The first pre-series aircraft, the Mirage F1-02, reached Mach 1.15 during its first flight on 20 March 1969, and Mach 2.03 during its third flight on 24 March. It completed the first phase of its flight test programme on 27 June 1969.

The F1-02, during its initial flight tests, was powered by an Atar 9K-31 turbojet engine developing 65.7 kN (14,770 lb st) with afterburning. It was re-engined in 1969 with the more powerful Atar 9K-50 turbojet; this engine was also fitted in the two later pre-series aircraft, and became the standard powerplant of the production versions.

The Mirage F1-03, which flew for the first time on 18 September 1969, had its wing leading edges extended for a greater proportion of the overall span than the preceding aircraft. It was followed by the final pre-series aircraft, the F1-04, on 17 June 1970. This had a complete electronics system and, after modification of its wing leading edges to be similar to those on the F1-03, became representative of the initial production version.

The Mirage F1 is dimensionally similar to the Mirage III series, and its swept wing is virtually a scaled-down version of that fitted to the F2 prototype, with improved high-lift devices which help to make possible take-offs and landings within 500–800 m (1,600–2,600 ft) at average combat mission weight. Operation from semi-prepared or even sod runways is possible.

Dassault-Breguet Mirage F1-C armed with two Matra Super 530 and two Matra 550 Magic air-to-air missiles.

The primary role of the single-seat Mirage **F1-C** production version, to which the detailed description applies, is that of all-weather interception at any altitude. It is equally suitable for visual ground-attack missions, carrying a variety of external loads beneath the wings and fuselage. Other versions have included the **F1-A**, a model for operation under VFR conditions, with much of the more costly electronic equipment deleted and the vacated space occupied by an additional fuel tank (production completed); **F1-B** two-seat version of F1-C, the first of which made its first flight on 26 May 1976; the **F1-D** two-seat version of F1-E; the single-seat **F1-E** multi-role air-superiority/ground-attack/reconnaissance version for export customers, with an inertial navigation system, nav/attack central computer, CRT head-up display, and a large inventory of external stores; and the single-seat **F1-R** (French Air Force **F1-CR**) day and night reconnaissance variant.

Many F1-Cs of the French Air Force were delivered or modified to **F1-C-200** standard by installation of a removable flight refuelling probe for long-range reinforcement capability. Export customers who have F1s equipped with refuelling probes include Iraq, Libya, Morocco, South Africa and Spain.

At the time of writing a total of 715 Mirage F1s had been ordered, comprising 252 (incl 6 prototypes) for the French Air Force and 463 for service with the air forces of Ecuador (F1-B and E), Greece (F1-C), Iraq (F1-B and E), Jordan (F1-B, C and E), Kuwait (F1-B and C), Libya (F1-A, B and E), Morocco (F1-C and E), Qatar (F1-B and E), South Africa (F1-A and C) and Spain (F1-B, C and E). A total of 672 had been delivered by 1 January 1987. The first production F1 flew on 15 February 1973 and was delivered to the French Air Force on 14 March 1973. The first unit to receive the F1 was the 30e Escadre at Reims, which became operational in early 1974. This now has three squadrons of F1-Cs; the 5e Escadre at Orange has two squadrons of F1-Cs and one of F1-Bs; the 12e Escadre at Cambrai has three squadrons of F1-Cs.

Deliveries of the F1-C series to the French Air Force totalled 166, made up of four prototypes, 81 F1-Cs and 81 F1-C-200s. Twenty two-seat F1-Bs began to equip the third squadron at Orange, as the F1 OCU, in June 1980; each aircraft is equipped with the same radar, weapon system and air-to-air missiles as the F1-C, but has no internal guns, and fuel capacity is reduced by 450 litres (119 US gallons; 99 Imp gallons).

The French Air Force has also purchased F1-CRs to replace Mirage III-R/RD aircraft equipping the three squadrons of the 33e Escadre de Reconnaissance, at Strasbourg. These aircraft are intended to carry internally an Omera 33 camera and either an Omera 40 panoramic camera or a SAT Super Cyclope SCM 2400 infra-red sensor, together with a Thomson-CSF Raphaël SLAR and an Omera 400 sight recorder. Further electromagnetic or optical sensors are intended to be carried in an underbelly pack, such as the Thomson-CSF Syrel elint pod. Other equipment includes a Sagem Uliss 47 inertial navigation system and ESD navigation computer. An in-flight refuelling probe is standard (hence -200 added to designation). The first of two F1-CR-200 prototypes, converted from F1-C-200s, flew on 20 November 1981. Sixty-four (incl the two prototypes) were ordered for the French Air Force. The first production F1-CR-200 flew on 10 November 1982, and the first squadron (2/33) became operational in July 1983.

Mirage F1-Cs and F1-C-200s of the French Air Force have Thomson-CSF Cyrano IVM radar of modular construction and optimised for air-to-air missions. The F1-CR-200 has a Cyrano IVMR with added air-to-ground functions for blind let-down, ground mapping, contour mapping and terrain avoidance, plus air-to-ground ranging. Export F1-Cs have a radar similar to Cyrano IV or IVM. Export F1-Es have radar similar to Cyrano IVMR but repackaged to save space.

Mirage F1-EQ5s and EQ6s of the Iraqi Air Force are equipped to carry Exocet anti-ship missiles and laser guided weapons such as the AS.30L missile and Matra 400 kg laser guided bomb.

The Mirage F1 is produced by Dassault-Breguet in co-operation with the Belgian company SABCA, in which Dassault-Breguet has a parity interest, and CASA of Spain, which is building fuselage sections for all Mirage F1s ordered. Dassault-Breguet also has a technical and industrial co-operation agreement with the Armaments Development and Production Corporation of South Africa Ltd, whereby the latter company has rights to build the Mirage F1 under licence.

The following description applies to the F1-C production version for the French Air Force, except where indicated:

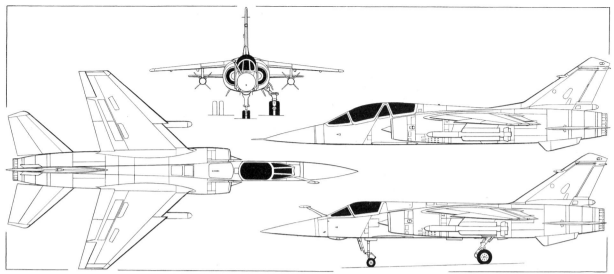

Dassault-Breguet Mirage F1-CR-200. Upper side view: Mirage F1-B. *(Pilot Press)*

TYPE: Single-seat multi-mission fighter and attack aircraft.

WINGS: Cantilever shoulder-wing monoplane. Anhedral from roots. Sweepback 47° 30′ on leading edges, with extended chord on approximately the outer two-thirds of each wing. Carbonfibre aileron skin on current production aircraft. Entire wing leading edge can be drooped hydraulically (manually for T-O and landing, automatic in combat). Two differentially operating double-slotted flaps and one aileron on each trailing edge, actuated hydraulically by servo controls. Ailerons are compensated by trim devices incorporated in linkage. Two spoilers on each wing, ahead of flaps.

FUSELAGE: Conventional semi-monocoque structure. Nose-cone over radar, and antennae fairings on fin, are of plastics. Large hydraulically actuated door-type airbrake in forward underside of each intake trunk.

TAIL UNIT: Cantilever structure, with sweepback on all surfaces. Single-spar fin. All-moving tailplane mid-set on fuselage, and actuated hydraulically by electric or manual control. Auxiliary fin beneath each side of rear fuselage.

LANDING GEAR: Retractable tricycle type, by Messier-Hispano-Bugatti. Hydraulic retraction, nose unit rearward, main units upward into rear of intake trunk fairings. Twin wheels on each unit. Nose unit steerable and self centering. Mainwheel tyres size 605×155. Nosewheel tyres size 360×135. Messier-Hispano-Bugatti brakes and anti-skid units. Brake parachute in bullet fairing at base of rudder.

POWERPLANT: One SNECMA Atar 9K-50 turbojet engine, rated at 70.6 kN (15,873 lb st) with afterburning. Movable semi-conical centrebody in each intake. Fuel in integral tanks in wings (combined capacity 375 litres; 99 US gallons; 82.5 Imp gallons), and three main tanks and one inverted-flight supply tank (combined capacity 3,925 litres; 1,037 US gallons; 863.5 Imp gallons) in fuselage. Total internal fuel capacity 4,300 litres (1,136 US gallons; 946 Imp gallons). Provision for two jettisonable auxiliary fuel tanks (each 1,130 litres; 298 US gallons; 248 Imp gallons) to be carried on inboard wing pylons, plus a single tank of 2,200 litres (581 US gallons; 484 Imp gallons) capacity on the underfuselage station. Non-retractable,

but removable, flight refuelling probe on starboard side of nose optional.

ACCOMMODATION: Single SEM Martin-Baker FIRM4 ejection seat for pilot, under rearward hinged canopy (SEM Martin-Baker F10M rocket seat in latest F1-Cs and in F1-E and F1-CR. Two Mk 10 seats with inter-seat sequence system in F1-B). Intertechnique liquid oxygen converter, miniature regulator and anti-g valve for pilot. No-delay through-the-canopy escape system, with pyrotechnic prefragmentation of canopy, on all versions.

AVIONICS AND EQUIPMENT: Thomson-CSF Cyrano IV fire control radar in nose. Two UHF transceivers (one UHF/VHF), Socrat 6200 VOR/ILS with Socrat 5600 marker beacon receiver, LMT Tacan, LMT NR-AI-4-A IFF, remote setting interception system, three-axis generator, central air data computer, SFIM spherical indicator with ILS pointers, Crouzet Type 63 navigation indicator, SFENA 505 autopilot and CSF head-up display, with wide-field-of-view double-converter. (Standard equipment on F-1E includes SAGEM Uliss 47 INS, EMD 182 central digital computer for nav/attack computations, TH C8F VE-120C CRT head-up display, Crouzet air data computer and digital armament/nav control panels.)

ARMAMENT AND OPERATIONAL EQUIPMENT: Standard installed armament of two 30 mm DEFA 553 cannon, with 135 rds/gun, mounted in lower central fuselage. Two Alkan universal stores attachment pylons under each wing and one under centre fuselage, plus provision for carrying one air-to-air missile at each wingtip. Max external combat load 6,300 kg (13,900 lb). Externally mounted weapons for interception role include Matra Super 530 air-to-air missiles under inboard wing pylons and/or Matra 550 Magic (or AIM-9J Sidewinder) air-to-air missiles at each wingtip station. For ground attack, typical loads may include one ARMAT anti-radar missile, or one AM39 Exocet anti-ship missile, or up to fourteen 250 kg bombs, thirty anti-runway bombs or 144 Thomson-Brandt rockets. Other possible external loads include auxiliary fuel tanks, laser designator pod with AS.30L missiles or 400 kg laser guided bombs, air-to-surface missiles, side looking airborne radar pod, active countermeasures pods such as the Thomson-CSF Remora, active ECM jamming pods such as the Thomson-CSF Caiman, a high-altitude/long-distance reconnaissance pod, and a four-camera reconnaissance pod with an SAT Super Cyclope infra-red scanner/recorder. Typical underwing ECM container for export aircraft is Matra Sycomor, which ejects heat-emitting infra-red cartridges and/or chaff.

DIMENSIONS, EXTERNAL (F1-C):	
Wing span: without missiles	8.40 m (27 ft 6¾ in)
over Magic missiles	approx 9.32 m (30 ft 6¾ in)
Length overall	15.30 m (50 ft 2½ in)
Height overall	4.50 m (14 ft 9 in)
Wheel track	2.50 m (8 ft 2½ in)
Wheelbase	5.00 m (16 ft 4¾ in)
AREA:	
Wings, gross	25.00 m² (269.1 sq ft)
WEIGHTS (F1-C):	
Weight empty	7,400 kg (16,314 lb)
T-O weight, 'clean'	10,900 kg (24,030 lb)
Max T-O weight	16,200 kg (35,715 lb)
PERFORMANCE (F1-C):	
Max level speed: high altitude	Mach 2.2
low altitude	
Mach 1.2 (800 knots; 1,480 km/h; 920 mph EAS)	
Max rate of climb at S/L (with afterburning)	
12,780 m (41,930 ft)/min	

Max rate of climb at high altitude (with afterburning)
14,580 m (47,835 ft)/min
Service ceiling 20,000 m (65,600 ft)
T-O run (AUW of 11,500 kg; 25,355 lb) 600 m (1,970 ft)
Landing run (AUW of 8,500 kg; 18,740 lb)
670 m (2,200 ft)
Combat radius:
hi-lo-hi at Mach 0.75/0.88, with fourteen 250 kg bombs and max internal fuel, with reserves
230 nm (425 km; 265 miles)
lo-lo-lo at 400–550 knots (740–1,020 km/h; 460–633 mph), with six 250 kg bombs and two external tanks, with reserves 325 nm (600 km; 374 miles)
hi-lo-hi at Mach 0.8/0.9, with two 250 kg bombs and three external tanks, with reserves
750 nm (1,390 km; 863 miles)
Combat air patrol endurance, with two Super 530 missiles and underbelly tank, with reserves, incl one attack at ceiling
2 h 15 min

Dassault-Breguet Etendard IV-P and Super Etendard

The Etendard was conceived as a low-cost, lightweight, single-engined interceptor and ground-support aircraft for the French Air Force and to meet NATO requirements. Several models were developed simultaneously, including: the Turboméca Gabizo turbojet-powered Etendard II, the lowest-thrust version, that was quickly abandoned; the afterburning Bristol Siddeley Orpheus BOr.3-engined Etendard VI; and the Etendard IV. The version most likely to

succeed was the Etendard VI, of which NATO ordered three prototypes, the first flying on 15 March 1957. However, this too was abandoned when NATO selected an Italian aircraft to fulfil its requirements.

Dassault's Etendard IV had been produced as a company-funded project, again to meet the same French Air Force requirements. The best version, it too failed to win orders, the prototype having first flown on 24 July 1956. However, a naval version was developed as the Etendard IV-M to operate from the French Navy's forthcoming new aircraft

Dassault-Breguet Etendard IV-P.

Dassault-Breguet Super Etendard carrier-based strike fighters.

carriers, *Clémenceau* and *Foch*. The prototype IV-M flew for the first time on 21 May 1958. Sixty-nine IV-Ms joined the Navy (Aéronavale) from early 1962, but none remain in use today. These were followed by 21 unarmed IV-P reconnaissance and flight refuelling tanker models, each with 5 Omera cameras in nose and ventral positions and refuelling equipment. The IV-P is still operational.

The Super Etendard was developed for the French Navy as an updated version of its Etendard IV-M carrier-based fighter. The airframe and equipment of the Super Etendard were expected to be 90 per cent common with those of the IV-M, except for the nav/attack system. In fact, the installation of a more powerful turbojet engine and equipment of enhanced capability, together with the adoption of improved aerodynamic features and modern manufacturing techniques, made the Super Etendard 90 per cent new. Like the IV, it is basically a transonic single-seat strike fighter, for low- and medium-altitude operations from ships in the class of the French Navy's *Clémenceau* and *Foch*. Its equipment includes a highly sophisticated and accurate nav/attack integrated avionics system. Inherent long range is increased by flight refuelling capability, and it is able to operate as a tanker for other aircraft.

The Atar 8K-50 turbojet engine is a non-afterburning version of the Atar 9K-50 used in the Mirage F1 multimission fighter and attack aircraft. It has a lower specific fuel consumption than the 43.15 kN (9,700 lb st) Atar 8B turbojet fitted in the Etendard IV-M. The thrust increase of about ten per cent, combined with a new wing leading edge and redesigned flaps, allows a significant increase in gross weight for catapulting and, hence, permits increased fuel load and armament.

Two prototypes were produced by conversion of standard IV-M airframes. The first of these flew initially on 28 October 1974. Its programme included engine development, followed in 1978 by tests of the Super Etendard's external load-carrying capability and firing trials of the Exocet AM39 air-to-surface anti-shipping missile.

The second prototype, which flew for the first time on 25 March 1975, was used for tests of the Super Etendard's navigation system and bombing capabilities. Its subsequent tasks included shipboard operation under open-sea conditions in waters other than the Mediterranean, where all early trials took place.

It was intended originally to build 100 production aircraft, but the number was reduced to 71 in order to conform with budget limitations. The first aircraft flew on 24 November 1977. Deliveries began on 28 June 1978, when the third production aircraft was accepted officially by the French Navy. The first export order, for 14, was placed by the Argentine Navy in 1979, and eight of these had been delivered by 1 May 1982. Their first known operational employment took place on 4 May, when an Exocet missile launched from a Super Etendard destroyed the Royal Navy's Type 42 destroyer HMS *Sheffield* off the Falkland Islands.

At the 1985 Paris Air Show, Dassault-Breguet announced its readiness to relaunch production of the Super Etendard against initial orders for about 40 aircraft. Changes by comparison with the original version would be limited to removal of equipment needed only for deck operations from aircraft carriers, and installation of new fire control and nav/attack systems.

Production of the original, carrier-based, version of this

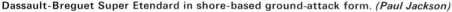

Dassault-Breguet Super Etendard in shore-based ground-attack form. *(Paul Jackson)*

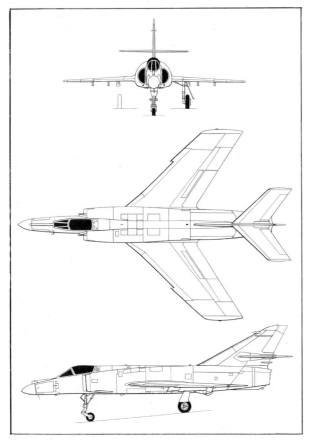

Dassault-Breguet Super Etendard. *(Pilot Press)*

wings and fuselage. Messier-Hispano-Bugatti disc brakes. Mainwheel tyres size 30 × 7.7-16; nosewheel tyre size 490 × 155-9. Brake-chute in fairing at junction of fin and tailplane trailing edges.

POWERPLANT: One SNECMA Atar 8K-50 non-afterburning turbojet, rated at 49 kN (11,025 lb st). Fuel in integral tanks in wings and rubber tanks in fuselage, with total capacity of 3,270 litres (845 US gallons; 719 Imp gallons). Provision for external tank of 625 or 1,100 litre (165 or 290.5 US gallon; 137 or 242 Imp gallon) capacity under each wing, and a 600 litre (158 US gallon; 132 Imp gallon) centreline tank or flight refuelling 'buddy' pack under the fuselage. Retractable flight refuelling probe in fairing in front of windscreen.

ACCOMMODATION: Pilot only, on Hispano-built Martin-Baker SEMMB CM4A lightweight ejection seat in pressurised cockpit. Extensively armoured.

AVIONICS AND EQUIPMENT: Sagem-Kearfott ETNA inertial navigation and attack system; Thomson-CSF/ESD Agave lightweight search/track/designation/telemetry/navigation radar; Thomson-CSF VE-120 head-up display; Crouzet Type 97 navigation display, armament control panel and selector box, and Type 66 air data computer; TRT radio altimeter; SFIM three-axis attitude indicator; LMT micro-Tacan and IFF, and Socrat VOR.

ARMAMENT: Two DEFA 30 mm guns, each with 125 rds, in bottom of engine air intake trunks. Underfuselage attachment for two 250 kg bombs, one 600 litre fuel drop-tank, a flight refuelling 'buddy' pack or a reconnaissance pod. Four underwing hardpoints for four 250 kg or 400 kg bombs, two Matra Magic air-to-air missiles, or four rocket pods (each eighteen 68 mm rockets). The inner wing hardpoints can carry two 625 litre or 1,100 litre fuel tanks, or one AM39 Exocet anti-ship missile and one fuel tank. Standard weapons include AN52 nuclear bomb, 18 (optionally 27) BAP 100 concrete-piercing bombs, 18 (optionally 27) BAT 120 bombs, and one self defence jamming pod (plus, optionally, one chaff/flare pod). Modification to carry ASMP nuclear missile completed.

single-seat transonic strike fighter for the navies of France and Argentina ended in 1983. However, the French Navy is reviewing the possibility of extending and updating the weapon system of aircraft in service, and Super Etendards have been modified to carry the ASMP medium-range air-to-surface nuclear missile under the 1984–88 defence programme.

The following details refer to the Super Etendard:

TYPE: Single-seat transonic carrier-based strike fighter.

WINGS: Cantilever mid-wing monoplane. Thickness/chord ratio varies from 6% at root to 5% at tip. Anhedral 3° 30′. Sweepback at quarter-chord 45°. Tips fold upward for carrier stowage. Inset ailerons, hydraulically-powered by Dassault irreversible dual circuits with artificial feel. Spoiler on top surface of each wing, ahead of special double-slotted flap with second slot in form of an integral 'gutter'. Flap travel increased by comparison with Etendard IV-M. Hydraulically-powered drooping leading edges, with extended chord on outer panels.

FUSELAGE: Semi-monocoque structure, 'waisted' in accordance with area rule. Perforated air-brake under each side of centre-fuselage.

TAIL UNIT: Cantilever structure, with tailplane mid-set on fin. All surfaces swept. All-moving tailplane (with electrically-powered pitch trim) and rudder are powered in same way as ailerons.

LANDING GEAR: Retractable tricycle type, with single wheel on each unit, manufactured by Messier-Hispano-Bugatti. Nosewheel retracts rearward, main units inward into

DIMENSIONS, EXTERNAL:

Wing span	9.60 m (31 ft 6 in)
Length overall	14.31 m (46 ft 11½ in)
Width, wings folded	7.80 m (25 ft 7 in)
Height overall	3.86 m (12 ft 8 in)
Wheel track	3.50 m (11 ft 6 in)
Wheelbase	4.80 m (15 ft 9 in)

AREA:

Wings, gross	28.4 m² (305.7 sq ft)

WEIGHTS:

Weight empty	6,450 kg (14,330 lb)
Max fuel, incl two 1,100 litre underwing tanks	
	4,800 kg (10,580 lb)
Max weapon load, internal fuel only	2,100 kg (4,630 lb)
Mission T-O weight	9,450–12,000 kg (20,833–26,455 lb)

PERFORMANCE:

Max level speed at height	approx Mach 1
Max level speed at low altitude	
	637 knots (1,180 km/h; 733 mph)
Approach speed for shipboard landing at AUW of 7,800 kg (17,200 lb)	135 knots (250 km/h; 155 mph)
Service ceiling	13,700 m (45,000 ft)
Radius of action, with AM39 missile and two external tanks, hi-lo-hi mission	460 nm (850 km; 530 miles)

Dassault-Breguet Atlantique 2 (ATL2) and Breguet Atlantic 1

The Atlantique 2, or ATL2 (formerly ANG–Atlantique Nouvelle Génération), is a twin-turboprop maritime patrol aircraft derived directly from the earlier Breguet 1150 Atlantic that was produced in 1964–73 for operation by the armed services of France (40, of which 3 were sold subsequently to Pakistan), the German Federal Republic (20, including 5 special-purpose ECM aircraft), Italy (18) and the Netherlands (9). The Atlantic 1 was designed to a specification drawn up by the NATO Armaments Committee for a maritime patrol aircraft to supersede the then widely-used Lockheed P-2 Neptune. The first prototype made its maiden flight on 21 October 1961, and the first production aircraft followed on 19 July 1965. Deliveries began with the first machines for the French Navy, on 10 December 1965. The Netherlands has withdrawn the Atlantic.

West German Marineflieger Dassault-Breguet Atlantic 1.

Powered by two SNECMA-built Rolls-Royce Tyne RTy.20 Mk 21 turboprop engines, the Atlantic 1 achieved a maximum speed of 355 knots (658 km/h; 409 mph) and a maximum range of 4,856 nm (9,000 km; 5,592 miles).

Design definition of the ATL2 was initiated by the French government in July 1977, with the aim of providing a replacement for the first-generation Atlantic (now known retrospectively as the Atlantic 1) during the period from 1988 to 1996. This led to launch of the development phase of the ATL2 programme in September 1978.

Two ATL2 prototypes were produced by modification of Atlantic 1 airframes. Work started in January 1979, and the first prototype flew for the first time in its new form on 8 May 1981, followed by the second on 26 March 1982. Series production was authorised on 24 May 1984, and five production aircraft had been ordered by early 1987. The first of these is scheduled to fly in July 1988, enabling deliveries to begin in 1989. The French Navy requirement is for 42 aircraft, of which five more were to be ordered in 1988, six in 1989, and five in 1990. The work is being shared by most members of the European SECBAT (Société d'Etude et de Construction du Breguet Atlantic) consortium that was responsible for the earlier Atlantic 1 programme, with some modification of the work-split to reflect varying national interests in the ATL2 aircraft. Companies involved, under Dassault-Breguet direction, are SABCA and Sonaca of Belgium, MBB and Dornier of Federal Germany, Aeritalia of Italy and Aérospatiale of France. The Tyne engines are being produced by SNECMA of France, Rolls-Royce of the UK, FN of Belgium and MTU of Federal Germany; and propellers by Ratier of France and British Aerospace.

Structural changes by comparison with the Atlantic 1 include use of a refined bonding technique, improved anti-corrosion protection, better sealing between skin panels, and design improvements offering longer fatigue life and more economical maintenance. These are intended to ensure increased serviceability, with 75 per cent of squadron aircraft permanently available for operations; readiness to take off within 30 minutes of an order to go; and an aircraft life of 30 years.

The basic mission performance requirements envisaged for the ATL2 are similar to those of the Atlantic 1: a high

Second prototype Dassault-Breguet Atlantique 2 (ATL2) maritime patrol aircraft.

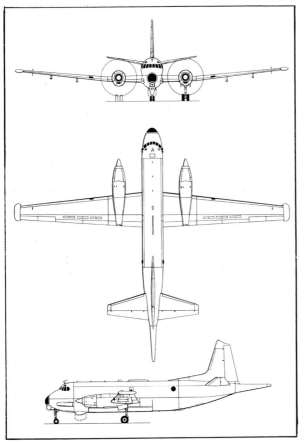

Dassault-Breguet Atlantique 2. *(Pilot Press)*

cruising speed to the operational area, quick descent from cruising altitude to patrol height, lengthy patrol endurance at low altitude, and a high degree of manoeuvrability at sea level. It is able to carry a wide variety of weapons and equipment for finding and attacking both submarines and surface targets in all weathers. In particular, its Thomson-CSF Iguane search radar can detect large ships at a range of 150–200 nm (275–370 km; 170–230 miles), and small targets such as submarine schnorkels over 'several dozen nautical miles' in rough seas.

Like the original Atlantic, the ATL2 is able to perform minelaying, logistic support, and passenger and freight transport missions. It could be adapted for advanced AEW duties, and is suitable for civilian tasks such as air/sea rescue and patrol of offshore fishing and oil interests.

TYPE: Twin-turboprop maritime patrol aircraft.

WINGS: Cantilever mid-wing monoplane, with streamlined ECM pods on tips. Wing section NACA 64 series. Dihedral 6° on outer panels only. Incidence 3°. Tapered planform, with 9° sweepback on leading edge. Two conventional ailerons on each wing. Slotted flaps in three segments on each wing, over 75 per cent of span. Three hinged spoilers on upper surface of each outer wing, forward of flaps. Airbrake above and below each wing. No trim tabs. Air Equipement/Kléber-Colombes pneumatic de-icing system on leading edges.

FUSELAGE: 'Double-bubble' fail-safe structure, with bonded honeycomb sandwich skin on pressurised central section of upper lobe, upward sliding weapons bay doors and nosewheel door. Larger air intake on each side of nose.

TAIL UNIT. Cantilever structure. Slightly bulged housing for ESM antennae at top of fin leading edge. Fixed-incidence tailplane, with dihedral. No trim tabs. Air Equipement/Kléber-Colombes pneumatic de-icing system on leading edges.

LANDING GEAR: Retractable tricycle type, supplied by Messier-Hispano-Bugatti, with twin wheels on each unit. Hydraulic retraction, nosewheels rearward, main units forward into engine nacelles. Kléber-Colombes or Dunlop tyres; size 39 × 13-20 on mainwheels, 26 × 8-13 on nosewheels. New Messier-Hispano-Bugatti disc brakes with higher braking energy, and Modistop anti-skid units.

POWERPLANT: Two 4,549 kW (6,100 ehp) Rolls-Royce Tyne RTy.20 Mk 21 turboprop engines, each driving a four-blade Ratier/British Aerospace constant-speed metal propeller type PD 249/476/3 on prototypes. Four pressure-refuelled integral fuel tanks in wings, with total capacity of 23,120 litres (6,108 US gallons; 5,085 Imp gallons).

ACCOMMODATION: Normal flight crew of 12, comprising observer in glazed nose; pilot, co-pilot and flight engineer on flight deck; a radio-navigator, ESM-ECM-MAD operator, radar-IFF operator, tactical co-ordinator and two acoustic sensor operators at stations on the starboard side of the tactical compartment; and two observers in beam positions at the rear. Provision for carrying relief crew, or 12 other personnel. Rest compartment, with eight seats, in centre fuselage, forward of crew room with tables and seats, galley, toilet and wardrobe.

ARMAMENT, AVIONICS AND OPERATIONAL EQUIPMENT: Main weapons bay in unpressurised lower fuselage can accommodate all NATO standard bombs, depth charges, up to eight Mk 46 or seven Murène torpedoes or two missiles (typical load comprises three torpedoes and one AM39 Exocet missile). Four underwing attachments for up to 3,500 kg (7,716 lb) of stores, including air-to-air and air-to-surface missiles or pods. More than 100 sonobuoys, with Alkan pneumatic launcher, in compartment aft of weapons bay, where whole of upper and lower fuselage provides storage for sonobuoys and marker flares. SAT/TRT forward looking infra-red sensor in turret under nose. Thomson-CSF Iguane retractable radar immediately forward of weapons bay, with integrated LMT IFF interrogator and SECRE decoder. Omera cameras in starboard side of nose and in bottom of rear fuselage. Crouzet MAD in lengthened tail sting. Thomson-CSF Arar 13A radar detector for ESM. Thomson-CSF Sadang system for processing active and passive acoustic detection data. A distributed data processing system around a data bus, with a CIMSA Mitra 125X tactical computer (512K words memory), two ESD bus computers, two Sagem magnetic bubble mass memories and Thomson-CSF display subsystem. Other equipment includes LMT NRAI 9A IFF responder and HF/BLU 400W transceiver, HF com, Tacan and DME by Thomson-CSF, VHF/AM/FM com by Socrat, VOR/ILS by EAS, TRT radio altimeter, Collins MF radio compass, ADF, HSI and autopilot/flight director by SFENA, dual Sagem Uliss 53 inertial navigation systems coupled to a Navstar receiver, Sagem high-speed printer and terminal display, Crouzet navigation table and air data computer.

DIMENSIONS, EXTERNAL:
Wing span, incl wingtip pods	37.42 m (122 ft 9¼ in)
Length overall	31.62 m (103 ft 9 in)
Height overall	10.89 m (35 ft 8¾ in)
Wheel track	9.00 m (29 ft 6¼ in)
Wheelbase	9.45 m (31 ft 0 in)
Propeller diameter	4.88 m (16 ft 0 in)
Main weapons bay: Length	9.00 m (29 ft 6¼ in)
Width	2.10 m (6 ft 10¾ in)

AREA:
Wings, gross	120.34 m² (1,295.3 sq ft)

WEIGHTS:
Weight empty, equipped, standard mission	25,700 kg (56,659 lb)
Military load:	
ASW or ASSW mission	3,000 kg (6,600 lb)
Mission T-O weight:	
ASW or ASSW mission	44,200 kg (97,440 lb)
combined ASW/ASSW mission	45,000 kg (99,200 lb)
Max overload T-O weight	46,200 kg (101,850 lb)

PERFORMANCE (with metal propellers, at T-O weight of 45,000 kg; 99,200 lb except where indicated):
Never-exceed speed	Mach 0.73
Max level speed at optimum height	350 knots (648 km/h; 402 mph)
Max level speed at S/L	320 knots (592 km/h; 368 mph)
Max cruising speed at 7,200 m (25,000 ft)	300 knots (555 km/h; 345 mph)
Normal patrol speed, S/L to 1,525 m (5,000 ft)	170 knots (315 km/h; 195 mph)
Stalling speed, flaps down	90 knots (167 km/h; 104 mph)
Max rate of climb at S/L, AUW of 30,000 kg (66,140 lb)	884 m (2,900 ft)/min
Max rate of climb at S/L, AUW of 40,000 kg (88,185 lb)	610 m (2,000 ft)/min
Service ceiling	9,145 m (30,000 ft)
T-O to 10.5 m (35 ft)	1,840 m (6,037 ft)
Landing from 15 m (50 ft)	1,500 m (4,922 ft)

Typical mission profiles, with reserves of 5% total fuel, 5% of fuel consumed and 20 min hold-off:

Anti-ship mission: T-O with max fuel and one AM39 missile; fly 1,800 nm (3,333 km; 2,071 miles) to target area; descend for two-hour search and attack at 90 m (300 ft); return to base

Anti-submarine mission: T-O at 44,300 kg (97,665 lb) AUW with 15,225 kg (33,565 lb) of fuel, four Mk 46 torpedoes, 78 sonobuoys, and a full load of markers and flares; cruise to search area at 290 knots (537 km/h; 333 mph) at 7,620 m (25,000 ft); descend for 8 h low-altitude patrol at 600 nm (1,110 km; 690 miles) from base, or 5 h patrol at 1,000 nm (1,850 km; 1,150 miles) from base; return to base at 9,145 m (30,000 ft). Total mission time 12 h 31 min

Ferry range with max fuel	4,900 nm (9,075 km; 5,635 miles)
Max endurance, no reserves	18 h

Dassault-Breguet Rafale A (Squall)

Known initially as the ACX (advanced combat experimental), the **Rafale A** is an experimental prototype that was built to demonstrate technologies applicable to the tactical combat aircraft (ACT) needed to replace French Air Force Jaguars in the 1990s, and to the ship-based combat aircraft (ACM: avion de combat marine) proposed for deployment on the French Navy's nuclear powered aircraft carrier. The production version will be known as **Rafale B**, and is described separately.

Essential characteristics of the Rafale A were revealed in the early weeks of 1983, at the time of Dassault-Breguet's decision to build it. On the basis of an airframe with overall dimensions little greater than those of the Mirage 2000, the company set out to produce a multi-role aircraft able to destroy everything from supersonic fighters to a helicopter in an air-to-air role, and able to deliver at least 3,500 kg (7,715 lb) of modern weapons on targets up to 350 nm (650 km; 400 miles) from its base. The ability to carry, and fire in rapid succession, at least six air-to-air missiles was considered

Dassault-Breguet Rafale A armed with four Mica and two Magic air-to-air missiles.

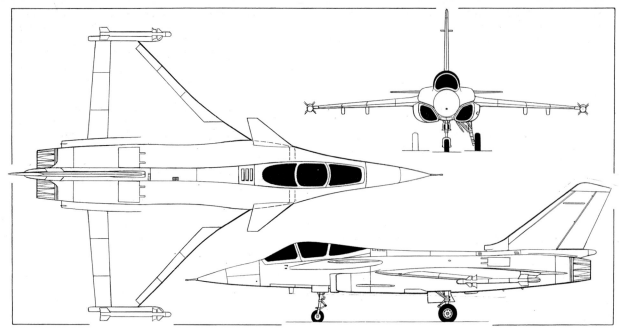

Dassault-Breguet Rafale A. *(Pilot Press)*

essential, together with the ability to launch electro-optically
guided and advanced 'fire and forget' standoff air-to-surface
weapons.

High manoeuvrability, high angle-of-attack flying capability under combat conditions, and optimum low-speed
performance for short take-off and landing were basic design
aims. This led to choice of a compound-sweep delta wing, a
large active canard foreplane mounted higher than the
mainplane, twin engines, air intakes of new design in a semi-
ventral position, and a single fin. To ensure a thrust-to-
weight ratio far superior to one, it was decided to make
extensive use of composites, such as carbon and Kevlar
fibres, and aluminium-lithium alloys throughout the
airframe, as well as the latest manufacturing techniques such
as superplastic forming/diffusion bonding of titanium
components.

Ergonomic cockpit studies suggested that the pilot's seat
should be reclined at an angle of 30° to 40° during flight
testing, and that equipment should include a sidestick
controller, a wide-angle holographic head-up display, an
eye-level display collimated to infinity (avoiding the need to
refocus from the HUD to the instrument panel), and lateral
multi-function colour displays.

The digital fly-by-wire control system will embody
automatic self-protection functions to prevent the aircraft
from exceeding its limits at all times. Functional recon-
figuration of the system in case of failure, and anti-
turbulence functions, would be embodied. Provisions would
be made for the introduction of fibre optics to enhance
nuclear hardening, and of voice-activated controls and voice
warning systems.

A full scale mockup of the original ACX design was
exhibited at the 1983 Paris Air Show, and construction of the
Rafale A began in March 1984. Compared with the mockup,
it embodies a number of significant refinements. In
particular, Dassault-Breguet was able to achieve improved
flow into the engine air intakes, and greater efficiency at high

angles of attack, by modifying the lower fuselage cross-
section to a V shape, enabling centrebodies and other
moving parts to be dispensed with. The size of the fin was also
greatly reduced.

Rafale A was rolled out of the Saint-Cloud assembly plant
on 14 December 1985, and exceeded Mach 1.3 during its first
test flight on 4 July 1986. Mach 1.8 was achieved during the
sixth flight, by which time the aircraft had been subjected to
load factors of + 6g in supersonic flight and + 8g in
subsonic flight, and angles of attack up to 23°.

TYPE: Single-seat twin-engined experimental combat aircraft.

WINGS: Cantilever multi-spar mid-wing monoplane of
compound delta planform. Most wing components
made from carbonfibre, including three-segment full-span
elevons on each trailing edge. Elevons can be deflected
identically or differentially. Full-span three-segment
leading-edge slats on each wing operate automatically
with the elevons to alter wing camber and provide high lift.
Slats made from titanium. Wing-root tip fairings of
aramid fibre. All movable surfaces actuated by fly-by-wire
control system, via hydraulic actuators.

FUSELAGE: Conventional semi-monocoque structure; 50 per
cent carbonfibre, including entire front fuselage and dorsal
spine fairings. Aramid fibre nosecone and jetpipe fairings.
Most centre- and rear-fuselage skin panels of aluminium-
lithium alloy. Wheel doors and engine doors of
carbonfibre. Dorsal spine fairing from rear of canopy to jet
nozzles. Forward hinged door-type airbrake above engine
duct on each side of fin leading edge.

FOREPLANES: Shoulder-mounted active foreplanes of sweptback planform, actuated hydraulically by fly-by-wire
control system. Made primarily of carbonfibre with
honeycomb core and aramid fibre tips.

TAIL UNIT: Fin and inset rudder only, of sweptback form,
made primarily of carbonfibre, with honeycomb core in
rudder. Aramid fibre fin tip. Air intake in base of fin

leading edge. Rudder actuated hydraulically by fly-by-wire control system. No tabs.

LANDING GEAR: Hydraulically retractable tricycle type supplied by Messier-Hispano-Bugatti, with single wheel on each unit. Hydraulically steerable nosewheel. All wheels retract forward. Designed for impact at vertical speed of 4 m (13 ft)/s, without flare-out. Michelin radial tyres. Mainwheel tyres size 810 × 275-15. Carbon brakes on all three wheels, controlled by fly-by-wire system. Brake chute for emergency use in cylindrical container at base of rudder.

POWERPLANT: Two General Electric F404-GE-400 augmented turbofan engines, in 71.2 kN (16,000 lb st) class, mounted side-by-side in rear fuselage. Kidney-shape plain air intakes, with splitter plates, mounted low on centre fuselage. Integral tanks in fuselage and wings for more than 4,250 kg (9,370 lb) of fuel. Inboard underwing pylons able to carry two 2,000 litre (528 US gallon; 440 Imp gallon) drop-tanks. Provision for flight refuelling.

ACCOMMODATION: Pilot only, on Martin-Baker Mk 10 zero/zero ejection seat, reclined at angle of 30–40°. One-piece blister windscreen/canopy, hinged to open sideways, to starboard. HOTAS (hands on throttle and stick) controls, with sidestick controller on starboard console and small-travel throttle lever.

AVIONICS AND EQUIPMENT: Provision for more than 780 kg (1,720 lb) of avionics equipment and racks, including Thomson-CSF RDX lookdown/shootdown radar with acquisition range in 50 nm (92 km; 57 mile) class, able to track up to eight targets simultaneously, with automatic threat assessment and allocation of priority. (Radar and some other advanced equipment are not installed initially.) Sagem Uliss 52X INS. Digital CRT display of fuel, engine, hydraulic, electrical, oxygen and other systems information. Wide-angle diffractive optics HUD, collimated eye-level display and lateral multi-function colour displays by Thomson-CSF/SFENA. TRT com. SOCRAT VOR/ILS. Crouzet voice activated radio controls and voice alarm warning system. LMT IFF. Internal ECM suite.

ARMAMENT: One 30 mm DEFA 554 gun in side of port engine duct. Twelve external stores attachments: four under fuselage, four under wings, two at wingtips, and two below engine air intakes for sensors. Basic armament of four fuselage mounted Matra Mica medium-range air-to-air missiles and two wingtip mounted Matra Magic close-range air-to-air missiles for air-defence role, with provision for four additional Micas under wings.

DIMENSIONS, EXTERNAL:
Wing span	11.2 m (36 ft 9 in)
Length overall	15.8 m (51 ft 10 in)

AREA:
Wings, gross	47.0 m² (506.0 sq ft)

WEIGHTS:
Weight empty	9,400–9,500 kg (20,725–20,945 lb)
Combat weight, with 4 Mica and 2 Magic missiles	
	14,000 kg (30,865 lb)

PERFORMANCE (estimated):
Max level speed	Mach 2
	(800 knots; 1,480 km/h; 920 mph IAS)
T-O run: at 14,000 kg (30,865 lb) AUW 400 m (1,313 ft)	
at 20,000 kg (44,100 lb) AUW under 700 m (2,300 ft)	
g limit	+ 9

Dassault-Breguet Rafale D and M

Rafale D/M are the planned production versions of Rafale A, to replace Air Force Mirage III-Es and Jaguars, and Navy Crusaders and Étendard IV-Ps, in the mid-1990s. They are intended to be slightly smaller than the Rafale A, although the general configuration will be identical except for deletion of the air intake at the base of the tail fin. Differences in the naval version (M) compared with the Air Force version (D) will include a reinforced main landing gear able to cope with rates of sink up to 6 m (19.7 ft)/s; a modified nose gear for nose gear catapult launch and possible use of a mini ski-jump T-O technique; and added arrester hook.

The proposed development programme for Rafale D/M envisaged design freeze in 1987, followed by construction of three 'D' prototypes and two 'M' prototypes, with flight testing to start in 1990. Other features of Rafale D/M announced in Summer 1986 are as follows:

POWERPLANT: Two SNECMA M88 turbofan engines, each rated at approx 50 kN (11,240 lb st) dry and 75 kN (16,860 lb st) with afterburning. Internal fuel capacity more than 4,000 kg (8,818 lb).

AVIONICS: Thomson-CSF RDX multi-function radar to permit terrain following/terrain avoidance/threat avoidance flight at low altitude, with simultaneous air-to-air search/track of multiple targets; and fire control of Mica and AMRAAM air-to-air missiles. Self protection ECM. Communications via SINTAC/JTIDS. Autonomous navigation, supplemented by use of GPS/Navstar satellite systems.

DIMENSIONS, EXTERNAL (calculated):
Wing span over missiles	10.75 m (35 ft 3¼ in)
Length overall	14.20 m (46 ft 7 in)

AREA:
Wings, gross	44.0 m² (474.0 sq ft)

WEIGHTS:
Avionics	more than 780 kg (1,720 lb)
Target operational weight, empty	8,600 kg (18,960 lb)

Socata
SOCIÉTÉ DE CONSTRUCTION D'AVIONS DE TOURISME ET D'AFFAIRES
(Subsidiary of Aérospatiale)

This company, formed in 1966, is a subsidiary of Aérospatiale, responsible for producing all of the group's piston engined light aircraft. As well as those described in this entry, Socata manufactures the Aérospatiale Epsilon military primary/basic trainer. Socata's works cover an area of 56,000 m² (602,775 sq ft).

Socata R 235 Guerrier

This military aircraft (known also as the Rallye 235 G) has four Alkan 663 underwing stores pylons which enable it to be used for a variety of armed and support missions. The pylons are connected to a weapon selection box installed centrally on the radio panel in the cockpit.

Customers for the Guerrier include Djibouti, Rwanda and Senegal.

TYPE: Light general-purpose STOL military aircraft.

WINGS: Cantilever low-wing monoplane. Wing section NACA 63A416 (modified). Dihedral 7°. Incidence 4°. Wide-chord slotted ailerons. Full-span automatic slats. Long-span slotted flaps. Ground adjustable aileron tabs.

FUSELAGE: Semi-monocoque structure.

TAIL UNIT: Cantilever structure. Fixed-incidence tailplane. One automatic tab and one controllable tab on elevator. One controllable tab on rudder.

LANDING GEAR: Non-retractable tricycle type, with single wheel on each unit. Castoring nosewheel. Cleveland mainwheels with tyres size 6.00-6; nosewheel tyre size 5.00-4. Cleveland hydraulic disc brakes.

POWERPLANT: One 175 kW (235 hp) Avco Lycoming O-540-B4B5 flat-six engine, driving a Hartzell HC-C2YK-1/8468-6 two-blade constant-speed metal propeller. Fuel in two metal tanks in wings, with total capacity of 282 litres (74.5 US gallons; 62 Imp gallons).

ACCOMMODATION: Two side-by-side seats, with dual controls, enabling aircraft to be used for basic and operational training as well as combat missions. Rear bench seat can be installed to permit the carriage of two passengers and a quantity of baggage or freight. Provision for carrying stretcher patient on casevac missions.

ARMAMENT AND OPERATIONAL EQUIPMENT: Underwing pylons can carry Matra F2 rocket launchers, each containing six 68 mm rockets; Type AA 52 pods, each containing two 7.62 mm machine guns with 500 rds/gun, and large enough to retain all spent cartridge cases and links after firing; 50 kg operational or smaller practice bombs; rescue packs for airdropping over water, desert, jungle or polar regions; flares for use during operational or rescue missions by night; a surveillance pack containing a TV camera and transmitter to send images to a ground station. The camera is fitted with a zoom lens, and can scan to 45° on each side of the aircraft, with a vertical scan of 110°. The pilot has a control box (normal and zoom), and a monitor on which to check precisely the images the camera is viewing. All underwing loads can be jettisoned in an emergency.

Socata Guerrier in ground-attack configuration, with two F2 rocket packs and bombs on underwing attachments.

Socata R 235 Guerrier. *(Pilot Press)*

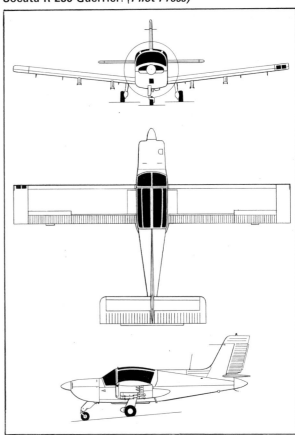

DIMENSIONS, EXTERNAL:
    Wing span   9.74 m (31 ft 11 in)
    Length overall   7.25 m (23 ft 9$\frac{1}{2}$ in)
    Height overall   2.80 m (9 ft 2$\frac{1}{4}$ in)
    Wheel track   2.01 m (6 ft 7 in)
    Wheelbase   1.71 m (5 ft 7$\frac{1}{4}$ in)
AREA:
    Wings, gross   12.76 m² (137.3 sq ft)
WEIGHTS:
    Weight empty   710 kg (1,565 lb)
    Max T-O weight   1,350 kg (2,976 lb)
PERFORMANCE:
    Max level speed   approx 148 knots (275 km/h; 171 mph)
    Range/endurance:
        armed reconnaissance with 2 gun pods at 70% power, 30 min
            fuel reserves
                        5 h or 556 nm (1,030 km; 640 miles)

armed reconnaissance with 4 rocket launchers at 70% power,
    30 min fuel reserves
                        2 h 40 min or 286 nm (530 km; 329 miles)
ground support with 2 gun pods at 75% power at 915 m (3,000
    ft), 30 min fuel reserves, 10 min over target
                        243 nm (450 km; 280 miles)
ground support with 4 rocket launchers at 75% power at 915 m
    (3,000 ft), 30 min fuel reserves, 10 min over target
                        130 nm (240 km; 149 miles)
ground support with 2 rocket launchers and 2 gun pods at 75%
    power at 915 m (3,000 ft), 15 min fuel reserves, 10 min over
    target
                        43 nm (80 km; 50 miles)
unarmed reconnaissance with TV pod at 70% power, 30 min
    fuel reserves
                        545 nm (1,010 km; 627 miles)

61

Germany (FEDERAL REPUBLIC)

MBB
MESSERSCHMITT-BÖLKOW-BLOHM GmbH

In May 1969 the former Messerschmitt-Bölkow GmbH and Hamburger Flugzeugbau GmbH merged to form a new group known as Messerschmitt-Bölkow-Blohm GmbH. Subsequently, in 1980, the Federal German government expressed its wish that MBB and VFW should merge, to strengthen the capabilities and competitive position of the two companies, and to help improve the structure of the German aerospace industry. The group employs about 36,915 people.

Helicopter and Military Aircraft Group
(Helicopter Division and Military Aircraft Division)

Helicopter activities of this Group include the manufacturing of civil and military versions of the MBB BO 105 helicopter, the MBB/Kawasaki BK 117 and Eurocopter programmes (described in the International section), and the ALH programme in co-operation with Hindustan Aeronautics Ltd. Main production centre for the BO 105 and BK 117 is MBB's Donauwörth factory. The Division also assumed the former VFW responsibility for overhaul and repair of Sikorsky CH-53G and Westland Sea King Mk 41 helicopters in service with the West German armed forces, and is currently upgrading 22 German Navy Sea Kings with Ferranti Seaspray Mk 3 radar, a Ferranti Link II target data transformer, AEG ALR-69 radar warning receiver, Tracor M130 chaff/flare dispenser and four BAe Sea Skua missiles.

Major military aircraft activities of the Group involve the Panavia Tornado (see International section), for which MBB is the German prime contractor; weapon system leadership for F-104G Starfighters of the Luftwaffe; modifications to improve the combat capability of Luftwaffe F-4F and RF-4E Phantoms; development of control configured vehicle (CCV) technology, using a modified F-104G aircraft; and participation in the European manufacturing programme for the General Dynamics F-16 combat aircraft.

In the Tornado programme, MBB is building centre-fuselages for all production aircraft, and is responsible for final assembly and flight testing of the aircraft required by the Luftwaffe and Marineflieger. Improvements are currently being made to the optical and electronic reconnaissance equipment in the Luftwaffe's RF-4E Phantoms, which are being armed to enable them to be used also in a fighter-bomber role. An enhancement programme for the F-4F tactical fighter is also under way.

The company has been engaged for a considerable time in intensive studies to define a new-generation tactical fighter aircraft for the Luftwaffe and other European air forces in the 1990s. In addition, it is conducting research and development programmes concerned with carbonfibre technology, and the creation of more simple, more reliable aircraft subsystems.

MBB BO 105

Design of this light utility helicopter was started in July 1962 and construction of prototypes began in 1964, under Federal German government contract. The first BO 105 prototype was fitted with an existing conventional rotor and two Allison 250-C18 turboshaft engines; subsequent aircraft, of which the first one flew in February 1967, have had a rotor system based on a rigid titanium hub, with feathering hinges only, and hingeless flexible glassfibre blades. From the Spring of 1970 'droop-snoot' rotor blades of MBB design have been standard.

Production of 100 BO 105 M (VBH) and 212 BO 105 P (PAH-1) military versions for the Federal Germany Army ended in 1984. Total civil/military production by early 1987 was over 1,200.

Details of combat-capable versions of the BO 105 follow:

BO 105 CB. Standard production version since 1975, with two Allison 250-C20B engines.

BO 105 CBS. Version with increased seating or cargo capacity in a 0.25 m (10 in) longer fuselage. Available in five-

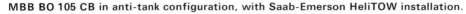

MBB BO 105 CB in anti-tank configuration, with Saab-Emerson HeliTOW installation.

BO 105 CBS operated in SAR role by the Swedish Air Force. *(Ivo Sturzenegger)*

seat executive or six-seat high-density configurations. Identified by small additional window aft of rear door on each side. Marketed in the USA by MBB Helicopter Corporation, under the name **Twin Jet II**. Certificated in early 1983 by FAA for IFR operation in accordance with SFAR Pt 29-4, requiring two pilots, radar, Loran-C and a separate battery, but not a stability augmentation system, though SAS is available as an option.

BO 105 LS. Produced in Canada since 1985, this 'hot and high' version of the BO 105 (L for Lift and S for Stretch) combines the enlarged cabin of the CBS version with more powerful engines and an uprated transmission, permitting operation at a higher gross weight. It was first flown on 23 October 1981. Certification was extended in April 1985 to cover 'hot and high' take-offs and landings at altitudes up to 6,100 m (20,000 ft).

BO 105 M (VBH). Liaison and light observation helicopter for the Federal German Army, with strengthened transmission gearing, reinforced rotor components, a tail rotor with improved thrust and performance, a rupture-proof fuel system, and a landing gear able to absorb higher energy levels. Production of 100 approved by the Federal government, to replace Alouette IIs. Deliveries completed in mid-1984.

MBB BO 105 P (PAH-1) anti-tank helicopters.

BO 105 P (PAH-1). Anti-tank version, with same airframe improvements as BO 105M, outriggers to carry six Euromissile Hot missiles, a stabilised sight above the co-pilot's position, and Singer AN/ASN-128 Doppler navigation system. The German Federal government gave approval for the procurement of 212 PAH-1s for the Federal German Army. Deliveries began on 4 December 1980 and were completed in mid-1984. First PAH-1 unit was Heeresfliegerregiment 16 at Celle. Empty equipped weight of the PAH-1, including pilot and weapons operator, is 1,913 kg (4,217 lb). Max T-O weight is 2,400 kg (5,291 lb). At max continuous power and ISA the PAH-1 has a forward rate of climb at S/L of 540 m (1,770 ft)/min and can hover OGE with T-O power at 1,580 m (5,180 ft). At max continuous power it has a max cruising speed at S/L of 119 knots (220 km/h; 137 mph) and a certificated service ceiling of 4,200 m (13,780 ft).

Twelve Mexican Navy BO 105 CBs are used for maritime patrol, fishery protection, anti-smuggling, and search and rescue duties from shore bases and corvettes of the 'Halcón' class. First BO 105s operated from ships designed especially for the purpose, these aircraft are equipped with Primus 500 search radar, flotation gear, rescue hoist, long range fuel tank, a system to wash salt deposits from the engines, special deck lashing fixtures, and folding rotor blades to permit stowage in the shipboard hangars.

Twenty BO 105 CBs, equipped with Saab/Emerson Heli-TOW missile systems, and Saab Helios sights providing night vision and laser capability, were ordered in July 1984 by the Swedish procurement agency FMV, for anti-tank operation by the Swedish Army. Deliveries of these began in 1987. In April 1985 the same agency ordered four BO 105 CBSs, in IFR search and rescue configuration, for use by the Swedish Air Force. All four were delivered in late 1985 and early 1986.

In Indonesia, IPTN is participating in a licence assembly programme for the BO 105. A contract for 60 BO 105 CBs was signed by the Spanish Ministry of Defence in late June 1979. Fifty-seven of these aircraft were assembled in Spain, including some parts manufacture, by CASA. They are operated by Spanish Army aviation units for armed reconnaissance (18), observation (14) and anti-tank (28)

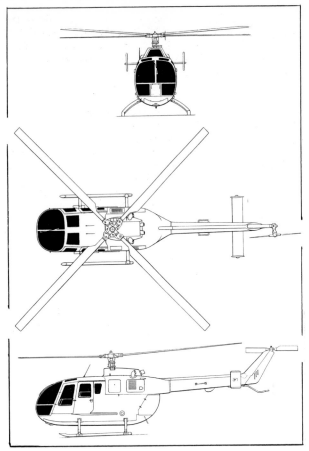

MBB BO 105 CBS. *(Pilot Press)*

missions. CASA is assembling further BO 105s.

The description which follows applies to the BO 105 CB except where indicated:

TYPE: Five-seat light helicopter.

ROTOR SYSTEM: Four-blade main rotor with MBB designed 'droop-snoot' blades of NACA 23012 asymmetrical section, having a specially designed trailing edge giving improved control in pitching moment. Roller bearings for pitch change. Main rotor blade folding optional. Two-blade semi-rigid tail rotor.

FUSELAGE: Conventional semi-monocoque structure of pod and boom type. Glassfibre reinforced cowling over powerplant.

TAIL UNIT: Horizontal stabiliser with small endplate fins.

LANDING GEAR: Skid type, with cross-tubes designed for energy absorption by plastic deformation in the event of a heavy landing. Inflatable emergency floats can be attached to skids.

POWERPLANT: Two 313 kW (420 shp) Allison 250-C20B turboshaft engines, each with a max continuous rating of 298 kW (400 shp). Bladder fuel tanks under cabin floor, capacity 580 litres (153 US gallons; 127.5 Imp gallons), of which 570 litres (150 US gallons; 125.3 Imp gallons) are usable. Auxiliary tanks in freight compartment available optionally.

ACCOMMODATION: Pilot and co-pilot or passenger on individual front seats. Optional dual controls. Bench seat at rear for three persons, removable for cargo and

stretcher carrying. Entire rear fuselage aft of seats and under powerplant available as freight and baggage space, with access through two clamshell doors at rear. Two standard stretchers can be accommodated side-by-side in ambulance role.

AVIONICS AND EQUIPMENT: A wide range of optional avionics and equipment is available, including stability augmentation system, Doppler navigation, search radar, dual controls, rescue winch, landing light, searchlight, externally mounted loudspeaker, external load hook, snow skids, and main rotor-blade folding. GEC Avionics AD 2780 Tacan in aircraft of Royal Netherlands Air Force. A completely equipped ambulance version is available.

ARMAMENT (military versions): Provision for a variety of alternative military loads, including six Hot or eight TOW anti-tank missiles and associated stabilised sight, or a Saab-Emerson HeliTOW installation.

DIMENSIONS, EXTERNAL:	
Main rotor diameter	9.84 m (32 ft $3\frac{1}{2}$ in)
Tail rotor diameter	1.90 m (6 ft $2\frac{3}{4}$ in)
Length, excl rotors: CB	8.56 m (28 ft 1 in)
CBS	8.81 m (28 ft 11 in)
Height to top of main rotorhead	3.00 m (9 ft 10 in)
Width over skids: unladen	2.53 m (8 ft $3\frac{1}{2}$ in)
laden	2.58 m (8 ft $5\frac{1}{2}$ in)
AREA:	
Main rotor disc	76.05 m² (818.6 sq ft)
WEIGHTS:	
Weight empty, basic: CB	1,276 kg (2,813 lb)
CBS	1,301 kg (2,868 lb)
Standard T-O weight	2,400 kg (5,291 lb)
Max T-O weight	2,500 kg (5,511 lb)
PERFORMANCE (A at 2,400 kg; 5,291 lb gross weight, B at 2,500 kg; 5,511 lb max T-O weight):	
Never-exceed speed at S/L:	
A	145 knots (270 km/h; 167 mph)
B	131 knots (242 km/h; 150 mph)
Max cruising speed at S/L:	
A, B	131 knots (242 km/h; 150 mph)
Max rate of climb at S/L, max continuous power:	
A	480 m (1,575 ft)/min
B	419 m (1,375 ft)/min
Vertical rate of climb at S/L, T-O power:	
A	183 m (600 ft)/min
B	91 m (300 ft)/min
Max operating altitude: A	5,180 m (17,000 ft)
B	3,050 m (10,000 ft)
Hovering ceiling IGE, T-O power:	
A	2,560 m (8,400 ft)
B	1,525 m (5,000 ft)
Hovering ceiling OGE, T-O power:	
A	1,615 m (5,300 ft)
B	457 m (1,500 ft)
Range with standard fuel and max payload, no reserves:	
at S/L: A	310 nm (575 km; 357 miles)
B	307 nm (570 km; 354 miles)
at 1,525 m (5,000 ft): A	355 nm (657 km; 408 miles)
B	321 nm (596 km; 370 miles)
Ferry range with auxiliary tanks, no reserves:	
at S/L: A	540 nm (1,000 km; 621 miles)
B	537 nm (995 km; 618 miles)
at 1,525 m (5,000 ft):	
A	600 nm (1,112 km; 691 miles)
B	550 nm (1,020 km; 634 miles)
Endurance with standard fuel and max payload, no reserves:	
at S/L: A	3 h 30 min
B	3 h 24 min

MBB F-4F ICE Programme

Under a German Defence Ministry programme known as ICE (improved combat efficiency), 75 Luftwaffe F-4F Phantom IIs of fighter wings JG 71 and JG 74 are to be upgraded to give them a lookdown/shootdown capability against multiple targets. The programme, for which MBB is the prime contractor, was initiated in late 1983 and reached the end of the definition phase some two years later. Initial operational capability is planned for 1991.

Main ingredient of this retrofit programme involves replacement of the existing Westinghouse APQ-120 radar by the all-digital multi-mode Hughes APG-65, built under licence in Germany by AEG. This advanced X band system has 30 air-to-air and air-to-ground modes, with a ten-target track-while-scan capability, of which eight can be displayed simultaneously. APG-65 subsystems include a low-sidelobe planar array antenna, a 16-bit (256 K) memory, and a radar data processor with advanced ECCM. Armament capability of the ICE Phantoms will be extended to include up to four Hughes AIM-120 (AMRAAM) air-to-air missiles. Other new avionics in the full ICE package are to include a new AEG radar control console, optimisation (by Hughes) of the cockpit display, installation of a new Litef digital fire control computer, Honeywell H-423 laser inertial platform, GEC Avionics CPU-143/A digital air data computer, new IFF system, a new guided missile launcher, a MIL-1553B digital data bus with advanced operational software, and improved resistance to electronic jamming and other countermeasures.

Some 75 other Luftwaffe F-4Fs, serving in the fighter-bomber role with JaboGs 35 and 36, are expected to undergo partial update (databus, INS and ADC only, initially), with the option of a full ICE installation later.

India

HAL
HINDUSTAN AERONAUTICS LIMITED

Hindustan Aeronautics Limited (HAL) was formed on 1 October 1964, and has 12 Divisions, six at Bangalore and one each at Nasik, Koraput, Hyderabad, Kanpur, Lucknow and Korwa, plus a Design and Development Complex. The total workforce is about 42,000. The new factory at Korwa, set up to manufacture inertial navigation systems, was commissioned on 3 April 1986.

HAL is currently manufacturing and overhauling a variety of aircraft, helicopters, aero engines, avionics, instruments and accessories. It is also manufacturing components for the Indian Space Research Organisation (ISRO).

The Bangalore Complex is engaged in the manufacture of military aircraft, helicopters and aero engines, both under licence and of indigenous design. These include the SEPECAT Jaguar International combat aircraft and its Adour engine, and the Kiran Mk II armed jet trainer. The Complex also undertakes repair and overhaul of airframes, engines, and allied instruments and accessories.

The Nasik and Koraput Divisions are manufacturing airframes and engines of the Soviet MiG-21 and MiG-27 in collaboration with the USSR. Hyderabad Division manufactures avionics for all aircraft produced by HAL, as well as airport radars.

The Korwa Division is to produce sophisticated INS and laser systems, intended to give India an indigenous capability in these fields.

In addition to its manufacturing programmes, HAL is pursuing design and development activities relating to aircraft, helicopters, small jet engines, avionics and accessories. A Light Combat Aircraft (LCA) programme was approved by the Indian government.

Bangalore Complex

The Bangalore Complex of HAL consists essentially of the former Hindustan Aircraft Limited. The Complex is subdivided into an Aircraft Division, Helicopter Division, Engine Division, Overhaul Division, Foundry and Forge Division, Services Division, and Design Complex.

HAL (SEPECAT) Jaguar International

The Bangalore Complex is responsible for the assembly and/or licence construction of SEPECAT Jaguar International combat aircraft (see International section) for the Indian Air Force. Current orders are for 76 aircraft. The first UK-built airframe components for final assembly in India were delivered to HAL in 1981, and the first Indian assembled Jaguar (JS136) made its initial flight on 31 March 1982.

Light Combat Aircraft

The Indian government confirmed a requirement for an air superiority and light close-air-support aircraft for service in the 1990s. Known as the LCA (light combat aircraft), it is being designed with assistance from a Western aerospace company but will probably be manufactured entirely in India. It is expected to embody composite materials in its construction, and to have a fly-by-wire flight control system. Empty and max T-O weights were originally believed to be in the order of 6,000 kg (13,230 lb) and 10,500 kg (23,150 lb), but the latter has reportedly now risen to 12,500 kg (27,558 lb). An indigenous afterburning engine of about 83.4 kN (18,740 lb st), designated GTX-35, entered development by the Gas Turbine Research Establishment at Bangalore, but General Electric F404 turbofans have been ordered to power the prototypes until this is ready. The project definition phase is currently under way, but a first flight is not expected before the early 1990s.

HAL HF-24 Marut (Wind Spirit)

The Marut has been long out of production, but it is thought that one Indian Air Force squadron retains Mk Is while awaiting replacement MiG-23BNs. A further 10–15 Mk IT two-seat trainer variants are still flown.

Development of the HF-24 Marut single-seat fighter was started by HAL in 1956, under the design leadership of Dr Kurt Tank, who was responsible for the wartime Focke-Wulf aeroplanes. The first prototype HF-24 Mk I flew for the first time on 17 June 1961. It was followed by the second Mk I prototype on 4 October 1962.

The HF-24 was built initially to Mk I standard as a ground-attack fighter, with Orpheus 703 non-afterburning engines. The first of 18 pre-production Maruts flew in March 1963, and a token delivery of two aircraft to the Indian Air Force was made on 10 May 1964. A further 12 were handed over to the IAF, the other four being used for test and development programmes. The latter included one Mk IA, for trials in 1966 with an afterburner fitted to its Orpheus 703 engine.

HAL HF-24 Marut Mk I ground-attack aircraft.

66

Mk IT two-seat training version of the HF-24 Marut.

The first series production Marut flew on 15 November 1967, and the Mk I equipped three squadrons of the Indian Air Force, which used its Maruts successfully, without loss, in the December 1971 war with Pakistan. A total of 129 Maruts was built.

The first of two prototype **Mk IT** tandem two-seat training versions began its flight tests on 30 April 1970, and was followed by the second Mk IT in March 1971. Differences by comparison with the Mk I were minimal. The internal Matra rocket launcher was removed to make way for the Martin-Baker Mk 84C second seat; full dual controls were fitted, and a wide choice of equipment enabled the Mk IT to be used for several advanced training roles, including dual and solo flying; operational training in the all-weather ground-attack role; and instrument flying and armament training. Eighteen Mk ITs had been delivered by the end of production in 1977.

The following description applies to the HF-24 Mk I, except where otherwise stated:

TYPE: Single-seat ground-attack fighter.

WINGS: Cantilever low-wing monoplane of thin section.

HAL HF-24 Marut Mk I. *(Pilot Press)*

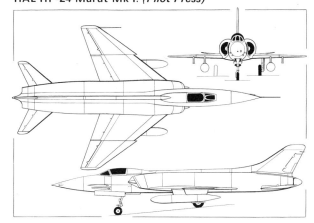

Sweepback approx 45° at quarter-chord. Extended-chord leading edges on outer panels. Hydraulically actuated ailerons and trailing-edge flaps, with provision for selecting manual control.

FUSELAGE: Conventional semi-monocoque structure, narrowed in accordance with area rule in region of wing trailing edge. Rear of fuselage detaches at transport joint for engine removal. Two hydraulically actuated airbrakes in lower part of fuselage aft of mainwheel wells, opening downward. Engine air intake, with non-adjustable half-cone centrebody, on each side of cockpit.

TAIL UNIT: Cantilever structure with sweepback on all surfaces. Hydraulically-operated low-set variable-incidence tailplane with electrical trim facility. Elevators can be operated either hydraulically or manually. Hydraulically actuated rudder.

LANDING GEAR: Retractable tricycle type, with single Dunlop wheel on each unit. Hydraulic-retraction, nosewheel retracting forward, main units inward into fuselage. Steerable nosewheel. Mainwheel tyres size 29 × 8-15. Nosewheel tyre size 19 × 6.25-9. Maxaret anti-skid system. RFD-GQ Type LB-52 Mk 2 ring-slot braking parachute, diameter 3.20 m (10 ft 6 in), located in top of rear fuselage.

POWERPLANT: Two HAL-built Rolls-Royce Bristol Orpheus 703 turbojet engines, each rated at 21.6 kN (4,850 lb st), side-by-side in rear fuselage. Fuel in main fuselage collector tank, wing centre-section supply tank and two integral wing tanks, with total usable capacity of 2,491 litres (658 US gallons; 549 Imp gallons). Provision for up to four 454 litre (120 US gallon; 100 Imp gallon) underwing drop-tanks, and an internal auxiliary tank of 400 litres (105 US gallons; 88 Imp gallons) capacity in place of the Matra rocket launcher.

ACCOMMODATION: Pilot only, on Martin-Baker Mk 84C zero-altitude ejection seat, under rearward-sliding blister canopy. Windscreen heated by sandwiched gold-film electrode.

67

AVIONICS AND EQUIPMENT: Includes a Bendix DFA 73 system; Bendix TA/RA 228 VHF com with 20 pre-set channels and mixing box; Ferranti ISIS F 124 sighting system; and BAT Mk 10 IFF transponder. To this equipment is added, in the Mk IT, a centralised warning system and fully duplicated control units for the radio communications system.

ARMAMENT: Four 30 mm Aden Mk 2 guns in nose, with 120 rds/gun, and Matra Type 103 retractable pack of 50 SNEB 68 mm air-to-air rockets in lower fuselage aft of nosewheel unit. Attachments for four 1,000 lb bombs, napalm tanks, Type 116 SNEB rocket packs, clusters of T10 air-to-surface rockets, drop-tanks or other stores, under wings.

DIMENSIONS, EXTERNAL:
Wing span	9.00 m (29 ft 6¼ in)
Length overall	15.87 m (52 ft 0¾ in)
Height overall	3.60 m (11 ft 9¾ in)
Wheel track	2.80 m (9 ft 2 in)
Wheelbase	5.555 m (18 ft 2¾ in)

AREA:
Wings, gross	28.00 m² (301.4 sq ft)

WEIGHTS:
Weight empty, equipped:	
Mk I with auxiliary ventral tank	6,195 kg (13,658 lb)
Mk IT	6,250 kg (13,778 lb)
T-O weight, 'clean':	
Mk I with auxiliary ventral tank	8,951 kg (19,734 lb)
Max T-O weight:	
Mk I	10,908 kg (24,048 lb)
Mk IT	10,812 kg (23,836 lb)

PERFORMANCE:
Max level speed attained at 12,000 m (39,375 ft):	
Mk I	Mach 1.02
Mk IT	Mach 1.00
Stalling speed at AUW of 8,951 kg (19,734 lb):	
flaps and landing gear up	138 knots (256 km/h; 159 mph)
flaps and landing gear down	133 knots (248 km/h; 154 mph)
Time to climb from S/L to 12,200 m (40,000 ft) ('clean' aircraft, ISA + 15°C)	9 min 20 sec
T-O run at S/L	850 m (2,790 ft)
Radius of action (Mk IT):	
at low level	129 nm (238 km; 148 miles)
interception mission at 12,000 m (39,375 ft)	214 nm (396 km; 246 miles)
Ferry range (Mk IT) at 9,150 m (30,000 ft)	780 nm (1,445 km; 898 miles)

HAL Kiran Mk II armament training and counter-insurgency aircraft.

The design and development phase was completed by March 1983. Deliveries of Kiran Mk IIs to the Indian Air Force began in April 1984. More than 100 may be ordered eventually.

HAL HJT-16 Kiran Mk II. *(Pilot Press)*

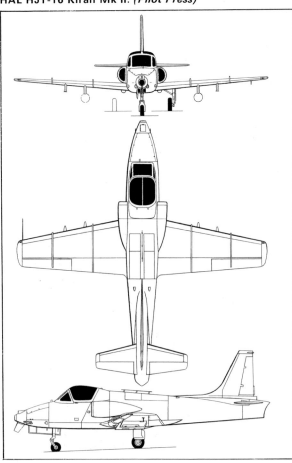

HAL HJT-16 Kiran Mk II

This version of the Kiran basic jet trainer, for armament training and counter-insurgency duties, was developed from the Mks I/IA by the Aircraft Design Bureau at Bangalore. The first prototype made its initial flight on 30 July 1976. Principal differences include improved weapon carrying capability, a more powerful engine, updated avionics and an improved hydraulic system. The Rolls-Royce Orpheus 701-01 turbojet, replacing the Viper engine of the Mks I/IA, gives the Kiran Mk II improved maximum speed, climb, and manoeuvrability.

TYPE: Two-seat jet trainer and light attack aircraft.

WINGS: Cantilever low-wing monoplane. Wing section NACA 23015 at root, NACA 23012 at tip. Dihedral 4° from roots. Incidence 0° 30′ at root. Sweepback 7° 28′ at quarter-chord. Frise differential ailerons, with balance tab in each aileron and ground-adjustable tab on port aileron. Hydraulically actuated trailing-edge split flaps. Two full-chord boundary-layer fences on upper surface of each wing.

FUSELAGE: Semi-monocoque fail-safe structure. Hydraulically actuated door-type airbrake under centre of fuselage, in line with flaps.

TAIL UNIT: Cantilever structure. Electrically operated variable-incidence tailplane, with elevators. Ground-adjustable tab on rudder.

LANDING GEAR: Retractable tricycle type, of HAL manufacture. Hydraulic actuation. Main units retract inward into fuselage; self-centering twin-contact non-steerable nosewheel retracts forward. Dunlop mainwheel tyres size 19 × 6.25-9. Nosewheel tyre size 15.4 × 4.6. Dunlop hydraulic brakes.

POWERPLANT: One Rolls-Royce Orpheus 701-01 turbojet engine, derated to 18.68 kN (4,200 lb st). Internal fuel in flexible main saddle tank in fuselage (625 litres; 165 US gallons; 137.5 Imp gallons), one 282 litre (75 US gallon; 62 Imp gallon) collector tank in wing centre-section, and two outboard integral wing tanks (each 218 litres; 57.5 US gallons; 48 Imp gallons), giving total internal fuel capacity of 1,345 litres (355 US gallons; 295.5 Imp gallons). Provision for two underwing tanks with total capacity of 454 litres (120 US gallons; 100 Imp gallons).

ACCOMMODATION: Crew of two side-by-side in air-conditioned and pressurised cockpit, on Martin-Baker H4HA zero-altitude fully automatic ejection seats. Clamshell type canopy, hinged at rear and opening upward. Dual controls and duplicated blind-flying instruments.

AVIONICS AND EQUIPMENT: HAL VUC 201 V/UHF multi-channel com transceiver; HAL COM 150A four-channel standby UHF; HAL ARC-610A ADF; HAL IFF Mk 10 (BAT). Blind-flying instrumentation standard.

ARMAMENT: Two 7.62 mm machine-guns in nose, with 150 rds/gun; G90 gun camera, and Ferranti ISIS gunsights with Teledyne camera. Two pylons under each outer wing, each with an ejector release unit capable of carrying a 227 litre (60 US gallon; 50 Imp gallon) drop-tank, a 250 kg bomb, a reusable pod containing eighteen 68 mm SNEB rockets, or a CBLS-200 carrier with four 25 lb practice bombs.

DIMENSIONS, EXTERNAL:	
Wing span	10.70 m (35 ft 1¼ in)
Length overall	10.60 m (34 ft 9½ in)
Fuselage: Max width	1.36 m (4 ft 5½ in)
Height overall	3.635 m (11 ft 11 in)
Wheel track	2.42 m (7 ft 11 in)
Wheelbase	3.50 m (11 ft 6 in)
AREA:	
Wings, gross	19.00 m² (204.5 sq ft)
WEIGHTS:	
Weight empty, equipped	2,995 kg (6,603 lb)
Normal T-O weight 'clean'	4,250 kg (9,369 lb)
Max T-O weight	5,000 kg (11,023 lb)
PERFORMANCE (at max T-O weight, ISA):	
Never-exceed speed	421 knots (780 km/h; 484 mph)
Max level speed at S/L	363 knots (672 km/h; 418 mph)

Max cruising speed at 4,575 m (15,000 ft)	335 knots (621 km/h; 386 mph) IAS
Econ cruising speed at 4,575 m (15,000 ft)	225 knots (417 km/h; 259 mph) IAS
Stalling speed:	
flaps and landing gear up	100 knots (185 km/h; 115 mph) IAS
flaps and landing gear down	85 knots (158 km/h; 98 mph) IAS
Max rate of climb at S/L	1,600 m (5,250 ft)/min
Service ceiling	12,000 m (39,375 ft)
T-O run	540 m (1,772 ft)
T-O to 15 m (50 ft)	730 m (2,395 ft)
Landing from 15 m (50 ft)	1,440 m (4,725 ft)
Range at 6,000 m (19,680 ft) with max internal fuel	397 nm (735 km; 457 miles)

HAL Ajeet (Invincible)

The Ajeet was built as a developed version of the 1950s Hawker Siddeley Gnat light fighter and fighter-bomber, which HAL had produced under licence. It differed in having improved communications and navigation systems; more reliable longitudinal control; and increased combat capability. The last-named characteristic was achieved by a redesigned fuel system, dispensing with the underwing drop-tanks in favour of integral wing tanks, so permitting additional underwing armament to be carried.

HAL Ajeet lightweight interceptor and ground-attack aircraft.

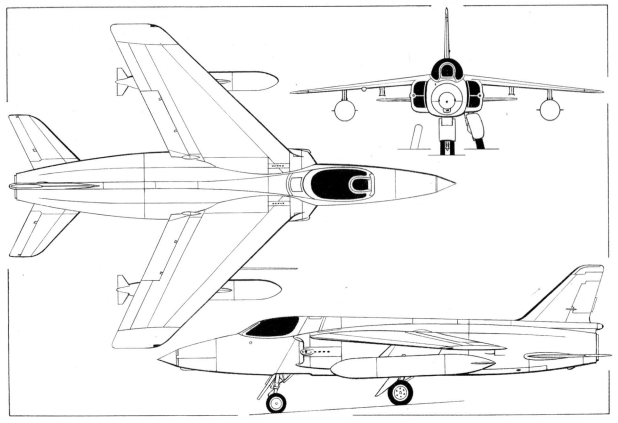

HAL Ajeet. *(Pilot Press)*

The last two HAL-built Gnat Mk Is were converted as prototypes for the Ajeet; the first of these was flown on 5 March 1975, and the second on 5 November 1975.

First flight of a production Ajeet was made on 30 September 1976, and a total of 80 had been delivered to the Indian Air Force by 1982, when the production line was closed. In addition, 10 Gnats were brought up to Ajeet standards.

TYPE: Single-seat lightweight interceptor and ground-attack aircraft.

WINGS: Cantilever shoulder-wing monoplane. Sweptback wings, of RAE 102 section. Thickness/chord ratio 8%. Anhedral 5°. Sweepback 40° at quarter-chord. One-piece wing, fitting into recess in top of fuselage and secured by bolts at four points. Inboard ailerons, powered by hydraulic actuators, droop 22° to serve as flaps when the landing gear is lowered.

FUSELAGE: Semi-monocoque structure.

TAIL UNIT: Cantilever structure. One-piece variable-incidence tailplane, operated hydraulically. Rear portions of tailplane can be unlocked to perform as elevators, or locked to provide the functions of an all-moving tailplane. Ground-adjustable tab on rudder.

LANDING GEAR: Retractable tricycle type, all units retracting rearward hydraulically into fuselage. Wheel-well fairings attached to individual landing gear units serve as airbrakes when landing gear is partly lowered, the relative movements of the airbrakes being so adjusted that no change of trim occurs at any speed. Dunlop mainwheel tyres size 20 × 5.25. Twin nosewheel tyres. Hydraulically operated brakes and Maxaret anti-skid units on main wheels. Braking parachute in fairing at base of fin.

POWERPLANT: One Rolls-Royce Orpheus 701-01 non-afterburning turbojet engine, rated at 20 kN (4,500 lb st). Compressed-air starting. Air intakes in sides of fuselage. Seven crashproof flexible tanks and two metal tanks in fuselage, and two 227 litre (60 US gallon; 50 Imp gallon) integral wing tanks. Total internal fuel capacity 1,350 litres (357 US gallons; 297 Imp gallons). Fuel supplied to engine by electrically-driven booster pump in one of the tanks. Provision for two 136.5 litre (36 US gallon; 30 Imp gallon) underwing drop-tanks.

ACCOMMODATION: Pilot only, on Martin-Baker GF4 zero-height/90 knot (167 km/h; 104 mph) lightweight ejection seat. Pressurised cockpit, with jettisonable canopy which is hinged at rear and opens upward.

AVIONICS AND EQUIPMENT: Bendix TA/RA-22 VHF transceiver (initially; V/UHF later) and BEL AX-3 standby VHF set; Bendix DFA-73 ADF; IFF Mk 10 (BAT) transponder. Ferranti navigation system.

ARMAMENT: Two 30 mm Aden Mk 4 cannon in air-intake fairings, one on each side of fuselage, with 90 rds/gun. Ferranti F 195R/3 ISIS weapons sight. Vinten G90 gun camera. Four underwing hardpoints, the inboard points each capable of carrying a BTV or BL-755 cluster bomb, a 500 lb bomb, a CBLS-200/IA cluster bomb, a Soviet 57 mm rocket pod, or a Matra Type 122 practice rocket pod. Outboard points can carry a 136.5 litre drop-tank.

DIMENSIONS, EXTERNAL:	
Wing span	6.73 m (22 ft 1 in)
Length overall	9.04 m (29 ft 8 in)
Height overall	2.46 m (8 ft 1 in)
Wheel track	1.55 m (5 ft 1 in)
Wheelbase	2.36 m (7 ft 9 in)
AREA:	
Wings, gross	12.69 m² (136.6 sq ft)
WEIGHTS:	
Basic weight empty	2,307 kg (5,086 lb)
T-O weight 'clean'	3,539 kg (7,803 lb)
Max T-O weight	4,173 kg (9,200 lb)

PERFORMANCE (in configurations indicated; A: ISA; B: ISA +15°C; C: ISA + 30°C):

Max Mach No. at 12,000 m (39,375 ft), at 'clean' T-O weight: A	0.96
B	0.953
C	0.948
Max level speed at S/L, at 'clean' T-O weight: A	595 knots (1,102 km/h; 685 mph)
B	612 knots (1,134 km/h; 705 mph)
C	622 knots (1,152 km/h; 716 mph)

Time to 12,000 m (39,375 ft) from brakes off, at 'clean' T-O weight: A	6 min 2 s
B	7 min 43 s
C	9 min 33 s
Service ceiling: A, B, C	13,720 m (45,000 ft)

T-O run at S/L, zero wind, at T-O weight of 4,136 kg (9,118 lb) with two rocket pods and two 30 Imp gallon drop-tanks:

A	1,034 m (3,390 ft)
B	1,180 m (3,870 ft)
C	1,376 m (4,515 ft)

Landing run 'clean' at S/L, zero wind, at normal landing weight, no brake-chute:

A	951 m (3,120 ft)
B	997 m (3,270 ft)
C	1,047 m (3,435 ft)

Combat radius (A, B and C), low-level ground-attack mission:
with two 250 kg bombs on inboard stations
93 nm (175 km; 107 miles)

MiG Complex

The MiG Complex was originally formed with the Nasik, Koraput and Hyderabad Divisions of HAL, which, under an agreement concluded in 1962, built respectively the airframes, powerplants and avionics of MiG-21 series fighters under licence from the USSR. Nasik has a workforce of 8,019. The Hyderabad Division is now a part of the Accessories Complex.

HAL (Mikoyan) MiG-21*bis*

NATO reporting name: Fishbed-N

Several versions of the MiG-21 have been supplied to or, since 1966, manufactured in India. These have included the MiG-21F (IAF designation Type 74), MiG-21PF (Type 76), MiG-21FL (Type 77), MiG-21U (Types 66-400 and 66-600), MiG-21M (Type 96), and MiG-21MF (160 built). The most recent version was:

MiG-21 *bis* ('Fishbed-N'). Deliveries of 75 Soviet-built examples of this version, initially for service with No. 21 Squadron of the IAF, were reported in 1977. Indian production of 220 MiG-21*bis* (initially from knocked-down components) and their Tumansky R-25 engines had begun by the end of 1979, and the 21*bis* superseded the MiG-21M as the current production version in 1981.

HAL (Mikoyan) MiG-21*bis*. *(Pilot Press)*

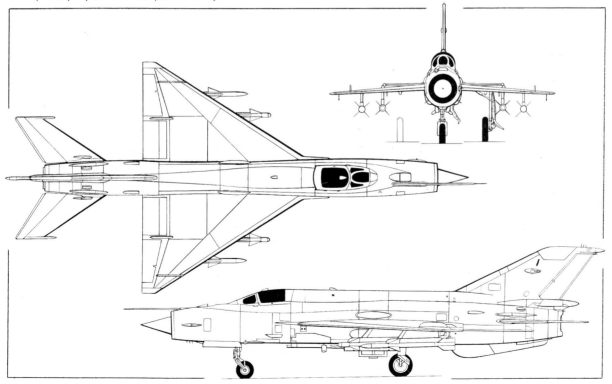

Indian production of MiG-21s was reported to be at the rate of about 30 per year in 1981–82. It is now being phased out, as production of the MiG-27M 'Flogger-J' increases. Details of the MiG-21 appear in the USSR section of this volume.

HAL (Mikoyan) MiG-27M

Indian Air Force name: Bahadur (Valiant)
NATO reporting name: Flogger-J

Licence assembly of some 165 MiG-27Ms (see USSR section) began at HAL in 1984, and the first example completed by HAL was rolled out in October of that year. These aircraft supplement Soviet-built MiG-23s and MiG-27s already supplied to the Indian Air Force, and are the first MiG-27s to be assembled outside the USSR. From 1988–89, MiG-27Ms assembled at Nasik are expected to incorporate components manufactured in India. First IAF unit to receive Bahadurs was No. 32 ('Tiger Sharks') Squadron, the type being formally inducted into IAF service on 11 January 1986.

POWERPLANT: One Tumansky R-29B turbofan engine, rated at 78.65 kN (17,681 lb st) dry and 112.78 kN (25,353 lb st) with afterburning.

ARMAMENT: One Gatling type cannon and up to 3,000 kg (6,614 lb) of external stores which can include 500 kg bombs, 57 mm S-24 rockets, two 'Kerry' air-to-surface or four R-60 air-to-air missiles.

WEIGHT:	
Max T-O weight	18,000 kg (39,685 lb)
PERFORMANCE:	
T-O run at S/L	800 m (2,625 ft)
Combat radius (low level)	210 nm (390 km; 242 miles)
Ferry range	1,349 nm (2,500 km; 1,553 miles)

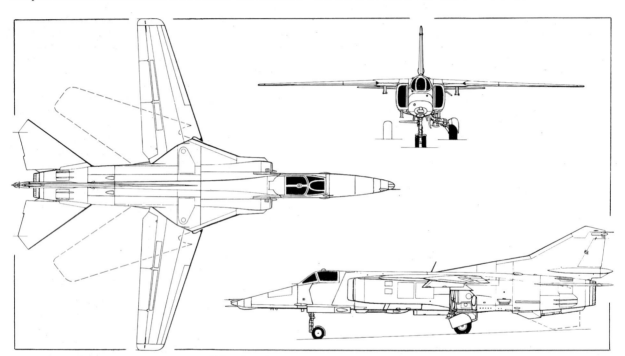

HAL (Mikoyan) MiG-27M Flogger-J. *(Pilot Press)*

International Programmes

AMX INTERNATIONAL
PARTICIPATING COMPANIES:
Aeritalia (Italy)
Aermacchi SpA (Italy)
**Embraer (Empresa Brasileira de Aeronáutica
   SA)** (Brazil)

AMX

Brazilian Air Force designation: A-1

The AMX, when it enters service in 1988, will represent the outcome of an Italian Air Force specification drawn up eleven years earlier. By that date the Aeronautica Militare Italiana's G91Rs, G91Ys and F-104Gs are expected to have reached the end of their useful life, so that the AMI's two basic front-line combat types will be the Tornado in the interdictor/strike and reconnaissance roles, and the Aeritalia-built F-104S for all-weather interception. The AMI decided that a need existed for a small tactical fighter-bomber to complement these types, optimised for direct air reconnaissance and weapons support of friendly ground and naval forces but capable also, when required, of carrying out missions which would otherwise require use of both the Tornado and F-104S.

In response to this AMI specification, design studies were initiated by Aeritalia in 1977. Earlier that year the Brazilian Air Force (Força Aérea Brasileira) had made known a broadly similar requirement, called A-X, for a single-seat attack aircraft to supplement its AT-26 Xavantes (Brazilian-built Aermacchi MB-326GBs). Collaboration between Embraer and Aermacchi on this project, involving an Aermacchi design known as the MB-340, had been discussed during the first half of 1977, and a decision on whether to go ahead with it was expected by the end of that year.

In the meantime, the AMI issued its own attack aircraft specification, an early result of which was the conclusion of a co-operation agreement between Aeritalia and Aermacchi in mid-1978, marking the beginning of an 18-month project definition phase of the AMX. In October 1978 the Italian Air Force selected the Rolls-Royce Spey Mk 807 turbofan engine as the powerplant for the AMX. In March 1980, soon after completion of the definition phase, the Brazilian government confirmed its intention of taking part in the AMX programme, and four months later Embraer became an industrial partner of the two Italian manufacturers. The development phase, initiated in January 1981, was followed by an initial memorandum of understanding between the two air forces concerned. A second MoU, signed in October 1981, covered the joint development and production phases of the AMX on a fully collaborative basis; a third was signed during 1983, laying down the terms of that collaboration during the development phase.

Six prototypes have been completed, plus one airframe (built by Aeritalia at Turin) for static testing, which was

Three of the Italian/Brazilian AMX prototypes equipped with various combinations of missiles, bombs and drop-tanks.

completed by the Spring of 1985. In addition, selected components for fatigue testing have been completed by each of the three manufacturers.

The Aeritalia-assembled A01 first prototype made its initial flight on 15 May 1984. On 1 June, on its fifth flight, it was lost in a crash. The second prototype (A02), completed by Aermacchi, made its first flight on 19 November 1984. These aerodynamic prototypes were followed by the Aeritalia-assembled A03 avionics testbed, which flew for the first time on 28 January 1985. Next to fly was a replacement for A01, designated A11, which made its initial flight on 24 May 1985. First Brazilian assembled (YA-1) prototype to fly, on 16 October 1985, was A04. A total of 1,400 flight hours is due to be completed during the development phase.

Based on present stated requirements for the air forces of Italy and Brazil, series production of the AMX is expected to continue until 1990. Manufacture of the first 30 production aircraft began, on schedule, in July 1986, and the first of these flew in 1987. Deliveries are planned to begin to the Italian Air Force in the Spring of 1988 and to the Brazilian Air Force in the Spring of 1989. The work split gives Aeritalia, the programme leader, 46.7 per cent (fuselage centre-section, nose radome, fin and rudder, elevators, flaps, ailerons and spoilers); Aermacchi has 23.6 per cent (forward fuselage, including gun and avionics integration, canopy, and tailcone); and Embraer 29.7 per cent (air intakes, wings, wing leading-edge slats, tailplane, wing pylons, external fuel tanks and reconnaissance pallets). There is single-source component manufacture only, but there are final assembly lines in both Italy and Brazil.

The series production phase entails building 266 aircraft – 187 for the Aeronautica Militare Italiana and 79 for the Força Aérea Brasileira. In the Italian Air Force the AMX is intended to take over duties performed at present by the G91R, now being phased out of its close-air-support role; the G91Y interdictor, also being phased out; and the F-104G and S Starfighter, scheduled for replacement in the strike role by 1987–88. The close-air-support and interdiction tasks will be undertaken fully by the AMX, while counter-air duties will be shared with the longer-range Tornado; the 187 aircraft to be ordered will be sufficient to equip eight squadrons.

The Brazilian Air Force aircraft differ primarily in avionics and weapon delivery systems, and have two internally mounted 30 mm cannon instead of the single multi-barrel 20 mm weapon of the Italian version.

The AMX is capable of performing missions at high subsonic speed and very low altitude, by day and night, in

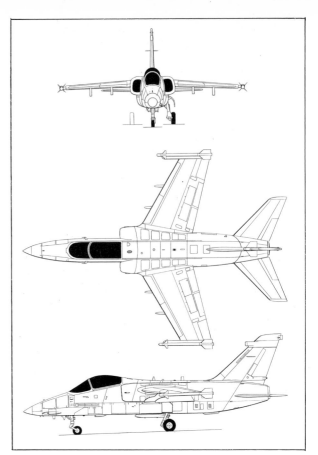

Aeritalia/Aermacchi/Embraer AMX. *(Pilot Press)*

poor visibility, and if necessary from bases with poorly equipped or partially damaged runways. Basic requirements included good take-off and landing performance, good penetration capability, and a proven, in-production power-plant requiring a minimum of adaptation to the AMX airframe. The primary flying control surfaces have manual reversion, to provide a fly-home capability even if both of the two independent hydraulic systems become inoperative.

The aircraft's modular design, coupled with sophisticated avionics and other airborne systems, gives it the flexibility to undertake additional roles. Definition has been completed of a two-seat version, with a second cockpit in tandem replacing the forward-fuselage fuel tankage, and this is seen as suitable for advanced training, operational conversion, all-weather day/night tactical fighter, maritime, electronic warfare or standoff weapon roles.

The following description applies to the single-seat AMX:

TYPE: Single-seat close-air-support, battlefield interdiction, anti-shipping and reconnaissance aircraft, with secondary capability for offensive counter-air.

WINGS: Cantilever shoulder-wing monoplane, with sweep-back of 31° on leading edges, 27° 30′ at quarter chord, and thickness/chord ratio of 12%. Leading-edge slats (two segments each side) over most of span, and two-segment double-slotted Fowler flaps over approx two-thirds of each trailing edge, are operated electrically and actuated hydraulically. Forward of each pair of flaps is a pair of hydraulically actuated spoilers, deployed separately in inboard and outboard pairs. These are controlled

Close-up of interchangeable reconnaissance pallet being test-flown in 1987 on Brazilian AMX prototype A04.

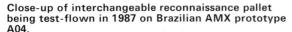

electronically by Aeritalia/GEC Avionics flight control computer, and serve also as airbrakes/lift dumpers. Hydraulically actuated ailerons, with manual reversion.

FUSELAGE: Conventional semi-monocoque oval-section structure. Forward section incorporates main avionics and equipment bays, airborne systems, gun(s), nose landing gear and cockpit; central section includes engine air intake ducts, main landing gear and engine bay. Extreme rear fuselage, complete with tailplane, is detachable for access to engine.

TAIL UNIT: Sweptback fin (of carbonfibre) and rudder. Variable-incidence tailplane, mid-mounted on fuselage. Tailplane and rudder movement controlled electronically by Aeritalia/GEC Avionics flight control computer. Hydraulically actuated carbonfibre elevators, with manual reversion.

LANDING GEAR: Hydraulically retractable tricycle type, of Messier-Hispano-Bugatti levered suspension design; built in Italy by Magnaghi (nose unit) and ERAM (main units). Single wheel on each unit. Nose unit retracts forward; main units retract forward and inward, turning through approx 90° to lie almost flat in underside of engine air intake trunks. Nosewheel is hydraulically steerable (60° to left and right), self-centering, and fitted with anti-shimmy device. Mainwheel tyres size 670 × 210-12; nosewheel tyre size 18 × 5.5-8. Hydraulic brakes and anti-skid system. No brake-chute. Prototypes fitted with runway arrester hook.

POWERPLANT: One 49.1 kN (11,030 lb st) Rolls-Royce Spey Mk 807 non-afterburning turbofan engine, built under licence in Italy by Fiat, Piaggio and Alfa Romeo, with Brazilian participation. Fuel in compartmented fuselage tank and two integral wing tanks. Auxiliary underwing fuel tanks of up to 1,000 litres (264 US gallons; 220 Imp gallons) capacity can be carried on each of the inboard underwing pylons, and up to 500 litres (132 US gallons; 110 Imp gallons) on each of the outboard pylons. Provision for in-flight refuelling.

ACCOMMODATION: Pilot only, on Martin-Baker Mk 10L zero/zero ejection seat; 18° downward view over nose. One-piece wraparound windscreen; one-piece hinged canopy, opening sideways to starboard. Cockpit pressurised. Tandem two-seat combat trainer/special missions version under development.

AVIONICS AND EQUIPMENT: Avionics and equipment are divided into six main subsystems: (1) UHF and VHF com, and IFF; (2) navigation (Litton Italia inertial system, with Tacan and standby AHRS, for Italian Air Force; VOR/ILS for Brazil); (3) Litton computer-based weapons aiming and delivery, incorporating an Elta/FIAR range-only radar and OMI/Selenia stores management system; (4) digital data display (OMI/Selenia head-up, multi-function head-down, and weapons/nav); (5) data processing, with Microtecnica digital air data computer; and (6) Elettronica active and passive ECM, including fin mounted radar warning receiver. The ranging radar, known as Pointer, is an I/J band set modified from the Elta (Israel) EL/M-2001B and built in Italy by FIAR. In terms of redundancy and monitoring, the avionics are designed to permit successful completion of mission, even in the event of initial failure. Modular design and space provisions within the aircraft permit retrofitting of alternative systems if and when required. All avionics/equipment packages are pallet mounted to facilitate removal and replacement, and are positioned to allow rapid access for routine maintenance and change of configuration.

ARMAMENT AND OPERATIONAL EQUIPMENT: One M61A1 multi-barrel 20 mm cannon, with 350 rds, in port side of lower forward fuselage (one 30 mm DEFA 554 cannon on each side in aircraft for Brazilian Air Force). Single twin-pylon stores attachment point under fuselage, on centreline, plus two attachments under each wing, and wingtip rails for two AIM-9L Sidewinder or similar infra-red air-to-air missiles (MAA-1 Piranha on Brazilian aircraft). Fuselage and inboard underwing hardpoints each stressed for loads of up to 907 kg (2,000 lb), outboard underwing points for 454 kg (1,000 lb) each. Total external stores load 3,800 kg (8,377 lb). Attack weapons can include free-fall or retarded Mk 82/83/84 bombs, cluster bombs, air-to-surface missiles (including area denial, anti-radiation and anti-shipping weapons), electro-optical precision guided munitions, and rocket launchers. For reconnaissance missions, three alternative and interchangeable pallet mounted photographic systems (panoramic, TV and photogrammetric) can be carried, installed internally in forward fuselage; an external infra-red/optronics pod can be carried on the centreline pylon. Each of these systems is fully compatible with the aircraft, and will not affect operational capability; the aircraft will therefore be able to carry out reconnaissance missions without affecting its normal navigation/attack and self-defence capabilities. Camera bay is in lower starboard side of fuselage, forward of mainwheel bay.

DIMENSIONS, EXTERNAL:

Wing span:	
excl wingtip missiles and rails	8.874 m (29 ft $1\frac{1}{2}$ in)
over missiles	10.00 m (32 ft $9\frac{3}{4}$ in)
Length overall	13.575 m (44 ft $6\frac{1}{2}$ in)
Height overall	4.576 m (15 ft $0\frac{1}{4}$ in)
Wheel track	2.15 m (7 ft $0\frac{3}{4}$ in)
Wheelbase	4.74 m (15 ft $6\frac{1}{2}$ in)

AREA:

Wings, gross	21.00 m² (226.04 sq ft)

WEIGHTS:

Operational weight empty	6,700 kg (14,770 lb)
Max external stores load	3,800 kg (8,377 lb)
T-O weight 'clean'	9,600 kg (21,164 lb)
Typical mission T-O weight	10,750 kg (23,700 lb)
Max T-O weight	12,500 kg (27,558 lb)

PERFORMANCE (A: at 10,750 kg; 23,700 lb mission T-O weight, B: at max T-O weight, ISA in both cases):

Max level speed	Mach 0.86
Service ceiling	13,000 m (42,650 ft)
T-O run at S/L: A	750 m (2,461 ft)
B	950 m (3,120 ft)
T-O to 15 m (50 ft) at S/L: B	1,525 m (5,000 ft)
Attack radius, with allowance for 5 min combat over target and 10% fuel reserves:	
A with 907 kg (2,000 lb) of external stores:	
hi-lo-hi	480 nm (890 km; 550 miles)
lo-lo-lo	300 nm (555 km; 345 miles)
B with 2,720 kg (6,000 lb) of external stores:	
hi-lo-hi	280 nm (520 km; 320 miles)
lo-lo-lo	200 nm (370 km; 230 miles)
Ferry range with two 1,000 litre (264 US gallon; 220 Imp gallon) drop-tanks, 10% reserves:	
A	1,700 nm (3,150 km; 1,957 miles)
g limits	+ 8/ − 4

DASSAULT-BREGUET/DORNIER

AIRFRAME PRIME CONTRACTORS:
Avions Marcel Dassault-Breguet Aviation
(France)
Dornier GmbH (Federal Republic of Germany)
On 22 July 1969 the French and Federal German governments announced a joint requirement for a new subsonic basic/advanced training and light attack aircraft to enter service with their armed forces in the 1970s. Each government had a potential requirement for up to 200 such aircraft, to replace Magister, Lockheed T-33A and Mystère IV-A trainers, and Fiat G91 attack aircraft, then in service.

Dassault-Breguet/Dornier Alpha Jet

Dassault-Breguet and Dornier are jointly producing the Alpha Jet, with Dassault-Breguet as main contractor and Dornier as industrial collaborator, the total workload being shared primarily between the two groups.

All production Alpha Jets have identical structure, powerplant, landing gear and standard equipment; there are assembly lines in France, West Germany and Egypt. The outer wings, tail unit, rear fuselage, landing gear doors and cold-flow exhaust are manufactured in West Germany; the forward and centre fuselage (with integrated wing centre-section) are manufactured in France. Fuselage nosecones and wing flaps are manufactured in Belgium by SABCA. The powerplant prime contractors are Turboméca and SNECMA in France, and MTU and KHD in West Germany; and, for the landing gear, Messier-Hispano-Bugatti in France and Liebherr Aero Technik in West Germany.

Four flying prototypes were built, plus two airframes for static and fatigue testing. The 01 made its first flight, at Istres, on 26 October 1973.

There are five versions of the Alpha Jet, as follows:
Advanced trainer/light attack version (formerly known as Alpha Jet E). Ordered for the air forces of France, Belgium (33), Egypt (30, designated **MS1**), Ivory Coast (7), Morocco (24), Nigeria (24), Qatar (6) and Togo (5). Those for Nigeria are from German assembly line, others from French production; 26 of Egyptian MS1s assembled in Egypt by AOI (which see). First production aircraft (E1 for French Air Force) flown on 4 November 1977; deliveries, starting with E2, began in the Summer of 1978, and the French Air Force had received its 176th by 1985. Aircraft for Belgian Air

French Air Force Alpha Jet advanced trainer and light attack aircraft.

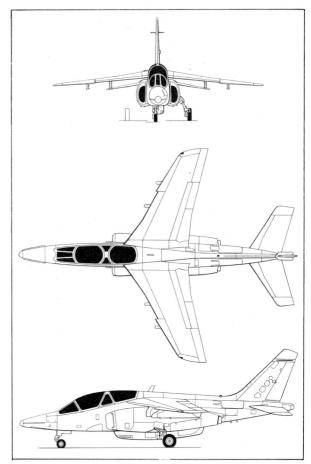

Dassault-Breguet/Dornier Alpha Jet, advanced trainer and light attack version. *(Pilot Press)*

Force, assembled by SABCA and delivered in 1978–80, serve with Nos. 7, 9 and 11 Squadrons.
Close-support version (formerly known as Alpha Jet A). Ordered for Federal German Luftwaffe (175). First flown (A1) on 12 April 1978; deliveries began in mid-March 1979 and were completed on 26 January 1983. These aircraft now equip Jagdbombergeschwader (fighter-bomber groups) JaboG 49 at Fürstenfeldbruck (from 20 March 1980), JaboG 43 at Oldenburg (from January 1981), and JaboG 41 at Husum (from January 1982), replacing Fiat G91Rs in the close-support and reconnaissance roles. Each of these units is allocated 51 aircraft. Eighteen others were assigned to the Luftwaffe base at Beja in Portugal for weapons training; these are earmarked to form an additional combat unit (JaboG 44) in the event of an emergency. An ICE (improved combat efficiency) update programme for the armament and avionics of Luftwaffe Alpha Jets is currently being devised by Dornier; under a separate programme, these aircraft are to be refitted with Larzac 04-C20 engines.
Alternative close-support version, developed by Dassault-Breguet and first flown on 9 April 1982. Equipped with new nav/attack system which includes inertial platform, head-up display, laser rangefinder in modified nosecone, and radar altimeter. Ordered by Egypt (15) and Cameroun (6) by mid-1987. Egyptian Air Force version, designated **MS2**, was co-produced with Aircraft Factory No. 36 at Helwan, near Cairo: eleven were co-produced, following delivery in 1983

of four French built MS2s. Egyptian MS2s are to be upgraded to Alpha Jet 2 standard with Larzac 04-C20 engines and Magic missile capability.

Alpha Jet 2 (formerly Nouvelle Génération pour l'Ecole et l'Appui). Improved attack version, incorporating the nav/attack system developed for the MS2; uprated Larzac 04-C20 engines, developing 7–13 per cent more power than C6 version of earlier Alpha Jets; capability of carrying Magic 2 air-to-air missiles, plus auxiliary fuel tanks of up to 625 litres (165 US gallons; 137.5 Imp gallons) on inboard underwing stations and 450 litres (119 US gallons; 99 Imp gallons) on inboard or outboard stations. Egyptian MS2s (see previous paragraph) to be upgraded to this standard.

Alpha Jet 3. Extended-capability version, derived from Alpha Jet 2, for day/night attack, anti-shipping strike, airspace denial and self-defence, and anti-helicopter missions. Incorporates fully tested core systems of AJ 2 (inertial platform and multiplex databus); added capabilities (a FLIR system providing a thermal image on the head-up display, Thomson-CSF/ESD Agave or Anémone multifunction radar in a lengthened nose and a CP 2084 computer with corresponding extension of capability); wider variety of weapons including anti-ship all-weather missiles, laser guided bombs and missiles; internal passive and active ECM; and greater external fuel capacity.

More than 500 Alpha Jets have been ordered.

TYPE: Tandem two-seat basic, low-altitude and advanced jet trainer and close-support and battlefield reconnaissance aircraft.

Dassault-Breguet/Dornier Alpha Jet MS2. *(Pilot Press)*

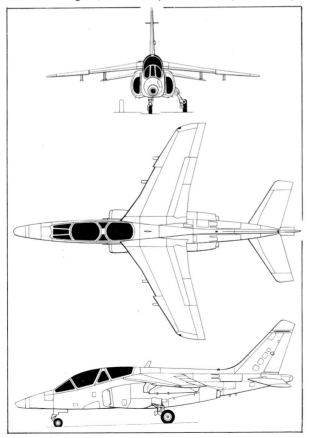

WINGS: Cantilever shoulder-wing monoplane, with 6° anhedral from roots. Thickness/chord ratio 10.2% at root, 8.6% at tip. Sweepback 28° at quarter-chord. Extended chord on outer wings. Hydraulically actuated Fowler slotted flaps on each trailing edge. Ailerons actuated by double-body irreversible hydraulic servo, with trimmable artificial feel system.

FUSELAGE: Semi-monocoque structure, of basically oval cross-section. Built in three sections: nose (including cockpit), centre-section (including engine air intake trunks and main landing gear housings) and rear (including engine mounts and tail assembly). Narrow strake on each side of nose of aircraft with no nav/attack system. Pointed nose, with pitot probe, on Luftwaffe close-support version. Electrically controlled, hydraulically actuated airbrake on each side of rear upper fuselage, of carbonfibre reinforced epoxy resin.

TAIL UNIT: Cantilever type, with 45° sweepback on fin leading edge and 30° on tailplane leading edge. Dorsal spine fairing between cockpit and fin. Aircraft equipped with radio compass have a long, narrow strake above the dorsal spine fairing to house the antenna for this equipment. All-flying tailplane, with trimmable and IAS-controlled artificial feel system. Glassfibre fin tip and tailplane tips. Yaw damper on close support versions.

LANDING GEAR: Forward retracting tricycle type, of Messier-Hispano-Bugatti/Liebherr design. All units retract hydraulically, main units into underside of engine air intake trunks. Single wheel and low-pressure tyre on each unit. Tyre size 615 × 255-10 on main units, 380 × 150-4 on nose unit. Steel disc brakes and anti-skid units on main gear (Minispad or Modistop). Emergency braking system. Hydraulic nosewheel steering and arrester hook on close-support version. Nosewheel offset to starboard to permit ground firing from gun pod.

POWERPLANT: Standard installation of two SNECMA/Turboméca Larzac 04-C6 turbofan engines, each rated at 13.24 kN (2,976 lb st), mounted on sides of fuselage. Alternative option (on any Alpha Jet) for 14.12 kN (3,175 lb st) Larzac 04-C20 turbofans, which are standard on the AJ2 version. Splitter plate in front of each intake. Fuel in two integral tanks in outer wings, one in centre-section and three fuselage tanks. Internal fuel capacity 1,900 litres (502 US gallons; 418 Imp gallons) or 2,040 litres (539 US gallons; 449 Imp gallons). Provision for 310 or 450 litre (82 or 119 US gallon; 68 or 99 Imp gallon) capacity drop-tank on each outer wing pylon, plus (on AJ2) a 450 or 625 litre (119 or 165 US gallon; 99 or 137.5 Imp gallon) tank on each inboard wing pylon.

ACCOMMODATION: Two persons in tandem, in pressurised cockpit under individual upward opening canopies. Dual controls standard. Rear seat is elevated. Martin-Baker AJRM4 (on French), B10N (on Belgian), E10N (on Egyptian) and Q10N (on Qatar) ejection seats. Aircraft for West Germany use Stencel S-III-S3AJ zero/zero ejection seats.

AVIONICS AND EQUIPMENT: Large avionics bays in rear fuselage, containing most of the radio and navigation equipment. Standard avionics, according to version, include V/UHF and VHF or UHF transceivers, IFF/SIF, VOR/ILS/marker beacon receiver, Tacan, radio compass, gyro platform and intercom. Basic French version has SFIM 550 gyro platform, LMT micro-Tacan, EAS 720 VOR/ILS/marker beacon receiver, TEAM com radio and intercom, and ESD 3300 IFF/SIF. West German version has Kaiser/VDO KM 808 head-up display, TRT AHV 6-18 radar altimeter, Lear Siegler LSI 6000 E attitude and heading reference system, and Litef LDN Doppler navigation system with LR-1416 navigation computer, Litef ABE control unit and Teledyne Ryan speed sensor, Elettronica (Italy) ECM, SEL Mitac/Setac Tacan with ILS, Siemens STR 700 IFF/SIF, Becker VCS 220 intercom, Rohde und Schwarz XT 3011 com radio, and EAS IMT 565 BDHI. AJ2 version has Sagem Uliss 81 inertial platform (replacing SFIM 550) and Una 81 nav/attack unit, Thomson-CSF VE 110C head-up display (VEM 130 in AJ3), Thomson-CSF TMV 630 laser rangefinder, TRT AHV 9 radar altimeter and ESD Digibus digital multiplexed avionics databus.

ARMAMENT AND OPERATIONAL EQUIPMENT: More than 75 different basic weapon configurations for training and tactical-air-support missions have been qualified for Alpha Jet users. For close support the Alpha Jet can be equipped with an underfuselage jettisonable pod containing a 30 mm DEFA or 27 mm Mauser cannon with 150 rds; or an underfuselage pylon for one 250 kg bomb or one 400 kg modular bomb. Provision also for two hardpoints under each wing, with non-jettisonable adaptor pylons. On these can be carried M155 launchers for eighteen 68

mm rockets; HE or retarded bombs of 50, 125, 250 or 400 kg; 625 lb cluster dispensers; 690 or 825 lb special-purpose tanks; practice launchers for bombs or rockets; Dassault-Breguet CC-420 underwing 30 mm gun pods, each with 180 rds; or two 310, 450 or 625 litre drop-tanks. Provision for air-to-air or air-to-surface missiles such as Magic or Maverick, or reconnaissance pod. Total load for all five stations more than 2,500 kg (5,510 lb). Dassault-Breguet CEM-1 (combined external multistore) carriers can be attached to inboard underwing pylons, permitting simultaneous carriage of mixed fuel/bomb/rocket loads, including six rockets and four practice bombs, or eighteen rockets with one 500 lb bomb, or six penetration bombs, or grenades or other stores. A special version of the CEM-1 allows carriage of a reconnaissance pod containing four cameras (three Omera 61 cameras and an Omera 40 panoramic camera) and a decoy launcher. Luftwaffe aircraft equipped with ML Aviation twin stores carriers, CBLS 200 practice bomb and rocket launcher carriers, and ejector release units. Fire control system for air-to-air or air-to-ground firing, dive bombing and low-level bombing. Kaiser/VDO KM 808 sight and gun camera in West German attack version; Thomson-CSF gun camera in AJ2 version.

DIMENSIONS, EXTERNAL:

Wing span	9.11 m (29 ft 10¾ in)
Length overall:	
close-support version, incl probe	13.23 m (43 ft 5 in)
Height overall (at normal T-O weight)	4.19 m (13 ft 9 in)
Wheel track	2.71 m (8 ft 10¾ in)
Wheelbase	4.72 m (15 ft 5¾ in)

AREA:

Wings, gross	17.50 m² (188.4 sq ft)

WEIGHTS:

Weight empty, equipped:	
close-support version	3,515 kg (7,749 lb)
Fuel load (internal)	1,520 kg (3,351 lb)
	or 1,630 kg (3,593 lb)
Fuel load (external)	500 kg (1,102 lb)
	or 720 kg (1,587 lb)
	or 1,440 kg (3,174 lb)
Max external load	more than 2,500 kg (5,510 lb)
Max T-O weight:	
with external stores	8,000 kg (17,637 lb)

PERFORMANCE (at normal 'clean' T-O weight, except where indicated):

Max level speed at 10,000 m (32,800 ft):	
Larzac 04-C6	Mach 0.85
Larzac 04-C20	Mach 0.86
Max level speed at S/L:	
Larzac 04-C6	540 knots (1,000 km/h; 621 mph)
Larzac 04-C20	560 knots (1,038 km/h; 645 mph)

Stalling speed: flaps and landing gear up	
	116 knots (216 km/h; 134 mph)
flaps and landing gear down	
	90 knots (167 km/h; 104 mph)
Max rate of climb at S/L	3,420 m (11,220 ft)/min
Time to 9,145 m (30,000 ft)	less than 7 min
Service ceiling	14,630 m (48,000 ft)
T-O run	370 m (1,215 ft)
Landing run at usual landing weight	
	approx 500 m (1,640 ft)
Lo-lo-lo mission radius (close-support version), incl combat at max continuous thrust and 54 nm (100 km; 62 mile) dash:	
with belly gun pod and underwing weapons	
	210 nm (390 km; 242 miles)
with belly gun pod, underwing weapons and external tanks	340 nm (630 km; 391 miles)
Hi-lo-hi mission radius (close-support version), incl combat at max continuous thrust and 54 nm (100 km; 62 mile) dash:	
with belly gun pod and underwing weapons	
	315 nm (583 km; 363 miles)
with belly gun pod, underwing weapons and external tanks	580 nm (1,075 km; 668 miles)
Ferry range (internal fuel and four 450 litre external tanks)	
	more than 2,160 nm (4,000 km; 2,485 miles)
Endurance (internal fuel only):	
low altitude	more than 2 h 30 min
high altitude	more than 3 h 30 min
g limits	+ 12/ − 6.4 ultimate

EHI
EH INDUSTRIES LIMITED

PARTICIPATING COMPANIES:

Agusta SpA (Italy)

Westland Helicopters Ltd (UK)

This company was formed in June 1980 by Westland Helicopters and Agusta to undertake the joint development, production and marketing of a new anti-submarine warfare

helicopter, for which the Royal Navy and Italian Navy both have a requirement. A formal contract for the naval version was signed on 7 March 1984. The programme is being handled on behalf of both governments by the British Ministry of Defence.

EH Industries EH 101

In the Spring of 1977 the British MoD (Navy) completed feasibility studies for a new ASW helicopter, and examined what sensors and performance standards it would require.

Westland's WG 34 design, marginally smaller than the Sea King but with substantially more payload capability, was selected by the MoD (Navy) for development in the late Summer of 1978. The Italian Navy, although it would place emphasis more on shore-based than shipboard operation, has a requirement broadly similar to that of the Royal Navy, and in 1980 Westland and Agusta decided to combine forces in a joint design, the EH 101, to meet the requirements of both services and for other military and civil applications. Development of this helicopter is now proceeding in three basic versions: naval, commercial transport, and utility.

The EH 101 has three engines, and incorporates composite materials, plus the latest available electronics and data handling systems. The physical dimensions of the helicopter are limited by frigate hangar size.

The naval EH 101 is designed for fully autonomous all-weather day and night operations, and will operate from land bases, large and small vessels (including merchant ships), and oil rigs. It will be capable of launch and recovery from a frigate of 3,445 tonnes (3,500 tons), in sea state 6, with the ship on any heading and in wind speeds, from any direction, of up to 50 knots (93 km/h; 57 mph).

Primary roles of the maritime version will be anti-submarine warfare, anti-ship surveillance and tracking, anti-surface-vessel, amphibious operations, and search and rescue. Other roles include airborne early warning, vertical replenishment, and electronic countermeasures (deception, jamming and missile seduction). For the Royal Navy, the EH 101 has been specified as equipment for its Type 23 general-purpose frigates; it has also been announced that the

PP1, the first pre-production EH 101, which began ground-running tests at Yeovil in the spring of 1987.

helicopter will operate from 'Invincible' class aircraft carriers, Royal Fleet Auxiliaries and other ships, as well as from land bases. Initial requirements are reportedly 50 for the Royal Navy and 42 for the Italian Navy. Canada also requires 30–50 to supersede CH-124A Sea Kings.

Ten pre-production aircraft are planned, one of which will be used for ground tests. The first of these made its initial flight at Yeovil in early 1987. Aircraft PP5 and PP6 will be devoted respectively to development of the Royal Navy and Italian Navy versions.

EH Industries EH 101, naval version. (Pilot Press)

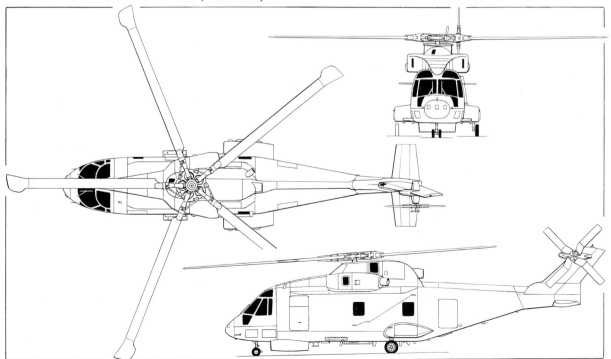

TYPE: Multi-role helicopter.

ROTOR SYSTEM: Five-blade main rotor. Blades, of composite construction, have an advanced aerofoil section, special high-speed tips resulting from the British Experimental Rotor Programme (BERP), and are attached to hub by multi-path loading including elastomeric bearings. Naval version has fully automatic powered folding of main rotor blades (optional on other versions) and tail-rotor pylon, with manual system for emergency backup. Electric de-icing of main and tail rotor blades (Lucas system) standard on naval version, optional on other versions. Four-blade tail rotor, mounted on port side of tail rotor pylon.

FUSELAGE AND TAIL UNIT: Modified rear fuselage and slimmer tailboom on military version, to accommodate rear-loading ramp/door in underside. Tailcone and tail-rotor pylon of composite construction; on naval version this folds forward and downward so that starboard half of tailplane passes underneath rear fuselage. Small ventral fin under tailcone.

LANDING GEAR: Hydraulically retractable tricycle type, with single mainwheels and steerable twin-wheel nose unit. Main units retract into fairings on sides of fuselage. Goodrich wheels, tyres and brakes.

POWERPLANT: Three General Electric T700-GE-401A turboshaft engines in naval version (assembled by Alfa Romeo), currently rated at 1,278 kW (1,714 shp) max contingency, 1,254 kW (1,682 shp) intermediate and 1,071 kW (1,437 shp) max continuous. A possible alternative engine is the Rolls-Royce Turboméca RTM 322. Computerised fuel management system. Dunlop electric anti-icing of engine air intakes, which are of Kevlar reinforced with aero-web honeycomb.

ACCOMMODATION: One or two pilots on flight deck (naval versions will be capable of single-pilot operation). ASW version will normally also carry observer and acoustic systems operator. Martin-Baker crew seats in naval version. Utility version will accommodate up to 38 combat-equipped troops or equivalent cargo. Cargo loading ramp/door at rear of cabin on utility version.

AVIONICS: Avionics system is based on two MIL-STD-1553B multiplex databuses which link the basic aircraft management and mission systems. Main processing element of the management system is a dual redundant aircraft management computer, which carries out navigation, control and display management, performance, 'health' and usage monitoring computation; it also controls the basic bus. Other basic aircraft system elements are the dual duplex digital AFCS; a complex military communications subsystem; and Doppler, inertial, global positioning and other navigation sensors. Advanced flight deck makes extensive use of colour CRTs for flight navigation and systems display, and features multi-function keyboard control. Main processing element of the naval version mission system is the dual redundant mission computer, which carries out tracking, sensor management, control and display management, and controls the mission bus. AFCS will include electronic ADI and HSI. Suppliers so far announced include British Aerospace for the ring laser gyro inertial navigation system, Smiths/OMI (automatic flight control system), Plessey/Elettronica (PA 5015 J-band radar altimeter), MEL (pilot's mission display units), GEC Avionics (air data system), Racal/Fiar (Doppler velocity sensor), Selenia/Ferranti (aircraft management computer) and Litton Italia (LISA-4000 strapdown AHRS).

ARMAMENT AND OPERATIONAL EQUIPMENT (naval and military utility versions): Naval version able to carry up to four homing torpedoes (probably Marconi Sting Ray in RN version) or other weapons. ASW version will have 360° search radar (Ferranti Blue Kestrel in RN aircraft) in a 'chin' radome, plus dipping sonar, two sonobuoy dispensers, advanced sonobuoy processing equipment, Racal ESM and an external rescue hoist. GEC Avionics AQS-903 ASW system and Fairey Hydraulics deck lock have been selected for Royal Navy aircraft. ASST (anti-ship surveillance and tracking) version will carry equipment for tactical surveillance and OTH (over-the-horizon) targeting, to locate and relay to a co-operating frigate the position of a target vessel, and for midcourse guidance of the frigate's missiles. On missions involving the patrol of an exclusive economic zone it can also, with suitable radar, monitor every hour all surface contacts within an area of 77,700 km² (30,000 sq miles); can patrol an EEZ 400 × 200 nm (740 × 370 km; 460 × 230 miles) twice in one sortie; and can effect boarding and inspection of surface vessels during fishery protection and anti-smuggling missions. ASV version is designed to carry air-to-surface missiles and other weapons, for use as appropriate, from strikes against major units using sea-skimming anti-ship missiles to small-arms deterrence of smugglers. Various duties in amphibious operations could include personnel/stores transportation (eg, 24 combat-equipped troops and their stores over a 200 nm; 370 km; 230 mile radius), casualty evacuation, surveillance over the beachhead, and logistic support. In logistic support the EH 101 can carry internal loads of up to 5,443 kg (12,000 lb), or 6,804 kg (15,000 lb) on an external sling.

DIMENSIONS, EXTERNAL:

Main rotor diameter	18.59 m (61 ft 0 in)
Length overall, both rotors turning	22.81 (74 ft 10 in)
Width, main rotor and tail pylon folded	
	5.49 m (18 ft 0 in)
Height overall, both rotors turning	6.65 m (21 ft 10 in)

AREA:

Main rotor disc	271.51 m² (2,922.5 sq ft)

WEIGHTS (naval version):

Basic weight empty	7,121 kg (15,700 lb)
Operating weight empty	9,298 kg (20,500 lb)
Payload (four torpedoes)	960 kg (2,116 lb)
Max T-O weight	13,000 kg (28,660 lb)

PERFORMANCE (estimated):

Never-exceed speed	167 knots (309 km/h; 192 mph) EAS
Average cruising speed	160 knots (296 km/h; 184 mph)
Best range cruising speed	140 knots (259 km/h; 161 mph)
Ferry range	1,000 nm (1,850 km; 1,150 miles)
Time on station for dunking cycle with full weapon and mission load	5 h

Eurocopter
EUROCOPTER GmbH

PARTICIPATING COMPANIES:

Messerschmitt-Bölkow-Blohm GmbH (Federal Republic of Germany)

Aérospatiale (France)

Following approval of a Franco-German co-operation programme on the basis of industry proposals, the defence ministers of West Germany and France signed on 29 May 1984 a memorandum of understanding covering the development of a new anti-tank helicopter for service with their two armies in the 1990s. Leadership and work will be shared equally between MBB and Aérospatiale. Eurocopter GIE is the instrument of co-operation in the field of helicopters between Aérospatiale and MBB. For the purpose of managing the Franco/German battlefield helicopter programme, Eurocopter GmbH was established in Munich on 18 September 1985 as a wholly owned subsidiary of Eurocopter GIE in Paris.

Executive authority for the battlefield helicopter programme is the Bundesamt für Wehrtechnik und Beschaffung (German federal defence technology and procurement agency).

Eurocopter CATH

The CATH programme, which will involve a total of 400 or more aircraft for the two countries, utilises a single basic helicopter design, from which three versions will be developed. These are:

HAP (Hélicoptère d'Appui et de Protection). Escort and fire support version for French Army, for delivery from 1997. Armed with a 30 mm GIAT AM-30781 automatic cannon in undernose turret, with 150–450 rds of ammunition. Releasable weapons, mounted on stub wings, comprise four Matra Mistral infra-red homing air-to-air missiles and two pods each with twenty-two 68 mm SNEB rockets. Roof mounted TV, FLIR, laser rangefinder and direct-optics sensors.

PAH-2 (Panzerabwehr Hubschrauber, 2nd generation). Anti-tank version for West German Army, for delivery from 1997. No gun turret. Underwing pylons for up to eight Hot 2 anti-tank missiles (inboard) and four Stinger 2 air-to-air missiles for self-defence (outboard). Mast mounted sight. Will have later, as alternative to Hot, the capability to carry up to eight Euromissile Trigat long-range 'fire and forget' infra-red homing missiles. An advanced Infra-Red Charge Coupled Device night vision system will enable night firing.

HAC (Hélicoptère Anti-Char with third-generation anti-tank missiles). Anti-tank version for French Army, for delivery from 1999. Wing pylons for up to eight Trigats inboard. Mast mounted TV/FLIR/tracker/laser rangefinder sighting system for gunner.

Seven development aircraft are expected to be built, including four unarmed aerodynamic prototypes to flight-test the common basic airframe. First flight is expected to take place in 1989–90. Requirements have been estimated at 212 PAH-2s for Germany, 75 HAPs and 140 HACs for France.

Mock-up showing the basic configuration of the Eurocopter Franco-German anti-tank helicopter.

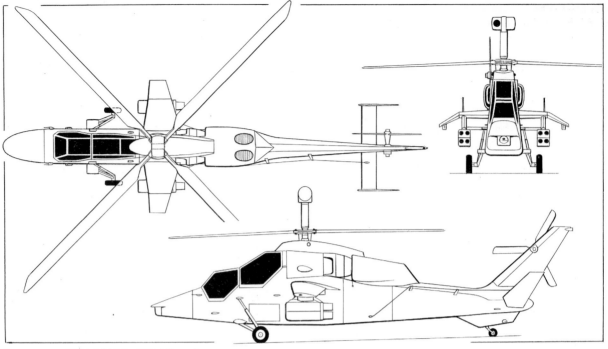

Eurocopter PAH-2/HAC. *(Pilot Press)*

TYPE: Twin-engined anti-tank helicopter.

ROTOR SYSTEM AND DRIVE: Four-blade semi-rigid main rotor, with composite blades; no flapping or lead-lag hinges; elastomeric pitch bearings. Rotorhead consists of two fibre composite starplates bolted together with a titanium spacer, a configuration which permits almost unrestricted installation of a mast mounted sight. Main features are a compact, robust construction, low aerodynamic drag, a very small number of parts, and ease of maintenance. Development of new blade aerofoil sections and geometries promises performance improvements of about 10 per cent over most present-day systems, and will provide the agility needed in typical anti-tank missions, ie in extreme nap-of-the-earth flights. Three-blade composite tail rotor, mounted on starboard side.

WINGS, FUSELAGE AND TAIL UNIT: Conventional semi-monocoque structures, meeting criteria for safety, crash resistance (to MIL-STD-1290 standard), and damage tolerance (survivable against hits from weapons of up to 23 mm calibre). Stub wings, with anhedral on outer panels, for releasable weapons. Sweptback fin/tail rotor pylon and underfin; horizontal stabiliser, with endplates, mounted low on main fin.

LANDING GEAR: Non-retractable tailwheel type, with single wheel on each unit.

POWERPLANT: Two 895 kW (1,200 shp) MTU/Rolls-Royce/Turboméca MTM 390 turboshaft engines, mounted side-by-side above centre fuselage. Self-sealing crashworthy fuel tanks, with explosion suppression.

ACCOMMODATION: Crew of two in tandem, with pilot in front and weapons system operator at rear. Armoured, impact-absorbing seats. Stepped cockpits, with flat-plate transparencies.

AVIONICS: Essential characteristics will be common to both French and German versions, and mainly European in origin. Systems architecture will be based on integrated digital avionics incorporating a 1553B databus, multiple cockpit displays, two symbol generators, a central operating unit, and a decentralised computer. Four-axis autopilot. Comprehensive ECM, including radar/laser warning receivers.

ARMAMENT: As listed under model descriptions.

DIMENSIONS, EXTERNAL:	
Main rotor diameter	13.00 m (42 ft 7¾ in)
Tail rotor diameter	2.70 m (8 ft 10¼ in)
AREA:	
Main rotor disc	132.7 m² (1,428.7 sq ft)
WEIGHTS:	
Mission T-O weight	approx 5,200 kg (11,464 lb)
Design max T-O weight	5,400 kg (11,905 lb)
PERFORMANCE (estimated):	
Cruising speed	
	135–151 knots (250–280 km/h; 155–174 mph)
Max rate of climb at S/L	600 m (1,970 ft)/min
Hovering ceiling OGE	1,000–2,000 m (3,280–6,560 m)
Endurance, incl 20 min reserves	3 h

Eurofighter
EUROFIGHTER JAGDFLUGZEUG GMBH
PARTICIPATING COMPANIES: See below

European Fighter Aircraft (EFA/JF-90)

The air chiefs of staff of five European nations – France, West Germany, Italy, Spain and the UK – agreed and issued in December 1983 an outline staff target for a new combat aircraft to enter service with all five air forces in the mid-1990s. France withdrew from this partnership in July 1985, participation by the remaining four countries then being set at 33% each for Great Britain and Germany, 21% for Italy and 13% for Spain. National design teams from MBB (with Dornier as co-contractor), Aeritalia, CASA and British Aerospace are collaborating in developing and harmonising individual national requirements, incorporating some of the design aspects and technology that became available via the BAe EAP programme (see UK section). The initial feasibility study, launched in July 1984, was followed in August 1985 by start of the project-definition phase. In June 1986 Eurofighter GmbH, with headquarters in Munich, was formed to manage the EFA programme. Eurojet Turbo GmbH was formed shortly afterwards to manage the engine programme.

The European air staff requirement was agreed in December 1985, and the project-definition stage was completed in September 1986. With a 1987 go-ahead from the four governments, the full scale engineering development stage should begin shortly afterwards, leading to a first flight in 1990–91, the start of series production in 1992, and initial deliveries in 1995–96. Eight or nine FSED prototypes are expected to be built.

The EFA will be configured primarily for the air defence role, but with a secondary capability for air-to-surface attack. Some 800 aircraft are expected to be required by the partner nations, in the approximate ratio of 250 for Germany, 200 for Italy, 75–100 for Spain and 250 for Great Britain; a proportion of two-seat trainer versions would be included in these totals. Export orders are also anticipated.

Full-authority four-channel ACT (active control technology) fly-by-wire flight control system, combined with mission-adaptive configuring and the aircraft's natural longitudinal instability, will provide the EFA with the required 'carefree' handling, gust alleviation and high sustained manoeuvrability throughout the flight envelope. Pitch control effected via foreplane/elevators ACT to provide artificial longitudinal stability; yaw control via all-moving tail fin. The quadruplex AFCS, which will operate through a NATO standard databus, is designed to ensure that the pilot cannot exceed the aircraft's flying limits.

TYPE: Single-seat, extremely agile STOL-capable fighter, optimised for air-to-air roles, with secondary ground-attack capability.

AIRFRAME: Cantilever low-wing monoplane, of canard delta configuration, having all-moving foreplanes and a fin with rudder. Wings are of low aspect ratio, with straight leading edges having 53° sweepback, inboard and outboard 'flaperons' on trailing edges. Airframe will incorporate 'stealth' technologies, and a substantial proportion of it will be built of composite materials, in conjunction with new lightweight metal alloys, using advanced manufacturing techniques such as superplastic forming and diffusion bonding.

POWERPLANT: Choice of engine for early EFA prototypes not yet made (Turbo Union RB199 and General Electric F404 are possible candidates). Later prototypes and the production aircraft will be powered by two Eurojet EJ200 advanced-technology turbofans (90 kN; 20,250 lb st class with afterburning), mounted side-by-side in rear fuselage with ventral intakes. Provision for external fuel tanks and in-flight refuelling.

ENGINE AIR INTAKES: Side-by-side intakes in underfuselage box, each having a fixed upper wedge/ramp and a variable-position lower cowl lip (vari-cowl).

AVIONICS: Primary sensor will be a multi-mode pulse-Doppler radar with an interception range of 50–80 nm (92.5–148 km; 57.5–92 miles), able to acquire at least 85 per cent of probable targets (including eight targets simultaneously), and to direct lookdown/shootdown and snap-up weapons against them. Other radar requirements include velocity and single-target search, track-while-scan and range-while-scan, target priority processing, auto-

Model of the European Fighter Aircraft (EFA), showing intake and other recent design changes.

matic weapons selection, and recommended combat tactics display. In attack mode, all have capability for ground mapping/ranging and terrain avoidance, but not terrain following. Proposals include Emerald, an adaptation of the F/A-18's APG-65 radar developed by Hughes Aircraft Company with GEC Avionics (UK) and AEG (Germany); the Ferranti Blue Vixen; and an all-new radar known as ECR 90 by Ferranti (UK), Fiar (Italy) and Inisel (Spain). Radar will form part of a comprehensive avionics suite which also includes extensive communications, and an advanced integrated defensive aids support system (DASS). All avionics, flight control and utilities control systems will be integrated through NATO standard databus highways with appropriate redundancy levels and full use of microprocessors. Special attention has been given to reducing pilot workload. New cockpit techniques will simplify flying the aircraft safely and effectively to the limits of the flight envelope while monitoring and managing the aircraft and its operational systems, and detecting/identifying/attacking desired targets while remaining safe from enemy defences. This will be achieved through a high level of system integration and automation, together with three large multi-function colour displays.

ARMAMENT: Interceptor will have an internally mounted cannon, plus a mix of AIM-120 AMRAAM and short-range (AIM-132 ASRAAM or Sidewinder) air-to-air missiles carried externally, four of the former being mounted in tandem pairs in a semi-recessed under-fuselage installation similar to that of the ADV Tornado. The short-range missiles are carried on underwing pylons. The EFA will, if necessary, be able to carry a considerable overload of air-to-air weapons. For air-to-surface weapons, and/or auxiliary fuel tanks, it will have a total of 15 external attachment points.

DIMENSIONS, EXTERNAL:
Wing span	10.50 m (34 ft 5½ in)
Length overall	approx 14.50 m (47 ft 7 in)

AREA:
Wings, gross	50.0 m² (538.2 sq ft)

WEIGHTS (approx):
Weight empty	9,750 kg (21,495 lb)
External stores load (weapons and/or fuel)	4,500 kg (9,920 lb)
Max T-O weight	17,000 kg (37,480 lb)

DESIGN PERFORMANCE:
Max level speed	greater than Mach 1.8
T-O and landing distance with full internal fuel and two AMRAAM plus two ASRAAM or Sidewinder missiles, ISA + 15°C	500 m (1,640 ft)
Combat radius (estimated)	250–300 nm (463–556 km; 288–345 miles)
g limits with full internal fuel and two AMRAAM missiles	+ 9/ − 3

JEH
JOINT EUROPEAN HELICOPTER Srl

Following industrial agreements between Agusta, CASA, Fokker and Westland, JEH was formed on 4 September 1986 to manage the multi-national programme to produce a third-generation multi-role light attack helicopter known as Tonal, based on the Agusta A 129 Mangusta.

JEH A 129 LAH Tonal

The Tonal programme came into being to meet the requirements of the Italian, British, Dutch and Spanish armed forces for an advanced multi-role combat helicopter for the late 1990s. Named after an ancient Aztec deity, Tonal will have a structure based on that of the Mangusta (see Italian section), but with equipment and weapons systems to give it anti-tank, scout and anti-helicopter capability. Primary armament will comprise third-generation anti-tank and air-to-air weapons, but a wide range of other ordnance, including guns and rockets, will also be deployable. Designed to be operable at night and in adverse weather, the Tonal is planned to enter service in 1997. At present, a joint Anglo-Italian Staff Target is forming the basis of a two-year feasibility and cost definition study which began on 1 June 1987, and a detailed description would therefore be premature. Reported requirements of the four partner nations are: Italy 90, UK 125, Netherlands 70 and Spain 70.

MBB/Kawasaki
AIRFRAME PRIME CONTRACTORS:
MESSERSCHMITT-BÖLKOW-BLOHM GmbH
(Federal Republic of Germany)
KAWASAKI HEAVY INDUSTRIES LTD (Japan)

MBB/Kawasaki BK 117 A-3M

MBB and Kawasaki agreed on 25 February 1977 to develop jointly a multi-purpose helicopter known as the BK 117. Four prototypes were built. Initial flight testing was undertaken by the second and third, which flew for the first time, in Germany and Japan respectively, on 13 June 1979 (D-HBKA) and 10 August 1979 (JQ-0003). An S-01 pre-production aircraft (D-HBKB) made its first flight on 6 March 1981. The first production BK 117 to fly was a Kawasaki-built aircraft (JQ1001), which flew for the first time on 24 December 1981. The first aircraft from the MBB production line (D-HBKC) flew on 23 April 1982.

The basic BK 117A-3 does not fall within the category of this book, but at the 1985 Paris Air Show the BK 117A-3M multi-purpose military version was shown publicly for the first time. This is a purely German development by MBB. The airframe and powerplant are virtually unchanged from the commercial 117 A-3, except for a new high-skid landing gear to provide clearance for an underfuselage Lucas turret housing a 0.50 in or 12.7 mm Browning automatic machine-gun, with 450 rounds of ammunition, controlled by a helmet mounted sight. Typical weapons load is eight Hot 2 anti-tank missiles, mounted on outrigger pylons (four missiles each side of cabin), with which are associated a SFIM APX-M397 stabilised roof mounted sight and digital weapons control avionics. Provisions exist for a mast mounted sight of up to 120 kg (264 lb) weight, infra-red jamming and chaff/flare ECM, a Racal Prophet radar warning system, and a Racal RAMS 3000 Series avionics management system which uses a dual MIL-STD-1553B databus and multi-function cockpit displays. Alternative ordnance can include TOW anti-tank missiles, air-to-air missiles, unguided rockets, machine-gun pods, fixed forward-firing cannon, or a doorway gunner's

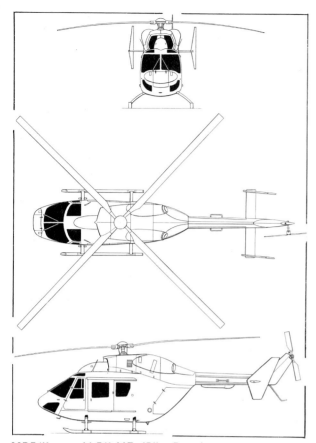

MBB/Kawasaki BK 117. *(Pilot Press)*

BK 117 A-3M multi-role military helicopter, equipped with undernose gun turret, roof and mast-mounted sights, and eight Hot 2 anti-tank missiles.

position with a 0.50 in machine-gun. The capacity to serve instead as an 11-troop or cargo transport helicopter is the same as for the commercial BK 117 A-3.

TYPE: Twin-turbine multi-purpose military helicopter.

ROTOR SYSTEM: Four-blade 'System Bölkow' rigid main rotor; head almost identical to that of BO 105; main rotor blades similar to those of BO 105, but larger. Fail-safe GRP blades of NACA 23012/23010 (modified) section with a stainless steel anti-erosion strip on each leading edge. Optional folding of two blades of main rotor. Two-blade semi-rigid (teetering) tail rotor, mounted on port side of vertical fin and rotating clockwise when viewed from that side. Blades are of GRP.

FUSELAGE: Of typical pod shaped configuration, comprising flight deck, cabin, cargo compartment and engine deck. Secondary components are compound-curvature shells with sandwich panels and Kevlar skins.

TAIL UNITS. Semi-monocoque tailboom, of tapered conical section, attached integrally to engine deck at forward end. Rear end, which is detachable, carries main fin/tail rotor support, and horizontal stabiliser with endplate fins set at an offset angle.

LANDING GEAR: Non-retractable tubular skid type, similar to that of BO 105. Skids are detachable from cross-tubes. Ground handling wheels standard. Emergency flotation gear, settling protectors and snow skids available optionally.

POWERPLANT: Two Avco Lycoming LTS 101-650B-1 turboshaft engines, each rated at 442 kW (592 shp) for take-off and 410 kW (550 shp) max continuous power. Fuel in four flexible bladder tanks (forward and aft main tanks, with two supply tanks between), in compartments under cabin floor. Two independent fuel feed systems for the engines and a common main fuel tank. Total standard fuel capacity 608 litres (161 US gallons; 133.75 Imp gallons). A 200 litre (53 US gallon; 44 Imp gallon) auxiliary tank is available optionally.

ACCOMMODATION: High-density layouts available for up to ten passengers in addition to pilot.

AVIONICS AND ARMAMENT: See introductory notes.

DIMENSIONS, EXTERNAL:	
Main rotor diameter	11.00 m (36 ft 1 in)
Tail rotor diameter	1.956 m (6 ft 5 in)
Main rotor blade chord	0.32 m (1 ft 0½ in)
Length overall, main and tail rotors turning	
	13.00 m (42 ft 8 in)
Fuselage: Max width	1.60 m (5 ft 3 in)
Height overall, main and tail rotors turning	
	3.85 m (12 ft 7½ in)
Width over skids	2.50 m (8 ft 2½ in)
AREA:	
Main rotor disc	95.03 m² (1,022.9 sq ft)
WEIGHTS:	
Weight empty, equipped	2,560 kg (5,644 lb)
Max T-O weight	3,200 kg (7,055 lb)

PERFORMANCE: (data based on commercial BK 117A-4 with gross weight of 3,200 kg; 7,055 lb):

Never-exceed speed at S/L	
	150 knots (278 km/h; 172 mph)
Max cruising speed at S/L	
	134 knots (248 km/h; 154 mph)
Max forward rate of climb at S/L	632 m (2,075 ft)/min
Hovering ceiling IGE (17 knot; 32 km/h; 20 mph cross-wind)	approx 2,440 m (8,000 ft)
Hovering ceiling OGE	1,980 m (6,500 ft)

McDonnell Douglas/BAe

AIRFRAME PRIME CONTRACTORS:
MCDONNELL DOUGLAS CORPORATION (USA)
BRITISH AEROSPACE PLC (UK)

McDonnell Douglas/British Aerospace Harrier II

US Marine Corps designations: AV-8B and TAV-8B

RAF designations: Harrier GR. Mk 5 and 7

Initial enthusiasm of the US Marine Corps for an advanced version of the AV-8A Harrier resulted in Anglo-American studies as long ago as 1973. After these foundered in 1975, McDonnell Douglas and Hawker Siddeley/British Aerospace at first pursued their own separate lines of development, both aimed broadly at doubling the payload/radius capability of the Harrier/AV-8A without departing too radically (or expensively) from the existing airframe/engine combination. The two companies subsequently joined forces in the current Harrier II programme, initially for the US Marine Corps (**AV-8B** and **TAV-8B**) and the Royal Air Force (**Harrier GR. Mk 5**).

As a first step, McDonnell Douglas and the USMC modified two AV-8As as prototype YAV-8Bs, these flying for the first time on 9 November 1978 and 19 February 1979. Four full-scale development (FSD) AV-8Bs were ordered on 12 April 1979, and the first of these made its initial flight on 5 November 1981. The remaining three first flew on 17 April, 9 April and 4 June 1982 respectively. Two airframes were built for structural and fatigue testing.

The decision to commit the AV-8B to production was announced on 24 August 1981, at which time the British Ministry of Defence and the main industrial partners in the programme indicated initial requirements of 257 for the USMC and 60 for the RAF. The total current USMC requirement is for 323 production aircraft (295 AV-8Bs and 28 two-seat TAV-8Bs), of which the first 12 (pilot production) AV-8Bs were ordered in FY 1982. The first of

these made its initial flight on 29 August 1983. Subsequent orders were placed in FYs 1983 (21 aircraft), 1984 (27, including one TAV-8B), 1985 (32, including two TAV-8Bs) and 1986 (46); funding for a further 42 aircraft was approved in FY 1987, and production is planned to continue into the early 1990s. The AV-8B is intended to re-equip three fleet operational AV-8A/C squadrons (VMA-331, VMA-542 and VMA-513), one training squadron (VMAT-203) and five A-4 Skyhawk squadrons by 1989. The first pilot production AV-8B was delivered to the USMC in October 1983. The first operational AV-8B squadron, VMA-331, was commissioned at MCAS Cherry Point, North Carolina, on 30 January 1985. Initial operational capability (IOC) was achieved in August 1985, and full operational readiness in 1986. VMA-231, the second operational AV-8B squadron, began receiving its aircraft in the Autumn of 1985, and the third (VMA-542) in mid-1986. The first 86 AV-8Bs had been delivered to the USMC by 9 July 1987.

First flight of the two-seat TAV-8B occurred on 21 October 1986, followed by initial deliveries to VMAT-203 in June 1987. This version has a longer forward fuselage and 0.43 m (1 ft 5 in) taller vertical tail than the AV-8B, with two cockpits in tandem. For weapons training it can carry Mk 76 practice bombs, LAU-68 rocket launchers or 1,135 litre (300 US gallon; 250 Imp gallon) external fuel tanks. BAe is the major subcontractor for the TAV-8B.

Deliveries of the GR. Mk 5 to the Royal Air Force began in 1987. First flight by a GR. Mk 5 (ZD318) was made on 30 April 1985; the second (ZD319) was flown on 31 July 1985. It has been announced that the RAF's initial requirement for 62 GR. Mk 5s will be followed by orders for 34 additional aircraft, for which long-lead production items were being authorised.

McDonnell Douglas/BAe AV-8B of US Marine Corps Squadron VMA-331.

McDonnell Douglas TAV-8B two-seat training version of the Harrier II on its first flight.

First export customer for the Harrier II is the government of Spain, which is acquiring 12 **AV-8Bs**, assembled by McDonnell Douglas, to supplement its carrier-based AV-8A Matadors. Deliveries began in October 1987.

A programme to develop a night-attack version of the Harrier II was announced by McDonnell Douglas in November 1984, and a USMC prototype of this version flew in 1987. Production deliveries could start in September 1989. The new nav/attack equipment includes two FD 4512 HUDs and a HUDWAC, an upgraded digital INS unit, projected map display, high-resolution head-down TV-type raster display in each cockpit, and video recording facilities, and is compatible with the aircraft's nose mounted FLIR sensor. 'Production' Nightbird Harrier IIs will be undertaken as a retrofit programme, requiring an enhanced (ACCS 2500) Computing Devices mission computer, and a multi-purpose colour display with a separate video map generator. They will be designated **Harrier GR. Mk 7**.

Features of the AV-8B include the use of graphite epoxy (carbonfibre) composite materials for the wings, and parts of the fuselage and tail unit; adoption of a supercritical-section wing; addition of lift improvement devices (LIDs) comprising fuselage mounted or under-gun-pod strakes and a retractable fence panel forward of the pods, to augment lift for vertical take-off; larger wing trailing-edge flaps and drooped ailerons; redesigned forward fuselage and cockpit;

redesigned engine air intakes to provide more VTO/STO thrust and more efficient cruise; and the Hughes Angle Rate Bombing Set. The leading-edge root extensions (LERX) developed originally by British Aerospace for the UK designed Big Wing Harrier have also been adopted as standard, although they are now only 64 per cent of the size originally proposed. This feature adds considerably to the AV-8B's instantaneous turn rate, enhancing still further its air combat capability. The landing gear is strengthened to cater for the higher operating weights and greater external stores loads made possible by these changes.

Work-split on the airframe for the AV-8B is 60 per cent to McDonnell Douglas and 40 per cent to British Aerospace; the GR.Mk 5 work-split is 50 per cent to each manufacturer. On any future third-party orders McDonnell Douglas would make 75 per cent of the aircraft deliveries and British Aerospace 25 per cent. Each manufacturer is responsible for the systems in those parts of the airframe which are its concern, and for their installation. British Aerospace provides the complete reaction control system for all aircraft in the programme, and undertakes final assembly of aircraft for the RAF. McDonnell Douglas assembles the aircraft for the USMC and Spain. Planned peak production rates are four US and two UK aircraft per month.

Pratt & Whitney manufactures up to 25 per cent by value of the engines for the USMC aircraft; Rolls-Royce builds the remainder. The production engine is the F402-RR-406

Prototype of the US night-attack version of the AV-8B Harrier II.

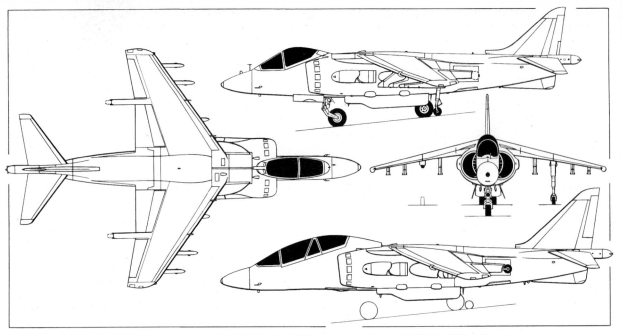

McDonnell Douglas/British Aerospace AV-8B Harrier II. Lower side view: TAV-8B. *(Pilot Press)*

(Pegasus Mk 105), an improved version of the Pegasus 11 with new features designed to offer substantially increased engine life and reduced peacetime operating costs. Beyond the current production engine, growth engines may offer some 13.3 kN (3,000 lb) more thrust, and Rolls-Royce began testing an uprated Pegasus known as the XG-15 in late 1985. Growth engines also form the basis of a supersonic engine using plenum chamber burning (PCB), and all four major airframe/engine partners are engaged in jointly funded R&D for the eventual development of a supersonic V/STOL combat aircraft. A digital engine control system (DECS) for the F402, developed by Dowty and Smiths Industries, was installed in the first TAV-8B in October 1986, and in production AV-8Bs from March 1987.

The following description applies to the production AV-8B and the Harrier GR. Mk 5:

TYPE: Single-seat V/STOL close support and (RAF only) reconnaissance aircraft.

WINGS: Cantilever shoulder-wing monoplane. Low-aspect-ratio sweptback wings, with non-swept inboard trailing edges and curved leading-edge root extensions (LERX). Span and area increased by approx 20 per cent and 14.5 per cent respectively compared with Harrier/AV-8A. Supercritical aerofoil section, with thickness/chord ratio of 11.5% at root, 7.5% at tip. Leading-edge sweep 10° less than that of Harrier/AV-8A. Marked anhedral. One-piece structure, of mixed construction, with extensive use of graphite epoxy (carbonfibre) and other composite materials in the main multi-spar torsion box, ribs, skins, flaps, ailerons, LERX, and outrigger pods and fairings. Wide-chord single-slotted trailing-edge flaps, with flap slot closure doors. Drooping ailerons, actuated by Fairey hydraulic jacks. Jet reaction control valve at each wingtip.

FUSELAGE: Conventional semi-monocoque structure, generally similar to that of AV-8A, but longer, owing to provision of a new forward fuselage built largely of graphite epoxy composite material. Lift augmenting underfuselage devices consist of a fixed strake on each of the two ventral gun packs, plus a retractable fence between forward edges of gun packs, just aft of forward main landing gear unit. During VTOL modes the 'box' formed by these surfaces, which are made of composite materials, traps the cushion of air bounced off the ground by the engine exhaust, providing sufficient additional lift to enable the AV-8B to take off vertically at a gross weight equal to its maximum hovering gross weight. Large forward hinged airbrake beneath fuselage, aft of rear main landing gear bay. Jet reaction control valves in nose and tailcone.

TAIL UNIT: One-piece variable-incidence tailplane, with marked anhedral, differing in planform from that of AV-8A in having constant sweep on leading edges and reduced sweep on trailing edges. Tailplane is built mainly of graphite epoxy, with aluminium alloy tips and leading edges. Fin has dielectric tip; manually operated graphite epoxy composite rudder, with inset trim tab. Dorsal airscoop, at base of fin, for equipment bay cooling system. Ventral fin under rear fuselage.

LANDING GEAR: Retractable bicycle type, permitting operation from rough unprepared surfaces of very low CBR (California Bearing Ratio). Hydraulic actuation, with nitrogen bottle for emergency extension. Single steerable nosewheel retracts forward, twin coupled mainwheels rearward, into fuselage. Small outrigger units, at approx mid span between flaps and ailerons, retract rearward into streamline pods. Dunlop wheels, tyres, multi-disc carbon brakes and anti-skid system. Mainwheel tyres size 26.0 × 7.75-13.00 and nosewheel tyre size 26.0 × 8.75-11. Outrigger tyres are size 13.5 × 6.00-4.00.

POWERPLANT: One 95.42 kN (21,450 lb st) Rolls-Royce F402-RR-406 (Pegasus 11-21) vectored-thrust turbofan engine in production AV-8B; one 96.75 kN (21,750 lb st) Pegasus Mk 105 in Harrier GR. Mk 5. Redundant digital engine control system (DECS), with mechanical backup, standard from March 1987. Zero-scarf front nozzles. Air intakes have an elliptical lip shape, leading edges reinforced against bird strikes, and a single row of auxiliary intake doors. Integral fuel tanks in wings; total internal fuel capacity (fuselage and wing tanks) 4,163 litres (1,100 US gallons; 915 Imp gallons). Retractable in-flight refuelling probe. Each of the four inner underwing stations capable of carrying a 1,135 litre (300 US gallon; 250 Imp gallon) auxiliary fuel tank.

ACCOMMODATION: Pilot only, on zero/zero ejection seat (Stencel for USMC, Martin-Baker for RAF), in pressurised cockpit. AV-8B cockpit raised approx 30.5 cm (12 in) by comparison with AV-8A/YAV-8B, with redesigned one-piece wraparound windscreen (thicker on RAF aircraft than on those for USMC) and rearward sliding bubble canopy, to improve all-round field of view. Windscreen de-icing and windscreen wiper.

AVIONICS AND EQUIPMENT: Include dual Collins RT-1250A/ARC U/VHF com (GEC Avionics AD3500 U/VHF-AM/FM in GR. Mk 5), R-1379B/ARA-63 all-weather landing receiver, RT-1159A/ARN-118 Tacan, RT-1015A/APN-194(V) radar altimeter, Sperry CV-3736/A com/nav/identification data converter, Bendix RT-1157/APX-100 IFF (Cossor IFF 4760 transponder in GR. Mk 5), Litton AN/ASN-130A inertial navigation system (Ferranti FIN 1075 in GR. Mk 5), Garrett AiResearch CP-1471/A digital air data computer, Smiths Industries SU-128/A dual combining glass head-up display and CP-1450/A display computer, IP-1318/A CRT Kaiser digital display indicator, and (RAF aircraft only) Ferranti moving map display. Litton AN/ALR-67(V)2 fore/aft looking radar warning receiver, and Goodyear flare/chaff dispenser (in lower rear fuselage). Primary weapon delivery sensor system for AV-8B and GR.Mk 5 is the Hughes Aircraft AN/ASB-19(V)2 or 3 Angle Rate Bombing Set, in the nose and comprising a dual-mode (TV and laser) target seeker/tracker. This system functions in conjunction with the CP-1429/AYK-14(V) mission computer (Computing Devices ACCS 2000 in GR. Mk 5), the Lear Siegler AN/AYQ-13 stores management system, the display computer and its associated cockpit displays, the head-up display, and the digital display indicator. Flight controls that interface with the reaction control system are provided by the Sperry AN/ASW-46(V)2 stability augmentation and attitude hold system currently being updated to the high-AOA-capable configuration. RAF aircraft will have an accident data recorder. Backup standby mechanical instrumentation includes airspeed indicator, altimeter, angle of attack indicator, attitude indicator, cabin pressure altitude indicator, clock, flap position indicator, horizontal situation indicator, standby compass, turn and slip indicator, and vertical speed indicator. Other equipment includes anti-collision, approach, formation, in-flight refuelling, landing gear position, auxiliary exterior lights, and console, instrument panel and other internal lighting.

ARMAMENT AND OPERATIONAL EQUIPMENT: Two under-fuselage gun/ammunition packs, mounting a five-barrel 25 mm cannon based on the General Electric GAU-12/U, with 300 rounds, in the AV-8B; or two 25 mm Royal Ordnance Factories cannon with 200 rds (derived from the 30 mm Aden) in the GR. Mk 5. Single 454 kg (1,000 lb) stores mount on fuselage centreline, between gun packs.

Three stores stations under each wing on AV-8B, the inner and centre ones each capable of carrying a 907 kg (2,000 lb) store, the centre one 281 kg (620 lb). The four inner wing stations are 'wet', permitting the carriage of auxiliary fuel tanks. Including fuel, stores, weapons and ammunition, and water injection for the engine, the maximum useful load for vertical take-off is approximately 3,062 kg (6,750 lb), and for short take-off nearly 7,710 kg (17,000 lb). Typical weapons include two or four AIM-9L Sidewinder, Magic or AGM-65E Maverick missiles; up to sixteen 500 lb general purpose bombs, 12 cluster bombs, ten Paveway laser guided bombs, eight fire bombs, ten rocket pods, six chaff or flare pods, or (in addition to the underfuselage gun packs) two underwing gun pods. ML Aviation BRU-36/A bomb release units standard on all versions. Provision for AN/ALQ-164 defensive ECM pod on centreline pylon (AV-8B). RAF aircraft have two additional underwing weapon stations, for Sidewinder air-to-air missiles, ahead of the outrigger-wheel fairings; a nose-mounted infra-red reconnaissance sensor; and a Marconi Defence Systems Zeus internal ECM system comprising an advanced radar warning receiver, and a multi-mode jammer with a Northrop RF transmitter.

DIMENSIONS, EXTERNAL:

Wing span	9.25 m (30 ft 4 in)
Length overall (flying attitude)	14.12 m (46 ft 4 in)
Height overall	3.55 m (11 ft 7¾ in)
Tailplane span	4.24 m (13 ft 11 in)
Outrigger wheel track	5.18 m (17 ft 0 in)

AREA:

Wings, excl LERX, gross	21.37 m² (230 sq ft)

WEIGHTS:

Basic operating weight empty:	
AV-8B	5,936 kg (13,086 lb)
GR. Mk 5	6,258 kg (13,798 lb)
Max fuel: internal only	3,519 kg (7,759 lb)
internal and external	7,180 kg (15,829 lb)
Max external stores	4,173 kg (9,200 lb)
Basic flight design gross weight for 7g operation	
	10,410 kg (22,950 lb)
Max T-O weight:	
500 m (1,640 ft) STO	14,061 kg (31,000 lb)
S/L VTO, ISA	8,595 kg (18,950 lb)
S/L VTO, 32°C	8,142 kg (17,950 lb)
Max vertical landing weight	8,459 kg (18,650 lb)

PERFORMANCE:

Max Mach number in level flight:	
at S/L	0.85 (562 knots; 1,041 km/h; 647 mph)
at altitude	0.91
STOL T-O run at max T-O weight	500 m (1,640 ft)

Operational radius with external loads shown:
short T-O (366 m; 1,200 ft), twelve Mk 82 Snakeye bombs, internal fuel, 1 h loiter

90 nm (167 km; 103 miles)

hi-lo-hi, short T-O (366 m; 1,200 ft), seven Mk 82 Snakeye bombs, external fuel tanks, no loiter (payload of 1,814 kg; 4,000 lb)

480 nm (889 km; 553 miles)

Combat air patrol endurance at 100 nm (185 km; 115 miles) from base   3 h

Unrefuelled ferry range, with four 300 US gallon external tanks   2,120 nm (3,929 km; 2,441 miles)

g limits   + 7/ − 3

Panavia

PANAVIA AIRCRAFT GmbH

Panavia, with its headquarters in Germany, was formed on 26 March 1969 to design, develop and produce an all-weather combat aircraft for the air forces of the United Kingdom, the Federal Republic of Germany and Italy, and the Federal German Navy. The name Tornado for this aircraft was adopted officially in March 1976. This programme is one of the largest European industrial programmes ever undertaken. The three component companies of Panavia are British Aerospace PLC (42.5% participation), MBB (42.5%) and Aeritalia (15%).

On 29 July 1976 the governments of Federal Germany, Italy and the Uk signed a memorandum of understanding for the production of 809 Tornados, enabling the three partner countries to embark upon the production programme.

Panavia Tornado IDS

RAF designation: Tornado GR. Mk 1

The Tornado is a twin-engined two-seat supersonic aircraft capable of fulfilling the agreed operational requirements of its three sponsoring countries. The use of a variable-geometry wing, and avionics which enable the aircraft to fly 'blind' in all weathers, day and night, at very low level, with automatic terrain following, give it the necessary flexibility to achieve all-weather penetration.

The aircraft is intended to fulfil six major requirements, some of which are shared by more than one of the partners. These are:

(a) Close air support/battlefield interdiction
(b) Interdiction/counter air strike
(c) Air superiority
(d) Interception/air defence
(e) Naval strike
(f) Reconnaissance

Design of the Tornado was completed in August 1972. Nine flying prototypes were built – four in the UK, three in West Germany and two in Italy. The first prototype (D-9591), assembled by MBB, made its first flight at Manching, West Germany, on 14 August 1974. The prototypes were followed by six pre-series Tornados.

The first 809 production aircraft ordered for the participating nations comprise 644 of the IDS (interdictor strike) version, and 165 examples of the ADV (air defence variant, described separately) for the RAF. These were ordered under six contracts with respective new-production totals of 43, 110, 164, 162, 171 and 155. Four of the early IDS pre-series batch will eventually be brought up to production standard (one for Great Britain, two for Germany, one for Italy) to make up the original 809 three-nation programme production total. A total of 643 will be operational aircraft, and 163 will be dual control trainers with full operational capability. A seventh Tornado production contract, for 124 aircraft, was signed on 10 June 1986. This figure, bringing the overall total (excluding the four pre-series aircraft) to 929, is made up of 72 for the Royal Saudi Air Force (48 IDS and 24 ADV), eight ADV for the Sultan of Oman's Air Force, nine more GR. Mk 1s for the RAF, and 35 of the ECR variant (also described separately) for the Federal German Luftwaffe. The first two IDS Tornados for the RSAF arrived in Saudi Arabia on 27 March 1986, and six had been delivered by the following August. In early 1988, Jordan decided to purchase eight IDS Tornados for delivery in 1991. The contract details were then being worked out.

German Navy IDS Tornado armed with four HARM anti-radiation missiles.

Two Panavia Tornado IDS of the Royal Saudi Air Force.

The RAF is to have 229 Tornados of the GR. Mk 1 interdictor/strike version, including 48 trainers. Squadron deliveries began on 6 January 1982 to No. IX Squadron (formerly flying Vulcans) at RAF Honington, Suffolk, which became Strike Command's first operational Tornado squadron on 1 June 1982. It now also equips Nos. 27 and 617 at Marham (UK), Nos. XV, 16 and 20 at Laarbruch (West Germany), and Nos. 14, 17 and 31 at Brüggen (Germany). A total of seven Tornado GR. Mk 1 strike/attack squadrons and a further GR. Mk 1 reconnaissance squadron will eventually be based in RAF Germany . In 1984, RAF GR. Mk1s based in West Germany began being modified to carry tactical nuclear weapons; they are also the first RAF Tornados to be equipped with the Hunting JP 233 anti-airfield weapon.

The Luftwaffe is to receive 212 IDS Tornados, to replace the Lockheed F-104G in the battlefield interdiction, counter-air and close-air-support roles. Six squadrons, two each with JaboG 31 at Nörvenich, JaboG 32 at Lechfeld and JaboG 33 at Büchel, are operational. The 112 for Marineflieger-geschwader 1 and 2 of the Federal German Navy are being equipped for strike missions against sea and coastal targets, and for reconnaissance. Two squadrons of IDS Tornados are in service with MFG. 1 at Jagel, and two with MFG.2.

The Italian Air Force will receive 100 Tornados (99 production aircraft plus the No. 14 pre-series Tornado brought up to production standard). Of these, 54 will be used to replace F/RF-104G aircraft in the air-superiority, ground attack and reconnaissance roles. Of the remainder, 34 will be kept in reserve and 12 will be equipped as dual-control trainers. First unit to be equipped was the 154° Gruppo (Squadron) of 6° Stormo (Wing) at Brescia-Ghedi, which received its first Tornados in August 1982. The second unit, the 156° Gruppo (36° Stormo) at Gioia del Colle (Bari), and the third, the 155° Gruppo, also at Ghedi, have also been equipped.

The first British production Tornado made its initial flight on 10 July 1979, the first West German on 27 July 1979, and the first Italian on 25 September 1981. More than 600 production Tornados have been delivered. Fifty of these were delivered to the Tri-national Tornado Training Establishment (TTTE) at RAF Cottesmore in 1981–82. Weapons training is carried out at two Tornado Weapons Conversion Units (TWCU) at RAF Honington (UK) and JaboG 38 at Jever (West Germany).

The first flight of the RAF camera-less reconnaissance version of Tornado took place in Autumn 1985. This version is identifiable by a small underbelly blister fairing, immediately behind the laser rangefinder pod, containing a BAe sideways looking infra-red (SLIR) system, BAe Linescan 4000 infra-red surveillance system and Computing Devices Company signal processing and video recording system. Also in 1985, an initial technology demonstration was completed by an RAF Tornado equipped with BAe's Terprom (terrain profile matching) self-contained navigation system, and a contract was awarded to GEC Avionics for a night vision FLIR system for the Tornado GR. Mk 1. The FLIR sensor is installed in the undernose fairing used currently to house a laser rangefinder.

RAF Squadrons Nos. IX, 27 and 617 have been SACEUR (Supreme Allied Commander, Europe) declared, RAF Germany Squadrons Nos. XV and 16 strike declared, and the six squadrons at German MFG. 1 and JaboGs 31, 32 and 33 were NATO assigned. The first operational batch of MW-1 weapons systems had been delivered to JaboG 31; and joint take-off and landing trials by RAF Germany and the Luftwaffe had been performed successfully on a motorway in north Germany.

Normal max weapons load of the IDS Tornado is approx 9,000 kg (19,840 lb), carried on seven fuselage and wing hardpoints: one centreline pylon fitted with a single ejection release unit (ERU), two fuselage shoulder pylons each with three ERUs, and, under each wing, one inboard and one outboard pylon each with a single ERU. The BAe Sea Eagle

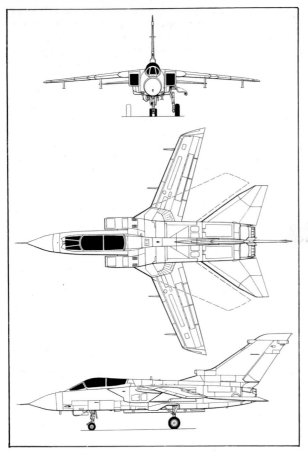

Panavia Tornado IDS. *(Pilot Press)*

air-to-surface missile can be carried by the RAF's GR. Mk 1. Primary armament of the Federal German Navy Tornados is four MBB Kormoran anti-shipping missiles. Italy's Tornados are to be equipped with the Selenia Aspide 1A air-to-air missile.

The following details apply to the basic IDS production version:

TYPE: Twin-engined all-weather multi-purpose combat aircraft.

WINGS: Cantilever shoulder-wing monoplane. Variable geometry wings, the outer panels having a leading-edge sweep of 25° in the fully forward position and 67° when fully swept. Fixed inboard portions have a leading-edge sweep of 60°. Krueger flap on the leading edge of each wing glove box. The wings each pivot hydraulically, on Teflon plated bearings, from a point in the centre-section just outboard of the fuselage. In the event of wing sweep failure, the aircraft can land safely with the wings fully swept. High-lift devices on the outer wings include full-span leading-edge slats (three sections on each side), full-span double-slotted fixed-vane trailing-edge flaps (four sections each side), and spoilers (two on upper surface on each side). Spoilers give augmented roll control at unswept and intermediate wing positions at low speed, and also act as lift dumpers after touchdown. No ailerons.

FUSELAGE: Conventional semi-monocoque structure, built in three main sections. Door-type airbrake on each side at top of rear fuselage.

TAIL UNIT: Cantilever structure, consisting of single sweptback two-spar fin and rudder, and low-set all-moving horizontal surfaces ('tailerons') which operate together for pitch control and differentially for roll control, assisted by use of the wing spoilers when the wings are not fully swept. Passive ECM antenna fairing near top of fin. Ram-air intake for heat exchanger at base of fin.

LANDING GEAR: Hydraulically retractable tricycle type, with forward retracting twin-wheel steerable nose unit. Single-wheel main units retract forward and upward into centre section of fuselage. Emergency extension system, using nitrogen gas pressure. Dunlop aluminium alloy wheels, hydraulic multi-disc brakes and low-pressure tyres (to permit operation from soft, semi-prepared surfaces) and Goodyear anti-skid units. Mainwheel tyres size 30 × 11.50-14.5, Type VIII (24 or 26 ply); nosewheel tyres size 18 × 5.5, Type VIII (12 ply). Runway arrester hook beneath rear of fuselage.

POWERPLANT: Two Turbo-Union RB199-34R Mk 101 turbofan engines in initial production aircraft, each rated at more than 40.0 kN (9,000 lb st) dry and more than 71.2 kN (16,000 lb st) with afterburning, fitted with bucket-type thrust reversers and installed in rear fuselage with downward opening doors for servicing and engine change. Mk 103 engines, offering approx 5 per cent more thrust, introduced on to production line from engine number 761 in May 1983; 100 modification kits ordered by RAF in 1983 to upgrade its Mk 101 engined aircraft to Mk 103 standard. All integral fuel in multi-cell Uniroyal self-sealing integral fuselage tanks and/or wing box tanks. RAF aircraft only have additional tank in fin. Detachable and retractable in-flight refuelling probe can be mounted on starboard side of fuselage, adjacent to cockpit. System also designed to accept a buddy-to-buddy refuelling pack. Provision for drop-tanks to be carried beneath fuselage (1,500 litres; 396 US gallons; 330 Imp gallons) and on inboard underwing pylons (1,500 or 2,250 litres; 396 or 594 US gallons; 330 or 495 Imp gallons). AEG-Telefunken intake de-icing system.

ACCOMMODATION: Crew of two on tandem Martin-Baker Mk 10A zero/zero ejection seats under Kopperschmidt/AIT one-piece canopy, which is hinged at rear and opens upward. Flat centre armoured windscreen panel and curved side panels, built by Lucas Aerospace, incorporate Sierracote electrically conductive heating film for windscreen anti-icing and demisting. Canopy (and windscreen in emergency) demisted by engine bleed air. Windscreen is hinged at front and can be opened forward and upward, allowing access to back of pilot's instrument panel. Seats provide safe escape at zero altitude and at speeds from zero up to 630 knots (1,166 km/h; 725 mph) IAS.

AVIONICS AND EQUIPMENT: Communications equipment includes Plessey PTR 1721 (UK and Italy) or Rohde und Schwarz (West Germany) UHF/VHF transceiver; AEG-Telefunken UHF/ADF (UK and West Germany only); SIT/Siemens emergency UHF with Rohde und Schwarz switch; BAe HF/SSB aerial tuning unit; Rohde und Schwarz (UK and West Germany) or Montedel (Italy) HF/SSB radio; Ultra communications control system; GEC Avionics central suppression unit (CSU); Epsylon voice recorder; Chelton UHF communications and landing system aerials.

Primary self-contained nav/attack system includes Texas Instruments multi-mode forward-looking ground mapping radar; Ferranti FIN 1010 three-axis digital inertial navigation system (DINS) and combined radar display; Decca Type 72 Doppler radar system, with Kalman filtering of the Doppler and inertial inputs for extreme navigational accuracy; Microtecnica air data computer; Litef Spirit 3 64K central digital computer; Aeritalia radio/radar altimeter; Smiths/Teldix/OMI electronic head-up display with Davall camera; Ferranti nose mounted laser rangefinder and marked target seeker; GEC Avionics TV tabular display, produced in partnership with AEG and Selenia; Astronautics (USA) bearing distance heading indicator and contour map display. Defensive equipment includes Siemens (West Germany) or Cossor SSR-3100 (UK and Saudi Arabia) IFF transponder; Elettronica passive warning radar.

Flight control system includes a GEC Avionics/Bodenseewerk triplex command stability augmentation system (CSAS), incorporating fly-by-wire and autostabilisation; GEC Avionics/Aeritalia autopilot and flight director (APFD), using two self-monitoring digital computers; GEC Avionics triplex transducer unit (TTU), with analog computing and sensor channels; GEC Avionics terrain following E-scope (TFE), produced in partnership with Selenia; Fairey/GEC Avionics quadruplex electro-hydraulic actuator; and Microtecnica air data set. The APFD provides preselected attitude, heading or barometric height hold, heading and track acquisition, and Mach number or airspeed hold with autothrottle. Flight director operates in parallel with, and can be used as backup for, the autopilot, as a duplex digital system with an extensive range of modes. Automatic approach, terrain following and radio height-holding modes are also available. Other instrumentation includes Smiths horizontal situation indicator, vertical speed indicator and standby altimeter; Lital standby attitude and heading reference system; SEL (with Setac) or (in UK aircraft) GEC Avionics AD2770 (without Setac) Tacan; Cossor CILS 75 ILS; Bodenseewerk attitude director indicator; Dornier System flight data recorder.

The avionics systems, while standardised as far as possible, retain the flexibility necessary to perform the various roles required. They provide accurate low- and high-level navigation; precision visual attack on ground targets in blind and poor weather conditions; air-to-ground and air-to-air attack with a wide variety of weapons; manually controlled and automatic attack; and comprehensive onboard checkout and mission data recording; with minimisation of ground support facilities at bases and the front line.

ARMAMENT: Fixed armament comprises two 27 mm IWKA-Mauser cannon, one in each side of the lower forward fuselage, with 180 rds/gun. Other armament varies according to version, with emphasis on the ability to carry a wide range of advanced weapons on three under-fuselage attachments and up to four swivelling hardpoints beneath the outer wings. A GEC Avionics/Selenia stores management system is fitted; Sandall Mace 355 and 762 mm (14 and 30 in) ejector release units, and ML Aviation CBLS 200 practice-bomb carriers, are standard. The battlefield interdiction version is capable of carrying weapons for 'hard' or 'soft' targets. Naval and interdictor strike versions have provision for carrying additional, externally mounted fuel tanks. For German Navy and Italian Air Force Tornados, MBB has

developed (first flight 14 April 1981) a multi-sensor reconnaissance pod to be carried on the centreline pylon. Some RAF Tornados will be fitted with infra-red cameras in ammunition bay. Among the weapons already specified for, or suitable for carriage by, the IDS Tornado are the Sidewinder and Aspide AAM, and ALARM or HARM anti-radiation missiles; JP 233 low-altitude airfield attack munition dispenser, Paveway laser guided bomb, AS.30, Maverick, GBU-15, Sea Eagle and Kormoran air-to-surface missiles; napalm; BL755 Mks 1 and 2 600 lb cluster bombs; MW-1 munitions dispenser; Mk 83 or other 1,000 lb bombs; 'smart' or retarded bombs; BLU-1B 750 lb fire bombs; Matra 250 kg ballistic and retarded bombs; Lepus flare bombs; LAU-51A and LR-25 rocket launchers; Marconi Skyshadow (jamming/deception) and BOZ 107 (chaff/flare) ECM pods; Pave Spike pods; data link pods; and chaff/flare dispensers. External fuel tanks can also be carried.

DIMENSIONS, EXTERNAL:	
Wing span: fully spread	13.91 m (45 ft $7\frac{1}{2}$ in)
fully swept	8.60 m (28 ft $2\frac{1}{2}$ in)
Length overall	16.72 m (54 ft $10\frac{1}{4}$ in)
Height overall	5.95 m (19 ft $6\frac{1}{4}$ in)
Wheel track	3.10 m (10 ft 2 in)
Wheelbase	6.20 m (20 ft 4 in)

WEIGHTS:	
Weight empty, equipped	14,091 kg (31,065 lb)
Nominal max weapon load	approx 9,000 kg (19,840 lb)
Max T-O weight:	
'clean', full internal fuel	20,411 kg (45,000 lb)
with external stores	approx 27,215 kg (60,000 lb)

PERFORMANCE:	
Max Mach number in level flight in altitude, 'clean'	2.2
Max level speed, 'clean'	
above 800 knots (1,480 km/h; 920 mph) IAS	
Max level speed with external stores	
Mach 0.92 (600 knots; 1,112 km/h; 691 mph)	
Time to 9,145 m (30,000 ft) from brake release	
	less than 2 min
Automatic terrain following	down to 61 m (200 ft)
Required runway length	less than 900 m (2,950 ft)
Landing run	370 m (1,215 ft)
Radius of action with heavy weapons load, hi-lo-lo-hi	
	750 nm (1,390 km; 863 miles)
Ferry range	approx 2,100 nm (3,890 km; 2,420 miles)
g limit	+ 7.5

Tornado Mid-Life Improvement Programme

In order to retain effective mission capability and survivability in the face of the increased threat in the 1990s, a mid-life improvement programme is currently being developed by the Tornado air arms and industry. It will confer more accurate navigation for 'blind' attacks, improved sortie-generation capability, increased range for better target coverage, increased target-acquisition capability, reduced penetration altitude, covert operation, improved electronic self-defence, improved threat suppression, and greater reliability and maintainability.

The first avionics upgrade modifications are already incorporated in the sixth Tornado production batch. They include a MIL-1553B databus, upgraded radar warning equipment and active ECM, an improved missile control unit, a 128K main computer, and integration of the Texas Instruments HARM anti-radar guided missile. A HARM-equipped Tornado began flight testing on 5 December 1985, following the first flight of ALARM on a Tornado, made on 13 February 1985.

Panavia Tornado ECR

The Federal German Luftwaffe has selected an ECR (electronic combat and reconnaissance) version of the IDS Tornado to replace tactical reconnaissance aircraft already in operation and to complement or supersede such NATO airborne electronic warfare types as the F-4G Phantom.

Retaining its air-to-surface role, except for the removal of the two 27 mm guns, the ECR Tornado is intended for standoff reconnaissance and border control, reconnaissance via image-forming and electronic means, electronic support, and employment of anti-radar guided missiles. For this purpose it is to be equipped with a direction-finding system for ground-based radar installations (emitter locator); IR linescanner system, FLIR, onboard systems for processing, storing and transmitting reconnaissance data; and advanced tactical displays for the pilot and weapons officer. The external load stations on fuselage and wings may be used in ECR or fighter-bomber missions, or a combination of both.

The ECR version will normally be configured to carry two HARMs, two Sidewinders, an active ECM pod, chaff/flare dispenser pod, and two 1,500 litre (396 US gallon; 330 Imp gallon) underwing fuel tanks.

The seventh Tornado production contract, signed on 10 June 1986, included an order for 35 Tornado ECRs, deliveries of which are due to be made in 1989–91. Pre-production Tornado P16 is being equipped for initial ECR flight trials, which began at Manching in 1987. Italy also has expressed interest in the ECR.

Panavia Tornado ADV

RAF designation: Tornado F. Mks 2, 2A and 3

A possible air-defence role for the Tornado was considered by the RAF when the interdictor/strike (IDS) programme

MBB model of Tornado in ECR configuration, with two HARM anti-radiation missiles under the fuselage, two Sidewinders and two drop-tanks (underwing, inboard), and chaff/flare dispenser (port) and AECM (starboard) pods under the outer wings.

was inaugurated in 1968, and low-key studies leading to an air defence variant (ADV) were initiated in the following year. These were given impetus in 1971, when the Ministry of Defence issued Air Staff Target (AST) 395 covering the development of an interceptor with a new advanced-technology radar and XJ521 Sky Flash air-to-air missiles. Changes from the IDS Tornado were to be minimal, and costs kept as low as possible.

It soon became clear that a configuration using the existing RB199 engines and having the four Sky Flash missiles on underwing pylons would have too high a drag factor and would not meet the performance requirement. The solution adopted was therefore to semi-submerge the Sky Flash missiles in tandem pairs under the fuselage, and to anticipate further performance benefits from ongoing development of the RB199 engine.

Full-scale development of the Tornado ADV was authorised on 4 March 1976, and the RAF includes 165 of this long-range interceptor model, designated F. Mk 2 and F. Mk 3, in its total procurement of 394 Tornados, to re-equip two Lightning squadrons, three squadrons of Phantoms, two new squadrons, and an OCU.

Most of the ADV Tornados will be based in the United Kingdom (including two squadrons at Leuchars in Scotland, two plus an OCU at Coningsby, Lincolnshire, and three at Leeming, Yorkshire), for air defence of the UK and to protect the northern and western approaches of NATO. Equipped with a tactical display that can cover the entire North Sea, they will also fulfil the RAF's commitments to provide long-range air defence of Britain's maritime forces, over a wide UK defence region extending from the Atlantic approaches to the Baltic and from Iceland to the English Channel; and to contribute towards air defence in the Central Region of Europe. The F. Mk 2/3 can loiter on patrol for several hours, using in-flight refuelling when necessary, and can detect, identify and destroy enemy aircraft approaching at supersonic speeds at high, medium or low altitudes, using its snap-up/snap-down missiles. Its fire control system is able to engage multiple targets in rapid succession; its weapons systems are highly resistant to enemy ECM; and it can operate from damaged airfields by virtue of its good short-field performance. Supersonic acceleration is better than that of the IDS version. A genuine long-range autonomous capability enables it to operate more than 350 nm (645 km; 400 miles) from its base at night, in bad weather, in heavy ECM conditions, against multiple targets at low level.

Two main airframe modifications distinguish the ADV from the IDS version. The principal one is an increase in fuselage length forward of the front cockpit, to accommodate the longer radome of the GEC Avionics AI-24 Foxhunter radar, and a small 'stretch' aft of the rear cockpit to allow the four Sky Flash missiles to be carried in two tandem pairs. The other is that the fixed inboard portions of the wings are extended forward at the leading edges (sweep angle 67° instead of 60°), to give increased chord and compensate for the shift in the CG. These changes also benefit performance by reducing drag, especially at supersonic speed, compared with the IDS version. Extension of the fuselage provides additional space for avionics and for an additional 10 per cent of internal fuel (909 litres; 240 US gallons; 200 Imp gallons).

Other changes include deletion of one of the two IWKA-Mauser 27 mm cannon; installation of RB199 Mk 103

Panavia Tornado F.Mk 3 of No 229 OCU, Royal Air Force.

engines in the first 18 production aircraft (**F. Mk 2**) and, thereafter (**F. Mk 3**), Mk 104 engines with extended nozzles, increased reheat combat thrust, and a Lucas DECU 500 digital engine control unit; fitting of a ram-air turbine, radar-dedicated cold air unit, and an internally mounted retractable in-flight refuelling probe; addition of a head-down display for the pilot, and replacement of the navigator's wet-film head-down display recorder by a displayed data video recorder; fitment of a second Ferranti 1010 INS platform; integration with the radar of a new Cossor IFF interrogator; incorporation (when its development is completed) of a Singer-Kearfott data link system; and introduction of new cockpit displays and redesign of symbology, together with an increase in computer storage capacity. The F. Mk 3 also introduced automatic wing sweep (AWS) and automatic manoeuvre device system (AMDS).

The F.2s are scheduled to be returned to BAe and largely upgraded to F.3 standard except for the Mk 104 engines, which could not be retrofitted without structural alterations to the rear fuselage. After upgrading, these F. 2s will be redesignated **F. Mk 2A**.

Although possessing some 80 per cent commonality with the IDS version, the Tornado ADV was sufficiently different for the initial production contract to include funding for three prototypes of the fighter version. These were identified by the manufacturer as the A01 to A03, making their first flights on 27 October 1979, 18 July 1980 and 18 November 1980. Flight development included successful guided firings of the Sky Flash and Sidewinder air-to-air missiles, and completion and service clearance of the rapid-rolling programme.

The first two production F. Mk 2s (RAF serial numbers ZD899/900), are conversion trainers, and were rolled out on 28 March 1984. First flights were made on 12 April and 5 March 1984 respectively. They were delivered to the Aeroplane and Armament Experimental Establishment at Boscombe Down in the Summer of 1984, and were followed on 5 November by the first two aircraft (AT003 and 005) for No. 229 Operational Conversion Unit at RAF Coningsby, Lincolnshire. The unit's full complement of 16 aircraft had been delivered by October 1985. Deliveries of the F. Mk 2 were completed by December 1985, and in February 1986 deliveries began of the F. Mk 3, which flew for the first time (ZE154) on 20 November 1985.

The first export order for the ADV Tornado, for eight aircraft for the Sultan of Oman's Air Force, was announced on 14 August 1985. Six weeks later, on 26 September, an order for 24 was announced by the Saudi Arabian government. These aircraft are included in the seventh Tornado production contract, which was signed on 10 June 1986.

TYPE: Twin-engined all-weather air defence interceptor.

WINGS: Similar to IDS version except that fixed inboard portions also have a leading-edge sweep of 67° and the Krueger leading-edge flaps are deleted. F. Mk 3 fitted with automatic wing sweep (AWS) and automatic manoeuvre device system (AMDS). With AWS, four different wing sweeps can be scheduled (25° at speeds up to Mach 0.73, 45° from there up to Mach 0.88, 58° up to Mach 0.95, and 67° above Mach 0.95), enabling specific excess power at transonic speeds and turning capability at subsonic speeds to be maximised. Buffet-free handling can be maintained, to the limits defined by the spin-prevention and incidence limiting system (SPILS), by use of the automatic manoeuvre device system (AMDS), which schedules with wing incidence to deploy either flaps and slats at 25° sweep angle or slats only at 45° sweep. Beyond 45°, both flaps and slats are scheduled 'in'.

FUSELAGE: Generally as for IDS version, but lengthened forward of front cockpit and aft of rear cockpit. Nosecone hinged in two places, providing access to front and rear of Foxhunter radar.

TAIL UNIT: As IDS version. On F. Mk 3, with extended afterburner nozzles, base of rudder is recontoured to clear the repositioned thrust reversers, and tailerons to clear the revised rear-fuselage outline.

95

LANDING GEAR: As IDS version. Nosewheel steering augmentation system to minimise 'wander' on landing.

POWERPLANT: Two Turbo-Union RB199-34R Mk 103 afterburning turbofan engines in F. Mk 2/2A; F. Mk 3 has Mk 104 engines with 360 mm (14 in) extension to afterburner nozzles to increase reheat thrust. Compared with the Mk 101 engine in early production IDS Tornados, the Mk 103 increases both dry and reheat thrust by 5 to 10 per cent; reheat combat thrust of the Mk 104 engine is increased by 7 per cent compared with that of the Mk 103. Max internal fuel capacity increased by 10 per cent compared with IDS version. Internally mounted, fully retractable in-flight refuelling probe in port side of nose, adjacent to cockpit. Provision for drop-tanks of 1,500 or 2,250 litres capacity, as on IDS version.

ACCOMMODATION: As for IDS version.

AVIONICS AND EQUIPMENT: Among those in the IDS Tornado which are retained in the ADV are the communications equipment (Plessey VHF/UHF transceiver, SIT/Siemens emergency UHF, Rohde und Schwarz HF/SSB, Ultra communications control system and Epsylon cockpit voice recorder); GEC Avionics triplex fly-by-wire command stability augmentation system and autopilot/flight director system (modified for increased-roll-rate and reduced pitch stick forces); Litef Spirit 3 central digital computer (with capacity increased from 64K to 128K) and data transmission system; Smiths electronic head-up and navigator's head-down display; Ferranti FIN 1010 inertial navigation system (to which is added a second 1010 to monitor the head-up display); GEC Avionics Tacan; Cossor ILS; and Cossor IFF transponder. Those deleted include the Texas Instruments nose radar, Decca 72 Doppler radar with terrain following, Ferranti laser rangefinder and marked target seeker, and Lital standby attitude and heading reference system.

The ADV's primary airborne interception system is based on a nose-mounted GEC Avionics AI-24 Foxhunter multi-mode track-while-scan pulse-Doppler radar with FMICW (frequency modulated interrupted continuous wave), with which is integrated a new Cossor IFF-3500 interrogator and a radar signal processor to suppress ground clutter. This system enables the aircraft to detect targets more than 100 nm (185 km; 115 miles) away, and to track several targets simultaneously. A ground mapping mode for navigation backup is also available. Ferranti is subcontractor for the Foxhunter transmitter and aerial scanning mechanism. A pilot's head-down display is added, a Ferranti displayed data video recorder (DDVR) replaces the navigator's wet-film display recorder, and an MSDS Hermes modular radar homing and warning receiver (RHWR) is added. Head-up/head-down displays are on front instrument panel only, radar control and data link presentations on rear panel only; both panels have weapon control and RHWR displays. A Ferranti FH31A AC driven 3 in horizon gyro in the rear cockpit, in addition to providing an attitude display for the navigator, feeds pitch and roll signals to other avionics systems in the aircraft in certain modes. Analog electronic engine control unit on F. Mk 2 replaced by Lucas digital unit (DECU 500) on F. Mk 3. ESM (electronic surveillance measures) and ECCM are standard; a Singer-Kearfott ECM-resistant data link system, interoperable with other NATO systems, is under development for installation later.

Because of its comprehensive avionics the Tornado ADV can contribute significantly to the transfer of vital information over the entire tactical area and can, if necessary, partially fulfil the roles of both AEW and ground-based radar.

ARMAMENT AND OPERATIONAL EQUIPMENT. Fixed armament of one 27 mm IWKA-Mauser cannon in starboard side of lower forward fuselage. Four BAe Sky Flash semi-active radar homing medium-range air-to-air missiles are semi-recessed under the centre fuselage, carried on internally mounted Frazer-Nash launchers; one or two European built NWC AIM-9L Sidewinder infra-red homing short-range air-to-air missiles on each of the inboard underwing stations. All four underwing stations are 'wet' for the carriage of auxiliary fuel tanks. Smiths Industries/Computing Devices Company missile management system (MMS), which also controls tank jettison, has provision for pilot override, optimised for visual attack. The Sky Flash missiles, each fitted with an MSDS monopulse seeker head, can engage targets at high altitude or down to 75 m (250 ft), in the face of heavy ECM, and at standoff ranges of more than 25 nm (46 km; 29 miles). Release system, designed specially for Sky Flash, permits the missile to be fired over the Tornado's full flight envelope. Furthermore, the missile is highly capable of tracking targets in a ground clutter environment, and of discriminating between closely spaced targets. A Thorn EMI active proximity fusing system allows these benefits to be realised fully in snap-down attacks against targets flying at very low level. For the future, the ADV will be able to carry, instead of Sky Flash and Sidewinder, up to six Hughes AIM-20 AMRAAM medium-range and four BAe/Bodenseewerk ASRAAM short-range air-to-air missiles; studies are being undertaken for a 1553B multiplex digital data bus associated with these weapons.

DIMENSIONS, EXTERNAL: As for IDS version, except:

Length overall	18.082 m (59 ft $3\frac{7}{8}$ in)

WEIGHTS (approx):

Operational weight empty	14,500 kg (31,970 lb)
Nominal max weapon load	8,500 kg (18,740 lb)
Max T-O weight	27,986 kg (61,700 lb)

PERFORMANCE:

Max Mach number in level flight at altitude, 'clean'	2.2
Max level speed, 'clean'	800 knots (1,480 km/h; 920 mph) IAS
Demonstrated roll rate at 750 knots (1,390 km/h; 864 mph) and up to 4g	180°/s
Operational ceiling	approx 21,335 m (70,000 ft)
T-O run:	
with normal weapon and fuel load	760 m (2,500 ft)
ferry configuration (four 1,500 litre drop tanks and full weapon load)	approx 1,525 m (5,000 ft)
T-O to 15 m (50 ft)	under 915 m (3,000 ft)
Landing from 15 m (50 ft)	approx 610 m (2,000 ft)
Landing run with thrust reversal	370 m (1,215 ft)
Intercept radius:	
supersonic	more than 300 nm (556 km; 345 miles)
subsonic	more than 1,000 nm (1,853 km; 1,151 miles)
*Endurance	
2 h combat air patrol at 300–400 nm (555–750 km; 345–460 miles) from base, incl time for interception and 10 min combat	
g limit attained (to Spring 1985)	7.5

*Prototype, using 1,500 litre drop-tanks and having more than 5% of internal fuel left at end of mission, has demonstrated a CAP of 2 h 20 min at 325 nm (602 km; 374 miles) from base, in a total flight time of 4 h 13 min without in-flight refuelling.

SEPECAT
SOCIÉTÉ EUROPÉENNE DE PRODUCTION DE L'AVION E.C.A.T.

AIRFRAME COMPANIES:

British Aerospace PLC (UK)

Avions Marcel Dassault-Breguet Aviation
(France)

This Anglo-French company was formed in May 1966 by Breguet Aviation and British Aircraft Corporation, to design and produce the Jaguar supersonic strike fighter/trainer. The Jaguar project was initiated by the Defence Ministries of Britain and France on 17 May 1965. The two governments appointed an official Jaguar Management Committee to look after their interests. SEPECAT is the complementary industrial organisation.

SEPECAT Jaguar

The Jaguar, which was developed from the Breguet Br121 project, was designed by Breguet and BAe to meet a common requirement of the French and British air forces laid down in early 1965. This requirement called for a dual-role aircraft, to be used as an advanced and operational trainer and a tactical support aircraft of light weight and high performance, to enter French service in 1972 and with the RAF in 1973.

The following versions of the Jaguar have been built:

Jaguar A. French single-seat tactical support version. Prototypes (A-03 and A-04) first flown on 23 March and 27 May 1969. Total of 160 ordered, the last of which was delivered on 14 December 1981. The final 30 were fitted with a Martin Marietta/Thomson-CSF target TV acquisition and laser designation pod, named ATLIS II, and can carry two AS.30 air-to-surface missiles.

The first operational Armée de l'Air Jaguar unit (Esc. 1/7 'Provence') was formed at St Dizier in eastern France on 19 June 1973. The French Air Force deployed the Jaguar A with nine squadrons: four with the 7th Escadre at St Dizier and Istres, four with the 11th Escadre at Toul-Rosières and Bordeaux, and one with the 3rd Escadre at Nancy. In December 1977 and May 1978, Jaguars of the Armée de l'Air were the first of their type to enter combat, when they were used to attack guerrilla forces in Mauritania.

Jaguar B (RAF designation: Jaguar T.Mk 2). British two-seat operational training version. Prototype B-08 (XW566) first flown on 30 August 1971. Total of 37 built initially; one more delivered in 1982.

Jaguar E. French two-seat advanced training version. Prototypes (E-01 and E-02) first flown on 8 September 1968 and 11 February 1969. Total of 40 built. First production Jaguar, designated E-1, flew for the first time on 2 November 1971, and deliveries to the CEAM at Air Base 118, Mont de Marsan, began in May 1972. The first unit to equip with this version was Esc. 1/7 at St Dizier.

Jaguar S (RAF designation: Jaguar GR. Mk 1). British single-seat tactical-support version, basically similar to A but with Ferranti FIN 1064 (originally GEC-Marconi navigation and weapon-aiming sub-system – NAVWASS). Prototypes first flown on 12 October 1969 and 12 June 1970. Total of 165 built. The first production GR. Mk 1 (XX108) flew on 11 October 1972. The RAF deployed the Jaguar S

SEPECAT Jaguar GR.Mk 1 of No 20 Squadron, RAF, with two laser-guided bombs on inboard pylons, Westinghouse AN/ALQ 101-10 ECM pod on port outer pylon and Phimat chaff dispenser on starboard outer pylon.

Two Jaguar Internationals serving with the Sultan of Oman's Air Force.

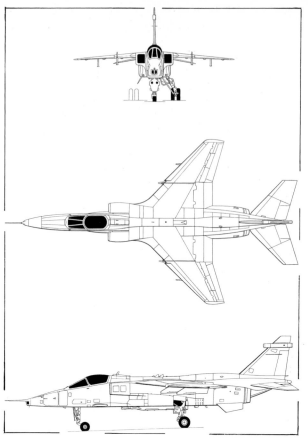

SEPECAT Jaguar GR.Mk 1. *(Pilot Press)*

with eight front-line squadrons: Nos. 2 (AC), 14, 17, 20 and 31 with the Second Allied Tactical Air Force in West Germany and Nos. 6, 41 and 54 at Coltishall in the UK, as well as No. 226 (Jaguar) OCU at RAF Lossiemouth in Scotland. Nos. 2 (AC) and 41 Squadrons were assigned as reconnaissance units.

All 403 Jaguars for the Royal Air Force (203) and Armée de l'Air (200) had been delivered by 1982. These aircraft were delivered with 22.75/32.5 kN (5,115/7,305 lb st) Adour Mk 102 turbofan engines. Between 1978 and 1984, RAF Jaguars were refitted with uprated Adour Mk 104 engines, equivalent to the Mk 804 which powered early Jaguar Internationals.

Jaguar International The export version, the first example of which made its initial flight on 19 August 1976. It has Adour Mk 804 or more powerful Mk 811 engines, which give improved combat performance with substantially enhanced manoeuvrability and acceleration in the low-level speed range. Other customer options include overwing pylons compatible with Matra R.550 Magic or similar dogfight missiles; a multi-purpose radar such as the Thomson-CSF Agave; up to four anti-shipping weapons such as Sea Eagle, Harpoon, Exocet and Kormoran on the underwing and underfuselage hardpoints; and night sensors such as low-light-level TV.

Orders were placed by the Sultan of Oman's Air Force (two batches of 12) and Ecuadorean Air Force (12), each order including two two-seaters. The first 12 aircraft for Oman and those for Ecuador were powered by Adour Mk 804 engines; the second SOAF batch have Mk 811 Adours. SOAF aircraft are fitted with a GEC Avionics 920ATC NAVWASS computer and carry AIM-9P Sidewinder air-to-air missiles on the outboard underwing pylons. In 1985 BAe Warton carried out a major servicing of the first 12 SOAF Jaguars, including fitment of a Ferranti FIN 1064 inertial navigation system. Second-batch Omani Jaguars were to receive this system.

An initial batch of 40 Jaguar Internationals with Adour Mk 804 engines was purchased from Britain by the Indian government; deliveries of these were completed in 1982. The 1979 agreement provided for a further 45 (with Mk 811

engines) to be assembled in India from European-built components, leading eventually to full manufacture of 31 additional aircraft under licence by Hindustan Aeronautics Ltd, Bangalore. The first Jaguar assembled at Bangalore made its initial flight on 31 March 1982. The Indian Air Force's first Jaguar squadron (No 14) was operational by the Summer of 1980, and the second (No. 5) in August 1981. Jaguars assigned to anti-shipping duty have nose mounted Agave radar and air-to-surface missiles.

The most recent customer for the Jaguar International was the Nigerian Air Force, which ordered 18 in 1983 (13 single-seat and five two-seaters). Deliveries were completed by June 1985. Total Jaguar sales amount to 573.

The following details refer to the current Jaguar International:

TYPE: Single-seat tactical support aircraft and two-seat operational or advanced trainer.

WINGS: Cantilever shoulder-wing monoplane. Anhedral 3°. Sweepback 40° at quarter-chord. Main portion built as single unit, with three-point attachment to each side of fuselage. Outer panels fitted with slat which also gives effect of extended chord leading edge. No ailerons: lateral control by two-section spoilers, forward of outer flap on each wing, in association (at low speeds) with differential tailplane. Hydraulically operated (by screwjack) full span double-slotted trailing-edge flaps. Leading-edge slats can be used in combat.

FUSELAGE: Built in three main units. Two door-type airbrakes under rear fuselage, immediately aft of each

Two-seat Jaguar International in the insignia of the Nigerian Air Force.

mainwheel well. Structure and systems, aft of cockpit(s), identical for single-seat and two-seat versions.

TAIL UNIT: Cantilever structure. Sweepback at quarter-chord 40° on horizontal, 43° on vertical surfaces. All-moving slab-type tailplane, with 10° anhedral, the two halves of which can operate differentially to supplement the spoilers. No separate elevators. Ventral fins beneath rear fuselage.

LANDING GEAR: Retractable tricycle type, all units having Dunlop wheels and low-pressure tyres for rough-field operation. Hydraulic retraction. Forward retracting main units each have twin wheels, tyre size 615 × 225-10. Wheels pivot during retraction to stow horizontally in bottom of fuselage. Single rearward retracting nosewheel, with tyre size 550 × 250-6. Dunlop hydraulic brakes. Anti-skid units and arrester hook standard. Irvin brake parachute of 5.5 m (18 ft 0½ in) diameter in fuselage tailcone.

POWERPLANT: Two Rolls-Royce Turboméca Adour Mk 804 turbofan engines, rated at 23.7 kN (5,320 lb st) dry and 35.75 kN (8,040 lb st) with afterburning, in aircraft for Ecuador, India (first 40) and Oman (first 12). Adour Mk 811, rated at 24.6 kN (5,520 lb st) dry and 37.4 kN (8,400 lb st) with afterburning, in remaining aircraft for India, second 12 for Oman, and those for Nigeria. Fixed-geometry air intake on each side of fuselage aft of cockpit. Fuel in six tanks, one in each wing and four in fuselage. Total internal fuel capacity 4,200 litres (1,110 US gallons; 924 Imp gallons). Armour protection for critical fuel system components. In basic tactical sortie the loss of fuel from one tank at halfway point would not prevent aircraft from regaining its base. Provision for carrying three auxiliary drop-tanks, each of 1,200 litres (317 US gallons; 264 Imp gallons) capacity, on fuselage and inboard wing pylons. Provision for in-flight refuelling, with retractable probe forward of cockpit on starboard side.

ACCOMMODATION (trainer): Crew of two in tandem on Martin-Baker 9B Mk II zero/zero ejection seats. Individual rearward hinged canopies. Rear seat 38 cm (15 in) higher than front seat. Windscreen bulletproof against 7.5 mm rifle fire.

ACCOMMODATION (single-seater): Enclosed cockpit for pilot, with rearward hinged canopy and Martin-Baker E9B (Ecuador), O9B (Oman), or IN9B (India) ejection seat as in two-seaters. Bulletproof windscreen, as in two-seat version.

AVIONICS AND OPERATIONAL EQUIPMENT: Differ according to individual customer requirements; details are generally still classified, but first 40 for India have a Smiths head-up display similar to that in RAF Jaguars. Indian assembled Jaguars will have a raster cursive head-up display, Sagem inertial navigation and weapon aiming system, and a Ferranti COMED 2045 combined map and electronic display.

ARMAMENT: Two 30 mm Aden or DEFA 553 cannon in lower fuselage aft of cockpit in single-seater; single Aden gun on port side in two-seater. One stores attachment on fuselage centreline and two under each wing. Centreline and inboard wing points can each carry up to 1,134 kg (2,500 lb) of weapons, outboard underwing points up to 567 kg (1,250 lb) each. Maximum external stores load, including overwing loads, 4,763 kg (10,500 lb). Typical alternative loads include one Martel AS.37 anti-radar missile and two 1,200 litre (317 US gallon; 264 Imp gallon) drop-tanks; eight 1,000 lb bombs; free-fall and retarded bombs, Hunting BL755 or Belouga cluster bombs, Matra R.550 Magic missiles and air-to-surface rockets, including the 68 mm SNEB rocket; a reconnaissance camera pack; or two drop-tanks. Jaguar International can also carry two Matra Magic air-to-air missiles on overwing pylons; aircraft for Oman carry two AIM-9P Sidewinders on outboard underwing pylons.

DIMENSIONS, EXTERNAL:
Wing span	8.69 m (28 ft 6 in)
Length overall, incl probe:	
single-seat	16.83 m (55 ft 2½ in)
two-seat	17.53 m (57 ft 6¼ in)
Height overall	4.89 m (16 ft 0½ in)
Wheel track	2.41 m (7 ft 11 in)
Wheelbase	5.69 m (18 ft 8 in)

AREA:
Wings, gross	24.18 m² (260.27 sq ft)

WEIGHTS:
Typical weight empty	7,000 kg (15,432 lb)
Normal T-O weight (single-seater, with full internal fuel and ammunition for built-in cannon)	
	10,954 kg (24,149 lb)
Max T-O weight with external stores	
	15,700 kg (34,612 lb)

PERFORMANCE:
Max level speed at S/L	
	Mach 1.1 (729 knots; 1,350 km/h; 840 mph)
Max level speed at 11,000 m (36,000 ft)	
	Mach 1.6 (917 knots; 1,699 km/h; 1,056 mph)
T-O run: 'clean'	565 m (1,855 ft)
with four 1,000 lb bombs	880 m (2,890 ft)
with eight 1,000 lb bombs	1,250 m (4,100 ft)
Landing run:	
normal weight, with brake chute	470 m (1,540 ft)
normal weight, without brake chute	680 m (2,230 ft)
overload weight, with brake chute	670 m (2,200 ft)
Typical attack radius, internal fuel only:	
hi-lo-hi	460 nm (852 km; 530 miles)
lo-lo-lo	290 nm (537 km; 334 miles)
Typical attack radius with external fuel:	
hi-lo-hi	760 nm (1,408 km; 875 miles)
lo-lo-lo	495 nm (917 km; 570 miles)
Ferry range with external fuel	
	1,902 nm (3,524 km; 2,190 miles)
g limits	+ 8.6/ + 12 ultimate

SOKO/CNIAR

PARTICIPANTS:
SOKO (Yugoslavia)
CENTRUL NATIONAL AL INDUSTRIEI AERONAUTICE ROMÂNE (Romania)

SOKO J-22 Orao (Eagle)/CNIAR IAR-93

This twin-jet close-support and ground-attack aircraft is in production to meet a joint requirement of the air forces of Romania and Yugoslavia. In the latter country it is known as the J-22 Orao (Eagle); in Romania it is known as the IAR-93. The joint programme is known as 'Yurom' (from *Yugoslavia-Rom*ania).

The Orao/IAR-93 was designed jointly by Yugoslav engineers from the Vazduhoplovno Tehnicki Institut in Zarkovo, near Belgrade, and by the Romanian engineers from the Institutul de Mecanica Fluidelor si Constructii Aerospatiale in Bucharest. Design began in 1970, and manufacture of a single-seat prototype was started simultaneously in the two countries in 1972. A first flight in each country was made on 31 October 1974. SOKO and CNIAR each then completed a two-seat prototype, these making simultaneous first flights on 29 January 1977. In that year construction began in each country of a pre-production batch of 15 aircraft, the first of these making their initial flights in 1978. The IAR-93 entered the series production phase in 1979, and the Orao about a year later.

The following production versions have been announced:

IAR-93A. Romanian version with non-afterburning Rolls-Royce Viper Mk 632 turbojet engines, first flown in 1981. Twenty ordered for Romanian Air Force. Total

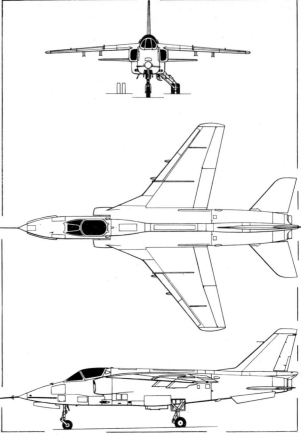

SOKO/CNIAR IAR-93B. *(Pilot Press)*

includes single- and two-seat versions, the latter having almost the same operational capabilities despite a 0.41 m (1 ft 4¼ in) longer front fuselage.

IAR-93B. Romanian version with Viper Mk 633 engines and licence-built afterburners. Total of 165 said to be ordered by Romanian Air Force, including two-seaters. First flight of production version made in 1985.

Orao 1. Yugoslav non-afterburning equivalent of IAR-93A, produced both as single-seat tactical reconnaissance aircraft and two-seat operational conversion trainer.

Orao 2. Yugoslav afterburning version, in production as

Second production single-seat SOKO Orao 2 attack aircraft of the Yugoslav Air Force.

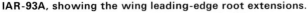

IAR-93A, showing the wing leading-edge root extensions.

single-seat attack aircraft. First flight 20 October 1983. Increased external stores load. Fuel system and capacities differ slightly from other versions.

TYPE: Single-seat close-support, ground-attack and tactical reconnaissance aircraft, with secondary capability as low-level interceptor. Combat capable two-seat versions used also for advanced flying and weapon training.

WINGS: Cantilever shoulder-wing monoplane, of NACA 65A-008 (modified) section and low aspect ratio. Anhedral 3° 30′ from roots. Incidence 0°. Sweepback 35° at quarter-chord and approx 43° on outer leading edges. Inboard leading edges extended forward (sweepback approx 70°) on production single- and two-seaters, but not on prototypes or pre-production aircraft. Wing spar box forms integral fuel tanks on IAR-93B/Orao 2; IAR-93A/Orao 1 have rubber fuel cells. Hydraulically actuated (EEMCO system) two-segment aluminium alloy leading-edge slats. Two small boundary-layer fences on upper surface of each wing. Hydraulically operated wide-chord plain ailerons and semi-Fowler trailing-edge flaps.

FUSELAGE: Conventional partly fail-safe semi-monocoque structure. Hydraulically actuated door-type perforated airbrake under fuselage on each side, forward of mainwheel bays. Narrow strake on each side of nose (not on prototypes). Dorsal spine fairing houses circuits, systems and flight controls. 'Pen nib' fairing above exhaust nozzles. Rear portion of fuselage is detachable to facilitate access for engine maintenance and removal.

TAIL UNIT: Cantilever structure, with sweepback on all surfaces. Low-set all-moving tailplane. Small dorsal fin. Auxiliary ventral fin on each side beneath rear fuselage (single-seat production versions). Development and early production aircraft have anti-flutter weights on tailplane tips; these were intended to be deleted on definitive production models.

LANDING GEAR: Hydraulically retractable tricycle type, with single-wheel hydraulically steerable nose unit and twin-wheel main units. All units retract forward into fuselage. Mainwheels and tubeless tyres on all versions are size 615 × 225 × 254 mm. Nosewheel and tubeless tyre are size 551 × 250 × 152.4 mm on IAR-93A/Orao 1; and size 451 × 190 × 127 mm on afterburning versions. Hydraulic disc brakes on each mainwheel unit, and electrically operated anti-skid system. Bullet fairing at base of rudder contains a hydraulically deployed 4.2 m (13 ft 9½ in) diameter braking parachute.

POWERPLANT (non-afterburning versions): Two 17.79 kN (4,000 lb st) Turbomecanica/ORAO (licence built Rolls-Royce) Viper Mk 632-41R turbojets, mounted side-by-side in rear fuselage; air intake on each side of fuselage, below cockpit canopy. Fuel normally in seven fuselage tanks and two collector tanks, with combined capacity of 2,480 litres (655 US gallons; 545.5 Imp gallons) and two 235 litre (62 US gallon; 51.75 Imp gallon) wing tanks, giving total internal fuel capacity of 2,950 litres (779 US gallons; 649 Imp gallons). Orao 2 has six fuselage and two collector tanks, with two fuselage and both wing tanks enlarged, giving total internal capacity of 3,100 litres (819 US gallons; 682 Imp gallons). Provision for carrying three 540 litre (143 US gallon; 119 Imp gallon) auxiliary fuel tanks, one on underfuselage stores attachment and one inboard under each wing.

POWERPLANT (afterburning versions). Two Turbomecanica/ ORAO (licence built Rolls-Royce) Viper Mk 633-41 turbojets, each rated at 17.79 kN (4,000 lb st) dry and 22.24 kN (5,000 lb st) with afterburning.

ACCOMMODATION: Single-seat or tandem two-seat cockpit(s), with Martin-Baker zero/zero seat for each occupant (RU10J in IAR-93, YU10J in Orao), capable of ejection through canopy. Canopy of single-seat IAR-93A and Orao 1/2 is hinged at rear and actuated electrically to open upward; single-seat IAR-93B, and all two-seaters, have manually opened canopies opening sideways to starboard. All accommodation pressurised. Dual controls in two-seat versions.

AVIONICS AND EQUIPMENT: Standard avionics include VHF/UHF air-to-air and air-to-ground com radio (20W transmission power); gyro unit, radio altimeter, radio compass and marker beacon receiver; IFF; and GEC Avionics three-axis stability augmentation system, incorporating a basic bank/attitude hold autopilot and emergency wings-level facility. Orao 1 and 2 also have Collins VIR-30 VOR/ILS and Collins DME-40; Orao 2 fitted with Iskra SO-1 radar warning receiver. Landing light under nose, forward of nosewheel bay; taxying light on nosewheel shock strut.

ARMAMENT (IAR-93 and Orao 1): Two 23 mm GSh-23L twin-barrel cannon in lower front fuselage, below engine air intakes, with 200 rds/gun. Gun camera and Ferranti D282 gyro gunsight. Five external stores stations, of which the inboard underwing pair and the fuselage centreline station are each stressed for loads up to 500 kg (1,102 lb); outboard underwing stations stressed for up to 300 kg (661 lb) each, giving a max external stores load of 1,500 kg (3,307 lb). Typical weapon loads can include two or three 500 kg bombs; four or five 250 kg bombs; four multiple carriers each with three 100 kg or 50 kg bombs; two such multiple carriers plus two L-57-16MD launchers each with sixteen 57 mm rockets; four L-57-16MD launchers; four launchers each with two 122 mm, one 128 mm or one 240 mm rocket (122 and 240 mm not used on Orao); a GSh-23L cannon pod with four L-57-16MD rocket launchers; four 160 kg KPT-150 or similar munition dispensers; or (Romanian aircraft only) four L-57-32 launchers each with thirty-two 57 mm rockets. Centreline and inboard underwing points are each plumbed to carry a 540 litre (143 US gallon; 119 Imp gallon) drop-tank; centreline point also capable of carrying a camera or infra-red reconnaissance pod or (not yet available for Orao) a night illumination pod.

ARMAMENT (Orao 2): Guns, gun camera, drop-tanks and centreline camera or infra-red reconnaissance pod as for Orao 1. Thomson-CSF VE-120T head-up display. All four wing stations stressed for 500 kg (1,102 lb), and fuselage station for 800 kg (1,763 lb), giving a max external stores capacity of 2,800 kg (6,173 lb). Typical weapon loads include five 50 kg, 100 kg, 250 kg or 500 kg bombs; four multiple carriers for a total of twelve 50 or 100 kg or eight 250 kg bombs; four PLAB-340 napalm bombs (each 360 kg; 794 lb); five BL755 bomblet dispensers, or eight on four multiple carriers; sixteen BRZ-127 5 in HVAR rockets; four pods of L-57-16MD or L-128-04 (4 × 128 mm) rockets, or eight pods on multiple carriers; five 500 kg AM-500 sea mines; or two launch rails for AGM-65B Maverick or Yugoslav developed Grom air-to-surface missiles. The 100 kg and 250 kg bombs can be parachute retarded. Chaff and IR decoy launch pods (up to 3 per aircraft) can also be carried.

DIMENSIONS, EXTERNAL:

Wing span	9.62 m (31 ft 6¾ in)
Length overall, incl probe:	
single-seater	14.90 m (48 ft 10⅝ in)
two-seater	15.38 m (50 ft 5½ in)
Fuselage: Max width	1.68 m (5 ft 6⅛ in)
Height overall	4.45 m (14 ft 7¼ in)
Wheel track (c/l of shock struts)	2.50 m (8 ft 2½ in)
Wheelbase: single-seater	5.42 m (17 ft 9⅜ in)
two-seater	approx 6.50 m (21 ft 4 in)

AREA:

Wings, gross	26.00 m² (279.86 sq ft)

WEIGHTS (A: IAR-93A, B: IAR-93B, C: Orao 2):

Weight empty, equipped: A	6,150 kg (13,558 lb)
B	5,700 kg (12,566 lb)
C	5,750 kg (12,676 lb)
Max external stores load: A	1,500 kg (3,307 lb)
B, C	2,800 kg (6,173 lb)
Basic operating weight: A	8,826 kg (19,458 lb)
B	8,400 kg (18,519 lb)
Max T-O weight: A	10,326 kg (22,765 lb)
B	11,200 kg (24,692 lb)
C	11,250 kg (24,800 lb)

PERFORMANCE (A at max T-O weight, B and C at 8,450 kg; 18,629 lb T-O weight):

Max level speed at S/L:	
A	577 knots (1,070 km/h; 665 mph)
B, C	626 knots (1,160 km/h; 721 mph)
Max cruising speed:	
A at 7,000 m (22,965 ft)	394 knots (730 km/h; 453 mph)
B at 9,000 m (29,525 ft)	354 knots (656 km/h; 407 mph)
Stalling speed at S/L: A	130 knots (241 km/h; 150 mph)
B, C	148 knots (274 km/h; 171 mph)
Max rate of climb at S/L: A	2,040 m (6,693 ft)/min
B, C	4,200 m (13,780 ft)/min
Service ceiling: A	10,500 m (34,450 ft)
B, C	13,500 m (44,300 ft)
T-O run: A	1,500 m (4,921 ft)
B, C	500 m (1,640 ft)
Landing run: A	720 m (2,362 ft)
B, C	1,050 m (3,445 ft)
Landing run with brake chute: A, B, C	670 m (2,200 ft)

Mission radius: B, C

lo-lo-lo with four rocket launchers, 5 min over target
140 nm (260 km; 161 miles)

hi-hi-hi patrol with three 500 kg (1,102 lb) auxiliary fuel tanks, 45 min over target   205 nm (380 km; 236 miles)

lo-lo-hi with two rocket launchers, six 100 kg bombs and one 500 kg auxiliary fuel tank, 10 min over target
243 nm (450 km; 280 miles)

hi-hi-hi with four 250 kg bombs and one 500 kg auxiliary fuel tank, 5 min over target
286 nm (530 km; 329 miles)

g limits: A, B, C   + 8/ − 4.2

Israel

IAI
ISRAEL AIRCRAFT INDUSTRIES LTD

This company was established in 1953 as Bedek Aircraft Company. The change of name, to Israel Aircraft Industries, was made on 1 April 1967.

IAI employs approx 21,000 people in all its facilities, which occupy a total covered floor area of 500,000 m² (5,381,950 sq ft). It is licensed by the Israeli Air Force, among others, as an approved repair station and maintenance organisation.

Israel Aircraft Industries underwent a major re-organisation in the latter part of 1977, and now comprises five divisions, as follows:

Bedek Aviation Division, incorporating Turbochrome, is an internationally approved multi-faceted single-site civil and military aircraft service centre. Present programmes include work on F-4, F-15 and F-16 fighters and military engines.

The **Aircraft Manufacturing Division** produces, among other civil and military aircraft, the Kfir fighter, Arava transport, and mini-RPVs. In addition, it is engaged in the manufacture of a vast variety of spares and assemblies for aircraft and jet engines, to meet Israeli Air Force requirements.

The **Engineering Division**, the largest establishment of its kind in Israel, employs some 1,800 technical, scientific and other skilled personnel. It is responsible for engineering research, design, development and testing of aerospace systems. It provides engineering support in system analysis, aerodynamics, materials and processing, landing and control systems, and in structural, flight and environmental testing. The Division's recent programmes have included development of a fly-by-wire system for flight testing in the Kfir, and research into materials, structures and electronic counter-measures. It also developed the Lavi strike fighter.

The **Electronics Division** incorporates Elta Electronics Industries, MBT Weapons Systems, Tamam Precision Instruments, and MLM Systems Engineering and Integration, together employing nearly 6,500 people in facilities. It specialises in the design, development and production of sophisticated electronic equipment such as airborne, ground and shipborne communications and radars, transceivers and navigational aids, general communications equipment, automatic test systems, and such electronic medical devices as cardiac resuscitation instruments.

Ramta Structures and Systems, Servo-Hydraulics Lod (SHL), MATA Helicopters, and Golan Industries, make up the **Technologies Division**. This designs, develops and manufactures hydraulic and fuel system components, hydraulic flight control servo-systems, landing gears and brake systems.

Through its **Military Aircraft Marketing Group**, IAI offers a number of services to foreign customers, based on the considerable capability of its five main divisions. Among these are combat aircraft upgrading, a retrofit package that can include improved systems, engines, avionics, design configuration and structures. This has proved a successful export item, and programmes are available for Mirage, Skyhawk, Hunter, Phantom, Northrop F-5 and other types.

In 1984–85 IAI had converted one Argentine Air Force Boeing 707 for ECM/sigint duties and was modifying two others as in-flight refuelling tankers. It also undertook the SINT upgrade of Argentine Daggers (see Nesher entry).

IAI Mirage Modifications

IAI is marketing a retrofit kit designed to increase, at relatively low cost, the combat capability and survivability of Mirage III/5 aircraft. The basic airframe modifications consist of installation of Kfir-type foreplanes and Kfir standard landing gear, the former permitting either a substantial reduction (305–457 m; 1,000–1,500 ft) in T-O run or a 907 kg (2,000 lb) increase in T-O gross weight, and the latter an increase in max T-O weight to 16,330 kg (36,000 lb). The foreplanes also offer a marked improvement in air turning radius (from 1,036 m; 3,400 ft to 610 m; 2,000 ft at 4,575 m; 15,000 ft altitude); improved sustained turn, a vastly extended usable angle-of-attack and low-speed envelope; and much improved handling qualities. By reducing air loads on the wings and fuselage, they extend the fatigue life of the airframe.

An additional fuselage fuel tank can be installed aft of the cockpit, and a Kfir type nose provides additional space for avionics such as control and stability augmentation systems. Other avionics include a radar warning system, with omnidirectional threat analysis and cockpit display, and a WDNS-391 fully inertial weapon delivery and navigation system with head-up operation in all air-to-surface and air-to-air modes. Additional external stores stations are provided, and flare/chaff dispensers can be installed under the rear fuselage.

IAI Phantom Modifications

Israeli Air Force approval has been given for an airframe and avionics upgrade programme for the service's F-4 Phantoms. Four prototypes were to be modified during 1986 with structural improvements, new (probably conformal) external fuel tanks, and possibly the addition of Kfir-type canard surfaces. New or upgraded avionics are expected to include a new Elta pulse-Doppler radar (derived from the EL/M-2021); Elbit ACE-3 radar data processor; Elop (Kaiser licence) wide-angle diffractive optics head-up display; Astronautics multi-function CRT displays; an avionics interface computer; and a multiplex digital databus. Elbit is overall integrator for the avionics refit. The programme is expected to involve about 140 Phantoms still in IAF service.

IAI Skyhawk Modifications

Major airframe improvements offered by IAI's Skyhawk retrofit programme (already applied to Israeli Air Force A-4s) include a life extension overhaul, replacement of all wiring, provision of dual disc brakes on the mainwheels, a steerable nosewheel, addition of wing lift spoilers, an extra hardpoint under each wing, extension of the tailpipe (to change the heat signature and make the tailpipe more survivable and easier to repair), and addition of a brake-chute in a fairing beneath the rear fuselage. The wingroot

IAI Nesher, delivered to the Israeli Air Force from 1972.

cannon are of increased calibre (30 mm instead of 20 mm), and a weapons delivery and navigation system (WDNS) similar to that in the Mirage package is installed. Additional space for lighter-weight avionics is made available in an extended nose compartment and in the 'saddleback' hump aft of the cockpit. As with the Mirage, flare and chaff dispensers can be installed under the rear fuselage, forward of the brake-chute fairing.

IAI Nesher (Eagle) and Kfir (Lion Cub)

US Navy and Marine Corps designation: F-21A

Following the French embargo on the delivery of Dassault Mirage 5 fighters to Israel, the decision was taken in Israel to manufacture aircraft of generally similar design to the Mirage. The ultimate outcome of this policy is the IAI Kfir, with a General Electric J79 turbojet instead of the SNECMA Atar fitted to French-built Mirage III/5s. As an interim step, IAI undertook responsibility for manufacturing spares for Mirage III-CJ fighters operated by the Israeli Air Force, and for putting into production an aircraft named the Nesher (Eagle). This comprised a locally-built airframe, similar to that of the Mirage III/5, fitted with an Atar 9C afterburning turbojet and Israeli electronics and equipment.

According to a book published in Israel in 1976, under the title *Israel, Army and Defence – a Lexicon*, the prototype Nesher flew for the first time in September 1969. Deliveries began in 1972, and some 40 Neshers are said to have taken part in the October 1973 war.

A total of 48 Nesher fighters was sold to the Argentinian Air Force from 1978. Known as Daggers in Argentina, the aircraft were initially operated by No. VI Brigada Aérea, from Tandil, near Buenos Aires. Under a contract known as 'Finger II', IAI subsequently installed a system called SINT (Sistema Integrado de Navigación y Tiro) to upgrade the nav/attack capability of Argentine Daggers with modern avionics, which include an Elta 2001 radar and a cockpit head-up display (HUD).

A prototype of the Kfir (a modified Nesher airframe adapted to the J79 engine) was first flown in June 1973, following almost three years of flight tests of this engine in a Mirage III-B. Existence of the Kfir was made public officially for the first time on 14 April 1975, when the first production example was displayed at Ben-Gurion Airport.

The Kfir has an airframe similar to the Dassault Mirage 5, the main changes being a shorter but larger-diameter rear fuselage, to accommodate the J79 engine; an enlarged and flattened undersurface to the forward portion of the fuselage; the introduction of four small fuselage airscoops, plus a larger dorsal airscoop in place of the triangular dorsal fin, to provide cooling air for the afterburner; and a strengthened landing gear, with longer-stroke oleos. Internal changes include a redesigned cockpit layout, addition of Israeli-built avionics, and revised fuel tankage compared with the Mirage 5. Intended for both air defence and ground attack roles, the Kfir retains the standard Mirage fixed armament of two 30 mm DEFA cannon, and can carry a variety of external weapons including Rafael Shafrir 2 air-to-air missiles. Two squadrons of the Israeli Air Force were equipped with this initial version, which flew its first combat mission in 1977.

A modified version known as the **Kfir-C2** was made public on 20 June 1976, having begun flight testing in 1974. This has a number of changes, including non-retractable, sweptback foreplanes just aft of the engine air intakes; a small strake on each side of the extreme nose; and extended wing leading edges, created by increasing the chord on approximately the outer 40 per cent of each wing. The foreplanes can be detached for missions not requiring high manoeuvrability.

IAI Kfir-C2s of the Israeli Air Force.

Kfir-TC2 two-seat training version of the Kfir multi-role fighter.

The modifications were designed to improve the aircraft's dogfighting manoeuvrability at the lower end of the speed range, and to enhance take-off and landing performance. It is claimed that, in particular, they give a better sustained turning performance, with improved lateral, longitudinal and directional control; contribute to a very low gust response at all operational altitudes, especially at very low level; offer improved handling qualities at all angles of attack, high g loadings, and low speeds; reduce take-off and landing distances, and landing speeds; and permit a more stable (and, if required, a steeper) approach, with a flatter angle of approach and touchdown. Later versions of the C2 have Elta EL/M-2001B nose radar in an extended nose, increasing the overall length by 0.80 m (2 ft $7\frac{1}{2}$ in). According to Israeli official sources, most of the 212 Kfirs produced were C2s, and some 27 C1s were later retrofitted to C2 configuration.

A two-seat version, known as the **Kfir-TC2**, was flown for the first time in February 1981, and is now in service. Overall dimensions, powerplant and performance are similar to those of the single-seat version, except for the insertion of a 0.84 m (2 ft 9 in) plug in the forward fuselage to accommodate a second cockpit in tandem. The nose is drooped in order to maintain a good field of view from both seats, and the second cockpit accommodates additional systems not present in the single-seat version.

Early in the series production of the Kfir, when the C2

version was anticipated, reinforced structure was built into the airframe so that it could subsequently be fitted with the C2 modifications. Those Kfirs that had already entered service without this reinforcement were later fitted with smaller canards, which were able to withstand the added aerodynamic stress while providing some increase in performance. These aircraft also carry strakes on the nose, but do not have the saw-tooth wing extensions. It is 12 aircraft of this version which, from April 1985, the US Navy leased for three years under the designation **F-21A**, for use with its VF-43 'Aggressor' squadron based at NAS Oceana, Virginia, as interim equipment pending delivery of the General Dynamics F-16N. Weights currently quoted for this version are: T-O 'clean', 10,390 kg (22,905 lb); max T-O, 14,700 kg (32,408 lb). Lease of a further 13 Kfirs by the US Marine Corps, for use in a similar role at MCAS Yuma, Arizona, was announced in the Summer of 1986.

Deliveries to the IAF began in Summer 1983 of the **Kfir-C7**, an improved version of the C2 in which the principal differences are higher augmented thrust, two additional hardpoints for increased payload/range capability, and a new HOTAS (hands on throttle and stick) cockpit

Latest version of the multi-role Kfir is the Kfir-C7, armed with Shafrir air-to-air missiles.

Early production Kfir supplied to the US Marine Corps in 1987 as F-21A interim 'aggressor' aircraft.

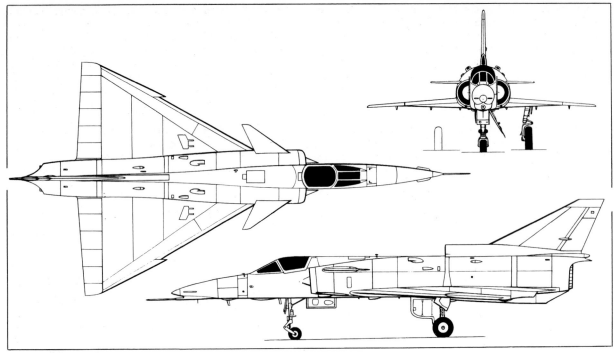

IAI Kfir-C2. *(Pilot Press)*

installation facilitated by new avionics. The C7 and two-seat **TC7** are now the principal IAF versions. IAI continues to overhaul and retrofit the Kfir, upgrading the C2 to C7 configuration, and the assembly line can be stepped up for series production at short notice.

The following description applies to the Kfir-C7:

TYPE: Single-seat strike, ground-attack and fighter aircraft.

WINGS: Cantilever low-wing monoplane of delta planform, with conical camber. Thickness/chord ratio 4.5% to 3.5%. Anhedral 1°. Incidence 1°. Sweepback on leading edges 60° 35′. Two-section elevons on each trailing edge, with smaller elevator/trim flap inboard of inner elevon. Small, hinged plate-type airbrake above and below each wing, near leading edge. Extended chord on outer leading edges. Small leading-edge fence on some aircraft, at approx one-third span.

FOREPLANES: Detachable sweptback canard surface above and forward of each wing, near top lip of engine air intake.

FUSELAGE: Semi-monocoque structure, 'waisted' in accordance with area rule. Cross-section of forward fuselage has a wider and flatter undersurface than that of Mirage 5. Nosecone built of locally developed composite materials, with a small horizontal strake or 'body fence' on each side near the tip. UHF antenna under front of fuselage, forward of nosewheel door. Enlarged-diameter rear fuselage, compared with Mirage 5, with approx 0.61 m (2 ft) shorter tailpipe. Ventral fairing under rear of fuselage.

TAIL UNIT. Cantilever fin; rudder has servo-assisted trim. UHF antenna in tip of fin. Triangular-section dorsal airscoop forward of fin, to provide cold air for afterburner cooling. No horizontal tail surfaces.

LANDING GEAR. Retractable tricycle type, with single SHL wheel on each unit. Electrically operated hydraulic actuation, nose unit retracting rearward, main units inward into fuselage. All units strengthened to permit higher operating weights. Low-pressure tubeless tyres on all units. Main-gear leg fairings shorter than on Mirage; inner portion of each main-leg door is integral with fuselage mounted wheel door. Steerable nosewheel, with anti-shimmy damper. SHL hydraulic disc brakes and anti-skid units. Braking parachute in bullet fairing below rudder.

POWERPLANT: One General Electric J79-J1E turbojet engine (modified GE-17), built by IAI's Bedek Division, with variable-area nozzle, rated at 52.89 kN (11,890 lb st) dry and 83.41 kN (18,750 lb st) with afterburning. Air intakes enlarged, compared with Mirage 5, to allow for higher mass flow. Adjustable half-cone centrebody in each air intake. Internal fuel in five fuselage and four integral wing tanks. Total internal capacity 3,243 litres (857 US gallons; 713.4 Imp gallons). Wet points for the carriage of one drop-tank beneath each wing (inboard), and one under fuselage; these tanks may be of 500, 600, 825, 1,300 or 1,700 litres (132, 159, 218, 343 or 449 US gallons; 110, 132, 181.5, 286 or 374 Imp gallons) capacity; max external fuel capacity 4,700 litres (1,242 US gallons; 1,034 Imp gallons). Provision for boom/receptacle or probe/drogue in-flight refuelling system, and for single-point pressure refuelling.

ACCOMMODATION: Pilot only, on Martin-Baker IL10P zero/zero ejection seat, under rearward hinged upward opening canopy. Cockpit pressurised. Two seats in tandem in TC7.

AVIONICS AND EQUIPMENT: C2 fitted with MBT twin-computer flight control system (ASW-41 control augmentation and ASW-42 stability augmentation systems), with Tamam inertial measurement unit (IMU), angle-of-attack transmitter and indicator, and accelerometer indicator. Elbit 2-8600 multi-mode navigation (Singer-Kearfott licence) and weapons delivery system or IAI/Elbit WDNS-141 or -341 weapons delivery and navigation system,

106

Tamam central air data computer, Elta EL-2001 X-band air-to-air and air-to-surface pulse-Doppler ranging radar, IFF/SIF and fire control, Electro-Optics head-up display and automatic gunsight. Two Elta AN/ARC-51 UHF transceivers. C7 differs in having an improved HOTAS (hands on throttle and stick) cockpit installation, facilitated by avionics which include a WDNS-391 as standard, an Elbit System 82 computerised stores management and release system, video subsystems, 'smart weapons' delivery capability, and updated electronic warfare systems. The EL-2001 ranging radar is replaced by an Elta EL/M-2001B, but the C7 can also mount Elta's EL/M-2021 advanced pulse-Doppler fire control radar, with lookup/lookdown capability, Doppler beam-sharpened mapping, terrain avoidance/following and sea search modes.

ARMAMENT: Fixed armament of one IAI-built 30 mm DEFA 552 cannon in underside of each engine air intake (140 rds/gun). Nine hardpoints (five under fuselage and two under each wing) for up to 5,775 kg (12,730 lb) of external weapons, ECM pods or drop-tanks. For interception duties, one Sidewinder, Python 3 or Shafrir 2 infra-red homing air-to-air missile can be carried under each outer wing. Ground-attack version can carry a 3,000 lb M118 bomb, two 800 or 1,000 lb bombs, up to four 500 lb bombs, or a Shrike, Maverick or GBU-15 air-to-surface weapon under the fuselage, and two 1,000 lb or six 500 lb bombs (conventional, 'smart' or 'concrete dibber' type) under the wings. Alternative weapons can include Mk 82/83/84 and M117/118 bombs; CBU-24/49 and TAL-1/2 cluster bombs; LAU-3A/10A/32A rocket launchers; napalm, flare, chaff, ECM and other podded systems.

DIMENSIONS, EXTERNAL:
Wing span	8.22 m (26 ft 11½ in)
Foreplane span	3.73 m (12 ft 3 in)
Length overall, incl probe: C7	15.65 m (51 ft 4¼ in)
TC7	16.36 m (53 ft 8 in)
Height overall	4.55 m (14 ft 11¼ in)
Wheel track	3.20 m (10 ft 6 in)
Wheelbase: C7	4.87 m (15 ft 11¾ in)
TC7	4.50 m (14 ft 9 in)

AREA:
Wings, gross	34.8 m² (374.6 sq ft)

WEIGHTS:
Weight empty (interceptor, estimated)	7,285 kg (16,060 lb)
Typical combat weight:	
interceptor, 50% internal fuel, two Shafrir missiles	9,390 kg (20,700 lb)
interceptor, two 500 litre drop-tanks, two Shafrir missiles	11,603 kg (25,580 lb)
combat air patrol, three 1,300 litre drop-tanks, two Shafrir missiles	14,270 kg (31,460 lb)
ground attack, two 1,300 litre drop-tanks, seven 500 lb bombs, two Shafrir missiles	14,670 kg (32,340 lb)
Max combat weight	16,500 kg (36,376 lb)

PERFORMANCE:
Max level speed above 11,000 m (36,000 ft)	
over Mach 2.3 (1,317 knots; 2,440 km/h; 1,516 mph)	
Max sustained level speed at height, 'clean'	Mach 2.0
Max level speed at S/L, 'clean'	750 knots (1,389 km/h; 863 mph)
Max rate of climb at S/L	14,000 m (45,930 ft)/min
Time to 15,240 m (50,000 ft), full internal fuel, two Shafrir missiles	5 min 10 s
Height attainable in zoom climb	22,860 m (75,000 ft)
Stabilised ceiling (combat configuration)	17,680 m (58,000 ft)
T-O run at max T-O weight	1,450 m (4,750 ft)
Landing run at 11,566 kg (25,500 lb) landing weight	1,280 m (4,200 ft)
Combat radius, without in-flight refuelling, 20 min fuel reserves:	
interceptor, one 825 litre and two 1,300 litre drop-tanks, two Shafrir missiles	419 nm (776 km; 482 miles)
combat air patrol, one 1,300 litre and two 1,700 litre drop-tanks, two Shafrir missiles, incl 60 min loiter	476 nm (882 km; 548 miles)
ground attack, hi-lo-hi, two 800 lb and two 500 lb bombs, two Shafrir missiles, one 1,300 litre and two 1,700 litre drop-tanks	640 nm (1,186 km; 737 miles)
Ferry range:	
three 1,300 litre drop-tanks	1,614 nm (2,991 km; 1,858 miles)
one 1,300 litre and two 1,700 litre drop-tanks	1,744 nm (3,232 km; 2,008 miles)
g limit	+ 7.5

IAI NAMMER (TIGER)

IAI is currently offering two concurrent remanufacturing/upgrading options for Mirage III and 5 airframes, under the name Nammer. **Option 1** involves replacement of the existing powerplant by a General Electric F404/RM 12 turbofan (55.6 kN; 12,500 lb st dry, 80.7 kN; 18,140 lb st with afterburning), permitting a shorter interception reaction time, better air combat performance, enhanced payload/range capability and improved fleet serviceability. In addition to providing some 30 per cent more thrust and up to 20 per cent better sfc, this re-engining saves some 453.5 kg (1,000 lb) in the aircraft's weight and enables it to carry an additional 544 kg (1,200 lb) of internal fuel.

Option 2 offers integration of the Elta EL/M-2011 or M-2032 lightweight fire control radar, conferring the following performance benefits: a coherent pulse-Doppler radar with low and medium PRFs; lookup/lookdown capability; target tracking by monopulse technique and tracking filter; ability to track low-altitude targets in heavy clutter; full utilisation of the launch envelopes and slaving capability of advanced missiles; all air target information presented on head-up display; improved air-to-ground ranging; extensive built-in testing and calibration; adaptability to other avionics systems; and growth potential through all-software-controlled LRUs and a MIL-STD-1553B interface.

Externally, the Nammer can be identified by a longer nose than the Mirage or single-seat Kfir, fitment of Kfir type canard surfaces on the engine air intake trunks, and a 'clean' fin without the large dorsal airscoop of the Kfir. Like current Kfirs, it is equipped with a contemporary weapon delivery and navigation system, HOTAS cockpit controls, and a related stores management and release system. There are nine external wing and fuselage stations for weapons, drop-

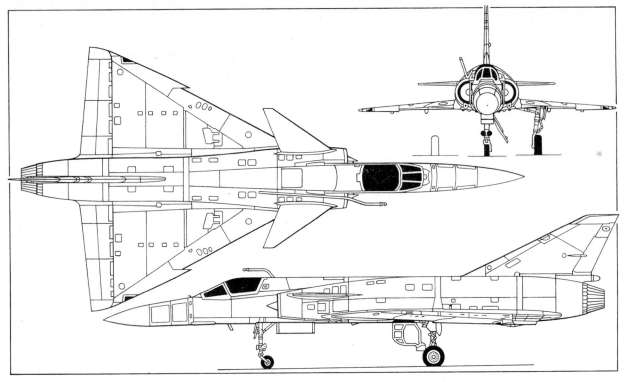

IAI Nammer upgraded version of the Mirage III and 5. *(Jane's/Mike Keep)*

tanks and other stores (similar to those listed for the Kfir, including capability for launching 'smart' weapons); UHF/VHF com and radio navigation systems would be to customer's requirements; and an ECM package (radar warning system, automatic chaff/flare dispensers and a jamming system) is available as an option.

DIMENSIONS, EXTERNAL, AND AREA: As listed for Kfir-C7 except:

Length overall	16.00 m (52 ft 6 in)
Wheel track	3.10 m (10 ft 2 in)

WEIGHTS:

Fuel: internal	2,994 kg (6,600 lb)
external	3,719 kg (8,200 lb)
Max external stores	6,260 kg (13,800 lb)
T-O weight 'clean'	10,251 kg (22,600 lb)
Typical combat weight	9,049 kg (19,950 lb)
Max T-O weight with external stores	
	16,511 kg (36,400 lb)

PERFORMANCE (at 9,049 kg; 19,950 lb combat weight except where indicated):

Max level speed:	
at S/L	750 knots (1,390 km/h; 863 mph)
at altitude	Mach 2.2
Stabilised ceiling	17,680 m (58,000 ft)
Max instantaneous turn rate at 4,575 m (15,000 ft)	21°/s

Combat radius (tanks dropped when empty):
  interceptor, one 1,300 litre tank and four IR air-to-air missiles, out and back at 12,200 m (40,000 ft) at Mach 1.8, incl 2 min combat

250 nm (463 km; 288 miles)
  combat air patrol at 9,150 m (30,000 ft) at Mach 0.85, one 1,300 litre and two 1,700 litre tanks and four IR air-to-air missiles, incl 60 min loiter and 2 min combat

746 nm (1,382 km; 859 miles)
  ground attack (hi-lo-lo-hi) at 544 knots (1,008 km/h; 626 mph) approach speed, two 1,700 litre tanks, two Mk 82 bombs and two IR air-to-air missiles

537 nm (995 km; 618 miles)
  ground attack (lo-lo-lo-hi) at 535 knots (991 km/h; 616 mph) approach speed, one 1,300 and two 1,700 litre tanks, four CBU-58 cluster bombs and two IR air-to-air missiles

573 nm (1,062 km; 660 miles)

g limit + 9

IAI 1124N Sea Scan

The Sea Scan is a maritime patrol version of the 1124 Westwind business transport. Three military Sea Scan types delivered to the Israeli Navy in 1977 for coastal patrol, tactical support and anti-terrorist duties were later brought up to full 1124N standard and equipped with thrust reversers, single-point pressure refuelling, anti-corrosion protection, fuselage-side stores pylons, bubble windows, Litton APS-504(V)2 360° search radar, Global GNS-500A VLF/Omega navigation system, operators' consoles, galley, and toilet. A low-altitude search range of 1,379 nm (2,555 km; 1,588 miles), and search endurance of more than 6 h 30 min, enables the Sea Scan to cover a search area of 82,740 nm² (268,056 km²; 103,496 sq miles) along a 60 nm (111 km; 69 mile) search band at a height of 915 m (3,000 ft). Increased search range and endurance to 2,500 nm (4,633 km; 2,878 miles) and over 8 h can be attained at altitudes up to 13,715 m (45,000 ft). Operational equipment can be matched to customer's specification.

Preliminary design and evaluation studies of a second-generation Sea Scan have been completed by IAI. No sales of either version have been reported, although Honduras and Panama are each said to operate one 'Westwind reconnaissance aircraft'. In addition to routine anti-terrorist low-level maritime patrol functions, a new Sea Scan could be deployed for ASW, signal intelligence (sigint) and anti-shipping air-to-surface missile attack operations. In the ASW role, search, detection, tracking, identification and attack would be carried out using high-performance maritime search radar, ESM, sonobuoys, onboard signal analysis, colour multi-purpose displays (MPDs), trailing MAD, long-range gyro stabilised sighting system (GSSS), and torpedoes. Search, localisation and attack at 100 nm (185 km; 115 miles) from base could be performed for approx 5 h, enabling a landing back at base with 45 min reserve fuel. Replacing torpedoes with Gabriel Mk III air-to-surface missiles, and removing some specific ASW mission equipment (sonobuoys, MAD etc), would allow anti-shipping missile attacks to be made from a standoff range of 32 nm (60 km; 37 miles) at distances greater than 1,000 nm

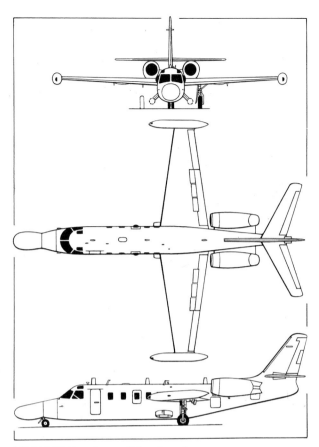

IAI 1124N Sea Scan. *(Pilot Press)*

(1,853 km; 1,151 miles) from base. Comint, elint and IDF equipment installed in the aircraft would permit long-range high-altitude sigint operations with an endurance of more than 8 h.

The following details refer specifically to the Westwind but

IAI 1124N Sea Scan maritime patrol aircraft.

can be viewed as generally applicable also to the Sea Scan, which is longer by virtue of its nose radar:

TYPE: Twin-turbofan maritime patrol aircraft.

WINGS: Cantilever mid-wing monoplane. Dihedral 2°. Incidence 1° at root, −1° at tip. Sweepback 4° 37′ at quarter-chord. Manually operated ailerons. Electrically operated double-slotted Fowler trailing-edge flaps. Electrically operated trim tab in port aileron. Hydraulically actuated speed brake and two lift dumpers above each wing, forward of flap. All primary control surfaces, including aileron tab, are fully mass balanced. Goodyear pneumatic de-icing boots standard.

FUSELAGE: Semi-monocoque structure, built in two main sections and joined at rear pressure bulkhead. Forward section, except for nosecone, is fully pressurised and fail-safe.

TAIL UNIT: Cantilever structure, with 28° sweepback at tailplane quarter-chord and 35° sweepback at fin quarter-chord. Variable incidence tailplane, actuated electrically. Manually operated statically balanced elevators and rudder. Electrically operated trim tab in rudder. Goodyear pneumatic de-icing boots on tailplane leading edges.

LANDING GEAR: Hydraulically retractable tricycle type, mainwheels retracting outward into wings, twin nosewheels rearward. No doors over mainwheels when retracted. Single wheels on main units. Nose unit steerable and self-centring. Goodyear multiple-disc brakes, with Hydro-Aire fully modulated anti-skid system having automatic computer/sensor to prevent wheel lock and maintain brake effectiveness. Parking brake.

POWERPLANT: Two 16.46 kN (3,700 lb st) Gàrrett TFE731-3-100G turbofan engines, with Grumman thrust reversers, pod mounted on sides of rear fuselage. 85 per cent of wing area forms an integral fuel tank, and additional fuel is carried separately in wingtip tanks and single rear of fuselage tank.

AVIONICS, EQUIPMENT AND ARMAMENT: See introductory paragraphs.

DIMENSIONS, EXTERNAL:

Wing span: incl tip tanks	13.65 m (44 ft 9½ in)
excl tip tanks	13.16 m (43 ft 2 in)
Fuselage: Max width	1.57 m (5 ft 2 in)
Max depth	1.83 m (6 ft 0 in)
Height overall	4.81 m (15 ft 9½ in)
Wheel track	3.35 m (11 ft 0 in)
Wheelbase	7.79 m (25 ft 6¾ in)

AREA:

Wings, gross	28.64 m² (308.26 sq ft)

WEIGHTS:

Weight empty	about 5,578 kg (12,300 lb)
Max T-O weight	10,660 kg (23,500 lb)

PERFORMANCE:

Max level speed, S/L to 5,900 m (19,400 ft)	
	about 471 knots (872 km/h; 542 mph)
Econ cruising speed at 12,500 m (41,000 ft)	
	about 400 knots (741 km/h; 460 mph)
Max rate of climb at S/L	about 1,524 m (5,000 ft)/min
Range/Endurance	see introductory paragraphs

Italy

Aeritalia
AERITALIA – SOCIETÀ AEROSPAZIALE ITALIANA p.A.

Aeritalia is a joint-stock company which was formed on 12 November 1969 by an equal shareholding of Fiat and IRI-Finmeccanica, to combine Fiat's aerospace activities (except those which concerned aero engines) with those of Aerfer and Salmoiraghi of the Finmeccanica group. The company became fully operational under the new title on 1 January 1972. On 28 September 1976 IRI-Finmeccanica purchased the Aeritalia stock owned by Fiat, thus acquiring complete control of the company's stock capital. In the Summer of 1981, following a general reorganisation of the Italian aerospace industry, Aeritalia acquired shareholdings of 100% in Aeronavali Venezia, 60% in Partenavia, and 50% in Meteor. A 25% holding in Aeronautica Macchi was acquired in 1983. Aeritalia has a total workforce of approx 14,500.

Aeritalia's organisation is based upon a centralised general management and seven operational groups: Combat Aircraft Group; Transport Aircraft Group; Avionics Systems and Equipment Group; Space Systems Group; Overhaul, Modification, Maintenance and General Aviation Group; RPVs and Missiles Group; and Alfa Romeo Avio.

Combat Aircraft Group

The Turin area factories of the Combat Aircraft Group are engaged, among other programmes, in the design, manufacture and testing of the AMX combat aircraft; design and manufacture of outer (movable) wings, final assembly and flight testing of the Panavia Tornado; definition, design and development of the Eurofighter European fighter aircraft, in partnership with other European companies; design and construction of wings for the EAP (Experimental Aircraft Programme) in collaboration with British Aerospace; manufacture of space vehicles; and design, development, manufacture and testing of an improved weapon system for the F-104S. Other activities include extensive research in various fields of aerodynamics and advanced technologies (eg weapon dispensers and STOL aircraft), and the repair, overhaul and maintenance of F-104G, TF-104F and F-104S aircraft.

Eurofighter

Aeritalia is collaborating in the design of this new-generation fighter, all available details of which can be found in the International section.

AMX

A description and illustration of this joint Italian–Brazilian attack aircraft programme, involving Aeritalia, Aermacchi and EMBRAER, can be found in the International section.

Tornado

Aeritalia has a 15% participation in the manufacturing programme for the Panavia Tornado (see International section), for which it is responsible for the radomes, the entire outer wings, including control surfaces, and the final assembly of aircraft for the Italian Air Force.

Aeritalia (Lockheed) F-104S

The first of two Lockheed-built F-104S prototypes, based upon the original Starfighter design, flew during December 1966. Aeritalia went on to build the F-104S under licence for the Italian Air Force, and the first was flown on 30 December 1968. Deliveries began in the Spring of 1969. These aircraft were put into service with the 4°, 5°, 6°, 9°, 36°, 51° and 53° Stormo (Wings) of the Italian Air Force. Forty F-104Ss were also delivered to the Turkish Air Force between December 1974 and mid-1976.

Aeritalia production of the F-104S ended in March 1979 after the manufacture of these 246 aircraft, including the 40

Aeritalia F-104S ASA with upgraded weapons systems. Armament comprises two Sidewinder and two Aspide air-to-air missiles. *(Aviodata)*

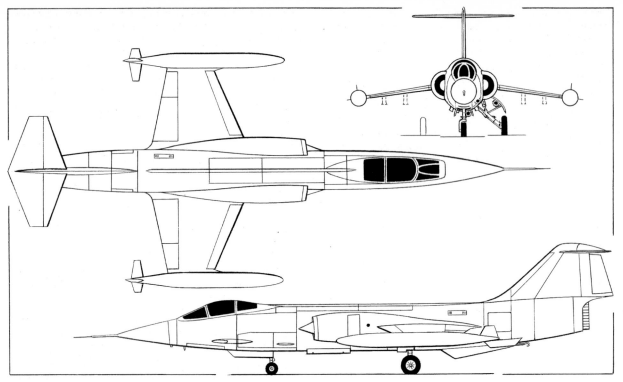

Aeritalia (Lockheed) F-104S. *(Pilot Press)*

for Turkey. Development was initiated in 1982 of a weapons system updating programme for the remaining 160 Italian aircraft, to increase their capability in the interception and interdiction/strike roles.

Now known as ASA (Aggiornamento Sistemi d'Arma), this programme is planned to include improved air-to-air self-defence and interception capability by the introduction of a Fiar R21G/M1 Setter radar; advanced ECM; improved IFF and altitude reporting system; improved electrical power generation and distribution system; improved weapons delivery (armament computer and time delay unit); and a new automatic pitch control computer. Weapons include Aspide 1A and AIM-9L Sidewinder.

An F-104S ASA demonstrator began flight testing in March 1985. Deliveries of production modification kits started in 1986.

TYPE: Single-seat multi-purpose combat aircraft.

WINGS: Cantilever mid-wing monoplane. Bi-convex supersonic wing section with a thickness/chord ratio of 3.36%. Anhedral 10°. No incidence. Sweepback 18° 6′ at quarter-chord. Full-span electrically-actuated drooping leading edge. Entire trailing edge hinged, with inboard sections serving as landing flaps and outboard sections as ailerons. Flaps are actuated electrically. Above each flap is the air delivery tube of a boundary layer control system, which ejects air bled from the engine compressor over the entire flap span when the flaps are lowered to the landing position.

FUSELAGE: Monocoque structure. Hydraulically-operated aluminium airbrake on each side of rear fuselage.

TAIL UNIT: T-type cantilever unit with 'all-flying' one-piece horizontal tail surface hinged at mid-chord point at top of the vertical fin and powered by a hydraulic servo. Tailplane has similar profile to wing. Narrow-chord

ventral fin on centreline and two smaller lateral fins under fuselage to improve stability.

LANDING GEAR: Retractable tricycle type. Main wheels raised in and forward. Steerable nosewheel retracts forward into fuselage. Mainwheel legs are hinged on oblique axes so that the wheels lie flush within the fuselage when retracted. Mainwheels size 26 × 8.0, with Goodrich tyres size 26 × 8.0 type VIII (18-ply rating). Nosewheel tyre size 18 × 5.5 type VII (14-ply rating). Bendix hydraulic disc brakes with Goodyear anti-skid units. Arrester hook under rear of fuselage. Braking parachute in rear fuselage.

POWERPLANT: One General Electric J79-GE-19 turbojet engine, rated at 52.8 kN (11,870 lb st) dry and 79.62 kN (17,900 lb st) with afterburning. Electrical de-icing elements fitted to air intakes. Most of the aircraft's hydraulic equipment mounted inside large engine bay door under fuselage to facilitate servicing. Internal fuel in five bag-type fuselage tanks with total standard capacity of 3,392 litres (896 US gallons; 746 Imp gallons). Provision for external fuel in two 740 litre (195 US gallon; 163 Imp gallon) pylon tanks and two 645 litre (170 US gallon; 142 Imp gallon) wingtip tanks. In-flight refuelling can be provided through Lockheed-designed probe-drogue system. Probe, mounted below port sill of cockpit, is removable but when installed is non-retractable.

ACCOMMODATION: Pressurised cockpit well forward of wings. Canopy hinged to starboard for access. Martin-Baker IQ-7A zero-zero ejection seat.

AVIONICS AND EQUIPMENT (pre-ASA modified): Integrated avionics system in which various communications and navigation components may be installed as a series of interconnecting but self-sustaining units which may be varied to provide for different specific missions. Equipment includes autopilot with 'stick steering', which includes modes for pre-selecting and holding altitude, speed, heading and constant rate of turn; multi-purpose R21G/H radar for air-to-air interception, ground and contour mapping, and terrain avoidance modes of operation; fixed-reticle gunsight; bombing computer; air data computer; dead reckoning navigation device; Tacan radio air navigation system; provision for data link-time division set and AN/ARC-552 UHF radio; Litton LN-3-2A lightweight fully-automatic inertial navigation system; Sperry C-2G compass system; AN/APN-198 radar altimeter; AIC-18 intercom; and AN/APX-46 IFF/SIF.

Provision for fitting a camera pod under the fuselage for reconnaissance duties. (See also introductory paragraphs.)
ARMAMENT: Nine external attachment points, at wingtips, under wings and under fuselage, for bombs, rocket pods, auxiliary fuel tanks and air-to-air missiles. Normal primary armament consists of two AIM-7 Sparrow air-to-air missiles under wings and/or two Sidewinders under fuselage and either a Sidewinder or 645 litre fuel tank on each wingtip. Alternatively, an M-61 20 mm multi-barrel rotary cannon can be fitted in the port underside of the fuselage instead of the AIM-7 missile control package. Max external weapon load 3,402 kg (7,500 lb).

DIMENSIONS, EXTERNAL:

Wing span without tip-tanks	6.68 m (21 ft 11 in)
Length overall	16.69 m (54 ft 9 in)
Height overall	4.11 m (13 ft 6 in)
Wheel track	2.74 m (9 ft 0 in)
Wheelbase	4.59 m (15 ft 0½ in)

AREA:

Wings, gross	18.22 m² (196.1 sq ft)

WEIGHTS:

Weight empty	6,760 kg (14,900 lb)
Max internal and external fuel load	5,153 kg (11,362 lb)
Max T-O weight	14,060 kg (31,000 lb)

PERFORMANCE (at 9,840 kg; 21,690 lb AUW except where indicated):

Never-exceed speed	Mach 2.2
Max level speed at 11,000 m (36,000 ft)	Mach 2.2 (1,259 knots; 2,330 km/h; 1,450 mph)
Max level speed at S/L	Mach 1.2 (790 knots; 1,464 km/h; 910 mph)
Max cruising speed at 11,000 m (36,000 ft)	530 knots (981 km/h; 610 mph)
Econ cruising speed	Mach 0.85
T-O speed at S/L, interceptor with two AIM-7 missiles	189 knots (350 km/h; 217 mph)
Max rate of climb at S/L	16,765 m (55,000 ft)/min
Service ceiling	17,680 m (58,000 ft)
Zoom altitude	more than 27,400 m (90,000 ft)
Time to accelerate from Mach 0.92 to Mach 2.0	2 min
Time to climb to 10,670 m (35,000 ft)	1 min 20 s
Time to climb to 17,070 m (56,000 ft)	2 min 40 s
T-O run at S/L, interceptor with two AIM-7 missiles	823 m (2,700 ft)
Typical landing run at S/L	762 m (2,500 ft)
Radius with max fuel	673 nm (1,247 km; 775 miles)
Ferry range (excl flight refuelling)	1,576 nm (2,920 km; 1,815 miles)

Aeritalia G91

The G91 light ground-attack and reconnaissance fighter was designed by Fiat in accordance with NATO operational requirements which were issued in the Spring of 1954 to the aircraft manufacturers of Western Europe.

While the G91 was still in the project stage, Fiat was awarded a contract for the construction of three prototypes and 27 pre-production aircraft, powered by the Bristol Siddeley Orpheus turbojet. The first prototype flew initially on 9 August 1956.

In the technical evaluation trials carried out at Brétigny, France, in the Autumn of 1957, the G91 proved itself able to meet the requirements of the official specification when operated from semi-prepared airstrips, with and without external stores. As a result, it was ordered into production as a standard NATO light tactical fighter.

Fiat received orders for the 30 prototypes and pre-production aircraft, 48 G91R/1s and 1As, 50 G91R/1Bs and more than 80 G91T/1s for the Italian Air Force, 50 G91R/3s and 66 G91T/3s for the German Air Force and 50 G91R/4s for the US Air Force (diverted to Federal Germany). In addition, the German aircraft industry manufactured 282 G91R/3s under licence for the German Air Force, the last of which was delivered in May 1966. As some German G91R/3s became surplus to requirements, Portugal took over their operation to build upon the original forty ex-German G91R/4s received from 1965. The last R/3s were taken into service by Portugal in 1980. Some Portuguese R/3s have RGS2 lead computing optical sights and Sidewinder missiles for interception missions, though most are fighter-bombers.

Versions of the G91 in service in 1987 were:

G91R/1, R/1A, R/1B. Attack and photographic-reconnaissance aircraft with differing standards of avionics. Used by two squadrons of Italian Air Force in 1986–87 (some 36 aircraft) but now being superseded by AMX.

G91R/3. Similar to G91R/1, but with 2 × 30 mm guns and equipment changes, including original installation of Bendix Doppler and Computing Devices of Canada Position and Homing Indicator. German examples superseded by Alpha Jets, leaving Portugal as the surviving operator.

G91R/4. Similar to G91R/1A, but with equipment changes.

G91T/1. Tandem two-seat version of G91 for advanced training at transonic speeds. Suitable also for use as tactical fighter. Similar to G91 except for two seats, rear one slightly raised, under electrically-operated two-section canopy, and increased internal fuel capacity. Only two underwing pylons. First G91T flew for the first time on May 31, 1960. Orpheus 803 turbojet. Taken into service by Italy.

G91T/3. Similar to G91T/1, but with equipment changes. Taken into service by Germany and, later, Portugal. Latter surviving operator.

G91Y. Twin-engined development of the earlier single-engined G91, based upon the airframe of the G91T version and powered by two 18.15 kN (4,080 lb st) with afterburning General Electric J85-GE-13A turbojets. Provision for JATO units for assisted take off. Fuel capacity 3,200 litres (845 US gallons; 703 Imp gallons). Wing span 9.01 m (29 ft 6½ in). T-O weight 7,000 kg (15,432 lb) and 8,700 kg (19,180 lb) from

Aeritalia G91Y twin-engined tactical strike-reconnaissance fighter.

semi-prepared and hard surfaces respectively. Max level speed at 9,145 m (30,000 ft), Mach 0.95. Max level speed at S/L, 600 knots (1,110 km/h; 690 mph). Armament and avionics comprise two 30 mm DEFA cannon and cameras in nose. Four underwing attachments for 1,000 lb bombs, 750 lb napalm tanks, four 7 × 2 in rocket packs, four 28 × 2 in rocket packs, four 5 in rocket containers, or AS.20 missiles. Total underwing load 1,816 kg (4,000 lb). Nav/attack system includes Computing Devices of Canada 5C-15 position and homing indicator, Sperry SYP-820 twin-axis gyro platform. Bendix RDA-12 Doppler radar and AiResearch air data computer, Ferranti ISIS B gyro-gunsight, Smiths electronic head-up display, Honeywell AN/APN-171 radar altimeter and Marconi-Elliott AD 370 ADF.

Two G91Y prototypes were built, of which the first flew for the first time on 27 December 1966. They were followed

Aeritalia G91Y. *(Pilot Press)*

by 20 pre-series G91Ys for the Italian Air Force, the first of which was flown in July 1968. All 20 were delivered to the 1° Group of the 8° Wing of the Italian Air Force, based at Cervia.

Delivery of the initial series of 35 production G91Ys to the Italian Air Force began in September 1971, and was completed by mid-1973. Delivery of an additional 10 aircraft was completed by mid-1976. The G91Y, as with Italian G91Rs, is expected to have reached the end of its useful life by 1988–89, when AMXs will be taking over.

The following details refer to the final production versions of the G91R and G91T, but are generally applicable to the other versions.

TYPE: Light tactical strike-reconnaissance fighter and trainer.

WINGS: Cantilever low-wing monoplane. Wing section NACA 65A112 at root, NACA 65A111 at tip. Thickness/chord ratio 12% at root, 11% at tip. Dihedral 1° 30′. Incidence 1° at root, − 1° at tip. Sweepback at quarter chord 37° 13′ 24″. Utilises integrally-stiffened panels. Easily-detachable outer wings. Internally-balanced ailerons. Electrically-actuated slotted flaps. No trim-tabs. Ailerons controlled through Jacottet irreversible hydraulic servo units with artificial feel and trimmer. No de-icing system.

FUSELAGE: Semi-monocoque structure. Rear portion detachable for engine replacement. Two hydraulically-actuated door-type airbrakes made of steel armour side-by-side under centre-fuselage.

TAIL UNIT: Cantilever structure. Rudder and elevators statically and aerodynamically balanced. Variable-incidence tailplane controlled by Rotax electric actuator. No de-icing system.

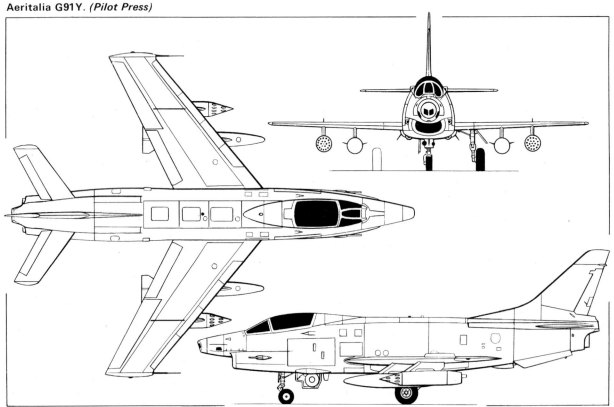

114

LANDING GEAR: Hydraulically-retractable tricycle type. Mainwheels retract inward into fuselage, nosewheel rearward. Messier mainwheels size 9.00-10, nosewheel size 7.25-6 and multi-disc hydraulic brakes. Braking parachute stowed at base of rudder.

POWERPLANT: One 22.24 kN (5,000 lb st) Fiat-built Bristol Siddeley Orpheus 803 turbojet engine. G91R has nine nylon-rubber fuel tanks in fuselage, with total capacity of 1,610 litres (425 US gallons; 354 Imp gallons). G91T has seven nylon-rubber fuel tanks in fuselage, with total capacity of 2,100 litres (555 US gallons; 462 Imp gallons). Provision for two pylon-mounted 260 litre (69 US gallon; 57 Imp gallon) or 520 litre (137 US gallon; 114 Imp gallon) underwing fuel tanks.

ACCOMMODATION (G91R): Pilot on Martin-Baker Mk W4 fully-automatic ejection seat in armoured, pressurised cockpit. Electrically-operated jettisonable rearward-hinged canopy.

AVIONICS AND EQUIPMENT (G91R): Built with AN/ARC-34 primary UHF, W.S. Electronics D.303A emergency UHF, Marconi AD722 radio-compass, PHI Mk 3B dead-reckoning navigation system, Bendix DRA-12A Doppler and IFF/SIF equipment. Three Vinten 70 mm cameras. Some Portuguese R/3s have Saab Instruments RGS 2 lead computing optical sighting system.

ARMAMENT (G91R): R/4 has fixed armament of 4×0.50-in Colt-Browning machine-guns in fuselage, two on each side of cockpit; R/3 has two DEFA cannon instead of machine-guns. Four underwing pylons for 500 lb bombs (inner pylons) and 250 lb bombs (outer pylons), 3 in rockets or rocket packs, or Sidewinder air-to-air missiles.

DIMENSIONS, EXTERNAL:

Wing span:		
G91R	8.56 m (28 ft 1 in)	
G91T	8.60 m (28 ft 3 in)	
Length overall:		
G91R	10.30 m (33 ft 9½ in)	
G91T	11.67 m (38 ft 3½ in)	
Height overall:		
G91R	4.00 m (13 ft 1½ in)	
G91T	4.45 m (14 ft 7¼ in)	
Wheel track:		
G91R	2.72 m (8 ft 11 in)	
G91T	2.82 m (9 ft 3 in)	
Wheelbase:		
G91R	3.16 m (10 ft 4½ in)	
G91T	3.51 m (11 ft 6¼ in)	
AREA:		
Wings, gross	16.42 m² (176.74 sq ft)	

WEIGHTS:

Basic operating weight:		
G91R	3,688 kg (8,130 lb)	
G91T	3,865 kg (8,520 lb)	
Basic T-O weight:		
G91R	5,390 kg (11,880 lb)	
G91T	5,500 kg (12,125 lb)	
Max T-O weight:		
G91R	5,500 kg (12,125 lb)	
G91T	6,050 kg (13,340 lb)	

PERFORMANCE (at basic T-O weight):

Max level speed at 5,000 ft (1,500 m):		
G91R	564 knots (1,045 km/h; 649 mph)	
G91T	556 knots (1,030 km/h; 640 mph)	
Stalling speed	125 knots (232 km/h; 144 mph)	
Service ceiling	12,200 m (40,000 ft)	
T-O to 50 ft (15 m):		
G91R	1,190 m (3,900 ft)	
G91T	1,450 m (4,760 ft)	
Landing from 50 ft (15 m):		
G91R	610 m (2,000 ft)	
G91T	670 m (2,200 ft)	
Landing run: G91R	305 m (1,000 ft)	
Typical combat radius at S/L: G91Y		
	323 nm (600 km; 372 miles)	

Aermacchi
AERMACCHI SpA (Subsidiary of Aeronautica Macchi SpA)

Aermacchi is the aircraft manufacturing company of the Aeronautica Macchi group. The company plants at Venegono airfield occupy a total area of 270,000 m² (2,906,260 sq ft). Total workforce is approximately 2,500.

The MB-339A two-seat trainer is in series production for the Italian Air Force and for export. A single-seat version, the MB-339K Veltro 2, is also in production. Other activities include the manufacture of wings for the Aeritalia G222 transport aircraft and underwing pylons for the Panavia Tornado; Aermacchi is also active in the field of aerospace ground equipment, with a complete line of hydraulic, electric and pneumatic ground carts for servicing civil and military aircraft.

AMX

Aermacchi is teamed with Aeritalia and EMBRAER in developing the AMX combat aircraft (see International section) for the Italian and Brazilian air forces.

Aermacchi MB-326

The MB-326 jet trainer flew for the first time on 10 December 1957, powered by a Rolls-Royce Viper 8 turbojet engine. The more powerful Viper 11 was provided for six production versions built for the air forces of Italy (MB-326 and 326E), Tunisia (MB-326B), Ghana (MB-326F), Australia (MB-326H) and South Africa (MB-326M/Impala Mk 1), and one version built for Alitalia (MB-326D).

Versions built with even more powerful Viper engines, armament changes and other modifications were as follows:

MB-326GB. Two-seat dual-control advanced training and attack version, with airframe modifications and Viper 20 Mk 540 engine. MB-326G prototype flew for first time in spring 1967; similar MB-326GB was production version. Customers included Argentinian Navy, and air forces of Zaïre and Zambia. In addition, 182 similar **MB-326GC**s were assembled in Brazil under licence by EMBRAER for the Brazilian Air Force, as the **AT-26 Xavante**, and for the

AT-26 Xavante version of the MB-326GB, operated by the Brazilian Air Force

air forces of Paraguay and Togo. AT-26 production outlasted Italian production.

MB-326K. Single-seat operational trainer and light ground-attack version. Retains most of structure and systems of MB-326GB, but has more powerful Viper 632 engine, no second cockpit, additional fuselage fuel tanks, increased weapon-carrying capacity. Prototype with Viper 540 engine first flown 22 August 1970; second prototype, with Viper 632, first flew 1971. Delivered to Dubai Defence Force, Ghana Air Force, South African Air Force, Tunisian Air Force and Zaïre Air Force. In South Africa, Atlas Impala Mk 2 was built as a Viper 540 powered version based on the MB-326K.

MB-326L. Two-seat advanced trainer, combining airframe of single-seat MB-326K with standard two-seat dual-control cockpit installation. One delivered to Dubai and four to Tunisian Air Force.

AT-26 Xavante. EMBRAER assembled under licence 166 Aermacchi MB-326GB jet trainer/ground attack aircraft for the Brazilian Air Force, by whom the type is known as the AT-26 Xavante, plus 16 others for the air forces of Togo (six) and Paraguay (ten). Eleven ex-Brazilian Air Force Xavantes were delivered to the Argentine Navy in 1983.

Atlas Impala Mk 2. The name Impala is given to two South African versions of the Aermacchi MB-326. The first Impala Mk 1s were 16 MB-326M trainers supplied by Aermacchi, the first of which made its initial flight in South Africa on 11 May 1966 and was delivered to the SAAF's Air Operational School at Langebaanweg in the following month. Gradual progress was then made, via ten more aircraft in the form of major assembly kits and a further 20 supplied in minor component form, to almost total local manufacture by Atlas. The first Atlas assembled Impala Mk 1 made its initial flight on 8 November 1966 and was delivered to the Air Operational School in February 1967. First Citizen Force squadron to operate this version was No. 4 at Zwartkop, Pretoria (from August 1972), followed by No. 5 Squadron at Durban (February 1973), No. 8 at Bloemfontein (April 1973), No. 6 at Port Elizabeth (February 1975), and No. 7 at Cape Town (June 1978). The Impala Mk 1 also served briefly with No. 1 (Fighter) Squadron at Pietersburg in May 1972; in the 1980s it was still in service with Nos. 4, 5, 6, 7, 8 and 40 Squadrons of the SAAF, and with the Flying Training School at Langebaanweg, including the SAAF's 'Silver Falcons' aerobatic team. A total of 151 Impala Mk 1s was built, the last example being delivered to the SAAF on 29 August 1974.

The MB-326KC Impala Mk 2 light ground-attack aircraft was based on the single-seat MB-326K, and is powered by a 14.95 kN (3,360 lb st) Rolls-Royce Viper Mk 540 turbojet engine. South African manufacture began with the assembly of seven aircraft from Italian-built components, the first of which made its initial flight on 13 February 1974 and was handed over to the SAAF on 22 April 1974. Mk 2s were supplied to Nos. 4, 5, 8 and 40 Squadrons. It is believed that approx 100 Mks 1/2 are in SAAF service, with about the same number in the reserve.

The following details refer to the MB-326GB/AR-26 Xavante, unless stated otherwise:

TYPE: Two-seat basic and advanced trainer (GB, GC and L) or single-seat operational trainer (K); all versions have light attack capability.

WINGS: Cantilever low/mid-wing monoplane. Wing section

Atlas MB-326KC Impala Mk 2 single-seat light ground-attack aircraft in South African Air Force markings.

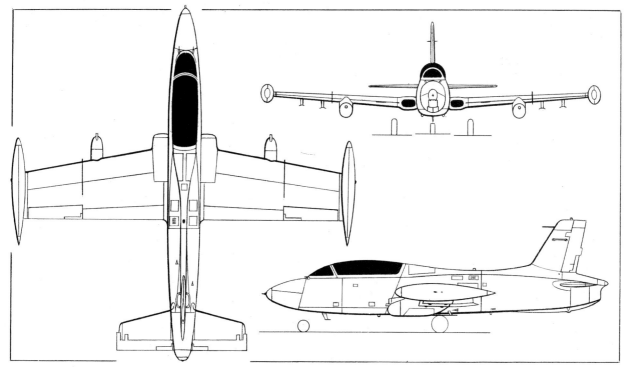

Aermacchi MB-326GB. *(Pilot Press)*

NACA 6A series (modified). Thickness/chord ratio 13.7% at root, 12% at tip. Dihedral 2° 55'. Incidence 2° 30'. Single fence on each wing at approx two-thirds span. Manually-operated ailerons and hydraulically-operated slotted flaps. Electrically-actuated balance and trim tab in port aileron. Geared balance tab in starboard aileron. MB-326K and L have strengthened structure, hydraulically-operated single-slotted flaps and hydraulically servo-powered ailerons. Automatic flap retraction on 326L above 160 knots (296 km/h; 184 mph).

FUSELAGE: Semi-monocoque structure. Hydraulically-operated airbrake under centre-fuselage.

TAIL UNIT: Cantilever structure. Electrically-actuated trim tab in rudder and each elevator.

LANDING GEAR (MB-326GB): Hydraulically-retractable tricycle type. Nosewheel retracts forward, main units outward into wings. Pirelli main wheels and tyres. Steerable and self-centering nosewheel with anti-shimmy device. Dunlop twin-contact nosewheel tyre, size 5-4.5. Hydraulic disc brakes.

LANDING GEAR (MB-326K and L): As MB-326GB, except for more powerful Dunlop high-capacity hydraulic disc brakes and separate emergency extension system.

POWERPLANT (GB): One Rolls-Royce Viper 20 Mk 540 turbojet engine, rated at 15.17 kN (3,410 lb st). Fuel in flexible rubber main tank in fuselage, capacity 782 litres (207 US gallons; 172 Imp gallons), and two 305 litre (81 US gallon; 67 Imp gallon) non-jettisonable wingtip tanks. Total standard fuel capacity 1,392 litres (369 US gallons; 306 Imp gallons). Provision for two 332 litre (88 US gallon; 73 Imp gallon) jettisonable underwing tanks, to give total capacity of 2,056 litres (545 US gallons; 452 Imp gallons). Fuel dump valves permit quick emptying of tip-tanks.

POWERPLANT (K and L): One Rolls-Royce Viper Mk 632-43 turbojet engine, rated at 18.79 kN (4,000 lb st). MB-326L fuel capacity same as for GB. Fuel in MB-326K contained in three rubber fuselage tanks and two permanent wingtip tanks, total usable capacity 1,660 litres (438 US gallons; 366 Imp gallons). Provision to install self-sealing fuselage tanks and reticulated foam anti-explosive filling in all tanks, including those at wingtips. Two underwing stations equipped normally to carry jettisonable auxiliary tanks of up to 340 litres (90 US gallons; 75 Imp gallons) each.

ACCOMMODATION (GB and L): Crew of two in tandem under a one-piece moulded Perspex canopy which hinges sideways to starboard. Pressurised cockpit. Dual controls and instruments. Blind-flying screens for pupil. Martin-Baker Mk 04A lightweight ejection seats in GB; Mk 06A zero-zero seats in L.

ACCOMMODATION (K): Pilot only, on Martin-Baker Mk 6 zero-zero rocket ejection seat in pressurised cockpit. Separately-controlled canopy jettison system provided, but seat is fitted with breakers to permit ejection through canopy in extreme emergency. Canopy hinges sideways to starboard. Provision for armour protection for pilot and other vital areas.

AVIONICS AND EQUIPMENT: Two Collins Type 618M-2B 360-channel VHF transceivers, Collins CIA-102A interphone system, Bendix DFA 73A-1 ADF, and a complete VOR/ILS system using a Collins 51RV-1 VOR/LOC/glideslope receiver, Collins 51Z-4 marker beacon receiver and AN/APX-72. Provision for IFF transponder.

ARMAMENT (GB and L): Provision for up to 1,814 kg (4,000 lb) of armament on six underwing attachments. Typical weapon loads include following alternatives: two LAU-3/A packs each containing nineteen 2.75 in FFAR rockets and two packs each containing eight Hispano-Suiza SURA 80 mm rockets; two 12.7 mm gun pods and four packs each containing six SURA 80 mm rockets; one 7.62 mm Minigun, one 12.7 mm gun pod, two Matra 122 rocket packs and two packs each containing six SURA 80 mm rockets; two 500 lb bombs and eight 5 in HVAR rockets; two AS.12 missiles; one 12.7 mm gun pod, one reconnaissance pack containing four Vinten cameras and two 272 kg (600 lb) drop-tanks, or two Matra SA-10 packs each containing a 30 mm Aden gun and 150 rounds. SFOM type 83 fixed gunsight or Ferranti LFS 5/102A gyro-sight. Gun camera in nose.

ARMAMENT (K): Standard fixed armament of two 30 mm DEFA electrically-operated cannon in lower front fuselage, with 125 rds/gun. Six underwing pylons, the inboard four stressed to carry up to 454 kg (1,000 lb) each and the outboard pair up to 340 kg (750 lb) each. Max external military load (with reduced fuel) is 1,814 kg (4,000 lb). Each pylon fitted with standard NATO 355 mm (14 in) MA-4A stores rack. Typical loads may include two 750 lb and four 500 lb bombs, four napalm containers, two AS.11 or AS.12 air-to-surface missiles, two machine-gun pods,

two Matra 550 air-to-air missiles, six SUU-11A/A 7.62 mm Minigun pods, and various Matra or other launchers for 37 mm, 68 mm, 100 mm, 2.75 in or 5 in rockets. A four-camera tactical reconnaissance pod can be carried on the port inner pylon without affecting the weapon capability of the other five stations.

ARMAMENT (AT-26): Six underwing points for bombs, gun pods or other stores. Typical loads include six 250 lb bombs; two 500 lb bombs; two 500 lb bombs and two twin 7.62 mm gun pods; four 250 lb bombs and two twin 7.62 mm gun pods; two twin 7.62 mm gun pods and two underwing drop-tanks; two twin 7.62 mm gun pods and four LM-70/7 rocket pods (each with seven SBAT 70 mm folding-fin air-to-ground projectiles); two twin 7.62 mm gun pods and two LM-37/36 rocket pods (each with thirty-six SBAT 37 mm air-to-ground rockets); six LM-70/7 rocket pods; or two LM-70/19 rocket pods (each with nineteen SBAT 70 mm air-to-ground rockets); or photographic reconnaissance pods. All armament loads are designed and manufactured in Brazil.

DIMENSIONS, EXTERNAL:		
Wing span over tip-tanks	10.854 m (35 ft 7¼ in)	
Length overall	10.673 m (35 ft 0¼ in)	
Height overall	3.72 m (12 ft 2 in)	
AREA:		
Wings, gross	19.30 m² (207.7 sq ft)	
WEIGHTS (A: Trainer; B: Attack):		
Basic operating weight, excl crew:		
A	2,685 kg (5,920 lb)	
*B	2,558 kg (5,640 lb)	
Max T-O weight (full internal fuel, wingtip and underwing tanks):		
A	4,577 kg (10,090 lb)	
B, no armament	4,447 kg (9,805 lb)	
B, with 769 kg (1,695 lb) armament	5,216 kg (11,500 lb)	
Max T-O weight (max armament):		
*B, with fuel in fuselage tank only and 1,962 kg (4,325 lb)		
armament	5,216 kg (11,500 lb)	

*Without tip-tanks and aft ejection seat

WEIGHTS (MB-326K):		
Weight empty, equipped	3,123 kg (6,885 lb)	
T-O weight ('clean')	4,645 kg (10,240 lb)	
Typical operational T-O weights:		
patrol and visual reconnaissance	5,048 kg (11,130 lb)	
photographic reconnaissance	5,111 kg (11,270 lb)	
Max T-O weight	5,897 kg (13,000 lb)	

PERFORMANCE: (A: Trainer at typical weight of 3,937 kg; 8,680 lb, representing max T-O weight without underwing tanks; B: Attack version at combat weight of 4,763 kg; 10,500 lb; C: Attack version at max T-O weight):

Never-exceed speed:		
A	Mach 0.82 (469 knots; 871 km/h; 541 mph EAS)	
B	Mach 0.75 (419 knots; 778 km/h; 483 mph EAS)	
Max level speed: A	468 knots (867 km/h; 539 mph)	
Max cruising speed:		
A	430 knots (797 km/h; 495 mph)	

Max rate of climb at S/L: A	1,844 m (6,050 ft)/min
B	1,082 m (3,550 ft)/min
C	945 m (3,100 ft)/min
Time to 3,050 m (10,000 ft): B	3 min 10 s
C	4 min 0 s
Time to 6,100 m (20,000 ft): A	4 min 10 s
B	8 min 0 s
C	9 min 20 s
Time to 9,150 m (30,000 ft): A	7 min 40 s
B	15 min 0 s
C	18 min 40 s
Time to 12,200 m (40,000 ft): A	13 min 5 s
Service ceiling: A	14,325 m (47,000 ft)
B	11,900 m (39,000 ft)
T-O run, ISA: A	412 m (1,350 ft)
B	640 m (2,100 ft)
C	845 m (2,770 ft)

Range (A, with 113 litres; 30 US/25 Imp gallons reserve):
fuselage and tip-tanks

998 nm (1,850 km; 1,150 miles)

fuselage, tip and underwing tanks

1,320 nm (2,445 km; 1,520 miles)

Combat radius (C):
max fuel, 769 kg (1,695 lb) armament, 90 kg (200 lb) fuel reserve, out at 6,100 m (20,000 ft), return at 7,620 m (25,000 ft)

350 nm (648 km; 403 miles)

fuselage tank only, 1,814 kg (4,000 lb) armament, 90 kg (200 lb) fuel reserve, cruise at 3,050 m (10,000 ft), five minutes over target

69 nm (130 km; 80 miles)

max fuel, 771 kg (1,700 lb) armament, 90 kg (200 lb) fuel reserve, cruise at 3,050 m (10,000 ft), 1 h 50 min patrol at 150 m (500 ft) over target

49.5 nm (92 km; 57 miles)

Aermacchi MB-339 and MB-339K Veltro 2 (Greyhound)

The MB-339A is a tandem two-seat trainer/ground-attack aircraft, powered by a Piaggio-built Rolls-Royce Viper 632 engine.

The first of two MB-339X flying prototypes was flown for the first time on 12 August 1976. The second aircraft, which

made its first flight on 20 May 1977, was built to pre-production standard; the third airframe was used for static and fatigue testing. The first production aircraft made its initial flight on 20 July 1978, and the first of an initial series of 51 aircraft for the Italian Air Force were handed over for pre-service trials on 8 August 1979. In addition to MB-339A

Aermacchi MB-399A of the Dubai Air Force Flying School.

trainers, this series included four **MB-339RM** (radio-misure) calibration aircraft delivered to 8° Gruppo Sorveglianza Elettronica of the 14° Stormo Radiomisure at Pratica de Mare from 16 February 1981, and fifteen **MB-339PAN**s (Pattuglia Acrobatica Nazionale) delivered to the Italian Air Force aerobatic team, the Frecce Tricolori, which began using the type on 27 April 1982. The PAN aircraft have the wingtip tanks deleted (to facilitate formation keeping) and a smoke generating system installed, but are otherwise similar to the standard MB-339A. At least two more MB-339As have since been converted to MB-339PAN standard to offset attrition. In September 1982 the Italian Air Force received the first of the second production batch of 30 aircraft, which are camouflaged and are to be used as an emergency close-air-support force. A total of 98 MB-339s had been delivered to the Italian Air Force by the beginning of 1987.

Ten MB-339As were delivered to the Argentine Navy in 1980, 16 to the Peruvian Air Force in 1981–82, 12 to the Royal Malaysian Air Force in 1983–84, five to Dubai in 1984–87, and 12 to Nigeria in 1985. A further order from an unspecified customer was announced in June 1987.

In 1985 Aermacchi introduced two new two-seat variants of the MB-339, both powered by the Viper 680 engine. The MB-339B is an advanced jet trainer, with enhanced light close-air-support capability compared with the MB-339A. The MB-339C is an improved trainer/close-air-support version with digital nav/attack system and other advanced avionics. It has the enlarged wingtip tanks of the MB-339B and a modified nose shape. It is intended for effective pilot training in modern mission-management techniques. Design and development began in 1982–83; the prototype flew for the first time on 17 December 1985. Power for the MB-339B and C is provided by one 19.57 kN (4,400 lb st) Rolls-Royce Viper Mk 680-43 turbojet engine.

The MB-339K Veltro 2, which perpetuates the name of the Macchi MC 205V fighter of the Second World War, is a single-seat development of the MB-339A, optimised for the roles of light close air support and operational training. The MB-339K private venture prototype flew for the first time on 30 May 1980, powered by a 17.8 kN (4,000 lb st) Viper Mk 632 engine, and has since successfully undertaken many weapon firing and compatibility trials. According to Aermacchi, construction of an initial production batch has been launched, but no orders for the K version had been announced at the time of writing.

Prototype MB-339C, equipped with Viper 680 engine and a digital nav/attack system. *(Aviodata)*

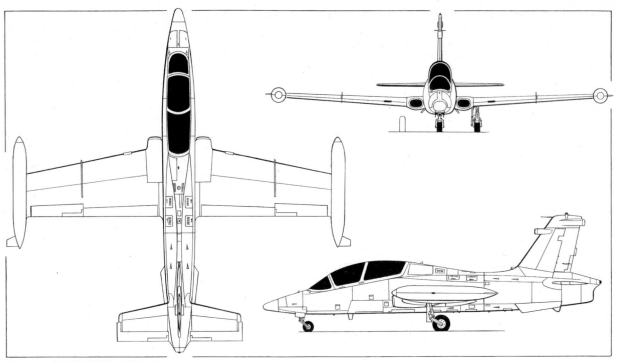

Aermacchi MB-339C. *(Pilot Press)*

The airframe of the MB-339A is retained, except for a new forward fuselage with redesigned single-seat cockpit, internally mounted cannon armament, auxiliary fuselage fuel tank and enlarged wingtip tanks. The other major changes in the production MB-339K concern the power-plant, and the avionics and equipment relevant to the different roles performed by the Veltro 2. Flight testing with the Viper Mk 680 engine in the second prototype MB-339A took place between the spring of 1983 and summer of 1984, and this engine became available for the production MB-339K from early 1986.

The following description applies to the basic MB-339K; operational capability can, at customer's option, be extended by adopting such additional features as a head-up display, cockpit TV display, ECM, and other improved avionics.

TYPE: Single-seat ground-attack aircraft and operational trainer.

AIRFRAME: Structural design criteria based on MIL-A-

Aermacchi MB-339K Veltro 2 light close air support aircraft, developed from the two-seat MB-339A.

8860 series of specifications; + 8/-4 limit load factor in 'clean' configuration. With a fatigue spectrum based on the ground-attack role only, service life will be more than 9,000 flying hours with 18,000 landings. Entire structure is specially treated to prevent corrosion.

WINGS: Cantilever low/mid-wing monoplane. Wing section NACA 64A-114 (mod) at centreline, NACA 64A-212 (mod) at tip. Leading edge swept back 11° 18'. Sweepback at quarter-chord 8° 29'. Wingtip tanks permanently attached. Single fence on each wing at approx two-thirds span. Servo powered ailerons embody 'Irving' type aerodynamic balance provisions, and are statically balanced along their entire span. Balance tabs facilitate reversion to manual operation in the event of servo failure. Hydraulically actuated single-slotted flaps.

FUSELAGE: Semi-monocoque structure, built in two main portions: forward (nose to engine mounting bulkhead), and rear (engine bulkhead to tailcone). Hydraulically actuated, electrically controlled airbrake under centre of fuselage, just forward of CG.

TAIL UNIT: Cantilever structure. Slightly sweptback vertical surfaces. Rudder and elevators are statically balanced, each having an electrically actuated dual-purpose balance and trim tab. Two auxiliary fins under rear fuselage.

LANDING GEAR: Hydraulically retractable tricycle type; suitable for operation from semi-prepared runways. Nosewheel retracts forward, main units outward into wings. Hydraulically steerable nosewheel. Low-pressure mainwheel tubeless tyres size 545 × 175-10 (12 ply rating); nosewheel tubeless tyre size 380 × 150-4 (6 ply rating). Emergency extension system. Hydraulic disc brakes with anti-skid system.

POWERPLANT: One 19.57kN (4,400 lb st) Rolls-Royce Viper Mk 680 turbojet engine. Fuel in one fuselage tank, consisting of three rubber cells with a total capacity of 1,030 litres (272 US gallons; 226.5 Imp gallons), and two constant-section integral wingtip tanks with a combined capacity of 1,020 litres (269 US gallons; 224.5 Imp gallons). Total usable internal fuel capacity 2,050 litres (541 US gallons; 451 Imp gallons).

ACCOMMODATION: Pilot only, on Martin-Baker IT10LK zero/zero ejection seat in pressurised cockpit. Rearview mirror standard. One-piece moulded transparent canopy, opening sideways to starboard.

AVIONICS AND EQUIPMENT: Typical avionics installation includes Collins AN/ARC-159(V)-2, or Magnavox AN/ARC-150(V), or Magnavox AN/ARC-164(V) UHF transceiver; Collins AN/ARC-186(V) VHF/AM and FM transceiver; Collins ICS-200 interphone; Collins AN/ARN-118(V) Tacan or King KDM 706A DME; Collins 51RV-4B or Bendix RNA-34A VOR/ILS and MKI-3 marker beacon receiver; GEC Avionics AD-620C computerised area and dead reckoning navigation system; and Bendix AN/APX-100(V) or Italtel SIT 421A IFF; and Collins 51RV-4B or Bendix RNA-34A VOR/ILS and strumentation includes Astronautics ARU-2B/A attitude director indicator; AQU-6/A horizontal situation indicator and flight director system; Sperry AS-339 attitude and heading reference system; and Microtecnica AG-5 standby attitude indicator.

ARMAMENT AND OPERATIONAL EQUIPMENT: Two 30 mm DEFA cannon, with 120 rds/gun, mounted internally in lower forward fuselage, with external fairings. Firing rate 1,200 rds/min. Loads on six underwing hardpoints. Aircraft is cleared for operation with rockets of 50 mm (SNIA), 68 mm, 81 mm (SNORA), 100 mm (Thomson-Brandt), 2.75 in and 5 in calibre, and with 500 lb Mk 82 and R bombs, 100 mm Thomson-Brandt special runway demolition bombs, 120 mm close-air-support bombs, 250 lb Expal BPR bombs and 500 lb Matra bombs. Elettronica ELT555 airborne deception jamming and warning pod can be carried underwing. Under study are two additional 30 mm guns in pods and a Sidewinder missile installation. Saab-Scania RGS 2 gunsight, with gyro lead computer; gunsight can be equipped with a fully automatic Teledyne TSC 116-2 gun camera. Provision for towing type A-6B (1.83 × 9.14 m; 6 × 30 ft) aerial banner target.

DIMENSIONS, EXTERNAL:	
Wing span over tip tanks	11.22 m (36 ft 9¾ in)
Length overall	10.85 m (35 ft 7 in)
Height overall	3.994 m (13 ft 1¼ in)
Wheel track	2.483 m (8 ft 1¾ in)
Wheelbase	4.369 m (14 ft 4 in)
AREA:	
Wings, gross	19.30 m² (207.74 sq ft)
WEIGHTS:	
Weight empty, equipped	3,245 kg (7,154 lb)
Max external stores load	1,935 kg (4,266 lb)
T-O weight 'clean', incl ammunition for internal guns	
	5,050 kg (11,133 lb)
Max T-O weight with external stores	
	6,350 kg (14,000 lb)

PERFORMANCE (with full gun ammunition load):	
Max limiting Mach number	0.85
Never-exceed speed	500 knots (927 km/h; 575 mph)
Max level speed at S/L	486 knots (900 km/h; 560 mph) IAS
Max rate of climb at S/L	2,400 m (7,875 ft)/min
Service ceiling	14,000 m (46,000 ft)
T-O run: 'clean'	580 m (1,900 ft)
at max T-O weight of 6,350 kg (14,000 lb)	
	910 m (2,985 ft)
Landing run	450 m (1,475 ft)
Combat radius with two 30 mm cannon (125 rds/gun) and four 500 lb Mk 82 bombs (total military load 1,088 kg; 2,400 lb):	
lo-lo-lo	205 nm (380 km; 236 miles)
hi-lo-hi	340 nm (630 km; 391 miles)
g limits	+8/ − 4

Agusta
AGUSTA SpA
Formed originally in 1977, the Agusta Group completely reorganised its structure from 1 January 1981 under a new holding company known as Agusta SpA. It is part of the Italian public holding agency EFIM, and has three main divisions employing nearly 10,000 people in 12 factories in various parts of Italy.

Costruzioni Aeronautiche Giovanni Agusta SpA
Agusta A 109

The first of three A 109 general-purpose helicopter prototypes flew for the first time on 4 August 1971. RAI and FAA certification for VFR operation was announced on 1 June

1975, and deliveries of the original A 109A production version started in early 1976.

Deliveries of the uprated A 109A Mk II began in September 1981. This has an increase in transmission rating, a new tail-rotor driveshaft, increased tail-rotor blade life and reliability, new self-damping engine mounts, integral-design oil coolers and blowers, a structurally redesigned tailboom, higher-pressure hydraulic system, improved avionics and instrument layout, and a removable floor in the baggage compartment. Civil and military deliveries of the A 109A/A MkII have included a VIP 'wide-body' version of the Mk II to be operated by 31° Stormo of the Italian Air Force, as a Presidential transport.

Several specifically non-commercial versions of the A 109A have been developed by Agusta. In general, their configuration, structure and powerplant are similar to those of the standard civil versions, although specially modified versions can be made available if required. Features of some or all military and naval versions include, as standard, dual controls and instrumentation; rotor brake; tail-rotor control magnetic brake; sliding doors; environmental control system; emergency flotation gear; armoured seats; heavy duty battery; particle separator; external cargo hook; multi-purpose universal supports for external stores; rescue hoist; and high-load cargo floor. The naval versions, specially configured for shipboard compatibility, can be equipped with four-axis AFCS, radar altimeter, internal auxiliary fuel tanks, non-retractable landing gear, search radar, anchorage points for deck lashings, and an automatic navigation system.

The principal military, paramilitary and naval versions are:

Aerial scout. Can be armed with a flexibly mounted 7.62 mm or 12.7 mm machine-gun, with stabilised sight, plus two XM157 launchers (each with seven 2.75 in rockets). Normal crew of three.

Light attack against tanks and other hard-point targets. Has been demonstrated with Hughes M65 TOW system incorporating undernose telescopic sight unit, plus four or eight TOW missiles. Normal crew of two. Argentine Army is adapting its A 109s to carry Mathogo anti-tank missiles.

Light attack against soft-point targets. Various combinations of armament include a pintle mounted 7.62 mm machine-gun in each doorway; a flexible, remotely controlled externally mounted 7.62 mm gun; twin trainable, remotely controlled, externally mounted 7.62 mm guns; two external machine-gun pods; or two gun pods and two rocket launchers. Normal crew of two.

Command and control. For target designation and direction of helicopter attack force. Can be armed with combination of rockets and flexible machine-guns, as described in preceding paragraph.

Utility. For up to seven troops; two stretcher patients and two medical attendants; externally mounted rescue hoist; or underfuselage hook for slung load.

Mirach. Version carrying two Mirach-100 RPVs for battlefield surveillance, reconnaissance, target acquisition, elint, ECM, attack on ground or naval targets, and enemy defence saturation or decoy.

ESM/ECM. Electronic warfare version, for military and naval use. Available with passive ESM only, plus weapon systems if required; and with passive ESM plus modularised active ECM (jamming), plus any required weapons. Provision for chaff dispenser to be mounted on tailboom.

Naval. Primary naval missions are anti-surface-vessel, electronic warfare, standoff missile guidance, reconnaissance, and anti-submarine classification. Secondary capabilities for search and rescue, troop transportation, ambulance, flying crane, coastguard patrol, and inter-ship liaison duties. Configurations for electronic warfare and utility roles generally similar to those described in preceding 'Utility' and 'ESM/ECM' paragraphs. For the ASW role, specialised equipment includes MAD, one or two homing torpedoes and six marine markers. For the ASV role the naval A 109 carries a high-performance long-range search radar with high discrimination in rough sea conditions. The surface attack is performed with air-to-surface wire-guided missiles. For the TG-2 (standoff missile guidance) mission, the helicopter is equipped with a special system to control and guide a ship-launched Otomat missile. For armed patrol, the naval A 109 is equipped with a search radar and armament to customer's requirements. The coastguard patrol configuration includes a search radar, a special installation for external high efficiency loudspeakers, and a searchlight.

Police and other patrol duties. For patrol (including armed patrol) and surveillance, search and rescue, firefighting, and similar utility missions. Principal SAR equipment includes search radar, rescue hoist, stretcher/first aid kits, radar altimeter, skis or emergency flotation gear, AFCS, and flare/smoke grenades. For aerial patrol it can include 360° radar, automatic stability control system, external loudspeakers, FLIR, pollution monitoring equipment, system for spraying chemical retardants, and other items depending upon requirements of mission.

Twenty-four examples of the new **A 109 EOA** version have been ordered by the Italian Army as advanced observation helicopters. Deliveries began in mid-1987.

The EOA has the lengthened nose and fixed, raised landing gear of the A 109K, but is powered by uprated Allison 250-C20R engines offering better 'hot and high' performance than the -C20Bs in the standard A 109A Mk II. Other features of the EOA include sliding cabin doors, crashworthy self-sealing fuel tanks, missile launchers and a 12.7 mm machine-gun, a SFIN gyro-stabilised sight, and electronic warfare equipment.

Agusta has also developed the **A 109K** multi-role 'hot and high' variant of the A 109A Mk II, aimed specifically at the military market in the Middle East and Africa. The A 109K has two 538 kW (722 shp) Turboméca Arriel IK turboshafts (instead of the A 109's usual 313 kW; 420 shp Allisons), an uprated transmission, a new main rotor hub made of composites, elastomeric bearings, composites blades with a hard surface coating that is resistant to abrasion by sand and hard dust, a new tail rotor of Wortmann blade section, a longer nose to house additional avionics, and a taller and non-retractable high-shock-absorption landing gear.

Intended for operation by a pilot and gunner in its primary combat role, the A 109K proved its capability during firing trials in Belgium. The first prototype flew for the first time in April 1983, and differed from the basic A 109A only in having the standard Allison 250-C20B turboshaft engines replaced by Arriel IKs. The second prototype, which began flying in March 1984, was fully representative of the planned production version.

The following details refer to the A 109K:

TYPE: Twin-engined multi-role helicopter.

ROTOR SYSTEM: Fully articulated four-blade single main

Agusta A 109K multi-role 'hot and high' variant of the A 109A Mk II.

Agusta A 109EOA, with uprated engines and transmission, non-retractable landing gear and other changes. *(Jane's/Mike Keep)*

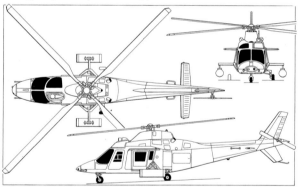

rotor and port side two-blade semi-rigid delta-hinged tail rotor. Main rotor blades have a 'droop snoot' aerofoil section, with thickness/chord ratios of 11.3% at root and 6% at tip. Composites main rotor blades and hub, with elastomeric bearings, and special blade surface coating, for greater corrosion/abrasion resistance. New tail rotor of slightly reduced diameter, with high-efficiency Wortmann aerofoil section.

FUSELAGE AND TAIL UNIT: Pod-and-boom type, built in four main sections (nose, cockpit, main cabin and tailboom). Nose lengthened by 40 cm ($15\frac{3}{4}$ in) and fitted with an upward hinged door on each side, for access to avionics, when compared with A 109A Mk II. Provision for ECM or other sensors on nose. Sweptback vertical fins (above and below tailboom). Non-swept elevator, mid-mounted on tailboom forward of fins, is linked to collective pitch control.

LANDING GEAR: Non-retractable tricycle type, giving increased clearance between fuselage and ground. Single mainwheels and castoring self centering nosewheel. Disc brakes on mainwheels. Tailskid under fin.

POWERPLANT: Two Turboméca Arriel IK turboshaft engines, each rated at 538 kW (722 shp) for 2.5 minutes, 522 kW (700 shp) for take-off (5 minutes) and 436 kW (585 shp) max cruise power. Engine particle separator added. Standard fuel capacity 700 litres (185 US gallons; 154 Imp gallons).

ACCOMMODATION: Normal crew of two for combat missions, comprising pilot (on right) and gunner. Up to six passengers in cabin of utility version. Smaller instrument panel to improve forward view.

AVIONICS: Basic installation comprises dual UHF/VHF AM-FM, Collins AN/ARN-126 VOR/LOC/ILS, Collins ADF-60, AG-06 intercom, SIT 421 IFF transponder, Sperry three-axis AFCS and AN/ASN-75 nav compass system.

ARMAMENT (optional): Total of four stores attachments, two on each side of cabin, on outriggers. Typical loads include two 7.62 mm or 12.7 mm gun pods, rocket launchers, or up to eight TOW anti-armour missiles (with roof mounted sight), plus a 7.62 or 12.7 mm side-firing gun in cabin.

DIMENSIONS, EXTERNAL:

Main rotor diameter	11.00 m (36 ft 1 in)
Tail-rotor diameter	2.00 m (6 ft $6\frac{3}{4}$ in)
Length overall, rotors turning	13.05 m (42 ft $9\frac{3}{4}$ in)
Length of fuselage	11.106 m (36 ft $5\frac{1}{4}$ in)
Height over tail fin	3.30 m (10 ft 10 in)
Elevator span	2.88 m (9 ft $5\frac{1}{2}$ in)
Width over mainwheels	2.45 m (8 ft $0\frac{1}{2}$ in)
Wheelbase	3.535 m (11 ft $7\frac{1}{4}$ in)

AREA:

Tail-rotor disc	3.143 m² (33.83 sq ft)

WEIGHTS:

Weight empty	1,595 kg (3,517 lb)
Max T-O weight	2,850 kg (6,283 lb)

PERFORMANCE (at max T-O weight except where indicated):

*Max level speed at S/L, 'clean':	
ISA	138 knots (255 km/h; 159 mph)
ISA + 20°C	140 knots (259 km/h; 161 mph)
*Max cruising speed at S/L, at average weight, 'clean':	
ISA	141 knots (261 km/h; 162 mph)
ISA + 20°C	144 knots (266 km/h; 166 mph)
**Econ cruising speed at S/L, at average weight, 'clean':	
ISA	128 knots (237 km/h; 147 mph)
ISA + 20°C	131 knots (243 km/h; 151 mph)
Max rate of climb at S/L:	
ISA	530 m (1,740 ft)/min
ISA + 20°C	509 m (1,670 ft)/min
Service ceiling:	
ISA or ISA + 20°C	6,100 m (20,000 ft)
Hovering ceiling IGE at average weight, 'clean':	
ISA	5,640 m (18,500 ft)
ISA + 20°C	4,970 m (16,300 ft)
Hovering ceiling OGE at average weight, 'clean':	
ISA	3,350 m (11,000 ft)
ISA + 20°C	2,680 m (8,800 ft)
Max range at S/L, 'clean':	
ISA	290 nm (537 km; 333 miles)
ISA + 20°C	284 nm (526 km; 326 miles)

*reduced by 9 knots (17 km/h; 11 mph) with two gun pods fitted
**reduced by 6 knots (11 km/h; 7 mph) with two gun pods fitted

Agusta A 129 Mangusta (Mongoose)

The Italian Army first made known its requirements for a light anti-armour helicopter in 1972, and the initial proposal, based on a derivative of the A 109A, was made in the following year. This was superseded by an all-new design, the A 129, which received Italian Army go-ahead in March 1978 and underwent several changes of configuration before reaching its final form in 1980. The first A 129 made an official first flight on 15 September 1983, following two earlier 'unofficial' flights of which the first took place on 11 September.

Initially, the A 129 is intended for service with the Italian Army, primarily for specialised attack against armoured targets with anti-tank or area-suppression weapons, and will have full night/bad-weather combat capability. It is also suitable for advanced scouting and other roles.

The development programme, including the building of five flying prototypes, has been fully funded (70 per cent by the Italian Army and 30 per cent by Agusta).

Italian government approval has been given for an initial production batch of 60 A 129s, to equip two Italian Army Aviation operational squadrons. A requirement exists for an additional 30 aircraft, plus reserves, to equip a third operational squadron. Manufacture of the first 15 Mangustas for the Italian Army was under way by mid-1986, and the first production example was completed by early 1987, permitting deliveries to start at the beginning of 1988. Twenty Mangustas have been ordered by the Dutch Army; they will be operated on behalf of the Army by the Royal Netherlands Air Force.

TYPE: Light anti-tank, attack and advanced scout helicopter.

ROTOR SYSTEM: Fully articulated four-blade main rotor and two-blade semi-rigid delta-hinged tail rotor, each with elastomeric bearings and low-noise tips (various tip designs evaluated before production). Main rotor blades, which have a very low vibration level, each consist of a

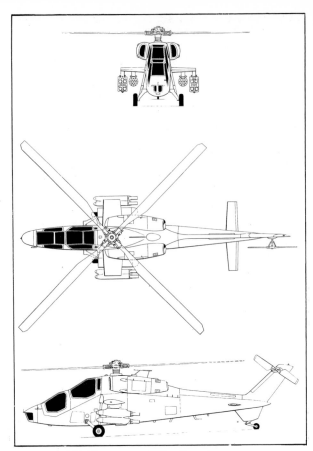

Agusta A 129 Mangusta. *(Pilot Press)*

carbonfibre and Kevlar spar, Nomex honeycomb leading and trailing edge, stainless steel leading-edge abrasion strip, frangible tip, and skin of composite materials. They are designed to have a ballistic tolerance against hits from 12.7 mm ammunition, but are expected also to have considerable tolerance against 23 mm hits. The hub has the same ballistic tolerance; all mechanical linkages and moving parts are housed inside the rotor mast to eliminate foreign object damage, decrease icing problems, and reduce radar signature. There are no lubricated bearings in the rotorhead. Tail-rotor blades are also of composite materials, with a stainless steel leading edge, and are tolerant to 12.7 mm hits.

WINGS: Cantilever mid-mounted stub wings, built of composite materials, aft of rear cockpit in plane of main rotor mast.

FUSELAGE: Conventional semi-monocoque structure. Composite materials, making up 45 per cent of total fuselage weight (excluding engine) and 16.1 per cent of total empty weight, are used for nosecone, tailboom, tail-rotor pylon, engine nacelles, canopy frame and maintenance panels. Small and narrow frontal area. Rollover bulkhead in nose and rollover bar in forward fuselage for crew protection; armour protection for vital areas of powerplant. Overall infra-red-absorbing paint finish. Airframe has a ballistic tolerance against 12.7 mm armour-piercing ammunition, and meets the crashworthiness standards of MIL-STD-1290 (vertical velocity changes of up to 11.2 m; 36.75 ft/s and longitudinal changes of up to 13.1 m; 43 ft/s).

Agusta A 129 armed attack helicopter for the Italian Army. *(Aviodata)*

TAIL UNIT: Sweptback main fin, with tail rotor mounted near top on port side. Small underfin, serving also as mount for tailwheel. Tailplane mid-mounted on tailboom in line with fin leading edge. All tail surfaces built of composite materials.

LANDING GEAR: Non-retractable tailwheel type, with single wheel on each unit. Gear designed to withstand hard landings at descent rates in excess of 10 m (32.8 ft)/s.

POWERPLANT: Two Rolls-Royce Gem 2 Mk 1004D turboshaft engines, each with a max continuous rating of 615 kW (825 shp) for normal twin-engined operation; intermediate contingency rating of 657 kW (881 shp) for 1 h; a max contingency rating of 704 kW (944 shp) for $2\frac{1}{2}$ min; and an emergency rating (S/L, ISA) of 759 kW (1,018 shp) for 20s. Production aircraft have engines licence-built in Italy by Piaggio. Two separate fuel systems, with crossfeed capability; interchangeable self-sealing and crash resistant tanks, self-sealing lines, and digital fuel feed control. Tanks can be foam-filled for fire protection. Single-point pressure refuelling. Infra-red exhaust suppression system and low engine noise levels. Separate independent lubrication oil cooling system for each engine. Provision for auxiliary (self-ferry) fuel tanks on inboard underwing stations.

ACCOMMODATION: Pilot and co-pilot/gunner in separate cockpits in tandem. Elevated rear (pilot's) cockpit. Each cockpit has a flat-plate low-glint canopy with upward hinged door panels on starboard side, blow-out side panel for exit in emergency, and armoured crashworthy seat.

AVIONICS AND OPERATIONAL EQUIPMENT: All main functions of the helicopter are handled and monitored by a fully integrated digital multiplex system, or IMS (first installation in prototype 904), which controls com, nav, flight director, autopilot, fly by wire, transmission and engine condition monitoring, fuel/hydraulic/electrical systems monitoring, aircraft performance, caution and warning systems, and rocket fire control. Processed information is presented to the pilot and co-pilot/gunner on separate graphic/alphanumeric head-down multi-function displays (MFDs) with standard multi-function keyboards for easy access to information, including area navigation and synthetic waypoint map, weapons status and selection, radio tuning and mode selection, caution and warning, and display of aircraft performance. The IMS computer can store up to 100 waypoints, or a maximum of ten flight plans with ten waypoints each, and 100 pre-set frequencies for HF, VHF and UHF radio management. Navigation is controlled by the navigation computer of the IMS coupled to a Doppler radar and a radar altimeter. Synthetic map presentation of waypoints, target areas and dangerous areas is shown on the pilot's or co-pilot's MFD.

The A 129 has a full day/night operational capability, with equipment designed to give both crew members a view outside the helicopter irrespective of light conditions.

A pilot's night vision system allows nap-of-the-earth (NOE) flight by night, a picture of the world outside being generated by the FLIR system inside the 'nose' of the pilot's night vision system (which is mounted at the nose of the aircraft) and presented to the pilot through the monocle of his integrated helmet and display sighting system (IHADSS). Symbology containing the information required for the flight is superimposed on to the image, giving a true head-up reference. The co-pilot/gunner is also equipped with an IHADSS. For night anti-tank engagements, the TOW target acquisition and missile guidance unit will be augmented by a FLIR. This vision equipment can also be used during daylight, especially the integrated helmet sight, which provides automatic weapon aiming and reduces reaction time against unexpected targets. An omnidirectional air data system is also installed.

As requested by the Italian Army, the A129 has provision to install a mast mounted sight (MMS) for target acquisition, TOW missile tracking, laser ranging, laser designation (eg for Hellfire launch), and automatic laser tracking of targets designated by other air or ground lasers. An MMS would give the A 129 greater flexibility and survivability by allowing it to aim and fire from behind trees or other terrain features. Feasibility studies for an MMS have been carried out successfully.

Active and passive self-protection systems (ECCM and ECM) will be standard on the Italian Army A 129. Passive electronic warfare systems will include a radar warning receiver, and a laser warning receiver, which can detect enemy radars or lasers locked on to the helicopter and signal them to the crew for evasive action or the appropriate use of active countermeasures. The latter may include a radar jammer and infra-red jammer, and a chaff/flare dispenser.

ARMAMENT: Four underwing attachments, inner pair stressed for loads of up to 300 kg (661 lb) each, outer pair (at wingtips) also for 300 kg each. All stations incorporate articulation which allows pylon to be elevated 2° and depressed 10° from armament datum line. They are aligned with the aircraft automatically, with no need for boresighting. Initial armament of up to eight TOW wire guided anti-tank missiles (two, three of four in pod suspended from each wingtip station); with these can be carried, on the inboard stations, either two 7.62, 12.7 or 20 mm gun pods, or two launchers each for seven air-to-surface rockets. For general attack missions, rocket launchers can be carried on all four stations (two nineteen-tube plus two seven-tube). Alternatively, is able to carry six Hellfire anti-tank missiles (three beneath each wingtip); two Sidewinder, Mistral or Stinger air-to-air missiles; eight Hot missiles; two gun pods plus two nineteen-tube rocket launchers; or grenade launchers. A 'chin' turret for a 0.50 in or 12.7 mm gun may be mounted under the nose.

DIMENSIONS, EXTERNAL:

Main rotor diameter	11.90 m (39 ft 0½ in)
Tail rotor diameter	2.24 m (7 ft 4¼ in)
Wing span	3.20 m (10 ft 6 in)
Width over TOW pods	3.60 m (11 ft 9¾ in)
Length overall, both rotors turning	14.29 m (46 ft 10½ in)
Fuselage: Length	12.275 m (40 ft 3¼ in)
Max width	0.95 m (3 ft 1½ in)
Height to top of rotorhead	3.35 m (11 ft 0 in)
Wheel track	2.20 m (7 ft 3½ in)
Wheelbase	6.955 m (22 ft 9¾ in)

AREA:

Main rotor disc	111.2 m² (1,196.95 sq ft)

WEIGHTS:

Weight empty, equipped	2,529 kg (5,575 lb)
Max external weapons load	1,000 kg (2,205 lb)
Max T-O weight	4,100 kg (9,039 lb)

PERFORMANCE:

At mission T-O weight of 3,700 kg (8,157 lb), at 2,000 m (6,560 ft), ISA + 20°C, except where indicated, the A 129 is designed to meet the following performance requirements:

Dash speed	170 knots (315 km/h; 196 mph)
Max level speed at S/L	140 knots (259 km/h; 161 mph)
Max rate of climb at S/L	637 m (2,090 ft)/min
Hovering ceiling: IGE	3,290 m (10,800 ft)
OGE	2,390 m (7,850 ft)

Basic 2 h 30 min mission profile with 8 TOW and 20 min fuel reserves

Fly 54 nm (100 km; 62 miles) to battle area, mainly in NOE mode, 90 min loiter (incl 45 min hovering), and return to base

Max endurance, no reserves	3 h 0 min
g limit	+ 3.5

Agusta A 129 (Developed versions)

Three possible variants of the A 129 Mangusta are being promoted by Agusta, which released first details at the 1985 Paris Air Show. The first of these, now named **Tonal** after an ancient Aztec deity, is an advanced multi-mission version to meet the requirements of the British, Dutch, Spanish and Italian armies. An agreement for a joint study was signed by Agusta, Westland and Fokker in 1985, with CASA joining in 1986. On 4 September 1986 the three original partners agreed to set up a new Joint European Helicopter company in Italy to carry out a technical and cost study for the Tonal, with CASA to sign shortly afterwards. Shareholdings are 38% each to Agusta and Westland, 19% to Fokker and 5% to CASA. Air-to-air, scout and anti-tank versions of the Tonal are planned.

Second proposed version is a ship- or shore-based **naval** development for anti-shipping and maritime support roles, with nose mounted radar, and an armament of two Marte Mk 2 or four Sea Skua missiles in the anti-shipping role or Mavericks, TOWs or rocket pods for maritime support.

The third proposal is for an **LBH** (light battlefield helicopter) tactical-support version which would combine the Mangusta's rotor system, powerplant and landing gear with an entirely new and larger fuselage having side-by-side crew seating and a cabin able to accommodate an eight-man assault squad, or six stretchers and two medical attendants. Provisions would be made for a 'chin' mounted gun turret, a 272 kg (600 lb) capacity rescue hoist, side looking airborne radar, and gun or rocket pods on the wing pylons.

Agusta-Bell 204AS and 212ASW

Agusta designed and built a special ASW version of the AB 204 (US Bell Model 204 built under licence) as the Agusta-Bell 204AS, for the Italian and Spanish navies. The 204AS was provided with electronic equipment for automatic stabilisation (ASE) and for automatic approach to hovering (AATH), in addition to complete instrumentation for all-weather flying. It was developed specifically for the anti-submarine search and attack role, for which task it is fitted with sonar, linked to the electronic equipment for stabilisation during search, and could be fitted optionally with AN/APN-195 search radar and two Mk 44 torpedoes.

The multi-role version of the AB 204AS, of which a substantial number was ordered, is capable of operation also against fast surface vessels, for which purpose it is provided with Bendix AN/AQS-13B search radar and Aérospatiale AS.12 or similar-type missiles. All AB 204s may be fitted with long-range auxiliary fuel tanks, rescue hoist and emergency flotation gear. Powerplant of the AB 204AS is the General Electric T58-GE-3, with a T-O rating of 1,290 shp.

As a follow-on to the AB 204AS, Agusta subsequently developed an extensively modified version of the AB 212 (the US Bell Model 212 built under licence in Italy), intended primarily for anti-submarine search and attack missions, and for attacks on surface vessels, but suitable also for search and rescue and utility roles. (The military version of the Bell Model 212 had first been delivered to the USAF in 1970 as the UH-1N for support operations of the Special Operations Force, followed by examples to other users.) A new Agusta SAR version has been developed recently with such additional features as a hydraulically operated external hoist and a four-channel Sperry autopilot. The 212 ASW benefits from considerable naval operational experience gained with the single-engined AB 204AS, and can operate from the same small ship decks. More than 100 are in service worldwide; recent customers have included the Greek Navy (12,

Agusta-Bell 212ASW in the insignia of the Italian Navy. *(Giovanni Masino)*

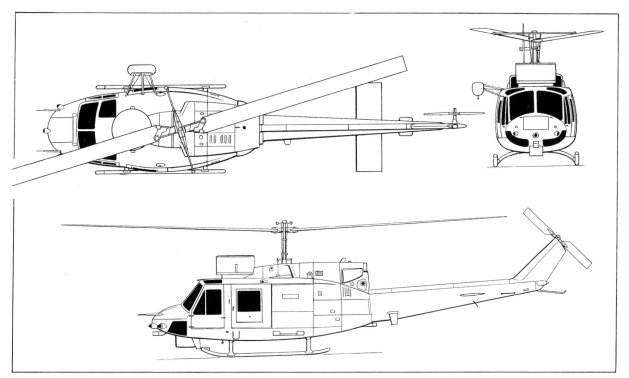

Agusta-Bell AB 212ASW. *(Pilot Press)*

including some in electronic warfare configuration), Iraqi Navy (5), Turkish Navy (12 in both ASW and ASV configurations), and Venezuela (6).

Apart from some local strengthening and the provision of deck mooring equipment, the airframe structure remains essentially similar to that of the commercial Model 212 and UH-1N.

The following details refer to the AB 212ASW, unless otherwise stated:

TYPE: Twin-engined anti-submarine and anti-surface-vessel helicopter.

ROTOR SYSTEM: Two-blade semi-rigid main rotor with interchangeable blades. Stabilising bar above and at right angles to main rotor blades. Underslung feathering axis head. Two-blade tail rotor. Rotor brake optional.

FUSELAGE: Conventional semi-monocoque structure.

TAIL UNIT: Small fixed stabiliser on rear fuselage.

LANDING GEAR: Tubular skid type. Lock-on ground handling wheels, fixed floats and inflatable nylon float bags optional.

POWERPLANT: One Pratt & Whitney Canada PT6T-6 Turbo Twin Pac, rated at 1,398 kW (1,875 shp). Protection against salt water corrosion. Provision for one internal or two external auxiliary fuel tanks.

ACCOMMODATION: Normal crew of three or four. Naval 212 can accommodate two pilots and seven passengers; or two pilots, four stretcher patients and attendant.

AVIONICS AND EQUIPMENT: Complete instrumentation for day and night sea operation in all weathers. Avionics installed are UHF transceiver, HF transceiver, and Agusta AG-03-M intercom, for communications; ADF, Tacan and homing UHF, for navigation assistance; radar altimeter, Doppler radar, ASW navigation computer, and automatic flight control system with General Electric SR-3 gyro platform, Sperry four-axis autopilot with AATH

(automatic approach to hover) mode for automatic navigation; IFF/SIF transponder; search radar and radar transponder; data link; and Bendix AN/AQS-13B/F sonar for ASW search.

ARMAMENT AND OPERATIONAL EQUIPMENT: Weapons may consist of two Motofides 244 AS or two Mk 44/46 homing torpedoes, or two Marte Mk 2 or Sea Skua type air-to-surface missiles. Rescue hoist, capacity 272 kg (600 lb), standard. Provisions for auxiliary installations such as a 2,270 kg (5,000 lb) capacity cargo sling, inflatable emergency pontoons, internal and external auxiliary fuel tanks, according to mission.

ASW MISSION: Basic sensor system for ASW search and attack is a Bendix AN/AQS-13B/F low-frequency variable-depth sonar, with a max operating depth of 137 m (450 ft). Automatic navigation system permits positioning of helicopter over any desired 'dip' point of a complex search pattern. Position of helicopter, computed by automatic navigation system, is integrated with sonar target information in radar tactical display where both surface and underwater tactical situations can be continuously monitored. Additional navigation and tactical information provided by UHF direction finding equipment, from an A/A mode-capable Tacan and a radar transponder. Automatic flight control system (AFCS) integrates basic automatic stabilisation equipment with signal output from radar altimeter, Doppler radar, sonar cable angle signals, and outputs from dry-cable transducer. Effectiveness of this system results in hands-off flight from cruise condition to sonar hover in all weathers and under rough sea conditions. Specially designed cockpit display shows pilots all flight parameters for each phase of ASW operation. Attack mission is carried out with two homing torpedoes, or with depth charges.

ASV MISSION: For this mission AB 212ASW carries a

Ferranti Seaspray long-range search radar, with very efficient scanner design and installation possessing high discrimination in rough sea conditions. Provisions made to permit incorporation of future radar system developments. Automatic navigation systems and search radar are integrated to permit continuously updated picture of tactical situation. Provisions also incorporated for installation of the most advanced ECM systems (Selenia or Elettronica is system most commonly used). Surface attack is performed with air-to-surface missiles of the Marte Mk 2 or Sea Skua type.

STANDOFF MISSILE GUIDANCE MISSION: In this mission the AB 212ASW, with special equipment, can provide mid-course passive guidance for the ship launched Otomat 2 surface-to-surface missile. Equipment includes an SMA/APS series 360° search radar and a TG-2 real-time target data transmission system for guidance of the missile.

DIMENSIONS, EXTERNAL:
Main rotor diameter (204AS and 212ASW)
    14.63 m (48 ft 0 in)
Tail rotor diameter   2.59 m (8 ft 6 in)
Length overall, main rotor turning:
  204AS   17.37 m (57 ft 0 in)
  212ASW   17.40 m (57 ft 1 in)
Fuselage length:
  204AS   12.67 m (41 ft 7 in)
  212ASW   12.92 m (42 ft 4¾ in)
Height: to top of rotorhead   3.91 m (12 ft 10 in)
  overall   4.53 m (14 ft 10¼ in)
Width: over skids   2.64 m (8 ft 8 in)
  overall (main rotor fore and aft)   2.86 m (9 ft 4½ in)
Stabiliser span   2.86 m (9 ft 4½ in)

AREA:
Main rotor disc   168.1 m² (1,809.5 sq ft)

WEIGHTS (204AS):
Weight empty, equipped (without armament)
    2,940 kg (6,481 lb)
T-O weight (incl armament) for multi-role mission
    4,310 kg (9,501 lb)

WEIGHTS (212ASW: A: ASW mission with Mk 46 torpedoes; B: ASV mission with AS.12 missiles; C: search and rescue mission; all at S/L, ISA):
Weight empty, equipped:
  A, B, C   3,420 kg (7,540 lb)
Mission equipment:
  A (two Mk 46 torpedoes)   490 kg (1,080 lb)
  B (AS.12 installation and XM-58 sight)
    180 kg (396 lb)
  C (rescue hoist)   40 kg (89 lb)
Full fuel (normal tanks)   1,021 kg (2,250 lb)
Auxiliary external tanks   32 kg (70 lb)
Auxiliary fuel   356 kg (785 lb)
Mission T-O weight: A   5,070 kg (11,176 lb)
  B   4,973 kg (10,961 lb)
  C   4,937 kg (10,883 lb)

PERFORMANCE (204AS: typical ASW mission at AUW of 4,082 kg; 9,000 lb):
Cruising speed at S/L   90 knots (167 km/h; 103 mph)
Time for sonar search operation (50% hovering OGE, 50% cruise)   1 hr 40 min
Operation radius for above time of search
    60 nm (111 km; 69 miles)

PERFORMANCE (212ASW, at max T-O weight except where indicated, ISA):
Never-exceed speed   130 knots (240 km/h; 150 mph)
Max level speed at S/L   106 knots (196 km/h; 122 mph)
Max cruising speed with armament
    100 knots (185 km/h; 115 mph)
Max rate of climb at S/L: A   396 m (1,300 ft)/min
Hovering ceiling IGE: A   3,200 m (10,500 ft)
Hovering ceiling OGE:
  A at AUW of 4,763 kg (10,500 lb)   396 m (1,300 ft)
Search endurance (A) with 50% at 90 knots (167 km/h; 103 mph) cruise and 50% hovering OGE, 10% reserve fuel
    3 h 12 min
Search range (B) with 10% reserve fuel
    332 nm (615 km; 382 miles)
Endurance (B), no reserves   4 h 7 min
Endurance (C) at 90 knots (167 km/h; 103 mph) search speed   5 h 4 min
Max range with auxiliary tanks, 100 knots (185 km/h; 115 mph) cruise at S/L, 15% reserves
    360 nm (667 km; 414 miles)
Max endurance with auxiliary tanks, no reserves
    5 h 0 min

Agusta-Bell Griffon

The first Bell prototype of the Model 412 was flown for the first time in August 1979, and customer deliveries began in January 1981. Licence production by Agusta was initiated later that year, and civil versions for a variety of applications are now available from the Italian manufacturer.

Agusta has also developed its own multi-purpose military version of the helicopter, known as the **Griffon**, for such applications as direct fire support, area suppression, scouting and reconnaissance, air defence, assault transport, combat equipment transport, and battlefield support. Special features include high-energy-absorbing landing gear, energy attenuating seats for crew and troops (the former also armour protected), and crash resistant self-sealing fuel tanks. Other survivability options can include passive (radar and laser warning, and missile detection) and active (ECM, radar jammer and decoy) systems, and a variety of ordnance can be carried. The Griffon is capable of performing medevac,

Agusta-Bell Griffon, armed with a 25 mm Oerlikon cannon.

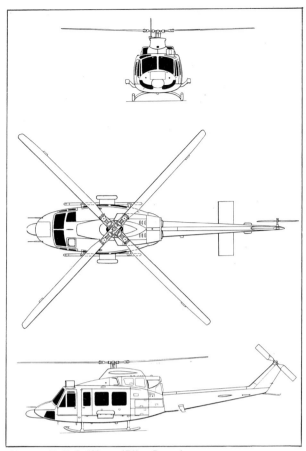

Agusta-Bell Griffon. *(Pilot Press)*

tactical support, logistic transport, maritime surveillance, pollution monitoring, search and rescue, and patrol duties, and of being used effectively against surface ships, tanks and other armoured vehicles.

A prototype of the Griffon was flown for the first time in August 1982, and deliveries began in January 1983. Customers include the Italian Army, Zimbabwe Air Force (10), Ugandan Army, and Finnish coastguard (2).

TYPE: Multi-purpose military helicopter.

ROTOR SYSTEM: Four-blade flex-beam soft-in-plane advanced technology main rotor. Blades are of similar construction to those described for the Model 214ST, but are interchangeable and have lightning protection mesh moulded into the structure and provisions for inclusion of de-icing heater elements. New design main rotorhead, with elastomeric bearings and dampers. Main rotor can be folded. Rotor brake standard. Two-blade tail rotor.

AIRFRAME: Generally similar to Model 212, but with reinforced impact-absorbing landing gear and armour protection in selected areas.

POWERPLANT: One 1,342 kW (1,800 shp) Pratt & Whitney Canada PT6T-3B Turbo Twin Pac (single-engine ratings 764 kW; 1,025 shp for 2½ min and 723 kW; 970 shp for 30 min). Fuel capacity 1,250 litres (330 US gallons; 275 Imp gallons), contained in crash resistant self-sealing tanks, three aft of cabin and two under cabin floor. Two 76 or 341 litre (20 or 90 US gallon; 17 or 75 Imp gallon) auxiliary fuel tanks optional.

ACCOMMODATION: One or two pilots on flight deck, on energy-absorbing, armour protected seats. Fourteen crash-attenuating troop seats in main cabin in personnel transport roles, six patients and two medical attendants in ambulance version, or up to 1,814 kg (4,000 lb) of cargo or other equipment. Space for 181 kg (400 lb) of baggage in tailboom. Total of 51 fittings in cabin floor for attachment of seats, stretchers, internal hoist or other special equipment.

AVIONICS AND EQUIPMENT: Typical avionics can include UHF/VHF (FM-AM) and HF secure voice com, ADF, VHF/UHF-DF, radar altimeter, IFF, DME, Tacan, VOR, navigation system, radar, Doppler radar, and four-axis AFCS. Optional avionics include AN/APR-39 radar warning receiver, laser warning receiver and pulse-Doppler radar missile detector system for passive warning of threats; active countermeasures options include AN/ALQ-144 ECM set, AN/ALQ-136 radar jammer, and chaff/flare system. A 272 kg (600 lb) capacity external rescue hoist can be fitted for search and rescue mission, and an external hook for cargo, battlefield support and other duties. Other optional equipment includes auxiliary fuel tanks, emergency floats, rotor brake, heavy duty heater, heated windscreen, loudspeakers, spectrolab, and searchlight, depending upon mission.

ARMAMENT: A variety of external weapon options for the Griffon includes two 25 mm Oerlikon cannon, four or eight TOW anti-tank missiles, two launchers each with nineteen 2.75 in SNORA rockets, two 12.7 mm machine-gun pods, four air-to-air or air defence suppression missiles, or, for attacking surface vessels, four Sea Skua or similar air-to-surface missiles.

DIMENSIONS, EXTERNAL:

Main rotor diameter	14.02 m (46 ft 0 in)
Tail rotor diameter	2.59 m (8 ft 6 in)
Length: overall (rotors turning)	17.07 m (56 ft 0 in)
fuselage (excl rotors)	12.92 m (42 ft 4¾ in)
Height: to top of rotorhead	3.29 m (10 ft 9½ in)
overall, tail rotor turning	4.32 m (14 ft 2¼ in)
Stabiliser span	2.86 m (9 ft 4½ in)

AREA:

Main rotor disc	154.40 m² (1,661.9 sq ft)

WEIGHTS:

Weight empty, equipped (standard configuration)	
	2,841 kg (6,263 lb)
Max T-O weight	5,400 kg (11,905 lb)

PERFORMANCE (at max T-O weight, ISA):

Never-exceed speed at S/L	
	140 knots (259 km/h; 161 mph)
Cruising speed:	
at S/L	122 knots (226 km/h; 140 mph)
at 1,500 m (4,920 ft)	125 knots (232 km/h; 144 mph)
at 3,000 m (9,840 ft)	123 knots (228 km/h; 142 mph)
Max rate of climb at S/L	438 m (1,437 ft)/min
Service ceiling, 30 m (100 ft)/min climb rate	
	5,180 m (17,000 ft)
Hovering ceiling: IGE	1,250 m (4,100 ft)
OGE	670 m (2,200 ft)
Range with max standard fuel at appropriate cruising speed (see above), no reserves:	
at S/L	354 nm (656 km; 407 miles)
at 1,500 m (4,920 ft)	402 nm (745 km; 463 miles)
at 3,000 m (9,840 ft)	434 nm (804 km; 500 miles)
Max endurance: at S/L	3 h 36 min
at 1,500 m (4,920 ft)	4 h 12 min

Agusta-Sikorsky AS-61 and ASH-3D/H

During 1967 Agusta began the construction under licence of Sikorsky S-61 and SH-3D helicopters. Deliveries of anti-submarine ASH-3Ds to the Italian Navy began in 1969. Additional orders have since been placed, both for the Italian armed forces and for other navies, in various configurations including ASW, VIP transport and rescue. Recent customers include the navies of Brazil (four) and Argentina (four). The VIP transport version, designated **SH-3D/TS** (Trasporto Speciale), serves with the 31° Stormo of the Italian Air Force and with some foreign air forces. Current production naval versions are to **SH-3H** standard.

Apart from some local strengthening, uprated engines and an improved horizontal tail surface, the Agusta-built airframe remains essentially similar to that of the Sikorsky built SH-3D/H, of which production has ended. The Agusta SH-3H is capable of operation in the roles of anti-submarine search, classification and strike; anti-surface-vessel (ASV); anti-surface-missile defence (ASMD); electronic warfare (EW); tactical troop lift; search and rescue (SAR); vertical replenishment; and casualty evacuation.

Starting in 1987, an SH-3 became the first airborne testbed for the BAe/Bendix HELRAS long-range high-resolution dipping sonar intended for naval versions of the Anglo-Italian EH 101 Sea King replacement helicopter.

The following description applies to the ASH-3H.

TYPE: Twin-engined amphibious all-weather anti-submarine helicopter.

ROTOR SYSTEM: Five-blade main and tail rotors. Fully articulated oil lubricated main rotor. Main rotor blades are interchangeable and are provided with an automatic folding system. Rotor brake standard. Tail rotor.

FUSELAGE: Single-step boat hull of semi-monocoque

Agusta-Sikorsky ASH-3H ASW helicopter of the Italian Navy.

construction. Tail section folds to reduce stowage requirements.

TAIL SURFACE: Fixed strut braced stabiliser on starboard side of tail section.

LANDING GEAR: Amphibious. Land gear consists of two twin-wheel main units, which are retracted rearward hydraulically into stabilising floats, and non-retractable tailwheel. Mainwheels and tubeless tyres size 6.50-10 type III. Tailwheel and tyre size 6.00-6. Hydraulic disc brakes. Boat hull and pop-out flotation bags in stabilising floats permit emergency operation from water.

POWERPLANT: Two 1,118 kW (1,500 shp) General Electric T58-GE-100 turboshaft engines, mounted side-by-side above the cabin. An optional anti-ice/sand shield can be provided. Fuel in underfloor bag tanks with a total

Agusta-Sikorsky AS-61. *(Pilot Press)*

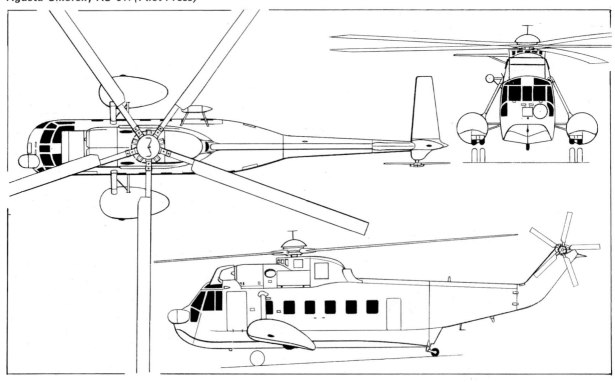

capacity of 3,180 litres (840 US gallons; 700 Imp gallons). Internal auxiliary fuel tank may be fitted for long-range ferry purposes.

ACCOMMODATION: Crew of four in ASW role (pilot, co-pilot and two sonar operators); accommodation for up to 31 paratroops in troop lift role, 15 stretchers and a medical attendant in casualty evacuation configuration, and up to 25 survivors in SAR role. Dual controls.

ARMAMENT AND OPERATIONAL EQUIPMENT (ASW/ASV roles): As equipped for these roles the ASH-3H is a fully integrated all-weather weapons system, capable of operating independently of surface vessels, and has the following equipment and weapons to achieve this task: low-frequency 360° depth AQS-18/AQS-13F sonar; Doppler radar and ASW automatic navigation system; SMA/APS-707 radar with one or two transceivers, with 'chin' radome for 360° coverage; radio altimeter; AFCS; marine markers and smoke floats; two or four homing torpedoes (A 244 AS, Mk 44 or Mk 46); or four depth charges. The AFCS provides three-axis stabilisation in pilot-controlled manoeuvres, attitude hold, heading hold and height hold in cruising flight; controlled transition manoeuvres to and from hover; automatic height control and plan position control in the hover; and trim facility. According to the threat, the Agusta SH-3H can be equipped with medium-range (four AS.12 air-to-surface wire-guided) missiles or long-range (two Marte Mk 2 or Exocet AM39/Harpoon type) missiles. The Oto Melara Marte Mk 2 is an all-weather day and night 'fire and forget' anti-ship missile with a range of 13.5 nm (25 km; 15.5 miles); guidance: sea skimming in elevation, terminal radar active homing in azimuth. The SMA/APS-707 radar has been specially designed to operate in a dense electronic emission environment and has a special interface to draw out target data to feed the computer for the long-range missiles. Provisions are also incorporated for the installation of MAD and advanced EW systems.

OPERATIONAL EQUIPMENT: (Search and rescue and transport roles): Search radar, and variable-speed hydraulic rescue hoist of 272 kg (600 lb) capacity mounted above starboard side cargo door.

DIMENSIONS, EXTERNAL:			
Main rotor diameter	18.90 m (62 ft 0 in)	Max external load capacity (with low-response sling)	
Tail rotor diameter	3.23 m (10 ft 7 in)		3,630 kg (8,000 lb)
Length overall, both rotors turning		Max T-O weight	9,525 kg (21,000 lb)
	21.91 m (71 ft 10.7 in)	PERFORMANCE (at max T-O weight):	
Length of fuselage	16.69 m (54 ft 9 in)	Never-exceed speed	144 knots (267 km/h; 165 mph)
Width (over sponsons), rotors folded	4.98 m (16 ft 4 in)	Typical cruising speed	120 knots (222 km/h; 138 mph)
Height to top of rotorhead	4.74 m (15 ft 6½ in)	Max rate of climb at S/L	670 m (2,200 ft)/min
Wheel track	3.96 m (13 ft 0 in)	Service ceiling	3,720 m (12,200 ft)
Wheelbase	7.18 m (23 ft 6½ in)	Hovering ceiling: IGE	2,500 m (8,200 ft)
AREA:		OGE	1,130 m (3,700 ft)
Main rotor blades (each)	4.14 m² (44.54 sq ft)	Range with 31 troops	314 nm (582 km; 362 miles)
WEIGHTS:		Range with max standard fuel	
Internal load capacity (cargo)	2,720 kg (6,000 lb)		630 nm (1,166 km; 725 miles)

SIAI-Marchetti SpA (Subsidiary of Agusta SpA)

Founded in 1915, the SIAI-Marchetti company produced a wide range of military and civil landplanes and flying-boats, including the transatlantic S.55 flying-boat of the 1930s and the S.M. 79 torpedo-bomber of the Second World War. Its current products include a full range of military trainers (the piston engined SF.260M/W, turboprop powered SF.260TP and turbofan engined S.211). Since the 1970s it has been engaged in the co-production with Agusta of licence-built Boeing Vertol CH-47C, Bell 204/205/212/412, and Sikorsky S-61A, SH-3D/H and HH-3F helicopters.

SIAI-Marchetti is also engaged in the overhaul and repair of various types of aircraft (notably the C-130 Hercules, DHC-5 Buffalo and Cessna Citation II). It participates in national or multi-national programmes, producing parts for the Aeritalia G222, Panavia Tornado, AMX, Atlantique 2 and other aircraft.

The company's works at Sesto Calende, Vergiate and Malpensa total 1,370,267 m² (14,749,416 sq ft) in area, and it employs about 2,000 people.

SIAI-Marchetti SF.260W Warrior

The prototype for the SF.260 series, known as the F.250, was designed by Dott Ing Stelio Frati and built by Aviamilano. Flown for the first time on 15 July 1964, it was powered by a 186.5 kW (250 hp) Avco Lycoming engine and was certificated for aerobatic flying.

The version developed initially, for civil production, was manufactured, at first under licence from Aviamilano, by SIAI-Marchetti, and is designated SF.260. It received FAA type approval on 1 April 1966. Subsequently SIAI-Marchetti became the official holder of the type certificate and of all manufacturing rights in the SF.260.

Current models include an improved civil version (SF.260D), military trainer (SF.260M), and the SF.260W Warrior as detailed below. The Warrior is operated by the air forces of Bolivia, Brunei, Burma, Burundi, Dubai, Ireland, Nicaragua, Singapore, Somali Republic, and Zimbabwe.

SF.260W Warrior. Trainer/tactical support version of SF.260M, first flown in May 1972. Two or four underwing pylons, for up to 300 kg (661 lb) of external stores, and cockpit stores selection panel. Able to undertake a wide variety of roles, including low-level strike; forward air control; forward air support; armed reconnaissance; and liaison. Also meets same requirements as SF.260M for use as a trainer. One aircraft was completed as the **SF.260SW Sea Warrior** surveillance/SAR/supply version.

SF.260TP. Turboprop powered development. Described separately.

TYPE: Two/three-seat fully aerobatic military light aircraft.

WINGS: Cantilever low-wing monoplane. Wing section NACA 64_1-212 (modified) at root, NACA 64_1-210 (modified) at tip. Dihedral 6° 20′ from roots (5° on SF.260D). Incidence 2° 45′ at root, 0° at tip. No sweepback. Differentially operating Frise balanced ailerons, and electrically actuated single-slotted flaps. Servo tab in each aileron.

FUSELAGE: Semi-monocoque safe-life structure.

TAIL UNIT: Cantilever safe-life structure, with sweptback vertical surfaces, fixed-incidence tailplane and one-piece elevator. Balanced rudder. Controllable trim tab in starboard half of elevator; ground adjustable tab on rudder.

LANDING GEAR: Electrically retractable tricycle type, with manual emergency actuation. Inward retracting main gear, of trailing arm type, and rearward retracting nose unit. Cleveland P/N 3080A mainwheels, with size 6.00-6 tube and tyre (6-ply rating). Cleveland P/N 40-77A nosewheel, with size 5.00-5 tube and tyre (6-ply rating). Cleveland P/N 3000-500 independent hydraulic single-disc brake and parking brake on each mainwheel. Nosewheel steering (20° to left or right) is operated directly by the rudder pedals. Up-lock secures main gear in retracted position during flight; anti-retraction system prevents main gear from retracting whenever strut is compressed by weight of aircraft.

POWERPLANT: One 194 kW (260 hp) Avco Lycoming O-540-E4A5 flat-six engine, driving a Hartzell HC-C2YK-1BF/8477-8R two-blade constant-speed metal propeller with spinner. IO-540 engine available optionally. Fuel in two light alloy tanks in wings, capacity of each 49.5 litres (13 US gallons; 10.9 Imp gallons); and two permanent wingtip tanks, capacity of each 72 litres (19 US gallons; 15.85 Imp gallons). Total internal fuel capacity 243 litres (64 US gallons; 53.5 Imp gallons), of which 235 litres (62 US gallons; 51.7 Imp gallons) are usable. Individual refuelling point on top of each tank. In addition, SF.260W may be fitted with two 80 litre (21 US gallon; 17.5 Imp gallon) auxiliary tanks on underwing pylons.

ACCOMMODATION: Side-by-side front seats, with third seat centrally at rear. Dual controls standard. Emergency canopy-release handle for each front seat occupant. Steel tube windscreen frame for protection in the event of an overturn.

AVIONICS AND EQUIPMENT: Basic instrumentation and military equipment to customer's requirements. Blind-flying instrumentation and communications equipment optional: typical selection includes dual Collins 20B VHF com; Collins VIR-31A VHF nav; Collins ADF-60A; Collins TDR-90 ATC transponder; Collins PN-101 compass; ID-90-000 RMI; and Gemelli AG04-1 intercom.

ARMAMENT: Two or four underwing hardpoints, able to carry external stores on NATO standard pylons up to a maximum of 300 kg (661 lb) when flown as a single-seater. Typical alternative loads can include one or two SIAI gun pods, each with one or two 7.62 mm FN machine-guns and 500 rds; two Aerea AL-8-70 launchers each with eight 2.75 in rockets; two LAU-32 launchers each with seven 2.75 in rockets; two Aerea AL-18-50 launchers each with eighteen 2 in rockets; two Aerea AL-8-68 launchers each with eight 68 mm rockets; two Aerea AL-6-80 launchers each with six 81 mm rockets; two LUU-2/B parachute flares; two SAMP EU 32 125 kg general-purpose bombs or EU 13 120 kg fragmentation bombs; two SAMP EU 70 50 kg general-purpose bombs; Mk 76 11 kg practice bombs; two cartridge throwers for 70 mm multi-purpose cartridges, F 725 flares, or F 130 smoke cartridges; one or two photo-reconnaissance pods with two 70 mm automatic cameras; two supply containers; or two 80 litre (21 US gallon; 17.5 Imp gallon) auxiliary fuel tanks.

DIMENSIONS, EXTERNAL:

Wing span over tip tanks	8.35 m (27 ft 4¾ in)
Length overall	7.10 m (23 ft 3½ in
Height overall	2.41 m (7 ft 11 in)
Wheel track	2.274 m (7 ft 5½ in)
Wheelbase	1.66 m (5 ft 5¼ in)
Propeller diameter	1.93 m (6 ft 4 in)

AREA:

Wings, gross	10.10 m² (108.70 sq ft)

WEIGHTS:

Manufacturer's basic weight empty	770 kg (1,697 lb)
Weight empty, equipped	830 kg (1,830 lb)

Typical mission weights:

Two 47 kg (103.5 lb) machine-gun pods and full internal fuel — 1,163 kg (2,564 lb)

One Alkan 500B cartridge thrower, one two-camera reconnaissance pod and full internal fuel — 1,182 kg (2,605 lb)

Trainer with 94 kg (207 lb) external stores — 1,249 kg (2,753 lb)

Self-ferry with two 80 litre (21 US gallon; 17.5 Imp gallon) underwing tanks — 1,285 kg (2,833 lb)

Two 125 kg bombs and 150 kg (331 lb) internal fuel — 1,300 kg (2,866 lb)

Two AL8-70 rocket launchers and 160 kg (353 lb) internal fuel — 1,300 kg (2,866 lb)

Max T-O weight — 1,300 kg (2,866 lb)

PERFORMANCE at 1,300 kg; 2,866 lb, except where indicated):

Max level speed at S/L	165 knots (305 km/h; 190 mph)
Max cruising speed (75% power), at 1,500 m (4,925 ft)	152 knots (281 km/h; 175 mph)
Stalling speed, flaps and landing gear up	88 knots (163 km/h; 102 mph)
Stalling speed, flaps and landing gear down	72 knots (134 km/h; 83 mph)
Max rate of climb at S/L	381 m (1,250 ft)/min
Time to 1,500 m (4,925 ft)	6 min 20 s
Time to 2,300 m (7,550 ft)	10 min 20 s
Time to 3,000 m (9,850 ft)	18 min 40 s
Service ceiling	4,480 m (14,700 ft)
T-O to 15 m (50 ft) at S/L	825 m (2,707 ft)
Landing from 15 m (50 ft) at S/L	645 m (2,116 ft)

Operational radius:

6 h 25 min single-seat armed patrol mission at 1,163 kg (2,564 lb) AUW, incl 5 h 35 min over operating area, 20 kg (44 lb) fuel reserves — 50 nm (92 km; 57 miles)

3 h 38 min single-seat strike mission, incl two 5 min loiters over separate en-route target areas, 20 kg (44 lb) fuel reserves — 250 nm (463 km; 287 miles)

4 h 54 min single-seat strike mission, incl 5 min over target area, 20 kg (44 lb) fuel reserves — 300 nm (556 km; 345 miles)

4 h 30 min single-seat photo-reconnaissance mission at 1,182 kg (2,605 lb) AUW, incl three 1 h loiters over separate en-route operating areas, 20 kg (44 lb) fuel reserves — 150 nm (278 km; 172 miles)

6 h 3 min two-seat self-ferry mission with two 80 litre (21 US gallon; 17.5 Imp gallon) underwing tanks, at 1,285 kg (2,833 lb) AUW, 30 kg (66 lb) fuel reserves — 926 nm (1,716 km; 1,066 miles)

SIAI-Marchetti SF 260TP of the Sri Lankan Air Force. *(Press Office Sturzenegger)*

SIAI-Marchetti SF.260TP

First flown in July 1980, the SF.260TP is a turboprop powered development of the SF.260M/W, the airframe remaining virtually unchanged aft of the firewall except for

SIAI-Marchetti SF.260TP. *(Pilot Press)*

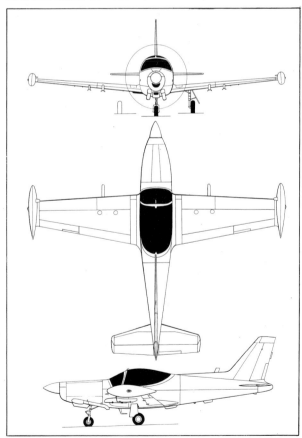

substitution of an inset rudder trim tab and provision of an automatic fuel feed system.

More than 60 SF.260TPs have been ordered by military customers, the most recent being the air force of Sri Lanka (6).

AIRFRAME: As SF.260W, except for increased overall length and provision of trim tab in rudder.

POWERPLANT: One Allison 250-B17D turboprop engine, flat rated at 261 kW (350 shp) and driving a Hartzell HC-B3TF-7A/T10173-25R three-blade constant-speed fully-feathering and reversible-pitch propeller with spinner. Fuel capacity as for SF.260M/W; automatic fuel feed system.

ACCOMMODATION, SYSTEMS, AVIONICS AND EQUIPMENT: Generally as for SF.260.

DIMENSIONS, EXTERNAL AND AREA:
As for SF.260 except:
Length overall 7.40 m (24 ft $3\frac{1}{4}$ in)
WEIGHTS: As for SF.260W except:
Weight empty, equipped 750 kg (1,654 lb)
PERFORMANCE (at trainer Utility T-O weight of 1,200 kg; 2,645 lb, ISA):
Never-exceed speed 236 knots (437 km/h; 271 mph)
Max level speed at 3,050 m (10,000 ft)
 228 knots (422 km/h; 262 mph)
Max cruising speed at 2,440 m (8,000 ft)
 216 knots (400 km/h; 248 mph)
Econ cruising speed at 4,575 m (15,000 ft)
 170 knots (315 km/h; 195 mph)
Stalling speed at S/L, flaps down, power off
 68 knots (126 km/h; 79 mph)
Max rate of climb at S/L 661 m (2,170 ft)/min
Service ceiling 7,500 m (24,600 ft)
T-O run 298 m (978 ft)
Landing run, without reverse pitch 307 m (1,007 ft)
Range at 4,575 m (15,000 ft) with max fuel, 30 min reserves 512 nm (949 km; 589 miles)

Japan

Kawasaki
KAWASAKI JUKOGYO KABUSHIKI KAISHA
(Kawasaki Heavy Industries Ltd)

With effect from 1 April 1969, Kawasaki Aircraft Co Ltd was amalgamated with the Kawasaki Dockyard Co Ltd and the Kawasaki Rolling Stock Mfg Co Ltd, to form Kawasaki Heavy Industries Ltd. The Aircraft Division of the former Kawasaki Aircraft Co Ltd, which employs some 3,900 people, continues its activities as the Aircraft Group of this company.

In addition to extensive overhaul work, Kawasaki has built many US aircraft under licence since 1955, including 48 Lockheed P2V-7 (P-2H) Neptune anti-submarine aircraft and 239 Bell Model 47 helicopters, plus another 211 Model KH-4 helicopters developed from the Bell 47 by its own design staff. From the Neptune it developed the P-2J anti-submarine aircraft, of which it delivered one prototype and 82 production examples.

Kawasaki is developing, as prime contractor, the Japan Defence Agency's new T-4 intermediate trainer to succeed both the Lockheed T-33A and the Fuji T-1. The company has developed, jointly with MBB of West Germany, the BK 117 twin-engined multi-purpose helicopter described in the International section.

Kawasaki is prime contractor for licence production of the Lockheed P-3C/Update II Orion, 100 of which are to be purchased by the JMSDF. Sixty-nine have so far been ordered. The first three (US-built) P-3Cs were handed over to the JMSDF in April 1981. The next four were assembled by Kawasaki from knocked-down assemblies; the first of these made its initial flight on 17 March 1982, and was delivered on 26 May that year to Fleet Squadron 51 at Atsugi Air Base. The remaining 62 are being built almost entirely in Japan, and the third and fourth P-3C squadrons, at Hachinohe, were equipped in 1985–86. Kawasaki is responsible for building the centre-fuselages, and for final assembly and flight testing. Kawasaki is also a subcontractor for rear fuselages, wings and tail units of the McDonnell Douglas

F-15J Eagles being licence-built in Japan by Mitsubishi.

Kawasaki has exclusive rights to manufacture and sell the twin-engined Boeing Vertol 107 Model II helicopter and its own KV107IIA development of it. McDonnell Douglas MD 500 series light observation helicopters are also being manufactured by Kawasaki under a licence agreement concluded in October 1967, while Kawasaki and Fuji are prime contractors for Japanese assembly of engines and airframes respectively for Bell AH-1S gunship helicopters for the JGSDF.

Kawasaki P-2J

JMSDF designation: P-2J

The P-2J was developed by Kawasaki, originally under the designation GK-210, to meet a JMSDF requirement for a new anti-submarine aircraft to replace its P2V-7 Neptunes in service during the 1970s. Design is based very closely upon that of the P2V-7 (P-2H), and began in October 1961. Work on the conversion of a standard P2V-7 as the P-2J prototype began in June 1965, and this aircraft flew for the first time on 21 July 1966.

The first production P-2J was flown on 8 August 1969, and was delivered to the JMSDF on 7 October. The second aircraft was also flown before the end of 1969, and nine contracts covered the delivery of 82 P-2Js by 1979. At least 55 P-2Js still operate in their original role. Two P-2Js have been converted to UP-2J configuration with equipment for target towing, ECM training and drone launch operations. Two others have been converted as EP-2J electronic intelligence (elint) aircraft, equipped with HLR-105 and HLR-106 systems. All four serve with No. 81 Squadron (3rd Fleet Air Wing) at Iwakuni. One P2V-7 was converted by Kawasaki, under Japan Defence Agency contract, as an experimental variable-stability aircraft.

Kawasaki P-2J anti-submarine and maritime patrol aircraft. *(K. Hinata)*

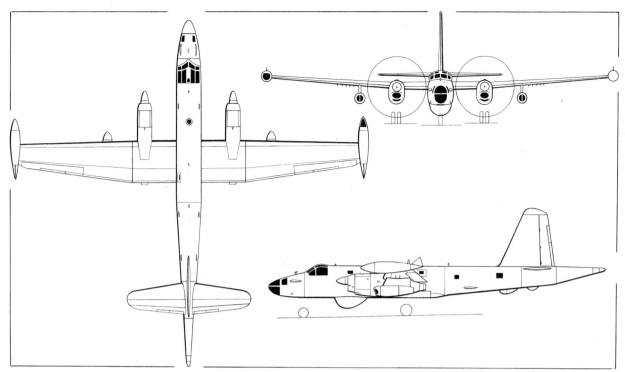

Kawasaki P-2J. *(Pilot Press)*

TYPE: Four-engined anti-submarine and maritime patrol aircraft.

WINGS: Cantilever all-metal mid-wing monoplane, with taper on outer panels. Wing section NACA 2419 (modified) at root, NACA 4410.5 at tip. Dihedral 5° on outer panels. Incidence 3° 30′ at root. No sweepback. Wing designed to give temporary flotation in event of ditching. Ailerons each incorporate a spring and trim tab. Fowler-type inboard and outboard trailing-edge flaps. Two-section spoilers in upper surface of outer wing panels, inboard of ailerons. Thermal de-icing of leading edges.

FUSELAGE: Conventional unpressurised semi-monocoque structure, basically as P2V-7 (P-2H) but with extra 1.27 m (4 ft 2 in) section inserted between wing leading edge and cockpit to house improved electronic equipment.

TAIL UNIT: Cantilever structure, incorporating 'Varicam' (variable camber), a movable trimming surface between the fixed tailplane and each elevator. Spring tab and trim tab in rudder, balance tab and spring tab in each elevator. Tail unit has thermal de-icing and is virtually unchanged from P2V-7 except for an increase in rudder area by extending the chord by 0.30 m (1 ft) at the top.

LANDING GEAR: Retractable tricycle type, with single steerable nosewheel and twin-wheel main units. Hydraulic retraction, nosewheel rearward, mainwheels forward into inboard engine nacelles. Goodyear Type VII tubeless tyres on all units, size 9.9 × 34-14 on nosewheel and 13 × 39-16 on mainwheels. Goodyear disc brakes and on/off-type anti-skid units on main units.

POWERPLANT: Two 2,282 kW (3,060 ehp) Japanese-built General Electric T64-IHI-10E turboprop engines, with water methanol injection, mounted on wing centre-section and each driving a Sumitomo Precision 63E60-19 three-blade variable-pitch metal propeller. Outboard of

these, on underwing pylons, are two pod-mounted Ishikawajima-Harima J3-IHI-7D turbojets, each rated at 15.2 kN (3,417 lb st). Fuel in inboard and outboard wing tanks with total capacity of 11,433 litres (3,020 US gallons; 2,515 Imp gallons), plus 1,514 litres (400 US gallons; 333 Imp gallons) in port wingtip tank. For ferry purposes a 2,650 litre (700 US gallon; 583 Imp gallon) auxiliary tank can be installed in the weapons bay.

ACCOMMODATION: Crew of 12, including two pilots on flight deck, seven men in tactical compartment in forward fuselage and three aft of centre-section wing box beam. Aft of the tactical compartment, in centre fuselage, are an ordnance room, galley and toilet. Crew escape hatches in flight deck, tactical and ordnance compartments.

ELECTRONICS AND EQUIPMENT (later, modernised version): Communications and navigation equipment comprises HIC-3 interphone, HRC-110 UHF transceiver, HRC-106 VHF transceiver, two HRC-107 HF transceivers, two N-CU-58/HRC HF antenna couplers, HGC-102 teletypewriter, HGA-101 TTY converter, HSC-1 TTY security unit, RRC-15 emergency radio, AN/APN-187B-N Doppler radar, N-PT-3 navigation plotter, N-OA-35/HSA tactical plotter, HRN-104 Loran, HRN-101 ADF, AN/ARA-50 UHF/DF, HRN-105 Tacan, AN/APN-171-NI radar altimeter, HRN-106B VOR/ILS/MKR receiver, PB-60J autopilot, MAD manoevure programmer and flight director system. ASW equipment comprises HSA-116 integrated data display system and digital data processor (for both navigation and tactical data), AN/APS-80-N search radar, AN/APA-125-N radar indicator, HLR-101 ESM, HSQ-101 MAD, HSA-102 AMC, HSA-103 SAD, AN/ASA-20B Julie recorder, AN/AQA-5-N Jezebel recorder, HQA-101 active sonobuoy indicator, AN/ARR-52A(V) sonobuoy receiver,

N-R-86/HRA OTPI, N-RO-22/HMH BT recorder, HQH-101 data recorder, AN/APX-68-N SIF transponder, HPX-101 IFF interrogator, N-KY-122/HPX IFF decoder, and HSA-1B sonobuoy data display system. Searchlight in starboard wingtip pod.

DIMENSIONS, EXTERNAL:

Wing span	29.78 m (97 ft 8½ in)
Wing span over tip-tanks	30.87 m (101 ft 3½ in)
Length overall	29.23 m (95 ft 10¾ in)
Height overall	8.93 m (29 ft 3½ in)
Wheel track (c/l of shock-absorbers)	7.62 m (25 ft 0 in)
Wheelbase	8.84 m (29 ft 0 in)
Propeller diameter	4.43 m (14 ft 6¼ in)

AREA:

Wings, gross	92.9 m² (1,000 sq ft)

WEIGHTS:

Weight empty	19,277 kg (42,500 lb)
Max T-O weight	34,019 kg (75,000 lb)

PERFORMANCE (at max T-O weight):

Never-exceed speed	350 knots (649 km/h; 403 mph)
Max cruising speed	217 knots (402 km/h; 250 mph)
Econ cruising speed at 3,050 m (10,000 ft)	200 knots (370 km/h; 230 mph)
Stalling speed, flaps down	90 knots (166 km/h; 103 mph)
Max rate of climb at S/L	550 m (1,800 ft)/min
Service ceiling	9,150 m (30,000 ft)
T-O to 15 m (50 ft)	1,100 m (3,600 ft)
Landing from 15 m (50 ft)	880 m (2,880 ft)
Range with max fuel	2,400 nm (4,450 km; 2,765 miles)

Mitsubishi
MITSUBISHI JUKOGYO KABUSHIKI KAISHA
(Mitsubishi Heavy Industries Ltd)

Mitsubishi began the production of aircraft in the present Oye plant of its Nagoya Engineering Works in 1921, and manufactured a total of 18,000 aircraft of approximately 100 different types during the 24 years before the end of the Second World War in 1945. The company was also one of the leading aero engine manufacturers in Japan, and produced a total of 52,000 engines in the 1,000–2,500 hp range. The conclusion of the Peace Treaty in 1952 enabled the aircraft industry in Japan to recommence, and in December of that year the company constructed its present Komaki South plant. This factory, together with Mitsubishi's Oye and Komaki North plants, was later consolidated as Nagoya Aircraft Works, with a combined floor area of 552,463 m² (5,946,666 sq ft).

By 1990 the Japan Defence Agency plans to procure a total of 187 McDonnell Douglas F-15 Eagles, including 14 US-built aircraft (two single-seat F-15Js and 12 two-seat F-15DJs) supplied as Foreign Military Sales. The first two US-built F-15s were followed by eight assembled in Japan from US supplied knocked-down assemblies. First aircraft of the latter batch flew on 26 August 1981 and was delivered on 11 December that year. First JASDF F-15 squadron was No. 202 (5th Air Wing) at Nyutabaru, which was activated in December 1982 with 20 F-15J/DJs. Other units now equipped are Nos. 201 and 203 Squadrons of the 2nd Air Wing at Chitose, Hokkaido; No. 204 (7th Air Wing, at Hyakuri); and No. 205. Mitsubishi is building the forward and centre-fuselages, and is responsible for final assembly and flight testing. Participants in the programme include Fuji (landing gear doors), Kawasaki (wings and tail assembly), Nippi (pylons and missile launchers), Shin Meiwa (drop-tanks), Sumitomo (landing gear), and IHI (engines). The J/ALQ-8 ECM and radar warning systems of all these aircraft are of Japanese design and manufacture. A total of 136 F-15J/DJs had been funded up to FY 1986.

Mitsubishi holds licence agreements to manufacture the Sikorsky S-61, S-61B (HSS-2/2A/2B) and S-61A helicopters. Between 1 April 1984 and 31 March 1987 Mitsubishi delivered seven HSS-2Bs (and one S-61A) to the JMSDF. By the latter date it had delivered to the JMSDF, for ASW and rescue, 131 helicopters of the HSS-2 series and 12 S-61As, out of a total order for 154 HSS-2/2A/2B/S-61As. Thirteen HSS-2Bs and one S-61A were approved in the FY 1986 budget. Under the FY 1985 budget Mitsubishi received funding to begin design work on the XSH-60J, a development of the Sikorsky SH-60B Seahawk ASW helicopter for the JMSDF.

Mitsubishi is prime contractor for the T-2 supersonic trainer and F-1 close support combat aircraft for the JASDF, with Fuji, Nippi and Shin Meiwa as principal subcontractors. It is producing forward and rear fuselages for the Lockheed P-3C Orions ordered by the JMSDF, under subcontract to Kawasaki.

Mitsubishi F-4EJKai

In co-operation with Kawasaki as subcontractor, Mitsubishi was the JDA's prime contractor in producing F-4EJ Phantom tactical fighters for the JASDF, under licence from McDonnell Douglas Corporation. The last of 140 F-4EJs was delivered to the JASDF on 20 May 1981; Mitsubishi is engaged currently in a major programme to update F-4EJ equipment and weapon systems. The prototype F-4EJKai (07-8431) was first flown on 17 July 1984 and delivered on the following 13 December. It has a Westinghouse AN/APG-66J fire control system, advanced avionics which include a Litton LN-39 INS, head-up display, and J/APR-4Kai radar warning receiver, lookdown/shootdown capability with

Mitsubishi F-4EJKai operated by 306 Squadron, 6th Wing, JASDF. (K. Hinata)

AIM-7E/F Sparrows or AIM-9P/4 Sidewinders, and can carry two ASM-1 anti-shipping missiles. Current plans are to convert 100 of the JASDF's remaining F-4EJs to F-4EJKai configuration and another 17 to RF-4EJ reconnaissance-fighters.

Mitsubishi F-1

Following the JASDF's decision to develop a single-seat close-air-support fighter from the T-2 supersonic trainer, design of this aircraft began in 1972. The second and third production T-2 trainers were converted as prototypes, in which form they made their first flights on 7 and 3 June 1975 respectively. They were delivered to the JASDF Air Proving Wing at Gifu in July and August 1975, and after a year of flight test and evaluation the aircraft was type approved in November 1976 and officially designated F-1.

Production orders were placed for 77 F-1s, of which all have been delivered. The first production F-1 made its first flight on 16 June 1977, and was delivered to the JASDF on 26 September 1977. F-1s serve with the 3rd Squadron of the 3rd Air Wing at Misawa and the 8th Air Wing at Tsuiki.

TYPE: Single-seat close-support fighter.

WINGS: Cantilever all-metal shoulder-wing monoplane. Wing section NACA 65 series (modified). Thickness/chord ratio 4.66%. Anhedral 9° from roots. Sweepback on leading edges 68° at root, 42° 29' inboard of extended chord outer panels and 36° on outer panels; basic sweepback at quarter-chord 35° 47'. Electrically actuated leading-edge flaps, the outer portions of which have extended chord. Electrically actuated single-slotted flaps. No conventional ailerons. Lateral control by hydraulically actuated two-section slotted spoilers ahead of flaps.

FUSELAGE: Conventional semi-monocoque structure. Generally similar to earlier T-2, but with rear cockpit area

Mitsubishi F-1 close-support aircraft.

modified as avionics compartment for bombing computer, inertial navigation system and radar warning system. Two hydraulically actuated door-type airbrakes under centre of fuselage, aft of mainwheel bays.

TAIL UNIT: Cantilever structure. One-piece hydraulically actuated all-moving swept tailplane, with 15° anhedral. Small ventral fin under each side of fuselage at rear. Hydraulically actuated rudder.

LANDING GEAR: Hydraulically retractable tricycle type, with pneumatic backup for emergency extension. Main units retract forward into fuselage, nose unit rearward. Single wheel on each unit. Nosewheel steerable through 72°. Nosewheel tyre size 18 × 5.5 Type VII (14 ply rating); mainwheel tyres size 25 × 6.75 Type VII (18 ply rating). Hydraulic brakes and Hydro-Aire anti-skid units. Runway arrester hook beneath rear fuselage. Brake parachute in tailcone.

POWERPLANT: Two Rolls-Royce Turboméca Adour Mk

Mitsubishi F-1. *(Pilot Press)*

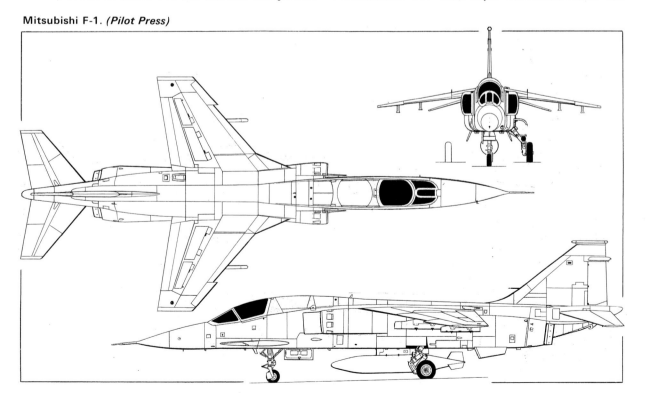

801A turbofan engines, each rated at 22.75 kN (5,115 lb st) dry and 32.49 kN (7,305 lb st) with afterburning, mounted side-by-side in centre of fuselage. (Engines licence-built by Ishikawajima-Harima, under designation TF40-IHI-801A.) Fixed-geometry air intake, with auxiliary 'blow-in' intake doors, on each side of fuselage aft of rear cockpit. Fuel in seven fuselage tanks with total capacity of 3,823 litres (1,010 US gallons; 841 Imp gallons). Three 821 litre (217 US gallon; 180 Imp gallon) auxiliary fuel tanks can be carried beneath the wings and fuselage.

ACCOMMODATION: Pilot only on Daiseru-built Weber ES-7J zero-zero ejection seat in pressurised cockpit. Fairing in place of second canopy.

AVIONICS AND EQUIPMENT: Dual UHF; Tacan; IFF/SIF; Mitsubishi Electric J/AWG-12 nose mounted air-to-air and air-to-ground radar, with Mitsubishi Electric (Thomson-CSF) head-up display; Ferranti 6TNJ-F inertial navigation system; radio altimeter; air data computer; Mitsubishi Electric J/ASQ-1 fire control system and bombing computer (replacing original fire control and bombing computer from January 1982, for compatibility with ASM-1 missile); strike camera system; radar homing and warning system; attitude and heading reference system.

ARMAMENT: Single JM61 multi-barrel 20 mm cannon. One underfuselage and four underwing hardpoints with detachable multiple ejector racks. Primary weapon is the Mitsubishi ASM-1 air-to-surface missile, of which two can be carried on underwing stations. Bombs of 500 or 750 lb can be carried on all five external stations, up to a maximum weight of 2,721 kg (twelve 500 lb bombs). Infra-red and laser guidance systems for free-fall 500 and 750 lb bombs were reported to be under development by the JASDF in 1983–84. The four underwing stations can each be used for rocket pods such as the JLAU-3A (with nineteen 70 mm), RL-7 (seven 70 mm) and RL-4 (four 125 mm). For air-to-air combat the F-1 can carry up to four AIM-9 Sidewinder missiles, one at each wingtip and one on each of the outboard underwing hardpoints. For long-range missions the F-1 can carry up to three auxiliary fuel tanks.

DIMENSIONS, EXTERNAL:	
Wing span	7.88 m (25 ft 10¼ in)
Length overall, incl probe	17.86 m (58 ft 7 in)
Height overall	4.39 m (14 ft 5 in)
Wheel track	2.82 m (9 ft 3 in)
Wheel track	2.82 m (9 ft 3 in)
Wheelbase	5.72 m (18 ft 9 in)
AREA:	
Wings, gross	21.17 m² (227.9 sq ft)
WEIGHTS:	
Operational weight empty	6,358 kg (14,017 lb)
Max T-O weight	13,700 kg (30,203 lb)
PERFORMANCE:	
Max level speed	Mach 1.6
Max rate of climb at S/L	10,670 m (35,000 ft)/min
Service ceiling	15,240 m (50,000 ft)
T-O run at max T-O weight	1,280 m (4,200 ft)

Mitsubishi (Sikorsky) XSH-60J

Detailed design work on this developed version of the Sikorsky SH-60B Seahawk anti-submarine helicopter, to meet the specific requirements of the JMSDF, was funded under the FY 1985 budget. Japanese avionics and equipment, including ring laser gyro AHRS, data link, tactical data processing and automatic flight management systems, will be integrated by the Technical Research and Development Institute of the Japan Defence Agency. The first of two prototype XSH-60Js, based on imported airframes, flew in 1987.

Shin Meiwa
SHIN MEIWA INDUSTRY CO LTD

The former Kawanishi Aircraft Company became Shin Meiwa in 1949 and established itself as a major overhaul centre for Japanese and US military and commercial aircraft.

Shin Meiwa PS-1

Shin Meiwa was awarded a contract in January 1966 to develop an anti-submarine flying-boat for the Japan Maritime Self-Defence Force. Company designation for the basic flying-boat was **SS-2**; in ASW configuration this was

Shin Meiwa PS-1 taking off near Oshima Island during a JMSDF review. *(Ryuta Watanabe)*

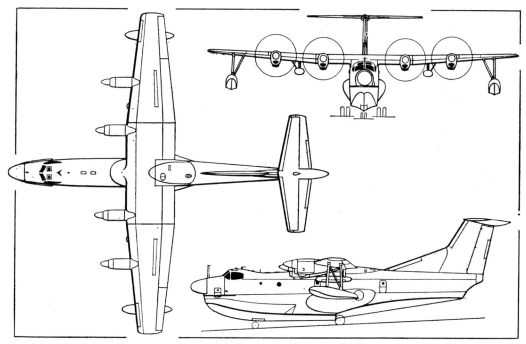

Shin Meiwa PS-1 Mod multi-purpose amphibian. *(Pilot Press)*

given the JMSDF designation **PS-1**. The later amphibious search and rescue version has the JMSDF designation **US-1/1A**.

The first PS-1 prototype (5801) flew for the first time on 5 October 1967. This, and the second, were delivered to the 51st Flight Test Squadron at Iwakuni.

In addition to the prototypes, Shin Meiwa delivered 23 production PS-1s by 1980, for use with the 31st Air Group of the JMSDF for ASW duties, most of them with No 31 Squadron of Iwakuni.

To enable very low landing and take-off speeds, the PS-1 has both a boundary layer control system and extensive flaps for propeller slipstream deflection. Control and stability in low-speed flight are enhanced by 'blowing' the rudder, flaps and elevators, and by use of an automatic flight control system.

The PS-1 was designed to dip its large sonar deep into the sea during repeated landings and take-offs, and can land on very rough water in winds of up to 25 knots (47 km/h; 29 mph). Take-offs and landings have been made successfully in seas with wave heights of up to 3 m (10 ft). To resist salt-water corrosion, much of the structure is of 2024-T3, 2024-T62, 7075-T73 and similar alloys, coated with a watertight polyurethane compound developed by Shin Meiwa.

In December 1986 No 71 SAR Squadron, JMSDF, received its tenth US-1 type amphibian, the seventh and subsequent aircraft having the revised designation US-1A to mark the adoption of T64-IHI-10J turboprops.

The following details refer to the PS-1, except where otherwise indicated:

TYPE: STOL anti-submarine flying-boat.

WINGS: Cantilever high-wing monoplane. Conventional structure, with rectangular centre-section and tapered outer panels. High-lift devices include outboard leading-edge slats extending over nearly 17% of the span and large outer and inner blown trailing-edge flaps extending 60° and 80° respectively. Two spoilers in front of outer flap on each wing. Powered ailerons. Leading-edge de-icing boots.

FUSELAGE: Semi-monocoque hull, with high length/beam ratio. V-shaped single-step planing bottom, with curved spray suppression strakes along sides of nose and spray suppressor slots in fuselage undersides aft of inboard propeller line. Double-deck interior.

TAIL UNIT: Cantilever T tail. Large dorsal fin. Tailplane has slats and de-icing boots on leading edge. Blown rudder and elevators. Tab in each elevator.

ALIGHTING AND BEACHING GEAR: Hull; and fixed stabilising floats near wingtips. Retractable tricycle-type beaching gear installed, with aft-retracting single-wheel main gear unit on each side of hull and forward-retracting twin steerable nosewheels, making aircraft independent of ground beaching aids.

POWERPLANT: Four 2,282 kW (3,060 ehp) Ishikawajima-built General Electric T64-ISI-10 turboprop engines, each driving a Sumitomo-built Hamilton Standard 63E60-19 three-blade constant-speed reversible-pitch propeller. Additionally, one 1,044 kW (1,400 ehp) T58-IHI-10 gas turbine is housed in upper centre portion of fuselage to provide power for boundary layer control system on rudder, flaps and elevators. Fuel in two bladder-type rear-fuselage tanks and five wing tanks, with total usable capacity of 19,500 litres (5,151 US gallons; 4,290 Imp gallons).

ACCOMMODATION (PS-1): Two pilots and flight engineer on flight deck, which has wide-view bulged windows at sides. Aft of this on the upper deck is a tactical compartment, housing two sonar operators, a navigator, MAD operator, radar operator, radio operator and a tactical co-ordinator. Electronic, magnetic and sonic equipment is installed on starboard side, with crew's rest area and bunks on port side. Aft of tactical compartment is the weapons compartment. On the lower deck, from nose to rear, are the avionics compartment, oxygen-bottle bay, main gear bay and two fuel tanks.

139

ACCOMMODATION (US-1): Search and rescue version has accommodation for crew of nine and 20 seated survivors or 12 stretchers, one auxiliary seat and two observers' seats. Sliding rescue door on port side of fuselage, aft of wing. Transport version can seat up to 69 passengers in mainly four-abreast seating with centre aisle; rear portion of cabin convertible to cargo compartment.

AVIONICS AND EQUIPMENT: Includes AN/ARA-50 UHF direction finder, HRN-105 Tacan, HRN-104 Loran, HPN-101B wave height meter, AN/APN-187C-N Doppler radar, A/A24G-9 TAS transmitter, AN/APS-80-N search radar, HGC-102 teletypewriter, AN/APN-125-N indicator group, HRN-101 ADF, N-PT-3 dead reckoning plotting board, AN/APX-68-N SIF, N-OA-35B/HSA tactical plotting group, HLR-102 countermeasure device, AN/ARR-52A sonobuoy receiver, HSQ-101 magnetic anomaly detector, HSA-103 error voltage monitor, HQS-101C dipping sonar, AN/ASA-20B recorder group, HQA-5 sonobuoy recorder, N-R-86/HRA OTPI (on top position indicator), HSA-116 integrated display system, HQH-101 sonobuoy data recorder, RRC-15 emergency transmitter, HSA-102 automatic magnetic compensator device, and N-CU-58/HRC antenna coupler.

ARMAMENT AND OPERATIONAL EQUIPMENT: Weapons bay on upper deck, aft of tactical compartment, in which are stored AQA-3 Jezebel passive long range acoustic search equipment with 20 sonobuoys and their launchers, Julie active acoustic echo ranging with 12 explosive charges, four 330 lb anti-submarine bombs, and smoke bombs. External armament includes underwing pod between each pair of engine nacelles, each containing two homing torpedoes, and a launcher beneath each wingtip for three 5 in air-to-surface rockets. Searchlight below starboard outer wing.

DIMENSIONS, EXTERNAL:

Wing span	33.15 m (108 ft 9 in)
Length overall	33.46 m (109 ft 9¼ in)
Height overall (on beaching gear)	9.82 m (32 ft 4¾ in)
Wheel track	3.10 m (10 ft 2 in)
Wheelbase	8.20 m (26 ft 10¾ in)
Propeller diameter	4.42 m (14 ft 6 in)

AREA:

Wings, gross	135.8 m² (1,462 sq ft)

WEIGHTS:

Weight empty	26,300 kg (58,000 lb)
Normal T-O weight	36,000 kg (79,365 lb)
Max T-O weight	43,000 kg (94,800 lb)

PERFORMANCE (at normal T-O weight):

Max level speed at 1,525 m (5,000 ft)	295 knots (547 km/h; 340 mph)
Cruising speed at 1,525 m (5,000 ft)	230 knots (426 km/h; 265 mph)
Stalling speed	40 knots (75 km/h; 46 mph)
Max rate of climb at S/L	690 m (2,264 ft)/min
Service ceiling	9,000 m (29,500 ft)
Time to 3,050 m (10,000 ft)	5 min
T-O run	250 m (820 ft)
Landing run	180 m (590 ft)
Normal range	1,169 nm (2,168 km; 1,347 miles)
Max ferry range	2,560 nm (4,744 km; 2,948 miles)
Endurance	15 h

Korea (REPUBLIC)

KA
KOREAN AIR

Following delivery by Hughes Helicopters of the USA of 34 Model 500MD Defender light helicopters to the Republic of Korea Air Force, Korean Air (a division of Korean Air Lines) began assembling Model 500 fuselages under licence in 1976 at its Kim Hae factory. The fuselages are shipped to the USA for final assembly, customer outfitting, flight test and delivery. Under a new 1984 offset agreement associated with the sale of Model 500MD Scouts to Korea, Korean Air assembles fuselages from US kits for the MD 500E and 530F commercial helicopters, and military Model 500s. It is also manufacturing main rotor blades and some other components for these aircraft. Descriptions of the MD 500 and 530 can be found under the McDonnell Douglas Helicopters entry in the US section.

In 1981 KA began to assemble under licence 68 Northrop F-5E Tiger IIs and F-5F combat trainers (48 and 20 respectively), ordered for the Republic of Korea Air Force. Deliveries of completed aircraft began in the Autumn of 1982 and all have since been delivered. Korean name for the F-5F is **Chegoong-Ho (Air Master)**.

Shin Meiwa US-1A air/sea rescue amphibian.

Romania

ICA
INTREPRINDEREA DE CONSTRUCTII AERONAUTICE (Aeronautical Construction Enterprise – a factory in the CNIAR group)

ICA, created in 1968, continues the work that was begun in 1926 by IAR-Brasov and was then undertaken in 1950–59 as URMV-3 Brasov. Today, it manufactures the Romanian designed IAR-28MA, IAR-823, IAR-825, IAR-827/828 and IAR-831 series of light aircraft/trainers; the Alouette III (sometimes carrying a 7.62 mm gun in the cabin, or a 20 mm cannon on an open turret-type mounting on the port side of the cabin, or two/four wire-guided missiles or 68 mm rocket pods on jettisonable launching rails) and Puma helicopters under licence from Aérospatiale of France (as the IAR-316B and IAR-330 respectively); and the IS-28/29 series of Romanian sailplanes and motor-gliders. It is developing its own IAR-317 Airfox attack helicopter version of the Alouette III, and also produces aircraft components and equipment.

ICA IAR-317 Airfox

Exhibited publicly for the first time at the 1985 Paris Air Show, the IAR-317 first prototype had then accumulated about 100 hours of flying since it first flew in April 1984. Completion of two more prototypes was planned; production, initially for the Romanian armed forces, had not begun by mid-1986.

Developed under the leadership of Dipl Ing Gheorghe Mitrea, the IAR-317 is modified from an IAR-316B Alouette

First prototype of the IAR-317 Airfox gunship helicopter. *(Brian M. Service)*

III. It is intended primarily as a light ground-attack, training and military liaison helicopter, although civil versions can also be produced to meet specific customer requirements. The modifications occur mainly ahead of the main rotor mast, the new cabin contours being considerably slimmer with tandem seating for a crew of two, the rear cockpit being elevated to improve the pilot's field of view. In the combat

ICA IAR-317 Airfox. *(Pilot Press)*

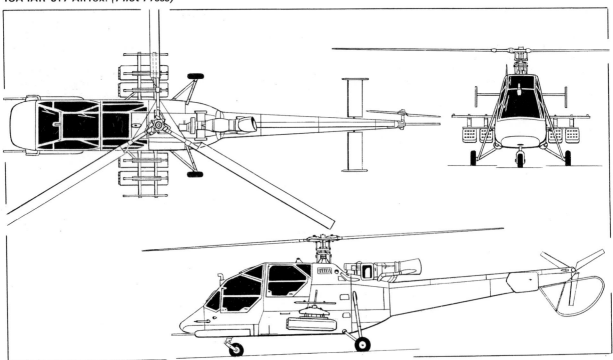

version, armour protection is provided for crew seats and fuel tank, toughened material is used in the cockpit transparencies, and attachments are provided for up to six external weapons.

TYPE: Tandem two-seat light attack and training helicopter.

ROTOR SYSTEM: Three-blade main and anti-torque rotors. Main rotor blades, of constant chord, on articulated hinges, with hydraulic drag-hinge dampers. Rotor brake and main rotor blade folding standard.

FUSELAGE: Welded steel tube centre-section, carrying the modified (duralumin) front section.

TAIL UNIT: Cantilever glassfibre fixed tailplane, with twin endplate fins, mounted on tailboom.

LANDING GEAR: Non-retractable tricycle type. Steerable nosewheel with optional locking device. Metal ski gear, floats and emergency flotation gear optional.

POWERPLANT: One 640 kW (858 shp) Turboméca Artouste IIIB turboshaft engine, as in Alouette III. Standard usable fuel capacity 573 litres (151 US gallons; 126 Imp gallons); one or two auxiliary fuel tanks optional, each of 125 litres (33 US gallons; 27.5 Imp gallons) capacity.

ACCOMMODATION: Crew of two in tandem, with elevated rear (pilot's) cockpit. Seats are of bucket type, adjustable vertically and horizontally, removable, and armoured in military versions. Windscreens and lower portions of side window/doors are flat-plate and of toughened material; forward and rear window/doors on each side can be jettisoned for escape in an emergency. Dual controls standard.

AVIONICS AND EQUIPMENT: Standard avionics include TR-800A VHF nav, AHV-6 radio altimeter, radio compass, marker beacon receiver, intercom, and pilot's gyro horizon, directional gyro and sideslip indicator. Pilot's main and secondary panels include altimeter, airspeed indicator, VSI, magnetic compass, tachometer, voltmeter, collective pitch indicator, temperature indicator, fuel gauge, oil pressure and temperature indicator, outside air temperature indicator, and clock. Pilot's main instruments (altimeter, airspeed indicator, variometer and collective pitch indicator) are repeated on co-pilot's panel; option also for co-pilot's gyro horizon and directional gyro. Standard equipment includes gunsight, roof mounted missile sight, position lights, anti-collision light, pilot's instrument failure warning lights, instrument and panel lights, and rotor brake. Optional equipment includes external cargo sling, rescue sling seat, 175 kg (386 lb) capacity rescue hoist and deck lock harpoon.

ARMAMENT: Fixed armament of two 7.62 mm machine-guns, one on each side of lower front fuselage. Load carrying beam aft of rear cockpit, with two (optionally three) weapon attachment points on each side. Typical stores loads, up to a maximum of 750 kg (1,653 lb), can include four rocket launchers (each with four or twelve 57 mm rockets), four twin-gun machine-gun pods, four 50 kg or 100 kg bombs, or '2 + 2' combinations of these weapons; four cartridge launchers or flare pods; four air-to-surface missiles; or six small 'Sagger' type anti-tank missiles. Naval weapons and stores can also be carried. RAD weapon aiming system, with PKV gyrostabilised sight, in front cockpit.

DIMENSIONS, EXTERNAL:

Main rotor diameter	11.02 m (36 ft 1¾ in)
Tail rotor diameter	1.912 m (6 ft 3¼ in)
Length overall, rotors turning	12.84 m (42 ft 1½ in)
Length of fuselage	9.80 m (32 ft 1¾ in)

AREA:

Main rotor disc	95.38 m² (1,026.6 sq ft)

WEIGHTS:

Weight empty	1,150 kg (2,535 lb)
Max T-O and landing weight	2,200 kg (4,850 lb)

PERFORMANCE (prototype: A at 1,700 kg; 3,748 lb gross weight, B at max T-O weight, no external stores, both in ISA zero wind conditions):

Never-exceed speed, and max level speed* at S/L:	
A, B	118 knots (220 km/h; 136 mph)
*Max cruising speed at S/L:	
A	108 knots (200 km/h; 124 mph)
B	102 knots (190 km/h; 118 mph)
Max rate of climb at S/L: A	510 m (1,673 ft)/min
B	270 m (886 ft)/min
Service ceiling: A	6,300 m (20,670 ft)
B	3,200 m (10,500 ft)
Hovering ceiling IGE: A	5,950 m (19,520 ft)
B	2,850 m (9,350 ft)
Hovering ceiling OGE: A	5,600 m (18,375 ft)
B	1,500 m (4,920 ft)
*Max range at S/L:	
with standard fuel: A	294 nm (545 km; 338 miles)
B	283 nm (525 km; 326 miles)
with auxiliary tanks: A	469 nm (870 km; 540 miles)
B	437 nm (810 km; 503 miles)
*Reduced by 10% with external stores	

Singapore

SAI
SINGAPORE AIRCRAFT INDUSTRIES PTE LTD

SAI was formed in early 1982 as a government owned industrial group under control of the Ministry of Defence's Sheng-Li Holding Company Pte Ltd. It has a combined workforce of more than 2,600, in six subsidiaries, of which the largest are SAMCO and SEEL. SAMCO was formed in 1975, initially to maintain and overhaul aircraft of the Republic of Singapore Air Force (RSAF), and began operating in April 1976, on both fixed-wing aircraft and helicopters.

Major programmes undertaken since that time have included rebuilding, refurbishing and A-4 to TA-4 conversion of Skyhawk aircraft for the RSAF and other air forces, and depot-level maintenance, overhaul, repair and refurbishment of many types of aircraft including the C-130 Hercules, F-5E/F Tiger II, Hunter, Strikemaster, and several models of Bell and Aérospatiale helicopters. Most of this work has been carried out at Seletar, but a new 15,000 m² (161,450 sq ft) factory at Paya Lebar was opened in October 1983. SAI's other subsidiaries have a substantial capability in the fields of aircraft and engine overhaul, maintenance and repair, component and equipment manufacture for civil and military aircraft and aero engines, external stores equipment, and defence avionics.

In late 1983 SAI began evaluating potential aircraft licence assembly and manufacturing programmes, and the first outcome of this is the assembly of 30 SIAI-Marchetti S.211 jet trainers for the RSAF, using kits supplied by the Italian manufacturer. It has also been reported that SAI will assemble 17 of the 22 Super Pumas ordered from Aérospatiale. In due course SAI is expected to be involved in production programmes for aircraft selected to replace the RSAF's Hunters and Strikemasters.

SAI A-4 Conversions

SAI is re-engining each of two Douglas A-4S-1 Skyhawk combat aircraft of the Singapore Air Force with a General Electric F404-GE-100D non-afterburning turbofan engine. The first of them made its first flight with the new powerplant in 1986. If flight testing shows major improvements, all of the Air Force's A-4S aircraft may undergo similar conversion, followed by a possible avionics update.

South Africa

Atlas
ATLAS AIRCRAFT CORPORATION OF SOUTH AFRICA (PTY) LIMITED

Atlas Aircraft Corporation, which was founded in 1963, built two versions of the Impala (MB-326) trainer/light attack aircraft under licence from Aermacchi. These programmes have now been completed.

Atlas continues to manufacture, under licence, components for Dassault Mirage F1-AZ and -CZ multi-purpose combat aircraft currently in service with Nos. 1 and 3 Squadrons respectively of the South African Air Force. It also undertakes maintenance and overhaul of SAAF aircraft. The company has developed the Cheetah combat aircraft for the SAAF, by modifying and upgrading the radar and other avionics of the service's Mirage IIIs. It has also developed a light attack helicopter, the Alpha XH-1, based on the French Alouette III.

Atlas Cheetah

The South African Air Force has given the name Cheetah to a redesigned and upgraded version of the Mirage III which is now undergoing modification by Atlas Aircraft Corporation. The new name, justified by the extensive changes, commemorates the fact that South Africa's first Mirage IIIs entered service, in March 1963, with the SAAF's No. 2 'Cheetah' Squadron.

Unveiled by Prime Minister P. W. Botha in Pretoria on 16 July 1986, the Cheetah has a configuration which invites immediate comparison with the Israel Aircraft Industries Nammer, although official South African statements imply that no outside assistance was given in its design. According to the SAAF, the modification is a mid-life update aimed at increasing the aircraft's operational life, made necessary by the continuing escalation of hostilities on South Africa's borders and the country's inability to procure modern front-line aircraft from elsewhere since the United Nations embargo on the sale of arms to South Africa in November 1977. Since then, and increasingly since the ending of Impala

Mk 2 production, Atlas has been charged with maintaining and updating the existing aircraft of the SAAF.

South Africa received some 74 Mirage IIIs from France between 1963 and the mid-1970s, and the majority of these remain in service. No. 2 Squadron at Hoedspruit in the Eastern Transvaal operates a mixture of the single-seat Mirage III-CZ, two-seat III-BZ trainer and reconnaissance III-RZ/R2Z models, while No. 85 Combat Flying School at Pietersburg flies mainly the III-EZ single-seater and III-DZ/-D2Z two-seat combat trainer versions. Most of these are powered by 60.8 kN (13,670 lb st) Snecma Atar 9C afterburning turbojet engines, but the later D2Z and R2Z have the higher rated (70.6 kN; 15,873 lb st) Atar 9K-50. In the mid-1970s Atlas acquired a licence to manufacture the latter engine, which also powers the SAAF's Mirage F1s, and refit with the 9K-50 may be an ingredient of the Cheetah modification.

According to the SAAF, the Cheetah programme includes new performance levels, and the replacement of many structural components and upgrading of flight systems, about 50 per cent of the existing airframe being reconstructed and equipped with the latest navigation and weapons systems. The Cheetah chosen for the July 1986 rollout was a two-seat III-D2Z, and exhibited many outward similarities to the TC2/TC7 two-seat versions of the Kfir, including the sweptback, intake mounted fixed foreplanes, small nose side-strakes, curved lower-fuselage side-strakes, and 'dog-tooth' wing leading edges. The nose extension appears to be shorter than that of the Kfir TC, and has rather more droop, but is large enough to accommodate a multi-mode radar. Beneath the nose-mounted pitot probe are box and blister shaped fairings which suggest the presence of such equipment as a Doppler or terrain following radar and an infra-red seeker. Retention of the Atar engine is confirmed by absence of the Kfir's large dorsal airscoop (for its bigger, heavier J79 engine) and also of the smaller, rearmost pair of over-

Cheetah multi-role fighter developed by Atlas from the Mirage III.

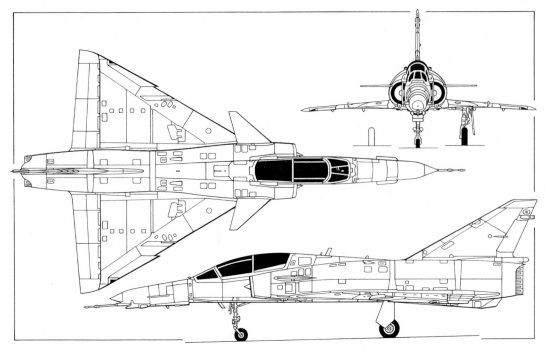

Atlas Cheetah. *(Jane's/Mike Keep)*

fuselage airscoops of the Israeli aircraft. The Cheetah displayed also retains the upward opening framed canopy of the two-seat Mirage. It appears that a radar warning receiver is carried on the fin, and small fences have been added to the wings.

The changes may be expected to confer upon the Cheetah the same kind of performance benefits as those claimed for the Kfir, namely improvements in dogfighting agility, especially in instantaneous and sustained turn rates (19°/s and 9.5°/s respectively in the case of the Kfir); handling and control at higher angles of attack; gust response, especially at low level; and take-off and landing distances. Other general performance figures are likely to remain similar to those of the Mirage III.

In addition to the pair of built-in 30 mm DEFA cannon, recent armament of SAAF Mirage IIIs has consisted primarily of Matra R.550 Magic or AIM-9 Sidewinder air-to-air missiles, medium-range Matra R.530 missiles, Matra JL-100 combined fuel/missile pods, and Nord AS 30 air-to-surface missiles. The Magic has already begun to be replaced by the domestic Armscor V3B infra-red homing missile, and it has been stated officially that all weaponry for the Cheetah is totally of South African origin.

Atlas Alpha XH-1

Revealing the existence of the Alpha XH-1 at a press conference in Johannesburg on 9 March 1986, the head of the South African Air Force, Lt Gen Dennis Earp, described this light attack helicopter prototype as 'entirely locally designed to SAAF specifications, using what the South African industry can provide'. In fact, this was a slight overstatement, since the XH-1 is based on the three-blade non-folding main and tail rotor and transmission systems, and almost certainly the powerplant, of the French Aérospatiale SA 316B Alouette III, albeit with many engine, gearbox and rotor system components manufactured in South Africa.

The Alpha XH-1 was developed under a SAAF contract

Atlas XH-1 prototype light attack helicopter.

awarded to Atlas in March 1981. Construction began in January 1983, and the XH-1 made its first flight on 3 February 1985, more than a year before its public disclosure. Although exhibiting some outward signs of its Alouette ancestry, it clearly does embody a considerable degree of new design. This is chiefly apparent in the almost all-new fuselage, which probably has no more than the tailboom and horizontal stabiliser in common with the Alouette III. In place of the latter's three-abreast cabin, the XH-1 has two single cockpits in tandem, resulting in a much narrower fuselage. The central portion has a mainframe of welded steel tube with metal skin, while the front portion is a semi-monocoque structure using components of both metal and composite materials. The hemispherical nosecone, probably containing only flight test instrumentation at this stage of the aircraft's development, could be of different shape on the production version. Compared with the Alouette III the max T-O weight is unchanged, and fuselage length probably differs very little, but the empty weight is increased by a little over 20 per cent.

A sweptback fin has been added to the port side of the tailboom opposite the three-blade tail rotor, and new endplate fins attached to the stabiliser are angular, sweptback structures with most of their area below the horizontal surface. To give clearance for the undernose gun which is the Alpha XH-1's main feature, the non-retractable tricycle landing gear of the Alouette has had to be replaced by a 'tailsitter' type. In this, the mainwheel units have been moved much further forward, to a position level with the rear cockpit instrument panel, while the tailwheel is carried on long V struts beneath the tailplane with a telescopic shock strut to the rear. The mainwheels are fitted with disc brakes.

Initial flight testing of the Alpha XH-1 has been completed, and some modifications were planned before the start of the next stage of flight trials, which were aimed not only at further XH-1 development but also at conducting requirement studies and expanding the degree of local technology involved. According to General Earp, 'we will be testing a wide range of airframe/engine/systems in the future, and technology derived from this programme will be tested on other helicopters in the SAAF inventory'. These plans

Atlas Alpha XH-1. *(Pilot Press)*

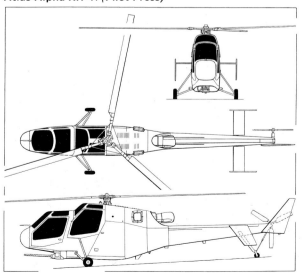

were expected to include provision of outriggers or stub-wings for the carriage of anti-tank guided weapons and unguided rockets. However, XM-1 development has since ended.

TYPE: Experimental light attack helicopter.

POWERPLANT (SA 316B): One 649 kW (870 shp) Turboméca Artouste IIIB turboshaft engine, derated to 425 kW (570 shp). Refuelling point in port side of rear fuselage.

ACCOMMODATION (XH-1): Two seats in tandem, with step down from rear (pilot's) cockpit to front cockpit occupied by weapons operator. Each cockpit has a forward opening door each side with very deep transparencies, giving an excellent field of view sideways and downward.

ARMAMENT (XH-1): Single-barrel GA1 20 mm cannon, with up to 1,000 rds of ammunition and max firing rate of 600 rds/min, in a servo controlled undernose turret. Gun is aimed by gunner's helmet mounted sight, and flexible mounting permits it to be traversed 120° to left and right and + 10°/ – 60° in elevation. Installation can accept alternative weapons, including a grouping of four 7.62 mm machine-guns.

DIMENSIONS, EXTERNAL (SA 316B):

Main rotor diameter	11.02 m (36 ft 1¾ in)
Tail rotor diameter	1.91 m (6 ft 3¼ in)
Length overall, rotors turning	12.84 m (42 ft 1½ in)
Height to top of rotor head	2.97 m (9 ft 9 in)

WEIGHTS (XH-1):

Weight empty	1,400 kg (3,086 lb)
Max T-O weight	2,200 kg (4,850 lb)

PERFORMANCE (XH-1 at S/L, estimated):

Max level speed	113 knots (210 km/h; 130 mph)
Max cruising speed	100 knots (185 km/h; 115 mph)
Max rate of climb	244 m (800 ft)/min
Combat radius	148 nm (275 km; 171 miles)

Atlas Impala Mk 2

The name Impala is given to two South African versions of the Aermacchi MB-326. The single-seat MB-326KC Impala Mk 2 light ground attack aircraft was based on the MB-326K. South African manufacture began with the assembly of seven aircraft from Italian-built components, the first of which made its initial flight on 13 February 1974. Production of the Mk 2 has now ended. (See Aermacchi entry in the Italian section.)

Atlas Impala Mk 2. *(Pilot Press)*

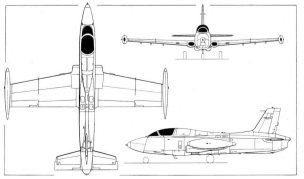

147

Spain

CASA
CONSTRUCCIONES AERONAUTICAS SA

This company was formed on 3 March 1923 for the primary purpose of producing metal aircraft for the Spanish Air Force. It began by building under licence the Breguet XIX, and has since manufactured many other aircraft of foreign design, recent examples including the Northrop F-5 fighter. It assembled 57 MBB Bo 105 helicopters ordered by the Spanish Army, and delivered 24 armed Bo 105s to the air force of Iraq. Output of Bo 105s continued with a further 32 aircraft in 1984. CASA also produces glassfibre doors and some rotorhead components for the German Bo 105 production line. Under an agreement signed with Sikorsky Aircraft on 13 June 1984, CASA is producing components (tailcones, tail rotor pylons and horizontal stabilisers) for S-70 helicopters. The agreement allows also for final assembly and flight testing of S-70s purchased by the Spanish armed forces, and development of additional helicopter marketing, product support, research and development, and other forms of collaboration. CASA will also assemble six of the 12 Aérospatiale AS 332B$_1$ Super Pumas ordered in 1986 for the Spanish Army.

CASA's own Project Office has designed several aircraft under contract to the Spanish Air Ministry, including the C-212 Aviocar transport and the C-101 Aviojet jet trainer, both of which are currently in production. In order to promote sales in the Far East, CASA established a C-212 assembly line in Indonesia, as well as full after-sales support in that area.

Under contract to Dassault-Breguet (which see), CASA is responsible for manufacturing centre fuselages for the Mirage F1 combat aircraft.

CASA undertakes maintenance and modernisation work for the Spanish Air Force and Navy, and for the US Air Force in Europe. Its principal current activities of this kind concern maintenance and specific modifications to the McDonnell Douglas F-15, and overhaul and maintenance of McDonnell Douglas F-4 and BAe Matador (Harrier) combat aircraft and Bell 47G, 204 and 205 helicopters.

CASA has six factories, employing about 10,240 people. Including production by the former Hispano Aviación SA, which it absorbed in 1972, the company has manufactured more than 3,500 aircraft and overhauled approx 6,250. CASA has a total covered area in the region of 270,000 m² (2,906,253 sq ft).

CASA C-101 Aviojet

Spanish Air Force designation: E.25 Mirlo (Blackbird)
Chilean Air Force designations: T-36 and A-36 Halcón

CASA and the Spanish Ministerio del Aire signed a contract for this basic and advanced military jet trainer aircraft on 16 September 1975. The contract covered the construction of four flying prototypes (first flights 27 June and 30 September 1977, 26 January and 17 April 1978) and two static and fatigue test airframes. MBB (West Germany) and Northrop (USA) collaborated in the design, the latter company

CASA C-101CC Aviojet light attack aircraft. *(Air Portraits)*

providing design assistance with the inlets and the 'Norcasa' wing section.

To minimise cost and maintenance, the C-101 is built on modular lines, with ample space within the airframe for equipment for any training mission likely to be required. The C-101 is fully aerobatic, and is able to carry out such additional duties as ground attack, reconnaissance, escort, weapons training, electronic countermeasures (ECM), and photographic missions.

CASA C-101CC Aviojet. *(Pilot Press)*

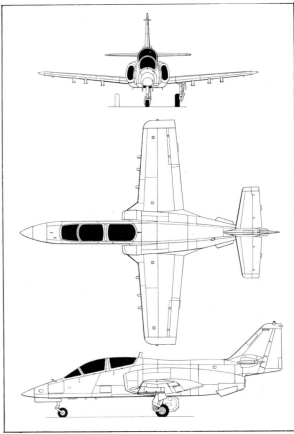

The training versions of the Aviojet are the C-101EB, C-101BB armed export model and the C-101DD enhanced model. The C-101CC light attack aircraft first flew as a prototype on 16 November 1983. Twenty-three CC-02s were ordered by Chile, including 19 for assembly and partial manufacture by ENAER as A-36 Halcóns, and 16 CC-04s ordered by the Royal Jordanian Air Force.

The following details refer to the C-101CC light attack version. Training versions of the C-101 will be covered in a companion publication.

TYPE: Tandem two-seat light attack aircraft and trainer.

WINGS: Cantilever low-wing monoplane. Wing section Norcasa 15, thickness/chord ratio 15%. Dihedral 5°. Incidence 1°. Sweepback at quarter-chord 1° 53'. Plain ailerons and slotted trailing-edge flaps, of glassfibre/honeycomb sandwich construction. Ailerons actuated hydraulically, with electrically actuated artificial spring feel and manual backup. Ground-adjustable tab on port aileron.

FUSELAGE: Semi-monocoque fail-safe structure. Hydraulically operated airbrake under centre of fuselage.

TAIL UNIT: Cantilever structure, with electrically actuated variable incidence tailplane. Electrically actuated trim tab in rudder. Twin ventral strakes under jetpipe.

LANDING GEAR: Hydraulically retractable tricycle type, with single wheel on each unit. Forward retracting Dowty Rotol nose unit, with non-steerable nosewheel and chined tubeless tyre size 457 × 146 (18 × 5.75-8). Inward retracting mainwheels with tubeless tyres size 622 × 216 (24.5 × 8.5-10) and hydraulically actuated multi-disc brakes.

POWERPLANT: One 19.13 kN (4,300 lb st) Garrett TFE 731-5-1J non-afterburning turbofan engine, with lateral intake on each side of fuselage abreast of second cockpit. Fuel in one 1,155 litre (305 US gallon; 254 Imp gallon) fuselage bag tank, one 575 litre (152 US gallon; 126.5 Imp gallon) integral tank in wing centre-section, and two outer wing integral tanks, for ferry missions, each of 342 litres (90 US gallons; 75.25 Imp gallons). Total usable internal fuel capacity 1,730 litres (457 US gallons; 380.5 Imp gallons) normal, 2,414 litres (638 US gallons; 531 Imp gallons) maximum. Fuel system permits up to 30 s of inverted flight. No provision for external fuel tanks.

ACCOMMODATION: Crew of two in tandem, on Martin-Baker Mk 10L zero/zero ejection seats, under individual canopies which open sideways to starboard and are separated by internal screen. Rear seat elevated 32.5 cm (12¾ in). Cockpit pressurised. Dual controls standard.

AVIONICS AND EQUIPMENT: C-101CC equipped with Magnavox AN/ARC-164 UHF com, Collins 21B VHF com, Collins VIR-31A VOR/ILS, Collins DME-40, Collins ADF-60, Andrea AN/AIC-18 interphone, Teledyne/CASA AN/APX-101 IFF/SIF, Sperry ZC-222 flight director, Sperry AS-339 gyro platform, ADI-500C, RD-550A HSI, Avimo RGS2 gunsight (front and rear cockpit), and CASA SCAR-81 armament control system. Wide range of alternative avionics and equipment available for export versions, including a Maverick pod.

ARMAMENT AND OPERATIONAL EQUIPMENT: Large bay below rear cockpit suitable for quick-change packages, including 30 mm DEFA cannon pod, a twin 12.7 mm M3 machine-gun pod, reconnaissance camera, ECM package or laser designator. Six underwing hardpoints, capacities 500 kg (1,102 lb) inboard, 375 kg (827 lb) centre and 250 kg (551 lb) outboard; total external stores load 2,250 kg (4,960 lb). Typical armament can include one 30 mm cannon with up to 130 rds, or two 12.7 mm guns, in the fuselage; and four LAU-10 pods of 5 in rockets, six 250 kg BR250 bombs, four LAU-3/A rocket launchers, four 125 kg BR125 bombs and two LAU-3/A launchers, two AGM-65 Maverick missiles, or four BIN200 napalm bombs.

DIMENSIONS, EXTERNAL:
Wing span	10.60 m (34 ft 9⅜ in)
Length overall	12.50 m (41 ft 0 in)
Height overall	4.25 m (13 ft 11¼ in)
Wheel track (c/l of shock struts)	3.18 m (10 ft 5¼ in)
Wheelbase	4.77 m (15 ft 7¾ in)

AREA:
Wings, gross	20.00 m² (215.3 sq ft)

WEIGHTS:
Weight empty, equipped	3,500 kg (7,716 lb)
Max external stores load	2,250 kg (4,960 lb)
T-O weight:	
trainer	4,850 kg (10,692 lb)
ground attack	6,300 kg (13,890 lb)

PERFORMANCE (C-101CC at 4,400 kg; 9,700 lb):
Max limiting Mach No.	Mach 0.80
Never-exceed speed	450 knots (834 km/h; 518 mph) IAS
Max level speed at S/L	415 knots (769 km/h; 478 mph)
Max level speed:	
at 6,100 m (20,000 ft)	435 knots (806 km/h; 501 mph)
at 4,575 m (15,000 ft)	450 knots (834 km/h; 518 mph)
Econ cruising speed at 9,145 m (30,000 ft)	
	Mach 0.60 (354 knots; 656 km/h; 407 mph)
Stalling speed:	
flaps up	99 knots (183 km/h; 114 mph) IAS
flaps down	88 knots (164 km/h; 102 mph) IAS
Max rate of climb at S/L	
	1,494–1,859 m (4,900–6,100 ft)/min
Time to 7,620 m (25,000 ft)	6 min 30 s
Service ceiling	12,800 m (42,000 ft)
T-O run	560 m (1,835 ft)
Landing run	480 m (1,575 ft)

Typical interdiction radius (lo-lo-lo) with four 250 kg bombs and 30 mm gun: 3 min over target, 30 min reserves
280 nm (519 km; 322 miles)
Typical close air support radius (lo-lo-lo):
with four 19 × 2.75 in rocket launchers and 30 mm gun, 50 min loiter over battle area, 8 min over target, 30 min reserves
200 nm (370 km; 230 miles)
with two 125 kg bombs, 30 min loiter, 10 min attack (max thrust) and 7% reserves
170 nm (315 km; 196 miles)
with two Maverick missiles and 30 mm gun, 8 min over target, 30 min reserves
325 nm (602 km; 374 miles)
Typical photo-reconnaissance radius (hi-lo-lo), 30 min reserves
520 nm (964 km; 599 miles)
Armed patrol, no underwing stores, 100 nm (185 km; 115 mile) transit from base to patrol area, with one 30 mm or two 12.7 mm guns, 45 min reserves
3 h 30 min at 200 knots (370 km/h; 230 mph) at S/L
Ferry range, 30 min reserves
2,000 nm (3,706 km; 2,303 miles)
Typical training mission endurance:
two 1 h 10 min general handling missions, incl aerobatics, with 20 min reserves after second mission

Max endurance	7 h

g limits:
at 4,800 kg (10,582 lb) AUW	+ 7.5/ – 3.9
at 6,300 kg (13,890 lb) AUW	+ 5.5/ – 1

CASA C-212 Series 200 maritime patrol Aviocar for the Swedish Coastguard. *(Brian M. Service)*

CASA C-212 Series 200 Aviocar
(ASW and Maritime Patrol Versions)

Swedish Navy designation: TP89

For service with the Spanish Air Force, and for certain foreign countries, CASA has developed a version of the C-212 Srs 200 STOL utility transport equipped for anti-submarine and maritime patrol duties. Nine have been

CASA C-212 Series 200 Aviocar. *(Pilot Press)*

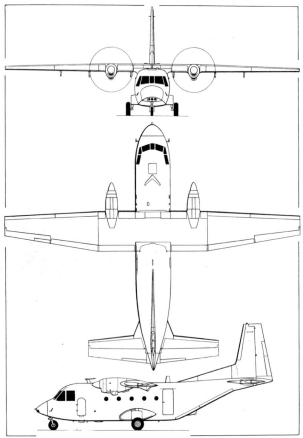

ordered by the Spanish Air Force for SAR duties, three by the Spanish Ministry of Finance, one ASW version by the Swedish Navy, two for maritime patrol (with a SLAR and IR/UV search equipment) by the Swedish Coastguard, four by the Venezuelan Navy, ten for maritime patrol by the Mexican Navy, two by Sudan and one by the Uruguayan Air Force.

The principal external differences from the transport version are the addition of a nose radome and the appearance of various antennae on the fuselage and tail fin. Two fuselage hardpoints are provided for the carriage of torpedoes, rocket pods and other weapons.

TYPE: Twin-turboprop ASW and maritime patrol aircraft.

WINGS: Cantilever high-wing monoplane. Wing section NACA 65_3-218. Incidence 2° 30′. No dihedral or sweepback. Ailerons and double-slotted trailing-edge flaps. Trim tab in port aileron. Pneumatic de-icing of leading edges (rubber boots and engine bleed air). Glassfibre extended wingtips optional.

FUSELAGE: Semi-monocoque non-pressurised fail-safe structure. Nose radome and various external antennae.

TAIL UNIT: Cantilever structure, with dorsal fin. Fixed-incidence tailplane, mid mounted on rear of fuselage. Trim tab in rudder and each elevator. Pneumatic de-icing of leading edges (rubber boots and engine bleed air). External antennae on tail fin.

LANDING GEAR: Non-retractable tricycle type, with single mainwheels and single steerable nosewheel. Goodyear wheels and tyres, main units size 11.00-12 Type III (10-ply rating), nose unit size 24-7.7 Type VII (8-ply rating). Goodyear hydraulic disc brakes on mainwheels. Anti-skid system optional.

POWERPLANT: Two Garrett TPE331-10R-511C turboprop engines, each flat rated at 671 kW (900 shp) and driving a Dowty Rotol R-313 four-blade constant-speed fully-feathering reversible-pitch propeller. Fuel in four integral wing tanks, with total capacity of 2,040 litres (539 US gallons; 449 Imp gallons), of which 2,000 litres (528 US gallons; 440 Imp gallons) are usable. Additional fuel can be carried in one 1,000 litre or two 750 litre (264 or 198 US gallon; 220 or 165 Imp gallon) optional ferry tanks inside cabin. Auxiliary fuel tanks, total capacity 1,400 litres (370 US gallons; 308 Imp gallons).

ACCOMMODATION (ASW version): Pilot and co-pilot on flight deck, with OTPI (on-top position indicator) and additional central console for radar repeater; control for radio navigation, Doppler, DME, ADF, UHF/DF, Omega and VOR/ILS; weapons delivery controls; and intervalometer for rockets. Avionics rack on port side, aft of pilot, for com/nav equipment; second rack on starboard side, aft of co-pilot, contains avionics for mission equipment (radar, sonobuoys, MAD and ESM). Immediately aft of the latter rack, along the starboard side of the cabin, are three control consoles for the mission crew members. The first console has the radar control and display. ESM control and display, and intercom switch control. The second has the tactical display and control, MAD recorder and control, and intercom switch. The rearmost of the three incorporates intercom switch, sonobuoy receiver control unit, acoustic control panel, and acoustic control and display units.

ACCOMMODATION (maritime patrol version): Pilot and co-pilot on flight deck, with central console for radar repeater; control for radio navigation, Doppler, DME, ADF, UHF/DF, Omega, VOR/ILS and searchlight. Avionics rack on port side, aft of pilot, for com/nav and radar equipment. On starboard side of cabin is a console for the radar operator. Posts for two observers are located at the rear of the cabin.

AVIONICS: Communications equipment includes two HF and two VHF transceivers, single UHF, and interphone. Navigation equipment includes automatic flight control system, flight director, VOR/ILS (including VOR/LOC), glideslope and marker beacon receiver, DME, two ADF, UHF/DF, radar altimeter, Doppler radar, VLF/Omega, autopilot and compass.

OPERATIONAL EQUIPMENT (ASW version): Underfuselage search radar with 360° scan, electronic support measures (ESM), sonobuoy processing system (SPS), OTPI, MAD, tactical processing system (TPS), IFF/SIF transponder, sonobuoy and smoke marker launcher, torpedoes, rockets and other weapons.

OPERATIONAL EQUIPMENT (maritime patrol version): Nose mounted AN/APS-128 100 kW search radar with 270° scan, searchlight, FLIR (optional), smoke markers and camera.

ARMAMENT: Includes option to carry torpedoes such as Mk 46 and Sting Ray, and light air-to-surface missiles such as Sea Skua and AS 15TT.

DIMENSIONS, EXTERNAL:

Wing span (standard, without optional glassfibre extended tips)	19.00 m (62 ft 4 in)
Length overall, not incl nose radome	15.15 m (49 ft 8½ in)
Fuselage: Max width	2.30 m (7 ft 6½ in)
Height overall	6.30 m (20 ft 8 in)
Wheel track	3.10 m (10 ft 2 in)
Wheelbase	5.55 m (18 ft 2½ in)

AREA:

Wings, gross (standard)	40.0 m² (430.56 sq ft)

WEIGHTS (ASW version):

Max T-O weight	8,400 kg (18,519 lb)
Max landing weight	7,350 kg (16,204 lb)

PERFORMANCE (at max T-O weight, ISA):

Max cruising speed at 3,050 m (10,000 ft)	190 knots (353 km/h; 219 mph)
Loiter speed at 457 m (1,500 ft)	105 knots (195 km/h; 121 mph)
Service ceiling	7,315 m (24,000 ft)
Max range	1,650 nm (3,055 km; 1,898 miles)
Max endurance	more than 12 h

CASA C-212 Series 200 Aviocar (Elint/ECM Version)

A version of the Srs 200 Aviocar for electronic intelligence and electronic countermeasures duties entered development in 1981, at which time four had been ordered by an export customer. Two more have since been ordered by an undisclosed customer, and two C-212s already delivered to the Portuguese Air Force have been modified retrospectively for elint/ECM duties.

The elint/ECM version carries equipment for automatic signal interception, classification and identification in dense signal environments, data from which enable a map to be drawn plotting the position and characteristics of hostile radar. Emitters for the jamming part of the mission are also carried.

Sweden

Saab-Scania
Saab-SCANIA AKTIEBOLAG

The original Svenska Aeroplan AB was founded at Trollhättan in 1937 for the production of military aircraft. In 1939 this company was amalgamated with the Aircraft Division (ASJA) of the Svenska Järnvägsverkstäderna rolling stock factory in Linköping. Following this merger, Saab moved its head office and engineering departments to Linköping, which is now the main aerospace factory. The company's name was changed to Saab Aktiebolag in May 1965.

Post-war expansions include a bombproof underground factory in Linköping, as well as important new production and engineering facilities in Linköping, Jönköping, Trollhättan and Gothenburg.

During 1968 Saab merged with Scania-Vabis, to strengthen the two companies' position in automotive product development, production and export. Malmö Flygindustri (MFI) was acquired in the same year.

Saab-Scania has more than 47,000 employees, organised in three operating divisions and two major subsidiaries (Saab-Scania Combitech and Saab-Scania Enertech). Of these, nearly 6,500 are employed by the Saab Aircraft Division, including 5,500 at Linköping.

Saab-Scania's current aerospace activities include production of the JA 37 Viggen supersonic STOL combat aircraft, and development of the Saab JAS 39 Gripen multi-role combat aircraft. Since 1949 the company has delivered more than 2,000 military jet aircraft to the air forces of four nations, and in 1985 received an order to refurbish 24 former Swedish Air Force Saab 35 Drakens for delivery to the Austrian Air Force. It has also delivered more than 1,500 piston engined aircraft to military and civil customers around the world.

Saab-Scania has greatly expanded its activities in the electronics field in recent years. Current production items include computer systems, autopilots, fire control and bombing systems for piloted aircraft, and electronics for guided missiles. A major production programme is the airborne computer for the Saab 37. The Saab RGS 2 lead-computing optical sighting system was selected for the Royal Netherlands Air Force Northrop NF-5A, the Italian Air Force Aermacchi MB-339A, and British Aerospace Hawks for the Finnish Air Force. Spaceborne computers, optronic fire control systems and field artillery computer systems are' also under development and in production.

Saab J 32 E Lansen

Details of this extensively modified electronic warfare and countermeasures version of the Lansen were released in 1985. It equips F13M target-flying squadron of the Swedish Air Force, which is based at Malmslätt, near Linköping, but operates throughout Sweden and provides target flying services for other nations such as Switzerland. Currently, F13M consists of two flying units. Flying unit 85 performs most of the Air Force's signal reconnaissance missions, using two specially equipped TP 85 Caravelles, supported by a Fairchild Metro for flight training. Flying unit 32 has 14 J 32E (for electronic) Lansens, six J 32D Lansen target tugs and three dual-control J 32B Lansens for training and radioactive sampling. The J 32Es can be used for a variety of missions, including jamming and countermeasures training, and 'aggressor' flying for SwAF combat squadrons.

The J 32E is a conversion of the standard J 32B, fitted with new flight instrumentation, a civil and military transponder, modernised autopilot and a range of specialised mission equipment, including:

Ingeborg, a micro-computer signal homing receiver for the S, C and part of L band, which works in parallel with the Adrian and G 24 systems to make possible optimum

Swedish Air Force Saab J 32E Lansen ECM/aggressor conversion. *(Swedish Air Force)*

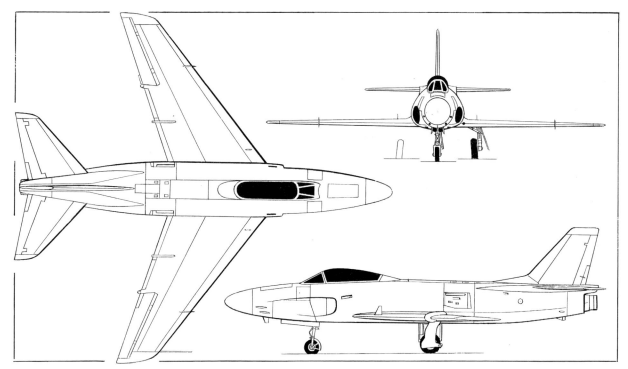

Saab J 32B Lansen. *(Pilot Press)*

jamming. Its three antennae are inside the aircraft's dielectric nosecone. The control unit replaces the original radar scope in the navigator's cockpit.

G 24, a nose mounted jamming transmitter which exists in three versions, covering the L, S and C bands, and is for use against ground and ship radars.

Boz 3 chaff dispenser pods, usually carried on each of the two outboard underwing pylons. Operator can select different dispensing programmes covering various radar bands.

Petrus jamming pod is intended mainly for use against X band fighter, attack aircraft and anti-aircraft radars. Microcomputer control equipment can transmit camouflage (roar) and disguise jamming, and generate radar signatures within wide ranges, ahead and rearward, and also warns of attacks from the rear. Petrus is carried on the J 32E's inboard underwing pylons.

Adrian jamming pod. Externally similar to, and interchangeable with, Petrus. Used mainly against ground and ship S and C band radars. Has forward and rearward pointing antennae.

Mera is a computerised radio jamming equipment and homing receiver for the VHF and UHF bands. Jamming can take place at several frequencies, such as FM/AM (roar), pulse and oscillating roar. Using a tape-recorded disguise, replay of commands and music can be transmitted. The jamming operator can also transmit misleading commands on a selected frequency.

TYPE: Two-seat electronic warfare aircraft.

WINGS: Swept low-wing cantilever monoplane, with 35° sweepback at quarter-chord. Thin laminar-flow wing section. Ailerons actuated by hydraulic booster system.

Fowler flaps. Two stall fences.

FUSELAGE: Conventional structure. Entire rear fuselage quickly removable for access to engine. Four airbrakes in rear fuselage sides.

TAIL UNIT: Cantilever monoplane type. Movable tailplane mounted on large fairings used to smooth the airflow around tailplane. Hydraulically-actuated elevator.

LANDING GEAR: Retractable nosewheel type, with mainwheels retracting into fuselage and nosewheel forwards. Goodyear wheels and brakes, with Dunlop Maxaret anti-skid device.

POWERPLANT: One 63.74 kN (14,330 lb st) with afterburning Svenska-Flygmotor-built Rolls-Royce RM6B (Avon) turbojet engine.

ACCOMMODATION: Crew of two in tandem, in pressurised cockpit. Ejector seats of Saab design.

AVIONICS AND EQUIPMENT: See introductory paragraphs.

DIMENSIONS, EXTERNAL:
Wing span	13.00 m (42 ft 7¾ in)
Length overall	14.65 m (48 ft 1 in)
Height overall	4.75 m (15 ft 7 in)

WEIGHT:
Max T-O weight	about 13,000 kg (28,660 lb)

PERFORMANCE:
Max level speed	608 knots (1,125 km/h; 700 mph)
Max restricted speed for target towing	
	297 knots (550 km/h; 340 mph)
Max rate of climb at S/L	about 3,600 m (11,800 ft)/min
g limit, to prolong structural life	+ 5

Saab 35 Draken

Swedish Air Force designations: J 35 and SK 35

The Saab 35 Draken single-seat fighter was originally designed to intercept bombers in the transonic speed range, and was provided with radar equipment to accomplish this under all weather conditions. It was also given the ability to carry substantial weapon loads for attack duties or cameras for photographic reconnaissance.

The first of three prototypes made its maiden flight on 25 October 1955, and the first version, the J 35A, entered service with the Swedish Air Force at the beginning of 1960. Subsequently the Draken went through several stages of development, and continuously improved versions for the Swedish Air Force included the J 35B, D and F fighter versions, the SK 35C trainer version and the S 35E reconnaissance version.

The versions of the Draken currently in service with the Swedish Air Force or the air forces of Austria, Denmark and Finland are as follows:

J 35D. Development of J 35B with more powerful Flygmotor RM6C turbojet engine. Saab FII5 autopilot. Increased fuel capacity. First flew on 27 December 1960 and deliveries to the SwAF began in 1962. No longer in Swedish use, but in 1985 Saab received an order to refurbish 24 former Swedish Air Force Saab 35 Drakens for delivery to the Austrian Air Force. All were delivered by the end of 1988, as Saab 35OEs.

Saab 35OE (modified J 35D) Draken for the Austrian Air Force.

J 35J. Under the revised designation J 35J (originally J 35F Mod), 66 remaining Draken fighters of F10 Wing of the Swedish Air Force, based near Ängelholm in southern Sweden, are being updated to extend their service life to the mid-1990s. Two additional inboard underwing stores pylons enable these aircraft to operate with four external fuel tanks and two missiles, or four missiles and two fuel tanks. The infra-red target seeker associated with the missile armament is updated. An altitude warning system and transponder are added, and instrument changes include a new horizon system. The aircraft's primary radar and IFF transponders are also modified.

Only F10 Wing will operate the J35J, which will continue

Additional underwing stores identify this J 35J Draken.

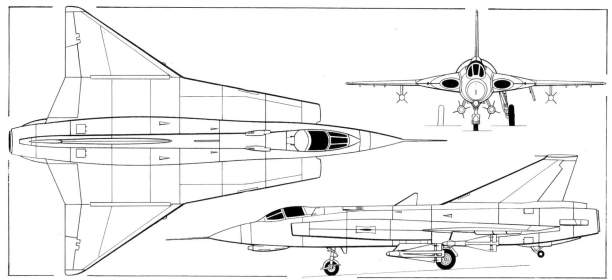

Saab J 35 Draken fighter. *(Pilot Press)*

in first-line service for three years after JAS 39 Gripens have
begun to enter service with other units of the Swedish Air
Force.

The J 35F had been developed from the J 36D, with an
improved Saab S7B collision-course fire-control system,
radar and normal armament of Saab-produced RB27 Falcon
HM-55 (radar guided) and two RB28 Falcon HM-58 (infra-
red) air-to-air missiles. An infra-red target seeker was placed
in a fairing under the nose, and one 30 mm Aden M/55
cannon was carried in the starboard wing.

SK 35C. Two-seat dual-control trainer version of J 35A,
with different front fuselage. Instructor and pupil in tandem
under a long canopy, with the instructor's seat raised slightly
to improve forward vision past the pupil. No radar. Same
weapons capability as tactical versions. First SK 35C flew on
30 December 1959.

Saab 35X. Long-range fighter/attack/reconnaissance
version developed for the export market. Externally similar
to the J 35F but possessing greatly increased attack
capability (max external load 9,920 lb; 4,500 kg) and range.
For reconnaissance duties, a nose similar to that of the S 35E
was fitted. T-O run with nine 1,000 lb bombs is 4,030 ft (1,210
m).

From 1968 the Danish Defence Ministry ordered 40
aircraft of this type, designated **Saab 35XD** (20 each of F-35
fighter-bombers and RF-35 reconnaissance-fighters), for the
Royal Danish Air Force, plus 11 TF-35 trainers.

In April 1970, 12 Drakens (designated **Saab 35S**) were
ordered by Finland. These were assembled in Finland by
Valmet Oy for delivery during 1974–75. For familiarisation
purposes, six Saab 35B Drakens (designated Saab 35BS)
were leased to Finland by the Swedish Air Force.

The following description refers to the exported Saab 35X
model:

TYPE: Single-seat supersonic all-weather fighter, reconnaissance and attack aircraft.

WINGS: Cantilever 'double delta' mid-wing monoplane.
Sweepback on centre wing leading edge 80°, on outer wing
leading edge 57°. Thickness/chord ratio 5%. Central wing
integral with fuselage.

FUSELAGE: Front and rear main sections, connected to each
other by a bolt joint. Fuselage front section integral with
front of centre wing structure. Two pairs of airbrakes,
above and below rear fuselage.

CONTROL SURFACES: Conventional delta-shape fin and
rudder. Elevons on wing trailing edge comprise two
inboard and two outboard surfaces, the latter being mass-
balanced. No part of load on control surfaces is fed into
stick and rudder pedals. Stick forces are generated
artificially. Three-axis stabilisation system.

LANDING GEAR: Retractable tricycle type. Hydraulic
actuation. Main units retract outward, the legs shortening
during retraction to reduce the space required inside wing.
Nosewheel retracts forward and is steerable. Goodyear
double-disc brakes and Dunlop anti-skid brake units.
Dual retractable tailwheels. Brake parachute in fairing
above rear fuselage. Arrester hook optional.

POWERPLANT: One Volvo Flygmotor (Rolls-Royce licence)
Avon 300-series engine (Swedish Air Force designation
RM6C) with Swedish-developed afterburner. Static thrust
approximately 56.88 kN (12,790 lb st) dry and 78.46 kN
(17,650 lb st) with afterburner. Internal fuel in integral
tanks in inner wings and fuselage bag tanks. Total internal
fuel capacity 4,000 litres (1,057 US gallons; 880 Imp
gallons). Provision for external tanks under fuselage and
wings, increasing total capacity to 9,000 litres (2,378 US
gallons; 1,980 Imp gallons). Additional internal tanks can
be fitted in place of guns for ferry purposes.

ACCOMMODATION: Pressurised and air-conditioned cockpit,
with fully-automatic Saab 73SE-F rocket-assisted ejection
seat and GQ parachute system permitting ejection within
the normal flight envelope and down to 54 knots (100
km/h; 62 mph) on the ground. Rearward-hinged canopy.

AVIONICS AND EQUIPMENT: Complete radar equipment with
nose scanner and pilot's scope, as well as Saab S7 collision-
course fire control equipment. Saab FH5 autopilot, with
air data system, stick-steering and various following
modes. Vertical tape instruments. Aga FR 21 VHF. DME.

ARMAMENT: Nine attachment points (each 454 kg; 1,000 lb)
for external stores: three under each wing and three under
fuselage. Stores can consist of air-to-air missiles and
unguided air-to-air rocket pods (19 × 7.5 cm), 12 × 13.5

155

cm Bofors air-to-ground rockets, nine 1,000 lb or fourteen 500 lb bombs, or fuel tanks. Two or four Sidewinder air-to-air missiles can be carried under wings and fuselage. Two 30 mm Aden cannon (one in each wing) can be replaced by extra internal fuel tanks. With two 1,275 litre (337 US gallon; 280 Imp gallon) and two 500 litre (132 US gallon; 110 Imp gallon) drop-tanks, two 1,000 lb or four 500 lb bombs can be carried.

DIMENSIONS, EXTERNAL:	
Wing span	9.40 m (30 ft 10 in)
Length overall	15.35 m (50 ft 4 in)
Height overall	3.89 m (12 ft 9 in)
Wheel track	2.70 m (8 ft 10½ in)
Wheelbase	4.00 m (13 ft 1 in)
AREA:	
Wings, gross	49.20 m² (529.6 sq ft)
WEIGHTS:	
T-O weight 'clean'	11,400 kg (25,130 lb)
T-O weight with two 1,000 lb bombs and two 1,275 litre drop-tanks	14,590 kg (32,165 lb)
Max T-O weight	15,000 kg (33,070 lb)
Max overload T-O weight	16,000 kg (35,275 lb)
PERFORMANCE (A: AUW of 25,130 lb; B: AUW of 32,165 lb):	
Max level speed with afterburning:	
A	Mach 2
B	Mach 1.4

Max rate of climb at S/L with afterburning:	
A	10,500 m (34,450 ft)/min
B	6,900 m (22,650 ft)/min
Time to 11,000 m (36,000 ft) with afterburning:	
A	2 min 36 sec
Time to 15,000 m (49,200 ft) with afterburning:	
A	5 min 0 sec
T-O run with afterburning:	
A	650 m (2,130 ft)
B	1,170 m (3,840 ft)
Landing run at normal landing weight:	
A and B	530 m (1,740 ft)
Radius of action (hi-lo-hi), internal fuel only:	
A	343 nm (635 km; 395 miles)
Radius of action (hi-lo-hi) with two 1,000 lb bombs and two drop-tanks:	
B	541 nm (1,003 km; 623 miles)
Ferry range with max internal and external fuel	1,754 nm (3,250 km; 2,020 miles)

Saab JA 37 Viggen (Thunderbolt)

The Saab 37 Viggen multi-mission combat aircraft has been produced to fulfil the primary roles of attack, interception, reconnaissance and training. Its STOL characteristics enable it to operate from narrow runways of about 500 m (1,640 ft) length. Viggens (all versions) are planned to equip a total of 17 Swedish Air Force squadrons.

The first of seven prototypes flew for the first time on 8 February 1967, and by April 1969 all six single-seat prototypes were flying. The seventh was the prototype for the two-seat SK 37 operational trainer.

Production deliveries of the AJ 37, SF 37, SH 37 and SK 37 versions, totalling 180 aircraft, have been completed.

Production of the final JA 37 type will end in 1988. Versions in service are as follows:

AJ 37. Single-seat all-weather attack version, with secondary interceptor capability. Initial production version, which began to replace the A 32A Lansen from mid-1971. First production AJ 37 flew on 23 February 1971 and deliveries began on 21 June 1971. First AJ 37 unit was F7 Wing at Såtenäs. The AJ 37 equips two squadrons of F6 Wing at Karlsborg, two squadrons of F7, and one squadron of F15 at Söderhamn.

JA 37. Single-seat interceptor, with more powerful Volvo Flygmotor RM8B engine. Improved performance, and

Saab AJ 37 all-weather attack aircraft.

Swedish Air Force Saab JA 37 in current blue-grey finish. *(Ivo Sturzenegger)*

secondary capability for attack missions. Four elevon hydraulic actuators under each wing, instead of three as on other versions, and a modified, taller tail fin similar to that of the SK 37. Total of 149 ordered, to re-equip eight Draken fighter squadrons of the Swedish Air Force: two squadrons each of Wings F4, F16 and F21, and one each of F13 and F17. First flight by a production JA 37 was made on 4 November 1977. Deliveries, to a squadron of F13 Wing at Norrköping, began in 1979, and the 100th JA 37 was delivered on 20 August 1985. Improvements added since the JA 37's entry into service include new-generation AIM-9L Sidewinder missiles, effective also against head-on targets, and an aircraft-to-aircraft communications system known as fighter link which makes possible efficient liaison between aircraft, even at night and in IMC conditions, regardless of their relative positions.

SF 37. Single-seat all-weather armed photographic reconnaissance version to replace the S 35E Draken. A production contract was awarded in early 1973. Intended normally for overland reconnaissance, the SF 37 has a modified nose containing cameras and other equipment, permitting reconnaissance at any hour of the day or night, at high or low altitudes and at long distances from its base. First flown on 21 May 1973. Deliveries, to F13 at Norrköping,

Saab JA 37 Viggen. *(Pilot Press)*

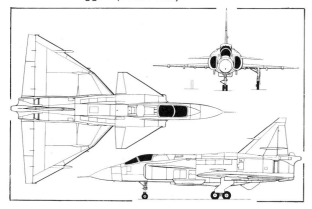

began in April 1977. Also in service with two mixed (SF 37/SH 37) squadrons: F21 at Luleå and F17 at Kallinge. Last SF 37 delivered on 7 February 1980.

SH 37. Single-seat all-weather maritime reconnaissance version, to replace the S 32C version of the Lansen. Production ordered at same time as the SF 37. Primarily intended to survey, register, and report activities in the neighbourhood of Swedish territory. Can also be used for attack missions. Prototype first flown on 10 December 1973. First production SH 37 delivered on 19 June 1975. In service with F13 at Norrköping (one squadron); and in two mixed (SF 37/SH 37) squadrons: F17 at Kallinge and F21 at Luleå.

SK 37. Tandem two-seat dual-control training version, in which the rear cockpit takes the place of some electronics and the forward fuselage fuel tank, and is fitted with bulged hood and twin periscopes. Modified, taller tail-fin of increased area. Capable of secondary attack role, with full range of attack armament as in AJ 37. Prototype first flown on 2 July 1970. First production SK 37 delivered in June 1972. In service with conversion unit of F15 at Söderhamn.

The following details refer to the JA 37 version:

TYPE: Single-seat all-weather multi-purpose combat aircraft.

WINGS: Tandem arrangement of delta foreplane, with trailing-edge flaps, and a rear mounted delta main wing with two-section hydraulically actuated powered elevons on each trailing edge, which can be operated differentially or in unison. Main wing has compound sweep on leading edge. Outer sections have extended leading edge.

FUSELAGE: Conventional semi-monocoque structure, using heat resistant plastics bonding. Four plate-type airbrakes, one on each side and two below fuselage. Quick-release handle permits nosecone to be pulled forward on tracks to give access to radar compartment.

TAIL UNIT: Vertical surfaces only, comprising main fin and powered rudder, supplemented by a small ventral fin. The main fin can be folded downward to port. More than 20 fins for JA 37s are being made of composite materials, to gain experience in preparation for the JAS 39 programme.

LANDING GEAR: Retractable tricycle type, designed for a max rate of sink of 5 m (16.4 ft)/s. Power steerable twin-wheel nose unit retracts forward. Each main unit has two

157

mainwheels in tandem and retracts inward into main wing and fuselage. Nosewheel tyres size 18 × 5.5. Mainwheel tyres size 26 × 6.6. Goodyear wheels and brakes. Dunlop anti-skid system.

POWERPLANT: One Volvo Flygmotor RM8B (supersonic development of the Pratt & Whitney JT8D-22) turbofan engine, fitted with a Swedish developed afterburner and thrust reverser. This engine is rated at 72.1 kN (16,203 lb st) dry and 125 kN (28,108 lb st) with afterburning. Thrust reverser doors are actuated automatically by compression of the oleo as the nose gear strikes the runway, the thrust being deflected forward via three annular slots in the ejector wall. The ejector is normally kept open at subsonic speeds to reduce fuselage base drag; at supersonic speeds, with the intake closed, the ejector serves as a supersonic nozzle. Fuel is contained in one tank in each side of the fuselage, and one aft of the cockpit. Provision for jettisonable external auxiliary tank on underfuselage centreline pylon.

ACCOMMODATION: Pilot only, on Saab-Scania fully adjustable rocket assisted zero/zero ejection seat beneath rearward hinged clamshell canopy. Cockpit pressurisation.

AVIONICS AND FLIGHT EQUIPMENT: Altogether, about 50 avionics units, with a total weight of approx 600 kg (1,323 lb), are installed in the Viggen. Flight equipment includes an automatic speed control system, a Smiths electronic head-up display, Bofors Aerotronics aircraft attitude instruments, radio and fighter link equipment, Singer-Kearfott SKC-2037 central digital computer, Garrett LD-5 digital air data computer, Singer-Kearfott KT-70L inertial measuring equipment, Honeywell/Saab-Scania SA07 digital automatic flight control system, Honeywell radar altimeter, Decca Doppler Type 72 navigation equipment, SATT radar warning system, Ericsson radar display system and electronic countermeasures, and AIL Tactical Instrument Landing System (TILS), a microwave scanning beam landing guidence system. Most avionics equipment is connected to the central digital computer, which is programmed to check out and monitor these systems both on the ground and during flight. Ram-air intake on underfuselage centreline, for cooling avionics compartment.

ARMAMENT AND OPERATIONAL EQUIPMENT: Permanent underbelly pack, offset to port side of centreline, containing one 30 mm Oerlikon KCA long-range cannon with 150 rounds, a muzzle velocity of 1,050 m (3,445 ft)/s, a rate of fire of 1,350 rds/min, and a projectile weight of 0.36 kg (0.79 lb). Improved fire control equipment. This gun installation permits retention of the three under-fuselage stores attachment points, in addition to the four underwing hardpoints. Advanced target search and acquisition system, based on a high-performance long-range Ericsson PS-46/A pulse-Doppler radar which is unaffected by variations of weather and altitude. This radar is not disturbed by ground clutter, and is highly resistant to ECM. Armament can include two BAe Sky Flash (Swedish designation RB71) and six AIM-9L Sidewinder (RB74) air-to-air missiles. For air-to-surface attack, a total of twenty-four 135 mm rockets can be carried in four pods.

DIMENSIONS, EXTERNAL:

Main wing span	10.60 m (34 ft 9¼ in)
Foreplane span	5.45 m (17 ft 10½ in)
Length overall (incl probe)	16.40 m (53 ft 9¾ in)
Height overall	5.90 m (19 ft 4¼ in)
Wheel track	4.76 m (15 ft 7½ in)
Wheelbase (c/l of shock absorbers)	5.69 m (18 ft 8 in)

AREAS:

Main wings, gross	46.00 m² (495.1 sq ft)
Foreplanes, outside fuselage	6.20 m² (66.74 sq ft)

WEIGHTS (approx):

T-O weight: 'clean'	15,000 kg (33,070 lb)
with normal armament	17,000 kg (37,478 lb)

PERFORMANCE:

Max level speed: at high altitude	above Mach 2
at 100 m (300 ft)	Mach 1.2
Time to 10,000 m (32,800 ft) from brakes off, with	
afterburning	less than 1 min 40 s
T-O run	approx 400 m (1,310 ft)
Landing run	approx 500 m (1,640 ft)
Required landing field length:	
conventional landing	1,000 m (3,280 ft)
no-flare landing	500 m (1,640 ft)
Tactical radius with external armament:	
hi-lo-hi	over 540 nm (1,000 km; 620 miles)
lo-lo-lo	over 270 nm (500 km; 310 miles)

Saab JAS 39 Gripen (Griffin)

In June 1980 the Swedish government approved funding for project definition and initial development during 1980–82 of a Viggen replacement to enter service from about 1992. Known officially as the JAS 39 (Jakt/Attack/Spaning: fighter/attack/reconnaissance), this multi-role combat aircraft is intended to replace, successively, the AJ/SH/SF/JA 37 versions of the Viggen. A similar financial commitment was made by Industri Gruppen JAS, a Swedish aerospace industry group formed in 1980 by Saab-Scania, Volvo Flygmotor, Ericsson and FFV.

On 3 June 1981 the group submitted to the Swedish Defence Materiel Administration (FMV) its detailed proposals for an aircraft to meet the JAS requirement. The airframe then had the Saab project design number 2105 (since superseded by the slightly modified Saab 2110), and is powered by a modified General Electric F404J afterburning turbofan engine developed and produced, as the RM12, in collaboration with Volvo Flygmotor.

Of similar aerodynamic configuration to the Viggen, with delta wings and all-moving foreplanes, the airframe is some 30 per cent manufactured from CFRP, permitting weight savings of up to 25 per cent and enabling the normal T-O weight to be kept down to approx 8,000 kg (17,635 lb). Performance will include supersonic speed at all altitudes and, like the Viggen, the JAS 39 will be adapted to the specific Swedish defence profile, using 800 m (2,625 ft) V-90 airstrips and ordinary roads as air bases as well as requiring only simple maintenance with turnaround service handled mainly by conscripts.

The FMV evaluated the Swedish industry proposals against aircraft from other countries, and recommended

Prototype of the Saab JAS 39 Gripen multi-role air defence and attack aircraft.

adoption of the Saab design. A procurement programme was agreed on 30 April 1982 between Industri Gruppen JAS and the FMV, and approved by the Swedish government on 6 May 1982. This covers the development and procurement of 140 aircraft by the year 2000. A JAS go-ahead was given by the Swedish parliament on 4 June 1982 as part of the next five-year (1982–87) defence plan, and a contract for the first 30 aircraft was signed on 30 June 1982. On 14 September 1982 a JA 37 Viggen testbed aircraft made its first flight equipped with the triplex fly-by-wire flight control system intended for the JAS 39. A second Viggen joined the programme as testbed for avionics and weapons systems. Overall programme go-ahead was confirmed in the Spring of 1983, and prototype construction began in 1984. The first wing/fuselage mating took place in 1986.

Five Gripen prototypes are being built, the first of which was rolled out on 26 April 1987 and will fly in 1988. Production deliveries are expected to begin in 1991.

The following description applies to the prototypes:

TYPE: Single-seat all-weather, all-altitude fighter, attack and reconnaissance aircraft.

AIRFRAME: Close-coupled canard configuration, with extensive use of composites in its construction. Cropped delta main wings, mid-mounted on fuselage, with leading-edge 'dog-tooth' and inboard and outboard elevons. Sweptback all-moving foreplanes, mounted on upper sides of engine air intake trunks. BAe is collaborating with Saab-Scania on design and construction of the carbonfibre wings, and manufactured those for the first two prototypes. Leading-edge sweepback approx 43° on foreplanes, 45° on main wings. Fin and rudder; no horizontal tail surfaces. Lear Siegler triple-redundant digital fly-by-wire flight control system, with Moog servo-actuators for primary flight control surfaces, Lucas Aerospace rotary actuators ('geared hinges') for leading-edge flaps, and Saab Combitech aircraft motion sensors and throttle actuator subsystem. Lucas Aerospace auxiliary and emergency power system.

Saab JAS 39 Gripen. *(Pilot Press)*

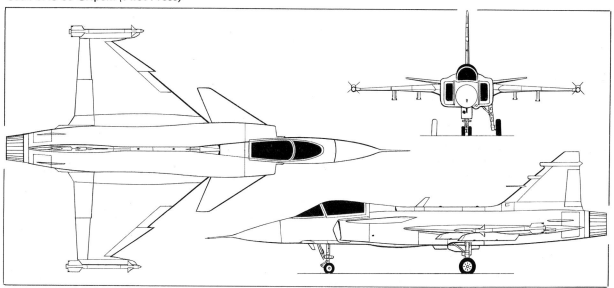

159

LANDING GEAR: Retractable tricycle type, mainwheels retracting forward and inward into fuselage; steerable twin nosewheel unit retracts rearward, turning through 90° to lie flat in underside of fuselage. Goodyear wheels, tyres, carbon disc brakes and anti-skid units.

POWERPLANT: One General Electric/Volvo Flygmotor RM12 (F404J) turbofan engine, rated at approx 80.5 kN (18,100 lb st) with afterburning. Wedge-shape intakes, each with splitter plate. Fuel in self-sealing main tank and collector tank in fuselage. Intertechnique fuel management system.

ACCOMMODATION: Pilot only, on Martin-Baker S10LS zero/zero ejection seat under 'teardrop' canopy. Canopy and one-piece wraparound windscreen by Lucas Aerospace. Design study for two-seat version, if required, has been carried out.

AVIONICS: Bofors Aerotronics AMR 345 VHF/UHF-AM/FM com transceiver. Honeywell laser inertial navigation system. Ericsson EP 17 electronic display system in cockpit, using one Hughes Aircraft wide-angle head-up and three Ericsson head-down CRT displays, with a Ferranti FD 5040 video camera, plus a minimum of conventional instruments for backup purposes only. The head-up display, using advanced diffraction optics, will present a combination of symbology and video images within the pilot's line of vision. Left-hand head-down display normally replaces all conventional flight instruments. Central display shows a computer generated map of the area surrounding the aircraft (indicating land, lakes, rivers, roads, population centres, and obstacles to low-level flying), on which tactical information is superimposed. Right-hand presentation is a multi-sensor display for information from the radar, video and FLIR. An Ericsson SDS 80 computing system controls the aircraft's central air data computer, radar, electronic displays and other computer controlled systems, and allows for multi-mode use and flexibility for further development.

OPERATIONAL EQUIPMENT: Ericsson/Ferranti PS-05/A multi-mode pulse-Doppler target search and acquisition system, comprising a nose mounted radar and pod mounted FLIR or a laser rangefinder pod. For fighter missions, this system provides target search, and tracking of several targets at long range; wide-angle quick-scanning and lock-on at short ranges; and fire control for missiles and cannon. In the attack and reconnaissance roles its operating functions are search against sea and ground targets; mapping, with normal and high resolution; fire control for missiles and other attack weapons; and obstacle avoidance and navigation. The pulse-Doppler radar is only some 60 per cent as large as current Swedish fighter radars but has three times the number of functions, is designed to detect targets at all altitudes and at longer ranges, and will have improved resistance to enemy ECM. It includes modes for surface surveillance, and is the basic part of the system for attack and reconnaissance missions. The FLIR pod, carried externally under the starboard engine air intake trunk, forward of the wing leading edge, is used for attack and reconnaissance missions at night, providing a 'heat picture' of the target on the cockpit right-hand electronic display. The JAS 39 will also carry advanced ECM, both built-in and externally.

ARMAMENT: Internally mounted 27 mm Mauser BK27 automatic cannon in fuselage. External attachment for FLIR pod under starboard intake (see preceding paragraph). Six other external hardpoints (two under each wing and one at each wingtip). Sidewinder, Sky Flash or AMRAAM infra-red or radar homing air-to-air missiles. Underwing stores can include Saab RBS 15F or other heavy anti-shipping missiles, electro-optically guided air-to-surface missiles and bombs, area weapons, or a day/night reconnaissance pod.

DIMENSIONS, EXTERNAL (approx):

Wing span	8.00 m (26 ft 3 in)
Length overall	14.10 m (46 ft 3 in)
Height overall	4.70 m (15 ft 5 in)
Wheel track	2.60 m (8 ft $6\frac{1}{2}$ in)
Wheelbase	5.30 m (17 ft $4\frac{3}{4}$ in)

WEIGHT (approx):

Normal max T-O weight	8,000 kg (17,635 lb)

PERFORMANCE:

Max level speed	supersonic at all altitudes
T-O and landing strip length	approx 800 m (2,625 ft)
g limit	+ 9

Saab 105

Swedish Air Force designation: SK 60

The first of two prototypes of this jet basic trainer and light attack aircraft flew for the first time on 29 June 1963. The Swedish Air Board ordered 130 production aircraft early in 1964, the first of which flew on 27 August 1965. A follow-up order for 20 more was placed in 1965. Today the SwAF operates about 135 SK 60s which, it has been announced, are to be upgraded under a SKr 50 million contract with Saab Aircraft Division. Under an existing contract, Swedish Saab 105s are having their wing spars modified.

The following versions were built, those with SK 60 designations for the Swedish Air Force:

SK 60A. Basic training and liaison version, of which deliveries to Ljungbyhed Air Base began in the spring of 1966. Two Turboméca Aubisque turbofan engines (each 7.29 kN; 1,640 lb st). All have certain provisions for conversion to attack configuration.

SK 60B. SK 60A with completed provision for ground attack use. These aircraft are still used mainly as trainers, but some 20 are actually assigned ground attack duties. The six underwing pylons can carry up to 700 kg (1,545 lb) of weapons, including missiles, two 30 mm gun pods and twelve 135 mm rockets.

SK 60C. A number of SK 60B aircraft were given a permanent reconnaissance camera installation in the nose, in addition to attack capability. The Fairchild KB-18 camera is of panoramic type. Prototype flew on 18 January 1967. About 20 are in SwAF use.

Saab-105XT. First flown on 29 April 1967, the Saab-105XT was a development of the SK 60B version, with improved performance and armament load capacity resulting from the installation of two General Electric J85-17B turbojet engines. To cater for the higher fuel consumption, compared with the SK 60s, internal fuel capacity was increased.

The wing structure was strengthened to permit a weapon load of up to 2,000 kg (4,410 lb) to be carried. Max T-O weight also increased, but the 105XT retained the ability to take off on one engine. It was intended for training, attack,

160

The Saab SK 60C multi-purpose reconnaissance-attack aircraft. *(I. Thuresson)*

liaison, interception or photo-reconnaissance duties. Provision was made for target towing reel and launcher to be installed beneath the port wing. Forty were built for the Austrian Air Force as Saab-105Ös, delivered from 1970. These trainers have a secondary air-defence role.

The following details refer to the Saab 105Ö version.

TYPE: Multi-purpose light twin-jet monoplane.

WINGS: Cantilever shoulder-wing monoplane. Sweepback 12° 48′ at quarter-chord. Anhedral 6°. Thickness/chord ratio 10.3% at root, 12% at tip. Aerodynamically balanced ailerons, with boosted control. Geared servo-tab in each aileron; starboard tab adjustable mechanically for

Saab 105. *(Pilot Press)*

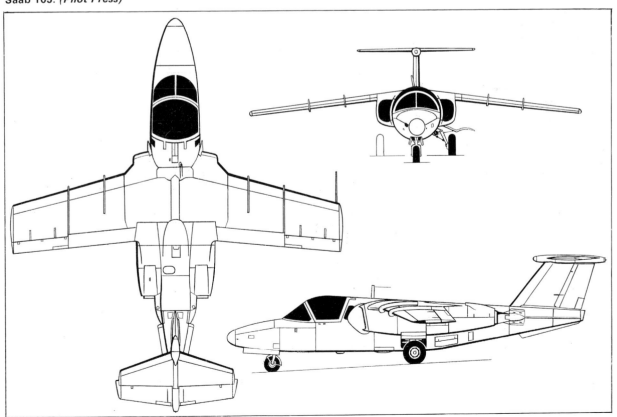

trimming. Hydraulically-operated single-slotted flaps. Two small fences on upper surface of each wing.

FUSELAGE: Semi-monocoque structure. Hydraulically-operated perforated airbrakes pivoted in transverse slots in lower fuselage aft of landing gear.

TAIL UNIT: Cantilever structure, with tailplane mounted at tip of fin. Control surfaces statically and aerodynamically balanced. Electrically-operated trim-tab in rudder. A pneumatic yaw-damper is also fitted. Geared servo-tab in each elevator, adjustable electrically for trimming. Small ventral fin.

LANDING GEAR: Retractable tricycle type. Hydraulic actuation. Main units retract into fuselage. Forward-retracting hydraulically-steerable nosewheel. Hydraulic disc brakes with anti-skid system.

POWERPLANT: Two General Electric J85-17B turbojet engines, each rated at 12.68 kN (2,850 lb st). Engine starting by internal battery. Fuel in two fuselage tanks and two wing tanks with total capacity of 2,050 litres (542 US gallons; 451 Imp gallons). Provision for overwing refuelling. Provision for two 500 litre (132 US gallon; 110 Imp gallon) underwing drop-tanks.

ACCOMMODATION: Two side-by-side ejection seats. Alternative provision for four fixed seats. Bird-proof windscreen. Electrically-actuated rearward-hinged canopy of double-curved acrylic glass. Dual controls standard.

AVIONICS AND EQUIPMENT: A wide range of navigational and communications equipment could be installed. The standard installation includes one VHF and one UHF unit with audio control, one VOR/ILS with marker beacon, one ADF, one transponder and one DME.

ARMAMENT AND OPERATIONAL EQUIPMENT: Three attachment points under each wing, the inner and outer points each capable of supporting a 275 kg (610 lb) load and the centre points each capable of supporting 450 kg (992 lb). Total weapons load 2,000 kg (4,410 lb). Wide range of weapons includes two 1,000 lb and four 500 lb bombs; ten 250 lb bombs; twelve 80 kg Lepus flare bombs; four 500 lb bombs and two 30-mm gun pods; four 500 lb napalm bombs and two Minigun pods; twelve 13.5-cm rockets; six pods each containing four 5-in rockets; twenty-two 7.5-cm rockets; two Saab RB05 air-to-surface and two infra-red (Sidewinder) air-to-air missiles and two Minigun pods; or a camera pod, flash pod, two Minigun pods and two drop-tanks. Ferranti Isis F-105 gyro gunsight standard.

DIMENSIONS, EXTERNAL:
Wing span	9.50 m (31 ft 2 in)
Length overall	10.50 m (34 ft 5 in)
Height overall	2.70 m (8 ft 10 in)
Wheel track	2.00 m (6 ft 7 in)
Wheelbase	3.90 m (12 ft 9½ in)

AREA:
Wings, gross	16.30 m² (175.0 sq ft)

WEIGHTS:
Weight empty	2,565 kg (5,655 lb)
Max T-O weight, trainer	4,530 kg (9,987 lb)
Max T-O weight, with armament	6,500 kg (14,330 lb)

PERFORMANCE (at max T-O weight):
Max speed at S/L	524 knots (970 km/h; 603 mph)
Max speed at 10,000 m (32,800 ft)	472 knots (875 km/h; 544 mph)
Landing run	575 m (1,890 ft)

Range at 13,100 m (43,000 ft), with 20 min reserves at 378 knots (700 km/h; 435 mph)
1,294 nm (2,400 km; 1,491 miles)

Range at 11,000 m (36,000 ft), with external tanks and 30 min reserves at 378 knots (700 km/h; 435 mph)
1,629 nm (3,020 km; 1,876 miles)

Typical attack radius, including reserves, with 1,360 kg (3,000 lb) bomb load:
hi-lo-hi mission	446 nm (827 km; 514 miles)
low altitude throughout	174 nm (324 km; 201 miles)

Typical attack radius, including reserves, with 907 kg (2,000 lb) bomb load and 2 drop-tanks:
hi-lo-hi mission	732 nm (1,360 km; 844 miles)
low altitude throughout	283 nm (523 km; 326 miles)

Switzerland

Swiss Federal Aircraft Factory (F + W)
EIDGENÖSSISCHES FLUGZEUGWERK – FABRIQUE FÉDÉRALE D'AVIONS – FABBRICA FEDERALE D'AEROPLANI

F + W is the Swiss government's official aircraft establishment for research, development, production, maintenance and modification of military aircraft and guided missile systems. It employs about 800 people in its works at Emmen, near Lucerne, which cover 140,000 m² (1,506,946 sq ft).

The Production Department covers the whole field of production capabilities, from mechanical and sheet metal parts to composite parts and subassemblies. Recent major activities have included licence manufacture of aircraft, helicopters and missile systems, and fabrication of the shroud of the Ariane space launcher (designed by F + W with Contraves as main contractor). In March 1985 F + W delivered to the Swiss Air Force the last of 110 Northrop Tiger IIs (98 F-5Es and 12 F-5Fs) ordered from the USA under two 'Peace Alps' contracts. All except the first 19 of these aircraft (13 Es and six Fs) were assembled and partially manufactured by F + W.

Under a $10.7 million USAF contract awarded jointly to Northrop and F + W in October 1984, the two companies are manufacturing more than 230 sets of new horizontal tail surfaces for the Northrop T-38 Talon supersonic jet trainer.

F + W conducts wind tunnel tests for foreign aircraft manufacturers, ground transportation developers and users, and for the building industry. It performs development and integration of internal stores and other modification work on military aircraft, including, currently, adding canard surfaces to Swiss Air Force Mirages, the first of which first flew in this configuration on 23 August 1983. F + W has also developed a low-level dispenser bombing system which is already integrated on Swiss Air Force Hunter and Tiger II aircraft. The system utilises aerodynamically retarded bomblets, carried in underwing pods and ejected by ram air. Integration on other types of aircraft is under way.

F + W Mirage Improvement Programme

The Swiss government approved funding at the end of 1985 for a retrofit programme for Mirage III aircraft of the Swiss Air Force, which currently has 52 of these aircraft (30 III-S, 18 III-RS, two III-BS and two III-DS) in its inventory. Main ingredients of this programme are the fitting of non-moving canard surfaces just aft of the engine air intakes, and addition of a very slim strake on each side of the extreme nose, the former to improve manoeuvrability and low-speed handling and eliminate buffeting, the latter to increase stability in yaw near the upper limit of the flight envelope. F + W began flight testing this configuration on a Swiss Air Force Mirage III-S on 23 August 1983, and a second aircraft was later converted for operational evaluation by Swiss Air Force pilots. The canards are of similar size and shape to those on the Mirage 3 NG, and have a span about one-third that of the wings. The nose strakes, which extend along part of the nose pitot and the tip of the radome, are approx 0.5 m (1 ft 7¾ in) long and less than 5 cm (1.97 in) wide.

Other improvements forming part of the upgrading package include new audible warning and visual angle-of-attack monitoring systems, to alert the pilot when approaching limits of the flight envelope; substitution of

Swiss Air Force Mirage III-S evaluation aircraft, modified by F + W with nose strakes and fixed foreplane surfaces. *(Swiss Air Force)*

Martin-Baker Mk 4 ejection seats for the present Mk 6 seats; addition of infra-red and passive/active ECM; provision of more powerful VHF radios; wing strengthening; ability to carry two underwing 500 litre (132 US gallon; 110 Imp gallon) IMI auxiliary fuel tanks and a 730 litre (193 US gallon; 160.5 Imp gallon) centreline tank; mounting of improved blast deflectors for the two internal guns, to allow firing at high angles of attack; and a new camouflage paint scheme. The retrofit programme is planned to be undertaken over the period 1986–1990.

F + W built Northrop F-5E Tiger II.

Taiwan

AIDC
AERO INDUSTRY DEVELOPMENT CENTER

The Aero Industry Development Center was established on 1 March 1969 as a successor to the Bureau of Aircraft Industry (BAI), which was formed in 1946 in Nanking and moved to Taiwan in 1948. AIDC, which employs more than 3,500 people, is now a subsidiary of the Chung Shan Institute of Science and Technology.

The AIDC has been engaged in licence building 248 Northrop F-5E Tiger II tactical fighter aircraft (see US section) and 36 two-seat F-5Fs for the Chinese Nationalist Air Force. The first Chinese-built F-5E (CAF name **Chung Cheng**) was rolled out on 30 October 1974, and all have now been delivered.

The AIDC designed and produced the T-CH-1 turboprop basic trainer for the Chinese Nationalist Air Force, and has since developed and put into production the twin-turbofan AT-3 jet trainer.

AIDC Fighter

Preliminary design has been completed of a supersonic lightweight air-defence fighter to replace the Lockheed F-104 and Northrop F-5E in Chinese Nationalist Air Force service in the 1990s. According to Taiwan's Defence Minister in late 1985, a development/production budget of $1,000 million had been approved for this programme, which is expected to lead to an aircraft with similar performance characteristics to the Northrop F-20A Tigershark, the sale of which to Taiwan has been forbidden by the US government. US technological assistance in developing an indigenous fighter is not, however, subject to the same restrictions, and AIDC is reported to have received such assistance from General Dynamics (airframe), Garrett (powerplant) and Lear Siegler (avionics), the fighter being likely to be powered by two 37.14 kN (8,350 lb st) Garrett TFE1042 turbofan engines. First flight is tentatively planned for 1989.

AIDC A-3 Lui-Meng

Reports have been received of a single-seat attack version of the AIDC AT-3 jet trainer, known as the A-3 Lui-Meng. It can carry a 2,700 kg (5,950 lb) weapon load, which can include wingtip Sidewinder air-to-air missiles. It is believed that AT-3 production by early 1988, amounting to about 50 units, includes some early A-3s.

Thailand

RTAF (SWDC)
ROYAL THAI AIR FORCE (Science and Weapon Systems Development Centre)

The RTAF-1, the first design for which engineers of the Royal Thai Air Force were responsible after the end of the Second World War, was followed by the RTAF-2 utility aircraft, now in the RTAF Museum at Don Muang, near Bangkok. No details of the RTAF-3 are known, except that a model underwent wind tunnel testing in Japan.

The Office of Aeronautical Engineering was set up in 1975, and has been responsible for all subsequent design activity.

RTAF-5

Most ambitious product of the Directorate of Aeronautical Engineering (DAE) to date, the RTAF-5 was a turboprop trainer and FAC aircraft designed and built entirely in Thailand. Design started in February 1975, and construction of the first of two prototypes began on 26 May 1976. This aircraft made a successful 12 min first flight at Don Muang

Prototype of the RTAF-5 trainer/FAC aircraft, designed and built by the Royal Thai Air Force.

Air Base on 5 October 1984. However, the programme has now been terminated.

RTAF-5. *(Pilot Press)*

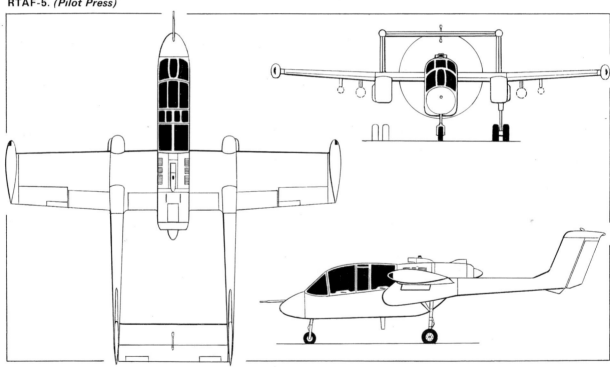

Turkey

TAI
TUSAŞ HAVACILIK VE UZAY SANAYii AS (Tusas Aerospace Industries Inc)

TUSAŞ was officially established on 11 July 1973, with joint funding by the Turkish government and the Turkish Air Force Foundation, with the objective of creating an aircraft manufacturing industry in Turkey. An area of 5 million m² (1.93 sq miles) at Mürted, near Ankara, was allocated for an aircraft manufacturing facility and auxiliary buildings.

Following selection of the General Dynamics F-16 in 1983 as the new fighter aircraft for the Turkish Air Force, TAI was established on 15 May 1984 as the corresponding industrial organisation, owned jointly by Turkish interests (51%), General Dynamics (42%) and General Electric (7%). Construction of the new facility began in the same year, and this came into operation in 1987. Co-production will include aircraft assembly, test, and airframe manufacture. A total of 160 F-16Cs and Ds is involved in the programme, and the first eight will be US built. Initial assembly by TAI will be from kits supplied by General Dynamics, progressing gradually towards local manufacture. Deliveries are planned to begin in 1988 and to be completed by 1994.

167

Union of Soviet Socialist Republics

Antonov
OLEG K. ANTONOV DESIGN BUREAU

This design bureau, based at Kiev, is named after its founder, Oleg Konstantinovich Antonov who, after establishing his reputation with a series of successful glider and sailplane designs, became one of the Soviet Union's leading designers of transport aircraft, particularly those types intended for short field operation. He died on 4 April 1984, at the age of 78.

Antonov An-12
NATO reporting name: Cub

More than 900 An-12 freighters were built for military and civil use before production ended in the Soviet Union in 1973. These, plus a Chinese version currently being built at the Hanzhong factory and known as the Y-8, are in Soviet and Chinese military service and are also operated by several other air forces. Full details of the An-12 freighter will be published in a companion edition to this book.

Four versions of electronic warfare An-12s have also been identified as follows:

Cub-A. Electronic intelligence (elint) version. Generally similar to basic 'Cub' but with blade aerials on front fuselage, aft of flight deck, and other changes.

Cub-B. Conversion of 'Cub' transport for elint duties with Soviet Naval Air Force. Examples photographed over international waters by the crews of Swedish and Norwegian combat aircraft each had two additional blister fairings

Electronic intelligence version of the Antonov An-12, known to NATO as 'Cub-B', is investigated by an F-104G of the Royal Norwegian Air Force.

under forward and centre fuselage, plus other antennae. About 10 produced.

Cub-C. ECM variant carrying several tons of electrical generation, distribution and control gear in cabin, and palletised jammers for at least five wavebands faired into belly, plus ECM dispensers. Glazed nose and undernose radar of transport retained. An ogival 'solid' fuselage tailcone, housing electronic equipment, is fitted in place of the usual gun position.

Cub-D. This further variant of the An-12 reflects the huge efforts being made by the Soviet Union to ensure effective

Antonov An-12 'Cub', a transport which forms the basis for four electronic warfare variants. *(Pilot Press)*

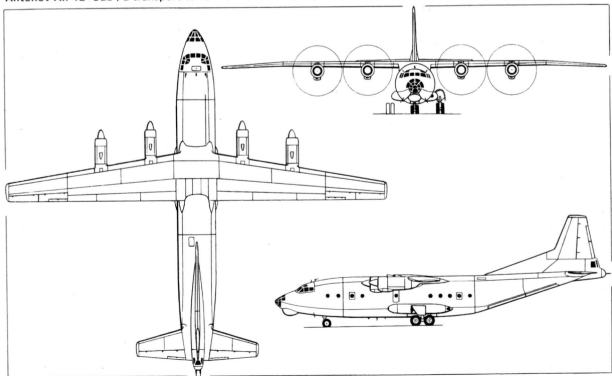

168

handling of every conceivable ECM task. Equipment differs from that of 'Cub-C', to handle different active counter-measures duties. Up to 25 'Cub-C and D' aircraft are believed to serve with the Soviet Air Force and Navy.

In addition to these operational variants, An-12s have been modified extensively as testbeds for advanced avionics, including anti-submarine MAD and radar.

A full structural description of this basically transport aircraft will appear in a companion publication.

POWERPLANT: Four 2,983 kW (4,000 ehp) Ivchenko AI-20K turboprops, driving AV-68 four-blade reversible-pitch propellers.
ARMAMENT: Usually two 23 mm NR-23 guns in tail turret.
DIMENSIONS, EXTERNAL:

Wing span	38.00 m (124 ft 8 in)
Length overall	33.10 m (108 ft 7¼ in)
Height overall	10.53 m (34 ft 6½ in)

AREA:

Wings, gross	121.70 m² (1,310 sq ft)

WEIGHT:

Max T-O weight	61,000 kg (134,480 lb)

PERFORMANCE:

Max level speed	419 knots (777 km/h; 482 mph)

Antonov An-74

This specialised variant of the An-72 twin-turbofan light STOL transport was due for certification in 1988. An AWACS model has also been developed, with a rotodome above the forward-canted tailfin. Its NATO codename is 'Madcap'. No more was known at the time of writing.

Soviet leader Mikhail Gorbachev's visit to the Antonov OKB resulted in the West's first glimpse of an AEW&C version of the An-74 (background), known to NATO as 'Madcap'.

Antonov An-74. The 'Madcap' AWACS version has a fin-top rotodóme. *(Pilot Press)*

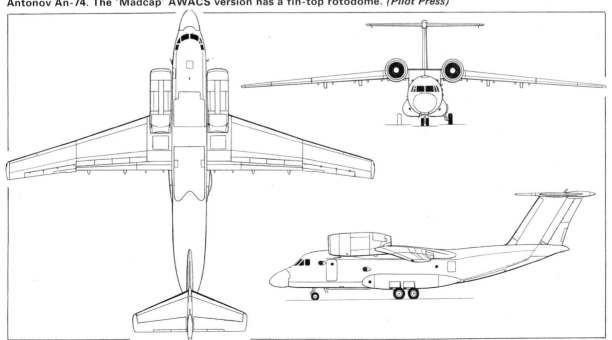

Beriev

This design bureau is named after Georgi Mikhailovich Beriev, whose death at the age of 77 was reported in July 1979. Based at Taganrog, it has been the centre for all Soviet seaplane development since 1945.

Beriev Be-12 (M-12) Tchaika (Seagull)

NATO reporting name: Mail

This twin-turboprop medium-range anti-submarine and maritime reconnaissance amphibian flew for the first time in 1960 and made its initial public appearance in the 1961 Aviation Day flypast at Tushino Airport, Moscow. Subsequently, during the period 23–27 October 1964, it established six international height records in Class C3 Group II. Data submitted in respect of these records revealed that the designation of the aircraft was M-12 (changed subsequently to Be-12) and the powerplant two 4,000 shp Ivchenko AI-20D turboprop engines. The aircraft was also, clearly, able to lift a payload of around 10 tons under record conditions.

The 1964 records have never been bettered. Subsequent record attempts ensured that the Be-12 retained all 22 FAI records in Class C3 Group II for turboprop amphibians, and all 22 current records in Class C2 Group II, for turboprop flying-boats. Two further records were set by Nikolai Shlikov and Sergei Tyukavkin (pilot and co-pilot respectively), for distance in a straight line, in 1983. They covered a distance of 2,647.634 km (1,645.163 miles) between Morskoy and Sukhoputny on 30 October to claim the class C3/II record. On the following day they covered a precisely similar distance between Severny and Morskoy to claim the class C2/II record.

Production started in 1964, and when three Be-12s took part in the 1967 air display at Domodedovo, the commentator said that the unit to which they belonged was 'one of those serving where the country's military air force began', implying that the aircraft were then in operational service. Be-12s have subsequently formed standard equipment at coastal air bases of the Soviet Northern and Black Sea Fleets, for anti-submarine and surveillance duties out to some 200 nm (370 km; 230 miles) from shore, and were operational for a period from bases in Egypt, in Egyptian

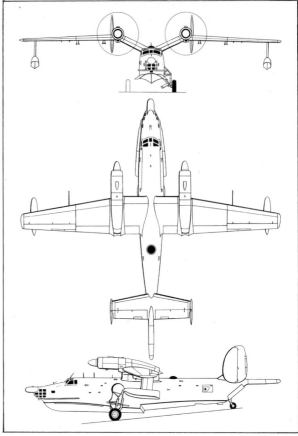

Beriev Be-12 'Mail'. *(Pilot Press)*

insignia. Production is believed to have totalled 100, of which about 95 remain in service.

TYPE: Twin-turboprop anti-submarine and maritime patrol amphibian.

WINGS: Cantilever high-wing monoplane of sharply cranked configuration to raise propellers clear of water. Unswept constant-chord centre-section; tapered outer panels. Hydraulically boosted ailerons. Two electrically operated

Beriev Be-12 Tchaika anti-submarine and maritime patrol amphibian flying-boat of the Soviet Naval Air Force. *(Royal Norwegian Air Force)*

tabs in each aileron. Hydraulically actuated trailing-edge flaps in two sections on each wing, from aileron to centre-section (passing under engine) and on centre-section.

FUSELAGE: Single-step semi-monocoque hull of high length to beam ratio. Two long strakes, one above the other, on each side of front fuselage to prevent spray from enveloping the propellers at take-off.

TAIL UNIT: Considerable dihedral on two-spar tailplane, which has two endplate fins and horn balanced rudders at tips. Electrically operated trim tab in each elevator and each rudder.

LANDING GEAR: Hydraulically retractable tailwheel type. Non-retractable wingtip floats.

POWERPLANT: Two Ivchenko AI-20D turboprop engines, each rated at 3,124 kW (4,190 ehp) and driving an AV-681 four-blade variable-pitch propeller. Metal cowlings open downward in halves, permitting their use as servicing platforms. Fuel tanks, between spars in wings and in fuselage, with total capacity of approx 11,000 litres (2,905 US gallons; 2,420 Imp gallons).

ACCOMMODATION: Crew of five on flight deck. Glazed navigation and observation station in nose. Astrodome observation station in top of rear fuselage. Side hatches in rear fuselage permit loading while afloat.

AVIONICS AND EQUIPMENT: No details available of com/nav systems or IFF. Radome above nose glazing. MAD (magnetic anomaly detection) 'sting' extends rearward from tail. APU exhausts through aperture in port side of rear fuselage.

ARMAMENT: Internal weapons bay in bottom of hull aft of step. One large and one smaller external stores pylon under each outer wing panel, for torpedoes, depth charges, mines and other stores.

DIMENSIONS, EXTERNAL:
Wing span	29.71 m (97 ft 5¾ in)
Length overall	30.17 m (99 ft 0 in)
Height overall	7.00 m (22 ft 11½ in)
Propeller diameter	4.85 m (16 ft 0 in)

AREA:
Wings, gross	105 m² (1,130 sq ft)

WEIGHTS:
Max operational load	10,000 kg (22,045 lb)
Max T-O weight	31,000 kg (68,345 lb)

PERFORMANCE:
Max level speed	328 knots (608 km/h; 378 mph)
Normal operating speed	172 knots (320 km/h; 199 mph)
Rate of climb at S/L	912 m (2,990 ft)/min
Service ceiling	11,280 m (37,000 ft)
Range with max fuel	4,050 nm (7,500 km; 4,660 miles)

Ilyushin

This design bureau is named after its former leader, Sergei Vladimirovich Ilyushin, who died on 9 February 1977 at the age of 83. Aircraft designed by Ilyushin and still in service include the Il-14 piston engined light transport and four-turboprop Il-18 transport, of which details will be made available in a companion publication alongside more modern transports, and the Il-28 twin-jet bomber, produced also in China (which see).

Ilyushin Il-20

NATO reporting name: Coot

The Il-18 prototype flew for the first time on 4 July 1957 and production models entered service with Aeroflot in 1959. Production exceeded 700 aircraft, of which more than 100 were exported for use by commercial airlines; a few were delivered for military and government use, usually as VIP transports.

An anti-submarine derivative, the **Il-38** (NATO reporting name 'May'), is in service and is described separately. Another military variant of the Il-18, seen for the first time in 1978, is the **Il-20** elint/reconnaissance aircraft, known to NATO as **Coot-A**. In this case, the airframe appears to be basically unchanged by comparison with the transport. It carries under its fuselage a container about 10.25 m long and 1.15 m deep (33 ft 7½ in × 3 ft 9 in), which is assumed to house side looking radar. There is a further container, about 4.4 m long and 0.88 m deep (14 ft 5 in × 2 ft 10½ in) on each side of the forward fuselage, containing a door over a camera or other sensor. Numerous other antennae and blisters can be seen, about eight of them on the undersurface of the centre and rear fuselage, with two large plates projecting above the forward fuselage.

The following abbreviated details of the Il-18D are retained as an indication of likely features of the military Il-20:

WINGS: Cantilever low-wing monoplane. Mean thickness/chord ratio 14%. Ailerons are mass-balanced and aerodynamically-compensated, and fitted with spring tabs. Double-slotted flaps. Electro-thermal de-icing.

Ilyushin Il-20 (NATO 'Coot-A') electronic intelligence and reconnaissance aircraft. *(US Navy)*

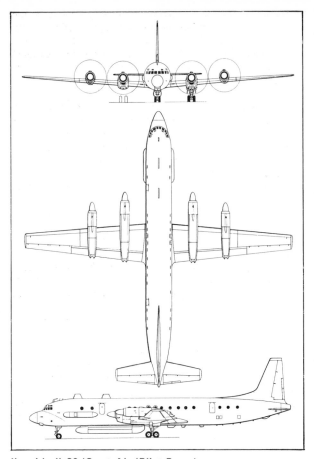

Ilyushin Il-20 'Coot-A'. *(Pilot Press)*

elevators. Additional spring tab in rudder. Electro-thermal de-icing.

LANDING GEAR: Retractable tricycle type. Four-wheel bogie main units, with 930 mm × 305 mm tyres and hydraulic brakes. Steerable (45° each way) twin nosewheel unit, with 700 mm × 250 mm tyres. Brakes and nosewheel steering. Pneumatic emergency braking.

POWERPLANT: Four 3,169 kW (4,250 ehp) Ivchenko AI-20M turboprop engines, each driving an AV-68I four-blade reversible-pitch propeller. Ten flexible fuel tanks in inboard panel of each wing and integral tank in outboard panel, with a total capacity of 23,700 litres (6,261 US gallons; 5,213 Imp gallons). Some Il-18 airliners have additional bag tanks in centre-section, giving a total capacity of 30,000 litres (7,925 US gallons; 6,600 Imp gallons).

DIMENSIONS, EXTERNAL:	
Wing span	37.42 m (122 ft 9¼ in)
Length overall	35.9 m (117 ft 9 in)
Height overall	10.17 m (33 ft 4 in)
Wheel track	9.00 m (29 ft 6 in)
Wheelbase	12.78 m (41 ft 10 in)
Propeller diameter	4.50 m (14 ft 9 in)
AREA:	
Wings, gross	140 m² (1,507 sq ft)
WEIGHTS (Il-18D airliner):	
Max payload	13,500 kg (29,750 lb)
Max T-O weight	64,000 kg (141,100 lb)
PERFORMANCE (Il-18D airliner, at max T-O weight):	
Max cruising speed	364 knots (675 km/h; 419 mph)
Econ cruising speed	337 knots (625 km/h; 388 mph)
Operating height	8,000–10,000 m (26,250–32,800 ft)
T-O run	1,300 m (4,265 ft)
Landing run	850 m (2,790 ft)
Range with max fuel, 1 h reserves	3,508 nm (6,500 km; 4,040 miles)
Range with max payload, 1 h reserves	1,997 nm (3,700 km; 2,300 miles)

FUSELAGE: Circular-section monocoque structure. The structure is of the fail-safe type. Fuselage mounted containers, as detailed in introductory paragraphs.

TAIL UNIT: Cantilever structure. Trim tabs in rudder and

Ilyushin Il-38

NATO reporting name: May

The airframe of this shore-based anti-submarine/maritime patrol aircraft was developed from that of the Il-18 airliner in the same way that the US Navy's P-3 Orion was based on the Lockheed Electra transport. The fuselage is lengthened, and the complete wing assembly is much farther forward than on the Il-18, to cater for the effect on the CG position of internal equipment and stores.

Il-38s of the Soviet Naval Air Force are encountered frequently over the Baltic and North Atlantic. A Treaty of Friendship and Co-operation signed with the People's Democratic Republic of Yemen permits patrols over the Red

Ilyushin Il-38 anti-submarine/maritime patrol aircraft. *(Royal Norwegian Air Force)*

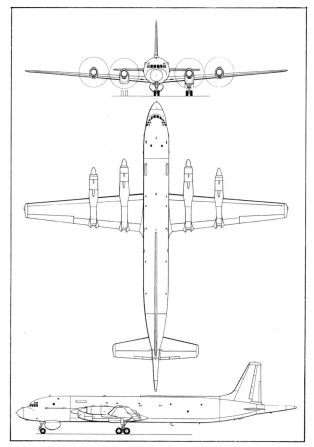

Ilyushin Il-38 'May'. *(Pilot Press)*

Sea, Gulf of Aden, Arabian Sea and Indian Ocean from a base in that country. Other Il-38s are deployed periodically to Libya, Tiyas in Syria, and Mozambique.

In 1975 the Indian Navy ordered an initial batch of three refurbished ex-Soviet Navy Il-38s, which equip INAS 315 at Dabolim, Goa. About 59 are believed to be operational with Soviet naval units.

TYPE: Four-turboprop maritime patrol aircraft.

WINGS: Cantilever low-wing monoplane. Dihedral 3° from roots. Mean thickness/chord ratio 14%. Ailerons are mass and aerodynamically balanced, and fitted with electrically actuated trim tabs. Flying controls cable actuated. Hydraulically actuated double-slotted flaps. Electro-thermal de-icing.

FUSELAGE: Circular-section semi-monocoque structure of fail-safe type, with rip-stop doublers around window cutouts, door frames and the more heavily loaded skin panels.

TAIL UNIT: Cantilever structure. Electrically actuated trim tabs in rudder and elevators. Additional spring tab in rudder. Electro-thermal de-icing.

LANDING GEAR: Retractable tricycle type, strengthened by comparison with that of Il-18. Four-wheel bogie main units, with 930 mm × 305 mm tyres and hydraulic brakes. Steerable (45° each way) twin nosewheel unit, with 700 mm × 250 mm tyres. Hydraulic brakes and nosewheel steering. Pneumatic emergency braking.

POWERPLANT: Four Ivchenko AI-20M turboprops, each rated at 3,169 kW (4,250 shp), driving AV-68I four-blade

reversible-pitch metal propellers. Multiple bag-type fuel tanks in centre-section and in inboard panel of each wing, and integral tank in outboard panel, with a total capacity of 30,000 litres (7,925 US gallons; 6,600 Imp gallons). Pressure fuelling through four international standard connections in inner nacelles. Provision for overwing fuelling. Engines started electrically.

ACCOMMODATION: Pilot and co-pilot side-by-side on flight deck, with dual controls; flight engineer to rear. Number of operational crew believed to be nine, but unconfirmed. Flight deck is separated from main cabin by a pressure bulkhead to reduce hazards following sudden decompression of either. Main cabin has few windows and contains search equipment, electronic equipment and crew stations appropriate to role.

AVIONICS AND EQUIPMENT: Navigation/weather radar in nose. Search radar in undernose radome. MAD tail 'sting'. Automatic navigation equipment, radio compasses and radio altimeter probably similar to those of Il-18.

ARMAMENT: Two weapons/stores bays forward and aft of wing carry-through structure on most aircraft, to accommodate a variety of attack weapons and sonobuoys.

DIMENSIONS, EXTERNAL:
As listed under Il-20 entry, except:
Length overall	39.60 m (129 ft 10 in)
Height overall	10.16 m (33 ft 4 in)

WEIGHTS:
Weight empty	36,000 kg (79,367 lb)
Max T-O weight	63,500 kg (140,000 lb)

PERFORMANCE:
Max level speed at 6,400 m (21,000 ft)	
	390 knots (722 km/h; 448 mph)
Max cruising speed at 8,230 m (27,000 ft)	
	330 knots (611 km/h; 380 mph)
Patrol speed at 600 m (2,000 ft)	
	216 knots (400 km/h; 248 mph)
T-O run	1,300 m (4,265 ft)
Landing run with reverse thrust	850 m (2,790 ft)
Range with max fuel	3,887 nm (7,200 km; 4,473 miles)
Patrol endurance with max fuel	12 h

Ilyushin Il-76

NATO reporting name: Candid
Indian Air Force name: Gajaraj

Towards the end of the 1960s, the Ilyushin design bureau, under the leadership of Mr G. V. Novozhilov, began design of a heavy transport to replace the turboprop An-12. Nominal task for the aircraft was to transport 40 tonnes of freight for a distance of 2,700 nm (5,000 km; 3,100 miles) in less than six hours. It had to be capable of operation from short unprepared airstrips, in the most difficult weather conditions experienced in Siberia, the north of Soviet Union and the Far East, while being much simpler to service and able to fly much faster than the An-12.

The prototype of the new transport, known as the Il-76, (SSSR-86712), flew for the first time on 25 March 1971. Test flying continued until 1975, when the Il-76 entered series production. Full details of the transport models will be made available in a companion publication.

It was clear from the start that the Il-76 had considerable

173

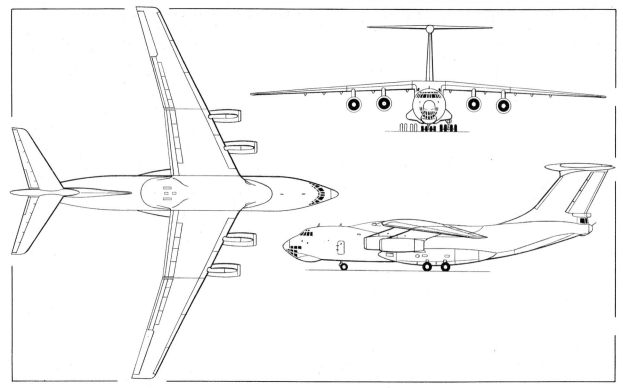

Ilyushin Il-76 'Candid'. *(Pilot Press)*

potential as a military transport. Evaluation by the Soviet Air Force had reached an advanced stage by 1974, when an official film depicted Il-76s with twin-gun rear turrets in use as vehicles for Soviet airborne troops, presumably with a development squadron. In addition, the Il-76 has formed the basis of two important derivatives, as detailed below:

Ilyushin Il-76 (AEW&C)

NATO reporting name: Mainstay

This AEW&C (airborne early warning and control system) version of the Il-76 has been under development since the 1970s as a replacement for the Tu-126s operated by the Soviet Voyska PVO home defence force and tactical air

First clear illustration of the Ilyushin Il-76 AEW&C aircraft, known to NATO as 'Mainstay'. *(Royal Norwegian Air Force)*

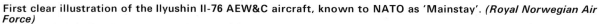

forces. Known to NATO as 'Mainstay', it is said by the US Department of Defense to provide the Soviet forces with the capability to detect aircraft and cruise missiles flying at low altitude over land and water; to help direct fighter operations over European and Asian battlefields; and to enhance air surveillance and defence of the USSR.

'Mainstay' has a conventionally located rotating 'saucer' radome, lengthened fuselage forward of the wings, and flight refuelling probe. In addition to a new IFF system, it is expected to have comprehensive ECM equipment. The first examples are operational in the Kola Peninsula region (particularly associated with Su-27 fighter control). 'Mainstay has no defensive guns, no forward observation window, and two dielectric blisters fore and aft. Radar warning receivers are believed to be positioned where the guns and observation windows on an Il-76 are usually found. A production rate of at least five aircraft per year is expected.

Ilyushin Il-76 (Flight Refuelling Tanker)

NATO reporting name: Midas

A version of the Il-76 had been under development since the mid-1970s as a probe-and-drogue flight refuelling tanker to replace the modified Myasishchev M-4 ('Bison') aircraft serving in this role. Now operational, it supports both tactical and strategic aircraft, improving significantly the ability of Soviet aircraft to conduct longer-range operations.

The following brief details refer to the Il-76T transport, but give an indication of the general characteristics of the 'Mainstay' and 'Midas'. A full structural description of the Il-76 will appear in a companion publication covering transports.

POWERPLANT: Four Soloviev D-30KP turbofan engines, each rated at 117.7 kN (26,455 lb st), in individual underwing pods. Each pod is carried on a large forward-inclined pylon and is fitted with a clamshell thrust reverser.

DIMENSIONS, EXTERNAL:

Wing span	50.50 m (165 ft 8 in)
Length overall*	46.59 m (152 ft 10¼ in)
Height overall	14.76 m (48 ft 5 in)

AREA:

Wings, gross	300.0 m² (3,229.2 sq ft)

WEIGHTS:

Max T-O weight	170,000–190,000 kg (374,785–418,875 lb)

PERFORMANCE:

Max level speed	459 knots (850 km/h; 528 mph)
Cruising speed	405–432 knots (750–800 km/h; 466–497 mph)

T-O speed	114 knots (210 km/h; 131 mph)
Normal cruising height	9,000–12,000 m (29,500–39,370 ft)
Absolute ceiling	approx 15,500 m (50,850 ft)
T-O run	850 m (2,790 ft)
Landing run	450 m (1,475 ft)
Nominal range with 40,000 kg (88,185 lb) payload	2,700 nm (5,000 km; 3,100 miles)
Max range, with reserves	3,617 nm (6,700 km; 4,163 miles)

*'Mainstay' is lengthened.

Kamov

This design bureau continues the work of Nikolai I. Kamov, a leading designer of rotating-wing aircraft since the late 1920s, who died on 24 November 1973, aged 71.

Kamov Ka-25

NATO reporting name: Hormone

The prototype of this military helicopter was first shown in public in the Soviet Aviation Day flypast over Tushino Airport, Moscow, in July 1961. It was allocated the NATO code name 'Harp', but this was changed to 'Hormone' for the production versions, of which about 460 were built in 1966–75. Together with the newer Mil helicopters known to NATO as 'Haze-A', these replaced piston engined Mi-4s in the Soviet Navy's ship and shore based force of around 250 helicopters. About 115 of them remain operational. In addition, five ex-Soviet Navy Ka-25s equip INAS 333 of the Indian Navy, for deployment on 'Kashin II' class destroyers. Nine are operated on coastal anti-submarine duties by the Syrian Arab Air Force and others by Yugoslavia and Viet-Nam (17).

As well as serving as an anti-submarine and missile support aircraft, the Ka-25 fulfils a number of other military roles. Three versions are identified by NATO reporting names:

Hormone-A. Basic ship-based anti-submarine version, operated from cruisers of 'Kresta II' and 'Kara' classes (one 'Hormone-A' each), the nuclear powered guided missile cruisers Kirov and Frunze, each of which carries three, carrier/cruisers of the 'Kiev' class, each of which can carry

about 14, the helicopter carrier/cruisers Moskva and Leningrad, each of which accommodates about 14, and missile frigates of the 'Krivak III' class (one each). Some have an underfuselage weapon bay. Search radar in undernose radome, diameter 1.25 m (4 ft 1 in); dipping sonar housed in compartment at rear of cabin. Canister for sonobuoys can be mounted to rear of main landing gear on starboard side. A major shortcoming is said to be lack of night and all-weather sonar dipping capability. Being replaced by Ka-27 ('Helix-A').

Kamov Ka-25 ('Hormone-A') anti-submarine helicopter. (Swedish Air Force)

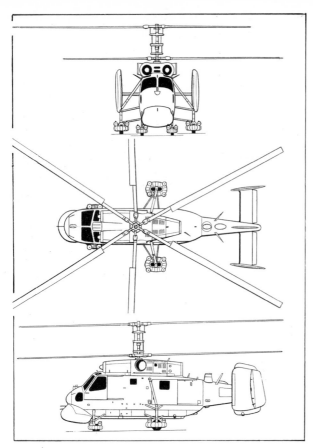

Kamov Ka-25 'Hormone-A'. *(Pilot Press)*

undernose radome with more spherical undersurface. Cylindrical radome under rear of cabin. Data link equipment.

Hormone-C. Utility and search and rescue model, generally similar to 'Hormone-A' but with inessential operational equipment and weapons removed. This version sometimes has a yagi aerial mounted on the nose.

TYPE: Twin-turbine anti-submarine, missile support and general-purpose helicopter.

ROTOR SYSTEM: Two three-blade coaxial contra-rotating rotors. Automatic blade folding.

FUSELAGE: Conventional semi-monocoque structure of pod and boom type.

TAIL UNIT: Cantilever structure, with central fin, ventral fin and twin endplate fins and rudders which are toed inward.

LANDING GEAR: Four-wheel type. Nosewheels are smaller than mainwheels and are of castoring type. Each wheel can be enclosed in an inflatable pontoon surmounted by inflation bottles to provide flotation in event of an emergency alighting on water. All legs are pivoted to retract upward about their wishbone supports, so that the wheels can be moved to a position where they offer least interference to signals from the nose radar.

POWERPLANT: Two 671 kW (900 shp) Glushenkov GTD-3F turboshaft engines, mounted side-by-side above cabin, forward of rotor driveshaft, on early aircraft. Later aircraft have 738 kW (990 shp) GTD-3BM turboshafts. Independent fuel supply to each engine. Provision for carrying external fuel tank on each side of cabin.

ACCOMMODATION: Pilot and co-pilot side-by-side on flight deck, with rearward sliding door on each side. Entry to main cabin is via a rearward sliding door to rear of main landing gear on port side. Cabin accommodates two or three systems operators in ASW role, but is large enough to contain 12 folding seats for passengers.

AVIONICS AND EQUIPMENT: Equipment available for all versions includes autopilot, navigational system, radio compass, radio communications installations, lighting system for all-weather operation by day or night, and hoist mounted above cabin door. IFF antennae (NATO 'Odd Rods') above nose and alongside central tail fin. Dipping sonar housed in compartment at rear of main cabin, immediately forward of tailboom, and search radar under

Hormone-B. Special electronics variant, able to provide over-the-horizon target acquisition for long-range cruise missiles launched from ships. These are believed to include SS-N-3B (NATO 'Shaddock') missiles launched from 'Kresta I' cruisers; SS-N-12 ('Sandbox') missiles from 'Kiev' class carrier/cruisers and 'Slava' class cruisers; SS-N-19 missiles from the battle cruisers *Kirov* and *Frunze*; and SS-N-22 missiles from 'Sovremenny' class destroyers. Larger

Ka-25 ('Hormone-B') with wheels retracted to prevent interference with signals from nose radar.

nose of anti-submarine version, which can have a canister of sonobuoys mounted externally aft of the starboard main landing gear. Some aircraft have a blister fairing over equipment mounted at the base of the centre tail fin; others have a cylindrical housing with a transparent top above the tailboom, probably for ESM, with a shallow blister fairing to the rear of the cylindrical housing. Provision for a camera pod on port side of cabin.

ARMAMENT: Doors under the fuselage of some aircraft enclose a weapons bay for two 450 mm (18 in) ASW torpedoes, nuclear depth charges and other stores.

Kamov Ka-27 'Helix-A' anti-submarine helicopter on board a Soviet aircraft carrier.

DIMENSIONS, EXTERNAL:

Rotor diameter (each)	15.74 m (51 ft 7$\frac{3}{4}$ in)
Length of fuselage	9.75 m (32 ft 0 in)
Height to top of rotorhead	5.37 m (17 ft 7$\frac{1}{2}$ in)
Width over tail-fins	3.76 m (12 ft 4 in)
Wheel track: front	1.41 m (4 ft 7$\frac{1}{2}$ in)
rear	3.52 m (11 ft 6$\frac{1}{2}$ in)

WEIGHTS:

Weight empty	4,765 kg (10,505 lb)
Max T-O weight	7,500 kg (16,535 lb)

PERFORMANCE:

Max level speed	113 knots (209 km/h; 130 mph)
Normal cruising speed	104 knots (193 km/h; 120 mph)
Service ceiling	3,350 m (11,000 ft)
Range with standard fuel, with reserves	217 nm (400 km; 250 miles)
Range with external tanks, with reserves	351 nm (650 km; 405 miles)

Kamov Ka-27

NATO reporting name: Helix

Ka-27 is the Soviet designation for military versions of the helicopter known as the Ka-32 in its civil forms. The basic airframe, powerplant, systems and equipment of the Ka-27 and Ka-32 are identical. Furnishings, avionics and mission equipment vary according to role.

First reference to a military version of this helicopter appeared in a 1981 document on *Soviet Military Power*, published by the US Department of Defense, which referred to 'Hormone variant' helicopters that could be carried in a telescoping hangar on the new 'Sovremenny' class of Soviet guided missile destroyers, for secondary ASW missions. Photographs of such helicopters were released to the technical press after two of them had been seen on the stern platform of the *Udaloy*, first of a new class of Soviet ASW guided missile destroyers, during the Zapad-81 (West-81) series of exercises in the Baltic in September 1981. The fact that one was finished in Aeroflot markings suggested that development of the military version might then have been at an early stage. The US Department of Defense first referred to the ASW helicopter as Ka-27 in 1982. At least 16 were observed on board the 'Kiev' class carrier/cruiser *Novorossiysk* during its maiden deployment in 1983.

Four versions of the Ka-27 have been identified by unclassified NATO reporting names:

Helix-A. Basic ASW version, as shown in accompanying illustration. Probable crew of three. Operational since 1982. About 60 in Soviet Naval Aviation service in 1987. Eight ordered for Indian Navy.

Helix-B. Infantry assault transport. Different undernose equipment. Can accommodate about sixteen troops. Carried by some Soviet naval vessels such as 'Ivan Rogov' class in support of amphibious assault forces.

Helix-D. Search and rescue and plane guard helicopter, first seen on the *Novorossiysk*. Features include an external fuel tank on each side of the cabin, as on the civil Ka-32 'Helix-C', and a winch beside the port cabin door.

'Helix-A' follows closely the configuration of 'Hormone' but has a longer and more capacious fuselage pod, no central

'Helix-B' infantry assault version of the Kamov Ka-27 on the assault ship *Ivan Rogov*. (Marine Nationale, Paris).

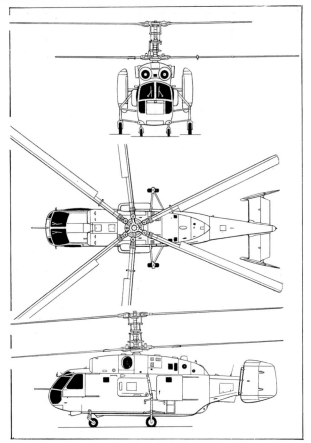

Kamov Ka-27 'Helix'. *(Pilot Press)*

tail fin, and different undernose radome. The overall dimensions of the two aircraft are generally similar, enabling 'Helix' to be stowed on board ship in hangars and via deck lifts built for its predecessor.

The general description of the Ka-32 given below applies also to the Ka-27. The IFF (NATO 'Odd Rods'), radar warning antennae and directional ESM radomes fitted to prototype SSSR-31000 are standard on the Ka-27. The rectangular containers on each side of the bottom centre fuselage may be used to house sonobuoys. Torpedoes and other stores are carried in the ventral weapons bay.

TYPE: Twin-turbine naval helicopter.

ROTOR SYSTEM: Two fully articulated three-blade coaxial contra-rotating rotors. Blades of all-composites construction, with carbonfibre and glassfibre main spars, pockets (13 per blade) of a material similar to Kevlar, and a filler similar to Nomex. As in all Soviet helicopters, blades have a non-symmetrical aerofoil section. Each blade is fitted with a ground adjustable tab. The three lower blades each carry an adjustable vibration damper, comprising two dependent weights, mounted on the root section, and there are further vibration dampers in the fuselage. Tip light on each blade of upper rotor. Blades fold manually outboard of all control mechanisms, to a folded width within the track of the main landing gear. Electrothermal de-icing of the entire profiled portion of each blade, operating at all times when engines are running. Heat generated by rotorhead prevents icing of droop stops. Rotor brake standard.

FUSELAGE: Conventional semi-monocoque structure of pod and boom type, making extensive use of titanium for primary components. Tailcone of composites material. Lower fuselage sealed for flotation.

TAIL UNIT: Braced structure, comprising fixed-incidence tailplane, elevators, twin endplate fins and rudders, with composite skins. Single bracing strut under each side of tailplane. Fins toe inward approx 25°. Fixed leading-edge slat on each fin prevents airflow over fin stalling in crosswinds or at high yaw angles.

LANDING GEAR: Four-wheel type. Nosewheels are smaller than mainwheels and of castoring type. Rear legs are pivoted on some versions, to retract upward about their wishbone supports so that the wheels can be moved to a position where they offer least interference to emissions from the undernose radar. Mainwheel tyres size 600 × 180. Nosewheel tyres size 400 × 150.

POWERPLANT: Two 1,660 kW (2,225 shp) Isotov TV3-117V turboshaft engines, with automatic synchronisation system, mounted side-by-side above cabin, forward of rotor driveshaft. Main gearbox brake standard. Electrothermal intake anti-icing. Cowlings hinge downward for use as maintenance platforms. All standard fuel in tanks under cabin floor and inside container on each side of centre fuselage. Provision for auxiliary tanks in cabin. Refuelling point behind small forward hinged door on port side, where bottom of tailboom meets rear of cabin. APU in rear of engine bay fairing on starboard side, for engine starting and to power all essential hydraulic and electrical services on the ground, eliminating need for GPU.

ACCOMMODATION: Pilot and navigator side-by-side on large air-conditioned flight deck, in fully adjustable seats. Rearward sliding jettisonable door with blister window on each side. Main cabin occupied according to role.

EQUIPMENT AND ARMAMENT: 'Helix-A' has undernose radome, dipping sonar, ESM and other equipment for ASW role. Weapons as for 'Hormone-A'.

DIMENSIONS, EXTERNAL:	
Rotor diameter (each)	15.90 m (52 ft 2 in)
Length overall: excl rotors	11.30 m (37 ft 1 in)
rotors folded	12.25 m (40 ft 2¼ in)
Width, rotors folded	4.00 m (13 ft 1½ in)
Height to top of rotorhead	5.40 m (17 ft 8½ in)
Wheel track: mainwheels	3.50 m (11 ft 6 in)
nosewheels	1.40 m (4 ft 7 in)
Wheelbase	3.02 m (9 ft 11 in)
WEIGHTS:	
Max payload: internal	4,000 kg (8,818 lb)
external	5,000 kg (11,023 lb)
Normal T-O weight	11,000 kg (24,250 lb)
PERFORMANCE (at AUW of 11,000 kg; 24,250 lb):	
Max level speed	135 knots (250 km/h; 155 mph)
Max cruising speed	125 knots (230 km/h; 143 mph)
Service ceiling at normal T-O weight	
	6,000 m (19,685 ft)
Hovering ceiling OGE	3,500 m (11,480 ft)
Range with max fuel	432 nm (800 km; 497 miles)
Endurance with max fuel	4 h 30 min

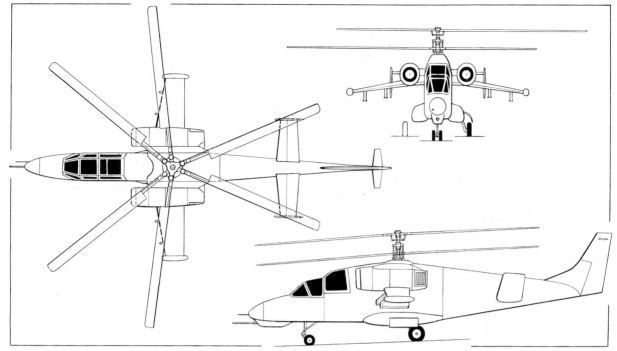

Kamov 'Hokum'. *(Pilot Press)*

Kamov Ka-?

NATO reporting name: Hokum

It became known in summer 1984 that the Kamov bureau had begun flight testing a new combat helicopter which has the NATO reporting name 'Hokum'. Few details are available except that it has co-axial contra-rotating and widely separated three-blade rotors, with swept blade tips; a streamlined fuselage with a tapered nose like that of a jet attack aircraft, with pitot, transducer to provide data for a fire control computer, and undernose sensor pack; and a retractable landing gear. DoD states that this helicopter has not been observed carrying anti-tank guided weapons. Instead, it is thought to have a primary air-to-air role (an assessment that is not universally accepted), with an armament of air-to-air missiles and a rapid-fire gun for employment as a low-level helicopter intercept system by day and night and in adverse weather conditions. Like other combat helicopters, 'Hokum' has a crew of two, in tandem, with elevated rear seat. Survivability is enhanced by use of infra-red suppressors, infra-red decoy dispensers and armour.

In 1987, 'Hokum' was still at the development stage, with only a few prototypes involved in flight and structural testing. If it enters production, the DoD expects that 'Hokum' will give the Soviets a significant rotary-wing air superiority capability. The system has no current Western counterpart'.

DIMENSIONS, EXTERNAL:
Rotor diameter (each)	14.0 m (45 ft 10 in)
Length overall, excl nose probe and gun	
	13.5 m (44 ft 3½ in)
Height overall	5.4 m (17 ft 8 in)

WEIGHT:
Max T-O weight	7,500 kg (16,500 lb)

PERFORMANCE (estimated):
Max level speed	189 knots (350 km/h; 217 mph)
Combat radius	135 nm (250 km; 155 miles)

MiG

Colonel-General Artem I. Mikoyan, who died on 9 December 1970 at the age of 65, was head of the design bureau responsible for the MiG series of fighter aircraft from 1940. With Mikhail I. Gurevich (1893–1976), a mathematician, he collaborated in the design of the first really modern Soviet jet fighter, the MiG-15, which began to enter squadron service in numbers in 1949.

The MiG-17, a progressive development of the MiG-15, was first observed in Soviet squadrons in 1953 or 1954, and was followed into service by the supersonic MiG-19, which appeared in 1955 and has been manufactured also in large numbers in China (which see).

Mikoyan-Gurevich MiG-15

Details of the remaining MiG-15s in service are given in the Chinese section of this book.

Mikoyan-Gurevich MiG-17 and Shenyang J-5

NATO reporting name: Fresco

Less than a year after the MiG-15 had been sanctioned for production (1948), this design bureau initiated work on a follow-on fighter that would approach the speed of sound mainly through refinement of the basic airframe configuration. The first prototype received the designation I-330, and flew for the first time in January 1950. Claims that the I-

330 managed to better Mach 1 during test flights are believed to be unsubstantiated, but the overall improvements in performance were important.

Following the loss of the first prototype, a second and further improved prototype took over, allowing testing to be completed in 1951, and production of the MiG-17 was given the go-ahead. Compared with the MiG-15, the MiG-17 had a lengthened fuselage with softer taper, larger-area tail surfaces to benefit handling characteristics, and thinner-section wings with rounded tips. Indeed, the wings were designed from scratch, with the inner leading edges extended forward; this resulted in greater root chord and varying leading-edge sweepback (45° along inner portions, 42° on outer panels). A mark of identification was the MiG-17's three boundary-layer fences on each wing.

Production began with a day fighter model (NATO 'Fresco-A'), which retained the VK-1 engine. The later MiG-17PF introduced all-weather capability, housing Izumrud S-band radar in a 'bullet' radome at the centre of the nose air-intake and in an extension on the upper lip of the intake. Subsequently, this S-band radar was superseded by an E/F-band version of 'Scan Fix', which still gave neither a large antenna nor a wide angle of scan and is now thought obsolescent.

In addition to the specialised two-seat trainer derivative of the MiG-17, known as the JJ-5 and exclusive to Chinese production (described in the Chinese section), the MiG-17 was also built (apart from in the USSR) in China, Czechoslovakia and Poland, with whom it was known as the J-5, S-104 and LiM-5 respectively. Soviet production alone is believed to have totalled some 6,000 aircraft, with the other countries adding at least half that number again.

While the MiG-17 is out of service (except perhaps in a training capacity) in the USSR, China is thought to operate about 300 J-5 types, with its Air Force of the People's Liberation Army and 'hundreds' with the Aviation of the People's Navy. These, like the MiG-17/J-5s flown by Afghanistan, Albania, Algeria, Bulgaria, Congo, Egypt,

Egyptian Air Force MiG-17F ('Fresco-C'). *(Denis Hughes)*

Equatorial Guinea, Ethiopia, Guinea, Malagasy, Mali, Mozambique, Pakistan, Poland, Romania, Somali, Syria, Tanzania, Uganda, North and South Yemen, are assigned fighter-bomber roles.

The initial production 'Fresco-A' and the similar 'Fresco-B' are no longer in operational use. The currently operated versions are:

MiG-17F (Fresco-C). Day fighter, superseding 'Fresco-A' in production in 1953. VK-1F engine gave way to more powerful VK-1A. MiG-17F was the most produced version.

MiG-17PF (Fresco-D). Limited all-weather version with radar as noted above. Initially (at least) fitted with afterburning Klimov VK-1F engine, rated at 33.14 kN (7,450 lb) thrust with afterburning.

J-5. Chinese-built version of the MiG-17F, constructed at Shenyang. Production is thought to have begun in late 1956; by 1959 these were almost entirely of Chinese local manufacture. VK-1 type engines were built at Harbin.

J-5A or J-5Jia. Chinese version of the MiG-17PF, constructed at Shenyang.

F-5/-5A. Chinese export models of the MiG-17,

Mikoyan-Gurevich MiG-17F 'Fresco-C'. *(Pilot Press)*

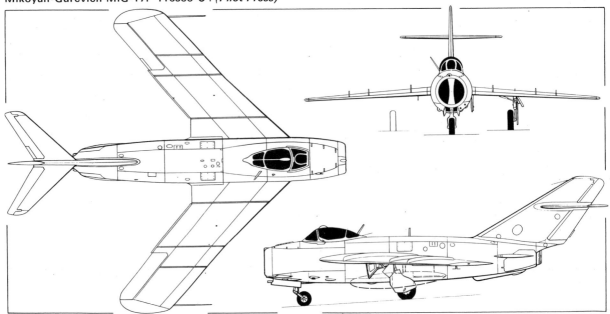

including those to Albania (30), Kampuchea and North Vietnam.

The following details refer specifically to the MiG-17F 'Fresco-C'.

TYPE: Single-seat fighter-bomber.

WINGS: Cantilever mid-wing monoplane. Sweepback 45° at roots, 42° on outer panels. Anhedral 3°. Split Fowler-type flaps. Three boundary-layer fences on each wing.

FUSELAGE: Semi-monocoque structure. Bulged rear air brakes.

TAIL UNIT: Sharply-swept surfaces. Fin-tip dielectric aerial.

LANDING GEAR: Retractable tricycle type. Mainwheel tyres diameter 60 cm.

POWERPLANT: One Klimov VK-1A turbojet engine, developing 33.83 kN (7,605 lb st) with afterburning. Normal fuel load in internal tanks 1,410 litres (372 US gallons; 310 Imp gallons). A 400 litre (106 US gallon; 88 Imp gallon) external tank may be fitted at half-span on each wing.

ACCOMMODATION: Pilot only in pressurised cockpit with ejection seat. Rearward-sliding canopy.

ARMAMENT. One 37 mm Nudelmann-Suranov NS-37 cannon and two 23 mm Nudelmann-Rikhter NR-23 cannon, or three 23 mm cannon. Provision for four underwing packs of 8 × 55 mm air-to-air rockets or a total of 500 kg (1,102 lb) of bombs under the wings.

AVIONICS: See introductory text.

DIMENSIONS, EXTERNAL:

Wing span	9.63 m (31 ft 7 in)
Length overall	11.36 m (37 ft 3¼ in)
Height overall	3.80 m (12 ft 5½ in)
Wheel track	3.85 m (12 ft 7½ in)

WEIGHTS:

Weight empty	3,930 kg (8,664 lb)
Max T-O weight	6,069 kg (13,379 lb)

PERFORMANCE:

Max level speed at 3,000 m (9,845 ft)	
	617 knots (1,145 km/h; 711 mph)
Max rate of climb at S/L	3,900 m (12,795 ft)/min
Service ceiling	16,600 m (54,460 ft)
Max range, with external tanks and bombs	
	755 nm (1,400 km; 870 miles)

Mikoyan MiG-19

NATO reporting name: Farmer

Soon after test flying began of the MiG-17 prototypes, work started on a supersonic fighter that entered service from 1955 as the MiG-19. It was the last of the early-style MiG jet fighters, but the first in the MiG-15/-17/-19 series to possess true supersonic performance in level flight. However, its traditional configuration belied its real strengths. Retaining a proven layout may well have been a prudent move because, in 1951, more radical Yakovlev and Lavochkin prototype fighters totally failed to meet a slightly earlier specification for a transonic fighter. The barrel fuselage with its wide circular nose air-intake housed twin engines in all MiG-19s with the exception of the very first prototype (which made its maiden flight in 1952), while the wing design was wonderfully suited to a wide speed range. The third prototype, the I-

350M, which first flew in September 1953, was the first to have the full MiG-19 configuration as we know it.

Unfortunately for the MiG-19, the experience of MiG-15s in the Korean War led the MiG bureau to pass on quickly from sweptwing fighters to a very different aircraft with a much improved power-to-weight ratio, the MiG-21. Indeed, it was the success of the MiG-21, which joined more air forces in greater number than any other jet fighter in history, that appeared to date the MiG-19 prematurely, and Soviet production up to 1959 covered fewer than half the number of MiG-17s built.

Perhaps the greatest compliment to the MiG-19 has been its amazingly successful production run in China. As the Shenyang J-6 (which see), it entered production in the early 1960s and first joined the Air Force of the People's Liberation Army in mid-1962, following genuine MiG-19s previously assembled in China from Soviet knock-down components. Chinese production of the J-6 greatly exceeded Soviet MiG-19 production, and only in the mid-1980s was full-scale building run down. Ironically, the Chinese initially built only small numbers of the J-7, a MiG-21 derivative.

Structural details of the MiG-19 are not included here, as a full description of the currently more important (and similar) J-6 is given in the Chinese section. The following versions of the MiG-19 are currently flown by the air forces of Afghanistan, Cuba and North Korea.

MiG-19SF (Farmer-C). (*Forsirovanny*: boosted). Day fighter-bomber, powered by two 31.9 kN (7,165 lb st) Klimov RD-9B turbojet engines. Three 30 mm NR-30 cannon. Underwing attachments for two air-to-air missiles, two rockets of up to 212 calibre, two packs of eight air-to-air rockets, two 250 kg bombs, drop-tanks or other stores. Has the all-moving tailplane and underfuselage as well as fuselage-side air-brakes introduced on the MiG-19S.

MiG-19PF (Farmer-D). (*Perekhvatchik*: interceptor). Limited all-weather model with Izumrud (Emerald) radar scanner inside its engine air-intake in a 'bullet' radome and ranging unit in the intake top lip. Armed with two wing-root cannon. Lower cockpit canopy.

MiG-19PM (Farmer-D). (*Modifikatsirovanny*; modified). As for MiG-19PF, but able to carry four first-generation 'Alkali' missiles. No cannon.

MiG-19R. Cannon-armed reconnaissance model, with two nose cameras.

Mikoyan MiG-19SF 'Farmer-C'. *(Pilot Press)*

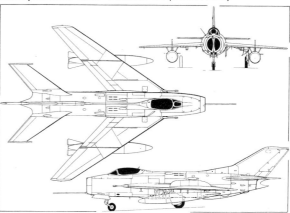

Mikoyan MiG-21

NATO reporting names: Fishbed and Mongol

The MiG-21 air superiority fighter was developed on the basis of experience of jet-to-jet combat between MiG-15s and US aircraft during the war in Korea. The emphasis was placed on good transonic and supersonic handling, high rate of climb, small size and light weight, using a turbojet engine of medium power. The first versions of the MiG-21 were, therefore, day fighters of limited range, with comparatively light armament and limited avionics. Subsequent development of the type was aimed mainly at improvements in range, weapons and all-weather capability, and the MiG-21 became the most widely used fighter in the world, as well as forming for many years the backbone of Soviet tactical air power.

According to pilots of the Egyptian Air Force, their late-model MiG-21MF remained deficient in IFF, navigation and other systems, but could be airborne in under 3 min from an order to go, and were capable of maintaining six sorties per day per aircraft for a two/three-day emergency period. Engine change of the Tumansky R-13-300 after 300 h reflects steady improvement in Soviet turbojet technology.

The E-5 aerodynamic prototype of the MiG-21 flew for the first time on 16 June 1956, and made its public debut during the flypast in the Soviet Aviation Day display at Tushino Airport, Moscow, on 24 June. The initial production version (NATO 'Fishbed-A') was built in only limited numbers, with a Tumansky R-11 turbojet engine rated at 38.25 kN (8,600 lb st) dry and 50 kN (11,240 lb st) with afterburning, and with an armament of two 30 mm NR-30 cannon. Meanwhile, the Soviet Union had been developing a small infra-red homing air-to-air missile, designated K-13 (NATO 'Atoll') and generally similar to the US AIM-9B Sidewinder 1A. Underwing pylons for two K-13s were fitted on the MiG-21F, the suffix 'F' standing for *Forsirovanny* (boosted), and indicating that this model also had a slightly more powerful turbojet. To save weight and provide room for avionics associated with the missiles, the port NR-30 cannon was removed and its blast-tube fairing on the lower fuselage was blanked off. Further details of this and subsequent operational versions of the MiG-21 follow.

MiG-21s continue to be flown by 32 air forces worldwide, but replacement with later fighters has left about 680 in first-line units of the Soviet tactical air forces, including 65 of the reconnaissance models known to NATO as 'Fishbed-H'. Early MiG-21F/PF/PFM variants (NATO 'Fishbed-C/D/F') are flown by various Warsaw Pact air forces.

MiG-21F (Fishbed-C). First major production version, built also in Czechoslovakia. Still in production in improved forms in China, with Chinese designation **J-7**. Short-range clear-weather fighter, with radar ranging equipment and a Tumansky R-11 turbojet rated at 42.25 kN (9,500 lb st) dry and 56.4 kN (12,676 lb st) with afterburning (designation of engine given in Soviet press statements as TDR Mk R37F). Two underwing pylons for UV-16-57 pods, each containing sixteen 57 mm rockets, or K-13 air-to-air missiles, and one NR-30 cannon in starboard side of fuselage (one each side on early aircraft and on the ten supplied to India). Internal fuel capacity of 2,340 litres (618 US gallons; 515 Imp gallons), plus underfuselage pylon for external fuel tank of 490 litres (129.4 US gallons; 108 Imp gallons) capacity. Small nose air intake of approximately 69 cm (27 in) diameter, with movable three-shock centrebody housing the radar ranging equipment. Undernose pitot boom, which folds upward on ground to reduce risk of ground personnel walking into it. Transparent blister cockpit canopy which hinges upward about base of integral flat bulletproof windscreen. Transparent rear-view panel (not on aircraft built in Czechoslovakia) aft of canopy at front of shallow dorsal spine fairing. Large blade antenna at rear of this panel, with small secondary antenna midway along spine. Fowler flap between fuselage and aileron on each trailing edge, with fairing plate under wing at outer extremity. Small forward-hinged airbrake under fuselage, forward of ventral fin; two further forward-hinged airbrakes, on each side of under-fuselage in line with wing root leading edges, integral with part of cannon fairings. Brake parachute housed inside small door on port underside of rear fuselage, with cable attachment under rear part of ventral fin. Semi-encapsulated escape system, in which canopy is ejected with seat, forming shield to protect pilot from slipstream, until the seat has been slowed by its drogue chute. Leading edge of fin extended forward on all but early aircraft, to increase chord.

MiG-21PF (Fishbed-D). Basic model of second series of operational versions with mid-fuselage waisted in accordance with area rule and forward fuselage of less

Mikoyan MiG-21*bis* 'Fishbed-L' of the East German Air Force, carrying 'Atoll' air-to-air missiles and a drop-tank.

tapered form. Intake enlarged to diameter of approximately 91 cm (36 in) and housing larger centrebody for R1L search/track radar (NATO 'Spin Scan A') to enhance all-weather capability (designation suffix letter 'P', standing for *Perekhvatchik*, is applied to aircraft adapted for all-weather interception from an earlier designed role). Remainder of airframe generally similar to that of MiG-21F, but pitot boom repositioned above air intake; cannon armament and fairings deleted, permitting simplified design for forward airbrakes; larger mainwheels and tyres, requiring enlarged blister fairing on each side of fuselage, over wing, to accommodate wheel in retracted position; dorsal spine fairing widened and deepened aft of canopy, to reduce drag and house additional fuel tankage, and rear-view transparency deleted; primary blade antenna repositioned to mid-spine and secondary antenna deleted. Uprated R-11 turbojet, giving 58.4 kN (13,120 lb st) with afterburning. Internal fuel capacity increased to 2,850 litres (753 US gallons; 627 Imp gallons) in seven fuselage tanks. Late production aircraft have attachments for a rocket assisted take-off unit (RATOG) aft of each main landing gear bay, and provision for a flap blowing system known as *Sduva Pogranichnovo Sloya* (SPS), which reduces the normal landing speed by some 22 knots (40 km/h; 25 mph). Flaps are larger than original Fowler type, do not move aft, and lack outboard fairing plates.

Fishbed-E. Basically similar to 'Fishbed-C' but with broad chord vertical tail surfaces. Brake parachute repositioned into acorn fairing, made up of clamshell doors, at base of rudder, above jet nozzle. Provision for GP-9 underbelly pack, housing GSh-23 twin-barrel 23 mm gun, in place of centreline pylon, with associated predictor sight and electrical ranging system. Identified in 1964.

MiG-21FL. Export version of late-model MiG-21PF series, with broad-chord vertical tail surfaces and brake parachute housing at base of rudder but no provision for SPS or RATOG. About 200 were initially assembled and later built under licence in India by Hindustan Aeronautics Ltd (which see), with the IAF designation Type 77. R-11-300 turbojet rated at 38.25 kN (8,598 lb st) dry and 60.8 kN (13,668 lb) with afterburning. Suffix letter 'L' (*Lokator*) indicates the installation of Type R2L ('Spin Scan B') search/track radar, reported to have lock-on range of 10 nm (19 km; 12 miles) but to be ineffective at heights below about 915 m (3,000 ft) because of ground 'clutter'. Can be fitted with GP-9 underbelly gun pack. Identified in 1966.

MiG-21PFS or **MiG-21PF(SPS).** Similar to 'Fishbed-D', but with SPS as standard production installation.

MiG-21PFM (Fishbed-F). Successor to interim MiG-21PFS, embodying all the improvements introduced progressively on the PF and PFS, the suffix letter 'M' indicating an exportable version of an existing design. Leading edge of fin extended forward a further 45 cm (18 in). Small dorsal fin fillet eliminated. Additional refinements, including sideways hinged (to starboard) canopy and conventional windscreen quarter-lights; simple ejection seat instead of semi-encapsulated type; and large dielectric portion at tip of tail fin. R2L radar. Max permissible speed at low altitude reported to be 593 knots (1,100 km/h; 683 mph). Built also in Czechoslovakia.

MiG-21PFMA (Fishbed-J). Multi-role version with Tumansky R-11-300 turbojet, rated at 38.25 kN (8,598 lb st) dry and 60.8 kN (13,668 lb) with afterburning. Deeper dorsal

Refuelling an Egyptian MiG-21MF 'Fishbed-J'.

spine fairing than on earlier versions, containing fuel tankage above fuselage, giving straight line from top of canopy to fin. Improved radar (NATO 'Jay Bird'). GSh-23 twin-barrel 23 mm gun in bottom of fuselage. Four underwing pylons, instead of former two, for a variety of ground attack weapons and stores, as alternative or supplementary to two or four air-to-air missiles. Latter can include radar homing 'Advanced Atoll' as well as infra-red K-13A 'Atoll'. Able to carry two underwing tanks in addition to standard underbelly tank, offsetting reduced internal fuel capacity of 2,600 litres (687 US gallons; 572 Imp gallons). Provision for GP-9 underbelly gun pack as alternative to centreline fuel tank. Small boat shaped fairing with angle-of-attack indicator added on port side of nose. Zero/zero ejection seat.

MiG-21R. Generally similar to MiG-21PFMA, but belly gun replaced by a pack of three reconnaissance cameras mounted on a side-hinged (to starboard) door which protrudes from underfuselage, immediately aft of nosewheel leg. Operated by Egyptian Air Force.

MiG-21R (Fishbed-H). Tactical reconnaissance version, basically similar to MiG-21PFMA. Equipment includes an external pod for forward facing or oblique cameras, or elint sensors, on fuselage centreline pylon. Suppressed ECM antenna at mid-point on dorsal spine and optional radar warning receivers in wingtip fairings.

MiG-21MF (Fishbed-J). Generally similar to MiG-21PFMA but re-engined with a Tumansky R-13-300 turbojet, lighter in weight and with higher performance ratings. Debris deflector beneath each suction-relief door forward of wingroot. Entered service with Soviet Air Force in 1969.

MiG-21M. Export variant of MiG-21MF. Generally similar to MiG-21PFMA, but with R-11F2S-300 engine. Superseded MiG-21FL on Hindustan Aeronautics production line in India, with IAF designation Type 96. First Indian-built MiG-21M handed over officially to IAF on 14 February 1973; HAL production ended 1981.

MiG-21RF (Fishbed-H). Tactical reconnaissance version of MiG-21MF. Equipment as for MiG-21R. Total of 65 'Fishbed-Hs' of both models estimated in service with Soviet tactical air forces in 1987.

MiG-21SMB (Fishbed-K). Similar to MiG-21MF, except for having deep dorsal spine extended rearward as far as brake parachute housing, to provide maximum possible fuel tankage and optimum aerodynamic form. Deliveries to Warsaw Pact air forces reported to have begun in 1971. Like the MiG-21PFMA and MiG-21MF, this version can carry

MiG-21RF 'Fishbed-H' tactical reconnaissance aircraft of the Polish Air Force. *(Swedish Air Force)*

K-13A 'Atoll' infra-red missiles and/or radar homing 'Advanced Atolls'.

MiG-21 bis (Fishbed-L). Third-generation multi-role air combat/ground-attack version, with Tumansky R-25 turbojet engine, rated at 73.6 kN (16,535 lb st) with afterburning, updated avionics and generally improved construction standards. Wider and deeper dorsal fairing than MiG-21MF. Max fuel capacity of seven internal self-sealing tanks 2,900 litres (766 US gallons; 638 Imp gallons).

MiG-21 bis (Fishbed-N). Advanced version of 'Fishbed-L' with further improved avionics, indicated by 'Swift Rod' ILS antennae under nose and on fin up. Standard equipment in Soviet Air Force. Empty weight reported to be 6,000 kg (13,225 lb), 'clean' T-O weight 8,500 kg (18,740 lb). Rate of climb at AUW of 6,800 kg (15,000 lb), with 50% fuel and two 'Atoll' missiles, is 17,700 m (58,000 ft)/min. Now carries two radar homing 'Atolls' outboard, two 'Aphids' inboard. Produced also by HAL from 1980; probably phased out in 1987.

MiG-21U (Mongol). Two-seat training versions. Initial version, 'Mongol-A', is generally similar to the MiG-21F but has two cockpits in tandem with sideways hinged (to starboard) double canopy, larger mainwheels and tyres of MiG-21PF, one-piece forward airbrake, and pitot boom repositioned above intake. Cannon armament is deleted. Later models, 'Mongol-B', have the broader-chord vertical tail sûrfaces and under-rudder brake parachute housing of the later operational variants, with a deeper dorsal spine and no dorsal fin fillet.

MiG-21US (Mongol-B). Similar to later MiG-21U but with provision for SPS flap-blowing, and retractable periscope for instructor in rear seat. Max internal fuel capacity 2,400 litres (634 US gallons; 528 Imp gallons).

MiG-21UM (Mongol-B). Two-seat trainer counter-part of MiG-21MF with R-13 turbojet and four underwing stores pylons.

In addition to these Soviet developed versions, the Chinese aircraft industry (which see) is producing fighters based on the MiG-21, under the designation **Xian J-7/F-7**.

The following details refer to the MiG-21MF ('Fishbed-J'):

TYPE: Single-seat multi-role fighter.

Mikoyan MiG-21SMB 'Fishbed-K'. *(Pilot Press)*

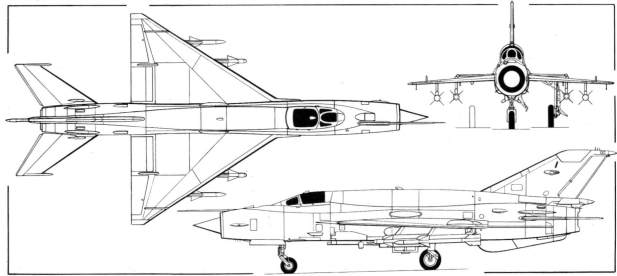

184

WINGS: Cantilever mid-wing monoplane of clipped delta planform, with 2° anhedral from roots. TsAGI section; thickness/chord ratio 5% at root, 4.2% at tip. No leading-edge camber. Sweepback on leading edges 57°. Small pointed fairing on each side of fuselage forward of wing root leading edge. Small boundary-layer fence above each wing near tip. Inset ailerons, hydraulically boosted. Large 'blown' plain trailing-edge flaps, actuated hydraulically.

FUSELAGE: Circular-section semi-monocoque structure. Ram air-intake in nose, with three-position movable centrebody. Forward hinged door in top of nose gives access to avionics. Large dorsal spine fairing along top of fuselage from canopy to fin, housing control pushrods, avionics, single-point refuelling cap and fuel tank. Forward hinged door type airbrake on each side of underfuselage below wing leading edge. A further forward hinged airbrake under fuselage forward of ventral fin. All airbrakes actuated hydraulically. Blister fairings above and below wing on each side to accommodate mainwheels when retracted.

TAIL UNIT: Cantilever structure, with all surfaces sharply swept. Conventional fin and hydraulically boosted rudder. Hydraulically boosted one-piece all-moving horizontal surface, mass balanced at tips, with two gearing ratios for use at varying combinations of altitude and airspeed. Tailplane trim switch on control column. No trim tabs. Single large ventral fin.

LANDING GEAR: Hydraulically retractable tricycle type, with single wheel on each unit. Non-steerable nosewheel unit, tyre size 500 × 180. Size 800 × 200 tyres on mainwheels, without normal operation from grass runways. Pneumatic disc brakes on all three wheels. Steering by differential mainwheel braking. Wheel doors remain open when legs are extended. Brake parachute housed inside acorn fairing at base of rudder.

POWERPLANT: One Tumansky R-13-300 turbojet engine, rated at 40 kN (9,000 lb st) dry and 64.73 kN (14,550 lb st) with afterburning. Fuel tanks in fuselage, and two integral tanks in each wing, with total capacity of 2,600 litres (687 US gallons; 572 Imp gallons), of which approx 1,800 litres (475 US gallons; 396 Imp gallons) are usable within CG limits at low speed. Provision for carrying one finned external fuel tank, capacity 490 litres (130 US gallons; 108 Imp gallons) or 800 litres (211 US gallons; 176 Imp gallons), on underfuselage pylon and two 490 litre drop-tanks on outboard underwing pylons. Two jettisonable solid propellant JATO rockets can be fitted under rear fuselage, aft of wheel doors.

ACCOMMODATION: Pilot only, on zero/zero ejection seat with spring loaded arm at top which ensures that seat cannot be operated unless hood is closed. Canopy is surmounted by a small rearview mirror. Flat bulletproof windscreen. Armour plating forward and aft of cockpit.

AVIONICS AND EQUIPMENT: Search and track radar (NATO 'Jay Bird') in intake centrebody, with search range of 10.8 nm (20 km; 12.5 miles). Other standard avionics include VOR, ARK automatic radio-compass, IFF and Sirena 3 radar warning system with an indicator marked in 45° sectors in front and behind the aircraft. Gyro gunsight maintains precision up to 2.75g. Automatic ranging can be fed into gunsight. Full blind-flying instrumentation, with attitude and heading indicators driven by remote central gyro platform.

ARMAMENT: One twin-barrel 23 mm GSh-23 gun, with 200 rounds, in belly pack. Four underwing pylons for weapons or drop-tanks. Typical loads for interceptor role include two K-13A 'Atoll' air-to-air missiles on inner pylons and two radar homing 'Advanced Atolls' or two UV-16-57 rocket packs (each sixteen 57mm rockets) on outer pylons; four K-13As/'Advanced Atolls'; or two drop-tanks and two K-13As or 'Advanced Atolls'. Typical loads for ground attack role are four UV-16-57 rocket packs; two 500 kg and two 250 kg bombs; or four S-24 240 mm air-to-surface rockets.

DIMENSIONS, EXTERNAL (MiG-21MF):

Wing span	7.15 m (23 ft 5½ in)
Length, incl pitot boom	15.76 m (51 ft 8½ in)
Fuselage length, intake lip to jetpipe nozzle	
	12.30 m (40 ft 4¼ in)
Height overall	4.00 m (14 ft 9 in)
Wheel track	2.69 m (8 ft 10 in)
Wheelbase	4.81 m (15 ft 9½ in)

AREA:

Wings, gross	23 m² (247 sq ft)

WEIGHTS (MiG-21MF):

T-O weight:	
with four K-13A missiles	8,200 kg (18,078 lb)
with two K-13A missiles and two 490 litre (130 US gallon; 108 Imp gallon) drop-tanks	8,950 kg (19,730 lb)
with two K-13As and three drop-tanks	9,400 kg (20,725 lb)

PERFORMANCE (MiG-21MF):

Max level speed above 11,000 m (36,000 ft)	
Mach 2.1 (1,203 knots; 2,230 km/h; 1,385 mph)	
Max level speed at low altitude	
Mach 1.06 (701 knots; 1,300 km/h; 807 mph)	
Design ceiling	18,000 m (59,050 ft)
Practical ceiling	about 15,250 m (50,000 ft)
T-O run at normal AUW	800 m (2,625 ft)
Landing run	550 m (1,805 ft)
Combat radius (hi-lo-hi):	
with four 250 kg bombs, internal fuel	
	200 nm (370 km; 230 miles)
with two 250 kg bombs and drop-tanks	
	400 nm (740 km; 460 miles)
Range, internal fuel only	593 nm (1,100 km; 683 miles)
Ferry range, with external tanks	
	971 nm (1,800 km; 1,118 miles)

PERFORMANCE (MiG-21US, 'clean'):

Max level speed above 12,200 m (40,000 ft)	
Mach 2.02 (1,159 knots; 2,150 km/h; 1,335 mph)	
Max level speed at S/L	
Mach 1.06 (701 knots; 1,300 km/h; 807 mph)	
Max rate of climb at S/L	6,400 m (21,000 ft)/min
Rate of climb at 11,000 m (36,000 ft)	
	3,050 m (10,000 ft)/min
Time to 1,500 m (4,920 ft)	20 s
Turn rate at 4,570 m (15,000 ft):	
instantaneous (Mach 0.5)	11.1°/s
instantaneous (Mach 0.9)	13.4°/s
sustained (Mach 0.9)	7.5°/s
T-O run	700 m (2,297 ft)

Mikoyan MiG-23

NATO reporting names: Flogger-A, B, C, E, F, G, H and K

The Ye-23IG prototype of this variable-geometry fighter was displayed in pubic for the first time on 9 July 1967,

The two-seat MiG-23UM, identical to the early MiG-23M except for the second cockpit. *(Letectvi + Kosmonautika)*

during the Aviation Day flypast at Domodedovo Airport, Moscow, soon after its first flight. Pre-series aircraft were delivered to the Soviet Air Force in 1970, followed by initial series production MiG-23 interceptors in 1973. Two Soviet fighter regiments, with a total of about 75 aircraft, were deployed to East Germany in 1973–74; since then the MiG-23 and related MiG-27 have superseded the MiG-21 progressively as primary equipment of the Soviet tactical air forces and Voyska PVO home defence interceptor force, with production continuing at the rate of several hundred a year. MiG-23s are flown by all the Warsaw Pact air forces, and have been exported to twelve other air forces.

US press reports suggest that former Egyptian operated MiG-23s are being flown by the US Air Force from an air base in the western USA, alongside MiG-21s, for realistic air-to-air combat training of USAF and allied pilots. At least one other was presented to China in a technology transfer deal.

There have been twelve versions of the MiG-23 of which details can be published:

MiG-23 (Flogger-A). Prototype shown at Domodedovo on 9 July 1967. One Lyulka AL-7F-1 afterburning turbojet, rated at 98.1 kN (22,046 lb st).

MiG-23S (Flogger-A). Pre-production version, with AL-7F-1 engine. Issued to complete fighter regiment in 1971 for development.

MiG-23SM (Flogger-A). As MiG-23S, but with four APU-13 pylons for external stores added under engine air intake ducts and fixed inboard wing panels.

MiG-23U. Tandem two-seat training counterpart of MiG-23S.

MiG-23M (Flogger-B). First series production version. Single-seat air-combat fighter with Tumansky R-27 turbojet, rated at 68.65 kN (15,430 lb st) dry and 100.0 kN (22,485 lb st) with afterburning. Wings moved forward about 61 cm (2 ft) to compensate for lighter engine, increasing gap between wing and tailplane. Length of rear fuselage reduced; size of dorsal fin increased; wing chord increased on movable panels, giving large dogtooth. Deliveries began in 1972.

MiG-23MF (Flogger-B). Improved version of MiG-23M, with more powerful R-29 engine and uprated equipment, including 'High Lark' J-band radar, Sirena 3 radar warning system, Doppler, and a small infra-red

search/track pod under the cockpit. The US *Military Posture* statement for FY 1979 described 'Flogger-B' as 'the first Soviet aircraft with a demonstrated ability to track and engage targets flying below its own altitude'. Standard version for Soviet Air Force from about 1975, and for other Warsaw Pact air forces from 1978.

MiG-23UM (Flogger-C). Tandem two-seat version suitable for both operational training and combat use. Individual canopy over each seat. Rear seat slightly higher than forward seat, with retractable periscopic sight for occupant. Dorsal spine fairing of increased depth aft of rear canopy. Otherwise identical to MiG-23M with R-27 turbojet. In service with Soviet and Warsaw Pact air forces and those of other countries, including Cuba, Egypt, India and Libya.

MiG-23MS (Flogger-E). Export version of 'Flogger-B', equipped to a lower standard. Smaller radar (NATO 'Jay Bird': search range 15 nm; 29 km; 18 miles, tracking range 10 nm; 19 km; 12 miles) in shorter nose radome. No infra-red sensor or Doppler navigation equipment. Armed with 'Atoll' missiles and GSh-23 gun. In service in Algeria, Cuba, Iraq, North Korea and Libya.

MiG-23BN (Flogger-F). Export single-seat fighter-bomber. Has the nose shape, raised seat, cockpit external armour plate and larger, low-pressure tyres of Soviet Air Force's MiG-27 ('Flogger-D'), but retains the powerplant, variable-geometry intakes and GSh-23 twin-barrel gun of the MiG-23MF interceptor. Provision for AS-7 'Kerry' missiles. Laser rangefinder instead of target seeking radar. Operated by Algerian, Cuban, Egyptian, Ethiopian, Iraqi, Libyan, Syrian and Vietnamese air forces.

MiG-23MF with underfuselage 'Aphid' and underwing 'Apex' missiles, plus drop tanks. *(US Department of Defense)*

'Flogger-H' can be distinguished from 'Flogger-F' by the avionics pods near the nosewheel doors, and from the MiG-27 'Flogger-D' by its variable-geometry intakes. *(Letectvi + Kosmonautika)*

MiG-23ML (Flogger-G). Identified when six aircraft from Kubinka air base made goodwill visits to Finland and France in the summer of 1978. Although basically similar to MiG-23MF version of 'Flogger-B', these aircraft had a much smaller dorsal fin. Absence of operational equipment, such as underwing pylons and infra-red and tracking pods, suggested initially that only a few aircraft had been modified to this standard for improved aerobatic capability as a display team. 'Flogger-G' has since been confirmed as a standard Soviet operational variant which has also been exported, to Czechoslovakia, the German Democratic Republic and Syria. The radar is lighter in weight, and the undernose sensor pod on some aircraft is of new design.

MiG-23BN (Flogger-H). As 'Flogger-F' but with small avionics pod on each side at bottom of fuselage, immediately forward of nosewheel doors. Operated by Bulgarian, Czechoslovakian and Polish air forces. Total of 80 delivered to Indian Air Force, beginning December 1980 with completion in 1982, to re-equip Nos. 10, 220 and 221 Squadrons. Has also been used by Soviet Air Force.

Notches in wing gloves identify the MiG-23 'Flogger-K'. *(US Navy)*

MiG-23 (Flogger-K). Photographed from F-4 of US Navy 100 nm off Vietnamese coast, near Cam Ranh Bay, in 1986. Identified by dog-tooth notch at junction of wing glove leading edge and intake trunk on each side, to generate vortices to improve stability in yaw at high angles of attack. This compensates for use of smaller ventral folding fin and small 'Flogger-G' type dorsal fin. New IFF antenna forward of windscreen. AA-11 'Archer' close-range air-to-air missiles on fuselage pylons. Pivoting weapon pylons under outer wings.

In spring 1987, it was estimated that about 420 'Flogger-B/G/K' interceptors served with the 1,210-strong Soviet strategic air defence interceptor force, and a further 1,570 in tactical air force regiments.

The following description refers specifically to the single-seat MiG-23MF ('Flogger-G') as supplied to the Soviet Air Force:

TYPE: Single-seat variable-geometry air-combat fighter.

WINGS: Cantilever shoulder-wing monoplane of conventional construction. Sweepback of main panels variable in flight or on the ground by manual control, at 16°, 45° or 72°. Two wing-sweep motors driven separately by main and control booster systems. If one system fails, wing-sweep system remains effective at 50 per cent normal angular velocity. Extended chord (dogtooth) on outer panels visible when wings are swept. Fixed triangular

Mikoyan MiG-23 'Flogger-K'. *(Pilot Press)*

inboard panels, with leading edges swept at 72°. Full span trailing-edge single-slotted flaps, each in three sections, permitting independent actuation of outboard sections when wings are fully swept. No ailerons. Two-section upper surface spoilers/lift dumpers, forward of mid and inner flap sections on each side, operate differentially in conjunction with horizontal tail surfaces (except when disengaged at 72° sweep), and collectively for improved runway adherence and braking after touch-down. Leading-edge flap on outboard two-thirds of each main (variable geometry) panel, coupled to trailing-edge flaps.

FUSELAGE: Conventional semi-monocoque structure of basic circular section; flattened on each side of cockpit, forward of lateral air intake trunks which blend into circular shape of rear fuselage. Large flat splitter plate, with boundary layer bleeds, forms inboard face of each intake. Two small rectangular suction relief doors in each trunk, under inboard wing leading edge. Perforations under rear fuselage, aft of mainwheel bays, are pressure relief vents. Four hydraulically actuated door-type air-brakes, mounted two on each side of rear fuselage above and below horizontal tail surface. Rear fuselage detachable between wing and tailplane for engine servicing.

TAIL UNIT: All-moving horizontal surfaces, swept back at 57° on leading edge, operate both differentially and symmetrically to provide aileron and elevator function respectively. Conventional fin, swept back at 65° on leading edge, with inset rudder. Fin and forward portion of each horizontal surface of conventional construction. Rudder and rear of each horizontal surface have honey-comb core. Ground adjustable tab on each horizontal surface at inboard trailing edge. Large ventral fin in two portions. Lower portion is hinged to fold to starboard when landing gear is extended, to increase ground clearance.

LANDING GEAR: Hydraulically retractable tricycle type, with single wheel on each main unit and steerable twin-wheel nose unit. Mainwheels fitted with brakes and anti-skid units. Brake parachute, area 21 m² (226 sq ft), housed in cylindrical fairing at base of rudder with split conic doors.

POWERPLANT: One Tumansky R-29B turbojet engine, rated currently at up to 122 kN (27,500 lb st) with max afterburning in aircraft for Soviet Air Force. Water injection system. Four fuel tanks in fuselage, aft of cockpit, and two in wings. Max internal fuel capacity 5,750 litres (1,519 US gallons; 1,265 Imp gallons). Variable-geometry air intakes and variable nozzle. Provision for carrying jettisonable external fuel tank, capacity 800 litres (211 US gallons; 176 Imp gallons), on underfuselage centreline pylon, and two more under fixed wing panels. Two additional external tanks of same capacity may be carried on non-swivelling pylons under outer wings for ferry flights, with wings in fully forward position. Attachment for assisted take-off rocket on each side of fuselage aft of landing gear.

ACCOMMODATION: Pilot only, on zero/zero ejection seat in air-conditioned and pressurised cockpit, under small hydraulically actuated rearward hinged canopy. Bullet-proof windscreen. Small electrically heated rearview mirror on top of canopy.

AVIONICS AND EQUIPMENT: J band radar dish (NATO 'High Lark': search range 46 nm; 85 km; 53 miles, tracking range 29 nm; 54 km; 34 miles) behind dielectric nosecone. ILS antennae (NATO 'Swift Rod') under radome and at tip of fin trailing edge; suppressed UHF antennae form tip of fin and forward fixed portion of ventral fin; yaw vane above fuselage aft of radome; angle-of-attack sensor on port side. SRO-2 (NATO 'Odd Rods') IFF antenna immediately forward of windscreen. Undernose infra-red sensor pod, Sirena 3 radar warning system, and Doppler equipment standard on Soviet Air Force version. Sirena 3 antennae in horns at inboard leading edge of each outer wing and below ILS antenna on fin.

ARMAMENT: One 23 mm GSh-23L twin-barrel gun in fuselage belly pack, with large flash eliminator around muzzles. One pylon under centre fuselage, one under each engine air intake duct, and one under each fixed inboard wing panel, for rocket packs, air-to-air missiles or other external stores. Use of twin launchers under air intake ducts permits carriage of four R-60 ('Aphid') missiles, plus two R-23 ('Apex') on underwing pylons.

DIMENSIONS, EXTERNAL:	
Wing span: fully spread	13.95 m (45 ft 9 in)
fully swept	7.77 m (25 ft 6 in)
Length overall, excl nose probe	15.88 m (52 ft 1¼ in)
Height overall	4.80 m (15 ft 9 in)
AREA:	
Wings, gross (spread)	27.30 m² (293.8 sq ft)
WEIGHTS:	
Weight empty	10,000 kg (22,050 lb)
Max external weapon load	3,000 kg (6,615 lb)
T-O weight	16,100–18,900 kg (35,495–41,670 lb)
PERFORMANCE:	
Max level speed: at height	Mach 2.025
at S/L	Mach 1.2
Service ceiling	18,000 m (59,055 ft)
T-O run	900 m (2,950 ft)
Landing run	1,600 m (5,250 ft)
Combat radius	485–700 nm (900–1,300 km; 560–805 miles)

Mikoyan MiG-25

NATO reporting name: Foxbat

Development of the MiG-25 interceptor was initiated as a high-priority programme to counter the threat of the US Air Force's Mach 3 B-70 strategic bomber, for which North American Aviation Inc was chosen as prime contractor in December 1957. When the B-70 was cut back to a research project by President Kennedy, in March 1961, work on the MiG-25 continued, with increased emphasis on the reconnaissance potential of the design.

First indication that the prototype had flown came with a Soviet claim, in April 1965, that a twin-engined aircraft designated Ye-266 had set a 1,000 km closed-circuit speed record of 1,251.9 knots (2,320 km/h; 1,441.5 mph), carrying a 2,000 kg payload. Photographs of the Ye-266 issued subsequently in the Soviet Union identified it as the twin-finned single-seat fighter of which four examples had taken part in the Aviation Day display at Domodedovo Airport, Moscow, in July 1967; the designation MiG-25 was confirmed later. NATO had, meanwhile, allocated the reporting name 'Foxbat' to the type.

The aircraft's performance in level flight was demonstrated further on 5 October 1967, when M. Komarov set a speed record of 1,608.83 knots (2,981.5 km/h; 1,852.61

Reconnaissance version of the MiG-25, known to NATO as 'Foxbat-B', in service with the Libyan Arab Air Force. Note the camera-carrying nose and dielectric panel. *(US Navy)*

mph) over a 500 km closed circuit. Other speed and height records followed. Three time-to-height records established by the Ye-266 on 4 June 1973 were beaten by the McDonnell Douglas F-15 *Streak Eagle* in January–February 1975; but two of them were recaptured by a Ye-266M (with uprated powerplant) on 17 May 1975. The late Alexander Fedotov climbed to 25,000 m in 2 min 34.2 s and P. Ostapenko reached 30,000 m in 3 min 9.85 s. Fedotov also set a new record by climbing to 35,000 m in 4 min 11.7s.

The current absolute height record was set by Fedotov on 31 August 1977, when he climbed to 37,650 m (123,524 ft) in a Ye-266M. He had, on 22 July, climbed to 37,080 m (121,654 ft) carrying a 2,000 kg payload, qualifying also for the record with 1,000 kg.

Four MiG-25 reconnaissance aircraft were deployed with Soviet Air Force units in Egypt in the sping of 1971, having been airlifted to that country in An-22 transports. First foreign operators, in 1979, were the Algerian and Syrian air forces, followed by the air forces of Iraq, Libya and India.

The first opportunity to study the MiG-25 interceptor outside the Soviet Union came when Lt Viktor Belenko defected in one from the Soviet air base of Sikharovka, 200 km (120 miles) from Vladivostok, to Hakodate airport, Japan, on 6 September 1976. Statements attributed to this pilot suggest that more than 400 MiG-25s had been built by that time, and that his particular aircraft left the production line less than three years earlier. Japanese and US military technicians who examined the aircraft reported that the airframe is constructed mainly of steel, with titanium only in places subjected to extreme heating, such as the wing leading edges. The inevitable weight penalty restricts the amount of equipment that can be carried. Belenko said that the aircraft

took a considerable time to accelerate to high speeds, which were then difficult to maintain.

Examination of the aircraft is said to have shown that the fuselage weighs about 13,600 kg (30,000 lb) with the wings, tail surfaces and afterburners removed; the fire control system is bulky and lacking in advanced technology, with its very high power (600 kW) devoted to anti-jamming capability rather than range, and with vacuum tubes rather than solid-state circuitry throughout the avionics. The number of cockpit instruments was described as 50 per cent of those in F-4EJ Phantoms of the JASDF, with a smaller and less versatile weapon sight; and the Machmeter has a 'red line' limit at Mach 2.8, which almost certainly represents a never-exceed speed when carrying missiles and pylons, rather than the maximum speed of which the 'clean' aircraft is capable. Of particular interest is the aircraft's high quality airborne computer which, in conjunction with a ground based flight control system, enables the interceptor to be vectored automatically on to its target over long ranges.

There are six variants of the MiG-25, as follows:

MiG-25 (Foxbat-A). Basic interceptor, with large radar (NATO 'Fox Fire') in nose and armed with four air-to-air missiles on underwing attachments. Slightly reduced wing leading-edge sweep towards tips. ECM and CW target illuminating radar in wingtip anti-flutter bodies. Production cut back in 1977–78, reflecting new emphasis on interception of low-flying targets. Most 'Foxbat-As' in service in the Soviet Union are being converted progressively to 'Foxbat-E' standard. 'Foxbat-As' remain operational in Algeria, Iraq and Syria.

MiG-25R (Foxbat-B). Basic reconnaissance version, with five camera windows and various flush dielectric panels

This photograph shows clearly the tandem cockpits in the nose of the MiG-25U 'Foxbat-C'.

MiG-25M ('Foxbat-E') interceptor of the Libyan Arab Air Force, armed with 'Acrid' and 'Aphid' air-to-air missiles. *(US Navy)*

aft of very small dielectric nosecap for radar. Equipment believed to include Doppler navigation system and side looking airborne radar (SLAR). No armament. Slightly reduced span. Wing leading-edge sweep constant from root to tip. Operated by Soviet tactical air forces, and in Algeria, Libya (one squadron, including 'Foxbat-Ds') and Syria. Eight delivered from summer 1981 to replace Canberras of No. 106 Squadron, Indian Air Force.

MiG-25U (Foxbat-C). Trainer, of which first photographs were published towards the end of 1975. Generally similar to operational versions, but with new nose, containing separate cockpit with individual canopy, forward of standard cockpit and at a lower level. No search radar or reconnaissance sensors in nose. In service with air forces of Soviet Union and India (two). The aircraft designated **Ye-133** in which Svetlana Savitskaya set a women's world speed record of 1,448.942 knots (2,683.44 km/h; 1,667.412 mph) on 22 June 1975 is believed to have been a MiG-25U. She has since set a women's sustained height record and closed-circuit speed records.

MiG-25R (Foxbat-D). Generally similar to 'Foxbat-B', but with larger SLAR (side looking airborne radar) dielectric panel, further aft on side of nose, and no cameras. Operated by Soviet Air Force and in Libya.

MiG-25M (Foxbat-E). Converted 'Foxbat-A' with changes to radar and equipment to provide limited lookdown/shootdown capability comparable with that of 'Flogger-B'. Undernose sensor pod. Engines uprated to 137.3 kN (30,865 lb st). Developed via aircraft known as the **Ye-266M**, which set three time-to-height records in 1975 and also holds the absolute height record.

MiG-25 (Foxbat-F). New version illustrated in Soviet press in 1986. Airframe generally similar to 'Foxbat' interceptors, but with dielectric panel aft of radome on port side (possibly both sides) of front fuselage. Probably an electronic reconnaissance or 'Wild Weasel' type of combat aircraft carrying missiles such as anti-radiation AS.11.

About 305 'Foxbat' interceptors served with the 1,210-strong Soviet home defence interceptor force in 1987; a further 105 interceptors and 195 reconnaissance MiG-25s served with the tactical air forces. Most 'Foxbat-As' in Soviet service are being converted progressively to 'Foxbat-E' standard. Some Libyan aircraft have been converted.

The following description applies to the MiG-25 ('Foxbat-A') interceptor except where indicated:
TYPE: Single-seat interceptor.
WINGS: Cantilever high-wing monoplane. Anhedral 4° from

First illustration of what could be a 'Foxbat-F' defence suppression version of the MiG-25 (copied from *Krasnaya Zvevda*)

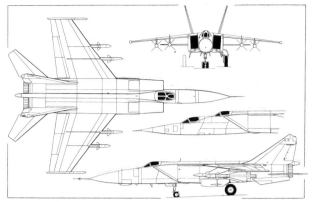

**Mikoyan MiG-25M 'Foxbat-E'. Scrap view: 'Foxbat-C'.
(Pilot Press)**

roots. Sweepback on leading edge approx 40° inboard, 38°
outboard of each outer missile attachment. Sweepback at
quarter-chord 32°. Upper surface fence in line with each
inboard weapon attachment; shorter shallow fence in line
with each outer attachment. Long anti-flutter body (max
diameter 30 cm; 11.8 in) at each wingtip, housing avionics.
Aileron at centre of each semi-span, with simple flap on
inboard 37 per cent of trailing edge. No other movable
wing surfaces.

FUSELAGE: Basic fuselage is quite slim, but is blended into
the rectangular air intake trunks, which have wedge inlets.
Inner walls of intakes are curved at top and do not run
parallel with outer walls; a hinged panel forms the lower
lip of each intake, enabling intake area to be varied
electronically. Airbrake beneath jetpipes, between ventral
fins.

TAIL UNIT: Cantilever structure comprising twin outward-
canted fins with inset rudders, and all-moving horizontal
surfaces. All surfaces sweptback (tailplane 50°, fins 60°),
without tabs. Two outward canted ventral fins, with
retractable sprung tailskids. Large areas of each main and
ventral fin form flush antennae.

LANDING GEAR: Retractable tricycle type. Single wheel,
with high pressure tyre of 1.20 m (47.25 in) diameter, on
each main unit. Twin-wheel nose unit. Twin brakechutes
in fairing above and between jet nozzles.

POWERPLANT: Two Tumansky R-31 (R-266) single-shaft
turbojet engines, each rated at 91.18 kN (20,500 lb st) dry,
and 120 kN (27,010 lb st) with afterburning. Water-
methanol injection standard. Fuel in two structural tanks
in fuselage, between cockpit and engine bay, in saddle
tanks around intake ducts, and in integral tank in each
wing, filling almost the entire volume inboard of outer
fence. Total fuel capacity approx 14,000 kg (30,865 lb) or
17,410 litres (4,600 US gallons; 3,830 Imp gallons).

ACCOMMODATION: Pilot only, on KM-1 zero-height, 80
knot (150 km/h; 93 mph) ejection seat similar to that fitted
to some versions of MiG-21.

AVIONICS AND EQUIPMENT: Main fire control radar (NATO
'Fox Fire': range believed to be 45 nm; 85 km; 52 miles) in
nose, forward of avionics compartment housing nav-
igation radar. SRZO-2 (NATO 'Odd Rods') IFF and
SOD-57M ATC/SIF, with antennae in starboard fin tip.
Sirena 3 360° radar warning system with receivers in centre
of each wingtip anti-flutter body and starboard fin tip.
Unidentified ECCM, decoys and jammers. RSB-70/RPS

HF, RSIU-5 VHF, R-831 UHF communications equipment, SP-50 (NATO 'Swift Rod') ILS, MRP-56P marker
beacon receiver and ARK-15 radio compass. Retractable
landing light under front of each intake trunk.

ARMAMENT: Four air-to-air missiles on underwing attachments. These may comprise one infra-red and one radar-
homing example of the missile known to NATO as 'Acrid'
under each wing. Alternatively, one 'Apex' and a pair of
'Archers' or 'Aphids' can be carried under each wing.
Backup optical weapon sight.

DIMENSIONS, EXTERNAL:	
Wing span: 'Foxbat-A'	13.95 m (45 ft 9 in)
'Foxbat-B'	13.40 m (44 ft 0 in)
Length overall	23.82 m (78 ft 1¾ in)
Height overall	6.10 m (20 ft 0¼ in)
AREA:	
Wings, gross: 'Foxbat-A'	56.83 m² (611.7 sq ft)
WEIGHTS (estimated):	
Basic operating weight, empty:	
'Foxbat-A'	at least 20,000 kg (44,100 lb)
'Foxbat-B'	19,600 kg (43,200 lb)
Max T-O weight: 'Foxbat-A'	37,425 kg (82,500 lb)
'Foxbat-B'	33,400 kg (73,635 lb)
PERFORMANCE (estimated):	
Max level speed at height:	
'Foxbat-B', 'clean'	Mach 3.2
Never-exceed combat speed: 'Foxbat-A', with four 'Acrid'	
missiles and 50% fuel	Mach 2.83
Max level speed at low altitude: 'Foxbat-A', with four 'Acrid'	
missiles and 50% fuel	Mach 0.85
Max rate of climb at S/L:	
'Foxbat-A'	12,480 m (40,950 ft)/min
Time to 11,000 m (36,000 ft) with afterburning:	
'Foxbat-A'	2 min 30 s
Service ceiling: 'Foxbat-A'	24,400 m (80,000 ft)
'Foxbat-B, D'	27,000 m (88,580 ft)
T-O run: 'Foxbat-A'	1,380 m (4,525 ft)
Landing run: 'Foxbat-A'	2,180 m (7,150 ft)
Normal operational radius:	
'Foxbat-A'	610 nm (1,130 km; 700 miles)
'Foxbat-B, D'	485 nm (900 km; 560 miles)
Max combat radius, econ power:	
'Foxbat-A'	780 nm (1,450 km; 900 miles)

Mikoyan MiG-27

NATO reporting names: Flogger-D and J
Indian Air Force name: Bahadur

Although the single-seat ground-attack aircraft known to
NATO as 'Flogger-D/J' have many airframe features in
common with the MiG-23, they differ in important respects
and are designated MiG-27. Their use of fixed air intakes and
a two-position afterburner nozzle is consistent with the
primary requirement of transonic speed at low altitude. Two
versions are operational in Soviet tactical air force regiments:

Flogger-D. Initial version for Soviet tactical air forces,
introduced in second half of the 1970s. Forward portion of
fuselage completely redesigned by comparison with interceptor versions of MiG-23. Instead of having an ogival
radome, 'Flogger-D' nose is sharply tapered in side
elevation, with a radar ranging antenna and a small sloping
window covering a laser rangefinder. Doppler navigation
radar in nose. Additional armour on flat sides of cockpit.

MiG-27 'Flogger-D' landing with wings swept forward and ventral fin folded. *(Flug Revue)*

Comparison of this photograph of a MiG-27 'Flogger-J' with that of 'Flogger-D' shows the restyled nose, absence of bullet antennae on the wing gloves, addition of wing root leading-edge extensions, and the angled-down barrel of the gun in the port underwing pod.

Seat and canopy raised to improve view from cockpit. Six-barrel 30 mm Gatling-type underbelly gun replaces GSh-23 of interceptor. Bomb/JATO rack under each side of rear fuselage in addition to five pylons for external stores, including tactical nuclear weapons and the air-to-surface missiles known to NATO as 'Kerry', 'Karen', 'Kegler' and 'Kedge'. Typical external load comprises six 500 kg bombs and two 800 litre (211 US gallon; 176 Imp gallon) jettisonable fuel tanks. Bullet-shape antenna above each glove pylon.

Flogger-J. Identified in 1981. New nose shape, with lip at top and blister fairing below. Enhanced electro-optical sensors, probably with rearward laser designation capability for laser guided bomb delivery. Bullet-shape antennae above wingroot glove pylons deleted. Wingroot leading-edge extensions added. Armament includes two gun pods on underwing pylons, with gun barrels that can be depressed for attacking ground targets. MiG-27M export version is being built under licence by HAL in India as the Bahadur (Valiant).

A total of about 830 'Flogger-Ds' and 'Js' is deployed with the Soviet tactical air forces, plus at least one squadron with the East German Air Force. The somewhat similar aircraft known to NATO as 'Flogger-F and H' are members of the MiG-23 series, with variable-geometry intakes and a GSh-23 twin-barrel gun, although having the nose shape, raised seat and larger, low-pressure tyres of 'Flogger-D'. Both versions have been operated by Soviet units; but the 'F' and 'H' are basically export counterparts of 'Flogger-D', with lower

standards of equipment and performance, and are described under the MiG-23 entry.

The following data are estimated for the MiG-27 'Flogger-D'.

POWERPLANT: Generally similar to MiG-23MF, but R-29-300 engine rated at 78.45 kN (17,635 lb st) dry and 112.8 kN (25,350 lb st) with max afterburning.

DIMENSIONS, EXTERNAL: As MiG-23, plus:	
Length overall	16.00 m (52 ft 6 in)
AREA:	
Horizontal tail surfaces	6.88 m² (74.06 sq ft)
WEIGHTS:	
Max external load	4,500 kg (9,920 lb)
Max T-O weight, 'clean'	15,500 kg (34,170 lb)
Max T-O weight	20,100 kg (44,313 lb)
PERFORMANCE (estimated):	
Max level speed: at height	Mach 1.7
at S/L	Mach 1.1
Service ceiling	16,000 m (52,500 ft)
T-O to 15 m (50 ft) at AUW of 15,700 kg (34,600 lb)	
	800 m (2,625 ft)
Combat radius, with underbelly fuel tank, four 500 kg bombs and two 'Atoll' missiles, lo-lo-lo	
	210 nm (390 km; 240 miles)
Max ferry range with three external tanks	
	1,350 nm (2,500 km; 1,550 miles)

Mikoyan MiG-29

NATO reporting name: Fulcrum
Indian Air Force name: Baaz (Eagle)

Operational since early 1985, the MiG-29 is a twin-engined aircraft comparable in size to the US F/A-18 Hornet. It is fitted with a large pulse Doppler lookdown/shootdown radar which gives it day and night all-weather operating capability against low-flying targets, as well as freedom from the outmoded ground control interception techniques that restricted Soviet air defence effectiveness in the past. Like other new Soviet air superiority fighters, it also has an infra-red search/track sensor, mounted inside a transparent dome in front of the windscreen, offset to starboard. It is expected

to replace MiG-21s, Su-21s and some MiG-23s in Soviet service.

References to this fighter first appeared in the Western press in 1979, after a prototype had been identified on photographs taken over Ramenskoye flight test centre by a US reconnaissance satellite. NATO allocated the reporting name 'Fulcrum' when it became clear that the MiG was intended as a production aircraft.

From the start, it was plain that 'Fulcrum' represented a concerted effort by the Soviet Union to close the technology gap with the West. Its sustained turn rate is much improved over that of earlier Soviet fighters, and thrust-to-weight ratio is better than 1. Although intended primarily as a single-seat counter-air fighter, it is likely to have a full dual-role air-

Photograph of 'Fulcrum-A' taken in Finland in July 1986 during the MiG-29's first appearance outside the Warsaw Pact countries. *(Hasse Vallas)*

combat/attack capability, and a combat-capable two-seater, lacking only the radar of the single-seater, is also in production and service.

The initial production version of the MiG-29 single-seater is known to NATO as 'Fulcrum-A'. Modifications have been made to the basic design: the first production aircraft lacked the current constant-depth strakes forward of the dorsal tail fins and had a ventral fin under each tail fin. Later aircraft have dorsal strakes and a small door over the extended nosewheel, but no ventral fins.

Production is centred at a factory in Moscow. Its status and scale are evident from the fact that export deliveries of an initial quantity of 44 MiG-29s ordered by India (40 single-seat, four two-seat) had been completed by mid-1987. Others had been delivered to Iraq and Syria. Reported potential operators include the air force of Zimbabwe. Meanwhile, more than 300 MiG-29s were already operational with Soviet tactical units stationed in East Germany, in the Soviet Union west of the Urals, and in the far eastern USSR.

On 1 July 1986, a detachment of six, from Kubinka air base, near Moscow, made a goodwill visit to Kuopio-Rissala air base in Finland. As the nosewheel of each aircraft made contact with the runway, doors were triggered to blank off the underslung engine air intakes. This surprising technique was adopted by the aircraft's designers to overcome problems caused by ingestion of stones, snow, slush, ice and foreign objects into the engine ducts during take-off and landing on the kind of runways used by Warsaw Pact front-line air forces, especially in winter. When the intake trunks are closed, engine air is taken in through a series of lateral louvres in the upper surface of the aircraft's deep wingroot leading-edge extensions.

There was nothing on the MiG-29s in Finland to suggest that the Soviet Union is yet equipping its fighters to refuel in flight. Also, although the MiG-29 has a high-set cockpit, giving its pilot a reasonable forward view over the sloping nose, he lacks the all-round field of view offered to the pilots of western fighters such as the F-15 and F-16 through 360° low-sill canopies. Nor can the bulky head-up display, IR sensor, and large wing leading-edge extensions be helpful in this respect.

Comparison of the general configurations of the MiG-29 Fulcrum and Su-27 Flanker prompts the thought that some authority, perhaps the TsAGI Central Aerodynamics and Hydrodynamics Institute, may be exerting a greater influence on current design concepts. The Sukhoi fighter

Later production version of MiG-29 armed with 'Alamo-A' and 'Aphid' missiles. *(Swedish Air Force)*

193

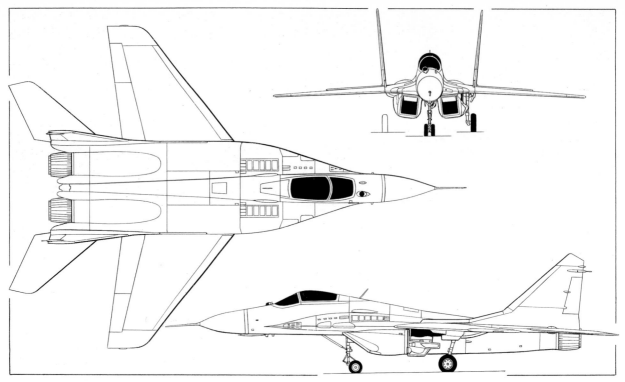

Mikoyan MiG-29 'Fulcrum'. *(Pilot Press)*

maintains the tradition of being larger and seemingly less sophisticated than the MiG, but the two designs are strikingly similar in most respects, even in such detail as current tail-fin location and the manner in which the mainwheels retract into the wing-roots.

TYPE: All-weather counter-air fighter, with attack capability.

WINGS: Cantilever low-wing monoplane. Leading-edge sweepback approx 42° on outer wings, with very large ogival root extensions. Anhedral approx 2°. Leading-edge manoeuvring flaps over full span except for tips. Plain flap and aileron on trailing edge of each wing. No tabs.

FUSELAGE: Semi-monocoque all-metal structure, sharply tapered and downswept aft of flat-sided cockpit area, with ogival dielectric nosecone.

TAIL UNIT: Cantilever structure, comprising twin fins, small inset rudders, and all-moving horizontal surfaces, all carried on slim booms alongside engine nacelles. Vertical surfaces sweptback at approx 40° and canted outward at 7°, each with dorsal fin that extends forward as an overwing fence. Horizontal surfaces sweptback at approx 50°. No tabs.

LANDING GEAR: Retractable tricycle type, with single wheel on each main unit and twin nosewheels. Mainwheel tyre size 770×200; nosewheel tyre size 530×100. Container for cruciform brake-chute recessed in centre of boat-tail between engine nozzles.

POWERPLANT: Two Tumansky R-33D turbofan engines, each rated at 50 kN (11,240 lb st) dry and 81.4 kN (18,300 lb st) with afterburning. Engine ducts are canted at approx 9° and have wedge intakes, sweptback at approx 35°, under wingroot leading-edge extensions. Doors inside each intake close the duct while the nosewheels are in contact with the runway, to prevent ingestion of foreign objects, ice, or snow. Air is then fed to each engine through

louvres in top of wingroot leading-edge extension. Attachment for single external fuel tank under fuselage, between ducts.

ACCOMMODATION: Pilot only on zero/zero ejection seat, under rearward-hinged transparent blister canopy in high-set cockpit. Sharply inclined one-piece curved windscreen.

ARMAMENT AND OPERATIONAL EQUIPMENT: Six medium-range radar homing AA-10 (NATO 'Alamo-A') and/or close-range AA-11 (NATO 'Archer') air-to-air missiles, bombs, rocket pods or other stores, on three pylons under each wing. Provision for carrying 'Amos' and 'Aphid' missiles. One 30 mm gun in port wingroot leading-edge extension. Equipment includes pulse-Doppler engagement radar, IR sensor, SRZO-2 (NATO 'Odd Rods') IFF, Sirena-3 360° radar warning system, and head-up display.

DIMENSIONS, EXTERNAL:

Wing span	11.50 m (37 ft 8¾ in)
Length overall, incl nose probe	17.20 m (56 ft 5 in)
Height overall	4.40 m (14 ft 5¼ in)
Wheel track	3.00 m (9 ft 10 in)
Wheelbase	3.60 m (11 ft 9¾ in)

AREA:

Wings, gross	35.20 m² (378.9 sq ft)

WEIGHTS (estimated):

Operating weight empty	8,175 kg (18,025 lb)
Normal T-O weight (interceptor)	16,500 kg (36,375 lb)

PERFORMANCE (estimated):

Max level speed: at height	
	Mach 2.2 (1,260 knots; 2,335 km/h; 1,450 mph)
at S/L	Mach 1.06 (700 knots; 1,300 km/h; 805 mph)
Max rate of climb at S/L	15,240 m (50,000 ft)/min
Service ceiling	20,000 m (65,600 ft)
Combat radius	620 nm (1,150 km; 715 miles)

MiG-31 photographed by a Royal Norwegian Air Force pilot in autumn 1985.

Mikoyan MiG-31

NATO reporting name: Foxhound

Evidence that the Mikoyan design team was developing an improved interceptor based on the general configuration of the MiG-25 (NATO 'Foxbat') came first from Lt Viktor Belenko, the Soviet pilot who defected to Japan in a 'Foxbat-A' in September 1976. He said that the airframe of the new fighter was strengthened to permit supersonic flight at low altitude; more powerful engines were fitted, each giving 137.3 kN (30,865 lb st) with afterburning; the avionics were improved; and fuselage mountings had been added to enable the aircraft to carry six air-to-air missiles.

In mid-1982 it became known that NATO had allocated the reporting name 'Foxhound' to what the technical press referred to as 'Super Foxbat', and which was subsequently identified as the MiG-31. A three-view displayed publicly for the first time in September of the following year, during briefings at the annual AFA Convention in Washington DC, showed significant new features, including tandem seating for a two-man crew, much enlarged engine air intakes, rearward extension of the jet nozzles, and wingroot leading-edge extensions on wings that were little changed in size and shape from those of the MiG-25. Its general accuracy was confirmed in the autumn of 1985, when the pilot of an F-16 of the Royal Norwegian Air Force intercepted a MiG-31 off the coast of Eastern Finnmark in Northern Norway.

The MiG-31's radar is said to embody technology found in the Hughes AN/APG-65 digital radar fitted in the US Navy's F/A-18 Hornet, providing true lookdown/shootdown and multiple-target engagement capability for the first time in a Soviet interceptor. Other equipment includes active counter-measures dispensers, and an infra-red search/track sensor.

Deployment of MiG-31s with Voyska PVO air defence regiments had begun by early 1983, and about 95 were known to be operational by October 1986, deployed from the Arkhangelsk area near the USSR's western borders to Dolinsk on Sakhalin Island, north of Japan. A further 30 were said by US official sources to be assigned to tactical and 24 to strategic reconnaissance missions. Production is centred at the Gorkiy airframe plant.

The detailed description which follows must be regarded as provisional. It is not yet possible, for example, to confirm that the arc-welded nickel steel structure of the MiG-25 has been retained on what has to be seen as a new design. The better heat-resistant characteristics of steel are not essential at the reduced maximum speed of the MiG-31; but a switch to light alloy construction would have required extensive redesign of such well proven features as the basic wing structure, as well as major manufacturing changes. It is doubtful if these would have been considered worthwhile.

TYPE: Two-seat all-weather interceptor.

WINGS: Cantilever high-wing monoplane. Anhedral 4° from roots. Sweepback on leading edge approx 40°, at quarter-chord 32°, with small sharply-swept wingroot extensions. Upper surface fence in line with each inboard weapon pylon. Aileron and flap on each wing, of greater span than those of MiG-25. No wingtip fairings or mountings.

MiG-31 all-weather interceptor, showing steerable mainwheels.

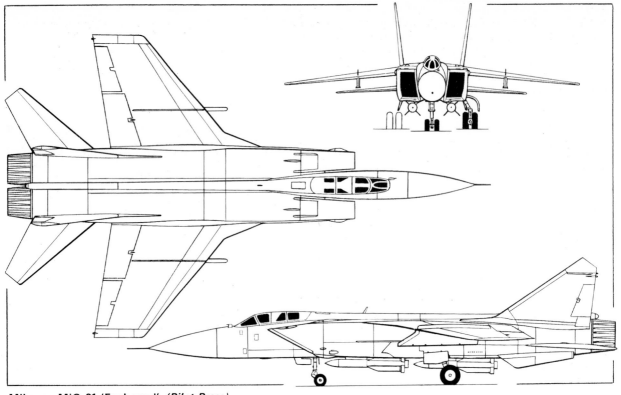

Mikoyan MiG-31 'Foxhound'. *(Pilot Press)*

FUSELAGE: Basic fuselage is slim, but is blended into wide rectangular air intake trunks, which have wedge inlets. Inner wall of each inlet is curved and does not run parallel with outer wall. Hinged panel forms lower lip of each inlet, and there is a large door towards the forward part of each top surface.

TAIL UNIT: Twin outward canted fins, with inset rudders, and all-moving one-piece horizontal surface. All surfaces sharply sweptback, without tabs. Two outward canted ventral fins. Large areas of each main and ventral fin form flush antennae. Aerodynamic fairings between base of each fin and engine duct, extending well forward of leading edge.

LANDING GEAR: Retractable tricycle type. Twin steerable wheels on each main unit and nosewheel unit.

POWERPLANT: Two Tumansky turbojet engines, each reportedly rated at 137.3 kN (30,865 lb st) with afterburning. Fuel tankage probably similar to that of MiG-25, which has two structural tanks in fuselage, between cockpit and engine bay, saddle tanks around intake ducts, and integral tank in each wing, filling almost the entire volume inboard of outer stores pylon, with total capacity of approx 17,410 litres (4,600 US gallons; 3,830 Imp gallons). Provision for two large external fuel tanks on outer underwing pylons.

ACCOMMODATION: Pilot and weapon systems operator in tandem. Canopy has only limited side glazing for rear cockpit, and blends into shallow dorsal spine fairing which extends to forward edge of jet nozzles.

AVIONICS AND EQUIPMENT: Main fire control radar of pulse-Doppler lookdown/shootdown type in nose, with reported search range of 165 nm (305 km; 190 miles) and tracking range of 145 nm (270 km; 167 miles). Infra-red sensor in bottom of front fuselage. Radar warning receivers, active IR and electronic countermeasures.

ARMAMENT: Aircraft illustrated has four AA-9 (NATO 'Amos') semi-active radar homing long-range air-to-air missiles in pairs under fuselage, and twin mounts for smaller stores such as AA-8 (NATO 'Aphid') air-to-air missiles on one large pylon under each wing. These pylons, and outer underwing pylons can probably increase the number of AA-9s carried by MiG-31 to reported total of eight.

DIMENSIONS, EXTERNAL (estimated):
Wing span 14.00 m (45 ft 11¼ in)
Length of fuselage, nosecone tip to end of jetpipe
21.50 m (70 ft 6½ in)
WEIGHTS (estimated):
Weight empty 21,825 kg (48,115 lb)
Max T-O weight 41,150 kg (90,725 lb)
PERFORMANCE (estimated):
Max level speed at height Mach 2.4
(1,375 knots; 2,550 km/h; 1,585 mph)
Max combat radius 1,135 nm (2,100 km; 1,305 miles)

Mil

Mikhail L. Mil was connected with Soviet gyroplane and helicopter development from at least 1930 until his death on 31 January 1970. His original Mi-1, which was designed in 1949, first flown in 1950, and introduced into squadron service in 1951, was the first helicopter to enter series production in the Soviet Union.

Mil Mi-8 (V-8)

NATO reporting name: Hip

This turbine powered helicopter was shown in public for the first time during the 1961 Soviet Aviation Day display. Since then, more than 10,000 Soviet built Mi-8s and uprated Mi-17s (described separately) have been delivered for military and civil use from two plants in Kazan and Ulan Ude, and production continues. Component production of the Mi-8 has also taken place at Harbin and Nanchang in China.

An estimated total of 1,950 Mi-8s and Mi-17s support Soviet armies in the field, in a variety of forms, but mainly for use as assault transports, some carrying extremely heavy weapon loads. It is because of the extensive armament available to many military versions of 'Hip' that the helicopter is included in this publication. Indeed, 'Hip-E' is one of the world's most heavily armed helicopters. Many other versions are operated by Soviet air forces, and military Mi-8s have been supplied to at least 39 other air forces.

The original prototype (NATO **Hip-A**) had a single 2,013 kW (2,700 shp) Soloviev turboshaft engine and four-blade main rotor. When fitted with the five-blade rotor that became standard on subsequent aircraft, it was redesignated **Hip-B**. The second prototype, which flew for the first time on 17 September 1962, introduced the now-standard Isotov twin-turbine powerplant and became **Hip-C** to NATO in both civil and military forms.

Military versions are identified by the following NATO reporting names:

Hip-C. Basic assault transport. Twin rack for stores on each side of cabin, able to carry total of 128 × 57 mm rockets in four packs, or other weapons.

Hip-D. For airborne communications role. Generally similar to 'Hip-C' but with canisters of rectangular section on outer stores racks and added antennae.

Mil Mi-8 ('Hip-E') military helicopter. 'Hip-E' differs from the commercial versions in having circular cabin windows, an optional nose gun, and weapon carriers on outriggers. This example carries rockets in six pods.

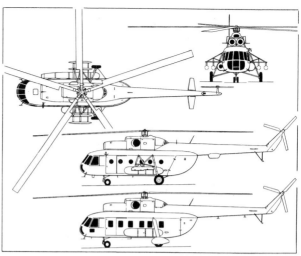

Mil Mi-8 'Hip-C'. Lower side view: Mi-8 commercial version. *(Pilot Press)*

Hip-E. Standard equipment of Soviet army support forces. One flexibly mounted 12.7 mm machine gun in nose. Triple stores rack on each side of cabin, able to carry up to 192 rockets in six suspended packs, plus four 'Swatter' anti-tank missiles on rails above racks.

Hip-F. Export counterpart of 'Hip-E'. Missile armament changed to six 'Saggers'.

Hip-G. Airborne communications version with rearward inclined antennae projecting from rear of cabin and from undersurface of tailboom, aft of box for Doppler radar.

Hip-H. See separate entry on Mi-17. Some Mi-8s being updated to this standard.

Hip-J. Additional small boxes on sides of fuselage, fore and aft of main landing gear legs, identify this ECM version.

Hip-K. Communications jamming ECM version with large antenna array on each side of cabin, of the kind seen previously on the Mi-4 ('Hound-C'). No Doppler radar box under tailboom.

TYPE: Twin-engined armed assault, communications and ECM helicopter.

ROTOR SYSTEM: Five-blade main rotor and three-blade tail rotor. Main rotor shaft inclined forward at 4° 30′ from vertical. All-metal main rotor blades of basic NACA 230 section. Main rotor blades are fitted with balance tabs, embody a spar failure warning system, and are interchangeable.

FUSELAGE: Conventional semi-monocoque structure of pod and boom type.

TAIL UNIT: Tail-rotor support acts as small vertical stabiliser. Horizontal stabiliser near end of tailboom.

LANDING GEAR: Non-retractable tricycle type, with steerable twin-wheel nose unit, which is locked in flight, and single wheel on each main unit. Mainwheel tyres size 865 × 280; nosewheel tyres size 595 × 185. Pneumatic brakes on mainwheels. Pneumatic system can also recharge tyres in the field, using air stored in main landing gear struts. Optional mainwheel fairings.

POWERPLANT: Two 1,267 kW (1,700 shp) Isotov TV2-117A turboshaft engines. Main rotor speed governed automatically, with manual override. Single flexible internal fuel tank, capacity 445 litres (117.5 US gallons; 98 Imp gallons), and two external tanks, one each side of cabin, with capacity of 745 litres (197 US gallons; 164 Imp gallons) in the port tank and 680 litres (179.5 US gallons; 149.5 Imp gallons) in the starboard tank. Total standard fuel capacity 1,870 litres (494 US gallons; 411.5 Imp gallons). Provision for carrying one or two additional ferry tanks in cabin, raising max total capacity to 3,700 litres (977 US gallons; 814 Imp gallons).

ACCOMMODATION: Two pilots side-by-side on flight deck, with provision for a flight engineer's station. Up to 32 troops, internal or external cargo (see 'Weights'), or 12 stretchers and a tip-up seat for a medical attendant. An electrically operated rescue hoist (capacity 150 kg; 330 lb) can be installed at the main passenger door. The rear of the cabin is made up of clamshell freight loading doors, with hook-on ramps for vehicle loading.

AVIONICS AND EQUIPMENT: Includes navigation equipment and instrumentation for all-weather flying by day and night, infra-red suppressors and infra-red decoy dispensers.

ARMAMENT: See individual model descriptions of military versions.

Mil Mi-14 anti-submarine helicopter ('Haze-A') with MAD 'bird' in stowed position. *(US Navy)*

Mil Mi-14 (V-14)

NATO reporting name: Haze

The Mi-14 shore-based amphibious helicopter flew for the first time in 1973 and subsequently entered service with the Soviet Navy in anti-submarine form, as a replacement for the Mi-4. Clearly derived from the Mi-8, it is known to NATO as 'Haze'.

Comparison of photographs of this aircraft and the Mi-8 shows that the Mi-14 has shorter engine nacelles, with the intakes positioned above the mid-point of the sliding cabin door. Such nacelles, found also on the Mi-24 'Hind' and Mi-17, house Isotov TV3-117 turboshaft engines in place of the lower-rated TV2s of the Mi-8. Overall dimensions and dynamic components of the Mi-14 are generally similar to those of the Mi-8, except that the tail rotor is on the port side of the vertical stabiliser. New features to suit it for its role include a boat hull planing bottom on the fuselage, a sponson on each side at the rear, and a small float under the tailboom, to confer a degree of amphibious capability. The fully retractable landing gear comprises two single-wheel nose units and two twin-wheel main units. There is a Doppler radar box under the forward part of the tailboom. Operational anti-submarine equipment can be seen to include a large undernose radome, a retractable sonar unit housed in the starboard rear of the planing bottom, forward of what appear to be two sonobuoy or signal flare chutes, and

Mil Mi-14 ('Haze-B') twin-turboshaft mine-countermeasures helicopter.

DIMENSIONS, EXTERNAL:

Main rotor diameter	21.29 m (69 ft 10¼ in)
Length overall, rotor turning	25.24 m (82 ft 9¾ in)
Length of fuselage, excl tail rotor	
	18.17 m (59 ft 7⅞ in)
Height overall	5.65 m (18 ft 6½ in)
Wheel track	4.50 m (14 ft 9 in)
Wheelbase	4.26 m (13 ft 11¾ in)

AREA:

Main rotor disc	356 m² (3,832 sq ft)

WEIGHTS:

Weight empty, typical	7,260 kg (16,007 lb)
Max payload: internal	4,000 kg (8,820 lb)
external	3,000 kg (6,614 lb)
Normal T-O weight	11,100 kg (24,470 lb)
T-O weight with 2,500 kg (5,510 lb) of slung cargo	
	11,428 kg (25,195 lb)
Max T-O weight for VTO	12,000 kg (26,455 lb)

PERFORMANCE:

Max level speed at 1,000 m (3,280 ft)	
normal AUW	140 knots (260 km/h; 161 mph)
Max level speed at S/L:	
normal AUW	135 knots (250 km/h; 155 mph)
max AUW	124 knots (230 km/h; 142 mph)
with 2,500 kg (5,510 lb) of slung cargo	
	97 knots (180 km/h; 112 mph)
Max cruising speed:	
normal AUW	122 knots (225 km/h; 140 mph)
max AUW	97 knots (180 km/h; 112 mph)
Service ceiling	4,500 m (14,760 ft)
Hovering ceiling at normal AUW:	
IGE	1,900 m (6,235 ft)
OGE	800 m (2,625 ft)
Ranges:	
cargo version at 1,000 m (3,280 ft), with standard fuel, 5% reserves:	
normal AUW	251 nm (465 km; 289 miles)
max AUW	240 nm (445 km; 276 miles)
with 28 troops at 1,000 m (3,280 ft), with 20 min fuel reserves	
	270 nm (500 km; 311 miles)
ferry range of cargo version, with auxiliary fuel, 5% reserves	647 nm (1,200 km; 745 miles)

described above. About 100 operational in 1987.

Haze-B. Mine-countermeasures version, identified by fuselage strake and pod on starboard side of cabin, and deletion of MAD. Seen also with a second equipment box under the centre of the tailboom. About 10 in service with Soviet Navy.

Three Mi-14s have been exported to Bulgaria, four to Cuba, twelve to Libya, an unknown quantity to Poland, six to Romania and eight to the German Democratic Republic. Production was continuing in 1987.

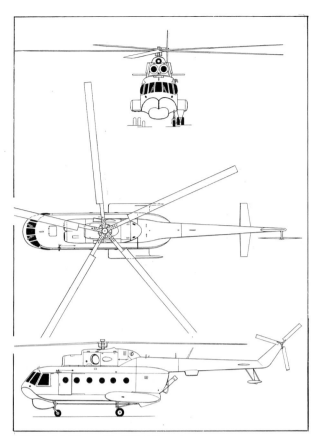

Mil Mi-14 'Haze-A'. *(Pilot Press)*

a towed magnetic anomaly detection (MAD) 'bird' stowed against the rear of the fuselage pod. Weapons include torpedoes and depth charges, carried in an enclosed bay in the bottom of the hull.

More than 100 Mi-14s are currently operated by the Soviet Naval Air Force. Two versions may be identified by NATO reporting names, as follows:

Haze-A. Basic ASW version, with crew of four or five, as

DIMENSIONS, EXTERNAL:
Main rotor diameter	21.29 m (69 ft 10¼ in)
Length overall, rotors turning	25.30 m (83 ft 0 in)
Height overall	6.90 m (22 ft 7¾ in)

WEIGHT
Max T-O weight	13,000 kg (28,660 lb)

PERFORMANCE:
Max level speed	124 knots (230 km/h; 143 mph)
Max cruising speed	108 knots (200 km/h; 124 mph)
Range with max fuel	500 nm (925 km; 575 miles)

MiL Mi-17

NATO reporting name: Hip-H

First displayed in public at the 1981 Paris Air Show, the Mi-17 combines the airframe of the Mi-8 with the uprated powerplant of the Mi-14. The basic civil and military version is known to NATO as 'Hip-H'. Many are operational side-by-side with Mi-8s in the Soviet armed forces, with the same armament options as the older aircraft. Export deliveries include 16 to Cuba in 1983, and others subsequently to Angola, India, North Korea and Peru. Mi-8s can be updated to Mi-17 standard.

The general description of the Mi-8 applies also to the Mi-17, except that the tail rotor is on the port side of the vertical stabiliser (as on the Mi-14). Externally, the new powerplant can be identified by the shorter nacelles, the air intakes extending forward only to the mid-point of the door on the port side at the front of the cabin. Also new is the small orifice on each side forward of the jetpipe. Take-off rating of each of

Mil Mi-17 ('Hip-H') used to patrol the border between East and West Germany.

mance compared with the Mi-8. Correct rotor speed is maintained automatically by a system which also synchronises the output of the two engines. Loss of power by one engine is offset automatically by increasing the output of the other. Should one engine stop, the output of the other is increased to a contingency rating of 1,640 kW (2,200 shp), enabling the flight to continue. An APU is carried to start the turboshafts pneumatically. If required, the engine air intakes can be fitted with deflectors to prevent the ingestion of sand, dust or foreign objects at unprepared landing sites.

Cabin configuration and payloads are unchanged by comparison with the Mi-8.

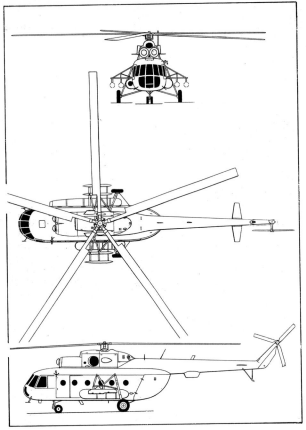

Mil Mi-17 'Hip-H'. *(Pilot Press)*

DIMENSIONS, EXTERNAL:	
As for Mi-8, except:	
Length overall, rotors turning	25.352 m (83 ft 2 in)
Length of fuselage, excl tail rotor	18.424 m (60 ft $5\frac{3}{8}$ in)
Height to top of main rotorhead	4.755 m (15 ft $7\frac{1}{4}$ in)
Wheel track	4.510 m (14 ft $9\frac{1}{2}$ in)
Wheelbase	4.281 m (14 ft $0\frac{1}{2}$ in)
WEIGHTS:	
Weight empty, equipped	7,100 kg (15,653 lb)
Max payload: internal	4,000 kg (8,820 lb)
external, on sling	3,000 kg (6,614 lb)
Normal T-O weight	11,100 kg (24,470 lb)
Max T-O weight	13,000 kg (28,660 lb)
PERFORMANCE (A at normal T-O weight; B at max T-O weight):	
Max level speed: B	135 knots (250 km/h; 155 mph)
Max cruising speed: B	129 knots (240 km/h; 149 mph)
Service ceiling: A	5,000 m (16,400 ft)
B	3,600 m (11,800 ft)
Hovering ceiling OGE: A	1,760 m (5,775 ft)
Range with max standard fuel, 5% reserves:	
A	267 nm (495 km; 307 miles)
B	251 nm (465 km; 289 miles)
Range with auxiliary fuel:	
A	513 nm (950 km; 590 miles)

the two Isotov TV3-117MT turboshafts is 1,417 kW (1,900 shp), which offers a considerable improvement in perfor-

Mil Mi-24

NATO reporting name: Hind

This assault helicopter was known to exist for two years before photographs became available to the technical press in 1974. The two versions shown in those first photographs (known to NATO as 'Hind-A and B') each carried a crew of three (with pilot and co-pilot side-by-side) and were designed to deliver a squad of eight combat-equipped troops into a

'Hind-A', first major production version of the Mil Mi-24, with original starboard tail rotor.

battle area. They had attachments under their auxiliary wings for a variety of ordnance with which to clear a path past any tanks, anti-aircraft guns or other obstructions encountered on the way, and to keep down the heads of enemy troops in the drop zone.

At least two units of approximate squadron strength were based at Parchim and Stendal, northwest and west of Berlin, near the border with West Germany, by the spring of 1974. Experience gained in training exercises soon led to a major change in tactics. Today, the Mi-24 is regarded as not only an effective anti-tank weapon, but capable itself of functioning as a high-speed nap-of-the-earth 'tank', and of destroying opposing helicopters in air-to-air combat. Other duties include escort of troop carrying Mi-8/17s and ground attack.

To exploit the Mi-24's potential, the Mil bureau first increased performance by replacing the original Isotov TV2-117 turboshaft engines with more powerful TV3-117s, at the same time transferring the tail rotor from the starboard to the port side of the tail fin. The front fuselage was then redesigned to give priority to the gunship role, with a two-man crew of weapon operator and pilot in tandem individual cockpits, while retaining the original transport capability. To reduce vulnerability to ground fire, steel and titanium were substituted for aluminium in critical components, and glassfibre-skinned rotor blades replaced the original metal-

Mil Mi-24 'Hind-D', with rocket launchers but no missiles on launch rails.

blade-pocket design. The gunship (beginning with the version known to NATO as 'Hind-D') then superseded the original versions in production.

Deliveries of all models are known to exceed 2,300, from plants in Arsenyev and Rostov, with production continuing at a rate of more than 15 a month. At Soviet army level, there are some 20 helicopter attack regiments, each with up to 60 Mi-8s and Mi-24s. At division level, helicopter detachments are expanding to squadrons. Other operators include the Warsaw Pact air forces of Bulgaria, Czechoslovakia, East Germany, Hungary and Poland. Export deliveries, mostly of the gunship version, have been made to Afghanistan, Algeria (including 'Hind-As'), Angola, Cuba, India, Iraq, Libya, Mozambique, Nicaragua, Viet-Nam (including uprated 'Hind-As') and South Yemen. Some of these are designated **Mi-25** (see separate entry). Many Mi-24s have been operated by Soviet forces in Afghanistan since December 1979, often in partnership with Sukhoi Su-25 fixed-wing ground-attack aircraft.

Except for the crew accommodation, the basic airframe, powerplant and transmission system appear to be common to all current versions of the Mi-24, with differences in armament, operational equipment and tail rotor location. Major variants of which details may be published are known by the following NATO reporting names:

Hind-A. Armed assault helicopter, with large enclosed flight deck for crew of three, comprising pilot, co-pilot/gunner and ground engineer, and places for up to eight fully equipped troops in main cabin. Auxiliary wings, with considerable anhedral, carry total of four underwing pylons for UB-32 rocket pods, special bombs, or other stores, and rails for four AT-2 (NATO 'Swatter') anti-tank missiles under endplate pylons at wingtips. One 12.7 mm single-barrel DShK machine-gun in nose, slaved to undernose sighting system. Camera at top of port inner underwing pylon. Anti-torque rotor, originally on starboard side of

offset tail pylon, repositioned to port side when original TV2-117 engines were replaced by TV3-117s on later and converted aircraft.

Hind-B. Similar to 'Hind-A' except that auxiliary wings have neither anhedral nor dihedral, and carry only the two inboard weapon stations on each side. This version preceded 'Hind-A' but was not built in large numbers.

Hind-C. Training version. Generally similar to late model 'Hind-A' but without nose gun and undernose blister fairing, and no missile rails at wingtips.

Hind-D. Basically similar to late model 'Hind-A', with TV3-117 engines and tail rotor on port side, but with completely new and heavily armoured accommodation for flight crew of two forward of the engine inlets and above the fuselage floor for primary gunship role. Weapon operator and pilot in tandem. Transport capability retained.

Rails carrying AT-2 'Swatter' anti-tank missiles on 'Hind-D'.

Mil Mi-24 'Hind-F' with twin-barrel cannon in place of earlier nose turret.

Undernose Gatling type 12.7 mm machine gun provides air-to-air as well as air-to-surface capability. Extended nosewheel leg to increase ground clearance of sensor pack; nosewheels semi-exposed when retracted. Weapons, equipment and other details listed in aircraft structural description.

Hind-E. As 'Hind-D', for Soviet armed forces, but with modified wingtip launchers and four underwing pylons for a total of up to twelve AT-6 radio guided tube-launched anti-tank missiles (NATO 'Spiral') in pairs, and enlarged

The new 'Hind-G' version of the Mi-24, with 'clutching hand' wingtip fittings. *(Soviet Military Review)*

undernose guidance pod on port side.

Hind-F. First shown in service with Soviet forces in photographs published in 1982. Generally similar to 'Hind-E' but with the nose gun turret replaced by a twin-barrel 30 mm cannon mounted inside a semi-cylindrical pack on the starboard side of the fuselage, and the bottom of the nose smoothly faired above and forward of sensors.

Hind-G. First identified at Chernobyl, after the accident at a nuclear power station, this version lacks the usual undernose electro-optical and RF guidance packs for anti-tank missiles. Instead of wingtip weapon attachments, it has unidentified 'clutching hand' mechanisms with are probably associated with radiation sampling, on lengthened pylons. Other features include a lozenge-shaped housing with cylindrical insert under the port side of the cabin, a bubble window on the starboard side, and a plate of triangular shape mounted in the tailskid. Small numbers of 'Hind-Gs' are deployed individually throughout the Soviet ground forces.

The following details apply to the 'Hind-D' gunship version:

TYPE: Gunship helicopter, with transport capability.

ROTOR SYSTEM: Dynamic components developed from those of Mi-8. Five-blade constant-chord main rotor with glassfibre skins, of NACA 230 blade section, and three-blade tail rotor; latter on port side of offset tail fin. Blade spars nitrogen pressurised for crack detection. Hydraulic lead/lag dampers. Balance tab and electric leading-edge de-icing on each blade. Main rotor brake standard.

FUSELAGE: Conventional semi-monocoque structure of pod and boom type. Forward portion, above shallow floor structure, embodies integral side armour.

AUXILIARY WINGS: Cantilever shoulder wings of tapered planform, with about 16° anhedral and 20° incidence. No movable surfaces. Wings contribute about 25 per cent of total lift in cruising flight.

TAIL UNIT: Swept fin, offset at 3°, serves also as tail-rotor pylon. Variable-incidence horizontal stabiliser at base of fin.

LANDING GEAR: Tricycle type, with rearward retracting steerable twin-wheel nose unit, and single-wheel main units with low-pressure tyres. Tubular tripod skid

202

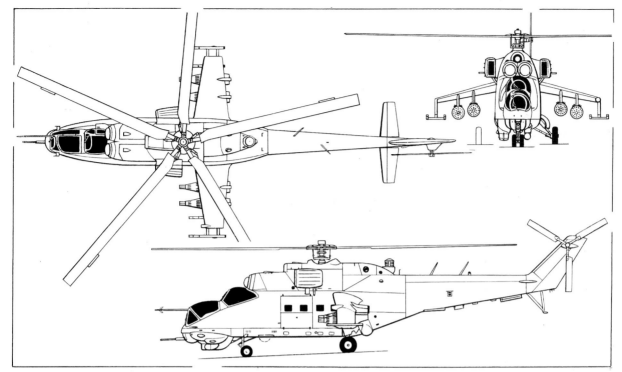

Mil Mi-24 'Hind-D'. *(Pilot Press)*

assembly, with shock strut, protects tail rotor in a tail-down take-off or landing.

POWERPLANT: Two Isotov TV3-117 turboshaft engines, each with max rating of 1,640 kW (2,200 shp), mounted side-by-side above the cabin, with their output shafts driving rearward to the main rotor shaft through a combining gearbox. Main fuel tank in fuselage to rear of cabin, with bag tanks under cabin floor and provision for auxiliary tank in cabin. Optional deflectors and separators for foreign objects and dust in air intakes; and infra-red suppression exhaust mixer boxes over exhaust ducts. APU mounted transversely inside fairing aft of rotor head.

ACCOMMODATION: Pilot (at rear) and weapon operator on armoured seats in tandem cockpits under individual canopies. Rear seat raised to give pilot an unobstructed forward view. Anti-fragment shield between cockpits. Main cabin can accommodate eight persons on folding seats, or four stretchers. Optically flat bulletproof glass windscreen, with wiper, for each crew member.

AVIONICS AND EQUIPMENT: Include VHF and UHF radio, autopilot, radar altimeter, blind-flying instrumentation, and ADF navigation system with map display. Air data sensor boom forward of top starboard corner of bulletproof windscreen at extreme nose. Undernose pods for electro-optics and RF missile guidance. Gun camera on port wingtip. Many small antennae and blisters, including IFF (NATO 'Odd Rods') and radar warning antennae. Infra-red suppressor in 'flower pot' container above forward end of tailboom; decoy flare dispenser under tailboom forward of tailskid assembly.

ARMAMENT: One remotely controlled four-barrel Gatling type 12.7 mm machine-gun in undernose turret with range of movement in azimuth and elevation, and slaved to undernose sighting system. Rails for four AT-2 'Swatter' anti-tank missiles under endplate pylons at wingtips. Four

underwing pylons for UV-32-57 rocket pods (each thirty-two S-5 type 57 mm rockets), pods each containing twenty 80 mm rockets, UPK-23 pods each containing twin 23 mm guns, up to 1,500 kg (3,300 lb) of chemical or conventional bombs, or other stores. PKV reflector gunsight for pilot. Provisions for firing AK-47 guns from cabin windows.

DIMENSIONS, EXTERNAL (estimated):	
Main rotor diameter	17.00 m (55 ft 9 in)
Tail rotor diameter	3.90 m (12 ft 9$\frac{1}{2}$ in)
Length overall:	
excl rotors and guns	17.50 m (57 ft 5 in)
rotors turning	21.50 m (70 ft 6$\frac{1}{2}$ in)
Height overall: rotors turnings	6.50 m (21 ft 4 in)
WEIGHTS:	
Weight empty	8,400 kg (18,520 lb)
Max external weapons	1,500 kg (3,300 lb)
Normal T-O weight	11,000 kg (24,250 lb)
PERFORMANCE ('Hind-D'):	
Max level speed	167 knots (310 km/h; 192 mph)
Max cruising speed	159 knots (295 km/h; 183 mph)
Max rate of climb at S/L	750 m (2,460 ft)/min
Service ceiling	4,500 m (14,750 ft)
Hovering ceiling OGE	2,200 m (7,200 ft)
Combat radius with max military load	
	86 nm (160 km; 99 miles)
Range with max fuel	405 nm (750 km; 466 miles)

Mil Mi-25

NATO reporting name: Hind

Some export variants of the Mi-24 ('Hind-D'), including those for India, are reportedly designated Mi-25. Such a change, presumably, signifies different equipment standards.

203

Artist's impression of Mil Mi-28 combat helicopters.
(US Department of Defense)

Mil Mi-28

NATO reporting name: Havoc

The existence of this Soviet combat helicopter was confirmed in the 1984 edition of *Soviet Military Power*, published by the US Department of Defense. The 1985 edition contained the first detailed artist's impression of the Mi-28, and the 1987 edition suggested that 'Havoc' might become operational during that year. There is, however, little reason to believe that it has yet emerged from the prototype development stage.

The DoD states that 'Havoc' has probably been built to meet the threat presented by NATO weapons using thermal-imaging systems.

Elimination of transport capability, by comparison with the Mi-24, should ensure much improved agility and survivability, as the result of a greatly reduced cross-section (almost certainly smaller than suggested by the DoD drawing). The following details should be regarded as provisional:

TYPE: Twin-engined combat helicopter.

ROTOR SYSTEM: Five-blade main rotor and three-blade tail rotor of new design. Tail rotor mounted on starboard side of tail fin, possibly at tip of small horizontal stabiliser.

WINGS: Cantilever mid-mounted wings of low aspect ratio, with sweptback leading edge. No movable surfaces.

FUSELAGE: Conventional semi-monocoque structure, embodying integral armour around cockpit area.

TAIL UNIT: Sweptback fin with small horizontal stabiliser at tip.

LANDING GEAR: Non-retractable tailwheel type, with single wheel on each unit. Mainwheels carried on side Vs.

POWERPLANT: Two unidentified turboshaft engines, possibly related to TV3-117 engines of Mi-24, in pods mounted above each wing root. Upward deflected jetpipes. Deflectors for dust and foreign objects forward of air intakes.

ACCOMMODATION: Co-pilot/gunner in front cockpit; pilot behind, on elevated seat. Flat, non-glint transparencies. Electro-optics pod under nose, probably enclosing low-light-level TV and/or laser designator and marked target seeker.

ARMAMENT AND OPERATIONAL EQUIPMENT: Heavy-calibre gun in undernose turret. Pylons under wings for external stores, including up to 16 anti-tank missiles or rocket packs. Wingtip pylons each capable of carrying two tube-launched missiles for air-to-air or air-to-ground use. Radar in small radome on nose. Infra-red suppressors and infra-red decoy dispensers fitted.

DIMENSIONS, EXTERNAL (estimated):	
Main rotor diameter	17.00 m (55 ft 9 in)
Length overall, excl rotors	17.40 m (57 ft 1 in)
WEIGHT (estimated):	
Max T-O weight	8,000 kg (17,635 lb)
PERFORMANCE (estimated):	
Max level speed	162 knots (300 km/h; 186 mph)
Combat radius	130 nm (240 km; 149 miles)

Mil Mi-28 'Havoc'. *(Pilot Press)*

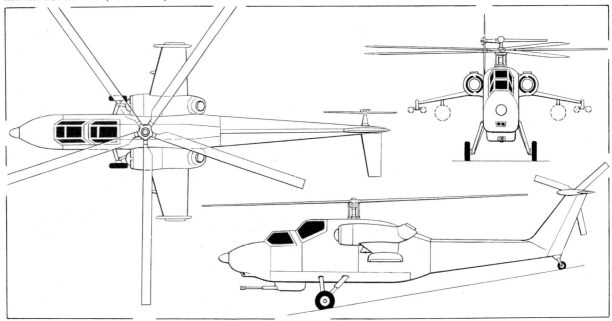

Myasishchev

This design bureau was formed in 1951, under the leadership of Professor Vladimir Mikhailovich Myasishchev, who died on 14 October 1978, at the age of 76. Its first product was the four-jet M-4 bomber (known in the West by the reporting name of 'Bison'), which remains in service as a strategic bomber, maritime reconnaissance aircraft and flight refuelling tanker.

Myasishchev M-4

NATO reporting name: Bison

Three major production versions of this four-jet aircraft were identified by NATO reporting names, as follows:

Bison-A. The Soviet Union's first operational four-jet strategic bomber, carrying free-fall weapons only. Design began in 1951 and the prototype was displayed over Moscow on 1 May 1954. Comparable with early versions of Boeing B-52 Stratofortress, it was powered by four 85.3 kN (19,180 lb st) Mikulin AM-3D turbojets, buried in wing roots. Defensive armament of eight 23 mm NR-23 cannon in twin-gun turrets in tail, above fuselage forward of wing and under fuselage fore and aft of three weapons bays.

Bison-B. Maritime reconnaissance version identified in service in 1964. 'Solid' nose radome in place of hemispherical glazed nose of 'Bison-A,' with large superimposed flight refuelling probe. Numerous underfuselage blister fairings for specialised avionics equipment. Forward portion of centre bomb bay doors bulged. Aft gun turrets above and below fuselage deleted, reducing armament to six 23 mm cannon. Few remain.

Bison-C. Improved maritime reconnaissance version. Generally similar configuration to 'Bison-B', but with large search radar faired neatly into longer nose, aft of centrally-mounted flight refuelling probe. Prone bombing/observation station, with optically-flat glass panels, below and to rear of radar; further small windows and a domed observation (and probably gunnery aiming) window on each side; under-fuselage blister fairings, bulged bomb bay and armament; all as 'Bison-B'. An example of this version with the experimental aircraft designation 201-M was used to set up a number of official records in 1959 and was exhibited statically in the Soviet Aviation Day display at Domodedovo Airport, Moscow, in 1967. Powered by four 127.5 kN (28,660

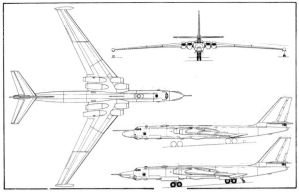

Myasishchev M-4 'Bison-C'. Upper side view: 'Bison-B'. *(Pilot Press)*

lb st) Soloviev D-15 turbojet engines, this testbed aircraft established seven payload-to-height records, including a weight of 55,220 kg (121,480 lb) lifted to 2,000 m (6,560 ft) and height of 15,317 m (50,253 ft) with a 10,000 kg payload. Few remain.

About 45 of these aircraft were available in October 1986, 15 as bombers for maritime and Eurasian missions and 30 as probe-and-drogue flight refuelling tankers for the 'Backfire/Bear/Bison/Blinder' attack force. Pending replacement, other 'Bisons' had been phased out of service and placed in storage.

DIMENSIONS, EXTERNAL ('Bison-A'):
Wing span   50.48 m (165 ft 7½ in)
Length overall   47.20 m (154 ft 10 in)
WEIGHT ('Bison-A'):
Max T-O weight   158,750 kg (350,000 lb)
PERFORMANCE ('Bison-A', estimated):
Max level speed at 11,000 m (36,000 ft)
     538 knots (998 km/h; 620 mph)
Service ceiling   13,700 m (45,000 ft)
Max unrefuelled combat radius
     3,025 nm (5,600 km; 3,480 miles)
Range at 450 knots (835 km/h; 520 mph) with more than 5,450 kg (12,000 lb) of bombs
     4,320 nm (8,000 km; 4,970 miles)

Myasishchev M-4 'Bison-B' maritime reconnaissance aircraft. *(Royal Air Force)*

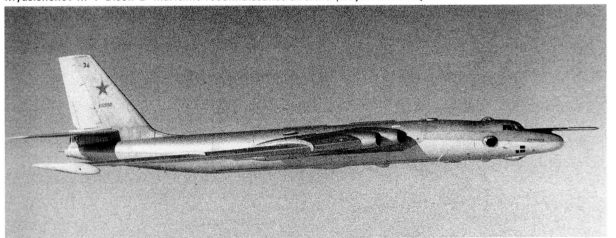

Sukhoi

This design bureau is named after Pavel Osipovich Sukhoi, who headed it from 1953 until his death in September 1975. It remains one of the two primary Soviet centres for fighter and attack aircraft development.

Sukhoi Su-7B

NATO reporting names: Fitter-A and Moujik

The Su-7B single-seat ground-attack fighter has been almost phased out of service in the Soviet air forces, but remains operational in the air forces of Afghanistan, Algeria, Czechoslovakia, Iraq, North Korea, Poland and Syria.

The first prototype of this single-seat fighter, designated S-1, was flown for the first time by test pilot A. G. Kochetkov on 8 September 1955, and was displayed in prototype form in the flypast over Moscow on the 1956 Soviet Aviation Day. It was the first Soviet aircraft to have all-moving horizontal tail surfaces and a fore-and-aft translating air intake centrebody to adjust supersonic airflow. Powerplant was, successively, an AL-7 turbojet and AL-7F; armament comprised three NR-30 guns.

The S-1 prototypes were followed by a number of S-2s, embodying certain aerodynamic refinements, and by a small number of pre-series aircraft designated **Su-7**. After evaluation of these, a new prototype, known as the S-22, was built in fighter-bomber form. It was flown for the first time, in April 1959, by E. Soloviev; and the S-22 was ordered into series production as the **Su-7B** fighter-bomber, air-combat and reconnaissance aircraft, to which NATO gave the reporting name **Fitter-A**. This model appeared in formations of up to 21 aircraft at the 1961 Tushino display.

In various versions, the Su-7 subsequently became the standard tactical fighter-bomber of the Soviet Air Force, but it is now almost out of service. Others were supplied to Afghanistan, Algeria, Cuba, Czechoslovakia, Egypt, Hungary, India, Iraq, North Korea, Poland, Romania, Syria, Viet-Nam and South Yemen, of which the remaining users are listed above.

The fuselage and tail unit of the Su-7B were almost identical with those of the delta-winged Su-9. Early production models had the pitot boom mounted centrally above the air intake, but it is offset to starboard on later versions, the first of which was the **Su-7BM** (S-22M). This had improved flight control and navigation equipment, and

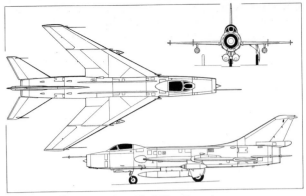

Sukhoi Su-7BM 'Fitter-A'. *(Pilot Press)*

introduced two slim duct fairings along the top of the centre fuselage; other detail changes followed progressively, including introduction of a zero-altitude ejection seat, Sirena tail warning radar, uprated engine, a second pair of underwing stores pylons, larger blast panels on the sides of the front fuselage by the muzzles of the wing-root guns, implying the use of cannon with a higher muzzle velocity or rate of fire, JATO attachments under the rear fuselage, and twin brake-chutes in a large container at the base of the rudder, instead of a single ribbon parachute attached under the rear fuselage. A demand for improved capability in operation from short, unprepared fields led next to the **Su-7BKL** (S-22KL = *koleso-lyzhny*, wheel-ski), with an AL-7F-1-200 turbojet, a low-pressure nosewheel tyre, requiring blistered doors to enclose it when retracted, and a small extensible skid outboard of each mainwheel. The final production single-seater, designated **Su-7BMK**, was strengthened to permit a heavier weapon load.

A variant of the Su-7 seen first at Domodedovo in 1967 is the two-seat **Su-7U** (U-22), with the second cockpit in tandem, aft of the standard cockpit and with a slightly raised, rearward-hinged canopy. The forward fuselage fuel tank is deleted, and the fuselage lengthened slightly, to make room for the second ejection seat, the occupant of which has a periscopic sight for forward view over the pupil's head. A prominent dorsal spine extends from the back of the rear canopy to the base of the tail fin. The two-seater, which exists in **Su-7UM** and **Su-7UMK** versions corresponding to the

Egyptian Sukhoi Su-7BM 'Fitter' ground-attack aircraft. *(Denis Hughes)*

single-seat 'M' and 'MK', is a standard operational trainer and has the NATO reporting name **Moujik**.

The following description applies to the Su-7BMK:

TYPE: Single-seat ground-attack fighter.

WINGS: Cantilever mid-wing monoplane. Thickness/chord ratio 8%. No dihedral or anhedral. Sweepback 60° on leading edges. Conventional structure. Wing root chord is extended, giving a straight trailing edge on inboard section of each wing. Hydraulically powered spring loaded ailerons. Large-chord flaps over entire trailing edge from root to inboard end of aileron on each wing. No slats or tabs. Two boundary layer fences on each wing, at approx mid-span and immediately inboard of tip.

FUSELAGE: Conventional semi-monocoque structure of circular section. Break joint at wing trailing edge permits removal of rear fuselage for engine servicing. Two intake suction relief doors on each side of nose. Two slim duct fairings along top of centre fuselage. Two hydraulically actuated door-type airbrakes, at top and bottom, on each side of rear fuselage.

TAIL UNIT: Cantilever structure, with 55° sweepback at quarter-chord on all surfaces. All-moving horizontal surfaces, with anti-flutter bodies projecting forward from tips. Conventional rudder with yaw damper. No tabs.

LANDING GEAR: Retractable tricycle type, with single wheel on each unit. Steerable nosewheel. Differential brakes on mainwheels. Twin brake-chutes in large container with clamshell doors, at base of rudder.

POWERPLANT: One Lyulka AL-7F-1-100 (TRD-31) turbojet engine, rated at 66.64 kN (14,980 lb st) dry and 94.08 kN (21,150 lb st) with afterburning. Time taken for afterburner light-up 6–7 s. Variable-area afterburner nozzle. Saddle fuel tanks in centre fuselage and integral tanks between spars of inner wings. Total internal fuel capacity 2,940 litres (777 US gallons; 647 Imp gallons). Gravity fuelling points above fuselage tanks and each wing tank. Provision for two drop-tanks side-by-side under fuselage, with total capacity of 1,200 litres (317 US gallons; 264 Imp gallons); and two ferry tanks, total capacity 1,800 litres (475.5 US gallons; 396 Imp gallons) on inner wing pylons. Two SPRD-110 solid-propellant rocket units, each 29.4 kN (6,610 lb st), can be attached under rear fuselage to shorten T-O run.

ACCOMMODATION: Pilot only in pressurised cockpit, on KS-4 zero-altitude rocket-powered ejection seat, under rearward sliding· blister canopy. Flat windscreen of armoured glass. Rearview mirror on top of canopy.

AVIONICS AND EQUIPMENT: Standard avionics include VHF/UHF radio, ILS, RSIU very-short-wave fighter radio, ADF, transponder, SRO-2M (NATO 'Odd Rods') IFF, Sirena 3 tail warning radar, ranging radar in air intake centrebody, autopilot. Launcher for Very cartridges or chaff under starboard wingroot leading edge. Provision for vertical and oblique cameras in belly aft of nosewheel bay.

ARMAMENT: Two 30 mm NR-30 guns, each with 70 rounds, in wingroot leading edges. ASP-5ND gyro gunsight. Six external stores pylons. Two underbelly pylons and inner underwing pylons each capable of carrying 750 kg (1,650 lb); outer underwing pylons each stressed for 500 kg (1,100 lb). Stores include UB-16-57U rocket pods (each sixteen 57 mm S-5, S-5M or S-5K rockets), S-24, 250 kg concrete piercing guided rockets, S-3K unguided rockets, and free-fall bombs (usually two 750 kg and two 500 kg), including

nuclear weapons. When underbelly fuel tanks are fitted, max external weapon load is 1,000 kg (2,205 lb).

DIMENSIONS, EXTERNAL:	
Wing span	8.77 (28 ft 9¼ in)
Length overall, incl probe	16.80 m (55 ft 1½ in)
Height overall	4.80 m (15 ft 9 in)
AREA:	
Wings, gross	23.0 m² (247 sq ft)
WEIGHTS:	
Operating weight empty	8,328 kg (18,360 lb)
Normal T-O weight	12,000 kg (26,450 lb)
Max T-O weight	13,440 kg (29,630 lb)
PERFORMANCE:	
Max level speed at 12,200 m (40,000 ft):	
'clean' Mach 1.6 (917 knots; 1,700 km/h; 1,055 mph)	
with external stores	
	Mach 1.2 (685 knots; 1,270 km/h; 788 mph)
Max level speed at S/L:	
without afterburning	460 knots (850 km/h; 530 mph)
with afterburning	625 knots (1,158 km/h; 720 mph)
Max rate of climb at S/L	9,000 m (29,525 ft)/min
Service ceiling	18,000 m (59,050 ft)
T-O run	2,400 m (7,875 ft)
Combat radius	
	135–187 nm (250–345 km; 155–215 miles)
Max range	780 nm (1,450 km; 900 miles)

Sukhoi Su-15 – See **Su-21**

Sukhoi Su-17, Su-20 and Su-22

NATO reporting names: Fitter-C, D, E, F, G, H, J and K

The prototype of this variable-geometry fighter series, designated S-22I or Su-71G (*Izmenyaemaya Geometriya*; variable geometry), was an R & D aircraft first flown on 2 August 1966 and shown at the Soviet Aviation Day display at Domodedovo Airport, Moscow, in July 1967, after which it was allocated the NATO reporting name 'Fitter-B'. Only 4.2 m (13 ft 9 in) of each wing was pivoted, outboard of a very large fence. The remainder of the airframe was virtually identical with that of the earlier fixed-wing Su-7, although the inboard glove panels were deepened in section. An attachment for an external store was built into each wing fence, but the Lyulka AL-7 powerplant was unchanged and there was no reason to expect 'Fitter-B' to form the basis of a production aircraft.

Discovery of two squadrons of 'improved Fitter-Bs' in service with the Soviet tactical air forces in 1972 came as a surprise, suggesting that even a small increase in range and endurance by comparison with the Su-7 was considered worthwhile. These aircraft still retained the AL-7 engine, had a Sirena 2 radar warning antenna on the fin tip, and a brake parachute.

A more powerful AL-21F-3 engine and rearward-hinged canopy were fitted to subsequent major production versions for the Soviet Air Forces, which were designated **Su-17** (S-32). Combined with the variable-geometry wings, the new engine permitted a doubled external load to be lifted from strips little more than half as long as those needed by the Su-7, and to be carried about 30 per cent further. Added to new avionics, this made the variable-geometry 'Fitters' so attractive that about 1,070 are deployed currently by Soviet

Single-seat Su-17 ('Fitter-H') of Soviet Air Force, armed with underbelly rocket pods, 'Atoll' air-to-air missiles and two AS-7 ('Kerry') air-to-surface missiles.

tactical air forces, 75 more by Soviet Naval Aviation units assigned to anti-shipping strike and amphibious support roles in the Baltic Sea area, and a further Naval unit of indeterminate size in the Pacific theatre. All aircraft of this type in Soviet service are designated Su-17. Differences between the various versions are as follows:

Su-17 (Fitter-C). Basic single-seat attack aircraft for Soviet tactical air forces, with Lyulka AL-21F-3 turbojet and eight stores pylons. Manual wing-sweep control. Additional wing fence on fixed centre section each side. Curved dorsal fin between tail fin and dorsal spine fairing. Operational since 1971, in relatively small numbers. Serves also with Soviet Navy.

Su-17M (S-32M, Fitter-D). Generally similar to 'Fitter-C', but forward fuselage lengthened by about 0.25 m (10 in). Added undernose electronics pod for Doppler navigation radar. Laser rangefinder in intake centrebody.

Su-17UM (U-32, Fitter-E). Tandem two-seat trainer for Soviet Air Force. Generally similar to 'Fitter-D', without electronics pod, but entire fuselage forward of wing drooped slightly to improve pilot's view. Deepened dorsal spine fairing, almost certainly to provide additional fuel tankage. Port wingroot gun deleted.

Su-17 (Fitter G). Two-seat trainer variant of 'Fitter-H', with combat capability. Deepened dorsal spine fairing and drooped front fuselage like 'Fitter-E'. Taller vertical tail surfaces. Shallow ventral fin (removable). Starboard gun only. Laser rangefinder fitted in intake centrebody.

Su-17 (Fitter-H). Improved single-seater for Soviet Air Forces. Basically as 'Fitter-D', but with wide and deep dorsal fairing aft of canopy, like 'Fitter-E/G'. Doppler navigation radar fitted internally in deepened undersurface of nose. Taller fin like 'Fitter-G'. Removable ventral fin. Retains both wingroot guns. About 165 'Fitter-H/Ks' are equipped for tactical reconnaissance duties.

Su-17 (Fitter-K). Latest single-seat version for Soviet Air Forces, identified in 1984. Dorsal fin embodies small cooling air intake at front. Also in Polish use.

It was deduced for some years that certain export versions of the variable-geometry 'Fitter' series had different engines from the Su-17 variants listed above. 'Fitter-C/D/E/G/H/K' operated by the Soviet Air Force and some other air forces have a rear fuselage of basically constant diameter and are powered by a Lyulka turbojet. Versions exported to Angola, Libya, Peru, Syria, Viet-Nam, and North and South Yemen were seen to have a more bulged rear fuselage, now known to house a Tumansky R-29BS-300 turbojet, as fitted in the MiG-27, with rearranged external air ducts, and a shorter plain metal shroud terminating the rear fuselage. This change of powerplant, and/or variations in equipment standard, is covered by the following changes to the Soviet type designation:

Su-20 (Su-17MK, S-32MK, Fitter-C). Generally similar to Soviet Air Force 'Fitter-C', with Lyulka engine, but with reduced equipment standard. Supplied to Algeria, Czechoslovakia, Egypt, Iraq and Poland. Two former Egyptian aircraft were acquired by Federal German Luftwaffe for evaluation during 1985 by Erprobungsstelle 61 at Manching.

Su-22 (Fitter-F). Export counterpart of 'Fitter-D', with slightly modified undernose electronics pod. Tumansky R-29B turbojet, rated at 112.8 kN (25,350 lb st) with

Sukhoi Su-17s ('Fitter-K') of the Polish Air Force, each with four flare/chaff dispensers visible beside dorsal spine.

A bulged rear fuselage and underfuselage electronics pod distinguish this Su-22 ('Fitter-F') of the Libyan Arab Air Force. *(US Navy)*

afterburning, in increased-diameter rear fuselage. Gun in each wingroot. Weapons include 'Atoll' air-to-air missiles. Aircraft supplied to Peru had Sirena 2 limited-coverage radar warning receiver, virtually no navigation aids, and IFF incompatible with that nation's SA-3 (NATO 'Goa') surface-to-air missiles.

Su-22 (Fitter-G). Export counterpart of Su-17 'Fitter-G', with R-29B engine.

Su-22 (Fitter-J). Generally similar to 'Fitter-H' but with Tumansky engine. Internal fuel tankage 6,270 litres

(1,656 US gallons; 1,379 Imp gallons). More angular dorsal fin. 'Atoll' air-to-air missiles. Supplied to Libya.

The following description applies to the Su-17 ('Fitter-C'):

TYPE: Single-seat ground-attack fighter.

WINGS: Cantilever mid-wing monoplane, with wide-span fixed centre-section and manually operated variable-geometry outer panels, with min sweep angle of 28° and max sweep angle of approx 62°. Slight sweepback on trailing edge of area-increasing centre-section flaps. Outboard of these flaps, centre-section trailing edge is

Sukhoi Su-17 'Fitter-K'. *(Pilot Press)*

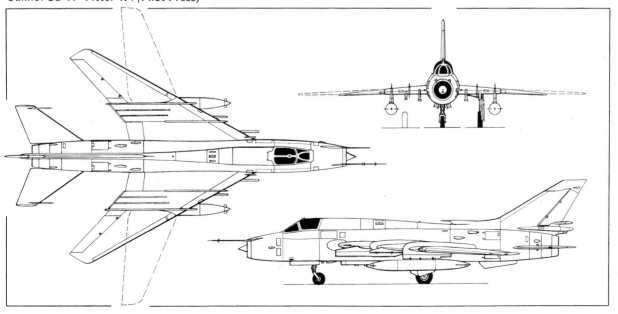

swept to align with trailing edge of outer panels when they are fully swept. Full span leading-edge slats on movable panels. Trailing edge of each movable panel made up of a slotted flap, operable only when the wings are spread, and a slotted aileron operable at all times. Large main fence on each side, at junction of fixed and movable panels, is square-cut at front and incorporates attachments for external stores. Shorter fence above centre-section on each side, inboard of main fence.

FUSELAGE: Conventional semi-monocoque structure of circular section. Large dorsal spine fairing along top of fuselage, from canopy to fin. Ram-air intake in nose, with variable shock-cone centrebody. Four door type airbrakes, at top and bottom on each side of rear fuselage, forward of tailplane. Pitot on port side of nose; transducer to provide pitch and yaw data for fire control computer and antennae on starboard side.

TAIL UNIT: Cantilever structure, with sweepback on all surfaces. All-moving horizontal surfaces, with anti-flutter body projecting forward on each side near tip. Conventional rudder. No tabs.

LANDING GEAR: Retractable tricycle type, with single wheel on each unit. Container for twin brake-chutes between base of rudder and tailpipe.

POWERPLANT: One Lyulka AL-21F-3 turbojet engine, rated at 76.5 kN (17,200 lb st) dry and 110 kN (24,700 lb st) with afterburning. Fuel capacity increased to 4,550 litres (1,202 US gallons; 1,000 Imp gallons) by added tankage in dorsal spine fairing. Provision for carrying up to four 800 litre (211 US gallon; 176 Imp gallon) drop-tanks on outboard wing pylons and under fuselage. When underfuselage tanks are carried, only the two inboard wing pylons may be used for ordnance, to a total weight of 1,000 kg (2,204 lb). Two solid-propellant rocket units can be attached to rear fuselage to shorten T-O run.

ACCOMMODATION: Pilot only, on ejection seat, under rearward hinged transparent canopy. Rearview mirror above canopy.

AVIONICS AND EQUIPMENT: SRD-5M (NATO 'High Fix') I-band ranging radar in intake centrebody; ASP-5ND fire control system; Sirena 3 radar warning system providing 360° coverage, with antennae in slim cylindrical housing above brake-chute container and in each centre-section leading edge, between fences; SRO-2M IFF; SOD-57M ATC/SIF, with transponder housing beneath brakechute container; and RSIU-5/R-831 VHF/UHF.

ARMAMENT: Two 30 mm NR-30 guns, each with 70 rds, in wing root leading edges. Total of eight weapon pylons (two tandem pairs under fuselage, one under each centre-section leading edge, one under each main wing fence) for more than 3,175 kg (7,000 lb) of bombs, including nuclear weapons, rocket pods and guided missiles such as the air-to-surface AS-7 (NATO 'Kerry').

DIMENSIONS, EXTERNAL:	
Wing span: fully spread	13.80 m (45 ft 3 in)
fully swept	10.00 m (32 ft 10 in)
Length overall, incl probes	18.75 m (61 ft 6¼ in)
Fuselage length	15.40 m (50 ft 6¼ in)
Height overall	5.00 m (16 ft 5 in)
AREAS (estimated):	
Wings, gross: fully spread	40.0 m² (430.0 sq ft)
fully swept	37.0 m² (398.0 sq ft)
WEIGHTS (estimated):	
Weight empty	10,000 kg (22,046 lb)
Max internal fuel	3,700 kg (8,157 lb)
T-O weight, 'clean'	14,000 kg (30,865 lb)
Max T-O weight	17,700 kg (39,020 lb)

PERFORMANCE (estimated for 'clean' aircraft, 60% internal fuel, except where indicated):

Max level speed: at height	Mach 2.09
	(1,200 knots; 2,220 km/h; 1,380 mph)
at S/L	Mach 1.05
	(693 knots; 1,285 km/h; 798 mph)
Max rate of climb at S/L	13,800 m (45,275 ft)/min
Service ceiling	18,000 m (59,050 ft)
T-O run at AUW of 17,000 kg (37,478 lb)	1,000 m (3,280 ft)
T-O to 15 m (50 ft) at AUW of 17,000 kg (37,478 lb)	
	1,400 m (4,600 ft)
Landing run	600 m (1,970 ft)
Combat radius with 2,000 kg (4,409 lb) external stores, incl fuel:	
hi-lo-hi	370 nm (685 km; 425 miles)
lo-lo-lo	240 nm (445 km; 275 miles)

Sukhoi Su-21

NATO reporting name: Flagon

Ten examples of the Su-15 twin-jet delta-wing fighter participated in the flying display at Domodedovo in July 1967. First to appear was a single black painted machine, piloted by Vladimir Ilyushin, son of the famous designer and known at that time to be a test pilot for Sukhoi. When a formation of nine similar aircraft appeared later, the identity of the design bureau responsible for them was confirmed by the obvious 'family likeness' to the earlier Su-9 and Su-11 in the shape of the wings and tail unit.

The Su-15 was developed to meet a Soviet Air Force requirement for a Mach 2.5 interceptor to follow the Su-11. It has served with the Soviet Air Force in several forms, identified by the NATO names Flagon-A, -C and -D, the 'A' and 'D' being single-seaters and the 'C' a two-seat training version of the 'D'.

The number of 'Flagons' currently in first-line home defence units is believed to have diminished to about 240, plus 260 in tactical units. Those remaining are of three variants, so different from early Su-15s that they are believed to be designated Su-21 in the USSR:

'Flagon-F' twin-jet interceptor armed with 'Anab' missiles and gun pods. (Swedish Coast Guard/Air Patrol)

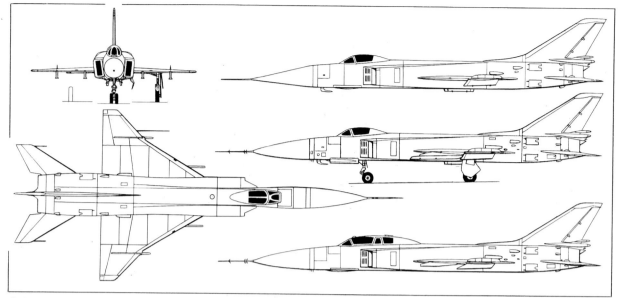

Sukhoi Su-21 'Flagon-F'. Additional side views: Su-15 'Flagon-D' (top), Su-21 'Flagon-G' (bottom). *(Pilot Press)*

Flagon-E. Single-seat interceptor. Longer-span wings than those of earlier 'Flagon-A', with compound sweep. Tumansky R-13F-300 turbojets, each rated at 64.73 kN (14,550 lb st), and increased fuel capacity, giving increased speed and range. Uprated avionics (NATO 'Twin Scan' replacing 'Skip Spin' radar). Major production version, operational since second half of 1973.

Flagon-F. Last known production version. Ogival nose radome instead of conical type of earlier variants. Generally similar to 'Flagon-E', but with uprated engines.

Flagon-G. Two-seat training version of 'Flagon-F', with probable combat capability. Individual rearward hinged canopy over each seat. Periscope fitted above rear canopy for enhanced forward view.

The following details apply to 'Flagon-F':

TYPE: Single-seat twin-jet all-weather interceptor.

WINGS: Cantilever mid-wing monoplane. Basic wings are of simple delta form, similar to those of earlier Su-11, but with new and extended outer panels. Sweepback 60° on inner wings, 45° on outer panels. No dihedral or anhedral. Single boundary layer fence above each wing at approx 70 per cent span. Large-chord flap extends from inboard end of aileron to fuselage on each side.

FUSELAGE: Cockpit section is basically circular with large ogival dielectric nosecone. Centre fuselage is faired into rectangular-section air intake ducts. Two door-type airbrakes at top and bottom on each side of rear fuselage, forward of tailplane.

TAIL UNIT: Cantilever structure, with sweepback on all surfaces. All-moving tailplane, with anhedral, mounted slightly below mid position and fitted with anti-flutter bodies near tips. Conventional rudder. No trim tabs.

LANDING GEAR: Tricycle type, with single wheel on each main unit and twin nosewheels. Container for brake-chute between base of rudder and tailpipe.

POWERPLANT: Two turbojets, with variable-area nozzles, mounted side-by-side in rear fuselage. These are reported to be Tumansky R-13F2-300s, each rated at 70.6 kN (15,875 lb st) with afterburning. Ram-air intakes, with variable ramps on splitter plates, embodying vertical slots

for boundary layer control. Blow-in auxiliary inlets between main intake and wing leading edge in side of each duct.

ACCOMMODATION: Single seat in enclosed cockpit, with rearward sliding blister canopy. Rearview mirror above canopy of some aircraft.

ARMAMENT: Two pylons for external stores under each wing. Normal armament comprises one radar homing and one infra-red homing air-to-air missile (NATO 'Anab') on outboard pylons, and an infra-red homing close-range missile (NATO 'Aphid') on each inboard pylon. Side-by-side pylons under centre fuselage for weapons, including GSh-23L 23 mm gun pods, or external fuel tanks.

AVIONICS AND EQUIPMENT: Large X-band radar (NATO 'Twin Scan') in nose, SOD-57M ATC/SIF nav system, SRO-2 (NATO 'Odd Rods') IFF, Sirena 3 radar warning system.

DIMENSIONS, EXTERNAL (estimated):	
Wing span	10.53 m (34 ft 6 in)
Length overall	20.5 m (68 ft 0 in)
WEIGHT (estimated):	
Max T-O weight	16,000 kg (35,275 lb)
PERFORMANCE (estimated):	
Max level speed above 11,000 m (36,000 ft):	
with external stores	Mach 2.1
Time to 11,000 m (36,000 ft)	2 min 30 s
Service ceiling	20,000 m (65,600 ft)
Combat radius	390 nm (725 km; 450 miles)

Sukhoi Su-24

NATO reporting name: Fencer

Although smaller and lighter than its USAF counterpart, the F-111, the variable-geometry Su-24 brought entirely new capability to Soviet tactical air power. Lt Gen Donald R. Keith, former US Army Deputy Chief of Staff for Research, Development and Acquisition, said that 'Fencer' is credited

Sukhoi Su-24 ('Fencer-C') two-seat attack aircraft. *(Swedish Air Force)*

with having terrain-avoidance radar, in addition to nav/attack radar, and 'has the capability to deliver ordnance in all weather within 55 m (180 ft) of its target'. The radar dish appears to have a diameter of at least 1.25 m (49 in), and is reported to be of the pulse-Doppler type. Equipment includes a laser rangefinder and marked target seeker.

Five variants have been identified by NATO reporting names:

Fencer-A. Identifiable by rectangular rear-fuselage box enclosing jet nozzles.

Fencer-B. Rear-fuselage box around jet nozzles has deeply dished bottom skin between nozzles. Larger brake-chute housing.

Fencer-C. Introduced in 1981. Important equipment changes. Multiple fitting on nose instead of former simple probe. Triangular fairing forward of each fixed wing root, on side of air intake (presumably housing ECM equipment of the kind seen on the fuselage sides, forward of the nosewheel doors, of ground attack MiG-23/27 'Floggers') and also on each side of fin, near tip.

Fencer-D. Introduced in 1983, with added flight refuelling capability. Slightly longer nose (approx 0.75 m; 2 ft 6 in) forward of windscreen; chord of lower part of tail fin extended, giving kinked leading edge; large overwing fences integral with extended wingroot glove pylons, probably for AS-14 (NATO 'Kedge') missiles in class of US Maverick; undernose aerials deleted; blister, probably for electro-optical sensor, added aft of nosewheel bay; and single long

Sukhoi Su-24 ('Fencer-D') with wings fully spread and landing gear extended. *(US Department of Defense)*

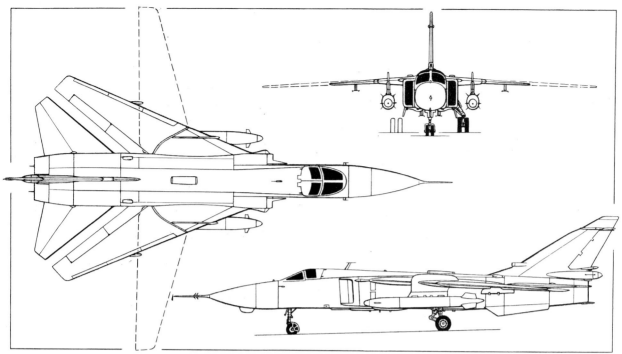

Sukhoi Su-24 'Fencer-D'. *(Pilot Press)*

noseprobe. A reconnaissance variant of 'Fencer-D' is operational with both tactical air force and naval forces.

Fencer-E. Electronic warfare version, replacing Yak-28s.

'Fencer' entered squadron service in December 1974, as a replacement for the Yak-28 (NATO 'Brewer'). In October 1986, an estimated 770 attack models and 65 reconnaissance 'Fencers' were serving with first-line units, including two full regiments at Tukums in Latvia, near the Gulf of Riga, and at Chernyakhovsk, near Kaliningrad on the Soviet Baltic coast. There are two more at Starokonstantinov and Gorodok in the Ukraine, and a single regiment in the Soviet Far East. No 'Fencer' was allowed to fly outside the Soviet Union or its home waters until July 1979, when an Su-24 regiment was deployed briefly with the 16th Air Army, at Templin air base, north of Berlin in East Germany. Not until 1982 was the first fully operational unit of 30 Su-24s deployed to East Germany as a regular component of the Frontal Aviation air forces stationed in Europe; on 24 September 1987 an Su-24 strayed into West German airspace for about five minutes, probably due to navigation error. About 450 of the aircraft now in service are assigned to strategic missions.

The following details apply specifically to 'Fencer-C' but are generally applicable to all versions:

TYPE: Two-seat variable-geometry attack aircraft.

WINGS: Cantilever shoulder-wing monoplane, each wing comprising a triangular fixed glove box and three-position pivoted outer panels. Slight anhedral from roots. Leading-edge sweepback on outer panels estimated at 16° fully forward, and 68° fully swept, with an intermediate sweep angle of 45°. Full span leading-edge slats and almost full span two-section double-slotted trailing-edge flaps on the outer panels. Differential spoilers forward of flaps for roll control at low speeds and for use as lift dumpers on landing.

FUSELAGE: Conventional semi-monocoque structure of slab-sided rectangular section, with integral engine air intake trunks. Splitter plate and outer lip of each intake are inclined slightly downward. Variable intake ramps. Air brake under each side of centre fuselage, curved to follow shape of underbelly fairing.

TAIL UNIT: Cantilever structure, comprising single swept-back fin with inset rudder, and all-moving horizontal surfaces which operate together for pitch control and differentially for roll control, assisted by use of the wing spoilers when the wings are not fully swept. Two slightly splayed ventral fins, one each side of fuselage under-surface.

LANDING GEAR: Retractable tricycle type, and twin wheels on each unit. Low-pressure tyres for operation from semi-prepared fields. Mudguard on nosewheels.

POWERPLANT: Two afterburning engines side-by-side in rear fuselage. These are believed to be related to the Lyulka AL-21F turbojet, as fitted in Su-17. Internal fuel capacity, estimated at 13,000 litres (3,434 US gallons; 2,860 Imp gallons), can be supplemented by four large external tanks.

ACCOMMODATION: Crew of two (pilot and weapon systems officer) side-by-side on ejection seats.

AVIONICS: Latest photographs show a small avionics pod at top of engine air intake duct on each side, immediately aft of lip, and on each side of fin. These pods appear similar to those immediately forward of the nosewheel bay of ground-attack versions of the MiG-23/27.

ARMAMENT: Eight pylons under fuselage, each wing root glove and outer wings for approx 11,000 kg (24,250 lb) of guided and unguided air-to-surface weapons, including nuclear weapons, missiles such as AS-7 (NATO 'Kerry'), AS-10 ('Karen') and AS-14 ('Kedge'), or external fuel tanks. Two pivoting underwing pylons were the first of their kind observed on a Soviet aircraft. No internal weapons bay. One six-barrel 30 mm Gatling-type gun inside fairing on starboard side of fuselage undersurface. Unidentified fairing on other side.

DIMENSIONS, EXTERNAL (estimated):

Wing span: spread	17.50 m (57 ft 5 in)
swept	10.50 m (34 ft 5½ in)
Length overall, excl probe	21.29 m (69 ft 10 in)
Height overall	6.00 m (19 ft 8¼ in)
Wheel track	4.00 m (13 ft 1½ in)

WEIGHTS (estimated):

Weight empty, equipped	19,000 kg (41,885 lb)
Max T-O weight	41,000 kg (90,390 lb)

PERFORMANCE (estimated):

Max speed, 'clean': at height	Mach 2.18
at S/L	Mach 1.2
Service ceiling	16,500 m (54,135 ft)
Combat radius:	
lo-lo-lo	over 174 nm (322 km; 200 miles)
lo-lo-hi with 2,500 kg (5,500 lb) weapons	
	515 nm (950 km; 590 miles)
hi-lo-hi, with 3,000 kg (6,615 lb) weapons and two external	
tanks	700 nm (1,300 km; 805 miles)

Sukhoi Su-25 combat aircraft of the Czechoslovak Air Force. *(Letectvi + Kosmonautika/Václav Jukl)*

Sukhoi Su-25

NATO reporting name: Frogfoot

First photographs of this Soviet counterpart to the US Air Force's single-seat A-10 Thunderbolt II attack aircraft became available in December 1982, following deployment of Su-25s to Afghanistan to support the Russian ground forces fighting in mountain terrain.

When first observed by satellite at Ramenskoye flight test centre in 1977, the Su-25 was given the provisional US designation Ram-J. The NATO reporting name 'Frogfoot' was released in 1982, and the Su-25 had attained full operational capability by 1984. The emphasis during operational use in Afghanistan is said to have been on techniques for co-ordinating low-level close support by fixed-wing aircraft and Mi-24 helicopter gunships. About 210 Su-25s were operational with Soviet forces by October 1986, plus one squadron serving with the Czechoslovak Air Force. Others have been exported to Iraq. Production is centred at the Tbilisi airframe plant.

TYPE: Single-seat close-support aircraft.

WINGS: Cantilever shoulder-wing monoplane. Anhedral from roots. Approx 20° sweepback. Entire trailing edge occupied by ailerons and double-slotted two-section flaps. Multiple tabs in each aileron. Full span leading-edge slats

Sukhoi Su-25 'Frogfoot'. *(Pilot Press)*

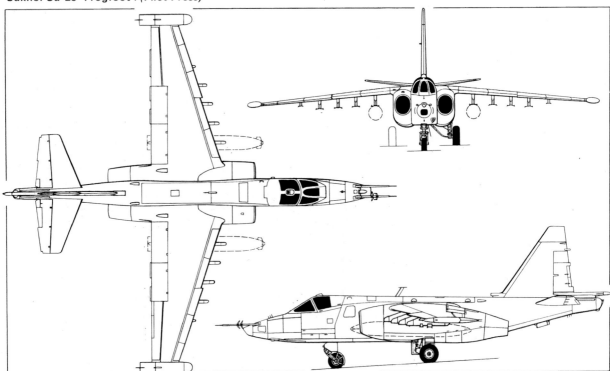

in two segments on each wing. Extended chord leading-edge 'dogtooth' on outer 50 per cent of each wing. Pods at wingtips each split at rear to form airbrakes which project above and below wing when extended, like those of Grumman A-6 Intruder. Retractable landing light in base of each pod, aft of dielectric nosecap for ECM.

FUSELAGE: Conventional semi-monocoque structure, with flat armoured sides around cockpit. Pitot on port side of nose; transducer to provide data for fire control computer on starboard side.

TAIL UNIT: Conventional cantilever structure. Variable-incidence tailplane, with slight dihedral. Two-section inset rudder. Tabs in lower rudder segment and each elevator.

LANDING GEAR: Hydraulically retractable tricycle type. Single wheel with low-pressure tyre on each unit. Mudguard on forward-retracting steerable nosewheel.

POWERPLANT: Two non-afterburning Tumansky R-13-300 turbojet engines in long nacelles at wingroots, each rated at 41.5 kN (9,340 lb st). Fuel tanks in fuselage between cockpit and wing front spar, and between rear spar and fin leading edge, and in wing centre section. Provision for external fuel tank on each inboard underwing pylon.

ACCOMMODATION: Single ejection seat under sideways hinged (to starboard) canopy, with small rearview mirror on top. Flat bulletproof windscreen.

AVIONICS: SRO-2 (NATO 'Odd Rods') IFF antennae forward of windscreen and under tail. Sirena 3 radar warning system antenna above fuselage tailcone.

ARMAMENT AND OPERATIONAL EQUIPMENT: One twin-barrel 30 mm gun in bottom of front fuselage on port side. Eight large pylons under wings for estimated 4,500 kg (9,920 lb) of air-to-ground weapons, including 57 mm and 80 mm rockets and 500 kg incendiary, anti-personnel and chemical cluster bombs. Two small outboard pylons for 'Atoll' or 'Aphid' air-to-air self-defence missiles. Laser rangefinder and marked target seeker under flat sloping window in nose. Chaff/flare dispenser in tailcone. Strike camera in top of nosecone.

DIMENSIONS, EXTERNAL:		
Wing span	14.30 m (46 ft 11 in)	
Length overall	15.40 m (50 ft 6¾ in)	
AREA:		
Wings, gross	33.7 m² (362.75 sq ft)	
WEIGHTS:		
Weight empty	9,500 kg (20,950 lb)	

Max T-O weight   18,120–19,200 kg (39,950–42,330 lb)
PERFORMANCE (estimated):
Max level speed   Mach 0.8
                                (530 knots; 980 km/h; 608 mph)
Combat radius, hi-lo-hi, with 2,000 kg (4,410 lb) air-to-ground weapons and two external fuel tanks.
                                        300 nm (556 km; 345 miles)

Sukhoi Su-27

NATO reporting name: Flanker

Responsibility for the larger of the Soviet Air Force's two new-generation single-seat fighters, equivalent to the USAF's F-15 Eagle, was assigned to the Sukhoi design bureau. Its general configuration is similar to that of the smaller MiG-29, suggesting that the two aircraft evolved from a common research programme by a central authority, such as the famous TsAGI Central Aerodynamic and Hydrodynamic Institute.

The first prototype of the Su-27 (NATO reporting name **Flanker-A**) began its flight testing in about 1977. An aircraft of the same configuration, with curved wingtips, and tail fins mounted centrally above each engine housing, was observed in a satellite picture taken overhead Ramenskoye flight test centre in the late 1970s and published openly in a US government document. The Soviet designation Su-27 was quoted by official sources in the West in 1982.

Nearly ten years of development, and considerable redesign, were needed before the production version (NATO

First Western photograph of the Sukhoi Su-27 ('Flanker-B'), taken from a P-3B of No 333 Squadron, Royal Norwegian Air Force.

215

Close-up of the cockpit area of the Su-27, showing the infra-red search/track sensor housing forward of the windscreen. *(Royal Norwegian Air Force)*

'**Flanker-B**') was able to achieve operational capability, with square wingtips carrying launchers for air-to-air missiles, outboard location of the tail fins, tailcone extension and other changes.

Following the type's deployment to the Kola Peninsula, in the far northern Murmansk region of the Soviet Union, first photographs of the operational version were taken by the crew of a Lockheed P-3B of No. 333 Squadron, Royal Norwegian Air Force. Two Su-27s were launched to identify the P-3B, each armed with six AA-10 air-to-air missiles of three different models.

Like the MiG-29, the Su-27 is described by the US Department of Defense as a supersonic all-weather counter-air fighter, with lookdown/shootdown weapon systems and beyond-visual-range air-to-air missiles, and with a possible secondary ground-attack role. The Su-27's range, thrust-to-weight ratio and manoeuvrability are all said to be improved by comparison with earlier Soviet fighters. Its large pulse-Doppler radar and heavy armament should give it formidable potential against low-flying aircraft and cruise missiles, particularly when it is deployed in partnership with the new Soviet AEW&C aircraft, based on the Il-76 transport and known to NATO as 'Mainstay'. DoD estimates suggest a combat radius as great as that of the Tupolev Tu-28P 'Fiddler', which is overdue for replacement, making the Su-27 capable of escorting missile armed bombers and deep-penetration ground-attack aircraft on sorties against the UK and western Europe.

The US Department of Defense estimated that, by October 1986, only five 'Flankers' had attained operational capability with the Voyska PVO, plus a further ten with the Soviet tactical forces. The total had probably increased to at least 50 operational aircraft by mid-1987.

Series production is centred in a plant at Komsomolsk, Khabarovsk territory. With the MiG-31, it is expected to replace many of the MiG-21, MiG-23/27, Su-21 and MiG-25 aircraft in the 17 tactical air forces assigned to Soviet military districts and groups of forces. It may also equip, in a navalised form, the large Soviet aircraft carrier now fitting out at Nikolayev.

There is reason to believe that the fighter designated **P-42**
by the Soviet Union is a specially prepared version of the Su-27. Flown by Viktor Georgiyevich Pugachev, a test pilot assigned to the Sukhoi design bureau, it set a record by climbing to 3,000 m in 25.373 seconds on 27 October 1986, beating by two seconds the previous record set by the F-15 *Streak Eagle*. On 15 November the same pilot claimed another record by taking the P-42 to 6,000 m in 37.050 seconds. On 10 March 1987 N. F. Sadovnikov flew the P-42 to 9,000 m in 44.176 seconds, and 12,000 m in 55.542 seconds. Data submitted with the claim for the November record gave the powerplant as two R-32 turbofans, each rated at 133.25 kN (29,955 lb st) with afterburning, and the take-off weight as 14,110 kg (31,110 lb).

TYPE: Single-seat all-weather counter-air fighter, with secondary ground-attack capability.

WINGS: Cantilever mid-wing monoplane. Basic wing sweepback approx 40° on leading edge, with long and smoothly curved leading-edge root extensions. Anhedral approx 2° 30′. Leading-edge manoeuvring flaps. Flap and aileron on trailing edge of each wing.

FUSELAGE: Short semi-monocoque all-metal structure of basically circular section, with cockpit high-set behind drooped nose. Large ogival dielectric nosecone. Long rectangular blast panel forward of gun on starboard side, above wingroot extension. Large forward hinged door type airbrake in top of centre-fuselage.

TAIL UNIT: Cantilever structure, comprising uncanted twin fins and rudders, mounted on narrow decks outboard of engine housings, and all-moving horizontal surfaces, all sharply sweptback. Fins have extensions beneath decks to form parallel but widely separated ventral fins.

LANDING GEAR: Retractable tricycle type, with single wheel on each unit. Mudguard on nosewheel unit. Brake-chute housed in fuselage tailcone.

POWERPLANT: Probably two Tumansky R-32 turbofans, each rated at 133.25 KN (29,955 lb st) with afterburning. Large auxiliary air-intake louvres in bottom of each engine duct near primary wedge intake. Two rows of small vertical louvres in each side wall of wedge.

ACCOMMODATION: Pilot only, under rearward sliding transparent blister canopy.

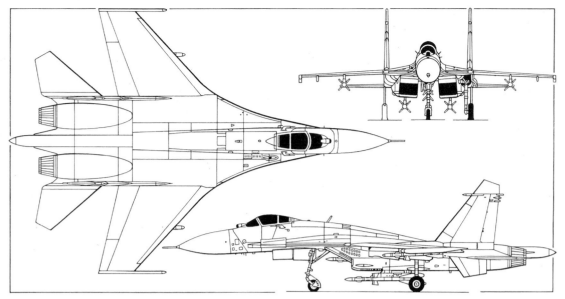

Sukhoi Su-27 'Flanker'. *(Jane's/Mike Keep)*

AVIONICS AND EQUIPMENT: Track-while-scan radar with reported search range of 130 nm (240 km; 150 miles) and tracking range of 100 nm (185 km; 115 miles). Infra-red search/track sensor in transparent housing forward of windscreen. Sirena-3 (or later) 360° radar warning receivers, outboard of each bottom air intake lip and at tail.

ARMAMENT: One 30 mm gun in starboard wingroot extension. Up to ten air-to-air missiles, on tandem pylons under fuselage between engine ducts, beneath each duct, under each centre-wing and outer-wing, and at each wingtip. Aircraft illustrated has two short-burn semi-active radar homing AA-10A missiles (NATO 'Alamo-A') in tandem under fuselage; two short-burn infra-red homing AA-10B ('Alamo-B') missiles on the centre-wing pylons; and a long-burn semi-active radar homing AA-10C ('Alamo-C') beneath each engine duct. The four outer pylons are unoccupied, but are believed to carry either AA-11 (NATO 'Archer') or AA-8 (NATO 'Aphid') close-

range infra-red missiles. Likely ability to carry up to 6,000 kg (13,225 lb) of external stores (e.g. twelve 500 kg bombs) for secondary attack role.

DIMENSIONS, EXTERNAL (estimated):

Wing span	14.70 m (48 ft 2¾ in)
Length overall, excl nose probe	21.60 m (70 ft 10½ in)
Height overall	5.50 m (18 ft 0 in)
Wheel track	4.40 m (14 ft 5¼ in)
Wheelbase	6.70 m (22 ft 0 in)

WEIGHT (estimated):

Max T-O weight	20,000–27,200 kg (44,000–60,000 lb)

PERFORMANCE (estimated):

Max level speed: at height	
	Mach 2.0 (1,150 knots; 2,120 km/h; 1,320 mph)
at S/L	Mach 1.1 (725 knots; 1,345 km/h; 835 mph)
Combat radius	810 nm (1,500 km; 930 miles)

Tupolev

Andrei Tupolev, born in 1888, was a leading figure in the Central Aero-Hydrodynamic Institute (TsAGI) in Moscow from the time when it was founded, in 1929, until his death on 23 December 1972. Current chief designers of the bureau which bears his name include his son, Dr Alexei A. Tupolev. The bureau has doubled in size during the past decade.

Tupolev Tu-16

NATO reporting name: Badger

The prototype of this intermediate-range bomber, which had the Tupolev design bureau designation Tu-88, was flown for the first time by N. Rybko in winter of 1951–2. The original strategic bomber version entered series production as the Tu-16 in 1953, and made its first major public appearance on 1 May 1954. An estimated 260 remained operational with the Soviet strategic bomber force in early 1987, equipped to carry both nuclear and conventional weapons. The bombers

are supported by 20 Tu-16 inflight-refuelling tankers and about 115 various versions equipped for ECM duties and for reconnaissance. Soviet Naval Aviation had, in 1987, about 190 attack models of 'Badger', plus 70 tankers and up to 80 reconnaissance and ECM models.

The original 1981 edition of *Soviet Military Power* stated: 'The prime strike force of Soviet Naval Aviation consists of . . . 'Badger' and 'Blinder' aircraft which are fitted to carry one or two of several types of anti-ship cruise missiles with standoff ranges varying from 90 to over 300 km (48–162 nm; 56–186 miles). Some missiles have variable flight paths and various homing techniques to help penetrate ship defences. All these missiles are assessed to carry either a nuclear or a high-explosive warhead of about 1,000 to 2,000 lb (450–900 kg) . . . In addition to naval aircraft armed with anti-ship missiles, certain 'Bear' and 'Badger' bombers of the Soviet strategic bomber force can be used for attacks against ships, and these aircraft regularly participate in naval exercises.'

Tupolev Tu-16 ('Badger-D') maritime/electronic reconnaissance aircraft. *(UK Ministry of Defence)*

Early production Tu-16s had AM-3 turbojet engines. These were replaced in later aircraft by improved RD-3M (AM-3M) engines, which increased maximum speeds by up to 54 knots (100 km/h; 62 mph), and range with max fuel to 3,885 nm (7,200 km; 4,470 miles). Eleven versions of the Tu-16 have been identified by unclassified NATO reporting names. All remain in service, as follows:

Badger-A. Basic strategic jet bomber, able to carry nuclear or conventional free-fall weapons. Glazed nose, with small undernose radome. Defensive armament of seven 23 mm cannon. Some equipped as flight refuelling tankers, using a unique wingtip-to-wingtip transfer technique to refuel other Tu-16s, or a probe-and-drogue system to refuel Tu-22s. Operational with Chinese Air Force, and production continues in China under the designation Xian **H-6**.

Badger-B. Similar to 'Badger-A' but equipped originally to carry two turbojet powered aeroplane-type anti-shipping missiles (NATO 'Kennel') underwing. Superseded by 'Badger-G'.

Badger-C. Anti-shipping version, first seen at 1961 Soviet Aviation Day display. Large air-to-surface winged missile (NATO 'Kipper') carried in recess under fuselage ('Badger-C Mod' carries 'Kingfish' on underwing pylons). Wide nose radome (NATO 'Puff Ball'), in place of glazing

and nose gun of 'Badger-A'. No provision for free-fall bombs. Operational with Soviet Northern, Baltic, Black Sea and Pacific Fleets in 1987.

Badger-D. Maritime/electronic reconnaissance version. Nose similar to that of 'Badger-C'. Larger undernose radome; three radomes in tandem under bomb bays.

Badger-E. Photographic and electronic reconnaissance version. Similar to 'Badger-A' but with cameras in bomb bay and two additional radomes under fuselage, larger one aft.

Badger-F. Basically similar to 'Badger-E' but with electronic intelligence pod on a pylon under each wing. No radomes under centre fuselage.

Badger-G. Converted from 'Badger-B' with underwing pylons for two rocket-powered air-to-surface missiles (NATO 'Kelt') which can be carried over a range greater than 1,735 nm (3,220 km; 2,000 miles). Free-fall bombing capability retained. Majority serve with anti-shipping squadrons of Soviet Naval Air Force. A few have been transferred to Iraq.

One Soviet Navy Tu-16, probably a 'Badger-G', has been seen with an ECM nose thimble of the kind seen beneath the inflight refuelling probe of 'Bear-G'. It can be assumed that it also carries further pods like those of 'Bear-G' on its centre or rear fuselage.

Tu-16 (Badger-G' modified) armed with an AS-6 'Kingfish' missile. *(Swedish Air Force)*

Badger-G modified. Specially equipped carrier for 'Kingfish' air-to-surface missiles, of which first photograph was released, by Swedish Air Force, in mid-1981. Large radome, presumably associated with missile operation, under centre fuselage, replacing chin radome. Device mounted externally on glazed nose might help to ensure correct attitude of Tu-16 during missile launch. Operational with Soviet Northern Black Sea and Pacific Fleets.

Badger-H. Stand-off or escort ECM aircraft, with primary function of chaff dispensing to protect missile carrying strike force. The dispensers, with a total capacity of up to 9,075 kg (20,000 lb) of chaff, are located in the weapons bay area. Hatch aft of weapons bay. Two teardrop radomes, fore and aft of weapons bay. Two blade antennae aft of weapons bay. Glazed nose and chin radome.

Badger-J. Specialised ECM jamming/elint aircraft to protect strike force, with some equipment located in a canoe-shaped radome protruding from inside the weapons bay and surrounded by heat exchangers and exhaust ports. Anti-radar noise jammers operate in A to I bands inclusive. Glazed nose as 'Badger-A'. Some aircraft have large flat-plate antennae at wingtips.

Badger-K. Electronic reconnaissance variant, with nose as 'Badger-A'. Two teardrop radomes, inside and forward of weapons bay; four small pods on centreline in front of rear radome.

Maritime reconnaissance versions of 'Badger' make regular flights over units of the US Navy and other NATO naval forces at sea in the Atlantic, Pacific and elsewhere. They also make electronic intelligence (elint) sorties around the coastlines of NATO and other countries. Strike, tanker and ECM variants of 'Badger' are deployed to Cam Ranh Bay, the former US Navy base in Viet-Nam.

TYPE: Twin-jet medium bomber and maritime reconnaissance/attack aircraft.

WINGS: Cantilever high mid-wing monoplane, with marked anhedral and with 35° of leading-edge sweep on outer panels; 42° sweep on inboard panels. Thickness/chord ratio 12½%. Two fences on each wing. Entire trailing edge made up of slotted flaps (max deflection 35°) and mass balanced ailerons, each with trim tab. Heavy engine nacelles form root fairings. Versions equipped for inflight refuelling have modified wingtips.

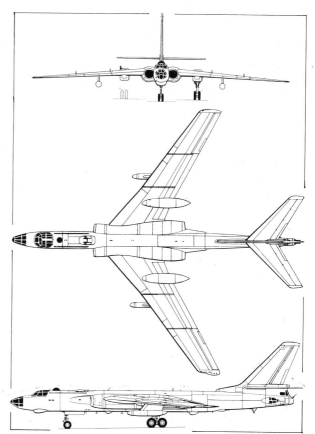

Tupolev Tu-16 'Badger-F'. *(Pilot Press)*

'Badger-J' ECM jamming version of the Tu-16. *(Swedish Air Force)*

FUSELAGE: Semi-monocoque structure of oval cross-section, made in five sections. The nose section houses the navigator's pressure cabin with double-glazed nose panels, the pilots' pressure cabin, the forward gunner's cabin, and radar equipment. The second and fourth sections house the aircraft's fuel tanks, with the weapon compartment between them; the tail section contains a pressure cabin for the radio operator and rear gunner.

TAIL UNIT: Cantilever structure, with 42° leading-edge sweepback on all surfaces. Trim tabs in rudder and each elevator.

LANDING GEAR: Retractable tricycle type. Twin-wheel nose units. Main four-wheel bogies retract into housings projecting beyond the wing trailing edge.

POWERPLANT: Early Tu-16s have two Mikulin AM-3 turbojet engines, each rated at 85.8 kN (19,285 lb st) at sea level. Later aircraft fitted with RD-3M (AM-3M) turbojets, each rated at 93.19 kN (20,950 lb st). Engines semi-recessed into side of fuselage. Divided air intake ducts: main duct passes through wing torque box between spars; secondary duct passes under wing to feed into primary airflow in front of engine. Jetpipes inclined outward 3° to shield fuselage from effects of exhaust gases. Fuel in wing and fuselage tanks, with total capacity of approx 45,450 litres (12,000 US gallons; 10,000 Imp gallons). Provision for underwing auxiliary fuel tanks and for flight refuelling. Tu-16 tankers trail hose from starboard wingtip; receiving equipment is in port wingtip extension.

ACCOMMODATION: Normal crew of six, with two pilots side-by-side on flight deck. Navigator, on seat with armoured sides and base, in glazed nose of all versions except 'Badger-C and D'. Manned tail position plus lateral observation blisters in rear fuselage under tailplane.

AVIONICS AND EQUIPMENT: Radio and radar aids probably include HF and VHF R/T equipment, as well as IFF and a radio compass and radio altimeter. Other equipment differs according to role.

ARMAMENT: Forward dorsal and rear ventral barbettes each containing two 23 mm NR-23 guns. Two similar guns in tail position controlled by an automatic gun ranging radar set. Seventh, fixed, gun on starboard side of nose of versions with nose glazing. Bomb load of up to 9,000 kg (19,800 lb) delivered from weapons bay 6.5 m (21 ft) long in standard bomber, under control of navigator. Naval versions can carry air-to-surface winged standoff missiles.

DIMENSIONS, EXTERNAL ('Badger-G'):
Wing span	32.93 m (108 ft 0½ in)
Length overall	36.25 m (118 ft 11¼ in)
Height overall	14.00 m (45 ft 11¼ in)
Wheel track	9.775 m (32 ft 0¾ in)

AREA:
Wings, gross	164.65 m² (1,772.3 sq ft)

WEIGHTS ('Badger-G'):
Weight empty, equipped	37,200 kg (82,000 lb)
Normal T-O weight	75,000 kg (165,350 lb)

PERFORMANCE ('Badger-G', at max T-O weight):
Max level speed at 6,000 m (19,700 ft)	
	535 knots (992 km/h; 616 mph)
Service ceiling	12,300 m (40,350 ft)
Range with 3,790 kg (8,360 lb) bomb load	
	3,200 nm (5,925 km; 3,680 miles)
Max unrefuelled combat radius	
	1,700 nm (3,150 km; 1,955 miles)

Tupolev Tu-22

NATO reporting name: Blinder

First shown publicly in the 1961 Aviation Day flypast over Moscow, the Tu-22 was the first operational Soviet supersonic bomber. Of the ten examples which took part in that display, only one carried visible weapons, in the form of an air-to-surface missile (NATO reporting name 'Kitchen'), some 11 m (36 ft) long, semi-submerged in the underside of its fuselage. This aircraft had also a wider nose radome.

A total of 22 Tu-22s took part in the 1967 display at Domodedovo. One was escorted by six MiG-21PFs, permitting a more accurate calculation of its overall dimensions than had previously been possible. Most carried 'Kitchen' missiles; all had a partially retractable nose refuelling probe and the wide radome seen on the single missile-armed aircraft in 1961.

About 250 Tu-22s were built, in four versions, as follows:

Blinder-A. Basic reconnaissance bomber, with fuselage weapons bay for free-fall nuclear and conventional bombs. 'Blinder-A' entered limited service, its range being inadequate for the originally intended strategic role.

Blinder-B. Generally similar to 'Blinder-A' but equipped to carry air-to-surface nuclear missile (NATO reporting name 'Kitchen') recessed in weapons bay. Larger radar and partially retractable flight refuelling probe on nose.

Blinder-C. Maritime reconnaissance version, with six camera windows in weapons bay doors. Flight refuelling probe like 'Blinder-B'. Modifications to nosecone, dielectric panels, etc, on some aircraft suggest possible electronic intelligence role or equipment for electronic countermeasures (ECM) duties. About 60 delivered, of which 35 remain in service, for operation primarily over sea approaches to the Soviet Union, from bases in the Southern Ukraine and Estonia.

Blinder-D. Training version. Cockpit for instructor in raised position aft of standard flight deck, with stepped-up canopy. In service in the Soviet Union and Libya.

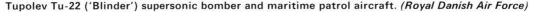

Tupolev Tu-22 ('Blinder') supersonic bomber and maritime patrol aircraft. *(Royal Danish Air Force)*

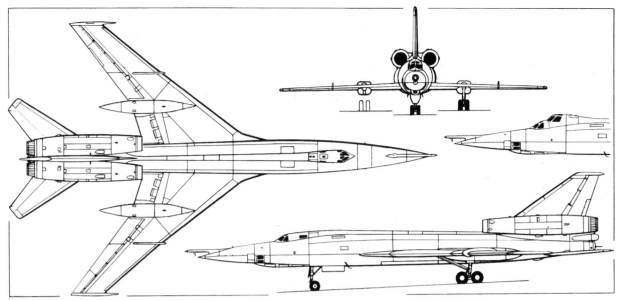

Tupolev Tu-22 'Blinder-A'. Scrap view: 'Blinder-D'. *(Pilot Press)*

About 135 'Blinder-As' and 'Blinder-Bs' remain operational with the Soviet air armies, plus 15 equipped for reconnaissance. The Soviet Naval Air Force has about 50, of which 20 are equipped for reconnaissance. The Libyan and Iraqi Air Forces each had seven or more Tu-22s, though the number of Iraqi aircraft may have altered as a result of the war with Iran. Also, a Libyan Tu-22 was destroyed over Chad in 1987.

The following details apply to 'Blinder-A and B' but are generally applicable to all versions except as noted under model descriptions:

TYPE: Twin-jet supersonic bomber and maritime patrol aircraft.

WINGS: Cantilever mid-wing monoplane. Constant slight anhedral from roots. Sweepback approx 45° on leading edge outboard of fence and 50° inboard of fence, increasing to acute sweep at roots. Conventional structure. Fully powered two-section ailerons, with tab in each inboard section. Flaps inboard and outboard of wheel pod on each wing trailing edge.

FUSELAGE: Semi-monocoque structure of circular section, with area rule 'waisting' at wing roots.

TAIL UNIT: Cantilever structure, with sweepback on all surfaces. Fully powered all-moving horizontal surfaces at bottom of fuselage. Aerodynamically balanced rudder, with inset tab.

LANDING GEAR: Retractable tricycle type. Wide-track four-wheel bogie main units retract rearward into pods built on to wing trailing edges. Main legs designed to swing rearward for additional cushioning during taxying and landing on rough runways. Twin-wheel nose unit. Small retractable skid to protect rear fuselage in tail-down landing or take-off. Twin brake-chutes standard.

POWERPLANT: Two Koliesov VD-7 turbojet engines, each rated at 137.5 kN (30,900 lb st) with afterburning, mounted in pods above rear fuselage, on each side of tail fin. Lip of each intake is in the form of a ring which can be translated forward by jacks for take-off. Air entering ram intake is then supplemented by air ingested through annular slot between ring and main body of pod. Jetpipes

have convergent-divergent nozzle inside outer fairing. Semi-retractable flight refuelling probe on nose of 'Blinder-B', with triangular guard underneath to prevent drogue damaging nosecone.

ACCOMMODATION: Crew of three in tandem. Row of windows in bottom of fuselage, aft of nose radome, at navigator/systems operator's station. Pilot has upward ejection seat; other crew members have downward ejection seats.

ARMAMENT AND OPERATIONAL EQUIPMENT: Weapons bay in centre-fuselage, with double-fold doors on 'Blinder-A'. Special doors with panels shaped to accommodate recessed 'Kitchen' missile on 'Blinder-B'. Single 23 mm NR-23 gun in radar directed tail turret, beneath 'Bee Hind' tail warning radar antenna. Radar in nose. Chaff/flare countermeasures dispensers and bombing assessment cameras carried in rear of wheel pods of some aircraft.

DIMENSIONS, EXTERNAL (estimated):	
Wing span	23.75 m (78 ft 0 in)
Length overall	40.53 m (132 ft 11½ in)
Height overall	10.67 m (35 ft 0 in)
WEIGHT (estimated):	
Max T-O weight	83,900 kg (185,000 lb)
PERFORMANCE (estimated):	
Max level speed at 12,200 m (40,000 ft)	
	Mach 1.4 (800 knots; 1,480 km/h; 920 mph)
Service ceiling	18,300 m (60,000 ft)
Max unrefuelled combat radius	
	1,565 nm (2,900 km; 1,800 miles)

Tupolev Tu-26 (Tu-22M)

NATO reporting name: Backfire

NATO first acknowledged the existence of a Soviet variable-geometry medium bomber in the autumn of 1969. Such an aircraft was not unexpected as the Tu-22 (NATO 'Blinder') replacement.

A prototype of the bomber was observed in July 1970, on the ground near the manufacturing plant at Kazan in Central

Missile-carrying 'Backfire-B' version of the Tupolev Tu-26, with wings spread and showing intake trunk stores racks. *(Swedish Air Force)*

Asia, and was confirmed subsequently as a twin-engined design by the Tupolev Bureau: At least two prototypes were built, and flight testing is believed to have started in 1971. Up to twelve pre-production models followed, for development testing, weapons trials and evaluation, by the beginning of 1973. Soviet delegates referred to the type as the **Tu-22M** during the SALT 2 treaty talks, but the current designation is believed to be **Tu-26**. The NATO reporting name allocated to the aircraft is 'Backfire'.

When drawing up the basic parameters for the bomber, the Tupolev Bureau is believed to have aimed at a maximum unrefuelled range of 4,775–5,200 nm (8,850–9,650 km; 5,500–6,000 miles) at high altitude. Unwillingness to depart from the Tupolev practice of retracting the main landing gear bogies into fairings on the wing trailing edges limited the variable geometry to the outer wings, as on the Sukhoi Su-17/20/22. There is reason to believe that the large size of these fairings, with the wheels stowed beneath the wing, caused excessive drag, so that 'Backfire's' range fell short of what had been planned. Redesign almost eliminated the fairings from later aircraft, after the main landing gear had been revised to retract inward into the fuselage.

By 1987, three versions of the Tu-26/Tu-22M had been identified by NATO reporting names:

Wedge-type air intakes and missile racks under the fixed wing panels identify 'Backfire-C'.

Backfire-A. Initial version, with large landing gear fairing pods on the wing trailing edges. Believed to have equipped only one squadron.

Backfire-B. Developed series production version, with increased wing span and landing gear fairing pods eliminated except for shallow underwing fairings, no longer protruding beyond the trailing edge. Inward retracting main landing gear units. During the abortive SALT 2 treaty negotiations, 'Backfire-Bs' were seen with the standard flight refuelling nose probe removed, although the housing remained. This was assumed to stress Soviet assertions that the aircraft are intended for peripheral/theatre operations rather than long-range strategic use, and were therefore exempt from the restrictions that would have been imposed on inter-continental bombers by the treaty. Initial armament was normally a single 'Kitchen' missile semi-recessed under fuselage. Current aircraft have a rack for a 'Kitchen' under each fixed wing centre-section panel, although fuselage mount is retained. External stores racks seen frequently under fuselage. Twin guns in tail mounting, initially beneath ogival radome, later with drum-shape radome of larger diameter.

Backfire-C. This advanced production version has wedge-type engine air intakes, like those of the MiG-25. By 1987, it was operational in large numbers, in both long-range bomber and maritime roles. Upturned nosecone with small pod at tip. No visible flight refuelling probe. Single twin-barrel gun in tail mounting, beneath large drum-shape radome.

'Backfire-B and C' are capable of performing nuclear strike, conventional attack, anti-ship and reconnaissance missions. Low-level penetration features make them more survivable than previous Soviet bombers, and they have adequate range to be employed against the contiguous United States on high-altitude subsonic missions, although such a flight profile would make them far more vulnerable. Their low-altitude supersonic-dash capability makes them formidable weapons with which to support military operations in Europe and Asia. A retractable flight refuelling nose probe on 'Backfire-B' makes possible extended-range missions.

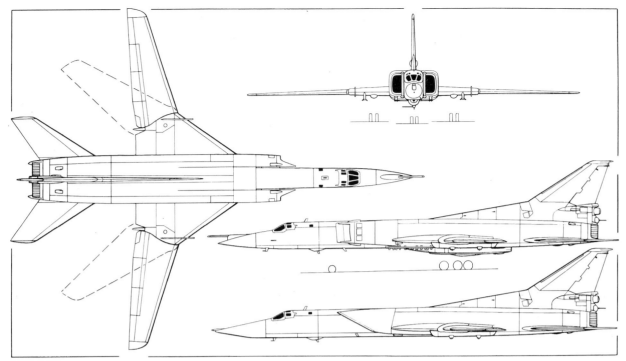

Tupolev Tu-26 'Backfire-B'. Lower side view: 'Backfire-C'. *(Pilot Press)*

About 320 'Backfire-Bs and Cs' are in service. Two-thirds of them oppose NATO in Europe and over the Atlantic, with the others in the far east of the Soviet Union. The latter are observed frequently over the Sea of Japan, and 30 of them are reportedly drawn from the 140 'Backfire-Bs and Cs' deployed in a maritime role by Soviet Naval Aviation. The FY 1979 Annual Report of the US Department of Defense stated: 'There is increasing evidence that the Soviet bomber and cruise missile force may be overtaking their submarine force as a threat to our fleet and to our forces necessary for the resupply of Europe. They can concentrate aircraft, co-ordinate attacks with air, surface, or submarine launched missiles, and use new technology to find our fleet units, jam our defences and screen their approach'.

It is expected that the 'Backfire' strategic/maritime force will be maintained eventually at a total of at least 400 aircraft. Production appears to be limited to the average rate of 30 aircraft a year which was specified by the unratified SALT 2 agreement. 'Backfires' have been used for development launches of new-generation Soviet cruise missiles, but are not expected to become designated AS-15 carriers.

The following details refer specifically to 'Backfire-B'.

TYPE: Twin-engined medium bomber and maritime reconnaissance/attack aircraft.

WINGS: Cantilever low mid-wing monoplane, made up of a large span fixed centre-section and two variable geometry outer panels. No anhedral or dihedral, but wing section is so thin that considerable flexing of the outer panels takes place in flight. Leading-edge fence towards tip of centre-section on each side. Each outer wing panel is believed to be fitted with a full span leading-edge slat, aileron, and slotted trailing-edge flaps aft of spoilers/lift dumpers. Wing sweep is believed to be variable from fully spread (20°) to fully swept (65°), rather than limited to one

intermediate position as on the MiG-23.

FUSELAGE: Forward of wings, fuselage is basically circular with large ogival dielectric nosecone. Centre fuselage is faired into rectangular section air intake trunks, each fitted with a large splitter plate and assumed to embody complex variable geometry ramps. There is no evidence to suggest external area-rule 'waisting' of these trunks.

TAIL UNIT: Cantilever structure, with sweepback on all surfaces. All-moving horizontal surfaces; conventional inset rudder.

LANDING GEAR: Retractable tricycle type. Each main unit carries a multi-wheel bogie.

POWERPLANT: Two unidentified turbofan engines with afterburners, mounted side-by-side in the rear fuselage. Reported to be uprated versions of the Kuznetsov NK-144 engines (each 196.1 kN; 44,090 lb st) that were developed for Tupolev's Tu-144 supersonic transport. Fuel tankage is believed to include integral tanks in the entire fixed portion of the wings and much of the centre-fuselage above the weapon bay. Removable flight refuelling nose probe; after one observed refuelling, a 'Backfire' prototype remained airborne for a further 10 h.

ACCOMMODATION: Pilot and co-pilot side-by-side on flight deck. Two crew members further aft, as indicated by position of windows between flight deck and air intakes.

AVIONICS AND EQUIPMENT: Large bombing and navigation radar (NATO 'Down Beat') inside dielectric nosecone. Radar (NATO 'Bee Hind') for tail turret, above guns. Fairing with flat glazed front panel under front fuselage is believed to be for a video camera to provide visual assistance for weapon aiming.

ARMAMENT: Primary armament of two 'Kitchen' air-to-surface missiles, carried under the fixed centre-section panel of each wing, or a single 'Kitchen' semi-recessed in the underside of the centre fuselage. Multiple racks for 12

500 kg bombs sometimes fitted under fuselage. Alternative weapon loads include up to 12,000 kg (26,450 lb) of conventional bombs. US reports have suggested that the Soviet Union is developing decoy missiles to assist penetration of advanced defence systems, in addition to very advanced ECM and ECCM. Twin 23 mm guns in radar directed tail mounting.

DIMENSIONS, EXTERNAL (estimated):
Wing span: fully spread	34.30 m (112 ft 6½ in)
fully swept	23.40 m (76 ft 9¼ in)
Length overall	39.60 m (129 ft 11 in)
Height overall	10.80 m (35 ft 5¼ in)

WEIGHTS:
Normal weapon load	12,000 kg (26,450 lb)
Max T-O weight	130,000 kg (286,600 lb)

PERFORMANCE (estimated):
Max level speed at high altitude	Mach 2.0
Max level speed at low altitude	Mach 0.9
Max unrefuelled combat radius	
	2,160 nm (4,000 km; 2,485 miles)

Tupolev Tu-28P ('Fiddler-B') with 'Ash' infra-red missiles on inboard underwing pylons and 'Ash' radar-homing missiles on outboard pylons.

Tupolev Tu-28P/Tu-128

NATO reporting name: Fiddler

Largest purpose-designed interceptor yet put into squadron service, this supersonic twin-jet aircraft was seen for the first time at Tushino in July 1961, with a large delta wing air-to-air missile (NATO 'Ash') mounted under each wing. It is thought to have the service designation Tu-28P (US Department of Defense has used Tu-128); its NATO reporting name is 'Fiddler'.

The Tu-28P has a large ogival nose radome and carries a crew of two in tandem. The shoulder intakes for its two afterburning turbojet engines have half-cone shock-bodies, and the jetpipes are side-by-side in the bulged tail. Each

engine is estimated to have a max rating of about 120.1 kN (27,000 lb st).

The sharply swept wings are mid-set, with slight anhedral, and have considerably increased chord on the inboard panels, which have both increased sweep and a straight trailing edge. The wide-track main landing gear units, comprising four-wheel bogies, retract into large fairings built on to the wing trailing edges.

The tail unit is also sharply swept, and the original two aircraft seen in 1961 ('**Fiddler-A**') were each fitted with two ventral fins. These were missing on the three Tu-28Ps ('**Fiddler-B**') which flew past at Domodedovo in July 1967, as was the large bulged fairing fitted under the fuselage in 1961.

'Fiddler-B' proved to be the production configured version, with an armament double that seen in 1961, each

Tupolev Tu-28P/Tu-128 'Fiddler-B'. *(Pilot Press)*

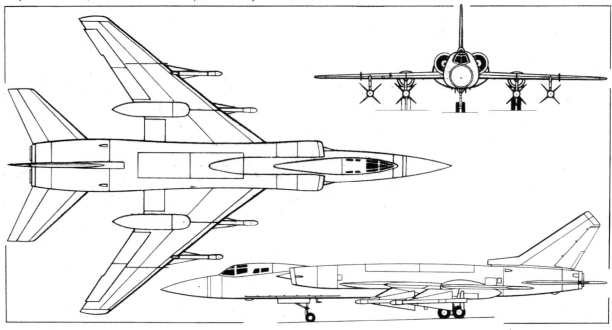

aircraft being equipped to carry two 'Ash' missiles under each wing, one usually of the radar homing type and the other of the infra-red homing type. This was confirmed as the standard armament of first-line service aircraft in a film released in 1969, showing units of the Soviet armed forces taking part in defence exercises.

About 80 'Fiddler-Bs' are thought to remain in service with the Soviet Union's Voyska PVO home defence fighter force, plus 20 with tactical air forces.

DIMENSIONS, EXTERNAL (estimated):
Wing span	18.10 m (59 ft 4½ in)
Length overall	27.20 m (89 ft 3 in)

WEIGHT (estimated):
Max T-O weight	45,000 kg (100,000 lb)

PERFORMANCE (estimated):
Max level speed at 11,000 m (36,000 ft)	Mach 1.65
	(950 knots; 1,760 km/h; 1,090 mph)
Service ceiling	20,000 m (65,620 ft)
Combat radius with max internal fuel	
	810 nm (1,500 km; 930 miles)

Tupolev Tu-95 and Tu-142

NATO reporting name: Bear

Documents issued in Washington concerning the SALT 2 negotiations, in 1979, revealed that the Soviet authorities use the designation **Tu-95** for the force of strategic attack 'Bears' that forms the major part of the long-range bombing force of the five Soviet strategic air armies, and for maritime reconnaissance 'Bear-Ds', but that the much changed 'Bear-Fs' used by the Soviet Naval Air Force are known as **Tu-142s**. The Naval aircraft, being employed only for reconnaissance and anti-submarine warfare, and being observably different from the bombers, have never been subject to SALT restrictions. Those air force and naval versions deployed to bases made available in Cuba and Angola are capable of covering the North and South Atlantic from the Mediterranean approaches westward to the US east coast, and southward to the Cape of Good Hope. Others operate regularly from Cam Ranh in Viet-Nam.

'Bear-G' has two large pylons under the wing roots on which to carry 'Kitchen' missiles. *(UK Ministry of Defence)*

Long range and endurance are only two of the attributes that have kept these huge four-turboprop aircraft in production for 33 years, an unprecedented length of time for a combat aircraft. Their high speed, exceeding that once considered possible for propeller driven aircraft, eclipsed the contemporary four-jet Myasishchev M-4. Their size and payload potential enabled them to accommodate the largest air-to-surface missiles and radars yet carried by operational aircraft. Thus, production to offset attrition continued into the 1980s, and in 1984 was increased to equip operational units with the new 'Bear-H' version, built at Kuybyshev.

Details of the nine versions identified by NATO reporting names, all of which remain in service, with constantly updated equipment, are as follows:

Bear-A. Basic Tu-95 strategic bomber, first flown in late summer of 1954 and shown in Aviation Day display at Tushino in July 1955. Internal stowage for two nuclear or a variety of conventional free-fall weapons. Fitted with chin radar, and defensive armament comprising three pairs of 23 mm cannon in remotely controlled rear dorsal and ventral barbettes and manned tail turret. Two glazed blisters on rear fuselage, under tailplane, are used for sighting by the gunner controlling all these weapons. The dorsal and ventral barbettes can also be controlled from a station aft of the flight deck. Max range with 11,340 kg (25,000 lb) bomb load is 8,000 nm (14,800 km; 9,200 miles). A small number remain in service.

Bear-B. First seen in 1961 Aviation Day flypast. Tu-95 version, as 'Bear-A' but able to carry a large air-to-surface aeroplane-type missile (NATO reporting name 'Kangaroo') under fuselage, with associated radar (NATO 'Crown Drum') in wide undernose radome, replacing the original glazing. Defensive armament retained. A few 'Bear-Bs' operate in maritime reconnaissance role, with flight refuelling nose-probe and, sometimes, an elint blister fairing on the starboard side of the rear fuselage. Some carry a pointed canister under each wing, for air sampling.

Bear-C. Another Tu-95 strike version, able to carry 'Kangaroo'; first observed near NATO naval forces during Exercise Teamwork in September 1964. Generally similar to 'Bear-B' but with an elint blister fairing on *both* sides of rear fuselage. Refuelling probe standard. Has been observed with a faired tail housing special equipment, like that illustrated on a 'Bear-D'.

Bear-D. Identified in August 1967, this maritime reconnaissance version of the Tu-95 has a glazed nose, an undernose radar (NATO 'Short Horn'), a large underbelly radome for I band surface search radar (NATO 'Big Bulge'), an elint fairing on each side of the rear fuselage like 'Bear-C', a nose refuelling probe, and a variety of other blisters and antennae, including a steamlined fairing on each tailplane tip. The housing for I band tail warning radar above the tail turret is much larger than on previous versions. Tasks include pinpointing of maritime targets for missile launch crews on board ships and for aircraft which are themselves too distant to ensure precise missile aiming and guidance. 'Bear-D' carries no offensive weapons.

A 'Bear-D' photographed in the second half of 1978, after interception by US Navy F-4s, had in place of the normal tail turret and associated radome a faired tail housing special equipment. A similar tail is now fitted to 'Bear-G'.

Bear-E. Reconnaissance version of Tu-95, basically similar in configuration to 'Bear-A' but with refuelling probe and rear-fuselage elint fairings as on 'Bear-C'. Six camera

Tu-95 ('Bear-D') maritime reconnaissance aircraft. *(US Air Force)*

windows in bomb bay, in pairs in line with the wing flaps, with a seventh window to the rear on the starboard side.

Bear-F. Anti-submarine aircraft. First of the Tu-142 series of extensively redesigned 'Bears', with more highly cambered wings and longer fuselage forward of the wings. Deployed initially by the Soviet Naval air force in 1970, since when several variants have been seen. Re-entered production in the mid-1980s. Originally had enlarged and lengthened fairings aft of its inboard engine nacelles, but later aircraft reverted to standard-size fairings. Some have no undernose radar; others have a radome in this position, but of considerably modified form compared with that of the maritime 'Bear-D'. On both models the main underfuselage J band radar housing is considerably farther forward than on 'Bear-D' and smaller in size; the flight deck windscreens are deeper, giving increased headroom; there are no large blister fairings under and on the sides of the rear fuselage; and the nosewheel doors are bulged prominently, suggesting the use of larger or low-pressure tyres. 'Bear-F' has two stores bays for sonobuoys, torpedoes and nuclear depth charges in its rear fuselage, one of them replacing the usual rear ventral gun turret and leaving the tail turret as the sole defensive gun position. Some examples have a MAD 'sting' projecting

from the rear of the fin tip and no tailplane tip fairings. The four 'Bear-F' models are:

1: As original 'Bear-F' but reverted to standard-size nacelles. Chin mounted J band radar deleted. Fewer protrusions.

2 (Tu-142M): Fuselage nose lengthened by 23 cm (9 in) and roof of flight deck raised. Angle of refuelling probe lowered by 4°.

3: MAD boom added to fin tip. Fairings at tips of tailplane deleted. Rear stores bay lengthened and made narrower.

4: Chin radar reinstated. ECM thimble radome on nose, plus other fairings.

Bear-G. Tu-95, generally similar to 'Bear-B/C' but reconfigured to carry two AS-4 ('Kitchen') air-to-surface missiles instead of one AS-3 ('Kangaroo'), on a large pylon under each wingroot. Other features include an ECM thimble under the inflight refuelling probe, a streamlined ECM pod on each side at the bottom of both the centre and rear fuselage, and a solid tailcone, containing special equipment, similar in shape to that on some 'Bear-Ds'. Operational.

Bear-H. New production version, based on the Tu-142 type airframe of 'Bear-F' but with a shorter fuselage of the same length as 'Bear-B' and 'C'. Equipped to carry long-range cruise missiles, including AS-15 (NATO 'Kent').

Tupolev Tu-142 'Bear-F Model 3' of the Soviet Naval Air Force with MAD 'sting' at the tip of its tail fin. *(UK Ministry of Defence)*

Deep flight-deck glazing and new undernose antennae are features of the 'Bear-H' cruise missile carrier. *(UK Ministry of Defence)*

Aircraft observed up to mid-1987 had only an internal (rotary?) launcher for these ALCMs, but additional pylon mountings can probably be attached under each wingroot. 'Bear-H' achieved initial operational capability in 1984, and at least 50 were deployed by spring 1987. Features include a larger and deeper radome built into the nose and a small fin-tip fairing. There are no elint blister fairings on the sides of the rear fuselage and the ventral gun turret is deleted. Some aircraft have only a single twin-barrel gun, instead of the usual pair, in the tail turret.

Bear-J. Identified in 1986, this is the Soviet equivalent of the US Navy's E-6A and EC-130Q Tacamo aircraft, equipped with VLF communications avionics to maintain an on-station/all-ocean link between national command authorities and nuclear missile-armed submarines under most operating conditions. Operational in comparatively small numbers, it appears to use a modified Tu-142 'Bear-F' airframe.

Most of the 150 'Bears' now serving with the air armies are of the 'G' and 'H' models; Soviet Naval Aviation units have about 15 'Bear-Ds', 60 'Bear-Fs' and a few 'Bear-Js'. Their duties include regular deployments to staging bases in Cuba and Angola, and eight are based permanently at Cam Ranh in Viet-Nam. 'Bears' are encountered frequently off the US east coast during transits between Murmansk and Cuba, and during elint missions from Cuba. 'Bear-Hs' also carry out simulated attack and training missions against the USA.

The Indian Navy reportedly ordered two ex-Soviet Navy

'Bear-Fs' for maritime reconnaissance, with delivery expected in 1988.

TYPE: Four-turboprop long-range bomber and maritime reconnaissance aircraft.

WINGS: Cantilever mid-wing monoplane. Slight anhedral. Sweepback 37° at quarter-chord on inner panels, 35° at quarter-chord on outer panels. Three-segment ailerons and two-segment Fowler flaps on each wing. Trim tab in each inboard aileron segment. Spoilers in top surface of wing forward of inboard end of ailerons. Three boundary layer fences on top surface of each wing.

FUSELAGE: Semi-monocoque structure of circular section, containing three pressurised compartments. Those forward and aft of the weapons bay are linked by a crawlway tunnel. The tail gunner's compartment is not accessible from the other compartments.

TAIL UNIT: Cantilever structure, with sweepback on all surfaces. Adjustable tailplane incidence. Hydraulically powered rudder and elevators. Trim tabs in rudder and each elevator.

LANDING GEAR: Tricycle type. Main units consist of four-wheel bogies, with tyres of approx 1.50 m (5 ft) diameter and hydraulic internal expanding brakes. Twin wheels on nose unit. Retractable tail bumper consisting of two small wheels. Braking parachute may be used to reduce landing run.

POWERPLANT: Four Kuznetsov NK-12MV turboprop engines, each with max rating of 11,033 kW (14,795 ehp) and driving eight-blade contra-rotating reversible-pitch Type AV-60N propellers. Fuel in wing tanks, with normal capacity of 95,000 litres (25,100 US gallons; 20,900 Imp gallons).

ACCOMMODATION AND ARMAMENT: See notes applicable to individual versions and under 'Fuselage'.

OPERATIONAL EQUIPMENT ('Bear-D'): Large I band radar (NATO 'Big Bulge') in blister fairing under centre fuselage, for reconnaissance and to provide data on potential targets for anti-shipping aircraft or surface vessels. In latter mode, PPI presentation is data linked to missile launch station. Four-PRF range J band circular and sector scan navigation radar (NATO 'Short Horn'). I band tail warning radar (originally NATO 'Bee Hind'; later 'Box Tail') in housing at base of rudder.

Tupolev Tu-142 'Bear-F Model 3'. *(Pilot Press)*

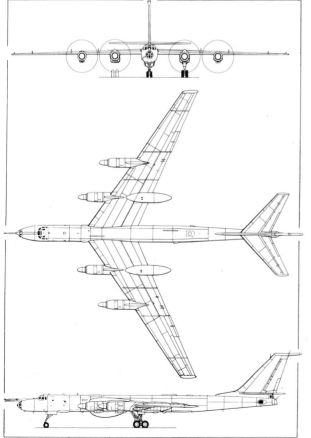

DIMENSIONS, EXTERNAL ('Bear-F', approx):	
Wing span	51.10 m (167 ft 8 in)
Length overall	49.50 m (162 ft 5 in)
Height overall	12.12 m (39 ft 9 in)
WEIGHT ('Bear-F', estimated):	
Max T-O weight	188,000 kg (414,470 lb)

PERFORMANCE:
  Max level speed at 7,620 m (25,000 ft)
    500 knots (925 km/h; 575 mph)
  Over-target speed at 12,500 m (41,000 ft)
    450 knots (833 km/h; 518 mph)
  Max unrefuelled combat radius
    4,475 nm (8,285 km; 5,150 miles)

Tupolev Tu-126

NATO reporting name: Moss

An officially released Soviet documentary film, shown in the West in 1968, included sequences depicting a military version

Tu-126 airborne early-warning and control system aircraft, known to NATO as 'Moss'. *(UK Ministry of Defence)*

of the Tu-114 four-turboprop transport carrying above its fuselage a rotating 'saucer'-type early warning radar with a diameter of about 11 m (36 ft). This was a logical development, as the Tu-114 had a fuselage of larger diameter than the military Tu-95, and could accommodate more easily the extensive avionic equipment and crew of 12 required by what was soon confirmed as the Soviet air forces' first-generation airborne early warning and control system aircraft, with the designation Tu-126. It proved also to have wings similar to those of the Tu-114, with extended-chord trailing-edge flaps, rather than the 'straight' trailing edge of

Tupolev Tu-126 'Moss'. *(Pilot Press)*

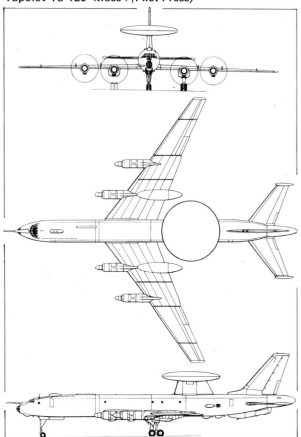

the Tu-95. The interior of the fuselage is fully air-conditioned. Few cabin windows are installed.

'Moss' (NATO name) has a flight refuelling nose-probe, ventral tail fin and numerous additional antennae and blisters for electronic equipment, including streamlined fairings and associated dielectric panels on the sides of the rear fuselage as on the Tu-95 'Bear-C/D'. The powerplant comprises four 11,033 kW (14,795 ehp) Kuznetsov NK-12MV turboprop engines. Wing fuel tanks have a capacity of 60,800 kg (134,040 lb).

The Tu-126 is intended to work in conjunction with advanced interceptors. After locating incoming low-level-strike aircraft, it would ideally direct towards them fighters armed with 'snapdown' air-to-air missiles able to be fired from a cruising height of 6,100 m (20,000 ft) or higher. It has a further, obvious application in assisting strike aircraft to elude enemy interceptors picked up by its radar.

About seven Tu-126s are operational with the Soviet air defence forces. They are said, by US defence experts, to have demonstrated some effectiveness in overwater exercises but to be ineffective over land.

DIMENSIONS, EXTERNAL:
Wing span	51.20 m (168 ft 0 in)
Length overall	55.20 m (181 ft 1 in)
Height overall	16.05 m (52 ft 8 in)
Wheel track	13.70 m (44 ft 11½ in)
Propeller diameter	5.60 m (18 ft 4½ in)

AREA:
Wings, gross	311.1 m² (3,349 sq ft)

WEIGHT (estimated):
Max T-O weight	170,000 kg (374,785 lb)

PERFORMANCE:
Max level speed	459 knots (850 km/h; 528 mph)
Normal operating speed	351 knots (650 km/h; 404 mph)
Max range without flight refuelling	
	6,775 nm (12,550 km; 7,800 miles)

New Tupolev Bomber

NATO reporting name: Blackjack

Tupolev's variable-geometry strategic bomber, known to NATO as 'Blackjack', is the long expected supersonic successor to the M-4 'Bison' and Tu-95 'Bear-A'. Apart from

Artist's impression of the new Tupolev strategic bomber known to NATO as 'Blackjack'. *(US Department of Defense)*

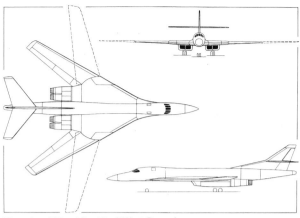

Tupolev 'Blackjack'. *(Pilot Press)*

artists' impressions prepared by the US Department of Defense, the only perspective picture of 'Blackjack' released is a poor-quality reconnaissance photograph taken over Ramenskoye flight test centre on 25 November 1981. Showing the aircraft parked alongside two Tu-144 supersonic airliners, this enabled its length, including nose probe, to be calculated as around 54.0 m (177 ft). What this implies in terms of weapon load and fuel tankage is easy to estimate. 'Blackjack' is about 25 per cent longer than Tupolev's last operational bomber, the supersonic 'Backfire', 20 per cent larger than USAF's B-1B, and 10 per cent longer than even the Boeing B-52. It is in no way a simple scale-up of 'Backfire'. Common features include low mounted variable-geometry wings, and large vertical tail surfaces with a massive dorsal fin; but 'Blackjack's' horizontal tail surfaces are mounted higher, at the intersection of the dorsal fin and main fin. The fixed root panel of each wing seems to be long and very sharply swept, like the inboard section of the Tu-144's delta wing. Sweepback is about 20° fully spread and 64° fully swept. The engine installation also seems to resemble that of the now-retired airliner rather than 'Backfire'; perhaps with four Koliesov Tu-144D-type engines. However, it must be borne in mind that the two bombers are designed for a similar subsonic cruise/supersonic-dash flight profile. As 'Blackjack's' max T-O weight is twice that of 'Backfire', it might have been logical to use four of the latter's turbofans. If the engines are mounted in pairs, inside two divided underwing ducts, as on the Tu-144, the gap between the ducts will determine the type and size of weapons that 'Blackjack' can carry.

About eight 'Blackjacks', including prototypes, were undergoing advanced flight testing in 1986, and the US Department of Defense expects the Soviet Union to build a production series of at least 100 in a new complex added to the huge Kazan airframe plant, with an initial operational capability in 1988. 'Blackjack's' primary weapons will be the AS-15 'Kent' air-launched cruise missile and supersonic BL-10 missile, each with a range of 1,620 nm (3,000 km; 1,850 miles); but it will have provision for carrying bombs or a mix of missiles and bombs.

DIMENSIONS, EXTERNAL (estimated):

Wing span: fully spread	55.70 m (182 ft 9 in)
fully swept	33.75 m (110 ft)
Length overall	54.00 m (177 ft)
Height overall	12.80 m (42 ft)
WEIGHTS (initial estimates):	
Max weapon load	16,330 kg (36,000 lb)
Max T-O weight	250,000 kg (551,150 lb)
PERFORMANCE (estimated):	
Max level speed at high altitude	Mach 2.0
Max unrefuelled combat radius	
	3,940 nm (7,300 km; 4,535 miles)

Yakovlev

Alexander Yakovlev is one of the most versatile Soviet designers, and products of his design bureau have ranged from transonic long-range fighters to the Yak-24 tandem-rotor helicopter, an operational VTOL carrier based fighter, and a variety of training and transport aircraft.

Yakovlev Yak-28

NATO reporting names: Brewer, Firebar and Maestro

First seen in considerable numbers in the 1961 Soviet Aviation Day flypast were three successors to the Yak-25/27 series, described by the commentator as supersonic multi-purpose aircraft and identified subsequently by the designation Yak-28. The two-seat tactical attack versions known to NATO as 'Brewer-A, B and C' were superseded by vastly superior Sukhoi Su-24s. Currently operated versions of the Yak-28 are:

Brewer-D. Reconnaissance version, with cameras or other sensors, including side looking airborne radar, in bomb bay. Two-seater, with pilot under blister canopy and navigator in glazed nose. Blister radome under fuselage forward of wings.

Brewer-E. First Soviet operational ECM escort aircraft, deployed in 1970. Active ECM pack built into bomb bay,

Examples of the Yakovlev Yak-28, known to NATO as 'Brewer-D'. *(Novosti/Camera Press)*

from which it projects in cylindrical form. No radome under front fuselage, but many additional antennae and fairings. Attachment under each outer wing, outboard of external fuel tank, for a rocket pod, chaff dispenser or anti-radiation missile.

US official sources estimated that about 195 Brewer-Ds and Es remained in service for tactical reconnaissance and ECM, and 102 for strategic reconnaissance and ECM, in October 1986.

Firebar. Tandem two-seat all-weather fighter. No internal weapons bay. Armament comprises one 'Anab' air-to-air missile under each wing. Identified as **Yak-28P** (*Perekhvatchik*; interceptor), the suffix 'P' indicating that the design had been *adapted* for the fighter role. Longer dielectric nosecone fitted retrospectively on many Yak-28Ps in squadron service does not indicate any increase in radar capability or aircraft performance. About 65 Yak-28P 'Firebars' continue to operate with the Soviet Voyska PVO

home defence interceptor force and 20 with the tactical forces.

Maestro (Yak-28U). Trainer version of 'Firebar'. Normal cockpit layout replaced by two individual single-seat cockpits in tandem, each with its own canopy.

The following details refer specifically to the Yak-28P, but are generally applicable to the other versions of the Yak-28:

TYPE: Two-seat all-weather interceptor.

WINGS: Cantilever shoulder-wing monoplane of basically constant chord. Extended leading edge on outer wings and also between fuselage and each engine nacelle. Outer extensions are drooped. Slotted flap, with unswept trailing edge, between fuselage and each engine nacelle. Basic wing sweepback 45°. Anhedral from root. Single fence on upper surface of each wing, between fuselage and engine nacelle. Large trailing-edge flap and short aileron, with tab, outboard of nacelle on each wing. Balancer-wheel fairings, inset from wingtips, are extended forward as lead filled

Yakovlev Yak-28P ('Firebar') all-weather fighter. *(Tass)*

230

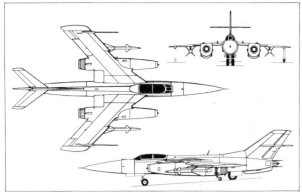

Yakovlev Yak-28P 'Firebar'. *(Pilot Press)*

DIMENSIONS, EXTERNAL (estimated):
Wing span   12.95 m (42 ft 6 in)
Length overall: Yak-28P (long nose)   23.00 m (75 ft 5½ in)
Height overall   3.95 m (12 ft 11½ in)
WEIGHTS (estimated):
Max T-O weight: Yak-28P   20,000 kg (44,000 lb)
PERFORMANCE (Yak-28P, estimated):
Max level speed at 10,670 m (35,000 ft)
    Mach 1.88 (1,080 knots; 2,000 km/h; 1,240 mph)
Cruising speed   496 knots (920 km/h; 571 mph)
Service ceiling   16,750 m (55,000 ft)
Max combat radius   500 nm (925 km; 575 miles)

wing balance weights.

FUSELAGE: Semi-monocoque structure of basically circular section. Finely tapered dielectric nosecone over radar scanner.

TAIL UNIT: Cantilever structure. Variable-incidence tailplane mounted midway up fin. All surfaces sweptback. Trim tab in rudder. Dorsal fin fairs into spine along top of fuselage. Shallow ventral stabilising fin.

LANDING GEAR: Two twin-wheel main units in tandem. Small balancer wheel near each wingtip.

POWERPLANT: Two afterburning turbojet engines, related to Tumansky R-11 fitted to some versions of MiG-21, with rating of 58.35 kN (13,120 lb st). Each fitted with centrebody shock cone. A pointed external fuel tank can be carried under the leading edge of each wing, outboard of the engine nacelle.

ACCOMMODATION: Crew of two in tandem on ejection seats in pressurised cabin under long rearward-sliding canopy.

AVIONICS: Reported to include tail warning radar.

ARMAMENT: Two pylons under each outer wing. Normal armament comprises two air-to-air missiles (NATO 'Anab'), with alternative infra-red or semi-active radar homing heads.

Yakovlev Yak-36MP/Yak-38

NATO reporting name: Forger

Known originally as the **Yak-36MP** (*Morskoy Palubnyi*: maritime carrier-borne), the **Yak-38** is the V/STOL combat aircraft deployed by a Soviet Navy development squadron on the *Kiev*, the first of its class of four 40,000-ton carrier/cruisers to put to sea in 1976, and subsequently on its sister ships, the *Minsk*, *Novorossiysk* and *Baku*. Two versions have been observed, as follows:

Forger-A. Basic single-seat combat aircraft, utilising a mixture of vectored thrust and direct jet lift. Prototype was completed in 1971 and production began in 1975. Twelve appear to be operational on each ship, in addition to 'Forger-Bs' and about 19 Kamov anti-submarine and missile targeting helicopters. Primary operational roles assumed to be reconnaissance, strikes against small ships, and fleet defence against shadowing maritime reconnaissance aircraft.

Forger-B. Two-seat trainer, of which two are deployed on each carrier/cruiser. Second cockpit forward of normal cockpit, with ejection seat at a lower level, under a continuous transparent canopy. To compensate for the longer nose, a 'plug' is inserted in the fuselage aft of the wing, lengthening the constant-section portion without requiring modification of the tapering rear fuselage assembly. In other

Yakovlev Yak-38 (NATO 'Forger-A') V/STOL combat aircraft on the carrier/cruiser *Novorossiysk*. Note the underwing gun and rocket pods. *(Royal Navy)*

Two-seat training version of the Yak-38 ('Forger-B').

respects this version appears to be identical to 'Forger-A', but has no ranging radar or weapon pylons.

Observers of deck flying by 'Forger-As' report that the aircraft appear to be extremely stable during take-off and landing. Initially, take-off was always made vertically, with the vectored-thrust nozzles up to 10° forward of vertical. This was followed by a smooth conversion about 5 to 6 m (15–20 ft) above the deck, achieved by lowering the aircraft's nose about 5° below the horizon and maintaining this attitude until the aircraft had accelerated to 30–40 knots (55–75 km/h; 35–46 mph). At this speed, a 5° nose-up attitude was assumed, and the accelerating transition was continued by vectoring aft the nozzles of the propulsion engine.

This VTO technique has been superseded by a STOL-type of take-off, with a short forward run, made possible by an automatic control system which ensures 'that the lift engines are brought into use, and the thrust vectoring rear nozzles rotated, at the optimum point in the take-off run'. As in the case of the British Harrier, STOL take-off can be assumed to offer improved payload/range capability.

Landing procedure begins with a gradual descent from far astern, with the last 400 m (1,300 ft) flown essentially level, about 30 m (100 ft) above the water. The aircraft crosses the ship's stern with about a 5 knot (10 km/h; 6 mph) closure rate, 10–14 m (35–45 ft) above the flight deck, then flares gently to a hover and descends vertically. Precise landings are

ensured by the automatic control system, perhaps in association with laser devices lining each side of the rear deck.

Development has been continuous throughout the period since the Yak-38 was first seen on the *Kiev*. Some early 'Forger-As' lacked the now-standard auxiliary intake doors aft of each engine air intake. A fence has been added on each side of the hinged door above the liftjets, extending back to a station in line with the wingroot leading edge, presumably to prevent ingestion of reflected exhaust efflux. Production is thought to have totalled some 75 aircraft by October 1986.

The following description applies to the single-seat 'Forger-A':

TYPE: Ship based V/STOL combat aircraft.

WINGS: Cantilever mid-wing monoplane, of very small area. Thickness/chord ratio estimated at 6% or less. Constant anhedral from roots. Sweepback on leading edge approx 45°. Conventional structure. Each wing comprises two panels of approx equal span, of which the outer panel folds vertically upward for stowage on board ship. Inboard panel has unswept trailing edge, occupied by a large single-slotted Fowler flap. Outer panel has a slightly sweptback trailing edge, occupied almost entirely by an aileron with setback hinges and inset trim tab. No leading-edge flaps or slats. Jet reaction control valve with upper and lower slots in each wingtip.

'Forger-A' combat aircraft, with hinged door over liftjets raised.

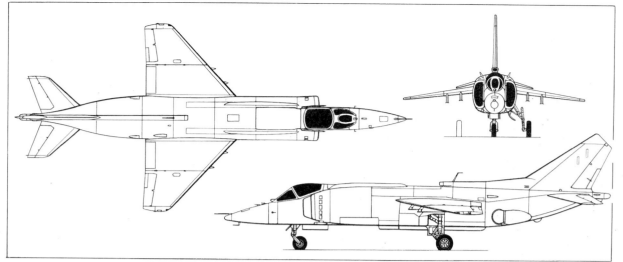

Yakovlev Yak-38 'Forger-A'. *(Pilot Press)*

FUSELAGE: Conventional semi-monocoque structure of oval cross-section. Integral engine air-intake ducts, with boundary-layer splitter plates and downward inclined lips forward of rear edge of transparent cockpit canopy. Row of small blow-in auxiliary intake doors a short distance aft of each intake. Rearward hinged door over liftjets, immediately aft of canopy, with 16 spring loaded louvres. Location of corresponding side-hinged underfuselage doors conforms with forward tilt of lift engines. Positions of these doors are controlled automatically during take-off and landing as part of control system. Fence on each side of door above liftjets. Small fence aft of each door beneath liftjets. Yaw reaction control nozzle to each side of small tailcone. No reaction control system in nose.

TAIL UNIT: Conventional structure, with sweepback on all surfaces and considerable tailplane anhedral. Rudder and each elevator have setback hinges and trim tab. Air intake at front of long duct extending forward from base of fin, to cool avionics bay in rear fuselage.

LANDING GEAR: Retractable tricycle type. Single wheel on each unit. Small bumper under upward curving rear fuselage.

POWERPLANT: Primary powerplant is a Lyulka AL-21 turbojet engine (approx 80 kN; 17,985 lb st), mounted in the centre fuselage and exhausting through a single pair of vectoring side nozzles aft of the wings. No afterburner is fitted. Two Koliesov liftjet engines (each 35 kN; 7,875 lb st) in tandem, immediately aft of cockpit, exhausting downward, and used also to adjust pitch and trim. Fuel tanks in fuselage, forward and aft of main engine. Drop-tanks, each estimated to have capacity of 600 litres (158 US gallons; 132 Imp gallons), can be carried on underwing pylons.

ACCOMMODATION: Pilot only, on zero-speed/zero-height ejection seat. Electronic system ejects pilot automatically if aircraft height and descent rate are sensed to indicate an emergency. Armoured glass windscreen.

AVIONICS: Ranging radar in nose. IFF (NATO 'Odd Rods') antennae forward of windscreen. Other avionics in rear fuselage. Fully automatic control system for use during take-off and landing, to ensure synchronisation of engine functioning, aerodynamic control operation, jet reaction nozzle operation, stabilisation and guidance.

ARMAMENT: No installed armament. Two pylons under fixed panel of each wing for 2,600–3,600 kg (5,730–7,935 lb) of external stores, including gun pods each containing a 23 mm twin-barrel GSh-23 cannon, rocket packs, bombs weighing up to 500 kg each, 'Kerry' short-range air-to-surface missiles, armour-piercing anti-ship missiles, 'Aphid' air-to-air missiles and auxiliary fuel tanks.

DIMENSIONS, EXTERNAL (estimated):

Wing span	7.32 m (24 ft 0 in)
Width, wings folded	4.88 m (16 ft 0 in)
Length overall: 'Forger-A'	15.50 m (50 ft 10¼ in)
'Forger-B'	17.68 m (58 ft 0 in)
Height overall	4.37 m (14 ft 4 in)
Wheel track	2.90 m (9 ft 6 in)
Wheelbase	5.50 m (18 ft 0 in)

AREA (estimated):

Wings, gross	18.5 m² (199.0 sq ft)

WEIGHTS (estimated):

Basic operating weight, incl pilot(s):	
'Forger-A'	7,485 kg (16,500 lb)
'Forger-B'	8,390 kg (18,500 lb)
Max T-O weight	11,700 kg (25,795 lb)

PERFORMANCE ('Forger-A', estimated, at max T-O weight):

Max level speed at height	
	Mach 0.95 (545 knots; 1,009 km/h; 627 mph)
Max level speed at S/L	
	Mach 0.8 (528 knots; 978 km/h; 608 mph)
Max rate of climb at S/L	4,500 m (14,750 ft)/min
Service ceiling	12,000 m (39,375 ft)
Combat radius:	
with air-to-air missiles and external tanks, 75 min on station	
	100 nm (185 km; 115 miles)
with max weapons, lo-lo-lo	130 nm (240 km; 150 miles)
with max weapons, hi-lo-hi	200 nm (370 km; 230 miles)

Aircraft of Unknown Design

Ram-M. Among aircraft observed at Ramenskoye flight test centre, and allocated a provisional 'Ram' designation, is a high-altitude reconnaissance aircraft in the class of the USAF's Lockheed TR-1. Few details are known except that it has twin tail fins. It was first reported in mid-1982.

233

United Kingdom

BAe
BRITISH AEROSPACE PLC

In 1977 the former companies of British Aircraft Corporation (Holdings) Ltd, Hawker Siddeley Aviation Ltd, Hawker Siddeley Dynamics Ltd and Scottish Aviation Ltd were brought together through nationalisation. In January 1981 the structure of British Aerospace was changed from a corporation in public ownership to a public limited company in the private sector, and in May 1985 HM Government sold its remaining shareholding. The Gyroscope division of Sperry was acquired in May 1982, forming the basis of the Naval and Electronic Systems Division. In August 1987 BAe acquired Steinheil-Lear Siegler AG of the Federal Republic of Germany.

The Company operates through six divisions, employing 76,000 people in the UK and overseas: Civil Aircraft Division, Military Aircraft Division, Air Weapons Division, Army Weapons Division, Space and Communications Division, and a new Division combining the former Naval Weapons and Electronic Systems and Equipment Divisions.

In April 1987 British Aerospace acquired Royal Ordnance PLC, formerly part of the Ministry of Defence with 17 manufacturing and R & D facilities. Royal Ordnance operates as a wholly owned subsidiary of BAe, and continues to trade under its original name.

Associated companies include SEPECAT (formed in May 1966 by BAC and Breguet Aviation to control the development and production of the Jaguar tactical strike fighter and trainer), Panavia Aircraft GmbH (formed in March 1969 by BAC, MBB and Aeritalia to manage the development and production of the Tornado all-weather combat aircraft), Eurofighter GmbH, Dulles International Aeroservices Inc (formed in 1976 by BAC(USA) Inc and Rolls-Royce Inc to supply customers in North America with spares and engineering support), BBG GmbH (formed with Bodenseewerk to develop and produce the ASRAAM missile, Arab-British Dynamics Co (inaugurated in 1977 by BAC Guided Weapons Division and the Egyptian government to manufacture the Swingfire missile in Egypt), and Frames Travel (Fylde) Ltd.

BAe Hawk (Two-Seat Versions)

RAF designation: Hawk T. Mk 1

After examining designs submitted by BAC and Hawker Siddeley to meet an RAF requirement for a basic and advanced jet trainer, the Ministry of Defence announced in October 1971 that the Hawker Siddeley P1182 had been selected to meet this requirement. Selection of a non-afterburning version of the Rolls-Royce Turboméca Adour to power the aircraft was announced on 2 March 1972, and later in the same month the Ministry of Defence confirmed an order for 176 HS P1182s, which were given the RAF name of Hawk T. Mk 1. These were to consist of one pre-production aircraft (XX154), which first flew on 21 August 1974, and 175 production Hawks. The first two production Hawks (XX162 and 163) were delivered to No. 4 Flying Training School at RAF Valley on 4 November 1976.

The Hawk is fully aerobatic and is designed to have a safe

Royal Air Force Hawk T.Mk 1A, armed with 30 mm gun and Sidewinder missiles, in formation with a Tornado F.Mk 3. *(G. H. Lee/British Aerospace)*

fatigue life of 6,000 hours. It replaced the Jet Provost, Gnat Trainer and Hunter in RAF service for advanced flying training, and for radio, navigation and weapons training. Full details of the training versions of the Hawk will be provided in an accompanying publication. It has since been adapted also for airfield defence and limited attack duties with the RAF. The design is capable of other operational roles, and has been developed through a succession of variants into a single-seat combat version. The following versions of the Hawk are important in a combat sense.

Hawk T. Mk 1A. Eighty-eight RAF Hawks have been modified to this war role standard for airfield defence and limited attack, of which 72 have been formally declared to NATO. Capable of carrying two AIM-9L Sidewinder air-to-air missiles on underwing hardpoints. One Adour 151 non-afterburning turbofan, rated at 23.13 kN (5,200 lb st).

Hawk 50 series. Initial export version, with Adour 851 turbofan, rated at 23.75 kN (5,340 lb st). Max operating weight increased by 30 per cent. Max disposable load increased by 70 per cent. Max range increased by 30 per cent. Revised tailcone shape to improve directional stability at high speed. Larger nose equipment bay. Two additional weapon pylons underwing. All four wing stations configured for single or twin store carriage; each pylon cleared to carry 515 kg (1,135 lb). 'Wet' inboard pylons for 455 litre (120 US gallon; 100 Imp gallon) fuel tanks. Improved nav/com. Improved cockpit, with angle-of-attack indication, fully aerobatic twin gyro AHRS, slim seat head boxes and weapon control panel. Optional brake-chute. Suitable for ground attack in day VMC, and armed reconnaissance with camera/sensor pod. Sold to Finland (50 **Mk 51** to replace Fouga Magisters; construction of components for 46 aircraft, and final assembly, undertaken in Finland by

234

Air Force of Zimbabwe Hawk Mk 60s armed with Sidewinder missiles and bombs.

Valmet); Kenya (12 **Mk 52**); and Indonesia (20 **Mk 53** ground attack/trainers). Deliveries began in 1980.

Hawk 60 series. Development of the 50 series with Adour 861 turbofan, rated at 25.35 kN (5,700 lb/st). Wing changes, including leading-edge devices and four-position flaps to improve lift capability. Low-friction nose leg, strengthened wheels and tyres, and adaptive anti-skid system. Drop-tanks of 592 or 864 litre (130 or 190 Imp gallon) capacity. Provision for Sidewinder or Magic air-to-air missiles. Max operating weight increased by further 17 per cent compared with Mk 50 series, disposable load by 33 per cent and range by 30 per cent. Improved field performance, acceleration, rate of climb and turn rate. Sold to Zimbabwe (eight **Mk 60**), Dubai (eight **Mk 61**), Abu Dhabi (16 **Mk 63**), Kuwait (12 **Mk 64**) and Saudi Arabia (30 **Mk 65**). Entered service 1982.

Hawk 100 series. To exploit the Hawk's five-pylon capability for carrying external stores, BAe announced this enhanced ground-attack development of the 60 series in mid-1982. Still basically a two-seater, it is likely to carry only a pilot on combat missions. The 100 series has a Singer Kearfott SKN 2416 inertial navigation unit of the type used on the F-16, an advanced Smiths Industries head-up display/weapon aiming computer (HUD/WAC), and new air data sensor package, with optional laser ranging and FLIR; improved weapons management system allowing pre-selection during flight and displaying weapon status; manual or automatic weapon release; passive warning radar; HOTAS (hands on throttle and stick) controls; full colour multi-purpose CRT display in each cockpit; and provision for carrying an ECM pod. Max external load is increased to

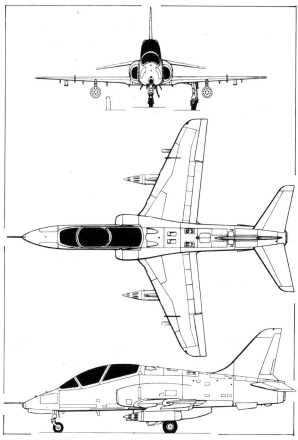
BAe Hawk 50 series. *(Pilot Press)*

3,265 kg (7,200 lb); T-O run reduced by typically 20 per cent and landing run by 15 per cent; max ferry range increased by over 50 per cent with two 864 litre (228 US gallons; 190 Imp gallon) external tanks; and hi-lo-hi combat radius improved to 660 nm (1,222 km; 759 miles) with two 1,000 lb bombs or 275 nm (509 km; 316 miles) with seven 1,000 lb bombs. In a combat air patrol mission, the Hawk Series 100 is able to loiter for 3½ h on station, 140 nm (260 km; 160 miles) from its base, armed with two Sidewinder type missiles and its 30 mm gun.

Hawk 200 series. Single-seat multi-role combat version. Described separately.

BAe's Hawk demonstrator, modified to the aerodynamic shape of the Hawk Series 100.

The following description applies to current UK production Hawks for export:

TYPE: Two-seat basic and advanced jet trainer, with capability for air-defence and ground-attack roles.

WINGS: Cantilever low-wing monoplane. Thickness/chord ratio 10.9% at root, 9% at tip. Dihedral 2°. Sweepback 26° on leading edge, 21° 30′ at quarter-chord. Double-slotted flaps and ailerons.

FUSELAGE: Conventional structure with large airbrake under rear fuselage, aft of wing.

TAIL UNIT: Cantilever structure, with sweepback on all surfaces. One-piece all-moving anhedral tailplane. Manually operated rudder, with electrically actuated trim tab. Two small ventral fins.

LANDING GEAR: Wide-track tricycle type, with single wheel on each unit. Dunlop mainwheels, brakes and tyres size 6.50-10. Nosewheel and tyre size 4.4-16. Tail bumper fairing under rear fuselage. Anti-skid wheel brakes. Tail braking parachute, diameter 2.64 m (8 ft 8 in), optional.

POWERPLANT: One Rolls-Royce Turboméca Adour non-afterburning turbofan engine, as described under individual series entries. Fuel in one fuselage bag tank of 868 litres (229 US gallons; 191 Imp gallons) capacity and integral wing tank of 836 litres (221 US gallons; 184 Imp gallons) capacity; total fuel capacity 1,704 litres (450 US gallons; 375 Imp gallons). Provision for carrying one 455, 592 or 864 litre (120, 156 or 228 US gallon; 100, 130 or 190 Imp gallon) drop-tank on each inboard underwing pylon, according to series.

ACCOMMODATION: Crew of two in tandem under one-piece fully transparent canopy. Improved windscreen fitted retrospectively to RAF Hawks, able to withstand a 1 kg (2.2 lb) bird at 528 knots (978 km/h; 607 mph). Rear seat elevated. Martin-Baker Mk 10B zero/zero rocket assisted ejection seats, with MDC (miniature detonating cord) system to break canopy before seats eject. The MDC can also be operated from outside the cockpit for ground rescue. Dual controls standard. Entire accommodation pressurised.

AVIONICS AND EQUIPMENT: The RAF standard of flight instruments includes Ferranti gyros and inverter, two Sperry Gyroscope RAI-4 4 in remote attitude indicators and a magnetic detector unit, and Louis Newmark compass system. Radio and navigation equipment includes Sylvania UHF and VHF, Cossor CAT.7000 Tacan, Cossor ILS with CILS.75/76 localiser/glideslope receiver and marker receiver, and IFF/SSR (Cossor 2720 Mk 10A IFF in aircraft for Finland).

ARMAMENT AND OPERATIONAL EQUIPMENT: Ferranti F.195 weapon sight and camera recorder in each cockpit of RAF, series 50 and 60 aircraft. (Saab RGS2 sighting system in aircraft for Finland.) Underfuselage centreline mounted 30 mm Aden gun and ammunition pack, and two or four hardpoints underwing, according to series. Provision for pylon in place of the ventral gun pack. In RAF training roles the normal max external load is about 680 kg (1,500 lb), but the uprated Hawk has demonstrated its ability to carry a total external load of 3,084 kg (6,800 lb). Typical weapon loadings on 60 series include a 30 mm or 12.7 mm centreline gun pod and four packs each containing eighteen 68 mm rockets; a centreline reconnaissance pod and four packs each containing twelve 81 mm rockets; seven 1,000 lb free-fall or retarded bombs; four launchers each containing four 100 mm rockets; nine 250 lb or 250 kg bombs; thirty-six 80 lb runway denial or tactical strike bombs; five 600 lb cluster bombs; four Sidewinder/Magic air-to-air missiles; nine 50 Imp gallon napalm canisters; four CBLS 100/200 carriers each containing four practice bombs and four rockets; or two 130 Imp gallon drop-tanks and two Stingray homing torpedoes. Maverick missiles could also be carried. Demonstrated configurations include a Sea Eagle anti-ship missile on the centreline pylon, plus two Sidewinder missiles and two 864 litre (228 US gallon; 190 Imp gallon) drop-tanks underwing.

DIMENSIONS, EXTERNAL:
Wing span	9.39 m (30 ft 9¾ in)
Length overall: excl probe	11.17 m (36 ft 7¾ in)
incl probe	11.86 m (38 ft 11 in)
Height overall	3.99 m (13 ft 1¼ in)
Wheel track	3.47 m (11 ft 5 in)

AREA:
Wings, gross	16.69 m² (179.6 sq ft)

WEIGHTS:
Weight empty: 60 series	3,635 kg (8,015 lb)
100 series	3,855 kg (8,500 lb)
T-O weight:	
60 series trainer, 'clean'	5,150 kg (11,350 lb)
Max T-O weight: T. Mk 1	5,700 kg (12,566 lb)
50 series	7,350 kg (16,200 lb)
60, 100 series	8,570 kg (18,890 lb)

PERFORMANCE:
Max speed in dive at height	575 knots (1,065 km/h; 661 mph)
Max Mach number in dive	1.2
Max level speed:	
50 series	535 knots (990 km/h; 615 mph)
60, 100 series	560 knots (1,037 km/h; 644 mph)
Max level speed Mach number	0.88
Max rate of climb at S/L	3,600 m (11,800 ft)/min
Time to 9,145 m (30,000 ft), 'clean'	6 min 6 s
Service ceiling	15,250 m (50,000 ft)
T-O run	550 m (1,800 ft)
Landing run	488 m (1,600 ft)
Combat radius:	
with 2,268 kg (5,000 lb) weapon load	538 nm (998 km; 620 miles)
with 908 kg (2,000 lb) weapon load	718 nm (1,448 km; 900 miles)
Ferry range 'clean'	1,313 nm (2,433 km; 1,510 miles)
Ferry range, 60 series, with two 864 litre (228 US gallon; 190 Imp gallon) drop-tanks	2,200 nm (4,075 km; 2,530 miles)
Endurance, 100 nm (185 km; 115 miles) from base	approx 4 h 0 min
g limits	+ 8/ − 4

BAe Hawk 200 Series (Single-Seater)

On 20 June 1984, British Aerospace announced its intention to build as a private venture a demonstrator single-seat combat version of the Hawk, and this aircraft (ZG200) flew for the first time on 19 May 1986. It was lost, through no apparent aircraft fault, on 2 July 1986, and was replaced by the first pre-production Hawk 200 in 1987.

The Hawk 200 is virtually identical with the current production two-seater aft of the cockpit, giving 80 per cent airframe commonality. Built-in twin-cannon armament frees the centreline pylon for other stores, including a 592 litre (156 US gallon; 130 Imp gallon) external fuel tank. Each of the four underwing pylons is capable of carrying 907 kg (2,000 lb), within the max external load of 3,084 kg (6,800 lb). The

BAe Hawk 200 single-seat multi-role combat aircraft.

wide range of missions that such capability permits include:

Airspace denial. Carrying two Sidewinder type missiles and two 864 litre (228 US gallon; 190 Imp gallon) drop-tanks, the Hawk 200 could loiter for 3.5 hours on station at 9,150 m (30,000 ft), 100 nm (185 km; 115 miles) from base; or for one hour on station 550 nm (1,018 km; 633 miles) from base. Max intercept radius is 720 nm (1,333 km; 828 miles).

Close air support. Five 1,000 lb and four 500 lb bombs could be delivered with precision up to 104 nm (192 km; 120 miles) from base in a lo-lo mission.

Battlefield interdiction. In a hi-lo-hi operation, the Hawk 200 has a radius of action of 579 nm (1,072 km; 666 miles), with a 1,360 kg (3,000 lb) military load.

Long-range photo reconnaissance. A wide area of search is made possible by the mission range of 1,723 nm (3,190 km; 1,982 miles) offered by two external tanks, carried with a pod containing cameras and infra-red linescan. A rapid role change could then permit follow-up attack by the same aircraft. Lo-lo radius by day or night is 510 nm (945 km; 586 miles).

Long-range deployment. Ferry range with two 864 litre (228 US gallon; 190 Imp gallon) and one 592 litre (156 US gallon; 130 Imp gallon) external tanks is 1,950 nm (3,610 km; 2,244 miles), unrefuelled and with 864 litre tanks retained. Reserves would allow 10 min over destination at 150 m (500 ft).

Anti-shipping strike. Armed with a Sea Eagle sea skimming anti-ship missile, and carrying two 864 litre (228 US gallons; 190 Imp gallon) tanks, the Hawk 200 could attack a ship 800 nm (1,480 km; 920 miles) from base, and return with 10 per cent fuel reserves. This puts ships almost anywhere in the North Atlantic within range of the Hawk from shore bases. Weapon release could be beyond the target's radar envelope.

Three standards of equipment are envisaged, depending on the customer's mission requirements, as follows:

Day operation. The most simple equipment fit would comprise a gyro stabilised attack sight and attitude heading reference system, with navigation by radio aids. Navigation and weapon aiming capabilities could be extended by adding an inertial navigation system, head-up display and weapon aiming computer. Other options are HOTAS controls, laser rangefinder, IFF, radar warning receiver.

Night operation. With a FLIR and laser rangefinder mounted in a modified nosecone, the Hawk 200 could carry out precision ground attacks and tactical reconnaissance by day and night.

All-weather operation. Installation of an advanced multi-mode radar (Westinghouse APG-66(V)) adds all-weather target acquisition and navigational fixing capabilities. Weapons like the anti-shipping Sea Eagle and air-to-air Sky Flash could also be employed.

Changes by comparison with the two-seat Hawk are as follows:

TYPE: Single-seat multi-role combat aircraft.

WINGS: As Hawk two-seater, except for detail modifications to leading-edge aerofoil section.

FUSELAGE: Modified to single-seat configuration. Unchanged design concept and criteria.

LANDING GEAR: Mainwheel tyres size 559 × 165-279. Nosewheel tyre size 457 × 140-203.

POWERPLANT: One Rolls-Royce Turboméca Adour Mk 871, with uninstalled rating of 26.0 kN (5,845 lb st).

ACCOMMODATION: Pilot only, on Martin-Baker Type 10L ejection seat, under side-hinged (to starboard) canopy.

ARMAMENT: One or two internally mounted 25 mm Aden guns beneath cockpit floor. Ferranti ISIS sight or Smiths head-up display optional.

DIMENSIONS, EXTERNAL:
As Hawk two-seater, except:

Length overall	11.38 m (37 ft 4 in)
Height overall	4.16 m (13 ft 8 in)
Wheelbase	3.298 m (10 ft 10 in)

WEIGHTS:

Weight empty	4,128 kg (9,100 lb)
Max fuel: internal	1,360 kg (3,000 lb)
internal + three drop-tanks	3,210 kg (7,080 lb)
Max weapon load	3,500 kg (7,700 lb)
Max T-O weight	9,101 kg (20,065 lb)

PERFORMANCE (estimated; no external stores or role equipment unless stated):

Never-exceed speed at height
Mach 1.2 (575 knots; 1,065 km/h; 661 mph)

Max level speed at S/L
560 knots (1,037 km/h; 644 mph)

237

Max cruising speed at S/L
850 knots (1,019 km/h; 633 mph)
Econ cruising speed at 12,500 m (41,000 ft)
430 knots (796 km/h; 495 mph)
Stalling speed, flaps down
106 knots (197 km/h; 122 mph) IAS
Max rate of climb at S/L   3,508 m (11,510 ft)/min
Service ceiling   15,250 m (50,000 ft)
T-O run with max weapon load   1,585 m (5,200 ft)
T-O to 15 m (50 ft) with max weapon load
2,134 m (7,000 ft)
Landing from 15 m (50 ft) at landing weight of 4,550 kg (10,030 lb): with brake-chute   854 m (2,800 ft)
    without brake-chute   1,250 m (4,100 ft)
Range:
    with internal fuel only   482 nm (892 km; 554 miles)
    with internal fuel plus three drop-tanks
1,950 nm (3,610 km; 2,244 miles)
g limits   + 8/ − 4

BAe Harrier

RAF designations: Harrier GR. Mk 3 and T. Mk 4/4A
USMC designations: AV-8A (Mk 50) and TAV-8A (Mk 54)
Spanish Navy designation: Matador (AV-8S and TAV-8S)

The Harrier was the world's first operational fixed-wing V/STOL strike fighter. The first of six single-seat prototypes (XV276) flew for the first time on 31 August 1966; the following versions have since been built:

Harrier GR. Mk 1, 1A and 3. Single-seat close-support and tactical reconnaissance versions for the RAF. First of initial series of 78 production GR. Mk 1s (XV738) flew on 28 December 1967. No. 1 Squadron at RAF Wittering received its first aircraft (XV744) on 9 April 1969. Deliveries to No. 233 OCU, also at Wittering, began on 5 May 1969 (aircraft XV747). Delivered subsequently to Nos. 3, 4 and 20 Squadrons in West Germany. These aircraft were designated

Harrier GR. Mk 1 when fitted initially with Pegasus 101 engines. When retrofitted subsequently with the Pegasus 102 they were redesignated GR. Mk 1A. Aircraft now in service have Pegasus 103 engines and are designated GR. Mk 3. A total of 120 GR. 1/3s has been delivered to the Royal Air Force.

The fourteen RAF Harrier GR. Mk 3s despatched to the South Atlantic in the spring of 1982 to take part in the Falklands campaign were converted to carry AIM-9L Sidewinder air-to-air missiles on their two outer underwing pylons. To enhance weapon commonality, they were also cleared to carry the 2 in rocket pods used by the Royal Navy. Four of the Harriers were flown from the UK to Ascension Island, using in-flight refuelling from Victor tankers for the non-stop 3,475 nm (6,435 km; 4,000 mile) flight of 9 h 15 min. They then flew directly to land on HMS *Hermes*, making a total of 6,950 nm (12,870 km; 8,000 miles) into a combat zone in some 18 flying hours, with one intermediate stop. Four GR. Mk 3s were lost in the campaign; all of the pilots were recovered.

A Harrier GR. Mk 1A, piloted by Sqn Ldr T. L. Lecky-Thompson, still holds two international time-to-height records after VTO, in Class H for jet lift aircraft, set on 5 January 1971. The aircraft reached 9,000 m (29,528 ft) in 1 min 44.7 s and 12,000 m (39,370 ft) in 2 min 22.7 s. The same RAF pilot also set a Class H altitude record of 14,040 m (46,063 ft) in a Harrier GR. Mk 1A on 2 January 1971.

Harrier T. Mk 2, 2A, 4 and 4A and Sea Harrier T. Mk 4RN. Two-seat versions, retaining the full combat capability of the single-seater in terms of equipment fit and weapon carriage. There is a large degree of commonality in structure and system components, ground support equipment and flight and ground crew training. Differences include a longer nose section forward of the wing leading edge, with two cockpits in tandem; a tailcone approx 1.83 m (6 ft) longer than that of the single-seat model; and enlarged fin surfaces. The two-seat Harrier can be used operationally with the rear seat and compensating tail ballast removed, thus minimising the weight penalty over its single-seat counterpart. First of two development aircraft (XW174) flew

Royal Air Force Harrier GR.Mk 3 V/STOL close support and reconnaissance aircraft.

on 24 April 1969, and the first of 21 production aircraft for the RAF (XW264) on 3 October 1969. The two-seater entered RAF service in July 1970.

The RAF Harrier T. Mk 2, like the GR. Mk 1, was powered originally by the Pegasus 101 engine. The designations T. Mk 2A and T. Mk 4 apply to aircraft retrofitted with, respectively, the Pegasus 102 and 103. The T. Mk 4A has a pointed nose, without LRMTS, to make it more suitable for training duties with No. 233 OCU at RAF Wittering because of decreased weight. Deliveries of T. Mk 2/4A aircraft totalled 23 by February 1984. Royal Navy two-seaters are designated Sea Harrier T. Mk 4RN; one was delivered in 1980 and three in 1983.

Harrier GR. Mk 5. Designation of AV-8B Harrier IIs ordered for the RAF. This version, which is being produced jointly for the US Marine Corps, the RAF and the Spanish Navy, is described under the McDonnell Douglas/BAe heading in the International section.

Harrier Mk 50 (USMC designation AV-8A). Single-seat close-support and tactical reconnaissance version for the US Marine Corps, delivery of which began on 26 January 1971. Dimensionally as GR. Mk 3, but without laser ranger and marked target seeker, and with modifications to customer's specification, including provision for the carriage of Sidewinder missiles. Total of 102 ordered for US Marine Corps, plus eight Harrier **Mk 54s** (a two-seat version designated **TAV-8A**); all of those still in service now have F402-RR-402 or -402A (Pegasus 803) engines.

The AV-8As equip three US Marine Corps combat squadrons: VMA 513, VMA 542 and VMA 231; and training squadron VMA(T) 203, at Cherry Point, North Carolina.

In the period from 1979 until FY 1984, the US Marine Corps upgraded 47 of its AV-8As to **AV-8C** standard. This was a CILOP (conversion in lieu of procurement) programme under which the AV-8As were fitted with forward looking passive radar warning equipment at the wingtips, tail warning radar in the tail 'bullet' fairing, improved UHF com aerial, a flare/chaff dispenser in the rear fuselage equipment bay, the LIDS (lift improvement devices: underfuselage strakes and forward flap) developed for the AV-8B, an onboard oxygen generating system, and KY 58 secure voice system. The ram-air turbine of the AV-8A was removed. Conversion of the first few AV-8As to AV-8C standard was undertaken by McDonnell Douglas, from kits supplied by BAe. The remaining conversions were carried out by the US Marine Corps at NAS Cherry Point, North Carolina, using BAe kits.

Eleven AV-8As and two TAV-8As were ordered, through USA, for the Spanish Navy, by whom they are known as **Matadors** and designated **AV-8S** and **TAV-8S** respectively. The first batch of six Spanish AV-8s are Mk 50 aircraft; the second batch of five are **Mk 55** aircraft; the TAV-8Ss are Mk 54s. They equip the 8a Escuadrilla of the Spanish Navy at Rota, Cadiz, and operate from the aircraft carriers *Principe de Asturias* and *Dedalo*. Like the AV-8As of the USMC, the Matador has a Sidewinder capability.

Harrier Mk 52. One aircraft built as a demonstrator using BAe and equipment suppliers' private funding. It is similar to the Harrier T. Mk 4, and is fitted with a Pegasus 103 engine; in recognition of its status as the first civil registered jet V/STOL aircraft in the UK, it was granted the civil registration G-VTOL. First flight was made on 16 September 1971, with a Pegasus 102 fitted initially.

Harrier T. Mk 60. Two-seat operational trainer version

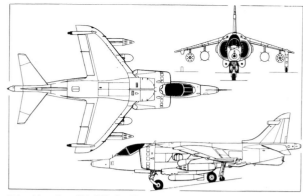

BAe Harrier GR.Mk 3. *(Pilot Press)*

for Indian Navy. T. Mk 4 configuration, but with complete Sea Harrier avionics except for Blue Fox radar. Two ordered.

Sea Harrier FRS. Mks 1 and 51. Versions for Royal Navy and Indian Navy. Described separately.

Harrier Mk 80. Export version, based on Sea Harrier but with laser ranger/seeker of GR. Mk 3 instead of Blue Fox radar. None yet delivered.

The following details apply generally to the Harrier GR. Mk 3 and T. Mk 4/4A, except where a specific version is indicated:

TYPE: V/STOL close-support and reconnaissance aircraft.

WINGS: Cantilever shoulder-wing monoplane. Wing section of BAe (HS) design. Thickness/chord ratio 10% at root, 5% at tip. Anhedral 12°. Incidence 1° 45′. Sweepback at quarter-chord 34°. Plain ailerons and flaps. Jet reaction control valve built into front of each outrigger wheel fairing. Entire wing unit removable to provide access to engine. For ferry missions, the normal 'combat' wingtips can be replaced by bolt-on extended tips to increase ferry range.

FUSELAGE: Conventional semi-monocoque safe-life structure with titanium skins at rear and some titanium adjacent to engine and in other special areas. Access to powerplant through top of fuselage, ahead of wing. Jet reaction control valves in nose and tailcone. Large forward hinged airbrake under fuselage, aft of mainwheel well.

TAIL UNIT: One-piece variable-incidence tailplane, with 15° of anhedral. Rudder is operated manually. Trim tab in rudder. Ventral fin under rear fuselage. Fin tip carries suppressed VHF aerial.

LANDING GEAR: Retractable bicycle type, permitting operation from rough unprepared surfaces of CBR as low as 3 to 5 per cent. Hydraulic actuation, with nitrogen bottle for emergency extension of landing gear. Small outrigger units retract rearward into fairings slightly inboard of wingtips. Dunlop wheels and tyres, size 26.00 × 8.75-11 (nose unit), 27.00 × 7.74-13 (main units) and 13.50 × 6.4 (outriggers). Dunlop multi-disc brakes and Dunlop-Hytrol adaptive anti-skid system.

POWERPLANT: One Rolls-Royce Pegasus Mk 103 vectored-thrust turbofan engine (95.6 kN; 21,500 lb st), with four exhaust nozzles of the two-vane cascade type, rotatable through 98.5° from fully aft position. Engine bleed air from HP compressor used for jet reaction control system and to power duplicated air motor for nozzle actuation.

The low-drag intake cowls each have eight automatic suction relief doors aft of the leading edge to improve intake efficiency by providing extra air for the engine at low forward or zero speeds. A 227 litre (60 US gallon; 50 Imp gallon) tank supplies demineralised water for thrust restoration in high ambient temperatures for STO, VTO and vertical landings. Fuel in five integral tanks in fuselage and two in wings, with total capacity of approx 2,865 litres (757 US gallons; 630 Imp gallons). This can be supplemented by two 455 litre (120 US gallon; 100 Imp gallon) jettisonable combat tanks, or two 864 litre (228 US gallon; 190 Imp gallon) tanks, or two 1,500 litre (396 US gallon; 330 Imp gallon) ferry tanks on the inboard wing pylons. Ground refuelling point in port rear nozzle fairing. Provision for in-flight refuelling probe above the port intake cowl.

ACCOMMODATION: Crew of one (Mk 3) or two (Mk 4) on Martin-Baker Mk 9D zero/zero rocket ejection seats which operate through the miniature-detonating-cord-equipped canopy of the pressurised cockpit. AV-8As of the US Marine Corps retrofitted with Stencel SIIIS-3 ejection seats. Birdproof windscreen, with hydraulically actuated wiper. Windscreen washing system.

AVIONICS AND EQUIPMENT: Plessey U/VHF, Ultra standby UHF, GEC Avionics AD 2770 Tacan and Cossor IFF, Ferranti FE 541 inertial navigation and attack system (INAS), with Sperry C2G compass, Smiths electronic head-up display of flight information, and air data computer. Marconi ARI.18223 radar warning receiver. INAS can be aligned equally well at sea or on land. The weapon aiming computer provides a general solution for manual or automatic release of free-fall and retarded bombs, and for the aiming of rockets and guns, in dive and straight-pass attacks over a wide range of flight conditions, and very considerable freedom of manoeuvre in elevation. Communications equipment ranges through VHF in the 100–156 MHz band to UHF in the 220–400 MHz band. Ferranti Type 106 laser ranger and marked target seeker (LRMTS) retrofitted to all RAF single-seat and some two-seat Harriers.

ARMAMENT AND OPERATIONAL EQUIPMENT: Optically flat panel in nose, on port side, for F.95 oblique camera, which is carried as standard. A cockpit voice recorder with in-flight playback facility supplements the reconnaissance cameras, and facilitates rapid debriefing and mission evaluation. No built-in armament. Combat load is carried on four underwing and one underfuselage pylons, all with ML ejector release units. The inboard wing points and the fuselage point are stressed for loads of up to 910 kg (2,000 lb) each, and the outboard underwing pair for loads of up to 295 kg (650 lb) each; the two strake fairings under the fuselage can each be replaced by a 30 mm Aden gun pod and ammunition. The Harrier is cleared for operations with a maximum external load exceeding 2,270 kg (5,000

lb), and has flown with a weapon load of 3,630 kg (8,000 lb). It is able to carry 30 mm guns, bombs, rockets and flares of UK and US designs, and in addition to its fixed reconnaissance camera can also carry a five-camera reconnaissance pod on the underfuselage pylon. A typical combat load comprises a pair of 30 mm Aden gun pods, a 1,000 lb bomb on the underfuselage pylon, a 1,000 lb bomb on each of the inboard underwing pylons, and a Matra 155 launcher with 19 × 68 mm SNEB rockets on each outboard underwing pylon. A Sidewinder installation is provided in the AV-8A and Matador versions (and retrospectively on some GR. Mk 3s), to give the aircraft an effective air-to-air capability in conjunction with the two 30 mm Aden guns. A flare/chaff dispenser can be fitted.

DIMENSIONS, EXTERNAL:

Wing span: combat	7.70 m (25 ft 3 in)
ferry	9.04 m (29 ft 8 in)
Length overall: single-seat	13.89 m (45 ft 7 in)
single-seat (laser nose)	14.27 m (46 ft 10 in)
two-seat (laser nose)	17.50 m (57 ft 5 in)
Height overall: single-seat	3.63 m (11 ft 11 in)
two-seat	4.17 m (13 ft 8 in)
Outrigger wheel track	6.76 m (22 ft 2 in)
Wheelbase, nosewheel to mainwheels	
	approx 3.45 m (11 ft 4 in)

AREA:

Wings, gross: combat	18.68 m² (201.1 sq ft)
ferry	20.1 m² (216 sq ft)

WEIGHTS:

Basic operating weight, empty:	
GR. Mk 3	6,140 kg (13,535 lb)
T. Mk 4	6,850 kg (15,100 lb)
Internal fuel	2,295 kg (5,060 lb)
Max T-O weight:	
single-seat	11,430 kg (25,200 lb)
two-seat	11,880 kg (26,200 lb)

PERFORMANCE:

Max speed at S/L	635 knots (1,176 km/h; 730 mph)
Max Mach number in a dive at height	1.3
Time to 12,200 m (40,000 ft) from vertical T-O	2 min 23 s
Service ceiling	15,600 m (51,200 ft)
T-O run: with 2,270 kg (5,000 lb) payload at max T-O weight	approx 305 m (1,000 ft)
Range: hi-lo-hi with 1,995 kg (4,400 lb) payload	360 nm (666 km; 414 miles)
lo-lo with 1,995 kg (4,400 lb) payload	200 nm (370 km; 230 miles)
Ferry range	1,850 nm (3,425 km; 2,129 miles)
Range with one in-flight refuelling	more than 3,000 nm (5,560 km; 3,455 miles)
Endurance:	
combat air patrol 100 nm (185 km; 115 miles) from base	1 h 30 min
with one in-flight refuelling	more than 7 h
g limits	+ 7.8/ − 4.2

BAe Sea Harrier

RN designation: FRS. Mk 1/2
Indian Navy designation: FRS. Mk 51

On 15 May 1975, the British government announced its decision to proceed with full development of a maritime version of the Harrier, subsequently designated Sea Harrier **FRS. Mk 1**. The first Sea Harrier to fly (XZ450) made its

first flight on 20 August 1978, and the first for the Royal Navy (XZ451) was handed over on 18 June 1979. The first Sea Harrier ship trials were carried out on board HMS *Hermes* during November 1979.

The initial Royal Navy order was for three development aircraft. Successive production orders for 21, 10, 14 and 9 had taken the total to 57 by summer 1986. The Naval

BAe Sea Harrier FRS.Mk 1s of the Royal Navy, some armed with Sidewinder missiles.

Intensive Flying Trials Unit for the Sea Harrier (No. 700A Squadron) was commissioned at RNAS Yeovilton on 19 September 1979. It became subsequently the shore based No. 899 HQ squadron, with eight aircraft. Front-line units, each nominally with five aircraft, are Nos. 800 and 801 Squadrons, able to operate from the anti-submarine cruisers HMS *Invincible, Illustrious* and *Ark Royal*. Six similar Sea Harriers, designated **FRS. Mk 51**, ordered by the Indian Navy, are now in service with No. 300 (White Tiger) Squadron and operate from INS *Vikrant*. Three standard, non-navalised T. Mk 4N two-seaters were delivered to the Royal Navy for land based training, and two T. Mk 60s to the Indian Navy. In November 1985 the Indian government ordered 10 additional FRS Mk 51 Sea Harriers and one more T. Mk 60 two-seat trainer. A letter of intent to purchase seven more FRS Mk 51s and a Mk 60 was issued in September 1986, to equip INS *Viraat*.

Following proposals by Lt Cdr D. R. Taylor, RN, tests were carried out successfully in 1977 with a 'ski-jump' launching ramp designed to boost the short take-off performance of vectored-thrust aircraft. This technique makes possible substantial benefits in Harrier operation both at sea and ashore, and is a feature of Royal Navy ships in which Sea Harriers are based. A 7° ski-jump ramp fitted to HMS *Invincible* and HMS *Illustrious*; that in former HMS *Ark Royal* was more steeply angled, at 12°, permitting an increase of 1,135 kg (2,500 lb) in launch weight for the same T-O run, or a 50–60 per cent reduction in T-O run for the same weight.

Major changes compared with the Harriers in service with the RAF, Spanish Navy and US Marine Corps comprise the elimination of magnesium components, introduction of a raised cockpit, revised operational avionics, and installation of multi-mode Ferranti radar in a redesigned nose that folds to port for carrier stowage. Known by the name Blue Fox, this radar is a derivative of the frequency-agile Seaspray radar fitted in the Royal Navy Lynx helicopter, but embodies changes to suit its different role, with air-to-air intercept and air-to-surface modes of operation.

The Royal Navy's Sea Harrier FRS. Mk 1 has a Rolls-Royce Pegasus 104 vectored-thrust turbofan engine, with the same rating as the Pegasus 103 fitted to current RAF Harriers. The two variants differ little in design, except that the Pegasus 104 incorporates additional anti-corrosion features and has the capability to generate more electrical power.

The Sea Harrier FRS. Mk 1 was intended to operate at approximately the same weights as the GR. Mk 3, and to be capable of lifting a full military load with a 152 m (500 ft) flat-deck run into an overdeck wind of 30 knots (55.5 km/h; 34.5 mph). It was first used operationally during the Falkland Islands campaign in 1982, from HMS *Hermes* and *Invincible*, when a total of 28 Sea Harriers flew 2,376 sorties. They destroyed 22 enemy aircraft in air-to-air combat without loss. Four Sea Harriers were lost in accidents and two to ground fire.

In January 1985 the UK Ministry of Defence awarded a contract to British Aerospace for the project definition phase of a mid-life update of Royal Navy Sea Harriers, of which 34 had been delivered by that time, with 23 more on order. The upgraded Sea Harriers are designated **FRS. Mk 2**.

Operational Sea Harrier FRS. Mk 1s began returning to BAe for conversion in early 1988, and will re-enter squadron service one year later. Delivery of new production FRS. Mk 2s could begin in 1990.

Externally, the Mk 2 differs from the Mk 1 in having role-change wingtip extensions that will increase the span by 61 cm (2 ft); a less pointed nose radome; a longer rear fuselage, resulting from insertion of a 35 cm (1 ft 1¾ in) plug aft of the wing trailing edge; and revisions of the antennae and external stores.

Installation of Ferranti Blue Vixen pulse-Doppler radar, instead of the original Blue Fox, will give the Sea Harrier FRS. Mk 2 all-weather lookdown/shootdown capability, with inherent track-while-scan, multiple target engagement, greatly increased missile launch range, enhanced surface target acquisition, and improved ECCM performance. In addition to the wide range of weapons with which the current operational Sea Harrier is compatible, the FRS. Mk 2 is equipped to carry the new air-to-air AIM-120 AMRAAM.

Improved systems are built around a MIL 1553B databus. This uses a dual redundant data highway, allowing computerised time sharing of information processed in the databus control and interface unit.

Redesign of the cockpit allows presentation of the total fleet defence picture, radar picture, threat data, target priority, and navigational information on dual multi-purpose displays. All time-critical weapon systems controls are positioned on the up-front control panel, or on the throttle and stick.

Operational efficiency is improved by the ergonomic integration of additional switches as part of the control column and throttle handle functions. HOTAS (hands on throttle and stick) controls provide simultaneous control of the aircraft, radar, and weapons systems without the need to operate separate controls and switches.

The Sea Harrier FRS. Mk 2 retains two external stores pylons under each wing, an underbelly centreline pylon, and mountings under the fuselage for two 30 mm Aden or new 25 mm gun packs, or AMRAAM missile pylons. Two 455 or 864 litre (120 or 228 US gallon; 100 or 190 Imp gallon) combat drop-tanks, or 1,500 litre (396 US gallon; 330 Imp gallon) ferry tanks, can be carried on the inboard underwing pylons. Alternative loadings include five free-fall or retarded 1,000 lb bombs, five cluster bombs, six Matra 115/116 packs

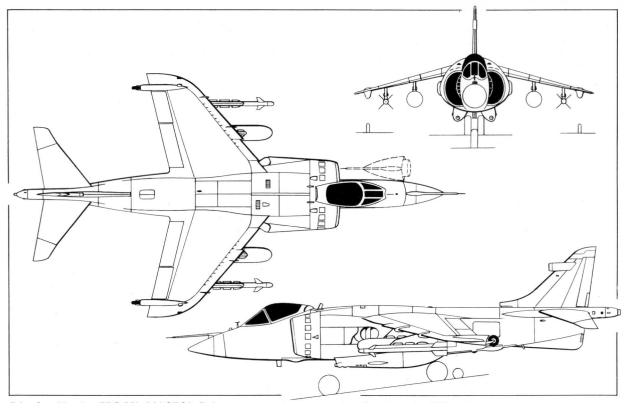

BAe Sea Harrier FRS Mk 1 V/STOL fighter, reconnaissance and strike aircraft. *(Pilot Press)*

of 68 mm rockets, eight Bofors Lepus flares, four Sidewinder, Magic or AMRAAM air-to-air missiles, two Sea Eagle air-to-surface missiles, or two ALARM anti-radiation missiles. Other standard weapons with which the aircraft is compatible include 250, 500, and 1,000 lb LDGP free-fall bombs, 250 and 500 lb Snakeye retarded bombs, LAU-10A, LAU-68A and LAU-69A rocket launchers, Mk 77 fire bombs, APAM cluster/Mk 7 dispensers, Rockeye 11 cluster/Mk 7 dispensers, and PMBR practice-bomb racks.

The description of the GR. Mk 3 applies also to the FRS. Mk 1, except as follows:

TYPE: V/STOL fighter, reconnaissance and strike aircraft.

POWERPLANT: As GR. Mk 3, except one Rolls-Royce Pegasus Mk 104 vectored thrust turbofan engine of 95.6 kN (21,500 lb st). Internal fuel capacity and external combat fuel capacity as for GR. Mk 3, except that 864 litre (228 US gallon; 190 Imp gallon) drop-tanks are in the regular RN inventory.

ACCOMMODATION: As GR. Mk 3, but with pilot raised 28 cm (11 in), on Martin-Baker Mk 10H zero/zero ejection seat.

SYSTEMS: As GR. Mk 3, except autopilot function on Fairey Hydraulics, giving throughput to aileron and tailplane power controls as well as to three-axis autostabs.

AVIONICS AND EQUIPMENT: Nose mounted Ferranti Blue Fox multi-mode radar, with TV raster daylight viewing tube which conveys flight information, as well as radar data, to pilot. New and larger Smiths electronic head-up display and 20,000-word digital weapon aiming computer. Autopilot, radar altimeter and Decca Doppler 72 radar. Ferranti self aligning attitude and heading reference platform and digital navigation computer. Radio navaids include UHF homing, GEC Avionics AD 2770 Tacan with offset facility and I band transponder. Radio com by

multi-channel Plessey PTR 377 U/VHF, with VHF standby via D 403M transceiver. Passive electronic surveillance and warning of external radar illumination by receiver with forward and rear hemisphere antennae in fin and tailcone respectively.

ARMAMENT AND OPERATIONAL EQUIPMENT: As GR. Mk 3, except for standard addition of four AIM-9 Sidewinder missiles on the outboard underwing pylons (Matra Magic instead of Sidewinder on Indian Navy aircraft), and provision for two air-to-surface missiles of Sea Eagle or Harpoon type.

Artist's impression of Sea Harrier FRS.Mk 2s embodying mid-life update modifications.

DIMENSIONS, EXTERNAL: As GR. Mk 3 except:

Wing span: FRS. Mk 1		7.70 m (25 ft 3 in)
FRS. Mk 2		8.31 m (27 ft 3 in)
Length overall: FRS. Mk 1		14.50 m (47 ft 7 in)
FRS. Mk 2		14.10 m (46 ft 3 in)
Length overall, nose folded:		
FRS. Mk 1		12.73 m (41 ft 9 in)
FRS. Mk 2		13.16 m (43 ft 2 in)
Height overall		3.71 m (12 ft 2 in)

WEIGHTS (FRS. Mk 1):

Operating weight empty	6,374 kg (14,052 lb)
Max fuel: internal	2,295 kg (5,060 lb)
external	2,404 kg (5,300 lb)
Max weapon load: STO	3,630 kg (8,000 lb)
VTO	2,270 kg (5,000 lb)
Max T-O weight	11,880 kg (26,200 lb)

PERFORMANCE (FRS. Mk 1):

Max Mach No. at high altitude — 1.25

Max level speed at low altitude
above 640 knots (1,185 km/h; 736 mph) EAS

Typical cruising speed:
high altitude, for well over 1 h on internal fuel
above Mach 0.8
low altitude
350–450 knots (650–833 km/h; 404–518 mph),
with rapid acceleration to
600 knots (1,110 km/h; 690 mph)

STO run at max T-O weight, without 'ski-jump'
approx 305 m (1,000 ft)

Time from alarm to 30 nm (55 km; 35 miles) combat area
under 6 min

High altitude intercept radius, with 3 min combat and reserves for
VL — 400 nm (750 km; 460 miles)
Strike radius — 250 nm (463 km; 288 miles)
g limits — +7.8/−4.2

COMBAT PROFILES (FRS. Mk 2, from carrier fitted with a 12° ski-jump ramp, at ISA + 15°C and with a 20 knot; 37 km/h; 23 mph wind over the deck):

Combat air patrol: Up to 1½ hours on station at a radius of 100 nm (185 km; 115 miles), carrying four AMRAAMs, or two AMRAAMs and two 30 mm guns, plus two 864 litre (228 US gallon; 190 Imp gallon) combat drop-tanks.

Reconnaissance: Low-level cover of 28,000 nm² (96,000 km²; 37,065 sq miles) at a radius of 525 nm (970 km; 600 miles) from the carrier, with outward and return flights at medium/high level, carrying two 30 mm guns and two 864 litre (228 US gallon; 190 Imp gallon) combat drop-tanks. Overall flight time 1 h 45 min.

Surface attack (hi-lo-hi): Radius of action to missile launch 200 nm (370 km; 230 miles), carrying two Sea Eagle missiles and two 30 nm guns.

Take-off deck run for the above missions is 137 m, 107 m and 92 m (450 ft, 350 ft and 300 ft) respectively, with vertical landing.

Interception: A typical deck-launched interception could be performed against a Mach 0.9 target at a radius of 116 nm (215 km; 133 miles), or a Mach 1.3 target at 95 nm (175 km; 109 miles), after initial radar detection of the approaching target at a range of 230 nm (425 km; 265 miles), with the Sea Harrier at 2 min alert status, carrying two AMRAAM missiles.

BAe EAP

British Aerospace exhibited at the 1982 Farnborough Air Show, and again at the 1983 Paris Air Show, a full-scale mockup of what was then known as the Agile Combat Aircraft (**ACA**). It represented the result of several years of private-venture research and development by BAe, with industry support from Rolls-Royce, Dowty, Ferranti, Lucas, GEC Avionics and Smiths Industries, at a total estimated cost of £25 million by mid-1983. MBB of Germany and Aeritalia of Italy had also contributed to the project.

No government support for the ACA was forthcoming but, at the 1982 Farnborough show, the UK government announced that it would make a financial contribution to an experimental aircraft programme (**EAP**) technology de-

monstrator based on the ACA design. The aims of the programme were to bring together a specific range of new and advanced technologies being developed by BAe and other aerospace manufacturers in Europe.

On 26 May 1983, BAe announced that a contract had been signed with the Ministry of Defence for the design, development and construction of a single demonstrator aircraft which would be used to prove advanced technological features, including advanced aerodynamics; active control technology for unstable aircraft; a digital databus system; advanced electronic cockpit; and advanced structural design including the extensive use of carbonfibre composites.

The EAP demonstrator was funded by the UK Ministry of Defence, BAe and its industrial partners. These included

BAe EAP advanced-technology demonstrator seen during its first flight.

Aeritalia, which designed and manufactured the carbonfibre wings jointly with BAe, and equipment suppliers in Britain, Italy and West Germany. The remainder of the airframe was designed and manufactured by BAe.

With the UK committed to participation in the international programme for a European fighter aircraft (EFA), the relevance of the EAP is that it is designed to demonstrate a complete weapon system that would meet a generally similar requirement. During its first flight, on 8 August 1986, the EAP demonstrator (ZF534) accelerated to Mach 1.1 at 9,150 m (30,000 ft).

TYPE: Advanced-technology demonstrator aircraft.

WINGS: Main wing aerofoil section varies from root to tip. Multi-spar carbonfibre composite co-bonded construction. Spars bonded to bottom skin; top skin bolted to spar flanges. Foreplanes of carbonfibre composite construction. Aerodynamic configuration provides high negative stability. The leading- and trailing-edge flight surfaces, and the foreplanes, are operated by a GEC Avionics computer controlled active control system, using quadruplex digital fly-by-wire technology developed in the Jaguar ACT programme. Dowty Boulton Paul actuators on the foreplane, rudder and inboard/outboard flaperon control surfaces are operated via a pilot's stick sensor assembly (PSSA) which uses spring damping and viscous loading to give the required stick resistance, to allow full and accurate movement of the stick in relation to aircraft speed and attitude.

FUSELAGE: Front fuselage is conventional metal semi-monocoque structure with carbonfibre composite side-skin panels. Engine air inlet duct of conventional aluminium alloy construction. Hinged forward lower lip. Centre and rear fuselage of conventional metal construction, using Tornado technology and components. Centre keel member of carbonfibre composite to save weight and space.

TAIL UNIT: Cantilever all-metal structure, consisting of single sweptback two-spar fin and rudder, essentially the same as those fitted to the Tornado.

LANDING GEAR: Tricycle type, with single wheel on each unit.

POWERPLANT: Two Turbo-Union RB199-34R Mk 104D turbofan engines, as fitted to the latest version of the IDS Tornado, rated in the 40.0 kN (9,000 lb st) class dry and 75.5 kN (17,000 lb st) class with afterburning. Installed in rear fuselage with downward opening doors for servicing and engine change. Lucas DECU 500 full-authority digital engine control system, developed in conjunction with Rolls-Royce. Fuel is carried integrally in the wings and in 14 tanks in the fuselage.

ACCOMMODATION: Pilot only, on Martin-Baker zero-zero ejection seat, in pressurised cockpit embodying advanced avionic management systems designed to reduce substantially the pilot's workload. Equipment includes three colour multi-function display CRTs supplied by Smiths Industries, and an advanced GEC Avionics head-up display embodying holographic optics, and an additional raster (TV-like) display for night flying. Sensors control level of integrated internal illumination to cater automatically for varying external conditions.

AVIONICS AND EQUIPMENT: Racal Acoustics RA 800 series digital audio control system (IDACS). GEC Avionics AD 3400 VHF/UHF multimode radio. GEC Avionics AD 2780 Tacan system. GEC Avionics television sensor in cockpit records what the pilot sees during flight. Ferranti FIN 1070 inertial navigation system and BAe SCR 300E flight data recorder. Major avionics units mounted in an innovative avionics equipment module in the front fuselage behind the cockpit. Information supplied to VDO cockpit multi-function displays by 1553B databus highways, replacing great lengths of multicored conventional wiring.

It is expected that the aircraft will be used for weapon system trials, and the avionics module will facilitate the evaluation of alternative equipment from other manufacturers.

DIMENSIONS, EXTERNAL:

Wing span	11.77 m (36 ft 7 in)
Length overall	14.70 m (48 ft 2¾ in)
Height	5.52 m (18 ft 1½ in)

AREA:

Wings, gross	52.0 m² (560 sq ft)

PERFORMANCE:

Max speed at height	Mach 2.0+

BAe Nimrod

The Nimrod was developed to replace the Shackleton maritime reconnaissance aircraft of RAF Strike Command, with which it is scheduled to serve until well into the 1990s. Design of the Nimrod, as the Hawker Siddeley 801, began in June 1964, and government authority to proceed was announced in June 1965.

Based substantially upon the airframe of the Hawker Siddeley (de Havilland) Comet 4C, the Nimrod was built as a new production aircraft with a 1.98 m (6 ft 6 in) shorter, modified pressurised fuselage; an unpressurised, underslung pannier for operational equipment and weapons; and Rolls-Royce Spey turbofan engines (instead of the Avon turbojets of the Comet), with wider air intakes to allow for the greater mass flow. Other external changes include enlarged flight deck main windows and 'eyebrow' windows; ESM and MAD equipment, in glassfibre fairings on top of the fin and in the tailboom respectively; and a searchlight in the starboard wing external fuel tank. The search radar is housed in a glassfibre fairing which forms the nose of the unpressurised lower fuselage.

The Nimrod was designed to combine the advantages of high altitude, fast transit speed with low wing loading and good low-speed manoeuvring capabilities when operating in its primary roles of anti-submarine warfare, surveillance and anti-shipping strike. When required, two of the four Spey engines can be shut down to extend endurance, and the aircraft can cruise and climb on only one engine. A wide range of weapons can be carried in the 14.78 m (48 ft 6 in) long bomb bay, and large numbers of sonobuoys and markers can be carried and released from the pressurised rear fuselage area.

In addition to its surveillance and ASW roles, the Nimrod can be used for day and night photography. As supplied originally to the RAF, the aircraft had a standoff surface missile capability. This was subsequently deleted, but was reactivated on some aircraft during the Falklands campaign in 1982. The Nimrod MR. Mk 1 could carry 16 additional personnel in the self-support role; the MR. Mk 2 can carry only 10 without the removal of equipment.

Two prototypes were built, utilising existing Comet 4C

BAe Nimrod R.Mk 1P of No 51 Squadron, RAF. Note the modified tailcone in place of the MAD boom and the flight-refuelling probe over the flight deck. *(Paul Jackson)*

airframes. The first of these (XV148), fitted with Spey engines, flew for the first time on 23 May 1967 and was used for aerodynamic testing. The second (XV147) retained its original Avon engines, was first flown on 31 July 1967, and was used for development of the nav/tac system and special maritime equipment. Both are now in storage in interim MR. Mk 2 condition.

The following versions have been produced:

Nimrod MR. Mk 1. Initial production version. First flown on 28 June 1968. Forty-six delivered, of which eleven were allocated to the now abandoned AEW. Mk 3 programme. All 35 operational MR. Mk 1s now upgraded to MR. Mk 2.

Nimrod R. Mk 1 and 1P. Three aircraft (additional to the MR. Mk 1s ordered for RAF Strike Command) were delivered to No. 51 Squadron at RAF Wyton. These aircraft (XW664-666), are employed for electronic intelligence (elint) missions, and can be identified by the absence of a MAD tailboom. XW664 now has a flight refuelling probe and is designated R. Mk 1P.

Nimrod MR. Mk 2 and **2P**. Thirty-five RAF Nimrod MR. Mk 1s have been refitted with new communications equipment, and advanced tactical sensor, ESM and navigation systems, under a programme which began in 1975 (one, XV256, has been lost subsequently through bird strike). Redelivery started on 23 August 1979 with XV236, the first completely refitted aircraft. After refit these aircraft were redesignated MR. Mk 2, and repainted in a NATO approved camouflage scheme. Equipment includes an advanced search radar, offering greater range and sensitivity coupled with a higher data processing rate; a new acoustic processing system, developed by GEC Avionics, which is compatible with a wide range of existing and projected sonobuoys, and Loral early warning support measures (EWSM) equipment in a pod at each wingtip. Aircraft deployed to Ascension Island during the Spring 1982 Falklands campaign were fitted with Sidewinder air-to-air missiles for self-defence, and were given an attack capability with bombs, Sting Ray torpedoes and, later, Harpoon missiles. Air-to-air refuelling probes were fitted at that time to 16 aircraft (redesignated MR. Mk 2P), making possible flights of up to 19 h with one additional pilot and navigator. Provision for such probes, and Sidewinder and Harpoon missile installations, have now been made on all MR. Mk 2

BAe Nimrod MR.Mk 2P in latest configuration, with wingtip EWSM pods, flight-refuelling probe and larger finlets on tailplane.

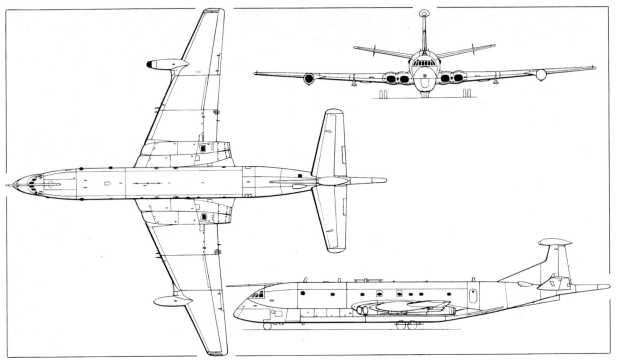

BAe Nimrod MR.Mk 2P. *(Pilot Press)*

aircraft. Associated with these changes are an added ventral fin, small finlets above and below the tailplane on each side, and eleven vortex generators on the leading edge of each outer wing.

Nimrod AEW. Mk 3. Airborne early warning version, now abandoned.

Ample space and power is available in the basic Nimrod design to accept additional or alternative sensors such as sideways looking radar, forward looking infra-red, infra-red linescan, low-light-level TV and digital processing of intercepted ESM signals.

The following description applies to the Nimrod MR. Mks 1 and 2:

TYPE: Four-turbofan maritime patrol aircraft.

WINGS: Cantilever low/mid-wing monoplane. Sweepback 20° at quarter-chord. Ailerons, with trim tabs. Plain flaps outboard of engines. Hot air anti-icing system.

FUSELAGE: Semi-monocoque structure. The circular-section cabin space is fully pressurised. Below this is an unpressurised pannier housing the bomb bay, radome and additional space for operational equipment. Segments of this pannier are free to move relative to each other, so that structural loads in the weapons bay are not transmitted to the pressure cell. Glassfibre nose radome and tailboom.

TAIL UNIT: Cantilever structure, with large dorsal and small ventral fin. Small finlets near leading edge of tailplane on each side. A glassfibre pod on top of the fin houses ESM equipment. Trim tab in each elevator. Hot-air anti-icing system.

LANDING GEAR: Retractable tricycle type. Four-wheel tandem bogie main units, with size 36 × 10-18 Dunlop tyres. Twin-wheel nose unit, with size 30 × 9-15 Dunlop tyres.

POWERPLANT: Four Rolls-Royce RB168-20 Spey Mk 250 turbofan engines, each rated at 54 kN (12,140 lb st).

Reverse thrust fitted on two outer engines. Fuel in fuselage keel tanks, integral wing tanks, and permanent external tank on each wing leading edge, with total capacity of 48,780 litres (12,886 US gallons; 10,730 Imp gallons). Provision for up to six removable tanks in weapons bay. Flight refuelling probe over flight deck.

ACCOMMODATION: Normal crew of 12, comprising pilot, co-pilot, and flight engineer on flight deck; routine navigator, tactical navigator, radio operator, radar operator, two sonics systems operators, ESM/MAD operator, and two observers/stores loaders in main (pressurised) cabin, which is fitted out as a tactical compartment. In this compartment, from front to rear, are a toilet on the port side; stations for the two navigators (stbd), radio and radar operators (port), and sonics systems operators (stbd) in the forward section; ESM/MAD operator's station, galley, four-seat dining area, rest quarters and sonobuoy stowage in the middle section; and buoy and marker launch area in the rear section. Three hemispherical observation windows forward of wings (one port, two stbd), giving 180° field of view. Two normal doors, emergency door, and four overwing emergency exits. Weapons bay can be utilised for additional fuel tanks (see under 'Powerplant') or for the carriage of cargo. Provision is made for a trooping role, in which configuration 45 passengers can be accommodated if some rear fuselage equipment is removed.

AVIONICS AND EQUIPMENT (As fitted to MR. Mk 1): Routine navigation by Decca Doppler Type 67M/GEC Avionics E3 heading reference system, with reversionary heading from a Sperry GM7 duplicated gyro compass system, operating in conjunction with a Ferranti routine dynamic display. Tactical navigation, and stores selection and release, by GEC Avionics nav/attack system utilising an 8K GEC Avionics 920B digital computer. Tactical display station to provide continually updated information about aircraft position, with present and past track, sonobuoy positions, range circles from sonobuoys, ESM bearings, MAD marks, radar contacts and visual bearings. Course information displayed automatically to the pilots on the flight director system; alternatively, the computer could be coupled to the autopilot to allow the tactical navigator to direct the aircraft to a predicted target interception, weapon release point, or any other point on the tactical display. ASW equipment: Sonic 1C sonar and long-range sonar system; Thorn EMI ASV-21D surface vessel detection radar in nose; Thomson-CSF ESM (electronic support measures) equipment in pod on top of fin; and Emerson Electronics ASQ-10A MAD (magnetic anomaly detector) in extended tailboom. Strong Electric 70 million candlepower searchlight at front of starboard external wing fuel tank. Aeronautical and General Instruments F.126 and F.135 cameras for day and night photography respectively, the latter having Chicago Aero Industries electronic flash equipment. Smiths SFS.6 automatic flight control system, embodying SEP.6 three-axis autopilot, integrated with the navigation and tactical system. Twin Plessey PTR 175 UHF/VHF, and GEC Avionics AD 470 HF, communications transceivers; twin GEC Avionics AD 260 VOR/ILS; GEC Avionics AD 2770 Tacan; Decca Loran C/A; GEC Avionics AD 360 ADF; Honeywell AN/APN-171(V) radar altimeter. Yaw damper and Mach trim standard.

AVIONICS AND EQUIPMENT (MR. Mk 2): New and more flexible operational system, using three separate processors for tactical navigation, radar and acoustics. GEC Avionics central tactical system, based on a 920 ATC computer with a greater storage capacity than that of MR. Mk 1, to provide improved computing and display facilities and, in conjunction with a Ferranti inertial navigation system, improved navigation capabilities. Thorn EMI Searchwater long-range surface vessel detection radar, with its own data processing subsystem incorporating a Ferranti FM 1600D digital computer. This system presents a clutter-free picture, can detect and classify surface vessels, submarine snorts and periscopes at extreme ranges, can track several targets simultaneously and is designed to operate in spite of countermeasures. Thorn EMI colour display for Searchwater now in use. AQS 901 acoustics processing and display system, based on twin GEC Avionics 920 ATC computers, is compatible with a wide range of passive and active sonobuoys, either in existence or under development, including the Australian BARRA passive directional sonobuoy, the Canadian TANDEM, the US SSQ-41 and SSQ-53, and the Ultra A size X17255 command active multi-beam sonobuoy (CAMBS), with a performance similar to that of helicopter dipping sonars. Communications improved by the installation of twin GEC Avionics AD 470 HF transceivers (instead of the original single AD 470), and a radio teletype and encryption system. Loral EWSM equipment in two wingtip pods. Onboard crew training system developed by the Maritime Aircraft Systems Division of GEC Avionics Ltd. Known as ACT-1 (Airborne Crew Trainer Mk 1), it consists of a single exercise control unit comprising a control and display panel with push-buttons, and a reel of magnetic tape containing the software programme, by means of which the AQS 901 processing and display system can operate in a training mode. Using the ACT-1, which physically resembles a TV game, one crew member can 'play' the part of a submarine, trying to outwit his colleagues operating the AQS 901 detection system. Although not a replacement for ground based simulator training, the ACT-1 onboard system enables a Nimrod captain to train his crew in authentic operational conditions, without the expenditure of sonobuoys.

ARMAMENT (MR. Mk 2): 14.78 m (48 ft 6 in) long weapons bay, with two pairs of doors, in unpressurised lower fuselage pannier, able to carry up to six lateral rows of ASW weapons, including up to nine torpedoes as well as bombs. Alternatively, up to six auxiliary fuel tanks can be fitted in the weapons bay, or a combination of fuel tanks and weapons can be carried. To ensure weapon serviceability, the weapons bay is heated when the ambient temperature falls below +5°C. Bay approx 9.14 m (30 ft) long in rear pressurised part of fuselage for storing and launching of active and passive sonobuoys and marine markers. Two rotary launchers, each capable of holding six size A sonobuoys, are used when the cabin is unpressurised; two single-barrel launchers are used when the aircraft is pressurised. A hardpoint is provided beneath each wing, just outboard of the mainwheel doors, on which can be carried two Sidewinder air-to-air missiles, a Harpoon air-to-surface missile, rocket or cannon pod, or mine, according to mission requirements.

DIMENSIONS, EXTERNAL:

Wing span	35.00 m (114 ft 10 in)
Length overall:	
MR. Mk 2 excl refuelling probe	38.63 m (126 ft 9 in)
MR. Mk 2 incl probe	39.35 m (129 ft 1 in)
R. Mk 2 excl probe	35.66 m (117 ft 0 in)
R. Mk 2 incl probe	36.60 m (120 ft 1 in)
Height overall	9.08 m (29 ft 8½ in)
Wheel track	8.60 m (28 ft 2½ in)
Wheelbase	14.24 m (46 ft 8½ in)

AREA:

Wings, gross	197.0 m² (2,121 sq ft)

WEIGHTS (as given for original MR. Mk 1):

Typical weight empty	39,000 kg (86,000 lb)
Max disposable load	6,120 kg (13,500 lb)
Fuel load: standard tanks	38,940 kg (85,840 lb)
max with six auxiliary tanks in weapons bay	
	45,785 kg (100,940 lb)
Normal max T-O weight	80,510 kg (177,500 lb)
Max overload T-O weight	87,090 kg (192,000 lb)
Typical landing weight	54,430 kg (120,000 lb)

PERFORMANCE (as given for original MR. Mk 1):

Max operational necessity speed, ISA + 20°C	
	500 knots (926 km/h; 575 mph)
Max transit speed, ISA × 20°C	
	475 knots (880 km/h; 547 mph)
Typical low-level patrol speed (two engines)	
	200 knots (370 km/h; 230 mph)
Operating height range	S/L to 12,800 m (42,000 ft)
T-O run at 80,510 kg (177,500 lb) AUW, ISA at S/L	
	1,463 m (4,800 ft)
Unfactored landing distance at 54,430 kg (120,000 lb)	
landing weight, ISA at S/L	1,615 m (5,300 ft)
Typical ferry range	4,500–5,000 nm
	(8,340–9,265 km; 5,180–5,755 miles)
Typical endurance	12 h

247

BAe (BAC 167) Strikemaster

The BAe Strikemaster was developed from the BAC Jet Provost trainer. It has the same airframe, but is powered by a Rolls-Royce Viper Mk 535 turbojet engine (15.2 kN; 3,410 lb st) and has eight underwing hardpoints, enabling it to carry up to 1,360 kg (3,000 lb) of stores. This makes it particularly suitable for counter-insurgency combat operations, reconnaissance, and pilot and weapons training.

The first Strikemaster (G-27-8) flew for the first time on 26 October 1967, and 146 (including five BAC 145s) were ordered. Deliveries were completed in 1978 (See Mks 89 and 90 below). Of the Strikemasters delivered, only the Mk 81s received by the People's Democratic Republic of Yemen (South) appear to be totally out of service.

Versions of the Strikemaster are:

Mk 55. In service with Sudan Air Force. Probably three remaining of five delivered.

Mk 80. For Royal Saudi Air Force. Twenty-five ordered in 1966. Deliveries began in 1968 and were completed in September 1969.

Mk 80A. Follow-on order, for ten aircraft, for Royal Saudi Air Force. An additional order for ten aircraft was placed during 1977.

Mk 82. For Sultan of Oman's Air Force. Twelve ordered; delivery completed in December 1969.

Mk 82A. For Sultan of Oman's Air Force. Eight ordered. Delivery of a further four was completed in July 1976.

Mk 83. For Kuwait Air Force. First order, for six, placed in October 1968; deliveries began in 1969. Order subsequently increased to 12, the last of which was delivered in July 1971.

Mk 84. For Singapore Air Defence Command. Sixteen ordered; delivery completed in September 1970.

Mk 87. For Kenya Air Force. Six ordered in 1969;

BAe (BAC 167) Strikemaster Mk 82A of the Sultan of Oman's Air Force.

delivery completed in 1971.

Mk 88. For Royal New Zealand Air Force. Ten ordered; delivery completed in October 1972. Six more ordered in spring 1974. Currently fifteen operated by single COIN squadron. Used also for advanced training.

Mk 89. For Ecuadorean Air Force. Initial order for eight (later increased to 12), of which delivery began in early 1973. Delivery of a further four was completed in July 1976. In 1986–87 Ecuador received another six, representing the last of the new Strikemasters held in store for future orders. These operate in a COIN role with 2113 Squadron.

Mk 90. Twelve final Strikemasters were assembled in UK in anticipation of further orders. From 1983 the Sudan received six as Mk 90s.

The following description applies primarily to later variants of the Strikemaster, such as the Mk 88, but is also substantially applicable to earlier versions:

TYPE: Two-seat tactical support aircraft and armed trainer.

BAe Strikemaster. *(Pilot Press)*

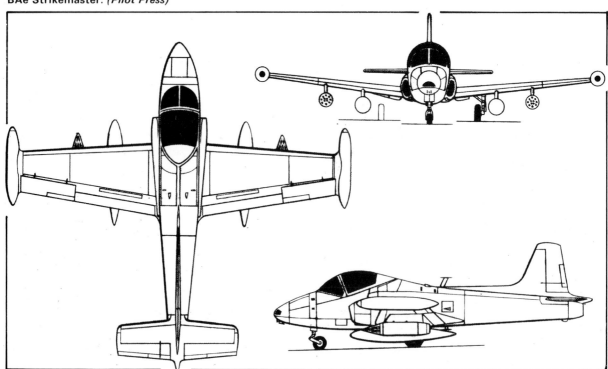

WINGS: Cantilever low-wing monoplane. Wing section NACA 23015 (modified) at root, NACA 4412 (modified) at tip. Dihedral 6°. Incidence 3° at root, 0° at tip. Ailerons with balance tabs. Slotted flaps. Air-brakes and lift spoilers on wings at rear spar position ahead of flaps.

FUSELAGE: Semi-monocoque structure. Hinged nose cap provides access to pressurisation, oxygen, radio and electrical equipment.

TAIL UNIT: Cantilever structure. One-piece tailplane, interchangeable elevators, fin and rudder. Combined trim and balance tab in starboard elevator; balance tabs in port elevator and rudder.

LANDING GEAR: Tricycle type. Dunlop main wheels with tubeless tyres size 21 × 6.75-9. Dunlop nosewheel and tubeless tyre size 6.00-4. Dunlop hydraulic disc brakes.

POWERPLANT: One Rolls-Royce Bristol Viper Mk 535 turbojet engine (15.2 kN; 3,410 lb st) in fuselage aft of cockpit. Lateral intake on each side of forward fuselage. Internal fuel capacity (one integral tank outboard and three bag tanks inboard in each wing) 1,227 litres (324 US gallons; 270 Imp gallons). Refuelling point near each wingtip. Two wingtip fuel tanks, total capacity 436 litres (115 US gallons; 96 Imp gallons), are a standard fit at all times. All tanks in wings are interconnected. System designed to permit 18 sec of inverted flight.

ACCOMMODATION: Two persons side-by-side in pressurised cabin, on Martin-Baker automatic ejection seats (Mk PB4/1 and PB4/2), suitable for use down to ground level and 90 knots (167 km/h; 104 mph). Power-operated rearward-sliding canopy, Dual controls standard.

AVIONICS: Varies to meet customer's requirements. The following radio equipment was installed in various combinations: ARC 51 BX and ARC 52 UHF; PV 141 UHF homer; D 403 UHF standby; PTR 175 UHF/VHF; Collins 618M VHF; Collins 618 FIA VHF standby; ARI 18120/2 Violet Picture; Sunair ASB 100 and SA 14-RA HF; and PTR 446, SSR 1600 and SSR 2100 IFF. The following navigation equipment was installed in various combinations: Bendix CNS 220B UHF; Bendix CNS 240B VHF; RCA AVQ-75 DME; AD 370B and ADF 722 ADF; Bendix 221 VOR/ILS; and ARN 84, ARN 52 and ARN 65 Tacan.

ARMAMENT: Two 7.62 mm FN machine-guns, with 550 rds/gun; one in the lower lip of each engine air intake duct. Later variants have SFOM gunsights; GM2L reflector gunsights fitted to some earlier models. Provision for a G90 gun camera and a Smiths camera sight recorder. Four underwing strongpoints for the carriage of external stores. Typical underwing loads include two 341 and two 227 litre (90 and 60 US gallon; 75 and 50 Imp gallon) drop-tanks; four Matra launchers each containing eighteen 68 mm SNEB rockets; four 540 LAU 68 rocket launchers, each with seven rockets; four 540 lb ballistic or retarded bombs, four 250 kg or 500 kg bombs; four PMBR carriers, each with six practice bombs; light-series bomb carriers to carry 8.5, 19 or 25 lb practice bombs; BAe/Vinten five-camera reconnaissance pod; or banks of SURA 80 mm rockets, with four rockets per bank. Other armament, to specific customer requirements, can include napalm tanks, 65 or 125 kg bombs, 2.75 in or 3 in rockets, and 7.62 mm or 20 mm gun packs. Max T-O weight of 5,215 kg (11,500 lb) includes one pilot only, full usable fuel (internal and wingtip tanks) and 1,200 kg (2,650 lb) of external stores. Max possible external stores load 1,360 kg (3,000 lb).

DIMENSIONS, EXTERNAL:
Wing span over tip-tanks	11.23 m (36 ft 10 in)
Length overall	10.27 m (33 ft 8½ in)
Height overall	3.34 m (10 ft 11½ in)
Wheel track	3.27 m (10 ft 8.9 in)
Wheelbase	2.93 m (9 ft 7.4 in)

AREA:
Wings, gross	19.85 m² (213.7 sq ft)

WEIGHTS:
Operating weight empty, equipped, incl crew
    2,810 kg (6,195 lb)
Typical T-O weights:
    pilot conversion training, 2 crew, full internal fuel
        4,219 kg (9,303 lb)
    armament training, 2 crew, full internal fuel, practice armament (bombs and racks)   4,808 kg (10,600 lb)
    ferry role, 2 crew, full internal fuel plus inboard and outboard drop-tanks   5,213 kg (11,493 lb)
    *Max T-O weight   5,215 kg (11,500 lb)
    *Details under 'Armament' paragraph

PERFORMANCE (at max T-O weight except where indicated):
Never-exceed speed   450 knots (834 km/h; 518 mph)
Max level speed, with 50% fuel, 'clean'
    at S/L   391 knots (724 km/h; 450 mph)
    at 5,485 m (18,000 ft)   418 knots (774 km/h; 481 mph)
    at 6,100 m (20,000 ft)   410 knots (760 km/h; 472 mph)
Stalling speed at 4,309 kg (9,500 lb) AUW:
    flaps up   98.5 knots (182 km/h; 113 mph)
    flaps down   85.5 knots (158 km/h; 98 mph)
Max rate of climb at S/L (training, full internal fuel)
    1,600 m (5,250 ft)/min
Service ceiling   12,200 m (40,000 ft)
T-O to 15 m (50 ft) at 5,215 kg (11,500 lb) AUW (combat)
    1,067 m (3,500 ft)
Landing from 15 m (50 ft) at 5,103 kg (11,250 lb) AUW (aborted armed sortie)   1,295 m (4,250 ft)
Combat radius (hi-lo-hi), 5 min over target, 10% reserves:
    with 1,360 kg (3,000 lb) weapons load
        215 nm (397 km; 247 miles)
    with 907 kg (2,000 lb) weapons load
        355 nm (656 km; 408 miles)
    with 454 kg (1,000 lb) weapons load
        500 nm (925 km; 575 miles)
Combat radius (lo-lo-lo, at S/L), 5 min over target, 10% reserves:
    with 1,360 kg (3,000 lb) weapons load
        126 nm (233 km; 145 miles)
    with 907 kg (2,000 lb) weapons load
        175 nm (323 km; 201 miles)
    with 454 kg (1,000 lb) weapons load
        240 nm (444 km; 276 miles)
    reconnaissance mission   300 nm (555 km; 345 miles)
Range with 91 kg (200 lb) fuel reserves:
    at 3,789 kg (8,355 lb) AUW (training)
        629 nm (1,166 km; 725 miles)
    at 4,558 kg (10,500 lb) AUW (combat)
        1,075 nm (1,922 km; 1,238 miles)
    at 5,215 kg (11,500 lb) AUW (max T-O)
        1,200 nm (2,224 km; 1,382 miles)

English Electric

ENGLISH ELECTRIC COMPANY

English Electric became part of BAC in 1960.

English Electric Canberra

Designed by the former English Electric company to Specification B.3/45, the Canberra remained in production for over ten years. The first prototype (VN799) flew for the first time on 13 May 1949. Deliveries of production Canberras to the Royal Air Force began in January, 1951, and versions were ordered subsequently by many Commonwealth and foreign air forces. The Canberra was the RAF's first operational jet bomber.

A total of 1,375 Canberras was built; 924 in the United Kingdom by English Electric, Short Bros & Harland, A. V. Roe and Handley Page; 48 under licence in Australia by the Department of Defence Production; and 403 under licence in the United States (under the USAF designation B-57) by the Martin Company.

The RAF's Bomber Command gave up the Canberra in 1961, although one squadron of Far East Command retained Canberras for an offensive role until 1970. Today the RAF uses Canberras only for ECM training, reconnaissance, calibration and target towing. However, some aircraft in foreign use retain major combat capability. These include the SAAF's B(I). Mk 12s, each of which has a new bomb rack giving a 40% increase in load and the ability to carry new-generation bombs, developed by Armscor and No 12 Squadron. SAAF Canberras already had a new weapons delivery system fitted to enhance accuracy.

The currently operated versions of Canberra are thought to be:

B Mk. 6. Early production bomber, with 28.9 kN (6,500 lb st) Avon 109 engines. Currently flown by the air force of Ecuador. B. Mk 6 can carry 2,720 kg (6,000 lb) of weapons internally, plus up to 907 kg (2,000 lb) of stores underwing on modified aircraft.

B (I). Mk 8. Developed as a two-seat long-range night intruder or high-altitude bomber and target marker. Currently used by Peru. See similar versions below.

B (I). Mk 12. Modified version of the B (I). Mk 8. Currently used by the South African Air Force. Prototype flew in 1958.

B (I). Mk 56. Similar to B (I). Mk 6, operated by Peru.

B (I). Mk 58. Modified version of the B (I). Mk 8 for the Indian Air Force. Total of 71 built in 1958–64. Remaining examples being replaced.

B. Mk 62, 72 and 82. Similar to original B. Mk 2, used by Argentina, Peru and Venezuela respectively.

B (I). Mk 88. Venezuelan intruder model, similar to B (I). Mk 8.

E. Mk 15. RAF radar and radio calibration model.

PR. Mk 9. High-altitude photographic reconnaissance aircraft to replace the PR.7. Span increased and chord of centre-section of wing inboard of nacelles extended. Offset fighter canopy as in B (I). Mk 8. Navigator's station in nose, the extremity of which is hinged for crew entry. Powered by Avon Mk 206 turbojets, each 48.9 kN (11,000 lb st). Built by Short Brothers & Harland. Prototype PR. Mk 9 (WH793) flew on 8 July 1955 and first production machine in July 1958. Supplied to the RAF and also currently flown by Chile. Five RAF Canberra PR. Mk 9s are undergoing major refurbishment for the UK Ministry of Defence, under a programme extending over several years and involving the design and embodiment of unspecified modifications.

PR. Mk 57. Modified version of the PR. Mk 7 for the Indian Air Force. Ten built in 1958–64.

PR. Mk 83. Venezuelan photographic reconnaissance model.

T. Mk 4. Dual-control trainer. Used by RAF, India (as T. Mk 54), Peru and South Africa.

T. Mk 17. This is a special electronic countermeasures training variant for the RAF, with a nose fairing similar to the tail-cone of the former Victor bomber.

Six of the 12 Canberra T. Mk 17s of No. 360 Squadron, Royal Air Force, are being modified to T. Mk 17A standard to increase their electronic jamming capability. First of the uprated T. Mk 17As delivered to the Squadron's base at RAF Wyton was WJ981. Externally, it is distinguished only by a new VHF/UHF radio antenna under each wing and overall hemp camouflage. Internally, it has a digital Omega navigation computer in place of its outdated analog set, and its suite of jammers has been modernised and expanded.

TT. Mk 18. This is a target towing conversion of the B. Mk 2, carrying a Flight Refuelling Rushton automatic winch pack on a pylon under each wing. These packs can tow interception targets on cables up to 48,000 ft (14,600 m) long.

TT. Mk 22. Royal Navy radar target version.

T. Mk 64. Designation of Argentine training version.

T. Mk 67. Indian training version.

T. Mk 84. Venezuelan training version.

Venezuelan Canberra B.Mk 82 light bomber.

First of six updated Canberra T.Mk 17As delivered to No 360 Squadron of the Royal Air Force.

Royal Air Force Canberra TT.Mk 18 target-towing conversion of the B.Mk 2. *(J. M. G. Gradidge)*

ASTOR Canberra. Thorn-EMI has supplied a modified Searchwater radar for installation in the Canberra held by the Royal Signals and Radar Establishment. The Canberra has undergone development and evaluation to assess the practicality of a high-altitude radar surveillance platform as part of the ASTOR battlefield surveillance system programme.

The following details apply to the B (I). (Mk 8, but are generally applicable to other versions.)

TYPE: Long-range interdictor and high-altitude bomber (see model listing for other roles).

WINGS: Cantilever mid-wing monoplane. RAE/D symmetrical high-speed wing section. Thickness/chord ratio 12% at root, 9% at tip. Dihedral 2° on centre-section, 4° 21′ on outer wings. Incidence 2°. Irving-Westland pressure-balanced ailerons with spring-tab in each. Four split trailing-edge flaps. Air-brakes consist of drag channels which can be extended from top and bottom wing surfaces aft of spar.

FUSELAGE: Semi-monocoque structure of circular section, built in nose, centre and rear portions.

TAIL UNIT: Cantilever metal structure, except for forward portion of fin, which is of wood construction with plywood covering. Variable-incidence dihedral (7° 57′) tailplane hinged at leading edge and operated by English Electric actuator in rear fuselage. Spring-tab in port elevator, geared tab in starboard elevator. Mass-balanced rudder with spring-tab.

LANDING GEAR: Tricycle type. Single wheel on each main unit. Dowty fully-castoring nose unit with twin wheels. Dunlop AH 51337 21 in main wheels and tyres. Dunlop AH 9590 nosewheels and tyres. Dunlop hydraulic disc brakes with Maxaret anti-skid units.

POWERPLANT: Two 32.9 kN (7,400 lb st) Rolls-Royce Avon 109 turbojet engines. Fuel in three main tanks in upper part of fuselage above bomb bay and two integral tanks in wings. Forward and centre fuselage tanks are of internally-braced self-sealing type, capacity 2,364 litres (624 US gallons; 520 Imp gallons) and 1,441 litres (381 US gallons; 317 Imp gallons) respectively. Rear lace-supported bag tank capacity 2,455 litres (648 US gallons; 540 Imp gallons). Integral wing tanks each 2,046 litres (540 US

English Electric Canberra PR. Mk 9. *(Pilot Press)*

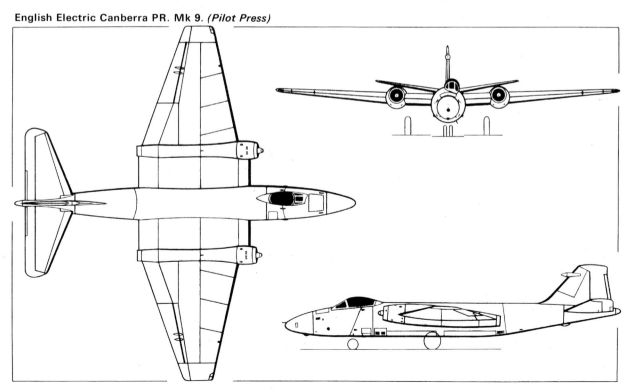

gallons; 450 Imp gallons). Provision for auxiliary wing-tip tanks, each with capacity of 1,109 litres (293 US gallons; 244 Imp gallons).

ACCOMMODATION: Pilot on Martin-Baker Type 2CB ejection seat under fighter-type canopy offset to port side of fuselage. Navigator's seat totally enclosed in nose.

ARMAMENT: In bomber role: six 1,000 lb, one 4,000 lb and two 1,000 lb, or eight 500 lb bombs internally, plus up to 907 kg (2,000 lb) of stores on underwing pylons. In intruder role, a pack of four 20-mm Hispano cannon can be installed in rear of weapons bay, leaving room in forward part for three 1,000 lb bombs. Alternatively, air-to-surface missiles can be carried.

DIMENSIONS, EXTERNAL:		
Wing span	19.50 m (63 ft 11½ in)	
Wing span over tip-tanks	19.96 m (65 ft 6 in)	
Length overall	19.96 m (65 ft 6 in)	
Height overall	4.77 m (15 ft 8 in)	
Wheel track	4.80 m (15 ft 9 in)	
Wheelbase	4.64 m (15 ft 2¾ in)	
AREA:		
Wings, gross	89.19 m² (960 sq ft)	
WEIGHTS:		
Basic operating weight (intruder)	12,678 kg (27,950 lb)	
Max T-O weight	24,925 kg (54,950 lb)	
PERFORMANCE:		
Max level speed at S/L	449 knots (832 km/h; 517 mph)	

Max level speed at 12,200 m (40,000 ft)		
at 19,958 kg (44,000 lb)	470 knots (871 km/h; 541 mph)	
Max level speed at 9,145 m (30,000 ft)		
B. Mk 6 version	504 knots (933 km/h; 580 mph)	
Max rate of climb at S/L	1,036 m (3,400 ft)/min	
Service ceiling	14,630 m (48,000 ft)	
T-O to 15 m (50 ft)	1,830 m (6,000 ft)	
Landing from 15 m (50 ft)	1,190 m (3,900 ft)	
Range with max fuel, no reserves		
	3,152 nm (5,842 km; 3,630 miles)	
Range with max payload, no reserves, at 610 m (2,000 ft) with 10 min over target at full power		
	699 nm (1,295 km; 805 miles)	
Range, B. Mk 6 version	3,290 nm (6,100 km; 3,790 miles)	

Hawker

HAWKER AIRCRAFT LTD

Hawker Siddeley Aviation, which superseded Hawker Aircraft Ltd, became part of BAe in 1977.

Hawker Hunter

Powered by one Rolls-Royce Avon RA.7 turbojet, the first of two prototype Hunter F. Mk 1 fighters (WB188) flew for the first time on 20 July 1951. Hunters first joined the RAF in 1954. WB188, having been modified into the single example of the RA-7R-powered F. Mk 3, set a world speed record over a 3 km straight course, and a 100 km closed-circuit record in September 1953, of 632 knots (1,171 km/h; 727.6 mph) and 616 knots (1,141.4 km/h; 709 mph) respectively.

A total of 1,985 Hunters was built, including 460 manufactured by Fokker and Aviolanda in Holland and by Avions Fairey and SABCA in Belgium. The final RAF version was the F(GA). Mk 9, a ground-support derivative of the F. Mk 6 fighter with a brake parachute and heavier weapon load. In the RAF it replaced the Venom for tropical work. This change of role put the Hunter back at the forefront of combat aircraft. As with the Canberra, however, the end of Britain's commitment to the defence of Malaysia in 1970 saw the end also of Hunters in RAF front-line service.

Many Hunters continue in front-line use with foreign air forces, notably with the Swiss Air Force which has 132 F. Mk 58s. This total includes examples of refurbished Hunters, sixty of which were ordered in the 1970s in two batches for final assembly at the Federal Aircraft Factory in Emmen. These were delivered by Hawker Siddeley Aviation from 1972. Hawker had refurbished Hunters for other air forces also, reconditioning and modification having been an important function of the company's Blackburn Division since the early 1960s.

Versions still in service are as follows:

T. Mk 7. Trainer/operational version with wider forward fuselage accommodating two side-by-side on Martin-Baker lightweight ejection seats. Was easily convertible from single-seat versions, by fitting new nose. Armament reduced to one 30 mm Aden gun in fairing under starboard side of forward fuselage. Brake parachute in fairing above jet-pipe. First prototype (XJ615), based on Mk 4, flew on 8 July 1955. Second prototype (XJ627), based on Mk 6, flew on 17 November 1956. First production T. Mk 7 (XL563) flew on 11 October 1957. Production included 45 for the RAF, of which some remain. Avon Mk 122 turbojet (34.25 kN; 7,700 lb st). AUW of 9,979 kg (22,000 lb). Thought to be used also by Oman in **T. Mk 67** form.

T. Mk 8. Naval counterpart of Mk 7 for Royal Navy with Avon Mk 122. Modifications included fitting of airfield arrester gear for training purposes. Prototype (WW664) flew on 3 March 1958, and 28 were built or converted. During 1960s a further quantity of conversions was ordered, with equipment changes, under the designations T. Mk 8B and 8C.

Royal Navy Hunter T.Mk 8M of No 899 Squadron.
(J. M. G. Gradidge)

Hunter GA.Mk 11s of the Royal Navy's Fleet Requirements and Air Direction Unit. *(Fleet Air Arm)*

T. Mk 8M. As part of the Sea Harrier development programme, two Hunter T. Mk 8 two-seat trainers of the Royal Navy were converted by British Aerospace at Brough to carry the complete suite of operational equipment selected for the Sea Harrier, including the Ferranti Blue Fox radar. The first of these aircraft, which have the designation **T. Mk 8M**, flew for the first time on 9 January 1978. They were being used for nav/attack system development trials, one by BAe at Dunsfold and the other by the RSRE at RAE Bedford. After completion of these trials, in 1981, the converted Hunters were returned to the Royal Navy for service as Sea Harrier airborne weapons system trainers.

F (GA). Mk 9. Development of Mk 6 single-seat fighter for ground-support duties with RAF in Middle East, with Avon Mk 207 turbojet, brake parachute and ability to carry 230 Imp gallon drop-tanks in addition to ground-attack weapons. Prototype (XE617) flew on 3 July 1959. In service in Aden by March 1960. Supplied to Royal Rhodesian Air Force and still used by Chile and Zimbabwe. Description below applies to this version.

GA. Mk 11. Conversion of F. Mk 4 for use by Royal Navy as single-seat advanced ground-attack trainer. Fitted with arrester hook and TACAN. Guns removed. With cameras in detachable nose-cone became PR. Mk 11.

F (GA). Mk 56. Mk 6 ground-attack fighter, powered by Avon Mk 203, for India. Delivery of 160 began in October 1957, and was completed in February 1961. First 48 were ex-RAF.

F. Mk 58. Mk 6 ground-attack fighter, with Avon Mk 203 engine, supplied to Switzerland. Equipped with gun blast deflectors and tail parachute. Delivery of 100 began in April 1958 and was completed in 1960. Sixty refurbished aircraft followed during 1970s.

F (GA). Mk 59. Eighteen ex-Mk 6 aircraft ordered by Iraq in 1963, to supplement 15 Mk 6 aircraft supplied earlier. Deliveries began in 1964.

T. Mk 66. Two-seat trainer for Indian Air Force, with Avon Mk 203 engine, two 30 mm Aden guns and tail parachute. Delivery of 22 began in 1959 and was completed in February 1961.

T. Mk 66B. Two-seat trainer, with Avon Mk 207 engine, two 30 mm Aden guns and tail parachute. Two delivered to Jordan in 1960–61. Thought to be used currently by Oman.

T. Mk 68. Swiss Air Force trainer.

T. Mk 69. Two two-seat trainers ordered by Iraq in 1963. Currently used also by Lebanon.

F. Mk 70. Perhaps seven fighters used by Lebanon.

F (GA). Mk 71. Fighter-bomber operated by Chile.

F (GA). Mk 73. Fighter-bomber operated by Oman.

F (GA). Mk 74. Fighter-bomber operated by Singapore.

FR. Mk 75. Reconnaissance version of F (GA). Mk 74 used by Singapore.

Swiss Air Force Hunter F.Mk 58 ground-attack fighters. *(Martin Fricke)*

F (GA). Mk 76. About ten fighter-bombers operated by Somali Republic.

T. Mk 77. Somali trainer.

F (GA). Mk 78. Fighter-bomber operated by Qatar. Based on Mk 6. Perhaps two only.

T. Mk 79. Single trainer used by Qatar.

T. Mk 80. Single trainer used by Zimbabwe.

All versions of the Hunter are supersonic in shallow dives at height.

The following details refer specifically to the Hunter F (GA) Mk 9, but are generally applicable to other versions.

TYPE: Single-seat ground-attack fighter.

WINGS: Cantilever mid-wing monoplane. Hawker high-speed symmetrical wing section. Thickness/chord ratio $8\frac{1}{2}\%$. Anhedral 1°. Incidence 1° 30′ at root. Sweepback at quarter-chord 39° 54′. Ailerons, with trim tab on port side. Split flaps.

FUSELAGE: Semi-monocoque structure built in three sections: nose section containing cockpit, armament pack and nosewheel unit; centre section with integral wing-root stubs, engine mounting attachments and intake ducts; and detachable rear fuselage with integral fin base and removable jet-pipe and tail-cone unit. Air-brake in form of hinged flap conforming to curvature of underside of rear fuselage.

TAIL UNIT: Cantilever structure with sweepback on all surfaces. Electrically-operated variable-incidence tailplane. Elevators. Interconnection between elevators and tailplane actuator made provision for operation of the units as an electrically-operated all-moving unit, which could be cut out by operation of a switch in the cockpit if desired. Trim-tab in rudder.

LANDING GEAR: Retractable tricycle type, with single wheel

Hawker Hunter F(GA). Mk 9. *(Pilot Press)*

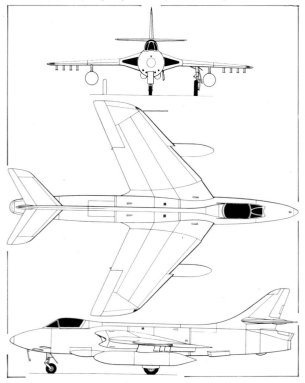

on each unit. Mainwheel tyres size 29 × 6.25-16: nosewheel tyre size 19 × 6.25-9. Hydraulic brakes with anti-skid units. One 3.05 m (10 ft) diameter ring-slot brake parachute in fairing over jet-pipe nozzle.

POWERPLANT: One 44.5 kN (10,000 lb st) Rolls-Royce Avon Mk 207 turbojet engine. Four flexible bag-type tanks in fuselage and four in each wing. Capacities: front fuselage 909 litres (240 US gallons; 200 Imp gallons), rear fuselage 236 litres (62 US gallons; 52 Imp gallons), wings 636 litres (168 US gallons; 140 Imp gallons). Total fuel capacity 1,782 litres (470 US gallons; 392 Imp gallons). Underwing attachments for 2 × 455 litre (120 US gallon; 100 Imp gallon) or 2 × 1,045 litre (276 US gallon; 230 Imp gallon) jettisonable tanks.

ACCOMMODATION: Pressurised cockpit with sliding jettisonable canopy. Martin-Baker Type 2H or 3H fully-automatic ejection seat.

ARMAMENT: Four 30 mm Aden guns (150 rpg) in self-contained removable package in underside of fuselage nose. Gun pack can be winched down for rearming, servicing, etc. Automatic gun-ranging radar in front fuselage with scanner in nose radome, and gyro gunsight. The following external stores may be carried: on the inboard wing pylons two 1,000 lb bombs, two 500 lb bombs, two carriers each with two 25 lb practice bombs, two clusters of six 3-in rockets, two containers, each with either 24 or 37 2 in folding-fin rockets, two 100 Imp gallon phenolic asbestos drop-tanks or two 230 Imp gallon steel drop-tanks; on the outboard wing pylons two 100 Imp gallon drop-tanks, or up to twenty-four 3 in rockets. The 100-gallon drop-tanks may be used as Napalm bombs. Combinations of the above loads may be carried. Oman's Mk 73s now carry AIM-9P Sidewinders.

AVIONICS AND EQUIPMENT: Original avionics: radio installation by Plessey of a UHF communications system and UHF stand-by system. A system to give the pilot audio warning of loss of hydraulic pressure is linked with UHF system. Murphy DME. Cossor IFF. Ekco radar ranging equipment.

DIMENSIONS, EXTERNAL:

Wing span	10.26 m (33 ft 8 in)
Length overall	13.98 m (45 ft $10\frac{1}{2}$ in)
Height overall	4.26 m (13 ft 2 in)
Wheel track	4.50 m (14 ft 9 in)
Wheelbase	4.80 m (15 ft 9 in)

AREA:

Wings, gross	32.42 m² (349.0 sq ft)

WEIGHTS:

Weight empty	6,019 kg (13,270 lb)
Max weapon load	3,357 kg (7,400 lb)
Max T-O weight	10,885 kg (24,000 lb)

PERFORMANCE (with two 230 Imp gallon drop-tanks):

Max level speed at S/L	616 knots (1,142 km/h; 710 mph)
Max cruising speed	Mach 0.84
Econ cruising speed	399 knots (740 km/h; 460 mph)
Stalling speed	125 knots (232 km/h; 144 mph)
Rate of climb at S/L	approx 2,440 m (8,000 ft)/min
Service ceiling	15,250 m (50,000 ft)
T-O run	640 m (2,100 ft)
T-O to 50 ft (15 m)	1,050 m (3,450 ft)
Landing run	960 m (3,150 ft)
Range, no reserves	1,595 nm (2,965 km; 1,840 miles)

Hawker Siddeley Buccaneer

The Hawker Siddeley (originally Blackburn) Buccaneer strike aircraft flew for the first time on 30 April 1958, and was produced initially for the Royal Navy (20 development aircraft, 40 S.Mk 1 and 84 S.Mk 2 production aircraft) and the South African Air Force (16 S.Mk 50s).

Many Royal Navy S. Mk 2s were later transferred to the RAF, the first four being delivered to No. 12 Squadron at RAF Honington on 1 October 1969. Those operated by the RAF became S. Mk 2As (without Martel missile capability) and S. Mk 2Bs (with Martel). Other airframe and equipment differences existed between these models, but the capability to carry Martel air-to-ground missiles was the fundamental definition of aircraft standard. The RAF, in addition to the ex-RN aircraft, ordered 43 new-production S. Mk 2Bs, the first of which flew on 8 January 1970. Delivery of these was completed in 1977, but the jigs have remained available to cope with repairs and modifications. Mk 2As were later brought up to Mk 2B standard. First RAF units to be completely equipped with the Buccaneer S. Mk 2B were Nos. 15 and 16 Squadrons, based at Laarbruch in Germany.

With the decommissioning of the Royal Navy's final large aircraft carrier, this Service passed its last Buccaneers to the RAF, these having been designated S. Mk 2C (without Martel) and S. Mk 2D (with). In RAF service they, too, became S. Mk 2As and S. Mk 2Bs.

It was announced in February 1985 that British Aerospace had been appointed prime contractor for a £40 million programme to update Buccaneer S.2Bs in service with the Royal Air Force, to improve the avionics, armaments and electronic countermeasures to meet Air Staff Requirement 1012.

A major element of the programme is the installation of a Ferranti FIN 1063 inertial navigation system. This is a

Hawker Siddeley Buccaneer S.Mk 2B of No 12 Squadron, RAF. *(J. M. G. Gradidge)*

derivative of the FIN 1064 which equips RAF SEPECAT Jaguars, minus the weapon aiming system. Ferranti will also update the Blue Parrot attack radar, and Marconi Defence Systems will update the radar warning/ESM suite to Guardian Series 200 standard.

The aircraft are being updated for further service in the maritime role, and will be armed with BAe Sea Eagle and the TV guided Martel anti-ship missiles. Complementary to the avionics update is a full-scale fatigue test intended to extend the airframe life for many years. The update programme involves 42 of the RAF's Buccaneers.

Six of the SAAF's Buccaneer S. Mk 50s remain in service. These were built with a Rolls-Royce Bristol BS. 60S two-chamber retractable rocket motor (8,000 lb thrust for 30 seconds) in the rear fuselage, to boost take-off performance from hot and high airfields.

The following details apply to the Buccaneer S. Mk 2B:
TYPE: Two-seat strike and reconnaissance aircraft.
WINGS: Cantilever mid-wing monoplane. Sweepback at

Hawker Siddeley Buccaneer S. Mk 2B. *(Pilot Press)*

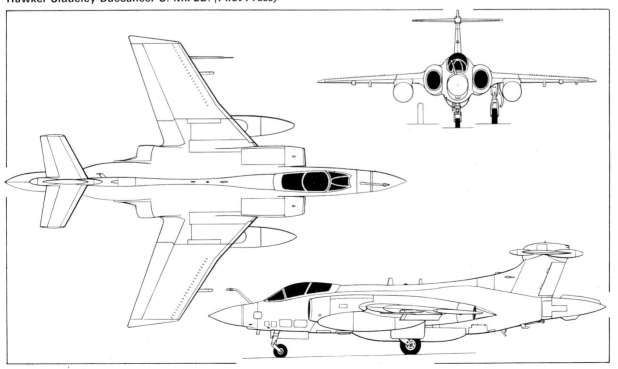

quarter-chord: 40° at root, decreasing first to 38° 36′ and then to 30° 12′. Thin section. No dihedral. Incidence 2° 30′. Ailerons can be drooped in conjunction with the inboard flaps to provide a full-span trailing-edge flap system. No trim tabs. Resin-bonded glassfibre tips on wings and ailerons. Super-circulation boundary layer control, with air outlet slots near leading edges and forward of the drooping ailerons and plain flaps. This system also provides thermal de-icing of the engines and intakes; use of the boundary layer system supplies sufficient heat to de-ice the wing and tailplane leading edges under most operational conditions. Outer wings fold upward hydraulically for stowage.

FUSELAGE: Semi-monocoque structure, bulged at rear end in conformity with area rule. Built in three main sections, comprising cockpit, centre fuselage and rear fuselage, plus nosecone and tailcone. Upper section of centre fuselage contains the fuel tanks, lower section contains the weapons bay. Engine and jetpipe firewalls and heat shields are titanium. Equipment bay in rear fuselage has strengthened floor, designed to absorb stresses when arrester hook was used and transfer them to main structure. Tailcone is made up of two petal-type airbrakes, hydraulically actuated to hinge sideways into the airstream; these can be opened fully or to any intermediate position. For stowage the resin-bonded glasscloth nosecone hinges sideways to port and the airbrakes can be fully opened.

TAIL UNIT: Cantilever T-tail. Large dorsal fin faired into fuselage dorsal fairing. All-moving tailplane attached to tip of fin, which is pivoted to move with it. Tailplane trim flap is used only when ailerons are deflected. Super-circulation boundary layer control system, with air outlet slots in underskin of tailplane, just aft of leading edge.

LANDING GEAR: Retractable tricycle type. Single wheels on all units. Goodyear or Dunlop main wheels and tubeless tyres, size 35 × 10. Goodyear or Dunlop nosewheel and tyre size 24 × 6.6. Hydraulically steerable nosewheel. Goodyear or Dunlop double-disc hydraulic brakes, with anti-skid system.

POWERPLANT: Two 49.4 kN (11,100 lb st) Rolls-Royce RB.168-1A Spey Mk 101 turbofan engines, housed in nacelle on each side of the fuselage. Standard internal fuel in eight integral tanks in upper part of centre fuselage, total capacity 7,092 litres (1,873 US gallons; 1,560 Imp gallons), with provision for cross-feed of all fuel to either engine. In addition, a 1,932 litre (510 US gallon; 425 Imp gallon) bomb-door fuel tank can be fitted, without detriment to the aircraft's bomb-carrying capability. Provision for additional 2,000 litre (528 US gallon; 440 Imp gallon) auxiliary tank in weapons bay, and/or two 1,136 or 1,955 litre (300 or 516 US gallon; 250 or 430 Imp gallon) underwing drop-tanks on the inboard pylons. Detachable flight refuelling probe standard. In the tanker role (max capacity 12,797 litres; 3,381 US gallons; 2,815 Imp gallons) the inboard starboard pylon is occupied by a 636 litre (168 US gallon; 140 Imp gallon) Mk 20B or 20C refuelling pod fed continuously from the main fuel system.

ACCOMMODATION: Crew of two in tandem on Martin-Baker zero-zero ejection seats in pressurised cockpit under single rearward-sliding blown Perspex canopy. Canopy can be jettisoned separately, if necessary, by explosive charge. Windscreen anti-icing by gold film electrical heating systems.

AVIONICS, ARMAMENT AND OPERATIONAL EQUIPMENT: Blue Parrot attack radar being reoptimised for over-water missions, in conjunction with use of Sea Eagle anti-ship missiles. Ferranti FIN 1063 inertial navigation system on updated S. Mk 2Bs, which have Marconi Defence Systems radar warning/ESM suite to Guardian Series 200 standard. Previous standard equipment included single-sideband HF and UHF/VHF communications equipment with centralised audio selection and telebriefing, air data system, and master reference gyro. The rotating weapons bay door can carry four 1,000 lb HE Mk 10 bombs, a 2,000 litre (528 US gallon; 440 Imp gallon) fuel tank, or a reconnaissance pack containing one vertical F97 night camera and six F95 day cameras (three vertical, two oblique and one forward) with low- or high-altitude 102 mm or 305 mm (4 in or 12 in) lenses. Other possible reconnaissance equipment includes linescan, electronic flash gear and different camera arrangements. Each of the four wing pylon stations can be adapted to carry a wide variety of external stores. Typical loads for any one pylon include one 1,000 lb HE Mk N1 or Mk 10 bomb; two 500 lb or 540 lb bombs on tandem carriers; one 18-tube 68 mm rocket pod; one 36-tube 2 in rocket pod; 3 in rockets; Sea Eagle anti-ship missile; or a TV-guided Martel air-to-surface missile (maximum 3 missiles and a Martel systems pod). Each pylon is also suitable for carrying three 1,000 lb stores on triple-release ejection units, or six 500 lb stores on multiple ejection release units, with only small restrictions on the flight envelope. In addition to a Mk 20 in-flight refuelling pod, when operating in the tanker role, an airborne low-pressure starter pod can be carried on an inner pylon; 1,136 litre (300 US gallon; 250 Imp gallon) or 1,955 litre (516 US gallon; 430 Imp gallon) drop-tanks can also be carried on these positions. Maximum internal and external stores load is 7,257 kg (16,000 lb).

DIMENSIONS, EXTERNAL:

Wing span	13.41 m (44 ft 0 in)
Wing span (folded)	6.07 m (19 ft 11 in)
Length overall	19.33 m (63 ft 5 in)
Length folded	15.79 m (51 ft 10 in)
Height overall	4.95 m (16 ft 3 in)
Height folded	5.08 m (16 ft 8 in)
Wheel track	3.62 m (11 ft 10½ in)
Wheelbase	6.30 m (20 ft 8 in)

AREA:

Wings, gross	47.82 m² (514.70 sq ft)

WEIGHTS:

Typical take-off weights	20,865 kg (46,000 lb) to 25,400 kg (56,000 lb)
Max T-O weight	28,123 kg (62,000 lb)

PERFORMANCE:

Max design level speed at 61 m (200 ft)	Mach 0.85 (560 knots; 1,038 km/h; 645 mph)
T-O run at S/L, ISA:	
at 20,865 kg (46,000 lb) AUW	720 m (2,360 ft)
at 25,400 kg (56,000 lb) AUW	1,160 m (3,800 ft)
Landing run at 15,876 kg (35,000 lb) landing weight, S/L, ISA	960 m (3,150 ft)
Typical strike range	2,000 nm (3,700 km; 2,300 miles)
Endurance with two in-flight refuellings	9 hr

Pilatus Britten-Norman

PILATUS BRITTEN-NORMAN LTD
(Subsidiary of Oerlikon-Bührle Holding Ltd)

In 1979 Pilatus Aircraft Ltd of Switzerland acquired all assets of Britten-Norman (Bembridge) Ltd, including the facilities on the Isle of Wight and the former Fairey SA Islander/Trislander production hardware at Gosselies in Belgium.

Pilatus Britten-Norman produces the Islander transport aircraft in a variety of forms, including versions of the military Defender.

Pilatus Britten-Norman Defender

The Defender is a variant of the civil Islander which can be adapted for a wide variety of government and military roles such as search and rescue, internal security, long-range patrol, forward air control, troop transport, logistic support and casualty evacuation. It is available with the same choices of wing configuration as the current civil versions, and can be equipped with a wide range of sophisticated avionics, including nose mounted weather radar, providing the aircraft with a marine search capability. For an electronic warfare role equipment can range from a simple radar warning receiver to a comprehensive passive electronics intelligence gathering system, ESM, and ECM coupled to the ESM to provide radar jamming or defensive chaff/IR flare dispensing. Other optional equipment includes four NATO standard underwing pylons for a variety of external stores, the inboard pair each carrying up to 317.5 kg (700 lb) and the outboard pair up to 204 kg (450 lb).

Typical underwing loads include twin 7.62 mm machine-guns in pod packs, 250 lb or 500 lb GP bombs, Matra rocket packs, SURA rocket clusters, wire guided missiles, 5 in reconnaissance flares, anti-personnel grenades, smoke bombs, marker bombs and 227 litre (60 US gallon; 50 Imp gallon) drop-tanks.

Military Britten-Norman Defenders/Islanders are in service with the Abu Dhabi Defence Force, Belgian Army, Belize Defence Force, Botswana Defence Force, British Army Parachute Association, Ghana Air Force, Guyana Defence Force, Jamaica Defence Force, Malagasy Air Force, Presidential Flight of the Mexican Air Force, Royal Hong Kong Auxiliary Air Force, Panamanian Air Force, Sultan of Oman's Air Force, Suriname Air Force, Mauritania Islamic Defence Force, the Seychelles Ministry of Agriculture and Fisheries, the Malawi Army Air Wing and the Rwanda Air Force. Those operated by the air forces of Iraq, Israel and Qatar are military Islanders, and are not equipped to carry offensive weapons; those which serve with the Cyprus National Guard, Indian Navy and Philippine Navy are Maritime Islanders.

TYPE: Twin-engined SAR, security, patrol, FAC, transport, logistic support and casualty-evacuation aircraft.

WINGS: Cantilever high-wing monoplane. NACA 23012 constant wing section. No dihedral. Incidence 2°. No sweepback. Flared-up wingtips of Britten-Norman design. Wingtip fuel tanks optional. Slotted ailerons and single-slotted flaps. Ground-adjustable tab on starboard aileron. Optional wingtip fuel tanks.

FUSELAGE: Conventional semi-monocoque structure.

TAIL UNIT: Cantilever structure. Fixed-incidence tailplane and mass balanced elevator. Trim tabs in rudder and elevator. Pneumatic de-icing of tailplane and fin optional.

LANDING GEAR: Non-retractable tricycle type, with twin wheels on each main unit and single steerable nosewheel. All five wheels and tyres size 16 × 7-7, supplied by Goodyear. Foot operated aircooled Cleveland hydraulic brakes on main units. Parking brake. Wheel/ski gear optional.

POWERPLANT: Two 224 kW (300 hp) Avco Lycoming IO-540-K1B5 flat-six engines standard. Total fuel capacity

Mauritania operates Pilatus Britten-Norman Islanders/Defenders in the counter-insurgency role.

(standard) 518 litres (137 US gallons; 114 Imp gallons). With optional wingtip fuel tanks, total capacity is increased to 855 litres (226 US gallons; 188 Imp gallons). Additional pylon mounted underwing auxiliary tanks, each of 227 litres (60 US gallons; 50 Imp gallons) capacity, optional.

ACCOMMODATION: Up to 10 persons, including pilot, on side-by-side front seats and four bench seats. No aisle. Special layouts available. Can be operated as freighter, carrying more than a ton of cargo; in this configuration the passenger seats can be stored in the rear baggage bay. In ambulance role, up to three stretchers and two attendants can be accommodated. Other layouts possible, including photographic, parachutist transport or trainer (with accommodation for up to eight parachutists and a dispatcher), or for military roles as detailed in introduction and for other Defender models (which see).

AVIONICS: Typical installation comprises 720 channel VHF nav/com transceivers with VOR/LOC and VOR/ILS, ADF, marker beacon receiver, transponder, HF com transceiver, weather radar and full autopilot. Optional equipment includes RWR, ESM and ECM.

DIMENSIONS, EXTERNAL:

Wing span	14.94 m (49 ft 0 in)
Length overall	10.86 m (35 ft 7¾ in)
Fuselage: Max width	1.21 m (3 ft 11½ in)
Max depth	1.46 m (4 ft 9¾ in)
Height overall	4.18 m (13 ft 8¾ in)
Wheel track (c/l of shock absorbers)	3.61 m (11 ft 10 in)
Wheelbase	3.99 m (13 ft 1¼ in)
Propeller diameter	1.98 m (6 ft 6 in)

AREA:

Wings, gross	30.19 m² (325.0 sq ft)

WEIGHTS:

Weight empty, equipped	1,925 kg (4,244 lb)
Max payload	870 kg (1,918 lb)
Max T-O weight	2,993 kg (6,600 lb)

PERFORMANCE (at max T-O weight)

Never-exceed speed:	183 knots (339 km/h; 211 mph) IAS
Max level speed at S/L	151 knots (280 km/h; 173 mph)
Max cruising speed (75% power) at 2,135 m (7,000 ft)	142 knots (264 km/h; 164 mph)
Cruising speed (67% power) at 2,750 m (9,000 ft)	137 knots (254 km/h; 158 mph)
Cruising speed (59% power) at 3,660 m (12,000 ft)	132 knots (245 km/h; 152 mph)
Stalling speed:	
flaps up	50 knots (92 km/h; 57 mph) IAS
flaps down	40 knots (74 km/h; 46 mph) IAS
Max rate of climb at S/L	344 m (1,130 ft)/min
Absolute ceiling	6,005 m (19,700 ft)
Service ceiling	5,240 m (17,200 ft)
T-O run at S/L, zero wind, hard runway	264 m (866 ft)
T-O to 15 m (50 ft) at S/L, zero wind, hard runway	352 m (1,155 ft)
Landing from 15 m (50 ft) at S/L, zero wind, hard runway	299 m (980 ft)
Landing from 15 m (50 ft) at 1,525 m (5,000 ft)	357 m (1,170 ft)
Landing run at 1,525 m (5,000 ft)	171 m (560 ft)
Landing run at S/L, zero wind, hard runway	140 m (460 ft)
Range at 75% power at 2,135 m (7,000 ft)	555 nm (1,028 km; 639 miles)
Range at 67% power at 2,750 m (9,000 ft)	577 nm (1,070 km; 665 miles)
Range at 59% power at 3,660 m (12,000 ft)	613 nm (1,136 km; 706 miles)

Pilatus Britten-Norman Maritime Defender

Generally similar to the Defender, the Maritime Defender differs in having a modified nose with a larger (Bendix RDR-1400) search radar, capable of detecting a 100 m² (1,076 sq ft) target in sea state 4-5 at a range of 36 nm (67 km; 41.5 miles). Scanning 60° on each side of the flight path, the radar provides a search width of 60 nm (111 km; 69 miles) at optimum altitude. The interior layout provides for pilot and co-pilot, a radar operator at a mid-cabin position on the starboard side, and two observers in the rear of the cabin, one aft of the radar operator, and one adjacent to a window on the port side.

Intended for coastal patrol, fishery and oil rig protection duties, as well as search and rescue support, the Maritime Defender is suitable for all-weather operation, by day or night, and carries the equipment necessary to fulfil such roles. This can include compass/HSI, horizon gyro (radar stabilisation), autopilot, ground mapping and weather radar, VLF/Omega, radio altimeter, dual VHF com, dual VHF nav/ILS, VHF marine band com, ADF, transponder, DME, encoding altimeter and SSB HF com. Specialised equipment includes a searchlight installation and hand-held camera; the four underwing pylons can be used to carry a loudspeaker pod, flares, parachute dinghy packs and a variety of weapons.

The description of the Defender applies also to the Maritime Defender, except that overall length is increased to 11.07 m (36 ft 3¾ in).

Pilatus Britten-Norman ASV Maritime Defender with Sea Skua missiles and Seaspray radar.

Pilatus Britten-Norman BN-2T Turbine Defender

On 2 August 1980 the prototype was flown of the civil BN-2T Turbine Islander, powered by two Allison 250-B17C turboprop engines. These enable the BN-2T to use available low-cost jet fuel instead of scarce and costly avgas, and offer a particularly low operating noise level.

The Turbine Defender is available for the same range of applications as the piston engined Defender.

The description of the Defender applies also to the Turbine Defender, except as follows:

TYPE: Twin-turboprop military aircraft.

FUSELAGE: Generally as for Defender.

POWERPLANT: Two 298 kW (400 shp) Allison 250-B17C turboprop engines, flat-rated at 238.5 kW (320 shp), and each driving a Hartzell three-blade constant-speed fully-feathering metal propeller. Fuel capacity 814 litres (215 US gallons; 179 Imp gallons). Pylon mounted underwing tanks, each of 227 litres (60 US gallons; 50 Imp gallons)

capacity, are available optionally for special purposes.

ACCOMMODATION: Generally as for Defender. Maritime Turbine Defender versions available for fishery protection, coastguard patrol, pollution survey, search and rescue, and similar applications. Offered as an option is an in-flight sliding parachute door.

AVIONICS AND EQUIPMENT: Standard avionics and equipment generally similar to that of Defender. Other equipment, according to mission, includes radar, VLF/Omega nav system, radar altimeter, marine band and VHF transceivers, dinghies, survival equipment, fixed tail 'sting' or towed 'bird' magnetometer, electromagnetic detection/analysis equipment, cameras, and special crew accommodation (maritime versions).

DIMENSIONS, EXTERNAL:
As for Defender, except

Length overall: standard nose	10.87 m (35 ft 7¾ in)
weather radar nose	11.07 m (36 ft 3¾ in)
Propeller diameter	2.03 m (6 ft 8 in)

WEIGHTS:

Weight empty, equipped (incl pilot)	1,914 kg (4,220 lb)
Payload with max fuel	608 kg (1,340 lb)
Max T-O weight	3,175 kg (7,000 lb)

PERFORMANCE (Turbine Defender, at max T-O weight, ISA, except where indicated):

Max cruising speed at 3,050 m (10,000 ft)	170 knots (315 km/h; 196 mph)
Max cruising speed at S/L	154 knots (285 km/h; 177 mph)
Cruising speed, 72% power at 3,050 m (10,000 ft)	150 knots (278 km/h; 173 mph)

Cruising speed, 72% power at 1,525 m (5,000 ft)	142 knots (263 km/h; 164 mph)
Stalling speed, power off:	
flaps up	52 knots (97 km/h; 60 mph) IAS
flaps down	45 knots (84 km/h; 52 mph) IAS
Max rate of climb at S/L	320 m (1,050 ft)/min
Service ceiling	over 7,620 m (25,000 ft)
T-O run	255 m (837 ft)
T-O to 15 m (50 ft)	381 m (1,250 ft)
Landing from 15 m (50 ft)	340 m (1,115 ft)
Landing run	228 m (747 ft)
Range (IFR) with max fuel, reserves for 45 min hold plus 10%	590 nm (1,093 km; 679 miles)
Range (VFR) with max fuel, no reserves	728 nm (1,349 km; 838 miles)

Pilatus Britten-Norman ASTOR Defender

ASTOR (Airborne STand-Off Radar) is the acronym for a British Ministry of Defence programme which is seeking to fulfil a requirement for an airborne surveillance radar to provide an overall picture of a battle area. The ASTOR programme is derived from the former CASTOR (Corps Airborne STand-Off Radar) programme.

Two ASTOR aircraft were completed for demonstrations of the radar systems, the one for Royal Air Force operation involving an English Electric Canberra fitted with a modified Thorn-EMI Searchwater radar. In parallel development for Army operation is the ASTOR Turbine Defender, which will have a lightweight all-weather multi-mode I-band data acquisition system, designed to meet UK General and Air Staff Requirement 3956, and to provide primary intelligence information in the immediate battle zone and beyond, while operating well within friendly territory. It will have full 360° scan, and will offer a wide area of coverage against moving and fixed targets. The associated transmitter, receiver and processing equipment will be housed in the fuselage of the aircraft, which will be flown and operated by a two-man crew. Data acquired will be processed and transmitted automatically, via an airborne link, to one or more ground stations.

The description of the Turbine Defender applies also to the ASTOR Defender, except as follows:

TYPE: Twin-turboprop experimental battlefield surveillance aircraft.

FUSELAGE: Modified nose.

LANDING GEAR: Modified BN-2A Mk III Trislander main landing gear. Longer nosewheel leg to provide adequate ground clearance for radome.

DIMENSIONS, EXTERNAL:

Wing span	14.94 m (49 ft 0 in)
Length overall	approx 11.89 m (39 ft 0 in)
Propeller diameter	2.03 m (6 ft 8 in)

WEIGHT:

Design max T-O weight	3,630 kg (8,000 lb)

Pilatus Britten-Norman AEW, AEW/MR and ASW/ASV Maritime Defenders

To meet a need for a lightweight AEW system, Pilatus Britten-Norman asked Thorn EMI Electronics to collaborate in the installation of the latter company's Skymaster multi-role radar in the Defender airframe and so create the **AEW Defender**. In an AEW role this long-range radar, using pulse-Doppler processing, can automatically acquire and track large numbers of targets flying at all altitudes against a land or sea background. For maritime reconnaissance (MR) the operator selects a non-coherent, frequency agile mode of operation, optimising the radar for the detection of small surface targets in high sea states out to the radar horizon.

The Defender's STOL performance enables it to be operated from forward unprepared strips, and in the air the

Pilatus Britten-Norman AEW Defender with nose-mounted Thorn EMI Skymaster radar.

aircraft's low radar cross-section aids survivability. The **AEW/MR Defender** is fitted with a second console to increase operational flexibility and target handling capacity. An air-to-air and air-to-ground data link, ESM, IFF and navigation equipments may be fully integrated with the radar display and control system.

Future developments will include a border surveillance role, with the radar optimised for the detection of moving targets at long range. A synthetic-aperture mode would provide high-resolution mapping video, which could be linked to provide ground commanders with an all-weather real-time display showing enemy dispositions and movements.

A further variant, the **ASW/ASV Maritime Defender**, made its first appearance at the Hanover Air Show in May 1984. This aircraft may be equipped to various standards, to the customer's specification. Equipment can include a 360° radar, FLIR, sonobuoys, acoustic processing equipment, and a magnetic anomaly detector. Four underwing hardpoints can be used to carry two Sting Ray lightweight torpedoes, four Sea Skua missiles, depth charges, ECM and ESM pods, survival packs, rockets, gun pods or other stores. A crew of three is normal, with room for a trainee.

The UK Ministry of Defence has purchased Pilatus Britten-Norman's former Turbine Defender demonstrator for use by the Royal Navy's Directorate-General of Underwater Weapons torpedo trials unit.

Pilatus Britten-Norman AEW Defender. *(Pilot Press)*

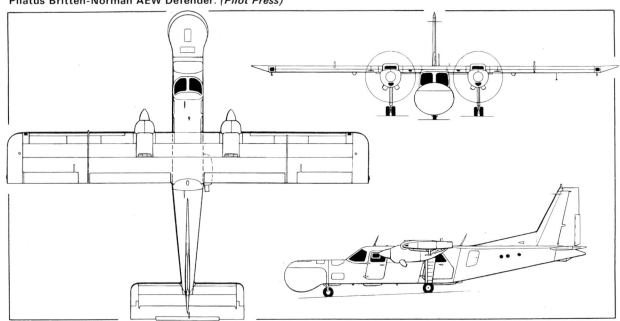

Westland

WESTLAND PLC

Westland Aircraft Ltd (now Westland plc) was formed in July 1935, to take over the aircraft branch of Petters Ltd, known previously as the Westland Aircraft Works, which had been engaged in aircraft design and construction since 1915. It entered the helicopter industry in 1947 by acquiring a licence to build the US Sikorsky S-51, which it produced as the Westland Dragonfly. This technical association with Sikorsky Division of United Technologies has continued since the decision was taken to concentrate on the design, development and construction of helicopters.

In 1959, Westland acquired Saunders-Roe Ltd. In 1960 it acquired the Helicopter Division of Bristol Aircraft Ltd and Fairey Aviation Ltd, and has been subsequently the only major helicopter design and manufacturing organisation in the United Kingdom.

A shareholders' meeting in 1986 approved a financial reconstruction package under which United Technologies (USA) and Fiat (Italy) acquired a minority holding in Westland plc.

Since 1 October 1966 the company's helicopter business has been conducted through a wholly owned company named Westland Helicopters Ltd.

The collaboration between Westland and Agusta of Italy, already well established with the EH 101 programme (see International section), has been extended to include design, manufacture and marketing across the joint product range.

A joint Westland/Agusta marketing company, EHI Limited, has been set up in Milan, initially to support the EH 101 helicopter. EHI Inc is a subsidiary of EHI in the USA.

Westland Helicopters Division

Helicopters in current production at Yeovil are the Sea King, Lynx, and Westland 30. In an international programme, Westland Helicopters and Agusta of Italy formed jointly a company named EH Industries Ltd to develop and produce the EH 101 naval, commercial and utility helicopter (see International section).

Work on advanced composite components is undertaken in a new production facility at Yeovil. Composite main rotor blades, based on carbonfibre and glassfibre materials, are in production as direct replacements for metal blades on S-61, SH-3 and Westland Sea King helicopters. Composite tail-rotor blades are also in production for the Westland 30.

Advanced design composite main rotor blades have been successfully test flown on Lynx, Lynx-3, Westland TT300 and EH 101.

Westland Lynx and Super Lynx

The Lynx is one of three types of aircraft (Puma, Gazelle and Lynx) covered by the Anglo-French helicopter agreement first proposed in February 1967 and confirmed on 2 April 1968. Westland has design leadership in the Lynx, which fulfils general-purpose and naval roles.

The first of 13 Lynx prototypes (XW835) flew for the first time on 21 March 1971. In-service and production versions are as follows:

Lynx AH. Mk 1. General-purpose and utility version for British Army, with Gem 2 engines, for tactical troop transport, logistic support, armed escort of troop carrying helicopters, anti-tank strike, search and rescue, casualty evacuation, reconnaissance and command post duties. Max T-O weight 4,354 kg (9,600 lb). Total of 113 built. First production aircraft (XZ170) flown on 11 February 1977. All delivered by February 1984.

A Westland owned aircraft (G-LYNX, first flown in May 1979), demonstrated the helicopter's multi-role capability with a wide range of weapons which included Hughes TOW and Euromissile Hot anti-tank guided missiles; SURA 80 mm, SNEB 68 mm and FZ 2.75 in rockets; twin 7.62 mm machine-gun pods and 20 mm automatic cannon; Matra Magic 550 air-to-air missiles; an AN/ALE-39 counter-measures dispenser with ECM chaff; and ECM warning equipment. It can also carry mine dispensers, or anti-tank teams armed with Milan missiles. Sixty Lynx AH. Mk 1 have been equipped with TOW missiles, for service with BAOR in the anti-tank role. The first six of these were delivered in the spring of 1981 to No. 654 Squadron of No. 4 Regiment, Army Aviation.

On 11 August 1986 the Lynx demonstrator G-LYNX set a new world's absolute speed record for helicopters by averaging 216.45 knots (400.87 km/h; 249.09 mph) over a 15/25 km course. Since officially ratified, this exceeded the former record held by a Soviet A-10 (Mil Mi-24). For the attempt the Lynx was fitted with Westland's new advanced technology BERP III main rotor blades, Westland 30-type horizontal and vertical tail surfaces, a water-methanol injection system and tuned jetpipes on the standard Gem 60 engines. The standard main gearbox was re-rated, and 32 kg (70 lb) of airframe drag removed by enhanced streamlining.

Lynx HAS. Mk 2. Version for Royal Navy, for advanced shipborne anti-submarine and other duties. Gem 2 engines. Ferranti Seaspray search and tracking radar in modified nose. Capable of operation on anti-submarine classification and strike, air-to-surface vessel search and strike, search and rescue, reconnaissance, troop transport, fire support, communication and fleet liaison, and vertical-replenishment duties. Total of 72 delivered. First production aircraft (XZ229) flown on 10 February 1976. First operational RN

Westland Lynx HAS. Mk 2 of the Royal Navy. *(J. M. G. Gradidge)*

unit, No. 702 Squadron, formed on completion of Navy intensive flight trials in December 1977. Able to carry Sea Skua anti-ship missiles.

Lynx Mk 2 (French Navy). Generally similar to British HAS. Mk 2 but with wheel brakes instead of sprag units, Alcatel dunking sonar, Omera-Seguid ORB-31-W radar, French radio, and AS. 12 wire-guided missiles. Delivery of initial batch of 26 began on 28 September 1978, and was completed during 1980.

Lynx HAS. Mk 3. Royal Navy aircraft with uprated powerplant, comprising two 835 kW (1,120 shp) Rolls-Royce Gem 41-1 turboshaft engines. Delivery of original series of 20, plus three Falklands War replacements, began in March 1982 and has been completed. One was built for the Empire Test Pilots School. Seven more were ordered in July 1985. In May 1985 it was announced that Westland, with Racal Avionics as subcontractor, is developing a central tactical system (CTS) for the Lynx HAS. Mk 3. This will ease the crew's workload by centrally processing all sensor data and presenting mission information on a multi-function electronic display. First flight of the CTS was scheduled for 1987.

Lynx Mk 4. Second batch of 14 aircraft ordered for French Navy in May 1980 with Gem 41-1 engines and uprated transmission to permit an increase in AUW to 4,763 kg (10,500 lb). Deliveries began on 28 January 1983 and have been completed.

Lynx AH. Mk 5. Uprated aircraft for British Army. Similar to AH. Mk 1 but with Gem 41-1 turboshaft engines, three-pinion main gearbox and 4,535 kg (10,000 lb) AUW. Two trials aircraft built initially for RAE Bedford: AH. Mk 1/5 (ZD285), first flown 21 November 1984, with uprated three-pinion gearbox and Gem 2 engines; Mk 5X (ZD559), first flown 11 February 1985, with Gem 41-1s, uprated transmission and max T-O weight of 4,535 kg (10,000 lb). Nine AH. Mk 5s ordered. Initial example (ZE375) flew on 23 February 1985 and was used for engine trials. Remainder transferred to AH. Mk 7 contract, although ZE376 flew initially as Mk 5 on 23 April 1986.

Lynx AH. Mk 7. Uprated aircraft to meet GSR 3947 requirement for the British Army. As Mk 5 but with improved systems, reversed-direction (clockwise when seen from port side) tail rotor with composite blades, and 4,876 kg (10,750 lb) AUW. The more powerful tail rotor reduces noise and improves the ability to hover for extended periods at high weights, important during anti-tank operations. Eight transferred from AH. Mk 5 contract, plus five more ordered

Royal Netherlands Navy Westland Lynx Mk 27 ASW helicopter using its Alcatel dunking sonar.

in 1985. First AH. Mk 7 (ZE376) flew for first time on 7 November 1985.

Lynx Mk 21. Naval version for Brazilian Navy, generally similar to HAS. Mk 2. Nine delivered.

Lynx Mk 23. ASW version for Argentine Navy, generally similar to HAS. Mk 2. Two delivered.

Lynx Mk 25. SAR version for Royal Netherlands Navy, with Gem 2 engines. In service with No. 7 Squadron; used also for communications and training. Six delivered; Dutch designation **UH-14A**.

Lynx Mk 27. Designation of initial ASW version for Royal Netherlands Navy, generally similar to HAS. Mk 2, but equipped with Gem 41-1 engines and Alcatel dunking sonar. Ten delivered. Dutch designation **SH-14B**.

Lynx Mk 28. General purpose military version, basically similar to AH. Mk 1, for State of Qatar Police. Three delivered, with uprated Gem 41-1 turboshafts.

Lynx Mk 80. ASW and maritime patrol version for Royal Danish Navy, generally similar to HAS. Mk 2 except for Gem 41-1 engines. Eight ordered and delivered.

Lynx Mk 81. ASW version for Royal Netherlands Navy, with Gem 41-1 uprated engines and equipped with MAD gear. Eight delivered; Dutch designation **SH-14C**.

Lynx Mk 86. SAR version for Royal Norwegian Air Force, generally similar to HAS. Mk 2 except for Gem 41-2 engines. Six ordered and delivered.

Lynx Mk 87. For Argentine Navy. Generally similar to Mk 23 but with Gem 41-2 engines and max AUW of 4,763 kg (10,500 lb). Eight ordered but only two delivered.

Lynx Mk 88. ASW version for use on board frigates of the Federal German Navy. Generally similar to HAS. Mk 2

Prototype Westland Lynx AH.Mk 7 for British Army.

but with Gem 41-2 engines, non-folding tail and Bendix AN/AQS-18 sonar. Original batch of 12 delivered. Two more ordered in 1984 for 1986 delivery. Another five ordered in February 1986 for delivery in 1988.

Lynx Mk 89. ASW/SAR version for Nigerian Navy, with Gem 42-1 engines and RCA 500 Primus radar. Three ordered, for delivery from December 1983.

Well over 300 Lynx are in service. Production is shared in the ratio of 70 per cent by Westland to 30 per cent by Aérospatiale.

Under development is a new version of the Navy Lynx known as **Super Lynx**, with extended range and payload and all-weather day/night capability, using advanced dipping sonar and 360° radar. Powered by 835 kW (1,120 shp) Rolls-Royce Gem 43 engines, it will be fitted with a new high-efficiency tail rotor and, optionally, Westland's new advanced-technology swept-tip composites main rotor blades. Weapons will include Penguin and Sea Skua missiles and Sting Ray torpedoes.

The following description applies to both the military general-purpose and naval versions with the Gem 2 powerplant, except where indicated:

TYPE: Twin-engined multi purpose helicopter.

ROTOR SYSTEM: Single four-blade semi-rigid main rotor and four-blade tail rotor. The main rotor blades, which are interchangeable, are of cambered aerofoil section and embody mass taper. Each blade has stainless steel box spar, to which is bonded a GRP rear skin stabilised by a Nomex plastics honeycomb core. Blade tips are of moulded GRP, with a stainless steel anti-corrosion sheath forward of the 50 per cent chord line. Each blade is attached to the main rotor hub by titanium root attachment plates and a flexible arm. The rotor hub and inboard portions of the flexible arms are built as a

complete unit, in the form of a titanium monobloc forging. Main rotor blades of both versions can be folded.

FUSELAGE AND TAIL UNIT: Conventional semi-monocoque pod-and-boom structure. Glassfibre components used for access panels, doors and fairings. Provision for internally mounted defensive armament, and for universal flange mountings on each side of the exterior to carry weapons or other stores. Tailboom is a monocoque structure bearing the sweptback vertical fin/tail rotor pylon, which has a half tailplane near the tip on the starboard side. Tail pylon leading and trailing edges, and bullet fairing over tail-rotor gearbox, are of glassfibre. Tail pylon of naval version can be folded and spread manually, to reduce overall length for stowage.

LANDING GEAR (general-purpose military version): Non-retractable tubular skid type. Provision for a pair of adjustable ground handling wheels on each skid. Flotation gear optional.

LANDING GEAR (naval versions): Non-retractable tricycle type. Single-wheel main units, carried on sponsons, are fitted at 27° toe-out for deck landing, and can be manually turned into line and locked fore and aft for movement of aircraft into and out of ship's hangar. Twin-wheel nose unit can be steered hydraulically through 90° by the pilot. Designed for high shock absorption to facilitate take-off from, and landing on, small decks under severe sea and weather conditions. Sprag brakes (wheel locks) fitted to each wheel prevent rotation on landing or inadvertent deck roll. These locks are disengaged hydraulically and will re-engage automatically in the event of hydraulic failure. Flotation gear and hydraulically actuated harpoon deck lock securing system, optional.

POWERPLANT: Two Rolls-Royce Gem 2 turboshaft engines, each with max contingency rating of 671 kW (900 shp) in

Westland Lynx HAS. Mk 2. *(Pilot Press)*

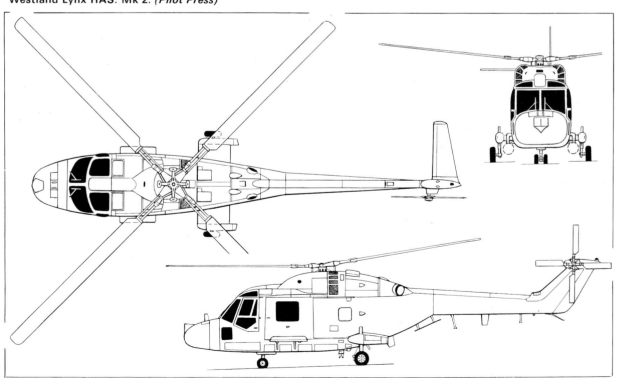

Lynx AH. 1, HAS. 2 and early export variants. Later versions have Gem 41-1 or 41-2 engines, each with max contingency rating of 835 kW (1,120 shp), or Gem 42-1 engines, each with max contingency rating of 846 kW (1,135 shp). Engine air intakes de-iced electrically. Fuel in five crashproof bag tanks, all within the fuselage structure, comprising two main tanks, two side-by-side collector tanks and an underfloor tank at the forward end of the cabin. Total fuel capacity 788 kg (1,737 lb). If required, ferry range can be increased by installing in rear of cabin two metal auxiliary tanks. A removable refuelling/defuelling pack can be fitted in the cabin and used to refuel aircraft from dump stocks on ground or containers suspended from hoist. It is also possible to raise fuel about 5 m (15 ft) while the aircraft is hovering. Fuel jettison capability for main and forward tanks. Provision for self-sealing of both collector tanks (except in Royal Navy versions).

ACCOMMODATION: Pilot and co-pilot or observer side-by-side. Dual controls optional. Additional crew members according to role. Maximum high-density layout (general purpose version) for one pilot and 10 armed troops or paratroops, on lightweight bench seats in soundproofed cabin. Alternative VIP layouts for four to seven passengers. Seats can be removed quickly to permit the carriage of up to 907 kg (2,000 lb) of freight internally. Tiedown rings are provided at approx 51 cm (20 in) intervals on main cabin floor, which is stressed for loads of up to 976 kg/m² (200 lb/sq ft). Alternatively, loads of up to 1,360 kg (3,000 lb) can be carried externally on freight hook mounted below the cabin floor and fitted with electrically operated emergency release system. In the casualty evacuation role, with a crew of two, the Lynx can accommodate three standard stretchers and a medical attendant. Both basic versions have secondary capability for search and rescue (up to nine survivors) and other roles.

AVIONICS AND FLIGHT EQUIPMENT: Avionics common to all roles (general-purpose and naval versions) include GEC Avionics duplex three-axis automatic stabilisation equipment; Sperry GM9 Gyrosyn compass system; Decca tactical air navigation system (TANS); Decca 71 Doppler, E2C standby compass; and S.G. Brown intercom system. Optional role equipment for both versions includes GEC Avionics automatic flight control system (AFCS); Plessey PTR 377 UHF/VHF with homing; Collins ARC-159 UHF with homing; Plessey PTR 1751 UHF; Ultra D 403M standby UHF; Collins ARC-182 VHF/UHF; AM/FM with homing; Collins VHF-20B VHF/AM; GEC Avionics AD 120 VHF/FM; Chelton 7 homer; Collins VOR/ILS; DME; Collins ARN-118 Tacan; I-band transponder (naval version only); Plessey PTR 446, Collins APX-72, Siemens STR 700/375 or Italtel APX-77 IFF; GEC Avionics AD 370 and AD 380 radio compass; and vortex sand filter for engine air intakes. Additional units are fitted in naval version, when sonar is fitted, to provide automatic transition to hover and automatic Doppler hold in hover.

ARMAMENT AND OPERATIONAL EQUIPMENT: For armed escort, anti-tank or air-to-surface strike missions, general-purpose version can be equipped with one 20 mm Oerlikon-Bührle KDA or similar cannon mounted in the cabin with 1,500 rds; or two 20 mm cannon mounted externally so as to permit the carriage also of anti-tank missiles or a pintle-mounted 7.62 mm GEC Minigun inside the cabin; or a side mounted 25 mm Oerlikon cannon; or a Minigun beneath cabin, in Emerson Minitat installation, with 3,000 rds. External pylon can be fitted on each side of cabin for a variety of stores, including two Minigun or other self-contained gun pods; two pods each carrying eighteen 68 mm SNEB, twelve 80 mm SURA, or nineteen 2.75 in rockets, the 2.75 in rockets containing illuminating flares if required; or up to six Aérospatiale AS.11, or eight Aérospatiale/MBB Hot, Rockwell Hellfire, Hughes TOW, or similar air-to-surface missiles. An additional six or eight missiles can be carried in cabin, for rearming in forward areas, and a stabilised sight is fitted for target detection and missile direction. British Army Lynx aircraft equipped with TOW missiles have roof mounted Hughes sight manufactured under licence by British Aerospace. The TOW roof sight is being upgraded under a £60 million mid-life improvement contract awarded to British Aerospace Army Weapons Division in 1986. The upgraded sight will have a night vision capability in the far infra-red waveband to increase operational versatility in low-light night conditions or poor daylight visibility. The Lynx can transport anti-tank teams of three gunners with missiles and launchers. For search and rescue role, with three crew, both versions can have a waterproof floor, eight 4 in flares in utility version (or six 4.5 in flares in naval version), and a 272 kg (600 lb) capacity electrically operated 'clip-on' hoist in starboard side of cabin. Alternative option of hydraulically operated hoist in naval version when third hydraulic system is installed. Optional equipment, according to role, can include lightweight sighting system with alternative target magnification, vertical and/or oblique cameras, up to six 4.5 in flares for night operation, low-light-level TV, infra-red linescan, searchlight, and specialised communications equipment. Naval version can carry out a number of these roles, but has specialised equipment for its primary duties. For ASW role this includes two Mk 44, Mk 46 or Sting Ray homing torpedoes, one each on an external pylon on each side of fuselage, and six marine markers; or two Mk 11 depth charges. Detection of submarines is by means of either Alcatel DUAV 4 or Bendix AN/AQS-18 dipping sonars or Texas Instruments AN/ASQ-81 magnetic anomaly detector. The dipping sonars are operated by a hydraulically powered winch and cable hover mode facilities within the AFCS. Ferranti Seaspray lightweight search and tracking radar, for detecting small surface targets in low visibility/high sea conditions. Armament includes four BAe Sea Skua semi-active homing missiles for attacking light surface craft; alternatively, four AS.12 or similar wire guided missiles can be employed in conjunction with AF 530 or APX-334 lightweight stabilised optical sighting system.

DIMENSIONS, EXTERNAL (A: general purpose version; N: naval version):

Main rotor diameter: A, N	12.80 m (42 ft 0 in)
Tail rotor diameter: A, N	2.21 m (7 ft 3 in)

Length overall:

A, N both rotors turning	15.163 m (49 ft 9 in)
A, main rotor blades folded	13.165 m (43 ft 2.3 in)

N, main rotor blades and tail folded

 10.618 m (34 ft 10 in)

Length of fuselage, nose to tail rotor centre:
 A 12.06 m (39 ft 6.8 in)
 N 11.92 m (39 ft 1.3 in)
Width overall, main rotor blades folded:
 A 2.94 m (9 ft 7¾ in)
 N 3.75 m (12 ft 3¾ in)
Height overall, both rotors turning:
 A 3.66 m (12 ft 0 in)
 N 3.60 m (11 ft 9¾ in)
 Skid track: A 2.032 m (6 ft 8 in)
 Wheel track: N 2.778 m (9 ft 1.4 in)
 Wheelbase: N 2.94 m (9 ft 7¾ in)
AREA:
 Main rotor disc 128.7 m² (1,385.4 sq ft)
WEIGHTS (A: general-purpose version, N: naval version):
 Manufacturer's empty weight: A 2,578 kg (5,683 lb)
 N 2,740 kg (6,040 lb)
 Manufacturer's basic weight: A 2,658 kg (5,860 lb)
 N 3,030 kg (6,680 lb)
 Operating weight empty, equipped:
 A, troop transport (pilot and 10 troops)
 2,787 kg (6,144 lb)
 A, anti-tank strike (incl weapon pylons, firing equipment and
 sight) 3,072 kg (6,772 lb)
 A, search and rescue (crew of three)
 2,963 kg (6,532 lb)
 N, anti-submarine strike 3,343 kg (7,370 lb)
 N, reconnaissance (crew of two) 3,277 kg (7,224 lb)
 N, anti-submarine classification and strike
 3,472 kg (7,654 lb)
 N, air-to-surface-vessel search and strike (crew of two and four
 Sea Skuas) 3,414 kg (7,526 lb)
 N, search and rescue (crew of three) 3,416 kg (7,531 lb)
 N, dunking sonar search and strike 3,650 kg (8,047 lb)
 Max T-O weight: A 4,535 kg (10,000 lb)
 N 4,763 kg (10,500 lb)
PERFORMANCE (at normal max T-O weight at S/L, ISA, except where
 indicated. A: general-purpose version, N: naval version):
 Max continuous cruising speed:
 A 140 knots (259 km/h; 161 mph)
 N 125 knots (232 km/h; 144 mph)
 A (ISA + 20°C) 130 knots (241 km/h; 150 mph)
 N (ISA + 20°C) 114 knots (211 km/h; 131 mph)
 Max continuous cruising speed (1h), one engine out:
 A 134 knots (248 km/h; 154 mph)
 N 122 knots (225 km/h; 140 mph)

 A (ISA + 20°C) 114 knots (211 km/h; 131 mph)
 N (ISA + 20°C) 99 knots (184 km/h; 114 mph)
 Speed for max endurance:
 A, N (ISA and ISA + 20°C)
 70 knots (130 km/h; 81 mph)
 Max forward rate of climb: A 756 m (2,480 ft)/min
 N 661 m (2,170 ft)/min
 A (ISA + 20°C) 536 m (1,760 ft)/min
 N (ISA + 20°C) 469 m (1,540 ft)/min
 Max vertical rate of climb:
 A 472 m (1,550 ft)/min
 N 351 m (1,150 ft)/min
 A (ISA + 20°C) 390 m (1,280 ft)/min
 N (ISA + 20°C) 244 m (800 ft)/min
 Hovering ceiling OGE: A 3,230 m (10,600 ft)
 N 2,575 m (8,450 ft)
 Typical range, with reserves:
 A, troop transport 292 nm (540 km; 336 miles)
 Radius of action, out and back at max sustained speed,
 allowances for T-O and landing, 30 min loiter in search area, 3
 min hover for each survivor, and 10% fuel reserves at end of
 mission:
 N, search and rescue (crew of 3 and 2 survivors)
 115 nm (212 km; 132 miles)
 N, search and rescue (crew of 3 and 7 survivors)
 96 nm (178 km; 111 miles)
 Time on station at 50 nm (93 km; 58 miles) radius, out and back at
 max sustained speed, with 2 torpedoes, smoke floats and
 marine markers, allowances for T-O and landing and 10% fuel
 reserves at end of mission:
 N, anti-submarine classification and strike, loiter speed on
 station 2 h 0 min
 N, anti-submarine strike, loiter on station 2 h 29 min
 N, dunking sonar search and strike, 50% loiter speed and 50%
 hover on station 1 h 5 min
 Time on station at 50 nm (93 km; 58 miles) radius, out and back at
 max sustained speed, with crew of 2 and 4 Sea Skuas,
 allowances and reserves as above:
 N, air to surface vessel strike, en-route radar search and loiter
 speed on station 1 h 36 min
 Max range: A 340 nm (630 km; 392 miles)
 N 320 nm (593 km; 368 miles)
 A (ISA + 20°C) 339 nm (628 km; 390 miles)
 N (ISA + 20°C) 320 nm (593 km; 368 miles)
 Max endurance: A 2 h 57 min
 N (ISA + 20°C) 2 h 50 min
 Max ferry range with auxiliary cabin tanks:
 A 724 nm (1,342 km; 834 miles)
 N 565 nm (1,046 km; 650 miles)

Westland Lynx-3

The Lynx-3 is a dedicated anti-tank helicopter, derived from the earlier production Lynx and incorporating its dynamic systems. It has a gross weight some 27 per cent greater, is engineered to offer increased survivability and is able to mount greater firepower. Advanced avionics allow Lynx-3 to operate by day or night, and in adverse weather conditions. Night vision and target acquisition systems are available in optional nose, roof or rotor-mast mounts. It can be equipped to carry and launch current and future versions of Euromissile Hot, Hughes TOW and Rockwell Hellfire air-to-surface missiles; for defence against air attack it can be armed with General Dynamics Stinger missiles. A naval version has also been announced.

A Lynx-3 (ZE477) flew for the first time on 14 June 1984 fitted temporarily with a standard Lynx main rotor. It has

since been retrofitted with the production standard BERP blades. The following details refer generally to the anti-armour version:

TYPE: Twin-engined anti-armour helicopter.

ROTOR SYSTEM: Advanced four-blade semi-rigid main rotor and four-blade tail rotor. Main rotor blades of Westland composite construction, incorporating BERP (British Experimental Rotor Programme) tips, which are claimed to increase rotor efficiency by up to 40 per cent. Main-rotor-blade folding optional (standard on naval version). The tail rotor, which is generally similar to that of the Westland 30, also has blades of composite construction; it rotates in the opposite direction to that of the standard Lynx and is considerably quieter.

FUSELAGE AND TAIL UNIT: Conventional semi-monocoque pod-and-boom structure. By comparison with the standard Lynx the fuselage has been lengthened by 30 cm

Pre-production Westland Lynx-3 armed with Hellfire missiles.

(11.8 in) to provide increased cabin volume. This makes it possible to seat the two-man crew slightly further forward, thus enhancing their view to the rear. It also provides increased storage space for missile reloads and allows for larger cabin doors. The tailcone is a monocoque structure with integral sweptback vertical fin/tail-rotor pylon. (Tailcone will fold on naval version.) Fixed-incidence tailplane of inverted aerofoil section.

LANDING GEAR: Non-retractable tricycle type, with single-wheel main units and twin-wheel nose unit. Shock absorption system designed to survive descent rates as high as 6.10 m (20 ft)/s.

POWERPLANT: Two Rolls-Royce Gem 60 turboshaft engines, each with a max continuous rating of 832 kW (1,115 shp) for normal twin-engined operation and a one-engine-inoperative max contingency rating of 1,004 kW (1,346 shp). Lateral engine air intakes incorporate particle filters. Crash-resistant fuel system. IR suppression optional.

ACCOMMODATION: Crew of two, side-by-side, in wide-view cockpit designed to meet the requirements of MIL-STD-1290. Crew seats have armour protection and are mounted on shock absorbing struts designed to ensure survival at descent rates tolerable to landing gear. Considerable space for storage of missile reloads, or to transport mobile anti-tank teams with missiles and launchers. Windscreen anti-icing, demisting and electrically operated wipers.

AVIONICS: Lynx-3 avionics are not yet finalised, but the inclusion of a mission avionics databus system, to MIL-STD-1553B, will allow integration of the latest systems, reduce wiring looms to a minimum, and simplify the introduction of alternative or new sensor and weapons fits. Navigation is likely to be based on the Sperry GM9 Gyrosyn compass system. Decca tactical air navigation system (TANS) and Decca Doppler. Mission avionics may include Martin Marietta target acquisition and designation system (TADS) and pilot's night vision sensor (PNVS), IFF, radar warning receivers, and IR jamming. Sensors for target acquisition, and enhanced viewing systems, will be mounted in optional positions including a mast mounted sight (MMS) or on the fuselage nose or roof. (Naval version will have 360° radar, MAD, dunking sonar, and active and passive sonobuoys).

ARMAMENT AND EQUIPMENT: Can be equipped with an Oerlikon or similar 20 mm cannon (25 mm cannon under evaluation); a pintle mounted 7.62 mm GEC Minigun inside the cabin; an 0.5 in machine-gun pod; air-to-surface missiles including Euromissile Hot, Hughes TOW and Rockwell Hellfire; air-to-air missiles including General Dynamics Stinger or Shorts Blowpipe; and SNEB, SNORA or SURA rockets. Goodyear chaff dispenser. Cable cutter mounted on roof, immediately above windscreen. (Naval version can carry Mk 44, Mk 46 or Sting Ray torpedoes; depth charges; and Sea Skua anti-ship missiles; and will have a harpoon deck lock and main-rotor negative thrust capability to simplify deck recover.)

DIMENSIONS, EXTERNAL:
Main rotor diameter	12.80 m (42 ft 0 in)
Tail rotor diameter	2.44 m (8 ft 0 in)
Length overall: rotors turning	15.47 m (50 ft 9 in)
main rotor folded	13.79 m (45 ft 3 in)
Width overall, main rotor folded	3.05 m (10 ft 0 in)
Height overall, rotors turning	3.30 m (10 ft 10 in)

AREA:
Main rotor disc	128.7 m² (1,385.4 sq ft)

WEIGHTS (estimated):
Max fuel weight	1,000 kg (2,204 lb)
Payload	1,542 kg (3,400 lb)
Normal max T-O weight	5,896 kg (13,000 lb)

PERFORMANCE (estimated):
Max level speed	165 knots (306 km/h; 190 mph)
Cruising speed	150 knots (278 km/h; 172 mph)
Range with max fuel, 20 min reserves	335 nm (620 km; 385 miles)
Endurance	3 h 30 min

Westland Sea King

The Westland Sea King development programme stemmed from a licence agreement for the S-61 helicopter concluded originally with Sikorsky in 1959. This permitted Westland to utilise the basic airframe and rotor system of the Sikorsky SH-3. Considerable changes were made in the powerplant and in specialised equipment, initially to meet a Royal Navy requirement for an advanced anti-submarine helicopter with prolonged endurance. The Sea King can also undertake secondary roles, such as search and rescue, tactical troop transport, casualty evacuation, cargo carrying and long-range self-ferry. A land-based general-purpose version is the Commando.

In-service versions of the Sea King are as follows:

Sea King Mk 2 AEW. Version developed in mid-1982 to provide Royal Navy with airborne early warning capability. Under a programme known as Project LAST (low-altitude surveillance task), it was developed in only 11 weeks, using two converted HAS. Mk 2 Sea Kings (XV650 and XV651) as testbeds. These aircraft (which first embarked aboard HMS *Illustrious* in August 1982 for deployment to the South Atlantic) each have a Thorn EMI Searchwater maritime surveillance radar in an air pressurised 'kettledrum' container of Kevlar impregnated fabric carried on a swivel mounting on the starboard side of the fuselage, in line with the dorsal radome. The container is swung, hydraulically, forward and downward below wheel level when deployed. The scanner is pitch and roll stabilised, and offers full 360° scan.

Two radar operator positions are provided for search and target classification. Radar classification is by raster displays having three modes; PPI (plan), B-scope (selected plan sector enlarged) and A-scope (profile, showing contact shape). A multiple-target track-while-scan capability permits tracking without interrupting search. A Cossor Electronics Jubilee Guardsman IFF interrogator is integrated with the radar.

An MIR-2 electronic support measures suite provides 360° detection of radar emissions and classifies them against stored signatures for positive identification of radar contacts. A UHF radio link provides voice and data communications with the fleet, enabling warning of a target's course, speed, coded identity, range and bearing to be transmitted quickly. Targets can be detected at a range of more than 87 nm (161 km; 100 miles), from a normal service ceiling of 3,050 m (10,000 ft). A four-hour endurance can be extended by refuelling at the hover.

The two original Mk 2 AEW aircraft formed the basis of No. 849 Squadron, which was reformed at RNAS Culdrose, Cornwall, on 9 November 1984. Eight more AEW Sea Kings are being acquired by modification of HAS. Mk 2 aircraft; and the Squadron's 'A' Flight was commissioned with three helicopters on 31 May 1985, for service in HMS *Illustrious* in August 1985.

Sea King HAS. Mk 2. Uprated version of HAS. Mk 1 for ASW and SAR duties with the Royal Navy. Twenty-one built; first flown (XZ570) on 18 June 1976. Equipment includes search radar and dunking sonar. Being upgraded to **Mk 5** standard (see below).

Sea King HAR. Mk 3. Uprated version for SAR duties with the Royal Air Force. Provision for flight crew of two pilots, air electronics/winch operator and loadmaster/winchman; up to six stretchers, or two stretchers and 11 seated survivors, or 19 persons. Nav system includes Decca TANS F computer, accepting inputs from Mk 19 Decca nav receiver and Type 71 Doppler. MEL radar. Sixteen ordered initially, to equip No. 202 Squadron at Lossiemouth, Scotland. First HAR. Mk 3 flew on 6 September 1977; deliveries of all 16 completed in 1979. Three more ordered in 1983 were delivered in 1985.

Sea King HC. Mk 4. Utility version of Commando Mk 2 for Royal Navy.

Sea King HAS. Mk 5. Uprated ASW and SAR version

Royal Navy Westland Sea King Mk 2 AEW.

for the Royal Navy. Thirty new-build aircraft ordered in three batches (17, 8 and 5), of which the first two (ZA126/127) were handed over officially on 2 October 1980. The nav/attack system of the Sea King HAS. Mk 5 utilises Tans G coupled to Decca 71 Doppler and MEL Sea Searcher radar. Also fitted are Racal MIR-2 ESM, passive sonobuoy dropping equipment, and associated GEC Avionics LAPADS acoustic processing and display equipment. The increased size of the rotating antenna has necessitated the Mk 5's larger dorsal radome.

Using this new equipment, the Sea King can pinpoint the position of an enemy submarine at far greater range than has been possible in the past, and attack it with torpedoes. In addition to monitoring signals from its own sonobuoys, the Sea King can handle information from buoys dropped by RAF Nimrod aircraft in a joint search. It can remain on station, up to 87 nm (160 km; 100 miles) from its parent ship, for long periods.

The Sea King HAS. Mk 5 carries a crew of four, with the dunking sonar operator also monitoring the LAPADS equipment at an additional crew station. To make room for the extra equipment, the cabin has been enlarged by moving the rear bulkhead further into the tail. Improvements envisaged for the future include the carriage of more-powerful torpedoes and improved anti-submarine sensors.

Max T-O weight of the Sea King HAS. Mk 5 is 9,525 kg (21,000 lb), the same as that of the Mk 2. Royal Navy HAS. Mk 2s are being upgraded to this standard.

Sea King Mk 41. Search and rescue version for Federal German Navy. First example (89 + 50) flown for the first time on 6 March 1972. Twenty-two ordered, of which production and delivery were completed in 1974. First unit to equip with these aircraft was MFG.5, based at Kiel-Holtenau. The 20 still in service are intended to undergo a combat capability improvement programme, with two being modified in 1984, three in 1985, and five in each of the years 1986–88.

Sea King Mk 42. ASW version for Indian Navy. Original order for six, which are in service with No. 330 Squadron. Delivery of a further six was completed in 1974, and these are in service with Nos. 330 and 336 Squadrons. Follow-on order announced in June 1977 for three uprated aircraft, designated **Mk 42A**, with hauldown capability for small-ship operation, which were delivered in March 1980.

Advanced Sea King. Version with 1,092 kW (1,465 shp)

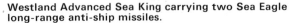

, **Westland Advanced Sea King carrying two Sea Eagle long-range anti-ship missiles.**

Sea King Mk 48, used for SAR by the Belgian Air Force. *(Aviation Picture Library)*

Rolls-Royce Gnome H.1400-1T engines, uprated main gearbox with emergency lubrication and strengthened main lift frames. Other changes include composite main and tail rotor blades, and improved search radar. Maximum AUW increased to 9,752 kg (21,500 lb) to give an improved payload/range performance. Through-life costs reduced.

Sea King Mk 42B. ASW version of the Advanced Sea King of which 12 were ordered for the Indian Navy in July 1983, with an option on eight more. Features include GEC Avionics AQS-902 sonobuoy processor and tactical processing system; MEL Super Searcher radar; Alcatel HS-12 dipping sonar; Chelton 700 sonics homing; Marconi Hermes ESM; and ability to carry British Aerospace Sea Eagle long-range anti-ship missiles.

Sea King Mk 42C. Utility transport version of the Advanced Sea King of which six have been ordered for the Indian Navy. Navigation systems similar to HAR. Mk 3, except that the MEL radar is replaced by Bendix RDR 1400C, nose mounted; the ADF and IFF are produced by HAL.

Sea King Mk 43. SAR version for Norwegian Air Force. Ten delivered. In service with No. 330 Squadron at Bodo.

Sea King Mk 43A. Uprated SAR version for Norwegian Air Force; one delivered in September 1978.

Sea King Mk 45. ASW version for Pakistan Navy. Six ordered, delivery of which was completed during 1975.

Sea King Mk 47. ASW version. Six ordered by Saudi Arabia on behalf of Egyptian Navy. Delivery completed in 1976.

Sea King Mk 48. SAR version for Belgian Air Force. Five ordered, including one aircraft with VIP interior capability. Delivery completed in November 1976. In service with No. 40 Squadron at Coxyde.

Sea King Mk 50. Version, developed from Mk 1, for No. 817 Squadron of Royal Australian Navy, which ordered 10. First flight 30 June 1974. Production included offset manufacture in Australia to 30 per cent of the contract value. Deliveries began in the autumn of 1974. The Mk 50 was the first fully uprated version of the Sea King to fly. It is capable of operation in the roles of anti-submarine search and strike, vertical replenishment, tactical troop lift, search and rescue,

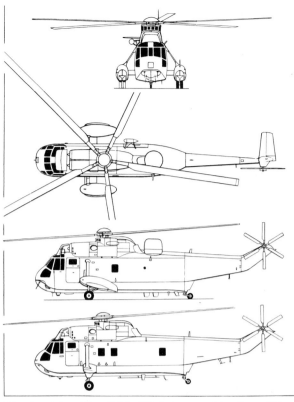

Westland Sea King HAS. Mk 5. Lower side view: HC. Mk 4. *(Pilot Press)*

casualty evacuation, and self-ferry. Two additional aircraft, designated **Mk 50a**, were delivered in early 1983.

A total of 316 Sea Kings and Commandos had been ordered by January 1987.

The following details apply to current production Advanced Sea Kings:

AIRFRAME: Generally similar to Agusta-Sikorsky ASH-3H (see Italian section), but with main and tail rotor blades of composite materials. Stabiliser on starboard side of tail pylon is unbraced.

POWERPLANT: Two 1,238 kW (1,660 shp) (max contingency rating) Rolls-Royce Gnome H.1400-1T turboshaft engines, mounted side-by-side above cabin. Transmission rating 2,200 kW (2,950 shp). Fuel in six underfloor bag tanks, total capacity 3,714 litres (981 US gallons; 817 Imp gallons). Internal auxiliary tank, capacity 863 litres (228 US gallons; 190 Imp gallons) may be fitted for long-range ferry purposes.

ACCOMMODATION: Crew of four in ASW role; accommodation for up to 22 survivors in SAR role; and up to 28 troops in utility role.

OPERATIONAL EQUIPMENT (ASW models): As equipped for this role, the Sea King is a fully integrated all-weather hunter/killer weapon system, capable of operating independently of surface vessels, and the following equipment and weapons can be fitted to achieve this task: Plessey Type 195, Bendix AN/AQS-13B or Alcatel HS-12 dipping sonar, GEC Avionics AD 580 Doppler navigation system, AW 391 search radar in dorsal radome, transponder beneath rear fuselage, Honeywell AN/APN-171 radar altimeter, Sperry GM7B Gyrosyn compass system, Louis Newmark Mk 31 automatic flight control system, two No. 4 marine markers, four No. 2 Mk 2 smoke floats, Ultra Electronics mini-sonobuoys, up to four Mk 46 or Sting Ray torpedoes, or four Mk 11 depth charges or one Clevite simulator. Observer/navigator has tactical display on which sonar contacts are integrated with search radar and navigational information. Radio equipment comprises Plessey PTR 377 UHF/VHF and homer, Ultra D 403M standby UHF, Collins 618-T3 HF radio, Ultra UA 60M intercom, Telebrief system and IFF provisions. For secondary role a mounting is provided on the aft frame of the starboard door for a general-purpose machine-gun. The Mk 31 AFCS provides radio altitude displays for both pilots; artificial horizon displays; three-axis stabilisation in pilot controlled manoeuvres; attitude hold, heading hold and height hold in cruising flight; controlled transition manoeuvres to and from the hover; automatic height control and plan position control in the hover; and an auxiliary trim facility.

OPERATIONAL EQUIPMENT (non-ASW models): A wide range of radio and navigation equipment may be installed, including VHF/UHF communications, VHF/UHF homing, radio compass, Doppler navigation system, radio altimeter, VOR/ILS, radar and transponder, of Collins, Plessey, Honeywell and GEC Avionics manufacture. A Sperry compass system and a Louis Newmark automatic flight control system are also installed. Sea Kings equipped for search and rescue have in addition a Breeze BL 10300 variable-speed hydraulic rescue hoist of 272 kg (600 lb) capacity mounted above the starboard side cargo door. Automatic main rotor blade folding and spreading is standard; for shipboard operation the tail pylon can also be folded. With search radar fitted, a total of 18 survivors and medical staff can be carried; this total can be increased to 22 if the search radar is omitted. In the casualty evacuation role the Sea King can accommodate up to 9 stretchers and two medical attendants, or intermediate combinations of seats and stretchers; a typical layout might provide for 15 seats and six stretchers. In the troop transport role, the Sea King can accommodate 28 troops. As a cargo transport, the aircraft has an internal capacity of 3,628 kg (8,000 lb) and the same max external load capacity when a low-response sling is fitted.

DIMENSIONS, EXTERNAL:		
Main rotor diameter		18.90 m (62 ft 0 in)
Length overall (rotors turning)		22.15 m (72 ft 8 in)
Length of fuselage		17.02 m (55 ft 10 in)
Length overall:		
main rotor folded		17.42 m (57 ft 2 in)
rotors and tail folded		14.40 m (47 ft 3 in)
Height overall: rotors turning		5.13 m (16 ft 10 in)
rotors spread and stationary		4.85 m (15 ft 11 in)
Width overall (rotors folded):		
with flotation bags		4.98 m (16 ft 4 in)
without flotation bags		4.77 m (15 ft 8 in)
Wheel track (c/l of shock absorbers)		3.96 m (13 ft 0 in)

AREA:
Main rotor disc   280.06 m² (3,020.3 sq ft)

WEIGHTS (A: anti-submarine, B: anti-surface vessel, C: airborne early warning, D: SAR, E: troop transport, F: external cargo):

Basic weight (depending on version)
      approx 5,530 kg (12,194 lb)

Weight equipped (typical): A	6,236 kg (13,749 lb)
B	6,454 kg (14,229 lb)
C	6,929 kg (15,275 lb)
D	6,280 kg (13,844 lb)
E	5,438 kg (11,990 lb)
F	5,424 kg (11,958 lb)
Max T-O weight	9,752 kg (21,500 lb)

PERFORMANCE (at max T-O weight, ISA):
Never-exceed speed (British practice) at S/L
      122 knots (226 km/h; 140 mph)

Cruising speed at S/L
      110 knots (204 km/h; 126 mph)
Max rate of climb at S/L   619 m (2,030 ft)/min
Max vertical rate of climb at S/L
      246 m (808 ft)/min
Hovering ceiling: IGE   1,982 m (6,500 ft)
   OGE   1,433 m (4,700 ft)
Range with max standard fuel, at 1,830 m (6,000 ft)
      800 nm (1,482 km; 921 miles)
Ferry range with max standard and auxiliary fuel, at 1,830 m (6,000 ft)   940 nm (1,742 km; 1,082 miles)
PERFORMANCE (at typical mid-mission weight):
Never-exceed speed (British practice) at S/L
      146 knots (272 km/h; 169 mph)
Cruising speed at S/L   132 knots (245 km/h; 152 mph)

United States of America

Bell
BELL HELICOPTER TEXTRON INC (Subsidiary of Textron Inc)

The business activities of Bell Helicopter Textron were conducted from 1970 until the end of 1981 as an unincorporated division of Textron Inc. Since 3 January 1982 the same activities have been conducted by Bell Helicopter Textron Inc, a wholly owned subsidiary of Textron Inc.

Available details of the range of military combat helicopters in current use, or under development, are published in this entry. Several Bell models are also built under licence by Agusta in Italy and Fuji in Japan. The Korea Bell Helicopter Company and Bell Helicopter Canada are also involved in manufacture.

By 1987, Bell, with its licensees, had manufactured more than 30,000 helicopters.

Bell Model 406 (AHIP)

US Army designation: OH-58D
The US Army announced on 21 September 1981 that Bell's Model 406 proposal had been selected as winner of its Army Helicopter Improvement Program (AHIP) competition to develop a near-term scout helicopter. Its configuration includes a mast mounted sight developed by McDonnell Douglas Astronautics in association with Northrop's Electro-Mechanical Division, and a cockpit control and display subsystem by Sperry Flight Systems. The US Army plans to modify at least 578 existing OH-58A Kiowa light observation helicopters by 1991, under the designation OH-58D, at an estimated cost of $2,000 million. This will provide the Army with a force of close-combat aerial reconnaissance helicopters capable of intelligence gathering and surveillance as well as supporting attack helicopter missions and directing artillery fire. In addition, the OH-58D has demonstrated its capability in a helicopter air-to-air combat role, using the onboard defensive missiles. Only 135 had been funded, in four lots, by summer 1987.

Bell was awarded an initial $151 million development contract, and the first of five prototypes made its first flight on 6 October 1983. US Army development and operational test programmes began in July 1984, at Yuma and at Edwards AFB, California, and were completed in February 1985. Two OH-58Ds were delivered in December 1985, and 64 were in the US Army inventory by the beginning of July 1987. The first shipment to units in Europe began on 11 June 1987, when 12 OH-58Ds were loaded on board a single C-5A Galaxy, complete with all needed support and maintenance equipment.

On 21 May 1984 Bell announced development of a lighter and simplified two/five-seat combat helicopter, with a four-blade soft-in-plane rotor and quick-chance weapons systems, known as the **Model 406CS (Combat Scout)**. It flew for the first time in June 1984. This multi-mission helicopter omits the MMS, specialised avionics and integrated multiplex cockpit of the AHIP 406, but incorporates many OH-58D (AHIP) features including a 548 kW (735 shp) Allison 250-C34R engine, AHIP dynamics and drive train, mated to a damage-resistant, 10,000 hour fail-safe four-blade rigid rotor of composites construction and a high-thrust composites tail rotor. Armament can comprise four TOW 2 anti-tank missiles, or a mix of Stinger air-to-air missiles, 70 mm rockets and 7.62 mm or 0.50 in machine-guns. Empty and max T-O weights are 1,028 kg (2,266 lb) and 2,041 kg (4,500 lb); hovering ceilings are 6,035 m (19,800 ft) IGE and 5,212 m (17,100 ft) OGE; range is 217 nm (402 km; 250 miles), and endurance 2 h 30 min. Max and cruising speeds are 124 knots (230 km/h; 143 mph) and 120 knots (222 km/h; 138 mph) respectively. No orders for the Combat Scout had been announced by mid-1987.

The following specification applies to the OH-58D:
TYPE: Two-seat armed scout helicopter.
ROTOR SYSTEM: Four-blade soft-in-plane main rotor. Blade section BHTI M406183. Glassfibre composite blades, with hollow spar, and afterbody skins supported by Nomex honeycomb core. Main rotorhead has glassfibre yoke and

Bell OH-58D (AHIP) with mast-mounted sight. *(Brian M. Service)*

Bell Model 406CS Combat Scout, armed with 70 mm rocket pack and pod containing two 7.62 mm machine-guns.

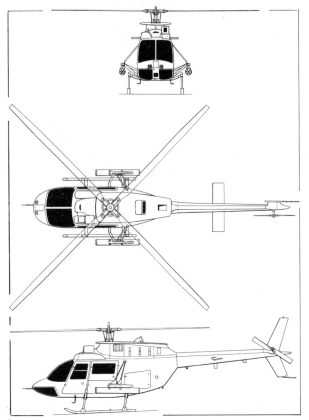

Bell Model 406CS. *(Pilot Press)*

starboard side of cabin. Provision for similar pack on port side. Model 406CS has wide range of weapon options, as detailed in introductory paragraphs.

DIMENSIONS, EXTERNAL:	
Main rotor diameter	10.67 m (35 ft 0 in)
Length: overall, rotors turning	12.85 m (42 ft 2 in)
fuselage, excl rotors	10.31 m (33 ft 10 in)
Width, rotors folded	1.97 m (6 ft 5½ in)
Skid track	1.88 m (6 ft 2 in)
AREA:	
Main rotor blades (each)	1.30 m² (13.95 sq ft)
WEIGHTS	
Weight empty	1,281 kg (2,825 lb)
Max T-O and landing weight	2,041 kg (4,500 lb)
PERFORMANCE (at max T-O weight, 'clean'):	
Never-exceed speed	130 knots (241 km/h; 149 mph)
Max level speed at 1,220 m (4,000 ft)	
	128 knots (237 km/h; 147 mph)
Max cruising speed at 610 m (2,000 ft)	
	120 knots (222 km/h; 138 mph)
Econ cruising speed at 1,220 m (4,000 ft)	
	110 knots (204 km/h; 127 mph)
Max rate of climb: at S/L, ISA	469 m (1,540 ft)/min
at 1,220 m (4,000 ft), 35°C (95°F)	
	over 152 m (500 ft)/min
Vertical rate of climb: at S/L, ISA	232 m (760 ft)/min
at 1,220 m (4,000 ft), 35°C (95°F)	
	over 152 m (500 ft)/min
Service ceiling	over 3,660 m (12,000 ft)
Hovering ceiling: IGE, ISA	over 3,660 m (12,000 ft)
OGE, ISA	3,415 m (11,200 ft)
OGE, 35°C (95°F)	1,735 m (5,700 ft)
Range with max fuel, no reserves	
	300 nm (556 km; 345 miles)
Endurance	2 h 30 min

elastomeric bearings. Main rotor blades fold and have a bendable tab at 60 per cent radius. No rotor brake. Two-blade non-lubricated tail rotor on port side of tailboom; blades of glassfibre composite with nickel coated abrasion strip.

FUSELAGE: Stressed semi-monocoque fail-safe structure. Tapered semi-monocoque tailboom.

TAIL UNIT: Fixed stabiliser of monocoque construction with inverted aerofoil section on starboard side of tailboom. Fixed vertical fin in sweptback upper and ventral sections.

LANDING GEAR: Tubular skids bolted to extruded cross-tubes.

POWERPLANT: One Allison 250-C30R turboshaft engine, with an intermediate power rating of 485 kW (650 shp) at S/L ISA. One self-sealing crash resistant fuel cell, capacity 399 litres (105.4 US gallons; 87.8 Imp gallons), located aft of the cabin area.

ACCOMMODATION: Pilot and co-pilot/observer seated side-by-side. Avionics in rear of cabin.

AVIONICS AND EQUIPMENT: Multi-function displays for vertical and horizontal situation indication, mast mounted sight day/night viewing and communications control, with selection via control column handgrip switches. Five com transceivers, data link and secure voice equipment. Doppler, strapdown INS. Equipped for day/night VFR. Mast mounted sight houses 12x magnification TV camera, auto-focusing IR thermal imaging sensor and laser rangefinder/designator, with automatic target tracking and in-flight automatic boresighting. Night vision goggles; AHRS; and airborne target handoff subsystem (ATHS).

ARMAMENT: Two Stinger air-to-air missiles in pack on

Bell Model 209 HueyCobra, SeaCobra and SuperCobra

US Army designations: AH-1G, AH-1Q and AH-1R
US Navy/Marine Corps designations: AH-1J, AH-1T and AH-1W

Bell Helicopter Textron initiated the Model 209 in March 1965 as a company funded development of the UH-1B/C Iroquois intended specifically for armed helicopter missions. The original design combined the basic transmission and rotor system and (in its standard form) the powerplant of the UH-1C with a new, streamlined fuselage designed for maximum speed, armament load and crew efficiency. Relatively small, its low silhouette and narrow profile make it easy to conceal with small camouflage nets or to move under cover of trees. Tandem seating provides the best possible field of view for the crew of two.

The Model 209 prototype made its first flight on 7 September 1965, and the US Army's intention to order the aircraft was announced on 11 March 1966, the initial model being known as the AH-1G HueyCobra. Total orders to date for all versions of the HueyCobra/SeaCobra exceed 1,400.

Versions announced so far are as follows:

AH-1G HueyCobra. Original version for US Army, powered by a single 1,044 kW (1,400 shp) Avco Lycoming T53-L-13 turboshaft engine, derated to 820 kW (1,100 shp) for T-O and max continuous rating. Development contract

Bell AH-1G HueyCobra of the United States Army.

for two pre-production aircraft placed on 4 April 1966, followed on 13 April by an initial order for 110 aircraft plus long-lead-time spares. Subsequent contracts raised the total US Army order to 1,075, deliveries of which began in June 1967. The US Marine Corps acquired 38 AH-1Gs during 1969, for transition training and initial deployment pending deliveries of the AH-1J. Six were supplied to Israel in 1974, and the Spanish Navy received eight (designated **Z.14**), for anti-shipping strike duties, giving an overall production total of 1,127 AH-1Gs. A number of AH-1Gs have been converted to **TH-1G** dual control trainers. Following the decision in 1977 to equip the HueyCobra with TOW missiles, 92 AH-1Gs were converted to interim AH-1Q standard; all of these, and 286 other AH-1Gs, had been converted to Mod AH-1S configuration by February 1984, completing contracts existing at that time. An order for 29 more conversions was announced in September 1984, followed by a contract for a further 29 in September 1985.

AH-1J SeaCobra. Initial twin-turboshaft version for US Marine Corps, powered by a 1,342 kW (1,800 shp) Pratt & Whitney Canada T400-CP-400 coupled free-turbine turboshaft engine, a military version of the PT6T-3 Turbo Twin Pac. Engine and transmission flat-rated at 820 kW (1,100 shp) continuous output, with increase to 932 kW (1,250 shp) available for T-O or 5 min emergency power. Total of 69 delivered to US Marine Corps between mid-1970 and February 1975, the last two being converted later as prototypes for the AH-1T. About 58 USMC AH-1Js remained operational in May 1982, when US Naval Air Systems Command awarded Bell a $4.7 million contract for phase 1 of a two-phase programme which calls for the company to integrate a Hellfire missile system and night vision cockpit in these helicopters. A further 202 TOW-capable AH-1Js were supplied to the Imperial Iranian Army Aviation from 1974, the US Army acting as purchasing agent.

AH-1Q HueyCobra. Interim anti-armour version for US Army, converted from AH-1G to fire Hughes TOW anti-tank missiles. Total of 92 converted; subsequently upgraded to Mod AH-1S standard.

AH-1S HueyCobra. Advanced and modernised TOW-capable version for US Army; described separately.

AH-1T Improved SeaCobra. Improved version of twin-engined AH-1J for US Marine Corps. Last two AH-1Js modified as prototypes under a US Army Aviation Systems Command contract, with uprated components for significantly increased payload and performance. Incorporates features of AH-1J airframe, but embodies dynamic system of Bell Model 214, some technology developed for Bell Model 309 Kingcobra, an upgraded powerplant (1,469 kW; 1,970 shp T400-WV-402) and transmission capable of transmitting the full rated engine power. Initial contract for 10 announced on 23 June 1975; total of 57 built, of which 51 were subsequently modified to TOW configuration. First AH-1T flew on 20 May 1976, and was delivered to US Marine Corps on 15 October 1977.

AH-1W SuperCobra. During 1980, Bell flight tested successfully an AH-1T powered by two General Electric T700-GE-700 turboshaft engines with a combined output in excess of 2,386 kW (3,200 shp). This installation was made in

US Marine Corps Bell AH-1T Improved SeaCobra twin-engined attack helicopters.

an AH-1T loaned by the US Marine Corps, as part of an R & D programme to establish the specification of a helicopter with enhanced capability for future procurement. Improvements that were proposed for a qualification configuration, suitable for retrofit to existing AH-1Ts, included installation of General Electric T700-GE-401 turboshafts with a combined output of 2,423 kW (3,250 shp); a new combining gearbox; and a number of detail improvements. The T700-GE-401 has intermediate and contingency ratings of 1,260 kW (1,690 shp) and 1,285 kW (1,723 shp) respectively. The fuel system is designed to survive 23 mm shell damage.

A T700-GE-401 testbed helicopter, then designated AH-1T+, made its first flight on 16 November 1983 and was evaluated by the US Marine Corps, beginning in December 1983. Early in 1984 Congressional approval was given for the procurement of 44 production AH-1W SuperCobras, 22 each in FYs 1985 and 1986. The first AH-1W delivered, on 27 March 1986, was intended to undergo a seven-month test programme with Naval Air Systems Command. A second AH-1W began a three-month electromagnetic interference test programme in the spring of 1986. Deliveries totalled 19 by June 1987, and were due to continue at the rate of two per month until February 1988. The USMC also plans to update its fleet of approximately 40 AH-1Ts to AH-1W standard, with the first modification beginning in November 1986, for delivery in 1989.

The first AH-1T uprated to AH-1W standard for the USMC was to be fitted with a larger main rotor based on Bell's Model 680 bearingless research rotor.

Missions assigned to the AH-1W include anti-armour, troop carrying helicopter escort, multiple weapon fire support, reconnaissance by fire, and search and target acquisition. The AH-1W is configured to carry seventy-six 2.75 in or sixteen 5 in Zuni rockets, or two GPU-2A self-contained 20 mm gun pods, or two AIM-9L Sidewinder air-to-air missiles plus 750 rounds of 20 mm ammunition for its three-barrel M197 gun, or up to eight TOW or Hellfire missiles. For other missions, the AH-1W carries flare dispensers for night illumination and the M118 smoke grenade dispenser for marking targets. Equipment includes dual radar warning, infra-red jamming and dual chaff dispensing systems. A night targeting system known as the Cobra Laser Night Attack System (CLNAS), is under

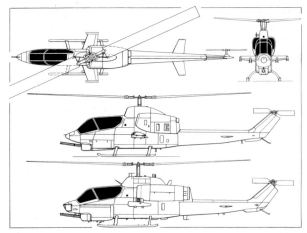

Bell AH-1T Improved SeaCobra. Lower side view: AH-1W. *(Pilot Press)*

development by Israel Aircraft Industries for USMC AH-1Ws and Israeli operated AH-1S HueyCobras. Max cruising speed is increased by 25 knots (46 km/h; 29 mph) to 160 knots (296 km/h; 184 mph) at 915 m (3,000 ft) on a hot day, by comparison with the AH-1T.

TYPE: Single-engined (AH-1G/S) and twin-engined (AH-1J/T/W) close-support and attack helicopters.

ROTOR SYSTEM (AH-1G/J): Model 540 two-blade wide-chord 'door hinge' main rotor, similar to that of UH-1C. Interchangeable blades. Rotor brake fitted. Blades do not fold. Two-blade flex-beam tractor tail rotor on starboard side, of honeycomb construction; blade chord increased on AH-1J.

ROTOR SYSTEM (AH-1T/W): Similar to that of Bell Model 214, with strengthened main rotorhead incorporating Lord Kinematics Lastoflex elastomeric and Teflon faced bearings. Main rotor blades have increased chord, and swept tips which reduce noise and improve high-speed performance. Tail rotor also similar to that of Model 214, with increased diameter and blade chord.

WINGS: Small mid-mounted stub wings, to carry armament and offload rotor in flight.

FUSELAGE: Conventional semi-monocoque structure, with

Bell AH-1W SuperCobra armed with rocket launchers.

low silhouette and narrow profile. AH-1T/W have forward fuselage lengthened by insertion of a 0.305 m (1 ft 0 in) plug, to accommodate tankage for additional 181.5 kg (400 lb) of fuel, and tailboom lengthened by 0.79 m (2 ft 7 in).

TAIL UNIT: Sweptback vertical fin/tail rotor pylon, strengthened on twin-engined models to cater for increased power. Elevator, of inverted aerofoil section, mid-mounted on tailboom forward of fin.

LANDING GEAR: Non-retractable tubular skid type. Ground handling wheels optional.

POWERPLANT: Single or twin turboshaft engines, as detailed under model listings. Fuel capacity: G and J, 1,014 litres (268 US gallons; 223 Imp gallons); T, two fuselage tanks, total capacity 1,158 litres (306 US gallons; 255 Imp gallons).

ACCOMMODATION: Crew of two in tandem, with co-pilot/gunner in front seat and pilot at rear. Crew are protected by seats and side panels of Norton Co 'Noroc' armour; other panels protect vital areas of aircraft.

AVIONICS (AH-1G): Communications equipment includes AN/ARC-54/131 FM radio; AN/ARC-51 and AN/ARC-134 voice com; KY-28 secure voice system.

AVIONICS (AH-1T): AN/ARC-159(V)1 UHF command set, AN/ARC-114A FM tactical set, AN/AIC-18 intercom, AN/ARN-84(V) Tacan, AN/ARA-50 UHF DF, AN/ASN-75B gyrosyn compass, AN/ARN-83 DF, AN/APN-171(V) radar altimeter, AN/APX-72 IFF transponder and AN/APN-154(V) radar beacon. Provision for TSEC/KY-28 com security unit and KIT-1A/TSEC Mk XII computer.

ARMAMENT AND OPERATIONAL EQUIPMENT (AH-1G): Initial production AH-1Gs were fitted with GAU-2B/A 7.62 mm Minigun in Emerson Electric TAT-102A undernose turret. This was superseded by an M28 turret, able to mount either two Miniguns (each with 4,000 rds), or two M129 40 mm grenade launchers (each with 300 rds), or one Minigun and one M129. The Miniguns in these turrets have two rates of fire, controlled by the gunner's trigger: 1,600 rds/min for searching or registry fire, or 4,000 rds/min for attack. The M129 fires at a single rate of 400 rds/min. Four external stores attachments under stub wings can accommodate seventy-six 2.75 in

rockets in four M159 launchers, 28 similar rockets in four M157 launchers, or two M18E1 Minigun pods. An initial batch of six AH-1Gs was delivered to the US Army in December 1969, equipped with a Bell/General Electric M35 armament subsystem. This unit consists of an M61 six-barrel 20 mm automatic cannon on the port inboard wing station, having a firing rate of 750 rds/min. Two ammunition boxes faired flush to the fuselage below the stub wings each accommodate 500 rds, and total installed weight of the system is 531 kg (1,172 lb). A total of 350 M35 kits was ordered subsequently by the US Army. All wing stores are symmetrically or totally jettisonable. In normal operation the co-pilot/gunner controls and fires the turret armament, and the pilot (aided by an M73 adjustable reflex rocket sight) normally fires the wing stores. The pilot can fire the turreted weapons only in the stowed (ie, dead ahead) position; the turret returns to the stowed position automatically when the gunner releases his grip on the slewing switch. The gunner also has the capability to fire the wing stores if required. Other operational equipment on the AH-1G includes an M130 chaff dispenser.

ARMAMENT (AH-1J): Electrically operated General Electric undernose turret, housing an M197 three-barrel 20 mm weapon (a lightweight version of the M61 cannon). A 750-rd ammunition container is located in the fuselage directly aft of the turret; firing rate is 750 rds/min, but a 16-round burst limiter is incorporated in the firing switch. Barrel length of 1.52 m (5 ft) makes it imperative that the M197 is centralised before wing stores are fired. Gun can be tracked 110° to each side, 18° upward, and 50° downward. Four attachments under stub wings for various loads, including LAU-68A/A (seven-tube) or LAU-61A/A (19-tube) 2.75 in rocket launchers, or M18E1 Minigun pods. Total possible armament load 245 kg (542 lb) internal, 998 kg (2,200 lb) external.

ARMAMENT (AH-1T): Chin turret as AH-1J. Underwing attachments for four LAU-61A, LAU-68A, LAU-68A/A, LAU-68B/A or LAU-69A 2.75 in rocket pods; or two CBU-55B fuel-air explosive weapons; four SU-44 flare dispensers; two M118 grenade dispensers; Mk 45 parachute flares; or two Minigun pods. Alternative TOW or Hellfire air-to-surface missile installations.

DIMENSIONS, EXTERNAL:

Main rotor diameter: G, J	13.41 m (44 ft 0 in)
T, W	14.63 m (48 ft 0 in)
Wing span (all)	3.23 m (10 ft 7 in)
Length overall, main rotor fore and aft:	
G	16.14 m (52 ft 11½ in)
J	16.26 m (53 ft 4 in)
T, W	17.68 m (58 ft 0 in)
Length of fuselage: G, J	13.59 m (44 ft 7 in)
T	14.68 m (48 ft 2 in)
Width of fuselage: G	0.965 m (3 ft 2 in)
J, T	0.98 m (3 ft 2½ in)
Height overall: G	4.12 m (13 ft 6¼ in)
J, W	4.15 m (13 ft 8 in)
T	4.32 m (14 ft 2 in)
Width over skids (all)	2.13 m (7 ft 0 in)
Width over TOW missile pods:	
G	3.26 m (10 ft 8¾ in)

AREAS:

Main rotor disc: G, J	141.26 m² (1,520.53 sq ft)
T	168.11 m² (1,809.56 sq ft)

WEIGHTS:

Operating weight empty, incl. amounts shown for crew, fluids, avionics and armour:	
G (404 kg; 891 lb)	2,754 kg (6,073 lb)
J (398 kg; 877 lb)	3,294 kg (7,261 lb)
Weight empty: T	3,642 kg (8,030 lb)
W	4,627 kg (10,200 lb)
Operating weight empty: T	3,904 kg (8,608 lb)
Max useful load (fuel and disposable ordnance):	
J	1,144 kg (2,523 lb)
T	2,445 kg (5,392 lb)
Mission weight: G	4,266 kg (9,407 lb)
J	4,523 kg (9,972 lb)
Max T-O and landing weight:	
G	4,309 kg (9,500 lb)
J	4,535 kg (10,000 lb)
T	6,350 kg (14,000 lb)
W	6,690 kg (14,750 lb)

PERFORMANCE (at max T-O weight, ISA):

Never-exceed speed:	
G	190 knots (352 km/h; 219 mph)

J	180 knots (333 km/h; 207 mph)	J, normal rated power	3,215 m (10,550 ft)
Max level speed at S/L:		T, max cont power	2,255 m (7,400 ft)
G, T	149 knots (277 km/h; 172 mph)	Hovering ceiling IGE: G	3,015 m (9,900 ft)
J	180 knots (333 km/h; 207 mph)	J	3,794 m (12,450 ft)
W	189 knots (350 km/h; 218 mph)	W	4,495 m (14,750 ft)
Max crosswind speed for hovering:		Hovering ceiling OGE: T	365 m (1,200 ft)
J	40 knots (74 km/h; 46 mph)	W	914 m (3,000 ft)
Vertical rate of climb at S/L:		Combat radius at 138 knots (255 km/h; 158 mph) at S/L:	
T	92 m (301 ft)/min	T	108 nm (200 km; 124 miles)
Max rate of climb at S/L:		Range at S/L with max fuel, no reserves:	
G, normal rated power	375 m (1,230 ft)/min	G	325 nm (602 km; 374 miles)
J, normal rated power	332 m (1,090 ft)/min	J	335 nm (620 km; 385 miles)
T	544 m (1,785 ft)/min	T	310 nm (574 km; 356 miles)
Service ceiling:		W	343 nm (635 km; 395 miles)
G, normal rated power	3,475 m (11,400 ft)		

Bell Model 209 HueyCobra (Modernised Version)

US Army designations: AH-1S and TH-1S

The AH-1S is an advanced version of the single-engined TOW-capable HueyCobra for the US Army, with upgraded powerplant, gearbox, transmission and many other improvements. The US Army's AH-1S fleet is being formed by procurement of new-production aircraft and by modification of AH-1Gs and other earlier models. Funds were provided in FY 1981 both to complete the new-production programme and to continue the conversions. By the end of 1985, 1,066 AH-1Ss had been manufactured and modified for US and foreign customers.

The first of a succession of US Army contracts was placed in 1975, and orders to the beginning of 1984 were as follows:

Mod AH-1S. This designation (the 'Mod' in this case indicating 'Modified') applies to 378 AH-1Gs retrofitted with the TOW missile system, and with a 1,342 kW (1,800 shp) Avco Lycoming T53-L-703 turboshaft engine, and the same rotor system dynamics as the Production AH-1S. The total includes the 92 AH-1Gs previously converted to AH-1Qs, which were further modified by Bell and Dornier to Mod AH-1S. An additional 29 conversions from AH-1G were ordered in September 1984, and 29 more in September 1985. Some Mod AH-1S have additional equipment

Bell AH-1S HueyCobra with eight TOW missiles and rocket launchers.

specified for Up-gun and Modernised AH-1S, including an M197 gun, ALQ-144 infra-red jammer, APR-39 radar warning receiver, AAS-32 laser rangefinder and tracker, hot metal and plume infra-red suppressor. Ten Mod AH-1S have been converted to **TH-1S** by Northrop's Electro-Mechanical Division, under a programme known as Night Stalker, to train US Army pilots in operation of the Martin Marietta FLIR-based night vision system and Honeywell integrated helmet and display sighting system (IHADSS) fitted to AH-64 Apache helicopters. Deliveries began on 31 July 1984, and were to be completed in April 1985. Each TH-1S has a pilot's night vision sensor (PNVS) and associated visual and avionics systems. Blue instrument lighting makes the cockpit compatible with night vision goggles.

Production AH-1S. Under Step 1 of a three-step new-production programme, 100 Production AH-1S HueyCobras were built and delivered to the US Army between March 1977 and September 1978. These aircraft have a flat-plate canopy, improved nap-of-the-earth (NOE) instrument panel layout, continental United States (CONUS) navigation equipment, radar altimeter, improved communication radios, uprated engine and transmission, push/pull anti-torque controls, and (from the 67th aircraft onwards) Kaman developed composite rotor blades. First unit to receive this version, in August 1977, was the 82nd Airborne Division at Fort Bragg, North Carolina.

Up-gun AH-1S. The next 98 new-production aircraft (Step 2) have all the improvements detailed for the Production AH-1S, plus a universal 20/30 mm gun turret, an improved wing stores management system for the 2.75 in rockets, automatic compensation for off-axis gun firing, and a 10k VA alternator to provide the necessary additional electric power. Deliveries of this version began in September 1978 and were completed in October 1979.

Modernised AH-1S. This version, not to be confused with the 'Mod AH-1S' referred to earlier, represents the fully upgraded AH-1S, and became standard from the 199th new-production aircraft. To the improvements already mentioned for the two preceding stages are added, as Step 3, a new fire control subsystem (comprising a laser rangefinder and tracker, ballistics computer, low-airspeed sensor, and pilot's head-up display), air data system, Doppler navigation system, IFF transponder, infra-red jammer, hot metal and plume infra-red suppressor, closed-circuit refuelling, new secure voice communications, and new composite rotor blades developed by Kaman. Total of 99 delivered to US Army. The Army National Guard also acquired an initial 27 Modernised AH-1Ss, with a further 23 to follow.

Under a $13 million 1980 contract awarded by the US Army Missile Command, Hughes Aircraft Company manufactured 157 Laser Augmented Airborne TOW (LAAT) stabilised sights for installation in Modernised AH-1S aircraft, and subsequently manufactured a further 120 new sights. The very small ($13 \times 13 \times 4$ cm; $5 \times 5 \times 1.5$ in) laser transmitter has been developed to fit within the existing sight turret of the AH-1S.

Three engineering development models of the LAAT were used for flight testing by Bell at Yuma Proving Grounds, Arizona. They demonstrated that the LAAT can significantly improve first-burst accuracy of gun and rocket fire. In use, the gunner sights a target and fires the laser. Reflected from the target, the returning beam provides accurate and almost instantaneous range information, enabling the aircraft's fire control computer to integrate range, wind and ammunition ballistics data to direct weapon firing with great accuracy.

To reduce the time taken by co-pilot/gunners to acquire targets and fire their missiles and guns, US Army AH-1S aircraft are to be fitted with an automatic airborne laser tracker (ALT) system produced by Rockwell. Delivery of 163 ALTs has been completed.

Hughes Aircraft has developed, as a further enhancement of the AH-1S TOW system, a FLIR-augmented Cobra TOW sight. This telescopic sight, mounted under the nose of the helicopter, enables the gunner to 'see' through darkness, smoke and haze, and offers a considerable improvement in round-the-clock combat capability. Delivery of the sight, now known as Cobra-Nite (C-Nite) began in mid-1986, with planned installation on some 500 AH-1Ss.

Thirty Modernised AH-1S, of a planned total of 54, were ordered by the Japan Ground Self-Defence Force for delivery between 1985 and 1987. These were assembled under licence in Japan, with Fuji as prime contractor under sub-licence from Mitsui. Other deliveries of the Modernised AH-1S have included 24 for Jordan and 20 for Pakistan. The

supply of a number to Israel was authorised, as well as four for Royal Thai Army Aviation.

The major differences between the current standard AH-1S and earlier single-engined HueyCobras may be summarised as follows:

TYPE: Anti-armour attack helicopter.

ROTOR SYSTEM AND DRIVE: Upgraded gearbox and transmission, the latter rated at 962 kW (1,290 shp) for take-off, 845 kW (1,134 shp) continuous. From 67th new-production AH-1S onward, main rotor blades of composite construction are fitted, developed by Kaman Aerospace Corporation and equipped with tungsten carbide bearing sleeves. The outer 15 per cent of these blades, which are tolerant of damage by weapons of up to 23 mm calibre, is tapered in both chord and thickness.

FUSELAGE: Tailboom strengthened to increase survivability against weapons of up to 23 mm calibre. Entire airframe has an anti-infra-red paint finish.

POWERPLANT: One 1,342 kW (1,800 shp) Avco Lycoming T53-L-703 turboshaft engine. Closed circuit refuelling on Modernised AH-1S. Fuel capacity 980 litres (259 US gallons; 216 Imp gallons).

ACCOMMODATION: New flat-plate canopy has seven panes of viewing surfaces, designed to minimise glint and reduce possibility of visual detection during nap-of-the-earth (NOE) flying; it also provides increased headroom for pilot. Improved instrument layout and lighting, compatible with use of night vision goggles.

AVIONICS AND EQUIPMENT: Standard lightweight avionics equipment (SLAE) includes AN/ARC-114 FM, AN/ARC-164 UHF/AM voice com, and E-Systems (Memcor Division) AN/ARC-115 VHF/AM voice com (compatible with KY-58 single-channel secure voice system). Other avionics include AN/ASN-128 Doppler nav system in Modernised AH-1S; APR-39 radar warning receiver; ALQ-144 infra-red jammer; HSI; VSI; radar altimeter; push/pull anti-torque controls for tail rotor; co-

Bell AH-1S Huey Cobra. *(Pilot Press)*

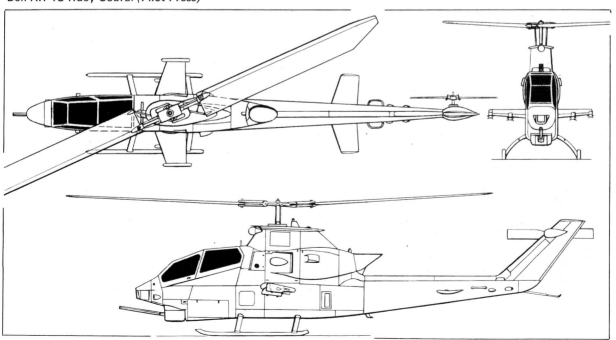

pilot's standby magnetic compass.

ARMAMENT AND OPERATIONAL EQUIPMENT: M65 system with eight Hughes TOW missiles, disposed as two two-round clusters on each of the outboard underwing stations. The inboard wing stations remain available for other stores. Beginning with the 101st new-production AH-1S (the first 'Up-gun' example), the M28 (7.62/40 mm) turret in earlier HueyCobras is replaced by a new electrically powered General Electric universal turret, designed to accommodate either a 20 mm or a 30 mm weapon and to improve stand-off capability. Initially, the 20 mm M197 three-barrel cannon (with 750 rds) is mounted in this turret. Rate of fire is 730 rds/min. Turret position is controlled by the pilot or co-pilot/gunner through helmet sights, or by the co-pilot using the M65 TOW missile system's telescopic sight unit. Field of fire is up to 110° to each side of aircraft, 20.5° upward and 50° downward. Also from the first 'Up-gun' AH-1S, the helicopter is equipped with a Baldwin Electronics M138 wing stores management subsystem, providing the means to select and fire, singly or in groups, any one of five types of external 2.75 in rocket store. These are mounted in launchers each containing from 7 to 19 tubes, and are additional to the TOW missile capability.

In addition to these installations the 199th new-built AH-1S (the first to full 'Modernised' standard) introduced a fire control subsystem which includes a Kaiser head-up display for the pilot, Teledyne Systems digital fire control computer for the turreted weapon and underwing rockets, omnidirectional airspeed system to improve cannon and rocket accuracy, Hughes laser rangefinder (accurate to 10,000 m; 32,800 ft), and provision for a Rockwell AN/AAS-32 airborne laser tracker. Other operational equipment includes a Hughes LAAT stabilised sight (see introductory copy), a GEC Avionics M-143 air data subsystem, AN/APX-100 solid-state IFF transponder, Sanders AN/ALQ-144 infra-red jammer (above engine), suppressor for infra-red signature from engine hot metal and exhaust plume, and AN/APR-39 radar warning receiver.

DIMENSIONS, EXTERNAL: As AH-1G except:

Wing span	3.28 m (10 ft 9 in)
Length overall, rotors turning	
	16.18 m (53 ft 1 in)
Width of fuselage	0.99 m (3 ft 3 in)
Width over TOW pods	3.56 m (11 ft 8 in)

WEIGHTS:

Operating weight empty	
	2,993 kg (6,598 lb)
Mission weight	4,524 kg (9,975 lb)
Max T-O weight	4,535 kg (10,000 lb)

PERFORMANCE (at max T-O weight, ISA):

Never-exceed speed (TOW configuration):	
	170 knots (315 km/h; 195 mph)
Max level speed (TOW configuration)	
	123 knots (227 km/h; 141 mph)
Max rate of climb at S/L, normal rated power	
	494 m (1,620 ft)/min
Service ceiling, normal rated power	3,720 m (12,200 ft)
Hovering ceiling IGE	3,720 m (12,200 ft)
Range at S/L with max fuel, 8% reserves	
	274 nm (507 km; 315 miles)

Bell/Boeing V-22 Osprey

Bell is teamed with Boeing Helicopter Company in a joint programme, based on the Model 301/XV-15, to meet the US government's Joint Services Advanced Vertical Lift Aircraft (formerly JVX) proposal, named V-22 Osprey in January 1985. The US Navy and US Air Force are currently participating in the programme, with the USN as executive service.

On 26 April 1983 the two companies received a US Naval Air Systems Command contract to proceed with preliminary design of the aircraft over the following 24 months. Two further contracts, totalling $17.5 million, were awarded in April 1985 for systems engineering, long-lead tooling, a V-22 mockup, and purchasing and design analysis for the aircraft's engine interface and avionics integration. Bell/Boeing, as prime contractors, have subcontracted Grumman to design and build the V-22's tail unit, General Electric the digital fly-by-wire flight control system, Lockheed-Georgia the wing control surfaces and fixed trailing edge, and Menasco of Canada and Dowty of Canada respectively the nose and main landing gear. Boeing will build the fuselage and overwing fairing; Bell is responsible for wings, nacelles, drive system and prop-rotor assemblies.

In January 1984 Bell began a simulated V-22 flight test programme, using data from wind tunnel tests and analyses. Formal evaluation by military pilots, using NASA/Ames simulation, began in the following March. Boeing has built a two-thirds scale rotor/wing model to prove hover perfor-

mance predictions. Testing of critical structural components was co-ordinated at Bell and Boeing.

In December 1985 the US Navy announced its selection of the 4,475 kW (6,000 shp) class Allison T406-AD-400 turboshaft engine for the V-22. Pratt & Whitney Government Products Division was named in April 1986 as second production source for the engine.

Artist's impression of Bell/Boeing MV-22A Osprey of the US Marine Corps.

On 2 May 1986 Naval Air Systems Command awarded Bell/Boeing $497.3 million as the first instalment of a $1,714 million fixed-price incentive award contract for a seven-year full scale development (FSD) programme for the V-22. This will include the manufacture of six flying prototypes, three to be completed by each partner, and three non-flying airframes for static, ground and fatigue testing. The V-22's first flight was scheduled for 18 June 1988, with production deliveries beginning in December 1991.

The V-22 Osprey has been conceived as a multi-mission aircraft. The US Marine Corps, which will receive the first production examples, has a requirement for 552 assault transport variants, designated **MV-22A**, to replace CH-46 and CH-53 helicopters. The MV-22A is required to carry 24 combat-equipped Marines at a speed of 250 knots (463 km/h; 288 mph) over an operational radius of 200 nm (370 km; 230 miles), with the ability to hover at 915 m (3,000 ft) at an ambient air temperature of 33°C. The US Navy has a requirement for up to 50 combat search and rescue aircraft, designated **HV-22A**, to replace HH-3 helicopters. In this role the Osprey would be required to operate at 250 knots (463 km/h; 288 mph) over a 460 nm (852 km; 530 mile) radius and hover mid-mission at 2,135 m (7,000 ft) OGE, with accommodation for four survivors. The US Navy has also expressed an interest in up to 300 V-22s for anti-submarine warfare duties, carrying dipping sonar and at least one torpedo.

The US Air Force requires 80 long-range special operations aircraft, designated **CV-22A**, to carry 12 special forces troops or up to 1,306 kg (2,880 lb) of internal cargo over a 700 nm (1,297 km; 806 mile) mission radius at 250 knots (463 km/h; 288 mph), with capability to hover OGE at 1,525 m (5,000 ft).

The US Army, although not involved in the development phase, currently has plans to procure 231 aircraft in the Marine Corps configuration for multi-mission transport duties, including utility operations, medical evacuation and corps area operations, making a total requirement for the US services of 1,213 aircraft.

Additional requirements specified by one or more of the services for the V-22 Osprey include an unrefuelled ferry range of 2,100 nm (3,892 km; 2,418 miles) for self-deployability; in-flight refuelling capability; ability to carry outsize external loads of up to 4,536 kg (10,000 lb); all-weather low-altitude capability; all-weather low-altitude navigation capability; self-protection; and low maintenance. To meet the Navy/Marine Corps requirement for operation from US Navy amphibious assault ships, the wing and rotor system must 'fold' in 90 seconds. After landing, the rotor blades are stopped and folded inboard automatically; nacelles are then rotated to the aeroplane mode, bringing the folded blades in line with the wing leading edge; finally, the entire wing is rotated automatically by a Lucas Aerospace actuator and locking unit, to align it with the fuselage. The Ospreys for the Navy and US Air Force will be fitted with Texas Instruments AN/APQ-168 multi-mode radar.

The Bell/Boeing team has begun a predesign study of a sea based anti-submarine warfare variant of the V-22 Osprey for the US Navy. Provisionally designated **SV-22**, this aircraft would have a modified fuselage interior for additional avionics and crew stations, and mountings for torpedoes and, possibly, air-to-surface missiles. Radar and FLIR systems are also anticipated in the design. As envisaged, SV-22s would be based on US Navy aircraft carriers for all

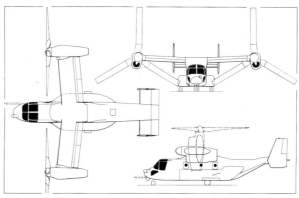

Bell/Boeing V-22 Osprey. *(Pilot Press)*

maintenance and berthing, but would operate for extended periods of time from smaller ships such as DD-963 class destroyers, providing long range ASW protection for non-carrier battle groups. The SV-22 could be available in the mid-1990s.

Concept studies for possible commercial variants of the V-22 Osprey have also been conducted. These range from a minimum-change version seating 36-44 passengers, which would have a max T-O weight of 19,958 kg (44,000 lb), a cruising speed of 300 knots (556 km/h; 345 mph) and a maximum range, with reserves, of 725 nm (1,343 km; 835 miles) to a series of five tilt-rotor derivative designs ranging from an eight-seat executive transport (**CTR-800**) and a 19-seat commuter/executive aircraft with Rolls-Royce/Turbomeca RTM.322 turboshafts (**CTR-1900**), to a 75-passenger short-haul airliner designated **CTR-7500**.

The concept studies, undertaken with the Department of Defense, Federal Aviation Administration and NASA, are looking at other possible roles for tilt-rotor craft, including AEW, tanker and gunship.

The following data are provisional:

DIMENSIONS, EXTERNAL:	
Rotor diameter (each)	11.58 m (38 ft 0 in)
Length overall	17.47 m (57 ft 4 in)
Height: over tail fins	5.28 m (17 ft 4 in)
overall, nacelles vertical	6.15 m (20 ft 2 in)
Width over mainwheels	4.64 m (15 ft 2½ in)
Nacelle ground clearance, nacelles vertical	
	1.58 m (5 ft 2½ in)
AREA:	
Rotor discs (each)	105.4 m² (1,134 sq ft)
WEIGHTS:	
Design weight empty	14,515 kg (32,000 lb)
Max T-O weight:	
STOL (20° forward tilt)	26,762 kg (59,000 lb)
VTOL	21,546 kg (47,500 lb)
PERFORMANCE:	
Max cruising speed at max STOL T-O weight	
	340 knots (630 km/h; 391 mph)
T-O run at max STOL T-O weight	
	less than 152 m (500 ft)

Bell ARTI and LHX

In 1982 the US Army invited manufacturers to submit design concepts for its Light Helicopter Experimental (LHX)

Artist's impression of possible Bell/McDonnell Douglas LHX contender.

programme, representing a requirement for some 5,000 helicopters in two variants: scout/attack (SCAT) and utility, both using the same dynamic systems. Bell began a contracted study which included derivative variants of the UH-1 and AH-1, as well as new designs for helicopters and high-performance (tilt-rotor) craft. The US Army subsequently announced that a conventional helicopter rather than a tilt-rotor was wanted for the LHX requirement. Accordingly, Bell and its partner, McDonnell Douglas Helicopter Company, concentrated on a single-main-rotor design incorporating the Model 680 bearingless main rotor system, composite materials adapted from the ACAP (Advanced Composite Airframe Program), a ring-fin tail rotor, and twin 895 kW (1,200 shp) T800 turboshaft engines. Specifications for the **LHX** design included main and tail rotor diameters of 11.58 m (38 ft) and 1.92 m (6.3 ft), max length with rotors turning of 14.02 m (46 ft), and width over landing gear of 2.29 m (7.5 ft). Primary mission gross weight was given as 3,402–3,855 kg (7,500–8,500 lb), with a fuel capacity of 700 litres (185 US gallons; 154 Imp gallons), and a speed of 170 knots (315 km/h; 196 mph) at max continuous power. In accordance with US Army specifications it was expected to fire Hellfire and Stinger missiles, 2.75 inch rockets and a single-barrel 20 mm cannon. Survivability equipment was being developed jointly by Northrop's Defense Systems Division and Eaton Corporation's AIL Division.

A major supporting contract for the LHX was the Advanced Rotorcraft Technology Integration (**ARTI**) effort. In December 1983 Bell received a contract to design a single-pilot cockpit for the SCAT LHX, which would fly all-weather, day and night nap-of-the-earth missions. The requirement called for an aircraft that could fly itself and simultaneously seek, identify and assign priority to targets. Bell went into partnership with Sperry Flight Systems, Honeywell Inc and Texas Instruments on the ARTI contract, and in early 1985 began conducting 'hands-off' flight tests of the digital fly-by-wire AFCS using the experimental YAH-1S four-blade Model 249 HueyCobra as the testbed aircraft. In fact, the FBW system was activated by 'hands-on' controls, but once selected the pilot could temporarily delegate his piloting task to the system while he performed navigation, target designation, weapon operating or other functions. He could interrupt the automatic flight mode and assume manual control at any time.

Boeing
THE BOEING COMPANY

Boeing Aerospace Company

The Boeing Aerospace Company has its headquarters at the company's space centre at Kent, Washington, some 12 miles south of Seattle. It consists of four major divisions: Information Systems; Space Systems; Ballistic Systems and Defense Systems. Major programmes and activities concern airborne warning and control, the E-4 advanced airborne command post, the E-6 Tacamo aircraft, the Inertial Upper Stage, Minuteman ICBM, Peacekeeper ICBM ground support system, air-launched cruise missile, ASW standoff weapon, and Roland. Responsible for much of Boeing's military and space effort, it has a labour force of approximately 17,000 employees.

Boeing E-3 Sentry

USAF designations: EC-137D and E-3

The E-3 Sentry AWACS (Airborne Warning and Control System) is effectively a mobile, flexible, survivable and jamming-resistant high-capacity radar station, command, control and communications centre, installed within a Boeing 707 airframe. It offers the potential of long-range high- or low-level surveillance of all air vehicles, manned or unmanned, and provides detection, tracking and identification capability within its surveillance capacity during all weathers and above all kinds of terrain. The radar system of later production aircraft also incorporates a maritime surveillance mode. Each of these aircraft is able to support a variety of tactical and/or air defence missions with no change in configuration. Its data storage and processing capability can provide real-time assessment of enemy action, and of the status and position of friendly resources.

In US Air Force service, the E-3 has a dual use: as a command and control centre to support quick-reaction deployment and tactical operations by Tactical Air Command units; and as a survivable early warning airborne command and control centre for identification, surveillance and tracking of airborne enemy forces, and for the command and control of NORAD (North American Air Defense) forces over the continental USA. The E-3 provides comprehensive surveillance out to a range of more than 200 nm (370 km; 230 miles) for low-flying targets, and still further for targets at higher altitudes.

Boeing's Aerospace Group, as it was then named, was awarded an initial contract as prime contractor and systems integrator for the AWAC system on 23 July 1970. To ensure that maximum effort and finance were devoted to the design and development of the most advanced radar and associated onboard systems, Boeing's design submission was based on the airframe of the Model 707-320B commercial jet transport. The only major change proposed for production E-3As was the installation of more powerful Pratt & Whitney TF33 turbofan engines, in lieu of the commercial turbofans then standard for the civil transport models. Two of these aircraft, with the prototype designation EC-137D, were modified initially for comparative trials with prototype downward looking radars designed by Hughes Aircraft Company and Westinghouse Electric Corporation. After several months of airborne tests, the Westinghouse radar was selected.

On 26 January 1973 the US Air Force announced approval for full scale AWACS development, and production received Congressional approval in the spring of 1975. The name Sentry was given subsequently to the E-3. The full-scale development test programme, completed at the end of 1976, involved a fleet of three aircraft completely equipped with mission avionics, and a fourth aircraft equipped for airworthiness testing. Thirty-five E-3s were delivered subsequently to the USAF, the last of them in June 1984. A further 18 were built for NATO.

These USAF and NATO AWACS have been developed and produced to four different standards, as follows:

Core E-3A. Initial form of the first 24 production Sentries delivered to USAF. Equipped with pulse-Doppler radar capable of detecting high- and low-flying aircraft; CC-1 computer; nine situation display consoles (SDCs) which provide the mission crew with all display and control features required to carry out their surveillance, weapons directing, and battle staff functions; two auxiliary display units (ADUs) which support the communications, maintenance and data processing functions; and 13 available communications links (seven UHF, three VHF/AM, one VHF/FM, and two HF/SSB), many of them in clear voice.

E-3B. Under the USAF Block 20 modification programme, the two prototypes and 22 USAF core-configured E-3As (aircraft Nos. 4 to 9 and 11 to 26) are being updated to E-3B standard by the installation of ECM-resistant voice communications; one more HF and five more UHF radios; a new and faster IBM CC-2 computer with much expanded memory and greatly increased processing speed compared with the CC-1; five additional SDCs; and an austere maritime surveillance capability which Westinghouse developed for incorporation in the basic radar system. The E-3B also has provisions for Have Quick anti-jamming improvements to UHF radios, self defence, and a radio teletypewriter. First E-3B was re-delivered to USAF, after modification, on 18 July 1984. Remaining 23 are being modified by USAF at Tinker AFB, using Boeing kits.

US/NATO Standard E-3A. Original standard for USAF aircraft Nos. 27 to 35, of which delivery began in December 1981, and of the updated aircraft No. 3. Radar modified to embody full maritime surveillance capability;

Boeing E-3 AWACS in Foreign Military Sales (FMS) configuration, with CFM56 turbofans.

NATO version of the Boeing E-3A Sentry AWACS aircraft. *(Air Photo Supply)*

CC-2 computer; additional HF radios; ECM-resistant voice communications; radio teletypewriter; provisions for self-defence and ECM. NATO aircraft are to this standard and retain E-3A designation.

E-3C. Under USAF Block 25 modification programme, begun in 1984, upgrading of the 10 USAF Standard E-3As to E-3C configuration is adding five more SDCs, five more UHF radios, and provisions for Have Quick anti-jamming improvements.

The USAF Electronic Systems Division has proposed a $425 million MSIP for the E-3, phased over five years, to give the radar greater 'detectability', add passive sensors, and make other improvements. Eventually, all USAF and NATO E-3s will be equipped with the Joint Tactical Information Distribution System (JTIDS) for anti-jam communications.

As a first step, in May 1987, Boeing was awarded a $241.5 million USAF contract for E-3 improvements that include full-scale development and integration into US and NATO E-3s of an ESM system to detect signals emitted by both hostile and friendly targets. Additional enhancements to be made to US E-3s, under what is known as the Block 30/35 programme, include upgrading of JTIDS to TADIL-J (tactical digital information link-J) capability; CC-2 computer memory upgrade, using VLSI (very large scale integration) and bubble memory electronics technologies; and ability to employ the GPS (Global Positioning System). IOC for the Block 30/35 improvements is scheduled for 1993.

The first production core-configured E-3A Sentry was delivered on 24 March 1977 to Tactical Air Command's 552nd Airborne Warning and Control Wing (later Division), based at Tinker AFB, Oklahoma. E-3As achieved initial operational status in April 1978, and have since completed deployments to Alaska, Iceland, West Germany, Saudi Arabia, Sudan, the Mediterranean area, and the Pacific. E-3 aircraft are also employed in support of the US drug enforcement programme.

E-3As began to assume a role in US continental air defence on 1 January 1979, when NORAD personnel started to augment E-3A flight crews from TAC on all operational NORAD missions from Tinker AFB. The operating component was redesignated 552nd AWAC Wing in April

1985; it consists of several subordinate units. At Tinker, these include the 963rd and 964th AWAC Squadrons, the 966th AWAC Training Squadron, the 552nd Aircraft Generation Squadron (systems support), the 552nd Component Repair Squadron, and the 8th Tactical Deployment Control Squadron (flying EC-135/WC-135 aircraft). Overseas units of the 28th Air Division include the 960th and 961st AWAC Support Squadrons. Based respectively at NAS Keflavik, Iceland, and Kadena AB, Okinawa, Japan, they provide command and control capability to CINCLANT (through the Commander, Iceland Defence Force) and CINCPAC.

Much of the avionics for NATO E-3As was produced in West Germany, with Dornier as systems integrator. NATO funded a third HF radio, to cover the maritime environment; a new data analysis and programming group; underwing hardpoints for self-defence-system stores; and a radio teletype to link the AWACS with the Organisation's maritime forces and commands. The first NATO production E-3A flew for the first time on 18 December 1980, from the manufacturing plant at Renton to Boeing Field, Seattle, where its rotodome and associated equipment were installed subsequently. It was delivered to Dornier's factory at Oberpfaffenhofen on 19 March 1981, and installation and checkout of mission avionics began on 1 April. Delivery of this first complete E-3A was made to NATO on 22 January 1982, and the final aircraft was delivered on 25 April 1985.

The NATO AWACS aircrafts' main operating base is at Geilenkirchen in West Germany. Initial forward operating bases were at Oerland, Norway, and Konya, Turkey. Additional forward operating bases became operational during 1985 at Preveza, Greece, and Trapani, Italy. The forward operating bases are manned by 20–35 NATO personnel, who provide turnaround maintenance services. E-3As are deployed periodically for training and surveillance missions. Eventually, aircraft are expected to be deployed to the forward bases nearly full-time.

The sale of five E-3 AWACS aircraft to the Royal Saudi Air Force was approved during October 1981, under a programme known as Peace Sentinel. Also included in the sale were six E-3 derivative tanker aircraft, which are designated **KE-3A**, and in 1984 the Saudi government exercised an option to increase the number of KE-3As to

Model of the RAF E-3, to be powered by CFM56s. *(Jay Miller/Aerofax)*

eight. In the same year, agreement was reached to equip the RSAF aircraft with CFM56-2 engines, fitted with Hispano-Suiza thrust reversers. The first Saudi E-3 was handed over on 30 June 1986. Aircraft delivered to Saudi Arabia are not

Boeing E-3A Sentry. *(Pilot Press)*

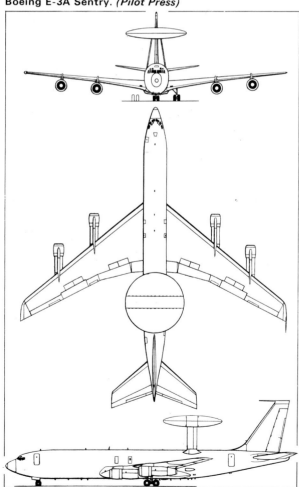

expected to be equipped with JTIDS, the latest-standard ECCM or Have Quick provisions.

On 18 December 1986 the British government announced its intention to order six E-3 AWACS aircraft for the Royal Air Force; a seventh has since been ordered. These will be powered by CFM56 engines and will be delivered to the UK for installation, integration and flight testing of avionics systems by British contractors. Boeing has offered 130 per cent offset to British companies on the RAF E-3 procurement. On 26 February 1987, the French Minister of Defence announced that France had ordered three similar aircraft, with a fourth ordered on 20 August, all for 1991 delivery. An option is held on a fifth aircraft.

The following details apply specifically to the USAF E-3A:

TYPE: Airborne early warning and command post aircraft.

WINGS: Cantilever low-wing monoplane. Dihedral 7°. Incidence 2°. Sweepback at quarter-chord 35°. Normal outboard aileron, and small inboard aileron on each wing. Two tracked and slotted flaps and one fillet flap on each wing. Full span leading-edge flaps. Four spoilers on each wing, forward of flaps. Primary flying controls are aerodynamically balanced and manually operated. Lateral control at low speeds by all four ailerons, supplemented by spoilers which are interconnected with the ailerons. Lateral control at high speeds by inboard ailerons and spoilers only. Operation of flaps adjusts linkage between inboard and outboard ailerons to permit outboard operation with flaps extended. Spoilers may also be used symmetrically as speed brakes. Thermal anti-icing of wing leading edges.

FUSELAGE: Semi-monocoque fail-safe structure strengthened by comparison with that of the commercial Model 707-320.

TAIL UNIT: Cantilever structure. Variable-incidence tailplane. Powered rudder. Anti-balance tab and trim tab in rudder. Trim and control tabs in each elevator.

LANDING GEAR: Tricycle type. Main units are four-wheel bogies. Twin-wheel nose unit. Mainwheels and tyres size 46 × 16. Nosewheels and tyres size 39 × 13. Multi-disc brakes by Goodyear. Hydro-Aire flywheel detector type anti-skid units.

POWERPLANT: Four Pratt & Whitney TF33-PW-100/100A

283

turbofans, each rated at 93.4 kN (21,000 lb st), mounted in pods beneath the wings. Fuel contained in integral wing tanks. Provision for in-flight refuelling, with receptacle for boom over flight deck.

ACCOMMODATION: Basic operational crew of 20 includes a flight crew complement of four plus 16 AWACS specialists, though this latter number can vary for tactical and defence missions. Aft of flight deck, from front to rear of fuselage, are communications, data processing and other equipment bays; multi-purpose consoles; communications, navigation and identification equipment; and crew rest area, galley and parachute storage rack.

AVIONICS AND EQUIPMENT: Prominent feature is the elliptical-cross-section rotodome of 9.14 m (30 ft) diameter and 1.83 m (6 ft) max depth, mounted 3.35 m (11 ft) above the fuselage. It comprises four essential elements: a turntable, strut mounted above the rear fuselage, that supports the rotary joint assembly to which are attached sliprings for electrical and waveguide continuity between rotodome and fuselage; a structural centre section which supports the AN/APY-1 surveillance radar and IFF/TADIL C antennae, radomes, auxiliary equipment for radar operation and environmental control of the rotodome interior; liquid cooling of the radar antennae; and two radomes constructed of multi-layer glassfibre sandwich material, one for the surveillance radar and one for the IFF/TADIL C array. For surveillance operations the rotodome is hydraulically driven at 6 rpm, but during non-operational flights it is rotated at only $\frac{1}{4}$ rpm, to keep the bearings lubricated. The Westinghouse radar operates in the S band and can function both as a pulse and/or a pulse-Doppler radar for detection of aircraft targets. A similar pulse radar mode with additional pulse compression and sea clutter adaptive processing is used to detect maritime/ship traffic. The radar is operable in six modes: PDNES (pulse-Doppler non-elevation scan), when range is paramount to elevation data; PDES (pulse-Doppler elevation scan), providing elevation data with some loss of range; BTH (beyond the horizon), giving long-range detection with no elevation data; Maritime, for detection of surface vessels in various sea states; Interleaved, combining available modes for all-altitude longer-range aircraft detection, or for both aircraft and ship detection; and Passive, which tracks enemy ECM sources without transmission-induced vulnerability. The radar antennae, spanning about 7.32 m (24 ft), and 1.52 m (5 ft) deep, scan mechanically in azimuth, and electronically from ground level up into the stratosphere. Heart of the data processing capability of the first 24 aircraft in their original core E-3A form is an IBM 4 Pi CC-1 high-speed computer, the entire group consisting of arithmetic control units, input/output units, main storage units, peripheral control units, mass-memory drums, magnetic-tape transports, punched-tape reader, line printer, and an operator's control panel. Processing speed is in the order of 740,000 operations/s; main memory size is 114,688 words (expandable to 180,224), and mass memory size 802,816 words (expandable to 1,204,224). An interface adapter unit developed by Boeing is the key integrating element interconnecting functional data between AWACS avionics subsystems, the data processing functional group, radar, communications, navigation/guidance, display, azimuth and identification, and also provides the central timing system. From the 25th aircraft, the new and improved IBM CC-2 computer was installed from the start, with a main storage capacity of 665,360 words. Data display and control are provided by Hazeltine Corporation high-resolution colour situation display consoles (SDC) and auxiliary display units (ADU). The core-configured E-3A carries nine SDCs and two ADUs. Navigation/guidance relies upon three principal sources of information: two Delco AN/ASN-119 Carousel IV inertial navigation platforms, a Northrop AN/ARN-120 Omega set which continuously updates the inertial platforms, and a Teledyne Ryan AN/APN-213 Doppler velocity sensor to provide airspeed and drift information. Communications equipment of the core-configured E-3As, supplied by Collins Radio, Electronic Communications Inc, E-Systems, and Hughes Aircraft, provides HF, VHF and UHF communication channels by means of which information can be transmitted or received in clear or secure mode, in voice or digital form. Identification is based on an AN/APX-103 interrogator set developed by Eaton Corporation's AIL Division. It is the first airborne IFF interrogator set to offer complete AIMS Mk X SIF air traffic control and Mk XII military identification friend or foe (IFF) in a single integrated system. Simultaneous Mk X and Mk XII multi-target and multi-mode operations allow the operator to obtain instantaneously the range, azimuth and elevation, code identification, and IFF status, of all targets within radar range. NATO E-3As carry, and USAF aircraft have provision for, a radio teletype. All aircraft from c/n 25 have an inboard underwing hardpoint on each side. There is no immediate requirement for either USAF or NATO AWACS to carry weapons; but on NATO E-3As these hardpoints may be used to mount additional podded items of ECM equipment.

DIMENSIONS, EXTERNAL:	
Wing span	44.42 m (145 ft 9 in)
Length overall	46.61 m (152 ft 11 in)
Height overall	12.73 m (41 ft 9 in)
WEIGHT:	
Max T-O weight	147,417 kg (325,000 lb)
PERFORMANCE:	
Max level speed	460 knots (853 km/h; 530 mph)
Service ceiling	over 8,850 m (29,000 ft)
Endurance on station, 870 nm (1,610 km; 1,000 miles) from base	6 h
Max unrefuelled endurance	more than 11 h

Boeing Advanced Airborne Command Post

USAF designation: E-4

On 28 February 1973 the US Air Force's Electronic Systems Division announced from its headquarters at Hanscom Field, Bedford, Massachusetts, that it had awarded The Boeing Company a $59 million fixed-price contract for the supply of two Model 747-200Bs to be adapted as **E-4A** airborne command posts under the 481B Advanced Airborne Command Post (AABNCP) programme. A further contract valued at more than $27.2 million was awarded in July 1973 for a third aircraft; in December 1973 a fourth aircraft was contracted at $39 million. This was to be fitted with more advanced equipment (see below) and designated **E-4B**.

The E-4s were intended to replace EC-135 Airborne Command Posts of the National Military Command System and Strategic Air Command, which are military variants of

Boeing E-4B AABNCP.

the Model 707. AABNCPs are intended to provide the critical communications link between US National Command Authority and the nation's strategic retaliatory forces during and following a nuclear or conventional attack on the United States. They were also equipped with the wiring that would be needed to add an ICBM launching ('Looking Glass') capability if ground control centres became inoperative; but the associated 'black boxes' were not fitted and there is no longer any intention to fit them.

E-Systems won the contract to install interim equipment in the three E-4As. This involved transfer and integration of equipment removed from EC-135s, providing aircraft with increased endurance and the ability to carry an expanded battle staff. The E-4A's floor space can accommodate almost three times the payload of the EC-135.

The first E-4A flew for the first time on 13 June 1973, and was delivered to Andrews AFB, Maryland, in December 1974. The second and third, also consigned to Andrews AFB, were received in May and September 1975. In their initial form, they were operated as National Emergency Airborne Command Posts (NEACPs), and provided operational experience that proved invaluable in finalising the design of equipment installed in the E-4B.

The third and fourth aircraft differed initially from the first two in having General Electric CF6-50E turbofan engines, each rated at 233.5 kN (52,500 lb st), instead of the JT9Ds that were then fitted normally to aircraft of the 747 series; CF6-50Es were fitted retrospectively to the first two aircraft during 1976, and have since been upgraded to CF6-50E2 standard, to improve fuel economy and T-O thrust under high ambient temperature conditions.

The total planned force was four E-4Bs, comprising the fourth aircraft, and the three E-4As brought up to the same standard retrospectively. Contracts covering modification of one E-4A to E-4B configuration, with options to modify the other two, were announced on 26 June 1980. The two options were duly exercised during December 1980 and October 1981, and the first converted E-4B was redelivered to USAF on 15 July 1983. The second was redelivered on 18 May 1984, and the third on 30 January 1985.

Boeing, E-Systems and a team of other companies were made responsible for designing and installing the advanced command post equipment in the E-4B, under a programme managed by Oklahoma City Air Logistics Centre. The first E-4B was delivered to the US Air Force in August 1975 in testbed configuration, with flight refuelling equipment installed but without the planned command, control and communications equipment. Next stage involved installation of the 1,200kVA electrical system (two 150kVA generators on each engine) designed to support the advanced avionics. Finally the operational systems were added, and the first flight of the fully equipped E-4B took place on 10 June 1978. US Air Force tests of operational capability began later that year.

The first E-4B (75-0125) was redelivered to the US Air Force on 21 December 1979, and entered service in January 1980. It has accommodation for a larger battle staff than that carried by the E-4A; an air-conditioning system of 226.5 m³ (8,000 cu ft)/min capacity to cool avionics components; nuclear thermal shielding; acoustic controls; an improved technical control facility; and new super-high-frequency (SHF) and dual Collins VLF/LF communications systems, the latter employing trailing short-wire and long-wire antennae of which the long-wire system has an antenna 4.3

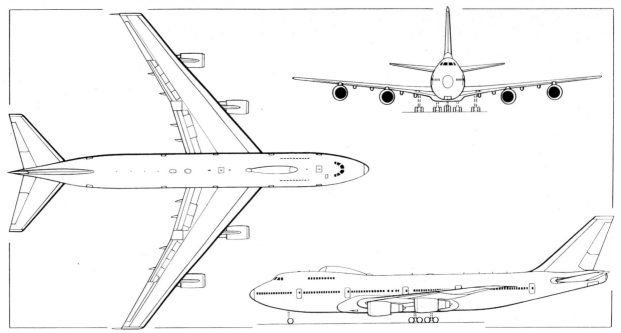

Boeing E-4B AABNCP. *(Pilot Press)*

nm (8 km; 5 miles) in length. The SHF antennae are housed in a dorsal fairing which is a recognition characteristic of the E-4B.

Strategic Air Command (SAC) is the sole operational manager of the AABNCP force. The main operating base for the E-4 fleet is at Offutt AFB, Nebraska.

ACCOMMODATION (E-4B): Up to 94 crew members on three decks. Upper deck contains flightdeck and flight crew rest area. Access to main deck compartments is by aisle on starboard side: these compartments include NCA (National Command Authority) area, conference room, briefing room, battle staff work area, communications control centre, technical control centre (where operators monitor and maintain quality of communications links), and crew rest area. Forward and rear lower lobes house electronic equipment, an onboard maintenance area, and a winch operator's station for the long-wire VLF antenna. The NCA's senior adviser conference room is equipped with a projection room, screen, and secure telephones at the conference table. Briefing room for second-level advisory staff contains table, podium, and a viewing screen served also by the projection room. Battle staff area accommodates up to 30 crew members responsible for information flow into and out of aircraft; their two-position consoles contain work surfaces and facilities for communications and data storage.

AVIONICS (E-4B): Command and control avionics, powered by 1,200kVA electrical power generation system, include 13 external communication systems operating through 46 antennae with configurations ranging from a small dish for SHF satellite links (in larger fairing aft of upper deck) to an 8 km (5 mile) trailing wire for VLF and LF communication. Ability to use satellite systems reduces dependence on ground stations and protects against jamming and direct tracking attempts. A long-range link, established with the high-power VLF system, resists atmospheric nuclear effects and is very difficult to jam. The HF, MF, VHF and UHF bands provide additional two-way radio channels. Secure voice and teletype links are achieved through HF, UHF and SHF bands, and the E-4B's high-speed secure-record communications equipment interfaces to the automatic digital network. The E-4B system is capable of tying in to commercial telephone and radio networks, and potentially could be used for radio broadcast to the general population. When it is on the ground it can also be connected to a ground communications network, which can be disconnected quickly. Other E-4B avionics and instrumentation include search radar in nosecone, Tacan, VHF Omni navigation, dual ADF, dual radio altimeters, glideslope and marker beacon receiver.

DIMENSIONS, EXTERNAL:	
Wing span	59.64 m (195 ft 8 in)
Length overall	70.51 m (231 ft 4 in)
Height overall	19.33 m (63 ft 5 in)
WEIGHTS:	
Max fuel weight	150,395 kg (331,565 lb)
Max T-O weight	362,875 kg (800,000 lb)
PERFORMANCE:	
T-O run for 8 h endurance	1,525 m (5,000 ft)
Mission endurance	72 h
Unrefuelled endurance	more than 12 h

Boeing Tacamo

US Navy designation: E-6A

On 29 April 1983, Boeing Aerospace Company received a contract to develop a survivable airborne communications system to provide an on-station/all-ocean link between the US National Command Authority and the US Navy's Trident ballistic nuclear submarine (SSBN) fleet. Designated E-6A, the new aircraft will replace the EC-130Q version of the Lockheed Hercules used currently for this mission, known as Tacamo (TAke Charge And Move Out), and is fitted with the EC-130Q's existing AVLF avionics.

The airframe of the E-6A is almost identical with that of

286

Boeing E-6A Tacamo prototype seen during roll-out, on 18 December, 1986.

the E-3 Sentry, and is assembled on the same production line. The prototype first flew on 19 February 1987. Initial operational capability is planned for early 1989, by which time the Trident force will have increased to ten SSBNs, while the EC-130 Tacamo fleet will have been reduced to 12 aircraft. During 1989–90 it is intended to deliver further E-6As, and the full Tacamo complement of 15 E-6As (including the refurbished prototype) and ten EC-130Qs is planned to be achieved by 1993, when all 14 Trident SSBNs will be in service.

Eight of the E-6As will be allocated to the Pacific Fleet, and the remainder to the Atlantic/Mediterranean. In each of these areas one E-6A will be required to be on station, in the air, at any given time, ready and able to relay emergency action messages to a high percentage of submarines, with an equally high chance of successful first-time reception. Another E-6A will be on standby alert, one on ready alert, and the remainder at dispersed bases or on maintenance or training.

The following details apply to the E-6A prototype:

TYPE: Long-endurance communications relay aircraft.

AIRFRAME: Retains more than 75 per cent commonality with that of the E-3A, main differences being deletion of the dorsal radome and its support structure, the addition of wingtip ESM/Satcom pods and HF antenna fairings, and increased corrosion protection. Also retained is the nuclear/EMP (electromagnetic pulse) 'hardening' of the E-3A airframe. Additions include incorporation of the large forward freight door of the commercial Boeing 707-320C. Landing gear is identical to that of the E-3A.

POWERPLANT: Four 97.86 kN (22,000 lb st) CFM International F108-CF-100 (CFM56-2A-2) turbofan engines in individual underwing pods, as on E/KE-3As for Saudi Arabia. Fuel contained in integral tanks in wings, with single-point refuelling. In-flight refuelling via boom receptacle above flightdeck.

ACCOMMODATION: Basic militarised interior sidewalls, ceilings and lighting are same as in E-3A. Interior divided into three main functional areas: forward of wings (flight deck and crew rest area), overwing (eight-man mission crew), and aft of wings (equipment). Forward crew area accommodates a four-man flight crew on flightdeck.

Compartment immediately aft of this contains food storage, galley, dining area, toilets, and an eight-bunk rest area for spare crew carried on extended or remote deployment missions. Then follows the C³ overwing compartment with central and other consoles, their operators, and an airborne control officer (ACO). Through this is reached, to the rear, the compartment containing the R/T racks, transmitters, trailing wire antennae and their winches, parachutes, equipment spares, and a baggage storage area. There is a bale-out door at rear of this compartment on the starboard side.

AVIONICS AND OPERATIONAL EQUIPMENT: Three Collins AN/ARC-182 VHF/UHF com transceivers, all with secure voice capability; two Collins AN/ARC-190 HF com (one transceiver, one receive only); and Hughes Aircraft AIC-29 crew intercom with secure voice capability. External aerials for Satcom UHF reception in each wingtip pod; fairings beneath each pod are antennae for standard HF reception. Navigation by triplex Litton LTN-90 ring laser gyro-based inertial reference system integrated with a Litton LTN-211 VLF/Omega system and duplex Smiths Industries SFM 102 digital/analog flight management computer system (FMCS). Bendix APS-133 colour weather radar, in nosecone, with capability for short-range terrain mapping, tanker beacon homing, and waypoint display. Honeywell APN-222 high/low-range (0–15,240 m; 0–50,000 ft) radio altimeter, and Collins low-range (0–762 m; 0–2,500 ft) radio altimeter, with ILS and GPWS. General Instruments ALR-66(V)4 electronic support measures (ESM), in starboard wingtip pod, provide information on threat detection, identification, bearing and approximate range. In overwing compartment, overseen by ACO, are two banks of three consoles and a new communications central console, which incorporate ERCS (emergency rocket communications system) receivers, Satcom cryptographic equipment, new teletypes, tape recorders, and other C³ equipment, all hardened against electromagnetic interference. In each operational area the E-6 links 'upward' with the airborne command posts and the Presidential E-4, to satellites, and to the ERCS; and 'downward' to VLF ground stations and the SSBN fleet. The main VLF antenna is a 7,925 m (26,000 ft) long trailing-wire aerial (LTWA), with a 41 kg (90 lb) drogue at the end, which is winched out from the middle part of the rear cabin compartment through an opening in the cabin floor. The LTWA, with its drogue, weighs about 495 kg (1,090 lb) and creates some 907 kg (2,000 lb) of drag when fully deployed. Acting as a dipole is a much shorter (1,220 m; 4,000 ft) trailing wire (STWA), winched out from beneath the rear fuselage just forward of the tailplane. At patrol altitude, with the LTWA deployed, the aircraft enters a tight orbit and the drogue stalls, causing the wire to be almost vertical (70 per cent verticality is required for effective sub-sea communications) and the aircraft/wire combination acts like a lasso being whirled above the head, only in reverse: i.e., the path of the drogue is that of the hand holding the rope, while the orbit of the aircraft is the lasso. Signals transmitted through the trailing-wire antennae use 200 kW of power, and can be received by submerged SSBNs via a towed buoyant wire antenna. Mean time between failures of complete mission avionics is approx 20 h, but the E-6 is able to carry spares, and a spare crew, to permit extended missions of up to 72 h with in-flight refuelling, and/or deployment to remote bases.

ARMAMENT: None.

DIMENSIONS, EXTERNAL:
Wing span	45.16 m (148 ft 2 in)
Length overall	46.61 m (152 ft 11 in)
Height overall	12.93 m (42 ft 5 in)
Wheel track	6.73 m (22 ft 1 in)
Wheelbase	17.98 m (59 ft 0 in)

AREA:
Wings, gross	283.4 m² (3,050.0 sq ft)

WEIGHTS:
Operating weight empty	78,378 kg (172,795 lb)
Max T-O weight	155,128 kg (342,000 lb)

PERFORMANCE:
Dash speed	530 knots (981 km/h; 610 mph)
Cruising speed at 12,200 m (40,000 ft)	
	455 knots (842 km/h; 523 mph)
Patrol altitude	7,620–9,150 m (25,000–30,000 ft)
Ceiling	12,800 m (42,000 ft)
Range (unrefuelled)	6,350 nm (11,760 km; 7,307 miles)
Endurance (unrefuelled)	15 h 24 min
Max mission endurance (with in-flight refuelling)	72 h

Boeing Military Airplane Company (BMAC)

Boeing Military Airplane Company, the formation of which was announced on 23 October 1979, is responsible for all work on the B-52 Stratofortress bomber and KC-135 jet tanker-transport series, and the offensive avionics system of the Rockwell B-1B strategic bomber. It manufactures parts and assemblies for the Boeing Model 707, 727 and 737 series of commercial transports, and is producing the nose section and nacelles of the Models 757 and 767, and pylons for the 747 and 767. It also undertakes conversion of Boeing aircraft from passenger to freight carrying and other configurations, installs new interiors and embodies structural modifications. BMAC is avionics integrator for the Bell/Boeing V-22 Osprey programme (see Bell entry) and Boeing/Sikorsky's development work for the LHX helicopter competition, and has been awarded an R & D contract for the US National Aerospace Plane trans-atmospheric aircraft. The Wichita

facility occupies an area of 376.5 hectares (930 acres), including 810,950 m² (8,729,000 sq ft) of covered space. BMAC also has facilities in Huntsville, Alabama, at Edwards AFB, California, and a major design and development centre in Seattle, Washington. At the beginning of 1987, BMAC had a total Kansas workforce of 21,000 persons.

In early 1985 BMAC was awarded a 26-month, $572,000 contract by the USAF to investigate the impact of advanced technologies on future fighter interceptors. BMAC will optimise aircraft configurations for continental air defence roles and conduct wind tunnel studies. BMAC is now teamed with General Dynamics and Lockheed-California in development work for the USAF's advanced tactical fighter (ATF) programme. In May 1985 the company was selected to design, develop and produce replacement wings for the US Navy's fleet of Grumman A-6 Intruder attack aircraft. Flight testing of the new wing was scheduled to begin in early 1988, and contracts for 120 sets had been received by March 1987, with options on a total of 336 (see Intruder).

In July 1985 BMAC was awarded a $995,175 study contract by USAF Aeronautical Systems Division to investigate requirements for improved penetration of enemy air defences by strategic systems including the B-52, FB-111, SRAM and cruise missiles.

During 1986 BMAC assumed marketing responsibility for the Skyfox modification of the Lockheed T-33 military jet trainer, and now holds an exclusive licence to produce the aircraft.

Boeing B-52 Stratofortress

In July 1948 a contract was issued for two prototype long-range strategic bombers, designated XB-52 and YB-52. The XB-52 appeared first, but was not flown until 2 October 1952; the YB-52 was flown on 15 April 1952.

The first Seattle-produced production bomber was a B-52A, which appeared in 1954, while Wichita production began with a B-52D. The 744th and final Stratofortress was a B-52H, completed at Wichita on 22 June 1962 and delivered to the USAF in October of that year. The B-52A, B, C, D, E and F are no longer operational, leaving only the B-52G and H in continued use. A total of 193 B-52Gs and 102 B-52Hs was built; 265 of these remain operational, serving with the 2nd, 7th, 42nd, 97th, 379th, 410th and 416th Bomb Wings of the Eighth Air Force; the 5th, 28th, 92nd, 93rd, 96th, 319th and 320th Bomb Wings of the Fifteenth Air Force; and the 43rd Strategic Wing of the 3rd Air Division of SAC.

B-52G. Developed version of the B-52F, with redesigned wing containing integral fuel tanks. Tail gunner positioned in forward pressure-cabin with rest of crew, operating guns remotely or with automatic fire-control system (see Armament). Vertical tail surfaces reduced in height. 25% greater range, increased climb performance and greater over-target altitude. Entered service in February 1959. (See following paragraphs for modification programmes.)

B-52H. Development of B-52G with TF33 turbofan engines. Single multi-barrel tail cannon. First flown on 6 March 1961. One set world straight-line distance record of 10,890.27 nm (20,168.78 km; 12,532.3 miles) between 10–11 January 1962.

Several programmes involving the **B-52G** and **H** have been undertaken or are now in progress to improve the avionics, equipment and operational capability. Under a

Boeing B-52G Stratofortress armed with AGM-86B air-launched cruise missiles.

1971 contract, 281 of these two models were modified to carry 20 Boeing SRAMs (short-range attack missiles), and the first of these became operational on 4 August 1972. Additionally, all B-52Gs and B-52Hs have been equipped with an AN/ASQ-151 Electro-optical Viewing System (EVS) to improve low-level-penetration capability. The EVS sensors are housed in two steerable, side-by-side chin turrets. The starboard turret houses a Hughes Aircraft AAQ-6 forward-looking infra-red (FLIR) scanner, while the port turret contains a Westinghouse AVQ-22 low light level TV camera.

The B-52Gs and Hs are being updated progressively with Phase VI avionics. This includes Motorola ALQ-122 SNOE (Smart Noise Operation Equipment) and Northrop AN/ALQ-155(V) advanced ECM; an AFSATCOM kit which permits worldwide communication via satellite; a Dalmo Victor ALR-46 digital radar warning receiver; Westinghouse ALQ-153 pulse-Doppler tail warning radar; and improved versions of the ITT Avionics ALQ-117 ECM system for the B-52G and ALQ-172 ECM system for the B-52H. Boeing is also producing an Offensive Avionics System (OAS) to upgrade the navigation and weapons delivery of the B-52G and H during low-level penetration missions. This is a digital (instead of analog) based, solid-state system, and includes Tercom (terrain comparison) guidance. The first flight by an OAS-equipped B-52G was made on 3 September 1980, and the first use of the OAS to launch a live SRAM occurred on 10 June 1981. The new equipment includes a Teledyne Ryan Doppler radar, Honeywell AN/ASN-131 gimballed electrostatic airborne inertial navigation system (GEANS), IBM/Raytheon ASQ-38 analog bombing/navigation system with IBM digital processing, Lear Siegler attitude heading and reference system, Honeywell radar altimeter, Sperry controls and displays, and Norden Systems modernised strategic radar. Under Phase II

of the programme, scheduled for completion by FY 1989, 168 B-52Gs and 96 Hs are being equipped with OAS, and contracts covering the total of 264 kits for B-52G and H aircraft had been placed by 1 January 1984.

A Collins Navstar Global Positioning System (GPS) was installed in a B-52G in late 1984 at Tinker AFB, before a 50-hour test flight programme carried out at the Yuma, Arizona, Proving Grounds test range.

A further major programme involves adaptation of the B-52G and B-52H force as carrier aircraft for AGM-86 air-launched cruise missiles. Full-scale development of B-52 carrier aircraft equipment began in early 1978, and three B-52Gs were modified for use in the fly-off programme at Edwards AFB, California. The current programme calls for 99 B-52Gs and 96 B-52Hs each to be modified to carry 12 AGM-86s externally (six on each inboard underwing pylon), in addition to an internal load of SRAMs and other weapons. The first B-52G with OAS and equipped to carry cruise missiles was delivered to the US Air Force in August 1981. SAC's 416th Bombardment Wing at Griffiss AFB, NY, became the first unit to attain operational capability with the AGM-86 in December 1982, with 12 missiles on each of its 14 B-52Gs. It was followed by the 379th Wing at Wurtsmith AFB, Michigan. Other stations equipped with ALCM-carrying B-52s are Blytheville AFB, Arkansas; Fairchild AFB, Washington, and Barksdale AFB, Louisiana. Towards the end of the 1980s the B-52H will be further modified to carry SRAMs, ALCMs, advanced cruise missiles or free-fall nuclear weapons on a common strategic rotary launcher (CSRL). Development of this internal carrying capability was initiated in 1982, and the first CSRL began flight testing in September 1985. A $44.5 million contract to initiate CSRL production was awarded to BMAC in February 1986.

Cruise missile carrying B-52Gs are fitted with a distinctive

Boeing Stratofortress launching a Harpoon anti-ship missile.

fairing (known as a 'strakelet') at the leading edge of each wing root to give these aircraft a recognisable appearance in accordance with provisions of the unratified SALT II agreement. B-52Hs will not need 'strakelets', as all will carry cruise missiles and are already recognisably different from other versions of the Stratofortress.

Those B-52Gs not scheduled for use as cruise missile carriers have replaced B-52Ds in a conventional maritime support role. First test launches of Harpoon anti-ship missiles from B-52s in spring 1983 all met their specified objectives, one after release at a height of 9,145 m (30,000 ft). Two squadrons of Harpoon-equipped B-52s are now operational.

On 11 February 1986 the US Air Force Aeronautical Systems Division began flight tests of an integrated conventional stores management (ICSM) software system in a B-52G at McConnell AFB, Kansas. The ICSM has been developed by BMAC for installation on 69 B-52Gs not configured as ALCM carrier aircraft, permitting aircraft normally configured for the carriage of nuclear weapons to

Boeing B-52H Stratofortress. *(Pilot Press)*

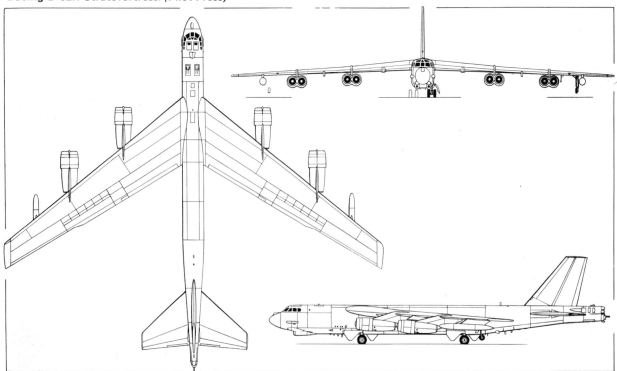

carry conventional weapons by rearranging data stored in the weapons systems computer by means of a pre-programmed removable software cassette. IOC for ICSM-equipped B-52Gs is planned for 1988.

The following details apply to the B-52G and B-52H:

TYPE: Long-range strategic bomber and maritime support aircraft.

WINGS: Cantilever high-wing monoplane, with anhedral and 35° sweepback. Conventional structure. Lateral control by inset ailerons between inner and outer flaps, supplemented by serrated spoilers on upper surface of wings. Spoilers can be used symmetrically as airbrakes. Area-increasing flaps.

FUSELAGE: Conventional semi-monocoque structure.

TAIL UNIT: Conventional cantilever type, with variable-incidence tailplane.

LANDING GEAR: Retractable tandem type. Four individually retractable twin-wheel units in tandem pairs. Small outrigger units outboard of engine positions. Ribbon braking parachute, 13.4 m (44 ft) diameter in compartment at top of fuselage, aft of rudder.

POWERPLANT (B-52G): Eight 61.2 kN (13,750 lb st) J57-P-43WB turbojet engines. Fuel capacity 174,130 litres (46,000 US gallons; 38,300 Imp gallons) internally, plus two 2,650 litre (700 US gallon; 583 Imp gallon) underwing drop-tanks.

POWERPLANT (B-52H): Eight 75.6 kN (17,000 lb st) Pratt & Whitney TF33-P-3 turbofan engines. Fuel capacity as for B-52G.

ACCOMMODATION (B-52G/H): Crew of six (pilot and co-pilot, side-by-side on flight deck, navigator, radar navigator, ECM operator and gunner).

ARMAMENT (B-52G): Four 0.50 in machine-guns in tail turret, remotely operated by AGS-15 fire control system, remote radar control, or closed circuit TV. Up to 20 Boeing AGM-69 SRAM short-range attack missiles: eight on rotary launcher in internal weapons bay, and six under each wing, plus nuclear free-fall bombs; ability to carry AGM-86 cruise missiles being introduced progressively on large proportion of fleet.

ARMAMENT (B-52H): As B-52G, except for single 20 mm Vulcan multi-barrel cannon in tail turret instead of four machine guns.

AVIONICS AND EQUIPMENT: See introductory paragraphs.

DIMENSIONS, EXTERNAL:

Wing span	56.39 m (185 ft 0 in)
Length overall	49.05 m (160 ft 10.9 in)
Height overall	12.40 m (40 ft 8 in)
Wheel track (c/l of shock struts)	2.51 m (8 ft 3 in)
Wheelbase	15.48 m (50 ft 3 in)

AREA:

Wings, gross	371.6 m² (4,000 sq ft)

WEIGHT:

Max T-O weight	more than 221,350 kg (488,000 lb)

PERFORMANCE:

Max level speed at high altitude	Mach 0.90 (516 knots; 957 km/h; 595 mph)
Cruising speed at high altitude	Mach 0.77 (442 knots; 819 km/h; 509 mph)
Penetration speed at low altitude	Mach 0.53 to 0.55 (352–365 knots; 652–676 km/h; 405–420 mph)
Service ceiling	16,765 m (55,000 ft)
T-O run: G	3,050 m (10,000 ft)
H	2,900 m (9,500 ft)

Range with max fuel, without in-flight refuelling:

G	more than 6,513 nm (12,070 km; 7,500 miles)
H	more than 8,685 nm (16,093 km; 10,000 miles)

Boeing C-135 Series

A turbojet-powered tanker-transport for service with the USAF was first flown as the Boeing Model 367-80 demonstrator on 15 July 1954. Subsequent commercial derivatives became the Model 707 airliner series, while the first of 732 KC-135A Stratotanker tanker-transports for the USAF flew on 31 August 1956. About 650 remain operational to support Strategic Air Command aircraft and those of other US Air Force commands, the US Navy and Marine Corps, and other nations. Various update programmes are also under way. The C-135 series will be fully detailed in an accompanying publication covering military transports, among other types.

In addition to tanker-transport roles, some KC-135As were modified to perform other duties, including airborne command post and communications relay (EC-135 series), advanced range instrumentation (EC-135N), airborne laser testbed (NKC-135), electronic reconnaissance (RC-135 series) and long-range weather reconnaissance (WC-135B). These versions, too, will be detailed in the accompanying publication.

A US Air Force programme for the replacement of turbojet engines by JT3D turbofans in its C-135s initially involved 18 special-purpose -135 aircraft, comprising three C-135Es, one KC-135E, two NKC-135Es, five EC-135Hs, two EC-135Ks, two EC-135Ns, two EC-135Ps, and one RC-

Boeing KC-135R of the US Air Force. *(Mike Jerram)*

291

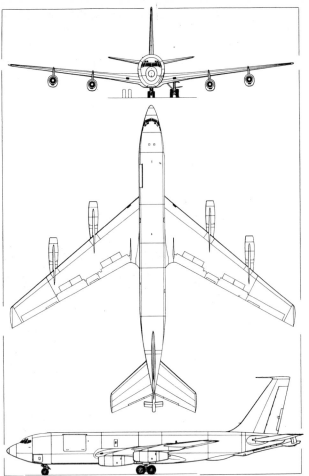

Boeing KC-135A Stratotanker. *(Pilot Press)*

135T. These re-engined special-purpose aircraft were redelivered to the Air Force between January and July 1981. Three more have since been re-engined.

USAF KC-135s and special-purpose -135s are also being retrofitted in service with a combined performance management system and integrated fuel management system

for which Delco Electronics Division of General Motors is prime contractor. The prototype system, installed in 1982, is being followed by an initial quantity of 371 systems, including spares. Options cover the eventual supply of a total of more than 700 systems.

Boeing EC-18B ARIA

In 1982 the Aeronautical Systems Division of the US Air Force procured six former American Airlines Boeing 707-323C transport aircraft, of which four will replace EC-135N Advanced Range Instrumentation Aircraft (ARIA) operated by its 4950th Test Wing. Like the ARIA EC-135Ns, each of the 707s is being converted to house the world's largest airborne steerable antenna in a bulbous nose, a probe antenna on each wingtip, and a totally new cockpit configuration, with navigation station, a new flight director, modified electrical system and improved environmental control system. Designated EC-18B after conversion, the aircraft have a greater payload capability than the EC-135Ns they replace, making them better able to support the expanding ARIA mission. This includes support of unmanned space launches, cruise missile and SDI tests, Army and Navy ballistic missile tests, and the Space Transportation System (Shuttle) programme.

The first EC-18B made its first flight after conversion on 27 February 1985 and entered operational service in January 1986. All four were expected to be fully operational by 1988, together with the three remaining EC-135s. A future modification will incorporate the sonobuoy missile impact location system (SMILS) currently installed on some US Navy P-3 Orion aircraft.

Boeing E-8A (J/STARS)

On 27 September 1985, Grumman Corporation received a $657 million contract for full-scale development of the USAF/US Army Joint Surveillance Target Attack Radar System (J/STARS). Boeing is modifying two C-18A (707-323C) airframes as vehicles for the airborne equipment. This will include a Norden multi-mode side-looking radar antenna in a canoe shaped radome some 9.1 m (30 ft) long, under the front fuselage of each aircraft. The radar will

Boeing EC-18B ARIA of the USAF's 4950th Test Wing.

operate in synthetic aperture radar (SAR) mode to detect and locate stationary objects such as parked tanks, and will alternate between SAR and Doppler to locate slow moving targets. The J/STARS system will then direct attack on the targets, via the Joint Tactical Information Distribution System (JTIDS).

The first J/STARS aircraft, designated E-8A, will fly for the first time in late 1988. The demonstration programme is scheduled for completion by 1991, when a decision will be taken on whether to proceed to production of ten operational E-8As and 107 ground stations to receive data from the aircraft.

Cessna

CESSNA AIRCRAFT COMPANY (Subsidiary of General Dynamics Corporation)

Cessna Aircraft Company was founded by the late Clyde V. Cessna, a pioneer in US aviation in 1911, and was incorporated on 7 September 1927. Its former Pawnee and Wallace aircraft divisions in Wichita were consolidated as production facilities within the company's Aircraft Division in mid-1984.

In September 1985, an agreement was announced between General Dynamics Corporation and Cessna whereby General Dynamics acquired the company as a wholly owned subsidiary.

By 1987 the company had produced a total of 176,819 aircraft, including units delivered by Reims Aviation of France.

Cessna OA-37B Dragonfly forward air control aircraft.

Cessna Dragonfly

USAF designation: OA-37B

The A-37 was developed from the T-37 trainer, produced for armed counter-insurgency (COIN) operations from short unimproved airstrips. Two YAT-37D prototypes were produced initially, for evaluation by the USAF, by modifying existing T-37 airframes. The first of these flew for the first time on 22 October 1963, powered by two 10.68 kN

(2,400 lb st) General Electric J85-GE-5 turbojets. There were two production versions, the A-37A designation covering the first 37 aircraft converted from T-37B trainers. A-37As were withdrawn from service in 1974.

The A-37B is the currently operated version, although it is no longer to be found in USAF or reserve units. However, a number of US A-37Bs have been converted into **OA-37B**

Cessna A-37B Dragonfly. *(Pilot Press)*

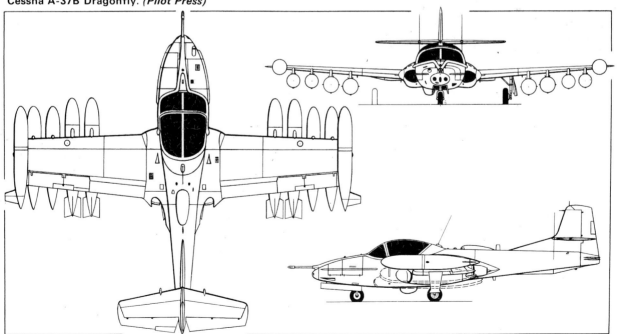

forward air control aircraft for operation by the Air National Guard, to supersede O-2As.

The A-37B (Model 318E) flew for the first time in September 1967. It has two General Electric J85-GE-17A turbojets, giving more than double the take-off power available for the T-37, permitting an almost-doubled take-off weight. A total of 577 had been delivered by 1977, when production ended. Current operators are Chile, Colombia, Dominican Republic, Ecuador, El Salvador, Guatemala, Honduras, Peru, Thailand and Uruguay.

TYPE: Two-seat light strike aircraft.

WINGS: Cantilever low-wing monoplane. Wing section NACA 2418 (modified) at root, NACA 2412 (modified) at tip. Dihedral 3°. Incidence 3° 38' at root, 1° at tip. No sweep at $22\frac{1}{2}\%$ chord. Conventional ailerons. Trim tab in port aileron with force-sensitive boost tabs in both ailerons, plus slot-lip ailerons forward of the flap on the outboard two-thirds of flap span. Slotted flaps of NACA 2h type. No de-icing equipment.

FUSELAGE: Semi-monocoque structure. Speed brake, measuring 1.14 m (3 ft 9 in) by 0.30 m (1 ft 0 in), below forward fuselage immediately aft of nosewheel well. Mountings for removable probe for in-flight refuelling on upper fuselage in front of cockpit.

TAIL UNIT: Cantilever structure. Fin integral with fuselage. Fixed-incidence tailplane mounted one-third of way up fin. Trim tabs in port elevator and rudder. No de-icing equipment.

LANDING GEAR: Retractable tricycle type. Steerable nosewheel. Goodyear tyres and single-disc brakes. Main-wheel tyres size 7.00–8 (14PR). Nosewheel tyre size 6.00–6 (6PR).

POWERPLANT: Two General Electric J85-GE-17A turbojet engines, each rated at 12.7 kN (2,850 lb st). Fuel tank in each wing, each with capacity of 428 litres (113 US gallons; 94 Imp gallons); two non-jettisonable tip-tanks, each of 360 litres (95 US gallons; 79 Imp gallons) capacity; sump tank in fuselage, aft of cockpit, capacity 344 litres (91 US gallons; 76 Imp gallons). Total standard usable fuel capacity 1,920 litres (507 US gallons; 422 Imp gallons). Four 378 litre (100 US gallon; 83 Imp gallon) auxiliary tanks can be carried on underwing pylons. Provision for in-flight refuelling through nose-probe.

ACCOMMODATION: Enclosed cockpit seating two side-by-side, with dual controls, dual throttles, full flight instrument panel on port side, partial panel on starboard side, engine instruments in between. Full blind-flying instrumentation. Standardised cockpit layout as in standard USAF combat aircraft. Cockpit not pressurised. Flak curtains of layered nylon are installed around the cockpit. A polycarbonate bird-resistant windscreen was available optionally.

AVIONICS: Radio and radar installations include UHF communications (AN/ARC-109A, ARC-151 and ARC-164), FM communications (FM-622A), Tacan (AN/ARN-65), ADF (AN/ARN-83), IFF (AN/APX-72), direction finder (AN/ARA-50), VHF communications (VHF-20B), VOR/LOC, glideslope, marker beacon (VIR-31A) and interphone (AIC-18).

ARMAMENT AND OPERATIONAL EQUIPMENT: GAU-2B/A 7.62 mm Minigun installed in forward fuselage. Each wing has four pylon stations, the two inner ones carrying 394 kg (870 lb) each, the intermediate one 272 kg (600 lb) and the outer one 227 kg (500 lb). The following weapons, in various combinations, can be carried on these underwing pylons: SUU-20 bomb and rocket pod, MK-81 or MK-82 bomb, BLU-32/B fire bomb, SUU-11/A gun pod, CBU-24/B or CBU-25/A dispenser and bomb, M-117 demolition bomb, LAU-3/A rocket pod, CBU-12/A, CBU-14/A or CBU-22/A dispenser and bomb, BLU-1C/B fire bomb, LAU-32/A or LAU-59/A rocket pod, CBU-19/A canister cluster and SUU-25/A flare launcher. Associated equipment includes an armament control panel, Chicago Aerial Industries CA-503 non-computing gunsight, KS-27C gun camera and KB-18A strike camera.

DIMENSIONS, EXTERNAL:

Wing span over tip-tanks	10.93 m (35 ft 10½ in)
Length overall, excl refuelling probe	8.62 m (28 ft 3¼ in)
Height overall	2.70 m (8 ft 10½ in)
Wheel track	4.28 m (14 ft 0½ in)
Wheelbase	2.39 m (7 ft 10 in)

AREA:

Wings, gross	17.09 m² (183.9 sq ft)

WEIGHTS:

Weight empty, equipped	2,817 kg (6,211 lb)
Max T-O and landing weight	6,350 kg (14,000 lb)

PERFORMANCE (at max T-O weight, except as detailed otherwise):

Never-exceed speed (Mach limitation)	455 knots (843 km/h; 524 mph)
Max level speed at 4,875 m (16,000 ft)	440 knots (816 km/h; 507 mph)
Max cruising speed at 7,620 m (25,000 ft)	425 knots (787 km/h; 489 mph)
Stalling speed at max landing weight, wheels and flaps down	98.5 knots (182 km/h; 113 mph)
Stalling speed at normal landing weight, wheels and flaps down	75 knots (139 km/h; 86.5 mph)
Max rate of climb at S/L	2,130 m (6,990 ft)/min
Service ceiling	12,730 m (41,765 ft)
T-O run	531 m (1,740 ft)
T-O to 15 m (50 ft)	792 m (2,596 ft)
Landing from 15 m (50 ft) at max landing weight	2,012 m (6,600 ft)
Landing run at max landing weight	1,265 m (4,150 ft)
Landing run at normal landing weight	521 m (1,710 ft)
Range with max fuel, including four 378 litre (100 US gallon; 83 Imp gallon) drop-tanks, at 7,620 m (25,000 ft) with reserves	878 nm (1,628 km; 1,012 miles)
Range with max payload, including 1,860 kg (4,100 lb) ordnance	399 nm (740 km; 460 miles)

Convair

Formerly known as Consolidated Vultee Aircraft Corporation (from 1943 merger), Convair became a division of General Dynamics in 1954.

Convair Delta Dart

USAF designation: F-106

All of the USAF's F-106 Delta Dart air defence fighters were to be phased out of service by 1988.

Of interest is the F-106B storm hazard test aircraft, used by NASA's Langley Research Center to penetrate storm cloud areas as part of a study into the effects of lightning strikes on aircraft. The Storm Hazards F-106B began storm cell penetrations in 1980, when only ten lightning strikes were recorded. In 1983 the aircraft was struck 250 times. Rates of current rise approaching 100 billion amperes per second have been recorded by sensors in the F-106B's nose boom, and the data are providing NASA with criteria for future lightning strike protection on commercial aircraft, particularly in regard to the effects on composites materials and electronic flight control systems. The F-106B also collects data for research studies on turbulence, windshear, and heavy rain effects.

Convair F-106A Delta Dart. Upper side view: F-106B.

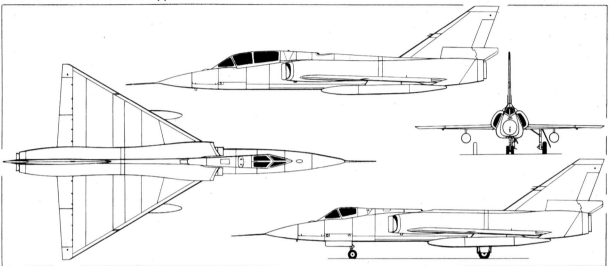

Fairchild Industries

FAIRCHILD REPUBLIC COMPANY

Founded on 17 February 1931, as the Seversky Aircraft Company, Republic operated as Republic Aviation Corporation from 1939 until September 1965, when it became a division of Fairchild Hiller Corporation, now Fairchild Industries Inc.

Its recent work included development and manufacture of the T-46 trainer, support of the A-10 Thunderbolt II aircraft, production of tail fins and rudders for the Grumman F-14 Tomcat, main landing gear fairings and doors for the Lockheed C-5B Galaxy, and manned spacecraft sub-assemblies and subsystems.

Following termination of the USAF T-46A trainer programme on 13 March 1987, the company announced the closure of its Farmingdale, Long Island, plant. Operations continue at Hagerstown, Maryland, and in the summer of 1987 the company was considering a plan to establish a support centre for USAF A-10A aircraft on Long Island.

Fairchild Republic Thunderbolt II

USAF designation: A-10A

Fairchild Republic built two YA-10A prototypes for evaluation under the US Air Force's A-X close-support aircraft programme, and the first of these flew for the first time on 10 May 1972. The first of six A-10A development test and evaluation aircraft flew on 15 February 1975. These six aircraft had production flight control and landing gear systems, an increase in wing area of 1.67 m² (18 sq ft), improved windscreens, streamlined ordnance pylons and pods, and production TF34-GE-100 engines instead of the YTF34s which powered the prototypes. The first aircraft was used to study flutter, stability and control, airloads, and general handling characteristics. The remaining five aircraft were for use by the USAF for stores certification, and for systems, performance and climatic testing. Only the first and fourth of these aircraft were not fitted with the GAU-8/A gun system.

The first flight by a production A-10A Thunderbolt II was made on 21 October 1975. Purchase of a total of 739 aircraft for the USAF was planned (including the six DT and E aircraft), but funding was terminated in 1983 after a total of 713 production A-10s had been ordered. Delivery of these was completed on 20 March 1984.

The first combat-ready A-10A wing was the 354th Tactical Fighter Wing, based at Myrtle Beach, South Carolina, to which deliveries began in March 1977. USAF operational units at the close of production were the 23rd, 57th, 354th

Fairchild Republic A-10A Thunderbolt II based at RAF Bentwaters, Suffolk, England. *(Dave Kindred)*

and 355th TFWs in the US and 343rd Composite Wing at Eielson AFB, Alaska; 81st TFW at RAF Bentwaters and Woodbridge in the UK; 51st TFW at Suwon AFB, South Korea; 174th TFW and 103rd, 104th, 128th and 175th Tactical Fighter Groups of the Air National Guard; 434th TFW and 422nd, 917th and 926th TFGs of the Air Force Reserve. The A-10A was the first front-line aircraft to be assigned to ANG units.

TYPE: Single-seat close-support aircraft.

WINGS: Cantilever low-wing monoplane, with wide-chord, deep aerofoil section (NACA 6716 on centre-section and at start of outer panel, NACA 6713 at tip) to provide low wing loading. Incidence –1°. Dihedral 7° on outer panels. Drooped (cambered) wingtips. Two-segment, three-position trailing-edge slotted flaps, interchangeable right with left. Wide span ailerons, made up of upper and lower surfaces that separate to serve as air-brakes. Flaps, airbrakes and ailerons actuated hydraulically. Small leading-edge slat inboard of each mainwheel fairing. Redundant and armour protected flight control system.

Fairchild A-10A Thunderbolt II. *(Pilot Press)*

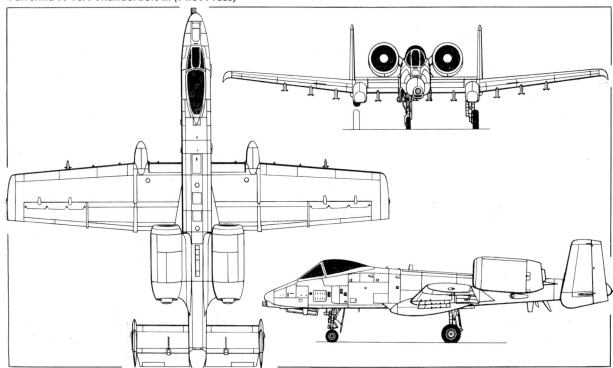

FUSELAGE: Semi-monocoque structure, built in front, centre and aft portions. Single curvature components aft of nose portion, interchangeable right with left.

TAIL UNIT: Cantilever structure, with twin fins and interchangeable rudders mounted at the tips of constant chord tailplane. Interchangeable elevators, each with trim tab. Redundant and armour protected flight control system.

LANDING GEAR: Retractable tricycle type with single wheel on each unit. All units retract forward, and have provision for emergency gravity extension. When fully retracted approximately half of each wheel protrudes from the fairing. Steerable nosewheel is offset to starboard to clear firing barrel of gun. Mainwheels size 36 × 11, Type VII; nosewheel size 24 × 7.7-10, Type VII.

POWERPLANT: Two General Electric TF34-GE-100 high-bypass-ratio turbofan engines, each rated at 40.3 kN (9,065 lb st). Maximum internal fuel capacity 4,853 kg (10,700 lb). All fuel cells are internally filled with reticulated foam, and all fuel systems pipework is contained within the cells except for the feeds to the engines, which have self-sealing covers. Three 2,271 litre (600 US gallon; 500 Imp gallon) jettisonable auxiliary tanks can be carried on underwing and fuselage centreline pylons. Provision for in-flight refuelling using universal aerial refuelling receptacle slipway installation (UARRSI).

ACCOMMODATION: Single McDonnell Douglas ACES II ejection seat operable at speeds from 450 knots (834 km/h; 518 mph) down to zero speed at zero height. Entire cockpit area is protected by an armoured 'bathtub' structure of titanium, capable of withstanding projectiles of up to 23 mm calibre.

AVIONICS AND EQUIPMENT: Kaiser head-up display giving airspeed, altitude and dive angle; weapons delivery package with dual-reticle optical sight for use in conjunction with underfuselage Pave Penny laser designation pod; target penetration aids; associated equipment for Maverick and other missile systems; IFF/SIF (AIMS); UHF/AM; VHF/AM; VHF/FM; Tacan; UHF/ADF; ILS/FDC; X-band transponder; INS (standard in last 283 production aircraft, retrofitted in earlier A-10As); heading and attitude reference system (HARS); ALR-46(V) radar homing and warning (RHAW); secure voice communications; active or passive electronic countermeasures (ECM); armament control panel; and gun camera. Space provisions for HF/SSB, and other 'growth' avionics and equipment.

ARMAMENT: General Electric GAU-8/A Avenger 30 mm seven-barrel cannon, mounted in nose with 2° depression and offset slightly to port so that, as the barrels rotate, the firing barrel is always on the aircraft centre-line. Gun and handling system for the linkless ammunition are mechanically synchronised and driven by two motors fed from the aircraft's hydraulic system. The single-drum magazine has a capacity of 1,174 rounds, and has a dual firing rate of either 2,100 or 4,200 rds/min. Four stores pylons under each wing (one inboard and three outboard of each mainwheel fairing), and three under fuselage, for max external load of 7,258 kg (16,000 lb). External load with full internal fuel is 6,505 kg (14,341 lb). The centreline pylon and the two flanking fuselage pylons cannot be occupied simultaneously. The centreline pylon has a capacity of 2,268 kg (5,000 lb); the two fuselage outer pylons and two centre-section underwing pylons 1,587 kg (3,500 lb) each; the two innermost outer-wing pylons 1,134 kg (2,500 lb) each; and the four outermost wing pylons 453 kg (1,000 lb) each. These allow carriage of a wide range of stores, including twenty-eight 500 lb Mk 82 LDGP or Mk 82 retarded bombs; six 2,000 lb Mk 84 general-purpose bombs; eight BLU-2 or BLU-27/B incendiary bombs; four SUU-25 flare launchers; twenty Rockeye II cluster bombs, sixteen CBU-52/71 dispenser weapons; six AGM-65A/B Maverick missiles; Mk 82 and Mk 84 laser guided bombs; Mk 84 electro-optically guided bombs; two SUU-23 gun pods; ALE-40 chaff/flare system; ALQ-119 ECM pods, or other jammer pods; or up to three drop-tanks. Typical combat load for an A-10A operating in Germany comprises the 30 mm gun with full ammunition, four Mavericks, Pave Penny pod, ALQ-119 pod and max internal fuel. Provision to be added for AIM-9 Sidewinder air-to-air missiles.

DIMENSIONS, EXTERNAL:

Wing span	17.53 m (57 ft 6 in)
Length overall	16.26 m (53 ft 4 in)
Height overall	4.47 m (14 ft 8 in)
Wheel track	5.25 m (17 ft 2½ in)
Wheelbase	5.40 m (17 ft 8¾ in)

AREA:

Wings, gross	47.01 m² (506.0 sq ft)

WEIGHTS:

Operating weight empty	11,612 kg (25,600 lb)
*Basic design weight, equipped	14,729 kg (32,472 lb)
**Forward airstrip weight	15,155 kg (33,412 lb)
Max external ordnance	7,258 kg (16,000 lb)
Max external ordnance with full internal fuel	6,214 kg (13,700 lb)
Max T-O weight	22,680 kg (50,000 lb)
Thrust/weight ratio	0.4

*including six 500 lb bombs, 750 rds of ammunition, and 1,134 kg (2,500 lb) of fuel

**with four Mk 82 bombs, 750 rds of ammunition, and 2,041 kg (4,500 lb) of fuel

PERFORMANCE (at max T-O weight except where indicated:

Never-exceed speed	450 knots (834 km/h; 518 mph)
Max level speed at S/L, 'clean'	381 knots (706 km/h; 439 mph)
Combat speed at 1,525 m (5,000 ft), with six Mk 82 bombs	380 knots (704 km/h; 438 mph)
Cruising speed at S/L	300 knots (555 km/h; 345 mph)
Cruising speed at 1,525 m (5,000 ft)	336 knots (623 km/h; 387 mph)
Stabilised 45° dive speed below 2,440 m (8,000 ft), AUW of 15,932 kg (35,125 lb)	260 knots (481 km/h; 299 mph)
Max rate of climb at S/L at basic design weight	1,828 m (6,000 ft)/min

T-O distance:

at max T-O weight	1,220 m (4,000 ft)
at forward airstrip weight	442 m (1,450 ft)

Landing distance:

at max T-O weight	610 m (2,000 ft)
at forward airstrip weight	396 m (1,300 ft)

Operational radius, 20 min reserve:

close air support, 1.7 h loiter	250 nm (463 km; 288 miles)
deep strike	540 nm (1,000 km; 620 miles)
Ferry range, headwind of 50 knots (93 km/h; 58 mph)	2,131 nm (3,949 km; 2,454 miles)

General Dynamics

GENERAL DYNAMICS CORPORATION

General Dynamics conducts its US aerospace activities at six divisions: Convair Division, with operations at San Diego, California; Fort Worth Division, with operations at Fort Worth, Texas; Pomona Division, with headquarters at Pomona, California; Electronics Division, with headquarters in San Diego; Valley Systems Division, with headquarters at Rancho Cucamonga, California; and Space Systems Division, with headquarters in San Diego. Convair Division is responsible for the design, development and production of offensive missile systems and aircraft structures. Current programmes include production of the Tomahawk sea-launched cruise missile for the US Navy, and the ground-launched version for the US Air Force. Fort Worth Division is engaged in the design, development and production of military aircraft and avionics. Pomona Division is engaged in the development and production of tactical missile and gun systems. Electronics Division is involved in new technology to support the development and production of advanced electronics systems. Major programmes include automatic test equipment for high-performance aircraft, sophisticated navigation positioning systems, tactical data and command control systems, and range measuring systems. Valley Systems Division produces Stinger and RAM missiles, and is developing terminally guided submunitions. Space Systems Division is responsible for the Corporation's development and manufacturing activities for the Atlas, Centaur, Space Shuttle Orbiter and other programmes.

Fort Worth is currently responsible for production of the F-16 Fighting Falcon multi-role fighter; spares, support and modification/update for the F-111 fighter-bomber; and various ground-based radar systems. Convair Division is responsible for production of a major portion of the fuselage for the McDonnell Douglas KC-10A Extender tanker/cargo aircraft.

On 3 March 1985 General Dynamics acquired the Cessna Aircraft Company of Wichita, Kansas.

General Dynamics F-16 Fighting Falcon

The F-16 had its origin in the US Air Force's Lightweight Fighter (LWF) prototype programme, in 1972. The first of two YF-16 prototypes made its official first flight on 2 February 1974, and attained a level speed of Mach 2 at 12,200 m (40,000 ft) on 11 March 1974. The second YF-16 (72-01568) flew for the first time on 9 May 1974. During subsequent weapon trials, this aircraft extended the planned operational capability of the design by launching successfully both Sparrow and Sky Flash missiles. In 1978, one of the prototypes, fitted with a Thomson-CSF Atlis II (Automatic Tracking and Laser Illumination System) pod, became the first single-seat fighter to hit ground targets with GBU-10 and GBU-16 laser guided bombs without assistance from air/ground locators.

On 13 January 1975 the Secretary of the US Air Force announced that the F-16 had been selected for full-scale engineering development. The original YF-16 requirement for an air-superiority day fighter was expanded, to give equal emphasis to the air-to-surface role, including provision of radar and all-weather navigation capabilities. The manufacture of eight pre-production aircraft, comprising six single-seat **F-16As** and two two-seat **F-16Bs**, began in July 1975. The first development F-16A made its first flight on 8 December 1976, and the first F-16B on 8 August 1977. The last of the eight development aircraft was the second two-seater, which made its first flight in June 1978.

Initially, the USAF planned to procure a total of 650

Royal Norwegian Air Force General Dynamics F-16A Fighting Falcon.

F-16s; this was increased subsequently to 1,388, including 204 two-seaters, to replace F-4s in the active force and to modernise the Air Force Reserve and Air National Guard. This has since been increased to a planned total of 3,047, of which 1,859 had been contracted and 1,000 delivered by September 1986.

The first production F-16A (78-0001) flew for the first time on 7 August 1978. The first to enter service was delivered to the US Air Force's 388th Tactical Fighter Wing at Hill AFB, Utah, on 6 January 1979; and the F-16 achieved combat-ready status in October 1980, with the 4th Tactical Fighter Squadron of the 388th TFW. In that year the name Fighting Falcon was adopted. By 1983 the type was serving also with the 56th Tactical Training Wing at MacDill AFB, Florida; the 58th TTW at Luke AFB, Arizona; the 363rd TFW at Shaw AFB, South Carolina; the 474th TFW at Nellis AFB, Nevada; the 8th TFW at Kunsan AB, South Korea (PACAF); the 50th TFW at Hahn AB, West Germany (USAFE); and the 401st TFW at Torrejon AB, Spain (USAFE).

In February 1982 the US Air Force announced that both the Air National Guard and Air Force Reserve would fly F-16s. First to receive the aircraft was South Carolina ANG's 169th TFG, in 1983. The 466th TFS of the AFR received its first F-16s on 28 January 1984, at Hill AFB, Utah.

On 7 June 1975 a joint announcement by the four NATO countries of Belgium, Denmark, the Netherlands and Norway confirmed their selection of the F-16 to replace F-104s in current service. The initial order was for 348 aircraft (Belgium 116, Denmark 58, the Netherlands 102 and Norway 72), of which 58 were to be two-seaters. Under co-production agreements, final assembly lines for these aircraft were established in Belgium and the Netherlands. About 30 European companies are producing F-16 components, avionics and equipment.

The first F-16 for Europe was delivered to the Belgian Air Force on 26 January 1979. The Royal Netherlands Air Force received its first two F-16s on 6 June 1979, and initial deliveries to the air forces of Norway and Denmark were

made respectively on 25 and 28 January 1980. First operational NATO F-16 unit (from 1 January 1981) was No. 349 Squadron of the Belgian Air Force, at Beauvechain. The first Dutch squadron (No. 322) became operational on the F-16 at Leeuwarden on 1 May 1981.

Non-NATO operators include Israel, which has initially acquired 75 (including eight two-seaters), Egypt (40), Pakistan (40), and Venezuela (24). South Korea began to equip with 36 in 1986, as the first step towards an eventual planned force of 156 F-16s. The Netherlands has ordered 54 more F-16s, and other follow-up orders have been announced by Belgium (44), Denmark (12), the Netherlands (a third batch totalling 57), Israel (75, with plans for 30 more) and Egypt (40, with plans for 36 more). Turkey is receiving 160, of which deliveries began in 1987; Greece has ordered 40, with deliveries beginning in 1988. Thailand and Indonesia each ordered eight F-16As and four F-16Bs. Singapore ordered eight F-16A/Bs. The fifteen foreign users of the F-16 have between them ordered 1,106 aircraft.

By the beginning of 1987 deliveries from Fort Worth totalled over 1,260, with a further 401 delivered from European assembly lines in Belgium and the Netherlands.

First combat use of the F-16 was by the Israeli Air Force, which used eight aircraft to destroy Iraq's Osirak nuclear reactor on 7 June 1981, with a top cover of six F-15s.

F-16s of the Pakistan Air Force can carry Thomson-CSF Atlis laser target designation pods.

A slightly modified version of the F-16 has been selected for the Japanese FSX support fighter programme. It will be built by Mitsubishi for introduction into service in 1997. The FSX is required for sea interdiction and secondary air defence duties.

Operational, experimental and planned or proposed versions of the F-16 are as follows:

A-16. Proposed close-air-support (CAS) version for US Air Force Tactical Air Command. If adopted, would be based on modified aircraft from current procurement. Unfunded by summer 1987.

F-16A. First production version, for air-to-air and air-to-surface roles. Production for USAF completed in March

Israeli Air Force F-16C Fighting Falcon.

1985, but still available to other customers. Pratt & Whitney F100-PW-200 turbofan, rated at approx 111.2 kN (25,000 lb st) with afterburning. Westinghouse APG-66 pulse-Doppler range and angle track radar. First aircraft flew for the first time on 7 August 1978. Standard equipment in TAC, USAFE, PACAF, ANG and AFRES, and with the Thunderbirds air demonstration squadron. Operated also by the air forces of Belgium, Denmark, Egypt, Israel, the Netherlands, Norway, Pakistan, Singapore (with potential force of 20) and Venezuela; ordered by Indonesia and Thailand (with potential force of 18). Extension of fin-root fairing houses Loral Rapport ECM equipment in Belgian F-16As and F-16Bs, a braking parachute in aircraft for Norway and Venezuela. F-16s of the Pakistan Air Force carry Thomson-CSF Atlis laser target designation pods.

USAF and NATO operators are co-operating in an operational capabilities upgrade (OCU) programme to enable F-16A/Bs to utilise next-generation air-to-air and air-to-surface weapons systems. Changes will be made to existing radar systems and software, and the aircraft's fire control and stores management computers will be improved. A data transfer unit and combined altitude radar altimeter will be installed.

F-16(ADF). In October 1986 the USAF awarded General Dynamics a contract to modify a total of 270 F-16As as air defence fighters (ADF) to replace F-4s and F-106s in eleven Air National Guard continental air defence squadrons. The aircraft's APG-66 radar will be upgraded with AMRAAM data link, improved ECCM and improved capability against cruise missiles. It will also be equipped with HF radio, IFF interrogator, ID light, a crash survivable flight data recorder and provisions for the Global Positioning System. The contract calls for addition of a drag chute and 2,271 litre (600 US gallon; 500 Imp gallon) external fuel tanks; requirements for these are under review. The aircraft will be modified to launch AIM-7 Sparrow missiles, two of which can be carried on underwing launchers. Alternatively, it will carry up to six AIM-120 AMRAAM or AIM-9 Sidewinder missiles, or combinations of all three air-to-air weapons. The F-16(ADF) will retain the M61 20 mm gun. Programme completion scheduled for FY 1992.

F-16B. Two-seat variant of F-16A with two cockpits in tandem, each fully systems-operational. Service use as for F-16A. Length unchanged.

F-16C/D. Single-seat (F-16C) and two-seat (F-16D) versions embodying results of USAF Multinational Staged Improvement Programme (MSIP) implemented in February 1980. MSIP expands the aircraft's growth capability to incorporate systems for ground attack and beyond-visual-range intercept missions by day and night, and in all weather conditions. Stage 1 of the programme, introduced on Block 15 F-16A and F-16B aircraft delivered from November 1981, included wiring and structural provisions for emerging systems. Stage II, applicable to Block 25 production deliveries of F-16C and F-16D aircraft from July 1984, incorporates core avionics, cockpit and other airframe changes. Stage III, begun during 1987, involves selected installation of advanced systems as these become available.

The only external feature distinguishing the F-16C from the F-16A is a slightly expanded forward tail-fin root fairing to house ASPJ when it becomes available. Internal changes include a Westinghouse APG-68 multi-mode radar offering increased range, sharper resolution, expanded operating modes and advanced ECCM by comparison with the APG-

The 2,000th F-16 to be built was this F-16D two-seat fighter-trainer.

66; an advanced cockpit with improved pilot/vehicle interface, including up-front controls, two multi-function displays, radar altimeter, GEC Avionics wide-angle HUD with FLIR video and Fairchild mission data transfer equipment; avionics growth capability through increases in both the speed and memory of core computers and solid-state cartridge system for loading mission data; increased capacity electrical power and cooling systems; structural changes for increased max T-O weight and gross weight manoeuvring limits; and MIL-STD-1760 weapons interface to provide compatibility with advanced 'smart' weapons such as AMRAAM and AGM-65D Maverick imaging infra-red missiles.

At Block 30 (July 1986 deliveries) a common engine bay was incorporated which facilitated incorporation of either of the Pratt & Whitney F100-PW-220 or General Electric F110-GE-100 engines developed under the USAF's Alternate Fighter Engines programme. Other changes included computer memory expansion and seal-bonded fuselage fuel tanks. At Block 30B (from spring 1987) a software change provides full level IV multi-target compatibility with AMRAAM. Further additions in 1987 included a voice message unit, Shrike anti-radiation missiles, crash survivable flight data recorder, and a modular common inlet duct which provides more air and full available thrust from the F110 engine at lower airspeeds.

At Block 40 (December 1988 delivery) planned upgrades include a digital flight control system, automatic terrain-following diffractive optics HUD, expanded-core computers, advanced IFF, increased max T-O weight,

LANTIRN (low altitude navigation and targeting infra-red for night) and GPS. Block 70 (mid-1991 delivery) is being planned to incorporate full HARM/Shrike missile capability, radar and cockpit improvements, an on-board oxygen generating system (OBOGS), reliability and maintainability improvements, ASPJ, advanced threat warning (ALR-74 or ALR-56M), ALE-47 advanced chaff/flares, and increased performance F100-PW-229 and F110-GE-IPE engines.

The first F-16C for the US Air Force (83-118) was delivered on 19 July 1984; the first F-16D was delivered in September 1984; first operational unit to equip with these models was the 33rd TFS at Shaw AFB, South Carolina. F-16Cs and F-16Ds were ordered also by Bahrain (12 F-16C/Ds with F110-GE-100 engines); Egypt (80), the first of which, handed over at Fort Worth on 15 August 1986, was also the first production F-16 to have the F100-PW-220 engine; Greece (40, with F110-GE-100 engines, deliveries commencing 1988, with potential force of 60); Israel (60 F-16Cs and 15 F-16Ds with F110-GE-100 engines, deliveries began early 1987 and were scheduled for completion by the end of the year, with potential for a further 30 aircraft); South Korea (36 with F100-PW-220 engines, the first delivered in March 1986, with a potential force totalling 156); and Turkey (136 F-16Cs and 24 F-16Ds with F110-GE-100 engines, deliveries from 17 July 1987). All but eight of the Turkish F-16C/Ds are to be built in Turkey.

F-16N. Selected in January 1985 as US Navy supersonic adversary aircraft (SAA). Contract was for 26 aircraft with deliveries stating in spring 1987 and continuing at the rate of two per month. The airframe is derived from that of Block 30 F-16Cs with minor structural modifications involving the substitution of titanium for aluminium in lower wing fittings and cold-working the lower wing skin holes to meet the increased frequency of g loading in adversary roles. The F-16N configuration includes the General Electric F110-GE-100 engine, substitution of the APG-66 radar for the APG-68, and deletion of the M61 gun. The F-16N normally carries only wingtip launchers for practice AIM-9 missiles and ACMI AIS pods, but is capable of carrying the full complement of F-16 fuel tanks and other external stores. The last four aircraft will be two-seat versions, similar to the F-16D and designated **TF-16N**.

F-16 Agile Falcon. Proposed successor to F-16C/D with composites wings of same planform but larger and lighter in weight, with refined aerodynamics. Updated avionics and a developed General Electric F110 turbojet developing 142.3 kN (32,000 lb st) with afterburning. Offered initially to European NATO operators of F-16A/B, and suggested as replacement for abandoned Israeli Lavi.

F-16 Recce. A reconnaissance capability is being designed for the F-16, using pod mounted sensors and requiring only minor changes to any existing F-16 model. Compatibility has been flight demonstrated with four existing European-built sensor pods, including that used on the Tornado. F-16s have been operational as tactical reconnaissance aircraft with one European NATO air force since 1983.

An extensive flight test programme conducted in 1986 verified the suitability of a new General Dynamics designed underbelly reconnaissance pod built especially for the F-16, and the feasibility and effectiveness of near-real-time reconnaissance capability. The semi-conformal pod, installed on an F-16B, housed advanced electro-optical and infra-red sensors for day/night operation, at all speeds and altitudes, and with stand-off capability. The three multi-position sensors served the function of seven cameras in current fixed-mount arrangements. The system provided real-time cockpit viewing and sensor positioning, imagery review/manipulation/frame selection, and digital data link of selected frames to distant ground stations. Ground station operators were able to analyse, annotate and disseminate this imagery and their reports electronically only minutes after the images were taken, compared with the hours required to process film-based systems. In addition to electro-optical equipment, a Texas Instruments RS-710 infra-red linescanner, extendable data link antenna and a Control Data Corporation imagery management system, the pod can also carry wide-angle and long-range Chicago Aerial KS-153 cameras. The pod is 4.40 m (14 ft 5 in) long, weighs 454–567 kg (1,000–1,250 lb), and has a design load factor of 9g. Development status of the F-16 Recce is uncertain, but highly probable by the early 1990s.

F-16/79. Essentially an F-16 powered by a General Electric J79-GE-119 afterburning turbojet, rated at 80.1 kN (18,000 lb st). Developed for US government's FX

General Dynamics AFTI/F-16 testbed.

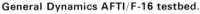

programme as an export fighter. Prototype, converted from second F-16B development aircraft, first flew on 29 October 1980; company certification flight testing completed on 19 December 1980. Aircraft demodified in 1986 and Pratt & Whitney F100 engine reinstalled.

AFTI/F-16. Modified F-16A testbed aircraft for Air Force Systems Command's Advanced Fighter Technology Integration (AFTI) programme; first flown on 10 July 1982. AFTI/F-16 has a digital flight control system and twin fuselage-mounted ventral foreplanes, permitting 'decoupled' or six-degrees-of-freedom flight modes and also providing integrated manoeuvring capability for making flat (un-banked) turns without sideslip and manoeuvre enhancement/gust alleviation. A major technology evaluated in the AFTI/F-16 was the automated manoeuvre and attack system (AMAS), which couples the fire control and flight control systems for dynamic precision weapons delivery. Other technologies included automatic terrain following, interactive voice control, automatic weapon fusing, digital colour moving map displays, helmet-mounted sight and automatic flight recovery. Information generated by the programme will be made available generally to the US aircraft industry for application to future fighter aircraft designs.

F-16XL. Advanced development of F-16 with 'cranked arrow' wing, embodying 50°/70° compound leading-edge sweep and an area more than twice that of a standard F-16 wing. Internal fuel capacity increased by 85 per cent, plus extra space for avionics and sensors. Two prototypes built; first flight on 3 July 1982. Demonstrated 48 per cent increase in combat radius on internal fuel, and 87 per cent increase with external tanks, compared with F-16A. Under the designation **F-16E** a two-seat F-16XL was proposed for the USAF's dual-role air-defence/ground-attack fighter requirement, for which the F-15E was selected on 24 February 1984. Since 1985 the prototypes have been held in flyable storage at General Dynamics' Fort Worth facility.

Development of the F-16 continues. Initial operational testing of LANTIRN began in mid-January 1986 on an F-16 from McChord AFB, Washington. Delivery of the first of 700 navigation pods was scheduled for April 1987.

Flight testing of an infra-red system known as Falcon Eye FLIR was scheduled to begin in mid-1987. This utilises a head-mounted display and head-steered FLIR sensor forward of the F-16's windscreen. Claimed advantages are night vision without need for an external pod and off-boresight field of vision correlated to the pilot's head position.

Other research and development subjects being investigated for the F-16 include artificial intelligence, modular avionics architecture, VHSIC, various weapons, sensors and cockpit displays, secure/anti-jam communications and data links, advanced navigation systems, chemical and electromagnetic pulse hardening, signature reduction and vulnerability reduction. The F-16 is a candidate for a defence suppression role in the USAF's Follow-On Weasel programme. A Falcon Century programme has been instituted to monitor and evaluate developments and to maintain a master plan for F-16 developments into the next century.

The following description applies to the F-16C and F-16D.
TYPE: Single-seat lightweight air-combat fighter (F-16C) and two-seat fighter/trainer (F-16D).
WINGS: Cantilever mid-wing monoplane, of blended wing/body design and cropped delta planform. The blended wing/body concept is achieved by flaring the wing/body intersection, thus not only providing lift from the body at high angles of attack but also giving less wetted area and increased internal fuel volume. In addition, thickening of the wing root gives a more rigid structure, with a weight saving of some 113 kg (250 lb). Basic wing is of NACA 64A-204 section, with 40° sweepback on leading

General Dynamics F-16C Fighting Falcon. *(Pilot Press)*

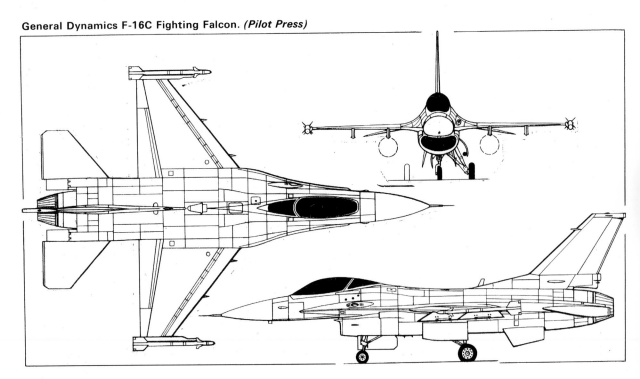

302

edges. Conventional construction. Leading-edge manoeuvring flaps are programmed automatically as a function of Mach number and angle of attack. The increased wing camber maintains effective lift coefficients at high angles of attack. The trailing edges carry large flaperons (flaps/ailerons), which are interchangeable left with right and are actuated by integrated servo-actuators. The maximum rate of flaperon movement is 52°/s.

FUSELAGE: Semi-monocoque structure, built in three main modules: forward (to just aft of cockpit), centre and aft. Highly swept vortex-control strakes along the fuselage forebody increase lift and improve directional stability at high angles of attack.

TAIL UNIT: Cantilever structure with sweptback surfaces. Fin structure has graphite epoxy skins, aluminium tip and dorsal fin. Optional extension of rear root fairing to house brake-chute (standard in Turkish F-16Cs) or Rapport III ECM. Interchangeable all-moving tailplane halves, constructed using graphite epoxy composite laminate skins. Split speed-brake inboard of rear portion of each horizontal tail surface to each side of nozzle, each deflecting 60° from the closed position.

LANDING GEAR: Retractable type. Nosewheel is located aft of intake, to reduce the risk of foreign objects being thrown into the engine during ground operation. Goodyear mainwheels and brakes; Goodrich mainwheel tyres, size 25.5 × 8-14. Steerable nosewheel with Goodrich tyre, size 18 × 5.5-8. All but two main unit components interchangeable. Brake by wire system on main gear, with Goodyear anti-skid units. Runway arrester hook under rear fuselage.

POWERPLANT: One General Electric F110-GE-100 or one Pratt & Whitney F100-PW-220 turbofan engine, rated at approx 129.0 kN (29,000 lb st) with afterburning, mounted within the rear fuselage. Fixed-geometry intake, with boundary layer splitter plate, beneath fuselage. Standard fuel contained in wing and five seal-bonded fuselage cells which function as two tanks; internal fuel weight is 3,162 kg (6,972 lb) in F-16C, and approx 17 per cent less in F-16D. In-flight refuelling receptacle in top of centre fuselage, aft of cockpit. Auxiliary fuel can be carried in drop-tanks on underwing and underfuselage hardpoints.

ACCOMMODATION: Pilot only in F-16C in air-conditioned cockpit. McDonnell Douglas ACES II zero/zero ejection seat. Transparent bubble canopy made of polycarbonate advanced plastics material. Windscreen/canopy design provides 360° all-round view, 195° fore and aft, 40° down over the side, and 15° down over the nose. To enable the pilot to sustain high g forces, and for pilot comfort, the seat is inclined 30° aft and the heel line is raised. A limited-displacement, force-sensing control stick is provided on the right hand console, with a suitable armrest, to provide precise control inputs during combat manoeuvres. The F-16D has two cockpits in tandem, equipped with all controls, displays, instruments, avionics and life support systems required to perform both training and combat missions. The layout of the F-16D second station is essentially the same as that of the F-16C, and is fully systems-operational.

SYSTEMS: Four dedicated, sealed-cell batteries provide transient electrical power protection for the fly-by-wire flight control system. Application of the control configured vehicle (CCV) principle of relaxed static stability produces a significant reduction in trim drag, especially at high load factors and supersonic speeds. The aircraft centre of gravity is allowed to move aft, reducing both the tail drag and the change in drag on the wing due to changes in lift required to balance the download on the tail. Relaxed static stability imposes a requirement for a highly reliable, full-time-operating, stability augmentation system, including reliable electronic, electrical and hydraulic provisions. The signal paths in this quad-redundant system are used to control the aircraft, replacing the usual mechanical linkages. Pilot commands are processed by a four-channel Lear Siegler flight control computer which generates the electrical signals for the servo actuators.

AVIONICS AND EQUIPMENT: Westinghouse APG-68 pulse-Doppler range and angle track radar, with planar array in nose. Radar provides air-to-air modes for range-while-search, uplook search, velocity search, air combat, track-while-scan (ten targets), raid cluster resolution, single-target track and (later) high PRF track to provide target illumination for AIM-7 missiles; and air-to-surface modes for ground mapping, Doppler beam sharpening, ground moving target, sea target, fixed target track, target freeze after pop-up, beacon for nav fix and offset weapon delivery with ground FAC, and air-to-ground ranging. Forward avionics bay, immediately forward of cockpit, contains radar, air data equipment, inertial navigation system, flight control computer, and combined altitude radar altimeter (CARA). Rear avionics bay contains ILS, Tacan and IFF, with space for future equipment. A Dalmo Victor AN/ALR-69 radar warning system is installed. Communications equipment includes Magnavox AN/ARC-164 UHF 'Have Quick' transceiver; provisions for a Magnavox KY-58 secure voice system; Collins AN/ARC-186 VHF AM/FM transceiver; government furnished AN/AIC-18/25 intercom; and Novatronics interference blanker. Sperry Flight Systems central air data computer. Litton LN-39 standard inertial navigation system; Collins AN/ARN-108 ILS; Collins AN/ARN-118 Tacan; Teledyne Electronics AN/APX-101 IFF transponder with a government furnished IFF control; government furnished National Security Agency KIT-1A/TSEC cryptographic equipment; Lear Siegler stick force sensors; GEC Avionics wide-angle holographic electronic head-up display with raster video capability and integrated keyboard; horizontal situation indicator; Teledyne Avionics angle-of-attack transmitter; Gull Airborne angle-of-attack indicator; Clifton Precision attitude director indicator; General Dynamics advanced stores management computer; Delco fire control computer; Sperry multi-function display set; data entry/cockpit interface by Litton-Canada and General Dynamics, Fort Worth; and cockpit/TV set. Cockpit and core avionics integrated on two MIL-STD-1553B multiplex buses. Optional equipment includes VIR-130 VOR/ILS and ARC-190 HF radio. Essential structure and wiring provisions are built into the airframe to allow for easy incorporation of future avionics systems under development for the F-16 by the US Air Force.

ARMAMENT: General Electric M61A1 20 mm multi-barrel cannon in the port side wing/body fairing, equipped with a General Electric ammunition handling system and a 'snapshoot' gunsight (part of the head-up display system) and 515 rounds of ammunition. There is a mounting for an air-to-air missile at each wingtip, one underfuselage centreline hardpoint, and six underwing hardpoints for additional stores. For manoeuvring flight at 5.5g the underfuselage station is stressed for a load of up to 1,000 kg (2,200 lb), the two inboard underwing stations for 2,041 kg (4,500 lb) each, the two centre underwing stations for 1,587 kg (3,500 lb) each, the two outboard underwing stations for 318 kg (700 lb) each, and the two wingtip stations for 193 kg (425 lb) each. For manoeuvring flight at 9g the underfuselage station is stressed for a load of up to 544 kg (1,200 lb), the two inboard underwing stations for 1,134 kg (2,500 lb) each, the two centre underwing stations for 907 kg (2,000 lb) each, the two outboard underwing stations for 204 kg (450 lb) each, and the two wingtip stations for 193 kg (425 lb) each. There are mounting provisions on each side of the inlet shoulder for the specific carriage of sensor pods (electro-optical, FLIR, etc); each of these stations is stressed for 408 kg (900 lb) at 5.5g, and 250 kg (550 lb) at 9g. Typical stores loads can include two wingtip mounted AIM-9J/L Sidewinders, with up to four more on the outer underwing stations; Sargent-Fletcher 1,400 litre (370 US gallon; 308 Imp gallon) or 2,271 litre (600 US gallon; 500 Imp gallon) drop-tanks on the inboard underwing stations; a 1,136 litre (300 US gallon; 250 Imp gallon) drop-tank on the underfuselage station; a Martin Marietta Pave Penny laser tracker pod along the starboard side of the nacelle; and single or cluster bombs, air-to-surface missiles, or flare pods, on the four inner underwing stations. Stores can be launched from Aircraft

Hydro-Forming MAU-12C/A bomb ejector racks, Hughes LAU-88 launchers, or Orgen triple or multiple ejector racks. Westinghouse AN/ALQ-119 and AN/ALQ-131 ECM (jammer) pods can be carried on the centreline and two underwing stations. Provision for future internal installation of Westinghouse/ITT AN/ALQ-165 airborne self-protection jammer (ASPJ) instead of ECM pods. ALE-40 internal chaff/flare dispensers. Current capabilities include air-to-air combat with gun and Sidewinder missiles; and air-to-ground attack with gun, rockets, conventional bombs, special weapons, laser guided and electro-optical weapons. Specific structure, wiring provisions, and system architecture, are built in to ensure acceptance of future sensor and weapon systems, including electro-optical and FLIR pods, and advanced beyond-visual-range missiles. Weapons already launched successfully from F-16s, in addition to Sidewinders and AMRAAM, include radar guided Sparrow and Sky Flash air-to-air missiles, AGM-65A/B/D Maverick air-to-surface missiles and Penguin Mk 3 anti-ship missile. Also, the GPU-5/A 30 mm gun pod has been fired successfully from the F-16 fuselage station. F-16s of the Belgian Air Force carry Matra Magic air-to-air missiles and those of the Norwegian Air Force carry Penguin anti-shipping missiles. F-16s can be equipped with a variety of reconnaissance pods and the Thomson-CSF Atlis laser designator pod.

DIMENSIONS, EXTERNAL (F-16C and D):	
Wing span over missile launchers	9.45 m (31 ft 0 in)
Wing span over missiles	10.00 m (32 ft 9¾ in)
Length overall	15.03 m (49 ft 4 in)
Height overall	5.09 m (16 ft 8½ in)
Wheel track	2.36 m (7 ft 9 in)
Wheelbase	4.00 m (13 ft 1½ in)
AREA (F-16C and D):	
Wings, gross	27.87 m² (300.0 sq ft)
WEIGHTS:	
Weight empty: F-16A	7,364 kg (16,234 lb)
F-16B	7,655 kg (16,876 lb)
F-16C	7,618 kg (16,794 lb)
F-16D	7,896 kg (17,408 lb)
Max external load: all models	5,443 kg (12,000 lb)
Structural design gross weight (9g) with full internal fuel:	
F-16A, B	11,113 kg (24,500 lb)
F-16C, D	11,839 kg (26,100 lb)

Max T-O weight:	
air-to-air, no external tanks:	
F-16A	11,094 kg (24,459 lb)
F-16B	10,849 kg (23,918 lb)
F-16C	11,372 kg (25,071 lb)
F-16D	11,114 kg (24,502 lb)
with external load:	
F-16A, B	16,057 kg (35,400 lb)
F-16C, D	17,010 kg (37,500 lb)
PERFORMANCE:	
Max level speed at 12,200 m (40,000 ft)	above Mach 2.0
Service ceiling	more than 15,240 m (50,000 ft)
Radius of action	more than 500 nm (925 km; 575 miles)
Ferry range, with drop-tanks	more than 2,100 nm (3,890 km; 2,415 miles)
Max symmetrical design load factor with full internal fuel, all models	+9

General Dynamics F-111

Following a detailed evaluation of design proposals submitted by General Dynamics and Boeing, the US Department of Defense announced on 24 November 1962 that General Dynamics had been selected as prime contractor for development of the F-111 variable-geometry tactical fighter (known originally by the designation TFX), with Grumman Aircraft as an associate. An initial contract was placed for 23 development aircraft (18 F-111As for the USAF, five F-111Bs for the US Navy), of which the first were scheduled for delivery within 2½ years. Subsequently, further orders were placed, covering F-111D, E and F improved tactical fighters for the USAF, 24 F-111Cs for the Royal Australian Air Force, 50 F-111Ks for the RAF, and the FB-

111A strategic bomber version for the USAF. However, the F-111B was cancelled after the five development aircraft and two of the 24 production models had been built. Likewise, the RAF's F-111K strike-reconnaissance fighter version was cancelled.

A total of 562 F-111s of all types, including the 23 development models, was covered by these contracts. The last F-111F, of which 106 were built, was delivered to the USAF in November 1976.

The specification to which the F-111 was designed called for a maximum speed of about Mach 2.5, capability of supersonic speed at sea level, short take-off capability from rough airfields in forward areas and short landing capability. The F-111 had to be able to fly between any two airfields in

General Dynamics F-111 with Mk 82 bombs. *(Erik Simonsen)*

the world in one day and to carry a full range of conventional and nuclear weapons including the latest air-to-surface tactical weapons.

On 15 April 1986, British-based USAF F-111s were used on a raid against Libya.

Versions are as follows:

F-111A. USAF two-seat tactical fighter-bomber. Development models built with two P & W TF30-P-1 turbofan engines: production version has 82.3 kN (18,500 lb st) with afterburning TF30-P-3 engines and Mk I electronics. First F-111A flew for the first time (with wings locked at sweepback of 26°) on 21 December 1964. Contracts covered the 18 development aircraft and 141 production models for the USAF Tactical Air Command.

During 1982 a Grumman/Norden Pave Mover battlefield surveillance radar was installed in a belly pod on an F-111A. Initial flight testing involved location of surface targets and directing attack aircraft on to them. Later tests were to evaluate the capability of directing surface-to-surface weapons equipped with guided submunitions under the DARPA Assault Breaker programme. Currently used by the 366th Tactical Fighter Wing. (See F-111C.)

EF-111A Raven. Grumman conversion of the F-111A for electronic warfare. (See Grumman).

F-111C. Strike aircraft with longer-span wings and strengthened landing gear. Outwardly similar to FB-111A, with Pratt & Whitney TF30-P-3 engines, Mk I electronics, cockpit ejection module and eight underwing attachments for stores. Twenty-four built for RAAF. Fifteen F-111Cs remain, plus four RF-111Cs and four ex-USAF F-111As fitted with 'C' avionics. Incorporation of reconnaissance capability in four F-111Cs (see RF-111C). AN/AVQ-26 Pave Tack (see F-111F) acquired for RAAF F-111Cs.

F-111D. Similar to F-111E, but with Mk II electronics, offering improvements in navigation and in air-to-air weapon delivery. AN/APQ-144 attack radar. Two 87.2 kN (19,600 lb st) with afterburning TF30-P-9 engines. Delivery of 96 by February 1973. Equips 27th Tactical Fighter Wing, Cannon AFB, New Mexico.

F-111E. Superseded F-111A from 160th aircraft. Modified air intakes improve engine/inlet compatibility above Mach 2.2. Total of 94 built; followed by F-111D. Most equip the 20th Tactical Fighter Wing, USAFE, at Upper Heyford, England. Between 1989 and 1993, replacement of the AJQ-20A analogue bombing and navigation systems by digital equipment will take place. This will allow the F-111A and E

General Dynamics F-111F two-seat tactical fighter-bomber.

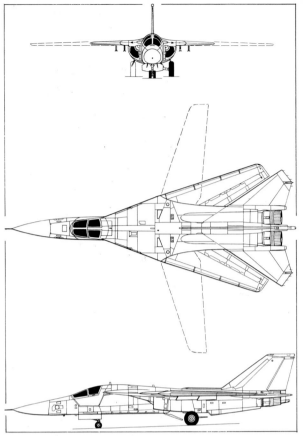

General Dynamics F-111E. *(Pilot Press)*

to handle modern guided munitions and advanced sensors in addition to future systems, like the Global Positioning System.

F-111F. Fighter-bomber version, with avionics that combine features of the F-111E and FB-111A systems. Uprated turbofan engines. A total of 106 produced. Equips 48th Tactical Fighter Wing, at Lakenheath. Following completion of a successful US Air Force flight test programme, a decision was made to incorporate AN/AVQ-26 Pave Tack/guided weapons capability into all F-111F aircraft. Kit proofing has been completed, and the first production kit was delivered in 1980. General Dynamics was the prime contractor for integration of the system in the F-111s. The major components of the system are the Ford Aerospace Pave Tack pod, General Electric controls and displays, and a Hughes Aircraft data link pod. The Pave Tack pod is carried inside the aircraft's weapon bay on a cradle which rotates 180° in 5 s to expose it for use. Embodying a data link for stand-off delivery, Pave Tack provides a day/night all-weather capability to acquire, track and designate ground targets for laser, infra-red and electro-optically guided weapons, from very low altitudes if necessary.

RF-111C. Four of the Royal Australian Air Force's remaining F-111C strike aircraft were allocated a strike/reconnaissance role. The modified aircraft, and trained crews with modification kits, returned to Australia in late 1979. Royal Australian Air Force personnel began

modification of the second aircraft in January 1980. Reconnaissance equipment includes a Fairchild KA-56E low-altitude panoramic camera, Chicago Aerial KS-87C vertical cameras, Chicago Aerial KA-93A high-altitude panoramic camera, Honeywell AN/AAD-5 infra-red line-scan, and Cardion Electronics TV.

The following details apply to the F-111F, except where otherwise indicated:

TYPE: Two-seat long-range variable-geometry interdiction fighter.

WINGS: Cantilever shoulder wing. Wing section of NACA 64A series, with conventional washout. Sweepback of outer portions variable in flight or on the ground from 16° to 72° 30′. Airbrake/lift dumpers above wing operate as spoilers for lateral control at low speeds. Full-span variable-camber leading-edge slats and full-span double-slotted trailing-edge flaps. General Electric flight control system.

FUSELAGE: Semi-monocoque structure. Main structural member is a T-section keel, under the arms of which the engines are hung.

TAIL UNIT: Conventional cantilever sweptback surfaces. All-moving horizontal surfaces operate both differentially and symmetrically to provide aileron and elevator functions. Two long, narrow ventral stabilising fins.

LANDING GEAR: Retractable tricycle type. Single wheel on each main leg. During mainwheel retraction, the legs pivot downward, the wheels tilt to lie almost flat against them, and the whole gear rotates forward so that the wheels are stowed side-by-side in fuselage between engine air intake ducts. Low-pressure tyres on main wheels, size 47-18 in. Disc brakes, with anti-skid system. Main landing gear door, in bottom of fuselage, hinges down to act as speed brake in flight.

POWERPLANT: Two Pratt & Whitney TF30-P-100 turbofan engines, each giving 111.5 kN (25,100 lb st) with afterburning. Fuel tanks in wings and fuselage. In-flight refuelling receptacle in top of fuselage aft of cockpit. Hydro-mechanical air intake system with movable shock-cone.

ACCOMMODATION: Crew of two side-by-side in air-conditioned and pressurised cabin. Zero-speed, zero-altitude (including underwater) emergency escape module developed by McDonnell Douglas Corpn and utilising a 178 kN (40,000 lb st) Rocket Power Inc rocket motor. Emergency procedure calls for both crew members to remain in capsule cabin section, which is propelled away from aircraft by rocket motor and lowered to ground by parachute. Airbags cushion impact and form flotation gear in water. Entire capsule forms survival shelter.

AVIONICS: See model listings. Electronic warfare capabilities being upgraded with ALQ-131 ECM pod system.

ARMAMENT: One M61 multi-barrel 20 mm gun plus one B-43 bomb, or two B-43s, in internal weapon bay. External stores are carried on three attachments under each wing. The two inboard pylons on each side pivot as the wings sweep back to keep the stores parallel with the fuselage. The outboard pylon on each wing is jettisonable and non-swivelling. To be given (with other versions) AIM-9L/M Sidewinder air-to-air capability. Since 1984 TAC F-111s have use of French Durandal parachute-retarded runway attack bombs. Also new is Gator air-delivered mine system.

DIMENSIONS, EXTERNAL (F-111F):
Wing span:
spread	19.20 m (63 ft 0 in)
fully swept	9.74 m (31 ft 11.4 in)
Length overall	22.40 m (73 ft 6 in)
Height overall	5.22 m (17 ft 1.4 in)

WEIGHTS (F-111F):
Weight empty	21,537 kg (47,481 lb)
Payload, external	11,340 kg (25,000 lb)
Max T-O weight	45,359 kg (100,000 lb)

PERFORMANCE (F-111F):
Max speed at height	Mach 2.5
Max speed at S/L	Mach 1.2
Service ceiling	over 18,000 m (59,000 ft)
T-O and landing run	under 915 m (3,000 ft)
Range with max internal fuel	
	over 2,540 nm (4,707 km; 2,925 miles)

The USAF's smallest strategic bomber is the two-seat General Dynamics FB-111A.

General Dynamics FB-111A

The FB-111A is a two-seat strategic bomber version of the F-111, operating with the USAF's Strategic Air Command. A requirement for 210 was announced by the US Secretary of Defense on 10 December 1965, to replace Boeing B-52C/F Stratofortresses and B-58A Hustler supersonic bombers. An initial contract for 64 was signed in the Spring of 1967. Subsequently, on 20 March 1969, it was announced that FB-111A production would total only 76 aircraft.

The first of two FB-111A prototypes was converted from a development F-111A and flew initially on 30 July 1967, followed by the first production aircraft on 13 July 1968 (fitted temporarily with TF30-P-3 engines). Long-span wings and a strengthened landing gear are features of this model, plus increased braking capability.

The first FB-111A was delivered to the 340th Bomb Group, a training unit of SAC, at Carswell Air Force Base, Texas, on 8 October 1969. In 1987 61 FB-111As remained on strength, 52 for active use and nine in reserve. When the B-2 becomes operational, FB-111As will assume a conventional-weapon role. To maintain their capabilities throughout the 1990s, several Class IV modifications are being made, including upgrading the avionics and powerplant, and escape capsule changes. Current radar is AN/APQ-114.

FB-111As currently equip the 380th and 509th Bomb Wings of the USAF, based at Plattsburgh AFB, New York,

and Pease AFB, New Hampshire, respectively.

The description of the F-111 applies generally to the FB-111A, except for the differences noted above and below.

POWERPLANT: Two 90.52 kN (20,350 lb st) with afterburning Pratt & Whitney TF30-P-7 turbofans.

ARMAMENT: 14,288 kg (31,500 lb) max load, comprising 42 × 750 lb bombs, of which two are carried in internal bay and 40 in clusters on eight underwing attachments. Full load is carried with wings swept at 26°, reducing to 32 bombs (six underwing attachments) at 54° of sweep, or 20 bombs at full sweep. Ability to carry six nuclear bombs or six AGM-69A SRAM missiles (four under wings and two in bay), or a combination of the two.

DIMENSIONS, EXTERNAL:
Wing span:
spread	21.34 m (70 ft 0 in)
fully swept	10.34 m (33 ft 11 in)
Length overall	22.40 m (73 ft 6 in)
Height overall	5.22 m (17 ft 1.4 in)

WEIGHTS:
Max T-O weight	approx 45,360 kg (100,000 lb)

PERFORMANCE:
Max level speed at 10,975 m (36,000 ft)	Mach 2.5
Max level speed at S/L	794 knots (1,472 km/h; 915 mph)
Service ceiling	more than 18,290 m (60,000 ft)
Range, with external fuel	
	approx 3,474 nm (6,437 km; 4,000 miles)

Grumman

GRUMMAN CORPORATION

The Grumman Aircraft Engineering Corporation was incorporated on 6 December 1929. Important changes in the corporate structure of the company were announced in 1969, resulting in the formation of Grumman Corporation, a small holding company, with Grumman Aerospace Corporation, Grumman Allied Industries Inc and Grumman Data Systems Corporation. In February 1985 Grumman Corporation announced the creation of nine operating divisions, each matched to a specific market: Aerostructures; Aircraft Systems; Allied (Vehicles and Marine); Data Systems; Electronics Systems; Melbourne Systems; Space Systems; St

Augustine; and Technical Services. In addition, a Corporate Services Division provides legal, purchasing, contracts and other common services to all the operating divisions.

Grumman Aircraft Systems Division

Current aircraft products of Grumman Corporation include versions of the A-6 Intruder, C-2A Greyhound, EA-6B Prowler, E-2C Hawkeye and F-14 Tomcat for the US Navy, and a tactical jamming version of the General Dynamics F-111A, designated EF-111A, for the US Air Force. In mid-1983, Grumman was selected to develop and build the composite graphite-expoxy wings and vertical tail for the prototype and early production models of Israel's new Lavi fighter (now cancelled). A contract to manufacture 270 shipsets of engine nacelles and thrust reversers for the Tay turbofans of Gulfstream IV and Fokker 100 transport aircraft was received in February 1984. An initial contract covering design and manufacture of the complete tail sections of the Bell/Boeing V-22 Osprey advanced vertical-lift aircraft (see Bell entry) was received in August 1984.

A contract was awarded in January 1987 by the government of Pakistan to study the technical feasibility of integrating US engines and avionics into Chinese manufactured jet fighter aircraft for the Pakistan Air Force. On 5 August 1987 the US Air Force awarded Grumman contracts totalling $245 million for the development, installation and flight testing of avionics upgrades for Chinese Shenyang F-8 II fighter aircraft. In April 1987 Grumman announced that it had been awarded an initial $28 million contract for the manufacture of two sets of composite structure ailerons, elevators and rudders for the McDonnell Douglas C-17A tactical airlifter.

Latest Grumman product is a small forward-swept-wing (FSW) technology demonstrator designated X-29A, built under contract from the US Defense Advanced Research Projects Agency.

Grumman Hawkeye

US Navy designations: E-2B, E-2C and TE-2C

The E-2 Hawkeye was developed as a carrier-borne early warning aircraft, but is suitable also for land based operations. The first of three prototypes flew for the first time on 21 October 1960; these were followed by 56 E-2As, all operational examples of which had been updated to E-2B standard by the end of 1971.

The first of two E-2C prototypes flew on 20 January 1971. Production began in mid-1971 and the first flight of a production aircraft was made on 23 September 1972. Orders from the US Navy for this version now cover 138 aircraft; 111 of these had been delivered by the beginning of 1987, and it is planned for production to continue at the rate of six per year until the early 1990s. Four E-2Cs were supplied to Israel in 1981; Japan accepted four each in 1982 and 1984. Egypt

has accepted five aircraft. The government of Singapore has taken delivery of four aircraft. The US Coast Guard and US Customs Service have each taken delivery of two aircraft for use in anti-narcotics smuggling operations.

The E-2C entered service, with airborne early warning squadron VAW-123 at NAS Norfolk, Va, in November 1973, and went to sea on board the USS *Saratoga* in late 1974. Sixteen other squadrons, including two naval reserve squadrons, have since received E-2C aircraft, and two **TE-2C** training aircraft are also in service.

The Hawkeye can maintain patrol on naval task force defence perimeters in all weathers, at an operating height of about 9,150 m (30,000 ft), and can detect and assess any threat from approaching enemy aircraft over ranges approaching 260 nm (480 km; 300 miles). An AN/APS-138 radar system replaced the original AN/APS-125 in new production E-2Cs in 1983. A retrofit programme is in progress for all previously delivered aircraft. The system includes a new total-radiation-aperture-control antenna (TRAC-A) to reduce sidelobes and offset increased jamming threats. The radar is capable of detecting airborne targets anywhere in a three million cubic mile surveillance envelope while simultaneously monitoring maritime traffic. Long-range detection, automatic target track initiation and high-speed processing combine to enable each E-2C to track, automatically and simultaneously, more than 600 targets and to control more than 40 airborne intercepts. A Randtron Systems AN/APA-171 antenna system is housed in a 7.32 m (24 ft) diameter saucer-shaped rotodome, mounted above the rear fuselage of the aircraft, which revolves in flight at 6 rpm. The Yagi-type radar arrays within the rotodome are interfaced to the onboard avionic systems, providing radar sum and difference signals plus IFF.

The AN/APS-138 search radar can detect targets as small as a cruise missile at ranges in excess of 145 nm (268 km; 167 miles). It also monitors movement of enemy ships and land vehicles. The AN/ALR-73 passive detection systems (PDS) alerts operators to the presence of electronic emitters at distances up to twice the detection range of the radar system, thus expanding significantly the surveillance capability of the E-2C.

In 1986 the US Navy began evaluation of an E-2C with

Land-based Grumman E-2C Hawkeye early-warning and control aircraft of the Egyptian Air Force.

US Navy Grumman E-2C Hawkeye on board a US carrier. *(Brian M. Service)*

new Grumman/General Electric APS-145 radar system, able to track more targets at greater ranges and decrease the effects of jamming, and having sharper overland vision. The APS-145 is expected to go into production aircraft towards the end of 1988.

The US Navy has awarded Grumman a $14 million contract to flight-test conformal microprocessor controlled phased array radar antennae installed in the wing leading edges, fuselage and horizontal tail surfaces of an E-2C. The passive array will be evaluated as an advanced anti-jamming ECM system. Tests began in 1986 and will last three years. Associated equipment will be provided by the General Electric Co. The conformal radar is a potential candidate for the US Navy's future Airborne Multi-Sensor (AMSS) requirement.

E-2Cs are used to monitor air traffic in the Florida skies surrounding Cape Canaveral during Space Shuttle launches and to direct US Coast Guard and US Customs fixed-wing and helicopter crews in many successful interceptions of drug smuggling aircraft. They are also used to direct Israeli fighters engaged in combat missions in the Middle East.

The following details apply to the E-2C Hawkeye:

TYPE: Airborne early warning aircraft.

WINGS: Cantilever high-wing monoplane of conventional construction. The outer wing panels fold rearward about skewed-axis hinge fittings mounted on the rear beams, to stow parallel with the rear fuselage on each side. Trailing edges of outer panels and part of centre-section consist of long-span ailerons and Fowler flaps. When flaps are lowered, ailerons are drooped automatically. All control surfaces are power operated and incorporate devices to produce artificial feel forces. Automatic flight control

Grumman E-2C Hawkeye. *(Pilot Press)*

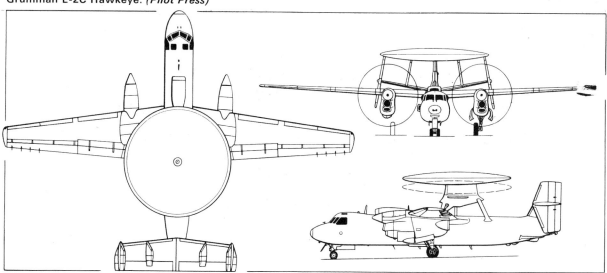

system (AFCS) can be assigned sole control of the system hydraulic actuators, or AFCS signals can be superimposed on the pilot's mechanical inputs for stability augmentation. Pneumatically inflated rubber de-icing boots on leading edges.

FUSELAGE: Conventional semi-monocoque structure.

TAIL UNIT: Cantilever structure, with four fins and three double-hinged rudders. Tailplane dihedral 11°. Portions of tail unit made of glassfibre to reduce radar reflection. Power control and artificial feel systems as for ailerons. Pneumatically inflated rubber de-icing boots on all leading edges.

LANDING GEAR: Retractable tricycle type. Pneumatic emergency extension. Steerable nosewheel. Twin wheels on nose unit only. Mainwheel tyres size 36 × 11 Type VII 24-ply. Hydraulic brakes. Hydraulically operated retractable tailskid. A-frame arrester hook under tail.

POWERPLANT: Two 3,661 kW (4,910 ehp) Allison T56-A-425 turboprop engines, driving Hamilton Standard type 54460-1 four-blade fully-feathering reversible-pitch constant-speed propellers. These have foam filled blades which have a steel spar and glassfibre shell. Spinners and blades incorporate electric anti-icing. E-2C under flight test with T56-A-427 engines, expected to offer a 24 per cent power increase and lower fuel consumption.

ACCOMMODATION: Normal crew of five on flight deck and in ATDS compartment in main cabin, consisting of pilot, co-pilot, combat information centre officer, air control officer and radar operator.

AVIONICS: Randtron AN/APA-171 rotodome (radar and IFF antennae), General Electric AN/APS-138 advanced radar processing system (ARPS) with overland/overwater detection capability (APS-139 in new-build aircraft from 1988, with APS-145 scheduled for introduction in 1990 and eventual retrofit in all E-2Cs), RT-988/A IFF interrogator with Hazeltine OL-76/AP IFF detector processor, Litton AN/ALR-73 passive detection system, Hazeltine AN/APA-172 control indicator group, Litton OL-77/ASQ computer programmer (L-304), ARC-158 UHF data link, ARQ-34 HF data link, ASM-440 in-flight performance monitor, Collins ARC-51A, UHF com, AIC-14A intercom, Litton AN/ASN-92 (LN-15C) CAINS carrier aircraft inertial navigation system, GEC Avionics standard central air data computer, APN-153 (V) Doppler, ASN-50 heading and attitude reference system, ARN-52 (V) Tacan, Collins ARA-50 UHF ADF, ASW-25B ACLS and Honeywell APN-171 (V) radar altimeter.

DIMENSIONS, EXTERNAL:		PERFORMANCE (at max T-O weight):	
Wing span	24.56 m (80 ft 7 in)	Max level speed	323 knots (598 km/h; 372 mph)
Width, wings folded	8.94 m (29 ft 4 in)	Max cruising speed	311 knots (576 km/h; 358 mph)
Length overall	17.54 m (57 ft 6¾ in)	Cruising speed (ferry)	268 knots (496 km/h; 308 mph)
Height overall	5.58 m (18 ft 3¾ in)	Stalling speed (landing configuration)	
Diameter of rotodome	7.32 m (24 ft 0 in)		74 knots (138 km/h; 86 mph)
Wheel track	5.93 m (19 ft 5¾ in)	Service ceiling	9,390 m (30,800 ft)
Wheelbase	7.06 m (23 ft 2 in)	Min T-O run	610 m (2,000 ft)
Propeller diameter	4.11 m (13 ft 6 in)	T-O to 15 m (50 ft)	793 m (2,600 ft)
AREA:		Min landing run	439 m (1,440 ft)
Wings, gross	65.03 m² (700 sq ft)	Ferry range	1,394 nm (2,583 km; 1,605 miles)
WEIGHTS:		Time on station, 175 nm (320 km; 200 miles) from base	
Weight empty	17,265 kg (38,063 lb)		3–4 h
Max T-O weight	23,556 kg (51,933 lb)	Endurance with max fuel	6 h 6 min

Grumman Intruder

US Navy designations: A-6, EA-6 and KA-6

The basic A-6A (originally A2F-1) Intruder was conceived as a carrier-borne low-level attack bomber equipped specifically to deliver nuclear or conventional weapons on targets completely obscured by weather or darkness. Of well over 600 A-6s built, in successive versions, approximately 350 currently equip operational US Navy and Marine Corps squadrons, and three readiness training squadrons. All older A-6s have been converted to the A-6E/TRAM configuration or into KA-6D tankers. The latest **KA-6D** configuration deletes all weapons systems capability. Grumman's St Augustine Division was awarded a $190 million contract to convert four A-6Es to KA-6D configuration and to update 49 existing KA-6Ds to the latest standard, which includes provision for the carriage of five 1,514 litre (400 US gallon; 333 Imp gallon) drop-tanks. Deliveries of updated KA-6Ds began in 1984.

Competition for the original A-6 contract was conducted from May to December 1957, Grumman's contender being selected on 31 December 1957. Seven variants of the basic design have been built, of which the A-6A, A-6B and A-6C are no longer operational. Current operational versions include the EA-6A (27 built) and KA-6D (78 converted from A-6A, and seven from A-6E, of which 68 are still in operation). The following versions are still in use:

EA-6A Prowler. Electronics development of the A-6A. Twenty-seven built for US Marine Corps, including six A-6As modified into EA-6As. See separate EA-6 Prowler entry.

EA-6B Prowler. Advanced electronics development of the EA-6A, described separately.

KA-6D Intruder. An A-6A was modified into a prototype flight refuelling tanker, with hose and reel in the rear fuselage, and flew for the first time on 23 May 1966. The KA-6D production model is fitted with Tacan and can transfer more than 9,500 kg (21,000 lb) of fuel immediately after take-off or 6,800 kg (15,000 lb) at a distance of 250 nm (463 km; 288 miles) from its carrier base. In addition, the KA-6D could act as a control aircraft for air-sea rescue operations or as a day bomber. A total of 78 A-6A/Es was modified to KA-6D configuration, of which 68 remain operational.

Grumman KA-6D tanker aircraft. *(Katsumi Hinata)*

A-6E Intruder. First produced as an advanced conversion of the A-6A with multi-mode radar and an IBM computer similar to that first tested in the EA-6B. First flight of an A-6E was made on 10 November 1970. First squadron deployment was made in September 1972, and the A-6E was approved officially for service use in December 1972. It was planned to acquire a total of 318 A-6Es. Procurement of new airframes is continuing beyond original termination date, with a total of 346 in service in 1986. Current Intruders are to

A-6E/TRAM (target recognition and attack multisensor) standard, the first example of which flew in October 1974. Delivery of fully provisioned TRAM aircraft began on 14 December 1978, and the first carrier deployment was completed successfully in May 1980. All older A-6Es have been converted to TRAM standard.

Under plans made in early 1981, 50 A-6Es were equipped to carry McDonnell Douglas Harpoon anti-shipping missiles (four per aircraft). Harpoon-capable A-6Es began to be

Grumman A-6E/TRAM Intruder being prepared for catapult launch.

deployed during 1981, and all subsequent new production and converted aircraft are equipped to carry this missile.

Intruder training is carried out using Grumman TC-4C (modified Gulfstream I) aircraft, eight of which are in US Navy/Marine Corps service. Grumman updated these aircraft to A-6E/TRAM standard during 1978–80.

A-6F Intruder II. Under a contract awarded in July 1984, Grumman initiated a major update programme for the Intruder, which was originally known as the A-6E Upgrade but was later designated A-6F. However, no funds were allocated to the programme for the current fiscal year and, instead, A-6E/TRAM Intruders will be further upgraded.

Boeing Military Airplane Company has contracts to manufacture 120 sets of new wings for the A-6E, to overcome fatigue problems believed to result from operation at heavier weights and higher load factors than were envisaged when the aircraft was designed. The new A-6 wing is made primarily of composites. Control surfaces are of aluminium alloy. Titanium is used in high-stress areas, such as the wing-fold fittings. Design improvements include split fuel tanks, so that supply can be maintained if one is damaged in combat; enhanced for protection; and easier repair and maintenance (see Boeing Military Airplane Company introductory text).

The following description applies to the A-6E:

TYPE: Two-seat carrier-based bomber for close-air-support, interdiction and deep strike missions.

WINGS: Cantilever mid-wing monoplane, with 25° sweep-back at quarter-chord. Almost full-span leading-edge slats and trailing-edge single-slotted, tracked, Fowler type flaps, with inset spoilers (flaperons) of same span as flaps forward of trailing-edge flaps for roll control. Trailing edge of each wingtip, outboard of flap, splits to form speed-brakes which project above and below wing when extended. Two short fences above each wing. Outer panels fold upward and inward.

FUSELAGE: Conventional semi-monocoque structure. Bot-tom is recessed between engines to carry semi-exposed store.

TAIL UNIT: Cantilever structure. All-moving tailplane, without separate elevators. Electronic antenna in rear part of fin, immediately above rudder.

LANDING GEAR: Retractable tricycle type. A-frame arrester hook under rear fuselage.

POWERPLANT: Two 41.4 kN (9,300 lb st) Pratt & Whitney J52-P-8B turbojet engines. Max internal fuel capacity 8,873 litres (2,344 US gallons; 1,952 Imp gallons). Provision for up to five external fuel tanks under wing and centreline stations, each of 1,135 litres (300 US gallons; 250 Imp gallons) or 1,514 litres (400 US gallons; 333 Imp gallons) capacity. Removable flight refuelling probe projects upward immediately forward of windscreen.

ACCOMMODATION: Crew of two on Martin-Baker GRU7 ejection seats, which can be reclined to reduce fatigue during low-level operations. Bombardier/navigator slightly behind and below pilot to starboard.

AVIONICS AND EQUIPMENT: Development of A-6E began with substitution of a single simultaneous multi-mode nav/attack radar, developed by Norden division of UTC, for the two earlier radar systems in A-6A. Following concept of EA-6B, IBM Corporation and Fairchild Camera and Instrument Corporation supplied a new nav/attack computer system and interfacing data converter. Conrac Corporation armament control unit. RCA video tape recorder for post-strike assessment of attacks. Norden AN/APQ-148 multi-mode radar provides simultaneous ground mapping; identification, tracking, and rangefinding of fixed or moving targets; and terrain clearance or terrain following manoeuvres. It can detect, locate and track radar beacons used by forward air controllers when providing close support for ground forces; and has mechanical scanning in azimuth, with a specially developed avionics system for simultaneous

First Grumman A-6F Intruder II development aircraft.

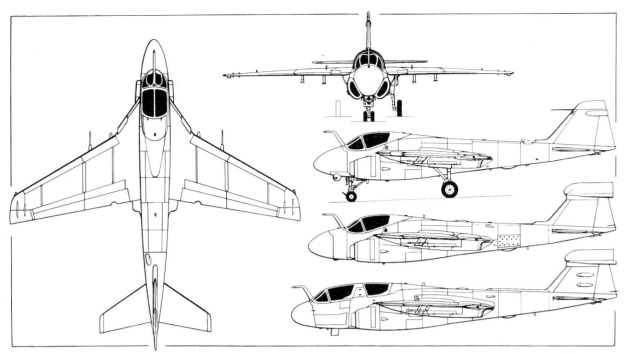

Grumman A-6E/TRAM Intruder. Additional side views: EA-6A (centre), EA-6B Prowler (bottom). *(Pilot Press)*

vertical scanning. During 1981–83, it was updated by an improved AMTI (airborne moving target indication) to enhance its ability to detect moving targets. Cockpit displays for pilot and bombardier/navigator; terrain data presented on vertical display indicator ahead of pilot. IBM AN/ASQ-133 solid-state digital computer is coupled to A-6E's radar, inertial and Doppler navigational equipment, communications and AFCS. As mission data is measured in flight by onboard aerodynamic and electronic sensors, computer compares data with programmed information, computes differences, and provides corrective data to alter parameters of mission. Fairchild Camera and Instrument Corporation signal data converter accepts analog input data from up to 60 sensors, converting data to a digital output that is fed into nav/attack system computer. Conrac armament control unit (ACU) provides all inputs and outputs necessary to select and release weapons. Master arming switch has a 'practice' position that allows ACU to be cycled up to point of firing command. Kaiser AN/AVA-1 multi-mode display serves as a primary flight aid for navigation, approach, landing and weapons delivery. Basic vertical display indicator (VDI) is a 0.20 m (8 in) CRT which shows a synthetic landscape, sky and electronically generated command flightpath that move to simulate the motion of these features as they would be seen by pilot through windscreen. Symbols are superimposed to augment basic attitude data, and for attack a second set of superimposed information provides a target symbol, steering symbol, and release and pull-up markers. A solid-state radar data scan converter can provide on the same display an apparent real-world perspective of terrain, ten shades of grey defining terrain elevation at ten different segmented contour intervals up to 8.7 nm (16 km; 10 miles) ahead of aircraft. This makes it possible for pilot to fly in either terrain following or terrain avoidance mode at low altitude. Flightpath and attack symbols can be super-

imposed over terrain elevation data on VDI, enabling pilot to attack while avoiding or following terrain in target area. Kaiser micromesh filter prevents 'washout' of data displayed on VDI in sunlight. Naval pilots use VDI as a primary flight instrument, for precise steering in navigation, weapons cues, progress, and status information during attack. For carrier landing, unit is used as a flight director and, linked to the APQ-148 radar, presents steering information, allowing pilot to select descent angle for final approach. Aircraft fitted with TRAM package have, in addition, an undernose precision-stabilised turret, with a sensor package containing both infra-red and laser equipment; INS updated with Litton AN/ASN-92 CAINS; new communications-navigation-identification (CNI) system; and automatic carrier landing capability. Sensor package is integrated with multi-mode radar, providing capability to detect, identify and attack a wide range of targets (as well as view the terrain) under adverse weather conditions, and with improved accuracy, using either conventional or laser guided weapons. Bombardier/navigator operates TRAM system by first acquiring target on his radar screen. He then switches to FLIR (forward looking infra-red) system, using an optical zoom to enlarge target's image. After identifying and selecting his targets, bombardier uses a laser designator to mark target with a laser spot, on which his own laser guided weapons, or those from another aircraft, will home. Using TRAM's laser spot detector, A-6E can also acquire a target being illuminated from another aircraft, or designated by a forward air controller on the ground. Under a contract awarded in Spring 1985, Northrop was to deliver in October 1986 the first pre-production examples of an infra-red video automatic tracking (IRVAT) system that will computerise and automate the tracking portion of the TRAM system.

ARMAMENT: Five weapon attachment points, each with a

1,633 kg (3,600 lb) capacity (max external stores load 8,165 kg; 18,000 lb). Typical weapon loads are twenty-eight 500 lb bombs in clusters of six, or three 2,000 lb general-purpose bombs plus two 1,135 litre (300 US gallon; 250 Imp gallon) drop-tanks. AIM-9 Sidewinder missiles can be carried for air-to-air use. Harpoon missile capability added to weapons complement of A-6E/TRAM. The HARM missile has been test flown on the A-6E, with operational introduction 1987. Flight and firing tests have been carried out with the AGM-123A Skipper II, also on an A-6E.

DIMENSIONS, EXTERNAL:

Wing span	16.15 m (53 ft 0 in)
Width, wings folded	7.72 m (25 ft 4 in)
Length overall	16.69 m (54 ft 9 in)
Height overall	4.93 m (16 ft 2 in)
Wheel track	3.32 m (10 ft 10½ in)
Wheelbase	5.24 m (17 ft 2¼ in)

AREA:

Wings, gross	49.1 m² (528.9 sq ft)

WEIGHTS:

Weight empty	12,132 kg (26,746 lb)
Max external load	8,165 kg (18,000 lb)
Max T-O weight:	
catapult	26,580 kg (58,600 lb)
field	27,397 kg (60,400 lb)
Max zero-stores weight	20,166 kg (44,460 lb)

PERFORMANCE (no stores, except where stated):

Never-exceed speed	700 knots (1,297 km/h; 806 mph)
Max level speed at S/L	560 knots (1,037 km/h; 644 mph)
Cruising speed at optimum altitude	412 knots (763 km/h; 474 mph)
Stalling speed:	
flaps up	142 knots (264 km/h; 164 mph)
flaps down	98 knots (182 km/h; 113 mph)
Max rate of climb at S/L	2,323 m (7,620 ft)/min
Service ceiling	12,925 m (42,400 ft)
Min T-O run	1,185 m (3,890 ft)
T-O to 15 m (50 ft)	1,390 m (4,560 ft)
Landing from 15 m (50 ft)	774 m (2,540 ft)
Min landing run	521 m (1,710 ft)
Range with max military load	878 nm (1,627 km; 1,011 miles)
Ferry range:	
tanks retained	2,380 nm (4,410 km; 2,740 miles)
tanks jettisoned when empty	2,818 nm (5,222 km; 3,245 miles)

Grumman G-134 Mohawk

US Army designation: OV-1 (formerly AO-1)

The Mohawk is a high-performance two-seat observation aircraft which Grumman developed for the US Army. An initial batch of nine service test aircraft was ordered, the first YOV-1A flying for the first time on 14 April 1959. Eighteen initial production OV-1As followed, then OV-1Bs with APS-94 side-looking airborne radar in an underfuselage container and AKT-16 VHF data link. The OV-1B also featured increased wing span and area. Neither of these early models remains operational.

Current versions of the Mohawk, which are only operated by the US Army, are:

OV-1C. Similar to second series of OV-1As, but with AAS-24 infra-red surveillance/mapping sensor and internal camera. Avco Lycoming T53-L-3 engines. Wing span 12.80 m (42 ft 0 in). Max T-O weight 8,723 kg (19,230 lb). Many converted to OV-1D standard (along with OV-1Bs).

OV-1D. Final new production version, convertible from infra-red to SLAR surveillance capability, and vice versa, so combining duties of OV-1B and C. Four pre-production prototypes followed by production aircraft built up to December 1970. Approximately 90 OV-1Bs and Cs were converted to OV-1Ds, enabling the US Army to maintain its inventory of 110 OV-1Ds.

RV-1D. Some 36 early Mohawks were converted into this latest electronic intelligence/emitter locating version for the US Army.

The description which follows applies in particular to the OV-1D:

TYPE: Two-seat army observation aircraft.

WINGS: Cantilever mid-wing monoplane. Wing section NACA 2412. Dihedral 6° 30'. Incidence 1° 30'. Inboard and outboard ailerons. Servo-tabs and manually adjustable trim-tabs in outboard ailerons. Trailing-edge flaps.

US Army Grumman OV-1D Mohawk.

FUSELAGE: Semi-monocoque structure. Forward-opening hydraulically-operated air-brake on each side, aft of wing.

TAIL UNIT: Cantilever structure. Central and two end-plate fins and rudders. Manually-adjustable trim-tabs in elevators and central rudder.

LANDING GEAR: Retractable tricycle type, with a single wheel on each unit. High-pressure pneumatic system for emergency extension. Main wheels and tyres size 8.50 × 10. Single nosewheel (steerable) tyre size 6.50 × 8. Goodyear hydraulically-operated disc brakes. Provision for wheel/ski gear.

POWERPLANT: Two 1,400 shp Lycoming T53-L-701 turbo-prop engines, driving Hamilton Standard Type 53C51-27 three-blade constant-speed fully-feathering reversible-pitch metal propellers. Fuel in self-sealing fuselage tank above wing, with capacity of 1,045 litres (276 US gallons; 230 Imp gallons). Provision for one 567 litre (150 US gallon; 125 Imp gallon) Aero 1C jettisonable tank under each wing, outboard of engine.

ACCOMMODATION: Flight compartment seating two side-by-side in nose on Martin-Baker Mk J5 ejection seats. Dual controls, except when electronic surveillance equipment is fitted. Armouring includes 0.64 cm ($\frac{1}{4}$ in) aluminium alloy cockpit floor, bullet-resistant windshields and removable flak curtains on fore and aft cockpit bulkheads.

AVIONICS AND EQUIPMENT: Photo-surveillance system consists of two KA-60C 180-degree panoramic camera systems and one KA-76 serial frame camera. Infra-red AN/AAS-24 surveillance system. Alternative AN/APS-94F side-looking airborne radar (SLAR) system. ADR-6 radiac system. AN/AYA-10 data annotation system. Nav/com systems include ARN-82 VOR, ARC-102 HF-SSB, ARC-114 VHF-FM primary and auxiliary, ARN-52 TACAN, ARN-89 loop, APX-72 IFF, APN-171(V) radar altimeter, ARC-114 VHF-FM homing, ARC-115 and -116 VHF/UHF, ARN-58 glideslope and marker beacon, ARN-89 LF-ADF, AN/ASN-33 flight director, PT489/ASQ-104 map readout unit, AN/ASW-12 automatic flight control, C-6533/ARC intercom, ASH-19 aural reproducer and continuous in-flight performance recorder (CIPR). ECM pods and an LS-59A photo-flash unit can be carried on underwing stations.

DIMENSIONS, EXTERNAL:

Wing span	14.63 m (48 ft 0 in)	Cruising speed (both)	210 knots (389 km/h; 242 mph)
Length overall	12.50 m (41 ft 0 in)	Econ cruising speed	180 knots (334 km/h; 207 mph)
Height overall	3.86 m (12 ft 8 in)	Stalling speed (landing configuration), 10% normal rated power,	
Wheel track	2.79 m (9 ft 2 in)	60% fuel:	
Wheelbase	3.56 m² (11 ft 8$\frac{1}{4}$ in)	infra-red mission	72 knots (134 km/h; 83 mph)
Propeller diameter	3.05 m (10 ft 0 in)	SLAR mission	73 knots (135 km/h; 84 mph)
AREA:		Rate of climb at S/L, maximum rated power:	
Wings, gross	33.45 m² (360.0 sq ft)	infra-red mission	1,102 m (3,620 ft)/min
WEIGHTS:		SLAR mission	1,056 m (3,465 ft)/min
Weight empty	5,328 kg (11,747 lb)	Service ceiling, 80% fuel	7,620 m (25,000 ft)
Useful load: infra-red version	800 kg (1,765 lb)	T-O to 50 ft (15 m):	
SLAR version	879 kg (1,939 lb)	infra-red mission	349 m (1,145 ft)
T-O weight for extended mission:		SLAR mission	358 m (1,175 ft)
infra-red version	8,085 kg (17,826 lb)	Landing from 15 ft (15 m):	
SLAR version	8,164 kg (18,000 lb)	infra-red mission	320 m (1,050 ft)
PERFORMANCE:		SLAR mission	323 m (1,060 ft)
Max level speed:		Range with two 150 US gallon drop-tanks:	
infra-red version	265 knots (491 km/h; 305 mph)	infra-red mission	938 nm (1,738 km; 1,080 miles)
SLAR version	251 knots (465 km/h; 289 mph)	SLAR mission	892 m (1,653 km; 1,027 miles)

Grumman EA-6 Prowler

The EA-6B is an advanced electronics development of the EA-6A for which Grumman received a prototype design and development contract in the autumn of 1966. Except for a 1.37 m (4 ft 6 in) longer nose section and large fin pod, the external configuration of this version is the same as that of the basic A-6.

The longer nose section provides accommodation for a total crew of four, the two additional crewmen being necessary to operate the more advanced ECM equipment. This comprises high-powered electronic jammers and modern computer-directed receivers, which provided the US Navy with its first aircraft designed and built specifically for tactical electronic warfare. The prototype of the upgraded EA-6B version flew for the first time on 25 May 1968.

Deliveries of production EA-6Bs began in January 1971 and have continued with six in 1985, 8 in 1986, and with 9 planned for 1988.

An ICAP (increased capability) version of the EA-6B, with substantially increased jamming efficiency, is now standard, and the first 21 production EA-6Bs were modified by Grumman to ICAP configuration. Modifications include an expanded onboard tactical jamming system with eight frequency bands, reduced response time, and a new multi-format display. In addition, an automatic carrier landing system (ACLS) to permit carrier recovery in zero-zero weather, a new defensive electronic countermeasures system (DECM) and new communications-navigation-identification (CNI) equipment are installed. The prototype of a more advanced ICAP-2 version, with further improved jamming capability, made its first flight on 24 June 1980. Each of the five pods carried under the EA-6B's wings and fuselage originally generated signals within a single frequency band. An ICAP-2 exciter in each pod generates signals in any one of seven frequency bands, and each pod

Grumman EA-6B Prowler with wings folded aboard USS *Nimitz*. *(Erik Simonsen)*

can jam in two different bands simultaneously. ICAP-2 attained IOC in 1984, on new aircraft and by retrofit. To follow this, an ADVCAP (advanced capability) programme was initiated in 1983, when Litton Industries' Amecom Division received a contract to develop a new receiver/processor group for the EA-6B's tactical jamming system. Delivery of the first of six systems for flight testing was scheduled for 1987, with production envisaged to start in 1991.

Ten US Navy squadrons (VAQ-129, 130, 131, 132, 133, 134, 135, 136, 137 and 138) were equipped with the Prowler by mid-1977. The first detachment of US Marine Corps Prowler squadron VMAQ-2 began training on the EA-6B in September 1977 at NAS Whidbey Island, Washington, and the detachment deployed in late 1978. Two additional detachments have since completed training, and at least one is deployed at all times.

The description of the standard A-6E Intruder applies also to the EA-6B, except as follows:

TYPE: Four-seat carrier- or land-based advanced ECM aircraft.

WINGS: As for A-6E, but reinforced to cater for increased gross weight, fatigue life and a 5.5*g* load factor.

FUSELAGE: As for A-6E, but reinforcement of underfuselage structure in areas of arrester hook and landing gear attachments, and lengthened by 1.37 m (4 ft 6 in).

TAIL UNIT: As for A-6E, except for provision of a large fin-tip pod to house ECM equipment.

LANDING GEAR: As for A-6E, except for reinforcement of attachments. A-frame arrester hook, and upgrading of structure to cater for increased gross weight.

POWERPLANT: Two Pratt & Whitney J52-P-408 turbojet engines, each rated at 49.8 kN (11,200 lb st).

ACCOMMODATION: Crew of four under two separate upward

Grumman EA-6B Prowler ICAP-2 tactical jamming aircraft.

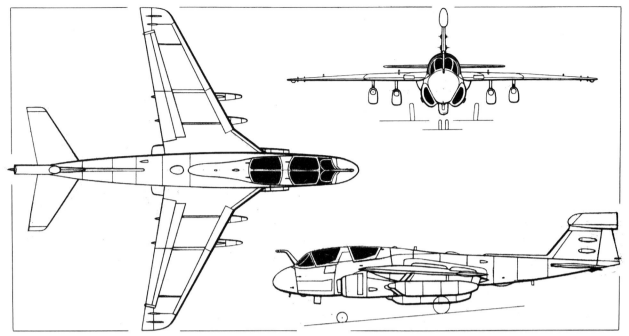

Grumman EA-6B Prowler ICAP-2. *(Pilot Press)*

opening canopies. Martin-Baker GRUEA 7 ejection seats for flight crew. The two additional crewmen are ECM Officers to operate the ALQ-99 equipment from the rear cockpit. Either ECMO can independently detect, assign, adjust and monitor the jammers. The ECMO in the starboard front seat is responsible for communications, navigation, defensive ECM and chaff dispensing.

AVIONICS: Eaton Corpn (AIL Division) AN/ALQ-99F tactical jamming system, in five integrally powered pods, with a total of ten jamming transmitters. Each pod covers one of seven frequency bands. Sensitive surveillance receivers in the fin-tip pod for long-range detection of radars; emitter information is fed to a central digital computer (AYK-14 in ICAP-2 aircraft) that processes the signals for display and recording. Detection, identification, direction-finding and jammer-set-on sequence can be performed automatically or with manual assistance from crew.

ARMAMENT: Originally unarmed, but currently being equipped to carry Texas Instruments AGM-88A HARM anti-radar missiles underwing.

DIMENSIONS, EXTERNAL: As for A-6E, except:
Width, wings folded	7.87 m (25 ft 10 in)
Length overall	18.24 m (59 ft 10 in)
Height overall	4.95 m (16 ft 3 in)
Wheelbase	5.23 m (17 ft 2 in)

WEIGHTS:
Weight empty	14,588 kg (32,162 lb)
T-O weight from carrier in standoff jamming configuration (5 ECM pods)	24,703 kg (54,461 lb)
T-O weight from field in ferry range configuration (max internal and external fuel)	27,492 kg (60,610 lb)
Max T-O weight, catapult or field	29,483 kg (65,000 lb)

PERFORMANCE (A: no stores, B: 5 ECM pods):
Never-exceed speed	710 knots (1,315 km/h; 817 mph)
Max level speed at S/L:	
A	566 knots (1,048 km/h; 651 mph)
B	530 knots (982 km/h; 610 mph)
Cruising speed at optimum altitude:	
A, B	418 knots (774 km/h; 481 mph)
Stalling speed, flaps up, max power:	
A	124 knots (230 km/h; 143 mph)
Stalling speed, flaps down, max power:	
A	84 knots (156 km/h; 97 mph)
Max rate of climb at S/L: A	3,932 m (12,900 ft)/min
B	3,057 m (10,030 ft)/min
Service ceiling: A	12,550 m (41,200 ft)
B	11,580 m (38,000 ft)
T-O run: B	814 m (2,670 ft)
T-O to 15 m (50 ft): A	869 m (2,850 ft)
B	1,065 m (3,495 ft)
Landing from 15 m (50 ft): A	823 m (2,700 ft)
Landing run: A	579 m (1,900 ft)
B	655 m (2,150 ft)
Range with max external load, 5% reserves plus 20 min at S/L:	
B	955 nm (1,769 km; 1,099 miles)
Ferry range with max external fuel:	
tanks retained	1,756 nm (3,254 km; 2,022 miles)
tanks jettisoned when empty	2,085 nm (3,861 km; 2,399 miles)

317

Grumman Tomcat

US Navy designation: F-14

Grumman announced on 15 January 1969 that it had been selected as winner of the design competition for a carrier-based fighter for the US Navy. Known as the VFX during the competitive phase of the programme, this aircraft was later designated F-14. First flight of the F-14A Tomcat prototype took place on 21 December 1970. It was lost in a non-fatal accident, and flight testing was resumed on 24 May 1971 with the second aircraft.

Under initial contracts, Grumman built for the US Navy 12 research and development aircraft. The planned programme was intended to provide 497 Navy Tomcats, including the 12 development aircraft. This total is now to be increased considerably, extending Tomcat production into the 1990s.

Carrier trials started in June 1972, and initial deployment with the fleet began in October 1972, the first two operational squadrons being VF-1 and VF-2. A total of 557 F-14As, including the 12 R&D aircraft, had been delivered to the US Navy by April 1987, when production of this version ended. By the end of 1987 the US Navy expected to have 28 Tomcat squadrons, including two reserve and four training squadrons, operating from 12 aircraft carriers and the Naval Air Stations at Miramar, California, Oceana, Virginia and Dallas, Texas. In addition, the Iranian Air Force took delivery of 80 F-14As in 1976-78. These aircraft retained the Phoenix weapon system, but had slightly different ECM equipment from US Navy Tomcats.

Since 1979 Northrop Corporation has been manufacturing television camera sets (TCSs) for installation on F-14s. The TCS is a closed-circuit TV system, offering both wide-angle (acquisition) and telescopic (identification) fields of view. Mounted beneath the nose of the F-14, the TCS automatically searches for, acquires and locks on to distant targets, displaying them on monitors for the pilot and flight

Grumman F-14A Tomcat of US Navy Squadron VF-21, embarked aboard USS *Constellation*. *(Katsumi Hinata)*

officer. By allowing early identification of targets, the system permits crews to make combat decisions earlier than was possible previously.

Between July and September 1981 a short flight test programme (29 flights by Grumman followed by five US Navy flights) was undertaken with an F-14 (the seventh development aircraft, originally the prototype F-14B) refitted with General Electric F-101 derivative fighter engines in place of then-standard Pratt & Whitney TF30-P-412As. F-14As delivered at the rate of 24 a year from FY 1983 to FY 1986 have improved TF30-P-414A engines. Only eight were scheduled for delivery in 1987, pending the beginning of deliveries of improved models of the Tomcat towards the end of that year.

In July 1984 Grumman was awarded a $984 million fixed-price contract for an F-14 update programme which provides for development of the **F-14A(Plus)** with F110-GE-400 engines, but otherwise unchanged, and for the **F-14D** with F110-GE-400, digital avionics and a new radar. Grumman is prime contractor for the engine and avionics upgrades, with General Electric and Hughes Aircraft as subcontractors. The F110-GE-400 selected for the F-14A(Plus) and F-14D has 82 per cent parts commonality with the F110-GE-100 engine for the USAF's F-15s and F-16s. A 1.27 m (4 ft 2 in) plug is inserted in the afterburner section to match the engine to F-14 inlet position and airframe contours, and only secondary structure requires modification to accept the new engine.

The F-14D upgrade modifies some 60 per cent of the F-14A's analog avionics, providing new weapons management, navigation, displays and control functions, with digital bus integration of the Litton ALR-67 threat warning and recognition system, Westinghouse/ITT ALQ-165 airborne self protection jammer (ASPJ), joint tactical information distribution system (JTIDS), infra-red search and track sensor (IRST) and television camera set (TCS), with emphasis on hardware and software commonality with the F/A-18 programme. The new radar, designated APG-71, is based on the AN/AWG-9 radar, with improved ECCM capability and incorporating monopulse angle tracking, digital scan control, target identification and raid assessment. The APG-71 features non-co-operative target identification and is able to counter sophisticated ECM by means of a low-sidelobe antenna and sidelobe blanking guard channel, frequency agility, and a new high-speed digital signal

Grumman F-14A Tomcat shipborne multi-mission fighter. *(Brian M. Service)*

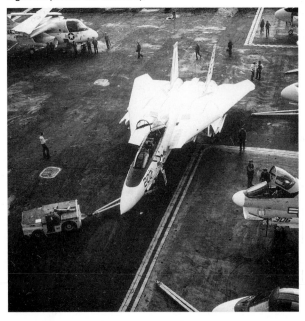

Development prototype for Grumman F-14A(Plus) and F-14D programmes.

processor based on elements of the USAF's multi-stage improvement programme (MSIP) of the F-15's APG-70 radar. Provision will also be made for integration of the AMRAAM missile. The F-14D is equipped with Martin-Baker Navy Aircrew Common Ejection Seat (NACES).

Grumman's full-scale development programme involves five aircraft, including the F-14B prototype which first flew with definitive F110-GE-400 engines on 29 September 1986 as part of the F-14A(Plus) programme. The remaining development aircraft are expected to fly at intervals from early 1988. Three will be used for avionics and radar development, in conjunction with a TA-3B Skywarrior

aircraft. One will be completed to full F-14D standard, and will join that programme after serving on the F-14A(Plus) development programme. The development schedule includes some 36 months of flight testing. Production of the F-14A(Plus) followed completion of the F-14A programme, with the first of 38 aircraft accepted by the US Navy in late 1987. In addition, 32 F-14As will be upgraded to F-15A(Plus) standard, with F110 engines. The first of 127 F-14Ds is scheduled to be delivered in March 1990, and 400 F-14A and F-14A(Plus) aircraft will be remanufactured to F-14D standard.

The F110-GE-400 powered F-14A(Plus) and F-14D are

Grumman F-14A Tomcat. *(Pilot Press)*

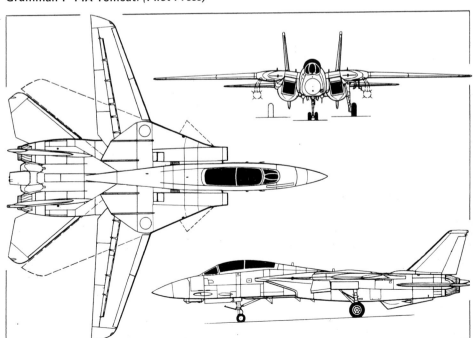

expected to show significant performance benefits resulting from the engine's 30 per cent increase in afterburning and non-afterburning thrust over the Pratt & Whitney TF30-P-414A engine. Specific excess energy is increased by 20 per cent, afterburning specific fuel consumption is reduced by 30 per cent, and deck launch intercept radius and combat air patrol time on station are expected to be increased by 60 and 35 per cent respectively, as a result of lower fuel burns and the F110 engined Tomcat's ability to be launched without use of afterburner.

The following description applies to the current operational F-14A:

TYPE: Two-seat carrier-based multi-role fighter.

WINGS: Variable-geometry mid-wing monoplane, with 20° of leading-edge sweep in the fully forward position and 68° when fully swept. Oversweep position of 75° for carrier stowage. Wing position is programmed automatically for optimum performance throughout the flight regime, but manual override is provided. A short movable wing outer panel, needing only a comparatively light pivot structure, results from the wide fuselage and fixed centre-section 'glove'. The inboard wing sections, adjacent to the fuselage, arc upward slightly to minimise cross-sectional area and wave drag. Small canard surfaces, known as glove vanes, swing out from the leading edge of the fixed portion of the wing, to a maximum of 15° in relation to the leading edge, as Mach number is increased. Spoilers on upper surfaces of wing. Stabilisation in pitch, provided by the canard surfaces, leaves the differential tailplane free to perform its primary control function. Trailing-edge flaps extend over almost entire span. Leading-edge slats.

FUSELAGE: Semi-monocoque structure. The aft section has a tapered aerofoil shape to minimise drag, with a fuel dump pipe projecting from the rear. Speed brakes located on the upper and lower surfaces, between the bases of the vertical tail fins.

TAIL UNIT: Twin vertical fins, mounted at the rear of each engine nacelle. Outward-canted ventral fin under each nacelle. The all-flying multi-spar horizontal surfaces have skins of boron epoxy composite material and honeycomb trailing edges.

LANDING GEAR: Retractable tricycle type. Twin-wheel nose unit and single-wheel main units. Original beryllium brakes were replaced by Goodyear lightweight carbon brakes from Spring 1981. Arrester hook under rear fuselage, housed in small ventral fairing. Nose-tow catapult attachment on nose unit.

ENGINE INTAKES: Straight two-dimensional external compression inlets. A double-hinged ramp extends down from the top of each intake, and these are programmed to provide the correct airflow to the engines automatically under all flight conditions. Each intake is canted slightly away from the fuselage, from which it is separated by some 0.25 m (10 in) to allow sufficient clearance for the turbulent fuselage boundary layer to pass between fuselage and intake without causing turbulence within the intake.

POWERPLANT: Early aircraft have two Pratt & Whitney TF30-P-412A turbofan engines of 93 kN (20,900 lb st) with afterburning, mounted in ducts which open to provide 180° access for ease of maintenance. Current production aircraft have TF30-P-414As of the same rating. Garrett ATS200-50 air turbine starter. Integral fuel tanks in outer wings, each with capacity of 1,117 litres (295 US gallons; 246 Imp gallons); between engines in rear fuselage, with capacity of 2,453 litres (648 US gallons; 539 Imp gallons); and forward of wing carry-through structure, capacity 2,616 litres (691 US gallons; 575 Imp gallons); plus two feeder tanks with combined capacity of 1,726 litres (456 US gallons; 380 Imp gallons). Total internal fuel capacity 9,029 litres (2,385 US gallons; 1,986 Imp gallons). An external auxiliary fuel tank can be carried beneath each intake trunk, each containing 1,011 litres (267 US gallons; 222 Imp gallons). Retractable flight refuelling probe on starboard side of fuselage near front cockpit.

ACCOMMODATION: Pilot and naval flight officer seated in tandem on Martin-Baker GRU7A rocket assisted zero/zero ejection seats, under a one-piece bubble canopy. Martin-Baker NACES seats on F-14D.

AVIONICS: Hughes AN/AWG-9 weapons control system, with ability to detect airborne targets at ranges of more than 65–170 nm (120–315 km; 75–195 miles) according to their size, and ability to track 24 enemy targets and attack six of them simultaneously at varied altitudes and distances. AN/AWG-15F fire control set; CP-1066/A central air data computer; CP-1050/A computer signal data converter; AN/ASW-27B digital data link; AN/APX-76(V) IFF interrogator; AN/APX-72 IFF transponder; AN/ASA-79 multiple display indicator group; Kaiser Aerospace AN/AVG-12 vertical and head-up display system. AN/ARC-51 and AN/ARC-159 UHF com; AN/ARR-69 UHF auxiliary receiver; KY-28 cryptographic system; LS-460/B intercom; AN/ASN-92(V) INS; A/A24G39 AHRS; AN/APN-154 beacon augmentor; AN/APN-194(V) radar altimeter; ARA-63A receiver-decoder; AN/ARN-84 micro Tacan; AN/ARA-50 UHF ADF; AN/APR-27/50 radar receiver; AN/APR-25/45 radar warning set. TV optical unit in undernose pod.

ARMAMENT AND OPERATIONAL EQUIPMENT: One General Electric M61A-1 Vulcan 20 mm gun mounted in the port side of forward fuselage, with 675 rounds of ammunition. Four Sparrow air-to-air missiles mounted partially submerged in the underfuselage, or four Phoenix missiles carried on special pallets which attach to the bottom of the fuselage. Two wing pylons, one under each fixed wing section, can carry four Sidewinder missiles or two additional Sparrow or Phoenix missiles with two Sidewinders. Various combinations of missiles and bombs to a max external weapon load of 6,577 kg (14,500 lb). ECM equipment includes Goodyear AN/ALE-29 and AN/ALE-39 chaff and flare dispensers, with integral jammers. Small undernose pod for Sanders AN/ALQ-100/126 deception jamming system, relocated under camera package of aircraft with Northrop TCS. During 1980–81 49 F-14s were allocated to carry TARPS (tactical air reconnaissance pod system), containing a KS-87B frame camera, KA-99 low-altitude panoramic camera, and AN/AAD-5 infra-red reconnaissance equipment, on underbelly attachment.

DIMENSIONS, EXTERNAL:		PERFORMANCE:	
Wing span: unswept	19.54 m (64 ft 1½ in)	Max speed at height	
swept	11.65 m (38 ft 2½ in)		Mach 2.34 (1,342 knots; 2,485 km/h; 1,544 mph)
overswept	10.15 m (33 ft 3½ in)	Max speed at low level	
Length overall	19.10 m (62 ft 8 in)		Mach 1.2 (792 knots, 1,468 km/h; 912 mph)
Height overall	4.88 m (16 ft 0 in)	Max cruising speed	
Wheel track	5.00 m (16 ft 5 in)		400–550 knots (741–1,019 km/h; 460–633 mph)
Wheelbase	7.02 m (23 ft 0½ in)	*Carrier approach speed	134 knots (248 km/h; 154 mph)
AREA:		*Stalling speed	115 knots (213 km/h; 132 mph)
Wings, gross	52.49 m² (565.0 sq ft)	Max rate of climb at S/L	over 9,140 m (30,000 ft)/min
WEIGHTS (P-414A engines):		Service ceiling	above 15,240 m (50,000 ft)
Weight empty	18,191 kg (40,104 lb)	Min T-O distance	427 m (1,400 ft)
T-O weight, clean	26,632 kg (58,715 lb)	Min landing distance	884 m (2,900 ft)
T-O weight with 4 Sparrow	27,086 kg (59,714 lb)	Max range with external fuel	
T-O weight with 6 Phoenix	32,098 kg (70,764 lb)		approx 1,735 nm (3,220 km; 2,000 miles)
Max T-O weight	33,724 kg (74,349 lb)	*carrier landing design gross weight	

Grumman (General Dynamics) Raven

US Air Force designation: EF-111A

The programme to convert General Dynamics F-111As into EF-111A electronic warfare aircraft, and to evaluate their ability to provide ECM jamming coverage for air attack forces, was initiated in 1972–73.

Three basic modes of deployment were foreseen for the EF-111A: standoff, penetration, and close air support. In the standoff role, jamming aircraft operate within their own airspace, at the FEBA (forward edge of the battle area). Out of range of the enemy's ground based weapons, orbiting EF-111As use their jamming systems to screen the routes of friendly strike aircraft. In the penetration role the EF-111As accompany strike aircraft to high-priority targets, their Mach 2 capability making them ideal escort aircraft for such a task. The close air support requirement calls for EF-111A escorts to neutralise anti-air radars while the strike force delivers its attack on enemy armour.

Primary electronic warfare equipment comprises the AN/ALQ-99E tactical jamming system, an improved version of the AN/ALQ-99 system carried by the US Navy's Grumman EA-6B Prowler. The ALQ-99E's jamming transmitters are mounted in the weapons bay, with their antennae covered by a narrow 4.9 m (16 ft) long canoe-shaped radome. The fin-tip pod, similar in shape to that of the EA-6B, houses the receiver and antennae.

Claimed to be the world's most powerful airborne ECM system, the ALQ-99E's frequency coverage, reliability, and effective use of available jamming power enable the EF-111A to penetrate the world's densest known electronic defences. Its electronic systems can be converted quickly to counter new threats as they develop, and, even if multiple hostile radars switch to a variety of frequencies, the EF-111A's broad range of jamming capabilities can handle them immediately. The electronic warfare officer (EWO) handles a tactical workload previously requiring (as in the EA-6B) several operators; for example, pre-flight programming of

EF-111A Raven electronic warfare aircraft.

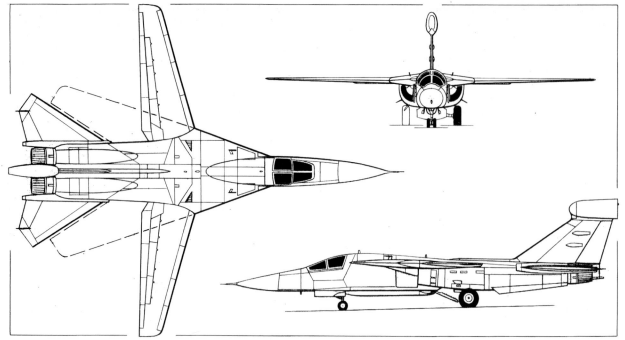

Grumman (General Dynamics) EF-111A Raven. *(Pilot Press)*

the computer with known radars frees the operator to concentrate on new and more urgent threat radars.

Design study contracts were awarded to General Dynamics and Grumman by the US Air Force in 1974, and in January 1975 it was announced that Grumman had been awarded an $85.9 million contract to convert two existing F-111As to EF-111A prototype configuration. A partially modified F-111A, fitted with the weapons bay radome only, was flown for the first time on 15 December 1975. The first flight of a fully aerodynamic prototype, with fin-tip pod and underbelly radome, was made from Grumman's Calverton, NY, facility on 10 March 1977; the complete system was flown for the first time on 17 May 1977, on the second prototype. USAF tests verified various mission operational concepts, flight formations, and the jammer's electromagnetic compatibility with other strike aircraft. (These latter tests dispelled an earlier concern that the friendly strike force, as well as enemy threats, might be jammed by the powerful signals emanating from the EF-111A.)

Including the two prototypes, which were subsequently brought up to full production standard, the US Air Force funded the conversion of 42 F-111As to EF-111A standard, to equip two squadrons. The first EF-111A was delivered to TAC for operational use in November 1981. The 390th Electronic Combat Squadron became operational on EF-111As in December 1983. In February 1984 the first EF-111A for USAFE arrived at RAF Upper Heyford, Oxfordshire, UK, assigned to the 42nd ECS of the 20th Tactical Fighter Wing.

Deliveries have been completed, but upgrading of the EF-111A's tactical jamming systems is being undertaken, to provide improved capability against EW radar, GCI and surface-to-air missile acquisition. When completed the update will have cost about $200 million.

In January 1987 the US Air Force awarded Grumman a contract for an EF-111A avionics modernisation programme (AMP). The upgrade will include improved cockpit control-display functions, enhanced terrain-following and navigation radars, installation of a ring-laser-gyro inertial navigation system and global positioning system (GPS), and the addition of two digital computers using two dual-redundant multiplex buses to provide digital interfacing. An FSD trials aircraft is scheduled to fly in January 1989, with delivery of production modernisation kits following a year later.

The description of the F-111A applies also to the EF-111A, except for the following additional or amended details:

TYPE: ECM tactical jamming aircraft.

WINGS: As detailed for F-111A. Wing section NACA 64A210.68 (modified) at pivot point, NACA 64A209.80, with modified leading edge, at tip. Dihedral, at 16° sweep, 1°. Incidence, at 16° sweep, 1° at root, −3° at tip.

TAIL UNIT: Fin reinforced to support 454 kg (1,000 lb) fin-tip antenna pod.

POWERPLANT: Two Pratt & Whitney TF30-P-3 turbofan engines, each rated at 82.3 kN (18,500 lb st) with afterburning. Fuel tanks in wings and fuselage, total capacity 18,919 litres (4,998 US gallons; 4,162 Imp gallons).

ENGINE INTAKES: External compression type with variable-diameter double-cone spike which expands from 8° 30′ to 26° for supersonic compression. The spike translates independently of the second cone position for more efficient air spillage at low supersonic speeds. Porous spike bleed is distributed over the spike shoulder for compression surface boundary layer control at high Mach numbers. An automatic air inlet control handles spike and cone movement as functions of engine duct and underwing glove Mach numbers.

ACCOMMODATION: Crew of two (pilot and electronic warfare officer) side-by-side in air-conditioned and pressurised cockpit. Zero-speed, zero-altitude (including underwater) emergency escape module.

AVIONICS AND EQUIPMENT: AN/ARC-112 HF com transceiver; Magnavox AN/ARC-164 UHF com transceiver; AN/AIC-25 intercom; AN/AJQ-20A INS; Collins AN/ARN-118 Tacan; Honeywell AN/APN-167 radar altimeter; Collins AN/ARA-50 UHF/DF; AN/ARN-58 ILS; IBM (Federal Systems Division) 4 Pi digital computer; Texas Instruments AN/APQ-110 terrain following radar; AN/APQ-160 attack radar; AN/APX-64 IFF/SIF; Eaton Corpn (AIL Division) AN/ALQ-99E tactical jamming system; Sanders AN/ALQ-137(V)4 ECM self-protection system (SPS); AN/ALR-62(V)4 terminal threat warning system (TTWS); AN/ALR-23 radar countermeasures receiver system (CMRS); AN/ALE-28 electronic countermeasures dispenser system (CMDS). All tactical jamming functions are managed by the EWO, who can, through computer management, handle a tactical electronic warfare workload which previously required several operators and more equipment. In addition, the automated system of the EF-111A has exceptional capability for locating, identifying, and assigning jammers to enemy emitters over a wide range of frequencies. The AN/ALQ-99E jamming system comprises ten transmitters (Raytheon high-band, AEL low-band), five Raytheon exciters, numerous receivers, computers, display systems, and one Raytheon RF calibrator per aircraft.

ARMAMENT: None.

DIMENSIONS, EXTERNAL:

Wing span: spread	19.20 m (63 ft 0 in)
fully swept	9.74 m (31 ft 11.4 in)
Length overall	23.16 m (76 ft 0 in)
Height overall	6.10 m (20 ft 0 in)
Wheel track	3.19 m (10 ft 0.4 in)
Wheelbase	7.44 m (24 ft 4.8 in)

AREA:

Wings, gross (16° sweep)	48.77 m² (525 sq ft)

WEIGHTS:

Weight empty	25,072 kg (55,275 lb)
Design T-O weight	33,000 kg (72,750 lb)
Combat T-O weight	31,751 kg (70,000 lb)
Max T-O weight	40,346 kg (88,948 lb)

PERFORMANCE (estimated for typical mission, at max T-O weight except where indicated. A: basic standoff; B: penetration; C: close air support):

Max level speed:	
A, B, C	1,227 knots (2,272 km/h; 1,412 mph)
Max combat speed at combat weight:	
A, B, C	1,196 knots (2,216 km/h; 1,377 mph)
Average speed, outbound:	
A, C	446 knots (826 km/h; 514 mph)
B	512 knots (949 km/h; 590 mph)
Average speed over combat area:	
A	321 knots (595 km/h; 370 mph)
B	507 knots (940 km/h; 584 mph)
C	462 knots (856 km/h; 532 mph)
Average speed, inbound:	
A, C	432 knots (800 km/h; 497 mph)
B	502 knots (930 km/h; 578 mph)
Stalling speed, power off:	
A, B, C	143 knots (264 km/h; 164 mph)
Rate of climb at S/L, intermediate power:	
A, B, C	1,006 m (3,300 ft)/min
Service ceiling with afterburning, at combat weight:	
A, B, C	13,715 m (45,000 ft)
T-O run: A, B, C	1,349 m (4,425 ft)
T-O to 15 m (50 ft): A, B, C	1,775 m (5,825 ft)
Landing from 15 m (50 ft) at weight of 26,968 kg (59,455 lb):	
A, B, C	945 m (3,100 ft)
Landing run at weight of 26,968 kg (59,455 lb)	
A, B, C	602 m (1,975 ft)
Combat radius, with reserves:	
A	200 nm (370 km; 230 miles)
B	807 nm (1,495 km; 929 miles)
C	623 nm (1,155 km; 717 miles)
Ferry range	2,000 nm (3,706 km; 2,303 miles)
Endurance without refuelling	more than 4 h

Grumman S-2 Tracker

The Tracker twin-engined carrier-based anti-submarine search and attack aircraft was developed for service with the US Navy, with whom it continued in S-2G upgraded form until superseded by the Lockheed Viking in 1976. However, several foreign forces still use the Tracker, as detailed under the model listings.

Grumman S-2E Tracker in service with the Brazilian Air Force. (Denis Hughes)

Grumman CP-121 Tracker of the Canadian Armed Forces.

The prototype Tracker, designated XS2F-1, made its first flight on 4 December 1952, and Grumman delivered more than 1,000 production S-2s before manufacture ended in 1968. Export deliveries were also made, but only Argentina, Brazil and Canada remain users among those that received newly built aircraft.

The following versions of the S-2 remain operational:

S-2A (formerly S2F-1). Two 1,525 hp Wright R-1820-82 engines. First production model. Total of 755 built. Currently used by Argentina, South Korea, Taiwan and Uruguay.

TS-2A. Training version of S-2A, operated by Turkey.

S-2E (formerly S2F-3S). Similar to S-2D (increased wing span and roomier crew accommodation), but with more advanced ASW electronic equipment and armament, comprising 60 echo-sounding charges in fuselage, one depth bomb or similar store in bomb bay, 32 sonobuoys in nacelles, four float lights, six underwing pylons for 5-in rockets, torpedoes, etc. Deliveries to US Navy (with nuclear depth bomb capability) began in October 1962. Total of 241 built. Currently used by Argentina, Brazil, South Korea, Peru, Turkey and Venezuela.

Grumman S-2 Tracker. *(Pilot Press)*

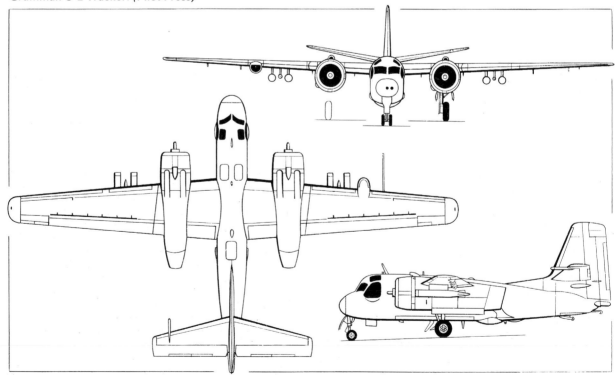

S-2F. Upgraded S-2B (the 'B' having begun as modified S-2A). Currently operated by Royal Thai Navy.

CP-121 (formerly CS2F). Canadian production version of S-2A built under licence for Royal Canadian Navy by de Havilland Aircraft of Canada Ltd. 100 built. Later fitted with improved operational equipment. Still in Canadian Armed Forces inventory.

TYPE: Twin-engined anti-submarine aircraft.

WINGS: Cantilever high-wing monoplane. Wings fold upward and inward hydraulically from outboard of the engine nacelles. Fixed leading-edge slots on outer wings. Small ailerons, supplemented by wide-span spoilers on upper surfaces. Long-span slotted flaps.

FUSELAGE: Semi-monocoque structure.

TAIL UNIT: Cantilever structure. Rudder split vertically into two sections: forward section actuated during take-off, landing and single-engined operation to increase rudder area.

LANDING GEAR: Retractable tricycle type. Twin wheels on nose unit only. Small aft wheel-bumper is extendable but not fully retractable.

POWERPLANT: Two 1,525 hp Wright R-1820-82 WA nine-cylinder air-cooled radial engines, driving three-blade constant-speed metal propellers.

ACCOMMODATION: Crew of four consisting of pilot, co-pilot (who serves as navigator, radio-operator and searchlight-operator), radar operator and MAD operator. Dual controls.

AVIONICS AND EQUIPMENT: Includes UHF direction finder, LF direction finder, TACAN, APN-122 Doppler radar, APN-117 low-altitude radar altimeter, UHF transmitter/receiver, HF transmitter/receiver, APX 6B and APA 89 IFF, ASA-13 ground position indicator, and ground track plotter on panel (giving aircraft position and ground track, including Doppler correction for drift and ground speed, target position from Julie computer, sonobuoy location, radar position, MAD mark on ground track and exhaust trail mark on ground track).

OPERATIONAL EQUIPMENT: S-2E has more advanced ASW electronic equipment than former S-2D, the equipment of which included AQA-3 Jezebel passive long-range acoustic search equipment, using sonobuoys; ECM instantaneous electronic countermeasures direction finder; Sniffer passive submarine-exhaust-trail detector; Julie active acoustic echo ranging by means of explosive charges, automatic target computer and automatic target plotting; retractable ASQ-10 MAD (magnetic anomaly detector) tail 'sting'; retractable 75 kW X-band 42 in × 20 in search radar under fuselage; 85 million candlepower remotely-controlled searchlight under starboard wing.

ARMAMENT: Two homing torpedoes or one depth bomb or four 385 lb depth charges in bomb bay. Six underwing attachments for torpedoes, 5 in rockets, Zuni rockets or 250 lb bombs. Housing for 32 sonobuoys and marine markers in rear of engine nacelles. Four float lights. Fuselage dispenser for 60 underwater sounding charges for echo ranging.

DIMENSIONS, EXTERNAL (S-2E):			
Wing span	22.13 m (72 ft 7 in)		
Width folded	8.33 m (27 ft 4 in)		
Length overall	13.26 m (43 ft 6 in)		
Height overall	5.06 m (16 ft 7 in)		
Wheel track	5.64 m (18 ft 6 in)		
AREAS:			
Wings, gross:			
S-2A, CP-121	45.1 m² (485.0 sq ft)		
S-2E	46.08 m² (496.0 sq ft)		
WEIGHTS (S-2E):			
Weight empty	8,505 kg (18,750 lb)		
Max payload	2,182 kg (4,810 lb)		

Max T-O weight	13,222 kg (29,150 lb)
PERFORMANCE (S-2E at max T-O weight):	
Max level speed at S/L	over 230 knots (426 km/h; 265 mph)
Patrol speed at 450 m (1,500 ft)	130 knots (241 km/h; 150 mph)
Stalling speed (landing configuration)	65 knots (119 km/h; 74 mph)
Service ceiling	6,400 m (21,000 ft)
T-O run	396 m (1,300 ft)
T-O to 50 ft (15 m)	572 m (1,875 ft)
Ferry range	1,128 nm (2,095 km, 1,300 miles)
Endurance with max fuel, 10% reserves	9 h

Kaman

KAMAN AEROSPACE CORPORATION
(a subsidiary of Kaman Corporation)

The original Kaman Aircraft Corporation was founded in 1945 by Mr Charles H. Kaman, who continues as President and Chairman of the Board of Kaman Corporation. Its initial programme was to develop and test a novel servo-flap control system for helicopter rotors, and the Kaman K-125 of 1947 was the first in a series of 'synchropter' designs with intermeshing contra-rotating rotors and the servo-flap control system. The later H-2 Seasprite naval helicopter utilises the servo-flap control system on a single main rotor.

Current research and development programmes at Kaman Aerospace are under the sponsorship of the US Army, US Air Force, US Navy and NASA, and include work in advanced design of helicopter rotor systems, blades and rotor control concepts, component fatigue life determination, and structural dynamic analysis and testing.

Kaman Aerospace is a major subcontractor in many aircraft and space programmes. This work includes design, tooling and fabrication of components in metal, metal honeycomb, bonded and composite construction, using techniques such as filament winding and braiding. Military and commercial aircraft programmes in which Kaman participates include the Grumman A-6 and F-14, Rockwell B-1B, Lockheed C-5B, Bell/Boeing V-22, Boeing 767, Sikorsky UH-60 helicopter and the NASA Space Shuttle Orbiter (for which the company provides baffle systems for the external fuel tank). Kaman also supplies acoustic engine ducts and spare parts for various aircraft types to the US military.

Kaman designed, and since mid-1977 has been producing,

all-composite rotor blades for Bell AH-1 HueyCobras in service with the US Army and several other countries. Improved performance, life and operational features have been demonstrated. Kaman is also a supplier of helicopter drone kits to the US Army for use in defence programmes.

Kaman Aerospace is part of Kaman Corporation's Diversified Technology Group. Kaman Sciences Corporation is engaged in high-technology applied research in space systems, C³I nuclear and non-nuclear effects, computer systems, engineering, and natural resources. Kaman Instrumentation Corporation specialises in high-precision instrumentation technology including neutron generators, displacement measuring systems, extreme environment transducers, and RF transmission lines. Kamatics Corporation designs and manufactures speciality products including high-performance self-lubricating bearings and specialised mechanical drive couplings. Electromagnetic Launch Research Corporation specialises in advanced electromagnetic energy and pulsed power research. AirKaman of Jacksonville, Florida, provides airline services, charters, flight training and manufacturing facilities. Locus Inc is an electronic research, development and engineering consulting firm engaged in electronic warfare studies and hardware, including radio frequency products and systems, digital systems and telecommunication products. Raymond Engineering Inc designs, develops, engineers and produces precision electromechanical systems and devices primarily for the military market.

Kaman Seasprite

US Navy designations: HH-2 and SH-2

The prototype Seasprite flew for the first time on 2 July 1959, and many versions were produced subsequently for the US Navy. Production of the SH-2F version was restarted in 1981.

From 1967, all of the original UH-2A/B Seasprites were converted progressively to UH-2C twin-engined configuration, with two 932 kW (1,250 shp) General Electric T58-GE-8B turboshaft engines in place of the former single T58. They have since undergone further modification, under the US Navy's Mk I LAMPS (Light Airborne Multi-Purpose System) programme, to provide helicopters for ASW (anti-submarine warfare), ASST (anti-ship surveillance and targeting), SAR (search and rescue), and utility operations. All but two of the US Navy's SH-2s have been upgraded to SH-2F standard, with stronger landing gear, T58-GE-8F engines and improved rotor system.

The following versions were in service in early 1987:

HH-2D. One aircraft, without LAMPS modifications, assigned to oceanography work.

NHH-2D. One aircraft assigned to special test programmes.

SH-2F. Deliveries of this developed Mk I LAMPS version began in May 1973, and the first unit became operational with squadron HSL-33, deployed to the Pacific, on 11 September 1973. Eighty-eight SH-2Fs were delivered, and 16 earlier SH-2Ds were uprated to SH-2F configuration, in a programme that was completed in 1982. Seventy-nine earlier production SH-2Fs remained in US Navy service in February 1987. Eighteen new production SH-2Fs were ordered in the FY 1982 defence budget, and 18 more in FY 1983, and six in FY 1984, and all had been delivered by February 1987. Six more were authorised in FY 1985 and six in FY 1986.

The US Navy plans an avionics improvement programme for the SH-2F, which includes a digital databus, onboard acoustic processor, multi-function raster display, Tacnav data transfer, 99-channel sonobuoys and a Global Positioning System. Other SH-2F enhancement programmes include the development of composite main rotor blades and the installation of new fuel-efficient T700-GE-401 engines.

Kaman SH-2F Seasprite Mk I LAMPS ASW helicopter.

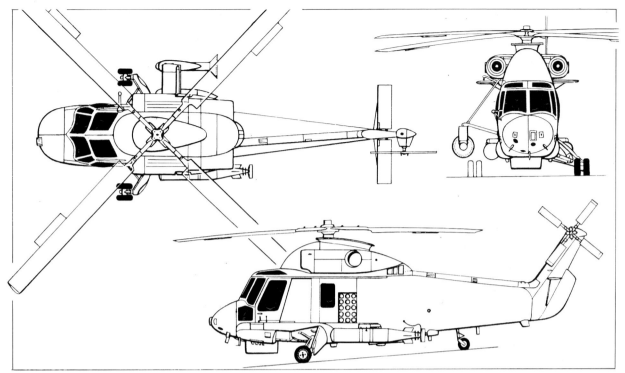

Kaman SH-2F Seasprite Mk I LAMPS. *(Pilot Press)*

Evaluation of a **YSH-2G** prototype fitted with these engines was completed in 1985. As a result, the six Seasprites ordered in FY 1987 will be to **SH-2G** standard, with the new engines and 1553B databus. In addition, in July 1987 the US Navy awarded Kaman Aerospace a contract for the modification of two SH-2Fs to the same configuration. Eventually, the Navy would like to upgrade its entire inventory of some 100 Seasprites to SH-2G standard.

A maximum gross weight of 6,123 kg (13,500 lb) has been authorised, effective on deliveries made from October 1985. This is 318 kg (700 lb) more than the previous standard SH-2F, and can be utilised as increased payload, or in the form of additional fuel in larger auxiliary tanks to provide extended range and endurance. US Navy tests have proved the SH-2 suitable for dipping sonar operations, air-to-surface missile firing, and equipping with various guns and rockets. Export models of the Seasprite are offered with dipping sonar, acoustic processor, mission computer, additional fuel, and search radar compatible with missiles like Sea Skua and Penguin.

Operational deployment of HSL LAMPS Mk I squadrons began on 7 December 1971. By January 1987 more than 520,000 flight hours had been accumulated by LAMPS Mk I detachments deployed on successive long cruises, primarily in the Mediterranean and Pacific, on the following ship classes: FFG-7, DD-963, DDG-993, CG-47, FFG-1, FF-1052, FF-1040, CG-26, CGN-35, CGN-38 and BB-61. The 80+ ships of the DD-963, DDG-993, CG-47 and FFG-7 classes are designed to operate with two LAMPS helicopters, and the 72 ships of the other classes with one LAMPS helicopter per ship. Formation of Naval Air Reserve HSL squadrons began in 1984, and at least 24 SH-2Fs will be transferred to Reserve units as new production aircraft are delivered. Active and Reserve LAMPS Mk I SH-2s are scheduled to remain operational, alongside LAMPS Mk III

(SH-60B), into the next century.

The following details apply to the uprated production version the SH-2F, effective from October 1985 deliveries:

TYPE: Naval anti-submarine warfare and anti-ship surveillance and targeting helicopter, with secondary capability for search and rescue, observation and utility missions.

ROTOR SYSTEM: Four-blade main and tail rotors. Kaman '101' main rotor utilises titanium hub and retention assemblies. Blades of aluminium and glassfibre construction, with servo-flap controls; composite blades effective from October 1987 deliveries. Blades folded manually. Main rotor rpm 298.

FUSELAGE AND TAIL UNIT: Semi-monocoque structure, with flotation hull housing main fuel tanks. Nose split on centreline, to fold rearward on each side to reduce stowage space required. Fixed horizontal stabiliser on tail-rotor pylon.

LANDING GEAR: Tailwheel type, with twin mainwheels and non-retractable tailwheel. Fully castoring tailwheel unit for taxying but locked fore and aft for T-O and landing. Mainwheels have 8-ply tubeless tyres size 17.5 × 6.25-11, tailwheel 10-ply tubeless tyre size 5.00-5.

POWERPLANT: Two 1,007 kW (1,350 shp) General Electric T58-GE-8F turboshaft engines, one on each side of rotor pylon structure. Basic fuel capacity of 1,802 litres (476 US gallons; 396 Imp gallons), including up to two external auxiliary tanks with a combined capacity of 757 litres (200 US gallons; 166.5 Imp gallons). Ship-to-air helicopter in-flight refuelling (HIFR).

ACCOMMODATION: Crew of three, consisting of pilot, co-pilot/tactical co-ordinator, and sensor operator. One passenger or litter patient, with LAMPS equipment installed; four passengers or two litters with sonobuoy launcher removed. Provision for transportation of internal or external cargo.

AVIONICS, ARMAMENT AND OPERATIONAL EQUIPMENT:
LAMPS Mk I mission equipment includes Canadian Marconi LN-66HP surveillance radar; General Instruments AN/ALR-66 electronic support measures (ESM); Teledyne Systems AN/ASN-123C tactical navigation system; dual Collins AN/ARC-159(V)1 UHF com radios; Texas Instruments AN/ASQ-81(V)2 magnetic anomaly detector; AN/ARR-75 sonobuoy receiver; AN/ASA-26B sonobuoy recorder and AN/AKT-22(V)6 sonobuoy data link; 15 DIFAR and DICASS sonobuoys; eight Mk 25 marine smoke markers; one or two Mk 46 torpedoes; cargo hook for external loads, capacity 1,814 kg (4,000 lb); and externally mounted rescue hoist, capacity 272 kg (600 lb).

DIMENSIONS, EXTERNAL:

Main rotor diameter	13.41 m (44 ft 0 in)
Length of fuselage, excl tail rotor	12.35 m (40 ft 6 in)
Height overall (rotors turning)	4.72 m (15 ft 6 in)
Width overall, incl MAD	3.74 m (12 ft 3 in)
Wheel track (outer wheels)	3.30 m (10 ft 10 in)
Wheelbase	5.11 m (16 ft 9 in)

WEIGHTS:

Weight empty	3,193 kg (7,040 lb)
Max T-O weight	6,123 kg (13,500 lb)

PERFORMANCE (at max T-O weight, except where indicated):

Max level speed at S/L	130 knots (241 km/h; 150 mph)
Normal cruising speed	120 knots (222 km/h; 138 mph)
Max rate of climb at S/L	744 m (2,440 ft)/min
Service ceiling	6,860 m (22,500 ft)
Hovering ceiling IGE	5,670 m (18,600 ft)
Hovering ceiling OGE	4,695 m (15,400 ft)
Personnel transfer radius, 10% reserves	180 nm (333 km; 207 miles)
Ferry range with max fuel, 10% reserves	375 nm (695 km; 431 miles)

Time on station (10% reserves):

ASW at 35 nm (65 km; 40 miles) from base, 1 torpedo	1 h 50 min
ASW as above, 2 torpedoes	1 h 10 min
ASW at 70 nm (130 km; 80 miles) from base, 1 torpedo	1 h 5 min
ASST at 70 nm (130 km; 80 miles) from base	2 h 20 min
SAR at 70 nm (130 km; 80 miles) from base	2 h 5 min

Lockheed

LOCKHEED CORPORATION

Built by the brothers Allan and Malcolm Lockheed, the first Lockheed aircraft, a tractor seaplane, first flew in 1913. Three years later the brothers established a company at Santa Barbara, California, to manufacture a twin-engined flying-boat, two seaplanes for the Navy and a small sport biplane that was a forerunner of the true streamlined aeroplane. Lockheed Aircraft Co, formed in 1926, moved to Burbank, California, in 1928 and was reorganised as Lockheed Aircraft Corporation in 1932.

On 30 November 1943 the Vega Aircraft Corporation, which had been formed in 1937 as an affiliate and in 1941 became a wholly-owned subsidiary of the Lockheed Aircraft Corporation, was absorbed and the name Vega abandoned. In September 1977 the former Lockheed Aircraft Corporation was renamed Lockheed Corporation, to reflect the company's diversified activities.

On 4 April 1983 Lockheed introduced a new corporate structure under which its operating companies and subsidiaries were grouped into four sectors according to their products and marketing. Lockheed's aircraft production was handled primarily by Lockheed-California Company, Lockheed-Georgia Company and Lockheed Aircraft Service Company. Its missile and space activities were centred at Lockheed Missiles and Space Company. By the end of 1982 Lockheed had built a total of approximately 37,000 aircraft. No later total has been released.

Early in 1984 Lockheed formed a new company, Lockheed Advanced Aeronautics Company (LAAC), based at the Kelly Johnson Research and Development Center, Rye Canyon, California. LAAC was made responsible for the design, manufacture and testing of all new Lockheed prototypes, and for aeronautical research and testing on behalf of all Lockheed companies in the Aeronautical Systems Group.

Lockheed Air Terminal Inc (LAT), a wholly owned subsidiary, operates and maintains the Hollywood-Burbank Airport, which belongs to the cities of Burbank, Glendale and Pasadena, and provides fuelling and related services at 25 other locations in 11 states, the territory of Guam, and Panama. Lockheed Aircraft Service Co designs and manufactures products for the aerospace industry, and carries out aviation maintenance, modification and management services in the USA and other nations. Much of its work outside the USA is done under subcontract for Lockheed Aircraft International AG, a separate subsidiary.

In April 1987 Lockheed Corporation's total facilities covered more than 2,322,575 m² (25,000,000 sq ft), and it had approximately 97,000 employees in 25 US states and on worldwide company assignments. On 3 September 1987, it announced that its aircraft design, development, manufacturing and modification programmes, undertaken previously by Lockheed-California Company, Lockheed-Georgia Company and Lockheed Aircraft Service Company, were being integrated under three divisions of a new Lockheed Aeronautical Systems Company (LASC), with headquarters in Burbank, California.

LASC Burbank Division

This division of LASC is responsible for production of the P-3 Orion land based anti-submarine warfare aircraft, TR-1 high-altitude tactical surveillance and reconnaissance aircraft, and components for Lockheed-Georgia's C-5B. It is engaged in several important research and development programmes, of which few details are yet available. One of them, covered in part by a $4.7 million USAF contract received in spring 1986, is a four-year four-phase programme involving integrated vehicle and propulsion system concepts applicable to future supersonic cruise aircraft.

Lockheed F-104G Starfighter of the Hellenic Air Force.

Lockheed F-104 Starfighter

Development of the F-104 began in 1951 as part of the USAF's so-called 'Century Series' of fighters. Two XF-104 prototypes were built (Lockheed Model 83s), each powered by a 46.7 kN (10,500 lb st) Wright J65-W-6 turbojet with afterburning, the first flying on 7 February 1954, only eleven months after the contract had been awarded.

An evaluation series of 17 F-104As was produced before full production, the single-seat F-104A using a 65.83 kN (14,800 lb st) with afterburning General Electric J79-GE-3B turbojet. Examples of this version were delivered to the USAF's Air Defense Command from January 1958. Twenty-five were subsequently re-engined with 79.62 kN (17,900 lb st) with afterburning J79-GE-19 turbojets and, upon withdrawal from USAF service, were handed over to Nationalist China. The F-104B was a two-seat training variant of the 'A'.

Today the F-104 is being superseded in service with most remaining users, the latest to give up the type being Japan (F-104Js). Apart from the Italian-built F-104S, which will continue for some time to come (see Italy), the only remaining single-seat version is the multi-role F-104G, which is accompanied by the TF-104G two-seat trainer. Generally, the details for the F-104S apply also to the older F-104G (which was the first version with an upward-ejecting ejector seat). Remaining operators of 'Gs' in early 1988 were West Germany, Greece, Italy, Taiwan (including the reconnaissance RF-104G) and Turkey, but most of these aircraft are scheduled for replacement in the near future.

Lockheed RF-19 and XST

In the so-called 'Skunk Works' at Burbank, this division has built, under a DARPA-funded contract from the USAF's Flight Dynamics Laboratory, a number of examples of a single-seat fighter/reconnaissance aircraft of which primary features are low radar, infra-red and optical signatures.

A proof-of-concept/demonstrator aircraft, known as **XST** (Experimental Stealth Technology), is believed to have made its first flight in 1977. The XST was reportedly a very small aircraft, powered by two 11.12–12.46 kN (2,500–2,800 lb st) General Electric CJ610 turbojet engines. Between five and

seven XSTs are believed to have been built, and two at least are thought to have crashed.

An operational derivative made its first flight during 1982, and was designed to offer minimal radar, infra-red, acoustic and visual signatures. General configuration is of blended wing/fuselage design, with anhedral foreplanes on blended fuselage chines. Two canted 'fins', on each side of the engine exhaust outlets, assist IR shielding. A special paint finish also reduces both IR and radar signatures. There are no electromagnetic emissions from the aircraft during its mission.

The aircraft is said to be powered by two General Electric F404-GE-400 turbofans, each rated at 48.0 kN (10,800 lb st) without afterburner. Its size is believed to be similar to that of the F/A-18 Hornet, with folding wings to permit air transportation by C-5 Galaxy. It is said to make little or no exhaust noise, even at close range. US Air Force designation is believed to be RF-19, and the official acronym for its assignment has been reported as CSIRS (covert survivable

This conjectural drawing of the Lockheed RF-19, by Hineo Maki, is reproduced by courtesy of *AiReview*, Tokyo.

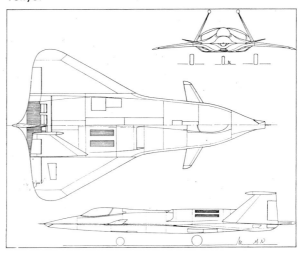

in-weather reconnaissance-strike). In early 1986 reports were received that the 'RF-19' was in series production and that up to 40 aircraft were operational, examples of which had been deployed outside the United States to bases which included one in the United Kingdom. The operating unit for the aircraft is believed to be the 4450th Tactical Test Group, based at Nellis AFB, Nevada. On 11 July 1986 a USAF pilot attached to this unit was killed in the crash of an unidentified aircraft near Bakersfield, California. The crash site was declared a national security area while wreckage was recovered.

The following data are estimated and highly provisional:

DIMENSIONS, EXTERNAL:

Wing span	9.65 m (31 ft 8 in)
Width, wings folded	5.0 m (16 ft 5 in)
Length overall	18.0 m (59 ft 0 in)
Height overall	4.0 m (13 ft 1½ in)

WEIGHTS:

Weight empty	10,000 kg (22,050 lb)
Max T-O weight	15,000 kg (33,070 lb)

PERFORMANCE:

Max cruising speed at S/L	560 knots (1,038 km/h; 645 mph)
Combat radius	300–400 nm (556–741 km; 345–460 miles)

Lockheed YF-22A (ATF)

LASC Burbank is contracted to build two YF-22A prototypes, in partnership with General Dynamics and Boeing, in connection with the US Air Force's Advanced Tactical Fighter (ATF) programme. See US Air Force Systems Command entry.

Lockheed SR-71 Blackbird

The existence of the Lockheed A-12 (then given as A-11) was announced by President Johnson on 29 February 1964. At a news conference he stated that this aircraft, developed in conditions of strict secrecy, had already been tested in sustained flight at speeds of more than 2,000 mph and at heights in excess of 70,000 ft at Edwards AFB, California.

Design of the A-12 was started in about 1959, almost certainly to supersede the Lockheed U-2 on long-range high-altitude reconnaissance missions. Like the U-2, it was designed by a team led by C. L. Johnson, Lockheed's Vice-President for Advanced Development Projects, in a restricted building known as the 'Skunk Works' at Burbank. About seven A-12s are believed to have been produced by October 1964, with 13 more covered by initial contracts. A further contract for six was placed in the Spring of 1966 to keep the assembly line open in case of any future need for such an aircraft. The first A-12 had been flown on 26 April 1962, with Mr Lou Schalk at the controls. Initially, the A-12 was powered by J75 engines, had a wing span of 17.37 m (57 ft), length of 31.09 m (102 ft) and take-off weight of about 54,430 kg (120,000 lb). The A-12 was last flown in May 1968.

President Johnson announced that the then-current flight tests were aimed at determining the A-12's capabilities as a long-range interceptor, and the service designation YF-12A was subsequently allocated to it. Five months later, on 24 July 1964, the President revealed that Lockheed were developing a second Mach 3 military aircraft, designated SR-71, as a 'long-range advanced strategic reconnaissance plane

Lockheed SR-71A Blackbird strategic reconnaissance aircraft.

for military use, capable of world-wide reconnaissance for military operations', and equipped with multiple sensors. He added that it used the same type of engines as the YF-12A. The YF-12A, which could attain a speed of Mach 3.6 at 28,950 m (95,000 ft), remained experimental, but the SR-71 went on to join the USAF. Versions are:

SR-71A. Unarmed strategic reconnaissance aircraft. Fuselage chines extend forward to nose. No ventral tail fins. Equipment carried internally ranges from simple battlefield surveillance systems to multiple-sensor high-performance systems for interdiction reconnaissance and strategic systems capable of specialised surveillance of up to 100,000 sq miles of territory in one hour. Uses synthetic-aperture radar (SAR-1). Improvements are scheduled as part of SAC's modernisation programme. Crew of two consists of pilot and reconnaissance systems officer. Development began in February 1963. First flight of an SR-71 was made on 22 December 1964, and deliveries of operational aircraft to the 9th Strategic Reconnaissance Wing at Beale AFB, California, began in January 1966. Can be used for national, theatre and strategic missions.

SR-71B. Tandem two-seat training version of SR-71A, with elevated second cockpit aft of normal cockpit. Fixed ventral tail fins reintroduced. First SR-71B delivered to Strategic Air Command's 4200th Strategic Reconnaissance Wing at Beale AFB, California, in early January 1966.

To make possible a cruising speed of Mach 3, extensive use is made of titanium and its alloys. The exterior paint finish is blue, and contains many millions of microscopic iron balls to conduct electricity. This, and the V-angled internal structure, ensure that only a weak radar signal is returned.

Each main unit of the tricycle landing gear has three wheels, while the nose unit has twin wheels. The powerplant comprises two Pratt & Whitney JT11D-20B (J58) turbojet engines, each with a thrust of 151.24 kN (34,000 lb) with

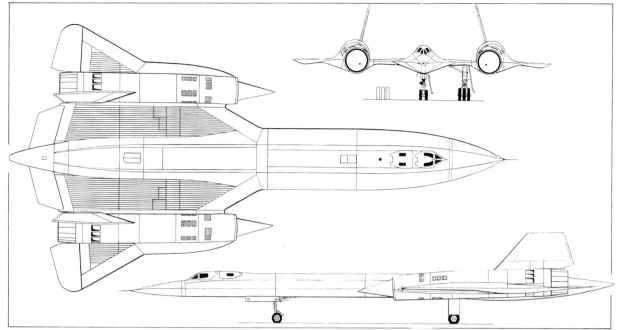

Lockheed SR-71A Blackbird. *(Pilot Press)*

afterburning. A large movable centre-body shock-cone is fitted at the front of each nacelle. At the rear, aft of the four-ring afterburner flameholder, is a ring of suck-in doors for cooling and area reduction at low speeds, and a variable-area final nozzle. Fuel capacity is 46,182 litres (12,200 US gallons; 10,159 Imp gallons).

On 1 May 1965 USAF pilots set up three world records and six international class records in two YF-12A aircraft, from Edwards AFB, California. Col Robert L. Stephens and Lt Col Daniel Andre achieved 1,797.72 knots (3,331.507 km/h; 2,070.102 mph) over a 15/25 km course at unlimited altitude, and a sustained height of 24,462.596 m (80,257.91 ft) in horizontal flight. Major Walter F. Daniel and Major Noel T. Warner averaged 1,426.85 knots (2,644.220 km/h;

1,643.042 mph) over a 500 km closed circuit. Major Daniel and Capt James P. Cooney averaged 1,466.66 knots (2,718.006 km/h; 1,688.891 mph) over a 1,000 km closed circuit, with a 2,000 kg payload, an absolute world record, and qualifying also for records without payload and with a 1,000 kg payload. The records were subsequently bettered by Soviet aircraft, but during 27–28 July 1976 the SR-71A established three still unbeaten Class C records: height in sustained horizontal flight of 25,929.031 m (85,069 ft); speed in a straight line over a 15/25 km course of 1,905.81 knots (3,529.56 km/h; 2,193.167 mph) and speed in a closed circuit over a 1,000 km course of 1,818.154 knots (3,367.221 km/h; 2,092.294 mph).

DIMENSIONS, EXTERNAL:

Wing span	16.95 m (55 ft 7 in)
Length overall	32.74 m (107 ft 5 in)
Height overall	5.64 m (18 ft 6 in)

WEIGHTS (estimated):

Weight empty	27,215 kg (60,000 lb)
Max T-O weight	77,110 kg (170,000 lb)

PERFORMANCE:

Max level speed at 24,000 m (78,740 ft)	more than Mach 3
Operational ceiling	more than 24,385 m (80,000 ft)
Range at Mach 3	2,822 nm (5,230 km; 3,250 miles)
Max endurance at Mach 3 (estimated), at 24,000 m (78,740 ft)	1 h 30 min

Lockheed U-2, ER-2 and TR-1

Development of the original U-2 began in the spring of 1954 as an unsolicited proposal to meet a joint CIA/US Air Force requirement for a high-altitude strategic-reconnaissance and special-purpose research aircraft. It took place in the Lockheed 'Skunk Works' at Burbank, California, where, after acceptance of the design in December 1954, two prototypes were hand-built in great secrecy by a small team of engineers. The aircraft's true purpose was cloaked under the US Air Force U-for-Utility designation U-2, and the first flight, by Lockheed test pilot Tony LeVier, took place on or about 1 August 1955 at Watertown Strip in the Nevada desert.

The configuration of the U-2 is basically that of a powered sailplane, which explains its unusual 'bicycle' landing gear, combined with underwing balancer units which provide stability during take-off and are then jettisoned. Range can, when necessary, be extended by shutting off the engine and gliding. Because of its configuration the U-2 (and later TR-1 models) requires unusually precise handling during take-off and landing—particularly the latter, since there is an extremely small margin between approach speed and stalling speed. After touchdown, the aircraft comes to rest on one of the down-turned wingtips, which serve as skids.

The original U-2A was a 7,710 kg (17,000 lb) aircraft with a wing span of 24.38 m (80 ft 0 in), powered by a single modified Pratt & Whitney J57 turbojet engine. It carried photographic equipment and was extremely successful. Added equipment led eventually to a reduction of about 1,525 m (5,000 ft) in service ceiling. To restore performance, the U-2C was produced, with a Pratt & Whitney J75 turbojet, and added elint and comint equipment that raised the T-O weight to 10,885 kg (24,000 lb). It was necessary only to modify the air intakes and nozzle to handle the increased airflow, but the aerodynamics and thrust were mismatched. At cruising speed above 21,335 m (70,000 ft), the U-2C had an envelope of only 4 knots (7.4 km/h; 4.6 mph) between Mach buffet and stall buffet. However, it overflew the Soviet Union continuously from 1956 until May Day 1960, followed sometimes by as many as 35 Soviet fighters, 6,100 m (20,000 ft) below.

The U-2A and U-2C were built under an initial FY 1956 contract calling for 48 single-seat and five two-seat U-2s. About 30 were U-2As. To match the thrust of the J75, designer Clarence (Kelly) Johnson developed a new wing for the U-2 in late 1965. Research showed that none of the then-new wing sections could improve on the L/D of the original U-2 section in an aircraft of this type, so the U-2A/C wing was simply scaled up to give a 40 per cent increase in area. The resulting U-2R was first given slipper fuel tanks and then large wing pods for increased range, increasing T-O weight to 18,144 kg (40,000 lb). It went into production until 1968, replacing some of the two dozen or more aircraft lost over hostile territory or in accidents. The production line was again reopened in 1980 to manufacture a new, tactical reconnaissance version, known as the TR-1.

All known versions of the U-2 (some now inactive), ER-2 and TR-1 are given below. U-2 models are similar in size except for the U-2R, which is now the main version (perhaps seven U-2Rs and CTs in active strategic force).

U-2A. Single-seat initial production version, powered by a 49.8 kN (11,200 lb st) Pratt & Whitney J57-P-37A turbojet engine with special wide-chord compressor blades for flight at very high altitudes. Approximately 30 built, of which most later converted to U-2B, others to WU-2A and U-2D. Deliveries to 1st, 2nd and 3rd Weather Reconnaissance Squadrons (Provisional) began in January 1956, and to 4028th and 4080th Strategic Reconnaissance Squadrons in early 1957.

WU-2A. Designation of small number of U-2As converted for atmospheric research. Bulged fairing on underside of fuselage, below air intakes. Used for weather reconnaissance flights over Europe, Turkey, Japan, Australia, the USA and Argentina. Took part in HI-CAT and HASP programmes, and in radioactivity sampling on behalf of SAC.

U-2B. Single-seat improved version of U-2A with strengthened airframe, more powerful J75 engine, and fully 'wet' wing. Total of 48 U-2A/Bs ordered (USAF serial numbers 56-6675 to 56-6722); from 1959 the last 18 (approx) of these, and most existing U-2As, were completed or re-engined to U-2B standard. Two supplied to Chinese Nationalist Air Force in July 1960, and at least four others later.

U-2C. Single-seat electronic intelligence (elint) version, converted from U-2B in early/middle 1960s and having similar performance. Bulged air intakes, and long dorsal spine fairing containing various additional avionics and other equipment. Two (NASA 708 and 709) delivered to NASA in April 1971 and used, *inter alia*, for Earth resources

monitoring on behalf of Ames Research Center.

WU-2C. Original designation of U-2R (which see).

U-2CT. Two-seat dual-control conversion trainer, with elevated rear cockpit for instructor. Dorsal spine fairing and bulged intakes, as U-2C. Converted from U-2C and U-2D. On training flights underwing balancer wheels retained to facilitate landings.

U-2D. Tandem two-seat development of U-2B for training and special duties, first displayed publicly at Wright-Patterson AFB in mid-1961. Five production aircraft (serials 56-6951 to 56-6955) built as U-2D; others converted from earlier models. Twin fairings above fuselage, one between cockpits and one above second cockpit, for antennae for infra-red, radioactivity or other sensors; these fairings could vary in shape between individual aircraft.

U-2EPX. Proposed ocean surveillance version for US Navy (EPX = electronics patrol experimental). Two aircraft, converted to carry AN/APS-116 radar similar to that in Lockheed S-3A Viking, test-flown by Lockheed in 1973 to evaluate use of U-2 as an airborne relay aircraft for surveillance data. Not adopted by USN.

U-2R. Single-seat strategic reconnaissance aircraft. Manufacture of original batch of 12 completed 1968. Originally designated WU-2C. Bulged intakes, as on U-2C, but longer nose and fuselage, without dorsal spine fairing: increased wing span and internal fuel capacity: rear fuselage slightly bulged on top, just forward of fin; mainwheels further aft, tailwheels further forward, than on earlier models. Non-US bases have included Mildenhall, England.

TR-1A. Single-seat tactical reconnaissance version, described by the Department of Defense as being 'equipped with a variety of electronic sensors to provide continuously available, day or night, high-altitude all-weather standoff surveillance of the battle area in direct support of the US and Allied ground and air forces during peace, crises, and war situations'. Tooling for the earlier U-2 had been kept in store at the USAF-owned Plant 42 at Palmdale, California, and the FY 1979 defence budget included $10.2 million to reopen the production line in FY 1980. The TR-1A has the same basic airframe as the U-2R, with a J75-P-13B engine, but with the significant addition of an advanced synthetic-aperture radar system (ASARS) in the form of a UPD-X side-looking airborne radar (SLAR) and modern electronic countermeasures (ECM). The TR-1A is primarily for use in Europe, where its SLAR provides the capability to 'see' approximately 30 nm (55 km; 35 miles) into hostile territory without the need to overfly an actual or potential battle area.

Close-up view of the Lockheed TR-1A tactical reconnaissance aircraft.

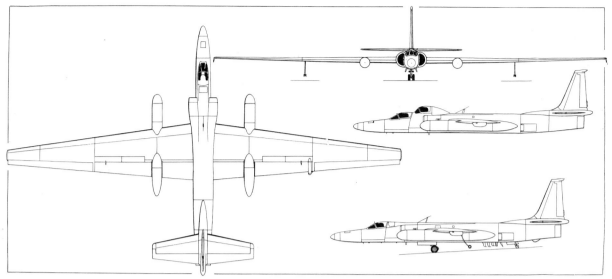

Lockheed TR-1A. Upper side view: TR-1B. *(Pilot Press)*

The first TR-1A flew for the first time on 1 August 1981. Deliveries began in September 1981, initially to Beale AFB, California.

TR-1B. Two-seat training version of TR-1A. Second cockpit in tandem, above and behind standard cockpit. First TR-1B delivered to Beale AFB in March 1983; second delivered in May 1983.

ER-2. Basically similar to TR-1A but modified for use by NASA as an Earth resources research aircraft. Delivered to Ames Research Center in June 1981.

Construction of the ER-2 and the first two TR-1As was funded by $42.4 million provided in the FY 1980 budget, the contract for the aircraft being received by Lockheed on 16 November 1979. A further 16 aircraft were ordered under the FY 1981–84 budgets, three more in FY 1985 and four in FY 1986, leaving three to be funded in FY 1987 to complete the planned inventory of 26 TR-1As for the USAF, plus the two TR-1Bs.

A TR-1A variant reported in 1984 has a satellite data link antenna mounted above its fuselage.

In early 1985 Lockheed began flight testing composites-structure speed brakes and elevators on a USAF TR-1A, and was reported to be considering testing a composites tailplane and fin on the aircraft. The company has also tested fibre-optic cables in place of wiring bundles on the TR-1A.

Fourteen TR-1s are stationed at RAF Alconbury, Cambridgeshire, England with the USAF's 95th Reconnaissance Squadron, 17th Tactical Reconnaissance Wing. A detachment of this aircraft has been housed at RAF Wethersfield. Although operating in Europe, they remain under the jurisdiction of Strategic Air Command, and not USAFE. The first of these TR-1s was flown to Alconbury during February 1983.

The following description applies to the TR-1A except where indicated:

TYPE: High-altitude reconnaissance and research aircraft.

Lockheed TR-1B two-seat training version of the TR-1A, with second cockpit above and behind the standard cockpit.

WINGS: Cantilever mid-wing monoplane, with special Lockheed wing section, and wingtip fittings which serve as skids during landing. Trailing-edge flaps (four segments on each wing, two inboard and two outboard of each underwing pod) occupy approx 70 per cent of each wing. Small tubular fuel-vent fairing between each outermost flap segment and aileron, projecting slightly aft of the trailing edge. Two small plate-type roll/lift spoilers on each wing, forward of outboard flap segments. Trim tab in each aileron. All primary flight controls manually operated, with high-density internal mass balance. Manually extended retractable stall strip in leading edge of each wing to assist pilot in settling aircraft on runway.

FUSELAGE: Semi-monocoque structure of circular cross-section. Fineness ratio approx 10:1. Forward opening door-type airbrake on each side of fuselage aft of wings, used mainly as a landing aid. Payload carrying nose sections and mission bay hatches interchangeable.

TAIL UNIT: Cantilever structure. Variable tailplane incidence, achieved by pivoting entire tail assembly around point at base of fin leading edge. Balanced rudder and elevators. Trim tab in each elevator.

LANDING GEAR: Retractable bicycle type, with twin mainwheels and twin 8 in diameter steerable tailwheels in tandem, each unit retracting forward into fuselage. Balancer units under outer wings, each with twin small wheels, are jettisoned on take-off. Brakes on mainwheels. Braking parachute in container under rudder. Provision for an arrester hook (TR-1 has foldable outerwing panels and can be operated from aircraft carriers without any change in aircraft structure or operating weights).

POWERPLANT: One 75.6 kN (17,000 lb st) Pratt & Whitney J75-P-13B turbojet engine. All fuel in inboard and outboard main tanks, filling each wing except for tip, each with overwing gravity refuelling point. Normal internal fuel capacity approx 4,448 litres (1,175 US gallons; 978 Imp gallons).

ACCOMMODATION: Pilot only, on ejection seat. Side-hinged transparent canopy, protected internally against ultra-violet radiation. Accommodation is air-conditioned and pressurised. Rearview periscope on most aircraft (positions vary). Food warmer, with spaceflight-type tubes of food. Second (instructor's) cockpit above and behind standard cockpit in TR-1B.

AVIONICS AND EQUIPMENT: Typical standard avionics
· include HF, UHF and VHF com, INS, Tacan, ILS, autopilot, ADF, air data computer, compass, and (for night flying) astro-compass. Equipment includes one vertical and two lateral cameras for training flights, or side-looking airborne radar and T-35 tracking camera for operational missions. Main avionics and equipment compartments are in detachable modular nose section, in a 'Q' bay aft of the cockpit (replaced by second cockpit in TR-1B), and in two large pods mounted underwing at approx one-third span. Each pod is approx 8.23 m (27 ft) long; has a volume of about 2.55 m³ (90 cu ft), and weighs about 544 kg (1,200 lb) complete with sensors and/or equipment. There is a smaller 'E' bay between the 'Q' bay and mainwheel bay; additional small areas in the bottom of the rear fuselage and in the tailcone can also be used to house mission equipment.

DIMENSIONS, EXTERNAL:
Wing span	31.39 m (103 ft 0 in)
Length overall	19.20 m (63 ft 0 in)
Height overall	4.88 m (16 ft 0 in)

AREA:
Wings, gross	approx 92.9 m² (1,000 sq ft)

WEIGHTS:
Weight empty, excl powerplant and equipment pods	under 4,535 kg (10,000 lb)
Max T-O weight	18,144 kg (40,000 lb)

PERFORMANCE:
Max cruising speed at normal operational height of 21,650 m (70,000 ft)	more than 373 knots (692 km/h; 430 mph)
Operational ceiling	27,430 m (90,000 ft)
Max range	more than 2,605 nm (4,830 km; 3,000 miles)
Max endurance	12 h
g limit	+2.5

Lockheed Model 185/285 Orion

US Navy designation: P-3
CAF designation: CP-140 Aurora

In 1958 Lockheed won a US Navy competition for an 'off-the-shelf' ASW aircraft with a developed version of its Electra four-turboprop commercial transport. An aerodynamic prototype flew for the first time on 19 August 1958. A second aircraft, designated YP-3A (formerly YP3V-1), with full avionics, flew on 25 November 1959.

One hundred and fifty-seven examples of the P-3A initial production version were built, plus four WP-3A weather reconnaissance aircraft. The 'A' was followed by the P-3B (144 built) and EP-3B.

P-3B. Follow-on production version to P-3A, with 3,661 kW (4,910 ehp) Allison T56-A-14 turboprop engines, which do not need water-alcohol injection. US Navy contracts covered 124 P-3Bs. In service also with air forces of Brazil, New Zealand, Norway and Portugal. Some USN P-3Bs became **EP-3Bs**. RNZAF P-3Bs were upgraded by Boeing under the 'Rigel I' programme, and a new upgrade is planned under the 'Rigel II' programme, mainly to improve the acoustic and electronic surveillance equipment. In late 1985 the Portuguese Air Force ordered six P-3Bs. These aircraft, formerly operated by the Royal Australian Air Force, will receive major systems updates to improve their ASW effectiveness. Following completion of a prototype by Lockheed in 1988, the remaining aircraft will be modified by Oficinas Gerais de Material Aeronáutico (OGMA) in Portugal (see P-3P).

P-3C. Advanced version with the A-NEW system of sensors and control equipment, built around a Univac digital computer that integrates all ASW information and permits retrieval, display and transmission of tactical data in order to eliminate routine log keeping functions. This increases crew effectiveness by allowing them sufficient time to consider all tactical data and devise the best action to resolve problems. First flight of this version was made on 18 September 1968, and the P-3C entered service in 1969. A total of 279 of this version had been delivered to the US Navy by 1 April 1986. Nine aircraft were funded in FY 1986, after which production was expected to switch to the new P-3G.

Aircraft delivered from January 1975 were to **P-3C Update** standard, with new avionics and electronics

Lockheed P-3C Orion of No 10 Squadron, RAAF *(Australian Department of Defence)*

software developed to enhance their effectiveness. Equipment includes a magnetic drum that gives a sevenfold increase in computer memory capacity, a new versatile computer language, Omega navigation system, improved acoustic processing sensitivity, a tactical display for two of the sensor stations, and an improved magnetic tape transport. A prototype with this equipment was handed over to the US Navy on 29 April 1974.

The US Navy and Lockheed began in 1976 a further P-3C avionics improvement programme known as **Update II**. This added an infra-red detection system (IRDS) and a sonobuoy reference system (SRS). The Harpoon missile and control system are included in Update II, which was incorporated into production aircraft from August 1977. The first Update II P-3C was delivered to the Naval Air Development Center in the same month. Ten Update II P-3Cs were delivered to the Royal Australian Air Force in 1978–79 for service with No. 10 Squadron. The RAAF ordered ten more in mid-1982, the last of which was delivered in May 1986. The Royal Netherlands Navy ordered 13 Update II P-3Cs, the first of which was delivered in November 1981. Japan has ordered 69 of a planned 100, of which four were assembled and the remainder are being licence-built in Japan by Kawasaki, following delivery of three US built aircraft during 1981. Thirty-two had been delivered by Kawasaki by 31 March 1987.

Update III, of which development began in February 1978, involves mainly ASW avionics, including a new IBM Proteus acoustic processor to analyse signals picked up from the sea, a new sonobuoy receiver which replaces DIFAR (directional acoustic frequency analysis and recording), an improved APU, and environmental controls to cater for increased heat from the avionics and to improve crew comfort further. A prototype Update III P-3C was delivered

The prototype P-3C Orion Update III photographed during test and evaluation by the US Navy.

to the US Navy for test and evaluation in August 1983. Production deliveries began in May 1984. The first delivery of P-3C Update IIIs to a US Navy reserve patrol squadron is scheduled for FY 1988. Two were ordered by the Royal Norwegian Air Force for delivery in 1989.

In addition to new production Update III aircraft, Lockheed has developed a retrofit kit, which was installed on a P-3C of VP-31 in early 1987. Installation of 18 more kits was scheduled to begin in June 1987, with the possibility of retrofitting a total of 113 P-3Cs eventually.

Update IV will have improved processing capabilities and a new family of acoustic sensors designed to counter the 'quieting' trend of the Soviet submarine force. Aerodynamic trials of a P-3C equipped with an Eaton AIL Division AN/ALR-77 tactical electronic support measures (ESM) system were expected to be followed by technical and operational evaluation at the Naval Air Test Center, Patuxent River, Maryland. The AN/ALR-77 system, which will form part of Update IV, comprises four wingtip quadrants providing 360° coverage with 36 interferometer antennae, each sub-band being covered by a triplet of antennae.

Two of the eight international records for turboprop aircraft set up in a P-3C by Cdr Donald H. Lilienthal, in early 1971, had not been beaten by 1987. They were a speed of 435.27 knots (806.10 km/h; 500.89 mph) over a 15/25 km course; and a time-to-height record, to 12,000 m in 19 min 42.24 s.

EP-3C. Elint version of P-3C being developed by Kawasaki for JMSDF. First example funded in 1987. Eight more to be funded at rate of one or two a year for operation by mid-1990s.

EP-3E. Ten P-3As and two EP-3Bs were converted to EP-3E configuration to replace Lockheed EC-121s in service with VQ-1 and VQ-2 squadrons. Identified by large canoe-shaped radars on upper and lower surfaces of fuselage and ventral radome forward of wing. EP-3E electronics suites are believed to comprise GTE-Sylvania AN/ALR-60 communications, interception and analysis system; Raytheon AN/ALQ-76 noise jamming pod; Loral AN/ALQ-78 automatic ESM system; Magnavox AN/ALQ-108 IFF

jammer; Sanders AN/ALR-132 infra-red jammer; ARGO Systems AN/ALR-52 instantaneous frequency measuring equipment; Texas Instruments AN/APS-115 frequency-agile search radar; Hughes AN/AAR-37 infra-red detector; Loral AN/ASA-66 tactical display; Cardion AN/ASA-69 scan converter; and Sperry Univac AN/ASQ-114 computer.

P-3F. Six aircraft, similar to the US Navy's P-3Cs, for the Iranian Air Force. Used initially for long-range surface surveillance and subsequently also for ASW missions. Delivery completed in January 1975.

P-3G. Proposed new variant, powered by a version of the Allison 501-M80C turboshaft engine adopted for the Bell/Boeing V-22A Osprey tilt-rotor aircraft. The US Navy is seeking competitive bids for 125 P-3Gs, to be acquired from 1990–94. In mid-1986 Boeing, Lockheed, McDonnell Douglas and Rockwell were reported to be discussing competitive procurement plans, while Lockheed and the US Navy were discussing ownership of the P-3 design and data.

P-3P. Designation of six ex-RAAF P-3Bs refurbished by Lockheed and OGMA for Esquadron 601 of the Portuguese Air Force.

CP-140 Aurora. Version for Canadian Armed Forces (18 built). First flown 22 March 1979. Each of these aircraft combines the P-3 Orion airframe, powerplant and basic aircraft systems with the avionics systems and data processing capability of the US Navy's carrier-based Lockheed S-3A Viking.

P-3 (Sentinel). Airborne early warning and control (AEW&C) variant. Prototype (N91LC), converted from ex-Royal Australian Air Force P-3B, made first flight on 14 June 1984, fitted with a 7.32 m (24 ft) diameter Randtron APA-171 rotodome above rear fuselage, but without radar. For military AEW&C operations the Sentinel would be equipped with General Electric AN/APS-138 radar (as on Grumman E-2C Hawkeye); a C³ system to receive, process and transmit tactical information through HF, UHF, VHF and Satcom channels; AR-187 satellite communications system and Collins EFIS-86B five-tube colour CRT electronic flight instrument system. Testing of an installed APS-138 is scheduled to begin in the Summer or Autumn of 1988.

US Navy Lockheed EP-3E version of the Orion. *(Air Photo Supply)*

Aerodynamic prototype of the P-3 Sentinel airborne early-warning and control version of the Orion.

In May 1987 the US Customs Service became launch customer for the P-3 Sentinel, with an order for one aircraft and options on three more. The first Sentinel for US Customs will be based on the company demonstrator airframe equipped with General Electric AN/APS-125 radar, which is expected to be installed in the aircraft in June 1988, for delivery in November of that year. The aircraft will be used for anti-drugs smuggling operations in the Caribbean and Gulf of Mexico.

Possible military customers for the P-3 Sentinel include Australia, which has a requirement for four AEW aircraft, Canada, Japan and the US Navy. The General Electric AN/APS-145 radar will be available for the aircraft from late 1989.

By 1 April 1986 Lockheed had delivered 601 P-3s of all versions, and held firm orders totalling 624 at that date.

In June 1987 Lockheed and MBB of West Germany signed a teaming agreement to propose the P-3 for the Federal

Lockheed P-3C Orion. *(Pilot Press)*

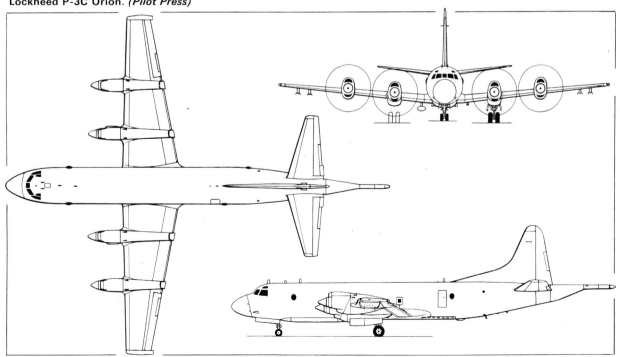

Republic of Germany's planned maritime patrol aircraft (MPA) programme, for which there is a requirement for up to 18 aircraft.

In addition, a number of Argentine **Electra** transports have been modified for maritime reconnaissance and elint duties.

The following details refer mainly to the P-3C.

TYPE: Four-turboprop ASW aircraft.

WINGS: Cantilever low-wing monoplane. Wing section NACA 0014 (modified) at root, NACA 0012 (modified) at tip. Dihedral 6°. Incidence 3° at root, 0° 30′ at tip. Lockheed-Fowler trailing-edge flaps. Hydraulically boosted ailerons. Anti-icing by engine bleed air ducted into leading edges.

FUSELAGE: Conventional semi-monocoque fail-safe structure.

TAIL UNIT: Cantilever structure with dihedral tailplane and dorsal fin. Fixed-incidence tailplane. Hydraulically boosted rudder and elevators. Leading edges of fin and tailplane have electric anti-icing system.

LANDING GEAR: Retractable tricycle type, with twin wheels on each unit. Mainwheels have size 40-14 type VII 26-ply tubeless tyres. Nosewheels have size 28-7.7 type VII tubeless tyres. Hydraulic brakes. No anti-skid units.

POWERPLANT: Four 3,661 kW (4,910 ehp) Allison T56-A-14 turboprop engines, each driving a Hamilton Standard 54H60 four-blade constant-speed propeller. Fuel in one tank in fuselage and four wing integral tanks, with total usable capacity of 34,826 litres (9,200 US gallons; 7,660 Imp gallons).

ACCOMMODATION: Normal ten-man crew. Flightdeck has wide-vision windows, and circular windows for observers are provided fore and aft in the main cabin, each bulged to give 180° view. Main cabin is fitted out as a five-man tactical compartment containing advanced electronic, magnetic and sonic detection equipment, an all-electric galley and large crew rest area.

AVIONICS AND EQUIPMENT: The ASQ-114 general-purpose digital computer is the heart of the P-3C system. Together with the AYA-8 data processing equipment and computer controlled display systems, it permits rapid analysis and utilisation of electronic, magnetic and sonic data. Nav/com system comprises two LTN-72 inertial navigation systems; AN/APN-227 Doppler; ARN-81 Loran A and C; AN/ARN-118 Tacan; two VIR-31A VOR/LOC/GS/MB receivers; ARN-83 LF-ADF; ARA-50 UHF direction finder; AJN-15 flight director indicator for tactical directions; HSI for long-range flight directions; glideslope indicator; on-top position indicator; two ARC-161 HF transceivers; two ARC-143 UHF transceivers; ARC-101 VHF receiver/transmitter; AGC-6 teletype and high-speed printer; HF and UHF secure communication units; ACQ-5 data link communication set and AIC-22 interphone set; APX-72 IFF transponder and APX-76 SIF interrogator. Electronic computer controlled display equipment includes ASA-70 tactical display; ASA-66 pilot's display; ASA-70 radar display and two auxiliary readout (computer stored data) displays. ASW equipment includes two ARR-72 sonar receivers; two AQA-7 DIFAR (directional acoustic frequency analysis and recording) sonobuoy indicator sets; hyperbolic fix unit; acoustic-source signal generator; time code generator and AQH-4(V) sonar tape recorder; ASQ-81 magnetic anomaly detector; ASA-64 submarine anomaly detector;

ASA-65 magnetic compensator; ALQ-78 electronic countermeasures set; APS-115 radar set (360° coverage); ASA-69 radar scan converter; KA-74 forward computer assisted camera; KB-18A automatic strike assessment camera with horizon-to-horizon coverage; RO-308 bathythermograph recorder. Additional equipment includes APN-194 radar altimeter; two APQ-107 radar altimeter warning systems; A/A24G-9 true airspeed computer and ASW-31 automatic flight control system. P-3Cs delivered from 1975 have the avionics/electronics package updated by addition of an extra 393K memory drum and fourth logic unit, Omega navigation, new magnetic tape transport, and an ASA-66 tactical display for the sonar operators. To accommodate the new systems a new operational software computer programme was written in CMS-2 language. GEC Avionics AQS-901 acoustic signal processing and display system in RAAF P-3Cs. AN/ALR-77 passive radar detection system (ESM), to be housed in wingtip pods, is under development by Eaton Corpn (AIL Division), and will also provide targeting data for the aircraft's Harpoon missiles. Wing span increased by some 0.81 m (2 ft 8 in) to accommodate ESM antennae and receivers. Update IV FSED contract awarded to Boeing Aerospace in Spring 1987, for completion in 1992. Subcontractors include Magnavox (acoustic system), Resdel (sonobuoy receiver), General Instrument (ESM), Honeywell (data recorders) and M/A Com (satellite communications).

ARMAMENT: Bomb bay, 2.03 m wide, 0.88 m deep and 3.91 m long (80 in × 34.5 in × 154 in), forward of wing, can accommodate a 2,000 lb Mk 25/39/55/56 mine, three 1,000 lb Mk 36/52 mines, three Mk 57 depth bombs, eight Mk 54 depth bombs, eight Mk 43/44/46 torpedoes or a combination of two Mk 101 nuclear depth bombs and four Mk 43/44/46 torpedoes. Ten underwing pylons for stores: two under centre-section each side can carry torpedoes or 2,000 lb mines; three under outer wing each side can carry respectively (inboard to outboard) a torpedo or 2,000 lb mine (or searchlight on starboard wing), a torpedo or 1,000 lb mine or rockets singly or in pods, a torpedo or 500 lb mine or rockets singly or in pods. Torpedoes can be carried underwing only for ferrying; mines can be carried and released. Search stores, such as sonobuoys and sound signals, are launched from inside cabin area in the P-3B. In the P-3C sonobuoys are loaded and launched externally and internally. Max total weapon load includes six 2,000 lb mines under wings and a 3,290 kg (7,252 lb) internal load made up of two Mk 101 depth bombs, four Mk 44 torpedoes, pyrotechnic pistol and 12 signals, 87 sonobuoys, 100 Mk 50 underwater sound signals (P-3B), 18 Mk 3A marine markers (P-3B), 42 Mk 7 marine markers, two B.T. buoys, and two Mk 5 parachute flares. Sonobuoys are ejected from P-3C aircraft with explosive cartridge actuating devices (CAD), eliminating the need for a pneumatic system. Australian P-3Cs use BARRA sonobuoys.

DIMENSIONS, EXTERNAL:

Wing span	30.37 m (99 ft 8 in)
Length overall	35.61 m (116 ft 10 in)
Height overall	10.27 m (33 ft 8½ in)
Wheel track (c/l shock absorbers)	9.50 m (31 ft 2 in)
Wheelbase	9.07 m (29 ft 9 in)
Propeller diameter	4.11 m (13 ft 6 in)

AREA:
Wings, gross 120.77 m² (1,300 sq ft)
WEIGHTS (P-3B/C):
Weight empty 27,890 kg (61,491 lb)
Max expendable load 9,071 kg (20,000 lb)
Max normal T-O weight 61,235 kg (135,000 lb)
Max permissible weight 64,410 kg (142,000 lb)
PERFORMANCE (P-3B/C, at max T-O weight, except where indicated otherwise):
Max level speed at 4,575 m (15,000 ft) at AUW of 47,625 kg
(105,000 lb) 411 knots (761 km/h; 473 mph)
Econ cruising speed at 7,620 m (25,000 ft) at AUW of 49,895 kg
(110,000 lb) 328 knots (608 km/h; 378 mph)
Patrol speed at 457 m (1,500 ft) at AUW of 49,895 kg (110,000
lb) 206 knots (381 km/h; 237 mph)
Stalling speed: flaps up 133 knots (248 km/h; 154 mph)
flaps down 112 knots (208 km/h; 129 mph)
Max rate of climb at 457 m (1,500 ft)
594 m (1,950 ft)/min
Service ceiling 8,625 m (28,300 ft)
T-O run 1,290 m (4,240 ft)
T-O to 15 m (50 ft) 1,673 m (5,490 ft)
Landing from 15 m (50 ft) at design landing weight
845 m (2,770 ft)
Mission radius (3 h on station at 457 m; 1,500 ft)
1,346 nm (2,494 km; 1,550 miles)
Max mission radius (no time on station) at 61,235 kg
(135,000 lb) 2,070 nm (3,835 km; 2,383 miles)

Lockheed Viking

US Navy designation: S-3
On 4 August 1969 Lockheed announced the receipt of a $461 million contract from the US Navy to develop a new anti-submarine aircraft under the designation S-3A. Development was carried out by Lockheed in partnership with Vought Systems Division of LTV and Univac Federal Systems Division of Sperry Rand. Univac was responsible for the digital computer, the heart of the weapon system, which provides high-speed processing of data essential for the S-3A's ASW role.

The selection of Lockheed-California as contractor for this aircraft followed more than a year of intensive competition between North American Rockwell,

Lockheed S-3A Viking anti-submarine aircraft of VS-22 aboard USS *John F. Kennedy*. *(Mike Jerram)*

McDonnell Douglas, Grumman, Convair Division of General Dynamics, and Lockheed-California in conjunction with LTV.

The Lockheed team was responsible for development, test and demonstration of the aircraft and its weapon systems. The first prototype was rolled out on schedule on 8 November 1971 at Burbank, California, and the first flight was made on 21 January 1972. An increased ceiling of $494 million on the contract, funded over a five-year period, provided for production of eight research and development aircraft in two lots.

On 4 May 1972 the US Navy announced an order for the first production lot of 13 S-3As, and orders for 35 and 45 more were received in April and October 1973 respectively. Other orders followed.

The Viking was introduced into the Fleet officially on 20 February 1974, during ceremonies held at North Island NAS, near San Diego, California. Initial deliveries were made to Squadron VS-41, the S-3A training squadron based at North Island NAS.

First operational deployment of the Viking, with Squadron VS-21, was made in July 1975, on board the USS *John F. Kennedy*. Viking squadrons are deployed aboard Atlantic and Pacific fleet carriers on a rotational schedule, with each deployment lasting about six months. The aircraft operate in Atlantic, Pacific and Mediterranean waters.

Shipboard maintenance is simplified by the provision of computerised fault-finding equipment, built-in test equipment (BITE), and versatile avionic shop test (VAST) compatibility. Complete deck-level servicing accessibility contributes to the attainment of a quick turn-around time.

Production of 187 **S-3As** for the US Navy ended in mid-1978. All tooling was then placed in storage at Burbank pending a US Navy decision on further orders, and in early 1980 demonstrator versions of the **US-3A** (COD) and **KS-3A** (tanker) were evaluated by the Navy. In 1982 three of the earlier production S-3As were modified to US-3A configuration. The sole KS-3A was also converted to US-3A configuration in late 1983.

As an alternative to the KS-3A dedicated tanker configuration, tests of an S-3A with a 'buddy' refuelling pack under its port wing were conducted in 1984. This technique transfers fuel from the tanker's standard internal tanks, and an external tank under the starboard wing, without affecting its multi-mission capability.

Lockheed announced on 18 August 1981 the receipt of a full-scale engineering development contract, from the US Naval Air Systems Command, for an improved avionics system for S-3A Vikings currently in service with the US Navy. With initial funding of $14.5 million, it follows a contract awarded by the Navy in 1980, under which Lockheed-California developed the specifications for an S-3A weapons system improvement programme (WSIP).

Aircraft modified under the WSIP are redesignated **S-3B**. Improvements include increased acoustic processing capacity, expanded electronic-support-measure capability, better radar processing, a new sonobuoy telemetry receiver system, and provisions for the Harpoon missile. It is anticipated that a total of 160 S-3As could be retrofitted under the programme. Two FSED (full-scale engineering development) S-3As were modified initially, the first of which was redelivered to Palmdale and began flight testing on 13 September 1984. A second aircraft joined the programme in February 1985, and the flight test schedule was completed in

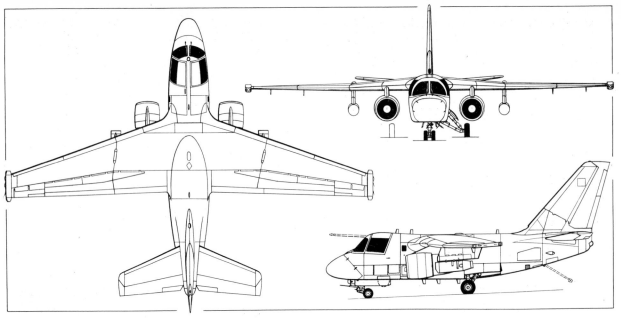

Lockheed S-3A Viking. *(Pilot Press)*

August 1985, with redelivery to the US Navy in October. Following a three-month technical evaluation by the Naval Air Test Center at Patuxent River NAS, Maryland, the two S-3Bs underwent a six-month operational evaluation in 1986.

Two prototype kits to convert S-3As to S-3B production standard have been ordered, and on 28 April 1986 the US Navy contracted Lockheed to supply a first production series of 22 modification kits, together with spares, support equipment and integrated logistics support. Valued at $170.5 million, the contract called for delivery of the two prototype kits in late 1987, followed by production deliveries at the rate of two per month, starting January 1988. Modification of S-3As to S-3B standard will be undertaken at Cecil Field NAS, Florida. To equip a projected 15-carrier fleet, Lockheed has also submitted proposals for follow-on production of 82 or 103 new S-3Bs.

The US Navy is to modify 16 S-3As for **electronic reconnaissance** duties, to replace EA-3 Skywarriors.

The following details refer to the S-3A, except where indicated:

TYPE: Twin-turbofan carrier-borne anti-submarine aircraft.

WINGS: Cantilever shoulder-wing monoplane. Sweepback at quarter-chord 15°. No dihedral. Incidence 3° 15′ at root, –3° 50′ at tip. Wings fold upward and inward hydraulically, outboard of engine pylons, for carrier stowage. Single-slotted Fowler-type trailing-edge flaps. Leading-edge flaps, extending from engine pylons to wingtips, are fully extended after 15° of trailing-edge flap movement. Ailerons augmented by under- and over-wing spoilers for roll control.

FUSELAGE: Semi-monocoque fail-safe structure, incorporating split weapons bays with clamshell doors. Launch tubes for 60 sonobuoys in belly. No provision for in-flight reloading of these launch tubes. Frangible canopies in top of fuselage are so designed that the crew can eject through them in emergency. Electronics bays with external access doors in forward and aft fuselage. An illuminated in-flight refuelling probe is mounted within the fuselage on the top centreline; it can be extended or retracted in emergency by

a hand crank. MAD boom, extensible in flight, housed in fuselage tail.

TAIL UNIT: Cantilever structure with swept vertical and horizontal surfaces. Fin and rudder are folded downward for carrier stowage. Variable-incidence tailplane. Trim tabs in elevators and rudder.

LANDING GEAR: Retractable tricycle type. Main units, similar to those of the Vought F-8 Crusader, are fitted with single wheels. Nose unit similar to that of the Vought A-7 Corsair II, with twin wheels and catapult towbar. Hydraulic brakes. Arrester hook.

POWERPLANT: Two General Electric TF34-GE-2 high-bypass-ratio turbofan engines, each rated at 41.25 kN (9,275 lb st), pylon-mounted beneath the wings. Fuel in integral wing tanks, entirely within the wing box beam, one on each side of the fuselage centreline and inboard of the wing fold-line. Usable fuel capacity approximately 7,192 litres (1,900 US gallons; 1,582 Imp gallons). Two 1,136 litre (300 US gallon; 250 Imp gallon) jettisonable fuel tanks can be carried on underwing pylons.

ACCOMMODATION: Crew of four. Pilot and co-pilot side-by-side on flight deck with transparent canopy. Tacco and Senso accommodated in aft cabin, with individual polarised side windows. All crew on McDonnell Douglas Escapac 1-E zero-zero ejection seats. Each seat has a rigid seat survival kit (RSSK), which can be opened during descent for inflation of life raft. Cabin pressurised, and each crewman's anti-exposure suit is ventilated with conditioned air from this system.

AVIONICS: ASW data processing, control and display includes Univac 1832A general-purpose digital computer, acoustic data processor, sonobuoy receiver, command signal generator and analogue tape recorder. Non-acoustic sensors comprise AN/APS-116 high-resolution radar, OR-89/AA forward-looking infra-red (FLIR) scanner in retractable turret, AN/ASQ-81 MAD and compensation equipment, and ALR-47 passive ECM receiving and instantaneous frequency-measuring system housed in wingtip pods. Primary navigation system composed of ASN-92(V) CAINS inertial navigator,

AN/APN-200 Doppler ground velocity system (DGVS), AYN-5 airspeed/altitude computing set (AACS), ASN-107 attitude heading reference system (AHRS), ARS-2 sonobuoy reference system (SRS), APN-201 radar altimeter and altitude warning system (RAAWS), ARN-83 LF/ADF and ARA-50 UHF/DF radio navigation aids, ARN-84(V) Tacan, and the aircraft's flight displays and interface system (FDIS). Communications equipment includes a 1 kW ARC-153 HF transceiver for long-range communications, dual ARC-156 UHF transceivers, AN/ARA-63 receiver/decoder set for use with shipboard ILS, data terminal set (DTS), OK-173 integral intercom system (ICS) and APX-72 IFF/APX-76A SIF units with altitude reporting, and AN/ASW-25B automatic carrier landing system (ACLS) communication set. Search stores are designated as LOFAR (SSQ-41), R/O (SSQ-47), DIFAR (SSQ-53), CASS (SSQ-50), DICASS (SSQ-62) and BT (SSQ-36) sonobuoys.

ARMAMENT: Split weapons bays equipped with BRU-14/A bomb rack assemblies can deploy either four MK-36 destructors, four MK-46 torpedoes, four MK-82 bombs, two MK-57 or four MK-54 depth bombs, or four MK-53 mines. BRU-11/A bomb racks installed on the two wing pylons permit carriage of SUU-44/A flare launchers, MK-52, MK-55 or MK-56 mines, MK-20-2 cluster bombs, Aero 1D auxiliary fuel tanks, or two rockets pods of type LAU-68/A (7 FFAR 2.75 in), LAU-61/A (19 FFAR 2.75 in), LAU-69/A (19 FFAR 2.75 in), or LAU-10A/A (4 FFAR 5.0 in). Alternatively, installation of TER-7 triple ejector racks on the BRU-11/A bomb racks makes it possible to carry three rocket pods, flare launchers, MK-20 cluster bombs, MK-82 bombs, MK-36 destructors, or MK-76-5 or MK-106-4 practice bombs under each wing.

AVIONICS, ARMAMENT AND OPERATIONAL EQUIPMENT (S-3B): AYS-1 Proteus acoustic signal processor; modified Sanders AN/OL-320/AYS data processing memory group integrated with IBM AN/UYS-1; updated Sperry Univac AYK-10A(V) air data computer, interfaced with Harpoon air-to-surface missile and other new systems; improved electronic support measures (ESM); Hazeltine AN/ARR-78 sonobuoy receiver system; Precision Echo AN/AQH-7 analog tape recorder; Cubic AN/ARS-2 sonobuoy reference system; Texas Instruments AN/APS-137(V)1 radar, incorporating inverse synthetic aperture radar (ISAR) techniques; modified Goodyear AN/ALE-39 chaff/flare dispensing system; IBM AN/ALR-76 ESM; and provision for carrying McDonnell Douglas Harpoon standoff air-to-surface missiles, and for future advanced navigation and communications systems including Global Positioning System and Joint Tactical Information Distribution System.

DIMENSIONS, EXTERNAL:	
Wing span	20.93 m (68 ft 8 in)
Wing span, wings folded	8.99 m (29 ft 6 in)
Length overall	16.26 m (53 ft 4 in)
Height overall	6.93 m (22 ft 9 in)
Height overall, tail folded	4.65 m (15 ft 3 in)
AREA:	
Wings, gross	55.56 m² (598 sq ft)
WEIGHTS:	
Weight empty	12,088 kg (26,650 lb)
Max design gross weight	23,831 kg (52,539 lb)
Normal ASW T-O weight	19,277 kg (42,500 lb)
Max carrier landing weight	17,098 kg (37,695 lb)

PERFORMANCE (at normal ASW T-O weight, unless otherwise indicated):	
Max level speed	450 knots (834 km/h; 518 mph)
Max cruising speed	370 knots (686 km/h; 426 mph)
Loiter speed	160 knots (296 km/h; 184 mph)
Approach speed	100 knots (185 km/h; 115 mph)
Stalling speed	84 knots (157 km/h; 97 mph)
Max rate of climb at S/L	over 1,280 m (4,200 ft)/min
Service ceiling	above 10,670 m (35,000 ft)
T-O run	671 m (2,200 ft)
Landing run at 16,556 kg (36,500 lb) weight	488 m (1,600 ft)
Combat range	more than 2,000 nm (3,705 km; 2,303 miles)
Ferry range	more than 3,000 nm (5,558 km; 3,454 miles)

LASC Georgia Division

The main building occupied by this division at Marietta is one of the world's largest aircraft production plants under a single roof. Aircraft in current production on its assembly lines are the C-5B Galaxy heavy logistics transport, the C-130 Hercules turboprop transport and its commercial counterpart, the L-100. A major modification programme has been completed on USAF C-5A Galaxy transports.

Lockheed Model 382 Hercules

US Air Force designations: C-130, AC-130, DC-130, EC-130, HC-130, JC-130, LC-130, MC-130, RC-130 and WC-130
US Navy designations: C-130, DC-130, EC-130 and LC-130
US Marine Corps designation: KC-130
US Coast Guard designation: HC-130

The C-130 Hercules military transport was designed to a specification issued by the USAF's Tactical Air Command in 1951. The prototype (YC-130) flew for the first time on 23 August 1954, and delivery of production C-130As began in December 1956. Full details of the Hercules transport and its variants will become available in an accompanying publication.

Of the special-duty versions of the Hercules, used for roles outside of transportation, the following are commensurate with this publication:

AC-130H 'Spectre'. Gunship version with side-firing weapons including 105 mm howitzer, 40 mm cannon, two 20 mm Vulcan cannon and two 7.62 mm Miniguns. Equipped with sensors and target acquisition systems including forward looking infra-red and low light level TV, and in-flight refuelling capability. In service with MAC's 1st Special Operations Wing. Improvement programme announced in Spring 1987 will include new fire control computers, navigation equipment and sensors, scheduled for completion in FY 1992.

ACP-130U 'Spectre'. It was announced on 6 July 1987 that the USAF had awarded a $155,233,489 contract to

Lockheed EC-130H Compass Call Hercules electronic warfare aircraft, identified by fuselage side blisters and undertail antennae. *(J. M. G. Gradidge)*

Rockwell's North American Aircraft Operations to cover research and development of this new gunship version of the Lockheed Hercules. This will lead to rollout of the first AC-130U at Palmdale in 1990, followed by ten months of flight testing at the Air Force Test Center, Edwards AFB, California. This aircraft, and eleven additional AC-130Us, will then enter service with the Special Operations Forces at Hurlburt Field, Florida, between late 1991 and the end of 1992.

All twelve gunship airframes will be new C-130Hs built by Lockheed's Georgia division. Conversion to gunship configuration will begin in 1988, and will include installation of a highly accurate suite of 105 mm, 40 mm and 25 mm guns which can be slaved to FLIR, low light level TV or strike radar, permitting night and/or adverse weather operations against ground targets. The AC-130U will utilise the highly-banked circular (pylon) turn technique first practised with 'Puff the Magic Dragon' C-47 gunships in Southeast Asia in the mid-1960s, and will combine intense firepower with the latest methods of target location and increased loitering capability. ECM will enhance survivability in a low-to-medium threat environment.

Apart from its primary role of precision fire suppression, the in-flight refuellable AC-130U will be capable of performing other special operations roles, including escort, surveillance, search, rescue and armed reconnaissance/interdiction.

C-130H-MP. Maritime patrol, search and rescue version, based on C-130H. Max T-O weight 70,310 kg (155,000 lb). Max payload 18,630 kg (41,074 lb). Four 3,362 kW (4,508 ehp) T56-A-15 engines. Standard and optional equipment includes sea search radar, scanner seats with

Lockheed Hercules transport forms the basis for many special versions. Drawing shows the C-130 H-30 *(Pilot Press)*

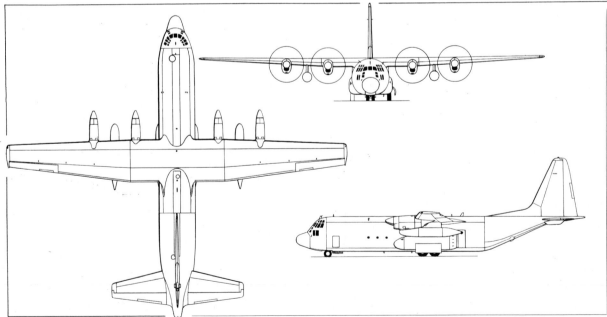

observation windows, computerised INS/Omega navigation system, crew rest and lavatory/galley slide-in module, flare launcher, loudspeaker system, rescue kit airdrop platform, side looking airborne radar, passive microwave imager, low-light TV, infra-red scanner, camera with data annotation, and ramp equipment pallet which includes a station for an observer. Search time at an altitude of 1,525 m (5,000 ft) is 2 h 30 min at a radius of 1,800 nm (3,333 km; 2,070 miles); 16 h 50 min at radius of 200 nm (370 km; 230 miles). One each delivered to the Indonesian Air Force and US Coast Guard, and three to the Royal Malaysian Air Force.

EC-130H 'Compass Call'. Operated by 41st Electronic Combat Squadron at Davis-Monthan AFB, Arizona and the 66th Electronic Combat Wing at Sembach, West Germany. Works with ground mobile C³CM systems to jam enemy command control and communications systems.

EC-130Q. Similar to earlier EC-130G, but with improved equipment and crew accommodation, for US Navy command communications (Tacamo) duties. Described as 'the only airborne, survivable, communications link with submarine forces, providing HF and VLF SIMOP (simultaneous operations) capability in a collocated environment'. Eighteen built.

C-130AEW. Lockheed-Georgia announced at the 1985 Paris Air Show a proposed airborne early warning system version of the C-130 Hercules with a GEC Avionics APY 920 radar installation in nose and tail fairings similar to those of the now abandoned BAe Nimrod AEW Mk 3. The C-130 AEW could be based on current production C-130H models or on conversions of earlier variants already in service.

MC-130E and MC-130H. The MC-130H is the Combat Talon II version of C-130H, modified by USAF for special tactical missions including day/night infiltration and exfiltration, resupply of Special Operations ground forces, psychological warfare missions, aerial reconnaissance, and airdropping and surface-to-air retrieval of personnel. Crew of 9–11. Deeper nose radome, carrying Fulton STAR retrieval yoke of type fitted to HC-130H. Other equipment includes terrain following radar, precision ground mapping, inertial navigation system, automatic computed air release point, high-speed low-level aerial delivery and container release systems, ground acquisition receiver/interrogator, secure voice UHF/VHF/FM radios, retractable FLIR pod, angle-of-attack probe and ALQ-8 ECM pod under port wing, plus in-flight refuelling capability. Six funded in FY 1983–86, with five more requested in FY 1987. By 1992 the USAF MC-130H inventory is expected to total 21 aircraft, supplementing earlier MC-130Es.

LTV

LTV Aircraft Products Group
(A unit of The LTV Corporation)

The former Chance Vought Aircraft Inc, founded in 1917 and a leading producer of aircraft for the US Navy throughout its history, became the Chance Vought Corporation on 31 December 1960. On 31 August 1961, Chance Vought Corporation merged with Ling-Temco Electronics Inc, to form a combined company known as Ling-Temco-Vought Inc (now The LTV Corporation).

The LTV Aerospace and Defense Operation was subsequently known as LTV Aerospace Corporation, Vought Corporation and LTV Aerospace and Defense Company. On 29 September 1986, LTV reorganised its aerospace/defense operations into two groups: LTV Aircraft Products Group, which consists of three divisions based in Dallas, Texas: Aircraft Modernization and Support, Military Aircraft and Commercial Aircraft; and LTV Missiles and Electronics Group, which consists of AM General Division, South Bend, Indiana; Sierra Research Division of Buffalo, New York; and the Missiles Division of Grand Prairie, Texas.

Current aerospace products include McDonnell Douglas KC-10 tailplanes and elevators, Boeing 747 tail assemblies, complete tailplane assemblies for the Boeing Model 767, complete tail units for the Boeing 757, including rear fuselage sections, and rear intermediate and rear fuselage sections of the Rockwell B-1B long-range multi-role bomber. In 1986 the company was selected by McDonnell Douglas Corporation to manufacture engine nacelles and tail unit sections for the C-17A tactical transport.

The company also has in production the Scout launch vehicle for NASA; components for manned and unmanned space vehicles; advanced missile, guidance, control and environmental systems; and advanced thermal protection systems.

LTV was selected in April 1980 as prime contractor for the Multiple Launch Rocket System (MLRS) for the US Army and NATO allies. It is also continuing development of vehicles embodying integral rocket/ramjet propulsion, as part of the US Navy's Supersonic Tactical Missile programme.

In October 1985 LTV's Sierra Research Division was awarded a $34 million US Air Force contract for two airborne platform/telemetry relay systems to be installed on two de Havilland Canada Dash 8 aircraft which operate as part of the Gulf Range Instrumentation System based at Tyndall AFB, Florida. The installation includes a large electronically steerable phased-array antenna mounted on the lower starboard fuselage side of the aircraft, an eight-channel UHF voice communication relay system, and an AN/APS-128D pulse compression radar for sea surveillance. The first Dash 8 for modification was delivered to LTV on 30 April 1986.

LTV Corsair II

US military designation: A-7

On 11 February 1964 the US Navy named the former LTV Aerospace Corporation winner of a design competition for a single-seat carrier-based light attack aircraft. The requirement was for a subsonic aircraft able to carry a greater load of non-nuclear weapons than the A-4E Skyhawk. To keep costs to a minimum and speed delivery it had been stipulated by the Navy that the new aircraft should be based on an existing design; the LTV design study was based, therefore, on the F-8 Crusader. An initial contract to develop and build three aircraft, under the designation A-7A, was awarded on 19 March 1964; first flight was made on 27 September 1965.

Several versions of the A-7 were evolved as Corsair IIs, for the US Navy, the USAF, the Hellenic Air Force and the Portuguese Air Force.

Orders for all versions totalled 1,545 new-build aircraft

LTV A-7D Corsair II of the Ohio Air National Guard, USAF. *(Erik Simonsen)*

when production ended in 1983. Versions currently in service are:

TA-7C. Designation of 60 A-7Bs and A-7Cs converted into tandem two-seat trainers, with operational capability; first example flew on 17 December 1976. Re-delivery began on 22 January 1985 of 49 aircraft upgraded with Allison TF41 engines, new Stencel ejection seats, automatic manoeuvring flaps and an engine monitoring system. Delivery of these was completed in 1986. Six other aircraft are fitted with forward looking infra-red and electronic warfare equipment and are designated EA-7L. The US Marine Corps has been testing a new night vision system in a TA-7C, which combines the use of the pilot's night goggles with a high-resolution, fixed-field-of-view FLIR sensor to project daylight visual capability in darkness. The system is expected to cost $1 million for retrofit to each aircraft already equipped with an inertial navigation system.

A-7D. Close-air-support/interdiction version, with a 64.5 kN (14,500 lb st) Allison TF41-A-1 non-afterburning turbofan engine. First flight 5 April 1968; last of 459 delivered in 1976. Assigned to ten states plus Puerto Rico Air National Guard units. Pave Penny laser target-designation pods installed. Seventy-two A-7Ds are being retrofitted with

FLIR and ATF (see A-7K for details; see also Corsair updates). 30 mm gun pod now added to weapon options.

A-7E. Light attack/close-air-support/interdiction aircraft for US Navy. All except first 67 aircraft (which were redesignated A-7C) powered by Allison TF41-A-2 (Spey) non-afterburning turbofan engine, rated at 66.8 kN (15,000 lb st). First flight 25 November 1968; deliveries began 14 July 1969. The A-7E entered combat service in Southeast Asia with Attack Squadrons 146 and 147 in May 1970, and equipped 26 Navy squadrons in 1980. Last of 596 A-7Es delivered in March 1981.

In early 1977 production began of an **A-7E FLIR** version. This was given a 327 kg (720 lb) pod under the starboard wing, housing a Texas Instruments FLIR gimballed sensor, and a Marconi raster-HUD cockpit display, to provide improved night capability. Deliveries of new-production FLIR-equipped A-7Es to the Navy began on 15 September 1978.

A-7H. Land-based version of A-7E, retaining the folding wings but without in-flight refuelling capability. First A-7H flew for the first time on 6 May 1975. Total of 60 delivered to three squadrons of the Hellenic Air Force.

TA-7H. Two-seat version for the Hellenic Air Force, with

LTV A-7K two-seat version of the A-7D. *(J. M. G. Gradidge)*

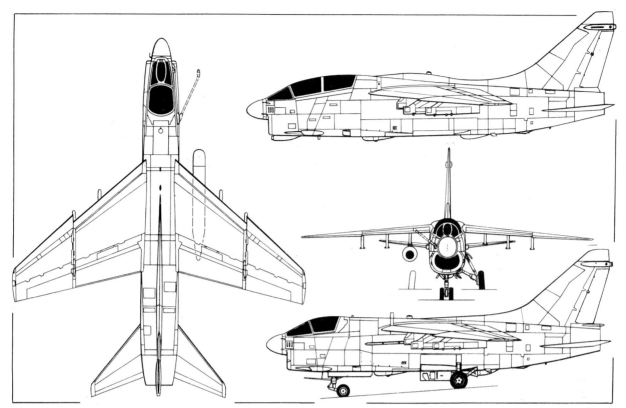

LTV A-7E Corsair II. Upper side view: A-7K. *(Pilot Press)*

an Allison TF41-A-400 engine. Configuration similar to TA-7C, but no in-flight refuelling capability. Five delivered between July and September 1980.

A-7K. Two-seat version of the US Air Force's A-7D, with fuselage lengthened by 0.86 m (2 ft 10 in), and powered by 64.5 kN (14,500 lb st) Allison TF41-A-1 engine. Total of 31 delivered to US Air National Guard. Basically trainers, these aircraft retain combat capability. A total of 78 ANG A-7Ds and A-7Ks are being equipped with low-altitude night attack (LANA) capability under contracts awarded by the Air Force's Oklahoma City Air Logistics Center. The first LANA equipped aircraft, an A-7K of the 152nd TFTS, Arizona ANG, made its first flight from Dallas on 2 October 1986. LTV is retrofitting 72 A-7Ds and eight two-seat A-7Ks with forward looking infra-red (FLIR) and automatic terrain-following (ATF) equipment to provide round-the-clock capability. LTV has also tested an augmented wing flap and spoiler that enables an A-7D or A-7K pilot to reduce landing speed, improve handling characteristics on the approach, and substantially reduce landing roll. The flap, which is 127 mm (5 in) wide, is mounted on the existing wing flap trailing edge and is intended for retrofit to Air National Guard A-7s. It is expected to be helpful to ANG pilots operating from the short runways and in the varying climatic conditions that they might encounter in Rapid Deployment Force roles.

EA-7L. Six US Navy TA-7Cs fitted with ECM and FLIR (see TA-7C).

A-7P. Designation of refurbished A-7As for Esquadra 302 (Grupo 52) of Portuguese Air Force at Mantijo, with TF30-P-408 engines and a mixture of A-7D and A-7E-standard avionics. Initial flight 20 July 1981. Deliveries of

initial 20 completed September 1982. A further 30, including six two-seaters, were ordered in 1983; deliveries of these began on 5 October 1984. These aircraft can carry a Northrop AN/ALQ-171(V) electronic countermeasures pod to defeat surface and airborne radar controlled terminal threat systems. About 37 remain operational.

TA-7P. Designation of Portuguese two-seat training version of A-7P.

The following description of the A-7E is generally applicable to other versions of the A-7 except as detailed under the individual model listings:

TYPE: Subsonic single-seat tactical fighter.

WINGS: Cantilever high-wing monoplane. Wing section NACA 65A007. Anhedral 5°. Incidence –1°. Wing sweepback at quarter-chord 35°. Outer wing sections fold upward. Plain sealed inset ailerons, outboard of wing fold. Leading-edge flaps. Large single-slotted trailing-edge flaps. Spoiler above each wing forward of flaps.

FUSELAGE: Semi-monocoque structure. Large door-type ventral speed-brake under centre fuselage.

TAIL UNIT: Large vertical fin and rudder, swept back 44° 16′ 48″ at quarter-chord. One-piece all-moving tailplane, swept back 45° at quarter-chord and set at dihedral angle of 5° 25′.

LANDING GEAR: Retractable tricycle type, with single wheel on each main unit and twin-wheel nose unit. Mainwheels and tyres size 28 × 9-12; nosewheels and tyres size 22 × 5.50. Nose gear launch bar formerly for carrier catapulting. Sting-type arrester hook under rear fuselage, formerly for carrier landings, emergency landings or aborted take-offs. Anti-skid brake system.

POWERPLANT: One Allison TF41-A-2 (Rolls-Royce Spey)

non-afterburning turbofan engine, rated at 66.7 kN (15,000 lb st). The A-7E has a pneumatic starter requiring ground air supply; A-7H, TA-7H and A-7K engines have self-start capability via a battery-powered electric motor and small gas turbine engine (jet fuel starter). Integral fuel tanks in wings and additional fuselage tanks. Maximum internal fuel 5,678 litres (1,500 US gallons; 1,249 Imp gallons). Maximum external fuel 4,542 litres (1,200 US gallons; 999 Imp gallons). The A-7E and A-7H have the fuselage sump tank filled with polyurethane fire-suppressing foam. Some fuselage tanks and fuel lines self-sealing. Flight refuelling capability of A-7E provided by a probe and drogue system; A-7K has a boom receptacle above the fuselage, on the centreline, in line with the wing leading edge. The A-7H and TA-7H do not have an air refuelling capability. Boron carbide (HFC) engine armour.

ACCOMMODATION: Pilot on McDonnell Douglas Escapac rocket powered ejection system, complete with US Navy life support system on the A-7E/H. Boron carbide (HFC) cockpit armour.

AVIONICS AND EQUIPMENT: AN/ASN-91(V) navigation/ weapon delivery computer displays continuously present position, using computed position and stored data to calculate navigation and weapon-delivery solutions, and monitors the reliability of data inputs and outputs. An AN/ASN-90(V) inertial measurement set is the basic three-axis reference system for navigation and weapon delivery. AN/APN-190(V) Doppler measures ground-speed and drift angle. AN/APQ-126(V) forward looking radar' provides the pilot with ten modes of operation: air-to-ground ranging; terrain following; terrain avoidance; ground mapping, shaped beam; ground mapping, pencil beam; beacon; cross-scan terrain avoidance; cross-scan ground mapping, pencil; TV; and Shrike integrated display system. An AN/AVQ-7(V) HUD receives and displays computed attack, navigation and landing data from the tactical computer; aircraft performance data from flight sensors: and discrete signals from various aircraft systems. CP-953A/AJQ solid-state servomechanical analog air data computer measures and computes continuously required altitude and airspeed information. The armament station control unit supplies electrical signals to arm and release or jettison external stores; controls and fires the Vulcan cannon; furnishes information to the tactical computer; supplies weapon status information to the pilot; determines weapon release according to priority of stations; and determines compatibility of selected release mode with the stores on selected stations. Standard aeronautical charts reproduced on 35 mm film in full colour are stored in an AN/ASN-99 projected map display set which provides a continuous display of the aircraft's geographical position. Other avionics include AN/ASN-54 approach power compensator; AN/ASW-30 AFCS; ARA-63 ACLS; dual AN/ARC-159 UHF com; AN/ARN-84 Tacan; AN/APX-72 IFF transponder; AN/APN-154 radar beacon; AN/ASW-25 data link; AN/ARA-50 ADF; and AN/AIC-25 audio system. ECM equipment includes ALR-45/50 internal homing and warning systems; ALQ-126 active ECM; chaff/flare dispensers; and external pod-mounted systems compatible with the aircraft's internal systems.

ARMAMENT: More than 6,805 kg (15,000 lb) of stores can be carried on six underwing pylons and two fuselage weapon stations, the latter suitable for Sidewinder air-to-air missiles. Two outboard pylons on each wing can each accommodate a load of 1,587 kg (3,500 lb). Inboard pylon on each wing can carry 1,134 kg (2,500 lb). Two fuselage weapon stations, one on each side, can each carry 227 kg (500 lb). Weapons carried include air-to-air and air-to-ground (anti-tank and anti-radar missiles); electro-optical (TV) and laser guided weapons; general-purpose bombs; bomblet dispensers; rockets; gun pods; Gator mines; and auxiliary fuel tanks. An M61A1 20 mm cannon is mounted in the port side of the fuselage, with 1,000 rds and selected firing rates of 4,000 or 6,000 rds/min. Strike camera in lower rear fuselage for damage assessment.

DIMENSIONS, EXTERNAL:		Max level speed at 1,525 m (5,000 ft):	
Wing span	11.80 m (38 ft 9 in)	with 12 Mk 82 bombs	
Width, wings folded	7.24 m (23 ft 9 in)		562 knots (1,040 km/h; 646 mph)
Length overall	14.06 m (46 ft 1½ in)	after dropping bombs	
Height overall	4.90 m (16 ft 0¾ in)		595 knots (1,102 km/h; 685 mph)
Wheel track	2.90 m (9 ft 6 in)	Sustained manoeuvring performance at 1,525 m (5,000 ft), at	
AREA:		AUW of 13,047 kg (28,765 lb) with 6 pylons and 2 Sidewinder	
Wings, gross	34.83 m² (375 sq ft)	missiles	
WEIGHTS:		1,615 m (5,300 ft) turning radius at 4.3g and	
Weight empty	8,676 kg (19,127 lb)		500 knots (925 km/h; 575 mph)
Max T-O weight	19,050 kg (42,000 lb)	T-O run at max T-O weight	1,705 m (5,600 ft)
PERFORMANCE:		Ferry range:	
Max level speed at S/L		max internal fuel	1,981 nm (3,671 km; 2,281 miles)
	600 knots (1,112 km/h; 691 mph)	max internal and external fuel	
Max level speed at S/L (A-7D)			2,485 nm (4,604 km; 2,861 miles)
	606 knots (1,123 km/h; 698 mph)		

LTV Corsair update programmes

Current activity is centred on a series of update programmes for the Corsair II, which include the **International Corsair II**. This is based on an A-7B airframe that is stripped, fitted with new avionics and communications equipment, overhauled engine, new wiring, and provision for night attack and the latest ordnance, providing, LTV claims, a low-cost multi-mission tactical fighter at one-third of the acquisition costs of new aircraft.

LTV has received a contract from the USAF Aeronautical Systems Division to upgrade two A-7Ds to supersonic **A-7 Plus** (formerly known as **Strikefighter**) configuration as a solution for its Close Air Support/Battlefield Air Interdiction (CAS/BAI) requirement. Up to 335 A-7Ds and A-7Ks from the Air National Guard may each be retrofitted

Artist's impression of the A-7 Plus supersonic conversion of the A-7D/K.

later to the same A-7 Plus standard, with an F100-PW-220 afterburning engine and additional fuel in a lengthened fuselage; an airframe mounted accessory drive unit for self contained ground operations; automatic manoeuvring flaps; lift dump spoilers; an extended tail fin; wingroot strakes; a new-technology wing trailing-edge flap structure; upgraded avionics which will include a replacement inertial navigation system, hands-on stick and throttle, GPS, LANA, FLIR, provision for Maverick and AIM-9 Sidewinder missile operation and automatic terrain following; all-new wiring; and an improved air-conditioning system. LTV says that the A-7 Plus will offer twice the thrust of existing A-7s, with 16 per cent greater speed (Mach 1.12 with afterburner), a 45 per cent decrease in take-off roll and 30 per cent in landing roll, and would provide greater agility and survivability while operating with minimal support in forward battle areas. It will have a common engine bay to accommodate the General Electric F110-GE-100 as an alternative to the Pratt & Whitney F100.

ARMAMENT (International Corsair II): Two internally mounted Mk 12 20 mm cannon, with 680 rounds of ammunition. Six underwing and two fuselage weapon stations, as on A-7E, capable of carrying all USN, USAF, and NATO munitions (max external load more than 6,805 kg; 15,000 lb). Weapon carriers include BRU-10A, MER-7, and TER-7 bomb racks; LAU-3 and LAU-32 wing mounted rocket launchers; LAU-7 fuselage mounted missile launchers; and pods containing 20 or 30 mm guns, ECM, chaff, or auxiliary fuel. Provision also to carry 'buddy' air-to-air refuelling pods.

WEIGHTS (International Corsair II):
Weight empty	9,496 kg (20,935 lb)
Max T-O weight	19,050 kg (42,000 lb)

TYPICAL MISSION PERFORMANCE (International Corsair II at T-O weight of 16,805 kg; 37,050 lb with six Mk 82 bombs and 500 rds of 20 mm ammunition):
Max level speed at S/L	645 knots (1,195 km/h; 743 mph)
Time to 9,145 m (30,000 ft)	1.6 min
T-O run	488 m (1,600 ft)

LTV F-8 Crusader

The former Chance Vought company was given a development contract for the F-8 in May 1953, after winning a design competition in which eight airframe manufacturers had participated. The prototype XF-8A Crusader flew for the first time on 25 March 1955, exceeding the speed of sound in level flight. The first production F-8A day fighter for the US Navy flew on 20 September 1955, and this version began

LTV F-8E (FN) Crusader flown by the French Navy. *(J. M. G. Gradidge)*

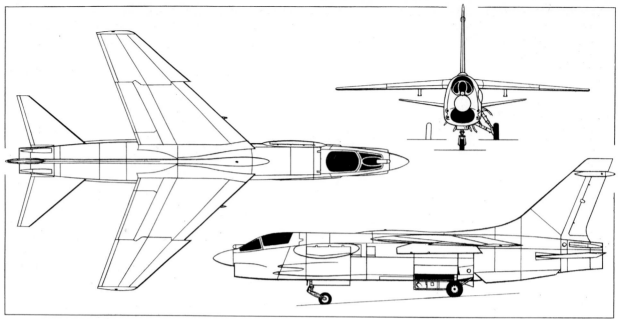

LTV F-8 Crusader. *(Pilot Press)*

reaching operational squadrons in March 1957. All-weather capability was introduced on the F-8D and E.

On 21 August 1956 an F-8A set up the first US national speed record of over 1,000 mph. Operating under restrictions, it recorded a speed of 881.8 knots (1,634.17 km/h; 1,015.428 mph). On 16 July 1957 an RF-8A photo-reconnaissance version of the Crusader set up the first supersonic US transcontinental record by flying from Los Angeles to New York in 3 hr 22 min 50 sec, at an average speed of 628.32 knots (1,164.39 km/h; 723.52 mph). A later modernised RF-8A version, the RF-8G, was the final Crusader type in US Navy service, operating with the Reserve in the 1980s.

An outstanding feature of the F-8 is its two-position variable-incidence wing. This provides a high angle of attack for take-off and landing, while permitting the fuselage to remain almost parallel to a flight deck or runway for good pilot visibility. Although the US Navy long since gave up its Crusaders as carrier fighters, French F-8E(FN)s still benefit from this feature for carrier operations.

Currently operated versions of the Crusader are:

F-8E(FN). Version of F-8E equipping French Navy squadrons for service on carriers *Clemenceau* and *Foch*. Main modifications were the incorporation of a boundary layer control system to provide 'blowing' of the flaps and ailerons, the introduction of two-stage leading-edge flaps to reduce landing speed on the comparatively small ships, and provision for carrying Matra air-to-air missiles in addition to Sidewinders. Contract for 42 placed in August 1963 through US Navy. Prototype, a converted F-8D, flew on 27 February 1964, but was lost in an accident on 11 April 1964. First production F-8E (FN) flew on 26 June 1964. Last F-8E (FN) was delivered in January 1965, bringing to an end the production of new Crusaders.

F-8H. Modernised and remanufactured F-8D, with new extended service-life wing, addition of attack capabilities, strengthened nose and main landing gear providing an increased carrier landing weight capability, strengthened arresting gear, armament system improvements involving improved fire control computer, expanded missile acquisition envelope and large APQ-94 radar. First F-8H flew on 17 July 1967. Acquired by the Philippine Air Force as a land based fighter-bomber, of which about 12 remain although these may be up for sale.

TYPE: Supersonic single-seat carrier-borne and land-based fighter.

WINGS: Cantilever high-wing monoplane. Thin laminar-flow section. Anhedral 5°. Sweepback 35°. Wing is adjustable to two incidence positions by hydraulic self-locking actuator. When wing is raised, the ailerons, the flaps and the 'dog-tooth' leading edge are all drooped 20° automatically. Outer wing sections fold upward for stowage. Inset ailerons, inboard of wing fold, function also as flaps. Small trailing-edge flaps. French F-8E(FN)s have boundary layer control system, to provide 'blowing' of flaps and ailerons, and two-stage leading-edge flaps to reduce landing speed.

FUSELAGE: Conventional structure in three main assemblies. Both magnesium alloy and titanium are used in the structure, the after section and a portion of the mid-section being of titanium, while 25 per cent of the wing and fuselage skins are of magnesium. Ventral speed-brake under centre fuselage.

TAIL UNIT: Large swept vertical fin and rudder and one-piece horizontal 'slab' tail.

LANDING GEAR: Retractable tricycle type. Sting-type arrester hook under rear fuselage.

POWERPLANT: One 80 kN (18,000 lb st) with afterburning Pratt & Whitney J57-P-20 turbojet. Integral fuel tanks in wings inboard of wing fold. Other tankage in fuselage. Total internal fuel capacity approx 5,300 litres (1,400 US gallons; 1,166 Imp gallons). Provision for in-flight refuelling.

ACCOMMODATION: Pilot on lightweight ejection seat in pressurised cockpit.

AVIONICS: See model listing.

ARMAMENT: Four 20 mm Colt cannon in fuselage nose, with 144 rpg. Matra R.550 Magic or Sidewinder missiles. Can carry attack weapons, including bombs, up to 2,000 lb weight, rockets, etc.

DIMENSIONS, EXTERNAL:
Wing span	10.87 m (35 ft 0 in)
Length overall	16.61 m (54 ft 6 in)
Height overall	4.80 m (15 ft 9 in)
Width folded	6.86 m (22 ft 6 in)
Wheel track	2.94 m (9 ft 8 in)

AREA:
Wings, gross	32.50 m² (350.0 sq ft)

WEIGHT:
Max T-O weight	15,420 kg (34,000 lb)

PERFORMANCE:
Max level speed	
	nearly 1,148 knots (2,127 km/h; 1,322 mph)
Service ceiling	17,680 m (58,000 ft)
Combat radius	521 nm (965 km; 600 miles)

McDonnell Douglas

MCDONNELL DOUGLAS CORPORATION

McDonnell Douglas Corporation was formed on 28 April 1967, by the merger of the former Douglas Aircraft Company Inc and the McDonnell company. It encompasses both of the original companies and their subsidiaries, and the former Hughes Helicopters Inc, which became a subsidiary in 1984.

At the end of March 1987 McDonnell Douglas employed 105,682 people, worldwide. Total office, engineering, laboratory and manufacturing floor area was 3,809,023 m² (41,000,000 sq ft).

Major operating components of McDonnell Douglas Corporation Aerospace Group are as follows:
McDonnell Aircraft Company
Douglas Aircraft Company
McDonnell Douglas Helicopter Company
McDonnell Douglas Astronautics Company

McDonnell Aircraft Company
(A Division of McDonnell Douglas Corporation)

Development and production at St Louis continues to be concentrated on versions of the F-15 Eagle air superiority fighter, AV-8B Harrier II and F/A-18 Hornet naval strike fighter.

McDonnell Douglas Phantom II
US Navy and USAF designations: F-4 and RF-4

The Phantom II was developed initially as a twin-engined two-seat long-range all-weather fleet air defence fighter for service with the US Navy. A letter of intent to order two prototypes was issued on 18 October 1954, at which time the aircraft was designated AH-1. The designation was changed to F4H-1 on 23 June 1955, with change of mission to missile fighter, and the prototype F4H-1 flew for the first time on 27 May 1958. The first production Phantom II was delivered to US Navy Squadron VF-121 on 29 December 1960. Trials in a ground-attack role led to USAF orders, and the basic USN and USAF versions became the F-4B and F-4C respectively. Many other variants appeared subsequently, and those versions currently in operational use are:

RF-4B (formerly F4H-1P). Multi-sensor reconnaissance version of F-4B for US Marine Corps. No dual controls or armament. Reconnaissance system as for RF-4C. J79-GE-8 engines. High-frequency single sideband radio. First flown on 12 March 1965. Overall length increased to 19.2 m (63 ft). Total of 46 built. Thirty updated from 1978 by addition of Honeywell AN/AAD-5 infra-red linescan equipment, AN/APD-10 side-looking radar, AN/ASN-92 carrier inertial navigation system and AN/ASW-25 carrier automatic landing system. Prototype updated to this configuration in 1977.

F-4C (formerly F-110A). Variant of F-4B for USAF, built with J79-GE-15 turbojets, cartridge starting, wider-tread low-pressure tyres size 30 × 11.5, larger brakes, Litton type LN-12A/B (ASN-48) inertial navigation system, APQ-100 radar, APQ-100 PPI scope, LADD timer, Lear Siegler AJB-7 bombing system, GAM-83 controls, dual controls and boom flight refuelling instead of drogue (receptacle in top of

McDonnell Douglas RF-4C multi-sensor reconnaissance aircraft in the markings of the Minnesota Air National Guard. *(Erik Simonsen)*

fuselage, aft of cockpit). Folding wings and arrester gear retained. For close support and attack duties with Tactical Air Command, PACAF and USAFE, and with the Air National Guard (ANG) from January 1972. First F-4C flew on 27 May 1963; 36 supplied to Spanish Air Force, which designated them **C.12**. The last of 583 was delivered to TAC on 4 May 1966. Replaced in production by F-4D. Still flown by ANG units.

RF-4C (formerly RF-110A). Multi-sensor reconnaissance version of F-4C for USAF, with radar and photographic systems in modified nose which increases overall length by 0.84 m (2 ft 9 in). Basic reconnaissance systems are infra-red detector to locate enemy forces under cover or at night by detecting exhaust gases and other heat sources, and forward and side-looking cameras, including panoramic models with moving-lens elements for horizon-to-horizon pictures. Sixteen RF-4Cs were fitted with side looking airborne radar for standoff battlefield surveillance and 24 with tactical electronic reconnaissance (TEREC) sensor for locating emitters. ARN-101 digital system for better navigation/reconnaissance accuracy, Pave Tack infra-red pod, and data link transmission. Systems are operated from rear seat. YRF-4C flew on 8 August 1963; first production RF-4C on 18 May 1964. Taken into service with ANG on 22 February 1971. Production ended December 1973. Total of 505 built, including two YRF-4C prototypes. In a programme begun in 1984, the Texas Instruments AN/APQ-99 terrain-following radar was expected to be fitted to RF-4Cs. Development is ongoing to replace film cameras with electro-optical sensors. RF-4Cs are currently flown by five active and six ANG squadrons of the USAF.

F-4D. Development of F-4C for USAF, built with J79-GE-15 turbojets, APQ-109 fire control radar, ASG-22 servoed sight, ASQ-91 weapon release computer, ASG-22 lead computing amplifier, ASG-22 lead computing gyro, 30 kVA generators, and ASN-63 inertial navigation system. First production F-4D flew on 8 December 1965; total of 793 supplied to USAF. Two squadrons of F-4Ds (32 aircraft) delivered to the Imperial Iranian Air Force and 36 to the Republic of Korea. Production completed. Total of 825 built, plus two prototypes converted from earlier models. USAF examples currently used by ANG and AFRES, the latter to receive grey paint finish by 1990. ANG F-4Ds are receiving AIM-9L/M Sidewinder capability.

F-4E. Multi-role fighter for air-superiority, close-support and interdiction missions with USAF. Has leading-edge manoeuvring slats, an internally-mounted M61A-1 20 mm multi-barrel gun, improved (AN/APQ-120) fire-control system and J79-GE-17 turbojets (each 79.6 kN; 17,900 lb st).

McDonnell Douglas F-4E Phantom II with Goodyear Aerospace wraparound windscreen.

Additional fuselage fuel cell. First production F-4E flown on 30 June 1967 and delivered to USAF on 3 October 1967. Total of 949 supplied to USAF, including many for MAP supply to other countries. Currently also used by Egypt, West Germany, Greece, Iran, Israel, South Korea and Turkey.

In early 1973 F-4Es began to be fitted with Northrop's target identification system electro-optical (Tiseo). Essentially a vidicon TV camera with a zoom lens, it aids positive visual identification of airborne or ground targets at long range. The Tiseo is mounted in a cylindrical housing on the leading edge of the port wing of the F-4E. F-4Es are replacing ANG F-4Cs and Ds as USAF F-15 and F-16 deliveries allow. ANG F-4Es being modified to carry AIM-9L/M Sidewinder.

RF-4E. Multi-sensor reconnaissance version in service with the air forces of West Germany, Greece, Iran, Israel, Japan (as RF-4EJ) and Turkey. Generally similar to the RF-4C, it differs by having the J79-GE-17 turbojets of the F-4E and changed reconnaissance equipment. First flown 15 September 1970.

F-4EJ. On 1 November 1968, the Japan Defence Agency selected the F-4E as the main fighter for the JASDF. Except for the first two, these aircraft were built in Japan under a licence agreement, with some components being supplied from St Louis. In co-operation with Kawasaki as subcontractor, Mitsubishi was the JDA's prime contractor in producing F-4EJ Phantom tactical fighters for the JASDF. The first US-built F-4EJ flew on 14 January 1971.

The Hellenic Air Force operates the F-4E and RF-4E versions of the Phantom II.

Equipment includes tail warning radar and launchers for Mitsubishi AAM-2 air-to-air missiles. Total of 140 built, the last delivered to the JASDF on 20 May 1981.

F-4EJ Kai. Mitsubishi is engaged currently in a major programme to update F-4EJ equipment and weapon systems. The prototype F-4EJ Kai was first flown on 17 July 1984 and delivered on the following 13 December. It has a Westinghouse AN/APG-66J fire control system, advanced avionics which include a Litton LN-39 INS, head-up display, and J/APR-4Kai radar warning receiver, look-down/shootdown capability with AIM-7F/M Sparrows or AIM-9L Sidewinders, and can carry two ASM-1 anti-shipping missiles. Current plans are to convert 110 of the JASDF's 125 remaining F-4EJs to F-4EJ Kai configuration and the other 15 to **RF-4EJ** reconnaissance-fighters.

F-4F. Two-seat fighter, with leading-edge slats to improve manoeuvrability and modified electronics. 175 ordered by Federal Germany for the Luftwaffe. First flown on 18 May 1973; last was delivered in April 1976.

F-4G (Advanced Wild Weasel). The USAF's Wild Weasel programme was concerned with the suppression of hostile weapon radar guidance systems. The provision of airborne equipment able to fulfil such a role, and modification of the necessary aircraft to create an effective force for deployment against such targets, had first priority in tactical Air Force planning in the spring of 1975. In the interests of force standardisation and airframe life, the F-4E Phantom was selected for modification to fulfil the Advanced Wild Weasel role, technical studies of the F-4D and F-4E having shown the latter aircraft to be easier to modify. External changes included the addition of a torpedo-shape fairing to the top of the fin to carry APR-38 antennae; removal of the M61A-1 gun system and its replacement by a chin pod containing APR-38 subsystems (receiver, homing and warning computer, computer interface system); and the addition of other APR-38 antennae, of which there are 56 in all on the fin-tip and fin sides, along the upper surface of the fuselage, and elsewhere. The chin pod is of laminated glassfibre construction, and there are fairing doors in place of the gun muzzle fairings.

Internal modifications consisted of a number of added and revised systems, chief of which was the McDonnell Douglas AN/APR-38 radar homing and warning system (RHAWS) itself. Changes were made to the LCOSS (lead-computing optical sight system) amplifier in the upper equipment bay, and the computer interface system (CIS) installations in the front and rear cockpits; suitable cockpit displays were provided. Additional equipment was installed in the compartment vacated by the ammunition for the M61 gun, and there was provision for further electronics packages if required. The gun purge scoop and entire gun hydraulic system of the F-4E were removed; pitot-static system drains were relocated in the chin pod; and a 7.5 cm (3 in) extension was added to the pitot-static nose boom. The radar cooling duct was modified, to provide open ducting for the APR-38 components on the equipment shelves in the nose. All gun control and APR-36/37 wiring in the F-4E was replaced by new wiring and co-axial cables for the APR-38 system in the radome, nose, inboard wing panels, and forward/centre/aft fuselage locations. New wiring used F-15 assembly techniques and materials, and additional wiring provided interface with new weapons launchers. The Advanced Wild Weasel F-4G was cleared for operation with AGM-45 Shrike, AGM-78 Standard ARM, AGM-88A HARM and AGM-65 Maverick (including IIR: imaging infra-red version) air-to-surface missiles. Use of the IIR Maverick greatly enhanced night and adverse-weather capability. For self-defence, AIM-7F Sparrow and/or AIM-9L Sidewinder air-to-air missiles can also be carried.

A digital computer receives, processes and displays emitter information to the crew in the form of CRT presentations, digital readouts, advisory/warning lights, and aural tones. Computerised information is also provided to the weapon system for use in munition delivery, and to various instruments used by the crew to perform delivery manoeuvres. This frees both the pilot and the electronics warfare officer (EWO) of many of the analytical and manual duties once required, presents them with an accurate view of the enemy's defence environment, and allows them an unprecedented flexibility in seeking-out and destroying those defences. The AN/APR-38 beam receivers (23 cm; 9 in arrays) which obtain range and azimuth information are located on the front and each side of the chin pod, and on the fin looking aft. The range and azimuth information for all ground threats received is displayed on the plan position indicator (PPI), which is one of three scopes in the rear cockpit. There is a repeater PPI in the front cockpit. Priorities are assigned to the top 15 targets by the computer. Threats are indicated by letter and number symbols. A triangle is placed around the highest-priority threat, which is determined by the computer classification table. If desired, the EWO may override and designate a threat for the Weasel to work: this threat is designated by a diamond around the symbol. The homing and warning computer (HAWC) is one of the most important parts of the system. It can be re-programmed to include new or changed threats. The optical sight, which has been modified, indicates the radar emitter position with its red reticle. Ground track of the aircraft in azimuth is indicated by a green cross caged in elevation to the radar boresight of the aircraft. The Weasel pilot can bomb 'blind' by positioning the green cross over the reticle, depressing the bomb button, and starting a recovery. The selected store will release automatically at the correct point. The mission recorder provides the capability to play back the mission on the ground for training and study purposes.

Although the Advanced Wild Weasel F-4G aircraft can operate independently in a hunter/killer role, their main utilisation is as a component of a strike force, where they detect, identify, locate and warn of hostile electromagnetic emitters, and deploy against them suitable weapons for their suppression or destruction.

The USAF sought funding in FY 1976 for the Advanced Wild Weasel concept, in order to provide an expansion in memory capability of the airborne processor and to extend coverage of low-frequency emissions. The programme provided for the first F-4G operational kit installation in the spring of 1976 and the second in the autumn of that year, followed by 15 installations in 1977, 60 in 1978, and 39 in 1979, to provide a force of 116 aircraft (96 for combat units, 20 for training and testing). The first F-4G was delivered on 28 April 1978, and the type entered service with the 35th Tactical Wing (39th Tactical Fighter Squadron, for training) at George AFB, California, in October 1978. The first two F-4Gs of 24 for the 81st TFS, USAFE, at Spangdahlem, Federal Republic of Germany, were delivered in the spring of 1979. About 72 F-4Gs remain active, and it is anticipated that modified F-15Es will eventually take over their role, though not for some years.

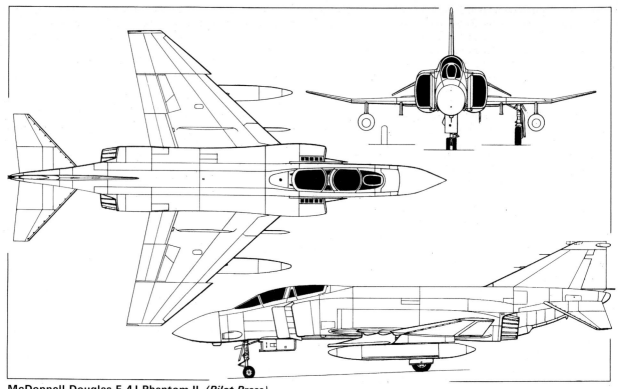

McDonnell Douglas F-4J Phantom II. *(Pilot Press)*

F-4J. Development of F-4B originally for US Navy and Marine Corps, primarily as interceptor but with full ground-attack capability. First flown in production form on 27 May 1966; 522 built up to 1972. Westinghouse AN/AWG-10 X-band pulse-Doppler fire control system. Underwent important avionics improvement programmes, initially aimed at improving electronic warfare equipment. Squadron taken into RAF service for air defence as Phantom FG.3s.

F-4K. Development of F-4B, originally for Royal Navy, with improvements evolved for F-4J plus other changes. Westinghouse AN/AWG-11 pulse Doppler fire-control radar system modified to allow the antenna to swing around with the radome. This 'foldable radome' reduced the length of the aircraft, making it compatible with the deck elevators

then in use on British aircraft carriers. Two Rolls-Royce Spey RB.168-25R Mk 201 turbofans initially (each rated at 55.6 kN; 12,500 lb st dry) with 70° afterburning; later the Mks 202/203 became standard, developing 91.25 kN (20,515 lb st) with afterburning. Air intake ducts 0.15 m (6 in) wider than on US models to cater for more powerful engines. Drooped ailerons. Tailplane has leading-edge fixed slot. Strengthened main landing gear. Nose landing gear strut extended to 1.02 m (40 in), compared with 0.51 m (20 in) on the F-4J, to permit optimum-incidence catapulting. Martin-Baker ejection seats. Weapons include Sparrow and Sky Flash missiles. Initial contracts for two YF-4Ks and two F-4Ks; ordered as Phantom FG. Mk 1. First flight (YF-4K) 27 June 1966. First operational Phantom unit, No. 892

Phantom FGR.Mk 2 flown by No 228 OCU, RAF. *(J. M. G. Gradidge)*

Squadron, commissioned at RNAS Yeovilton on 31 March 1969. Now operated by Royal Air Force as interceptors. Total of 52 built, including YF-4K prototypes.

F-4M. For Royal Air Force. Generally similar to F-4K, but with larger brakes and low-pressure tyres of F-4C, no tailplane leading-edge slot, and AN/AWG-12 radar. Folding wings and arrester gear retained. Up to 50% of the components manufactured in the UK. First YF-4M flew on 17 February 1967. Deliveries began on 23 August 1968. RAF designation is Phantom FGR. MK 2. Total of 118 built, including two YF-4M prototypes. Some delivered with dual controls for use as conversion trainers.

F-4N. The US Navy updated 227 F-4Bs under this designation. The first was flown for the first time on 4 June 1972, and the initial delivery was made on 21 February 1973, the last in December 1978.

F-4S. The US Navy modified F-4Js under this designation for Marine Corps use, with structural strengthening to increase operational life, improvements to the electrical system, replacement of the original wing leading-edge flaps by highly-cambered, bulbous nosed leading-edge slats, and an improved AN/AWG-10A digital weapon control system. Delivery of modified aircraft from the Naval Air Rework Facility, North Island, California, began on 26 May 1978.

A total of 5,057 completed Phantoms had been delivered from St Louis when production ended on 26 October 1979. This total included 2,597 for the US Air Force, 1,264 for the US Navy/Marine Corps, and 1,196 for foreign customers. In addition, 11 Phantoms were supplied in kit form to Japan for assembly by Mitsubishi, which built further aircraft under licence in that country. McDonnell Douglas also completed RF-4Es ordered by Iran before the change of government in that country in 1979.

Because of the continuing importance of the F-4, many modification programmes have recently been introduced or offered to improve safety, increase power and/or enhance systems. These have included:

Mitsubishi F-4EJKai. See model listings.

IAI. Israeli Air Force approval was given for an airframe and avionics upgrade programme for the service's F-4 Phantoms. Four prototypes were modified during 1986 with structural improvements and new external fuel tanks. New or upgraded avionics were expected to include a new Elta pulse-Doppler radar (derived from the EL/M-2021); Elbit ACE-3 radar data processor; Elop (Kaiser licence) wide-angle diffractive optics head-up display; Astronautics multi-function CRT displays; an avionics interface computer; and a multiplex digital databus. Elbit is overall integrator for the avionics refit. The programme was then expected to involve about 140 Phantoms still in IAF service.

MBB F-4F ICE. Under a German Defence Ministry programme known as ICE (improved combat efficiency), 75 Luftwaffe F-4F Phantom IIs of fighter wings JG 71 and JG 74 are to be upgraded to give them a lookdown/shootdown capability against multiple targets. The programme, for which MBB is the prime contractor, was initiated in late 1983 and reached the end of the definition phase some two years later. It was expected to achieve initial operational capability in 1991.

Main ingredient of this retrofit programme involves replacement of the existing Westinghouse APQ-120 radar by the all-digital multi-mode Hughes APG-65, built under licence in Germany by AEG. This advanced X-band system has 30 air-to-air and air-to-ground modes, with a ten-target track-while-scan capability, of which eight can be displayed simultaneously. APG-65 subsystems include a low-sidelobe

McDonnell Douglas F-4E Phantom II. *(Pilot Press)*

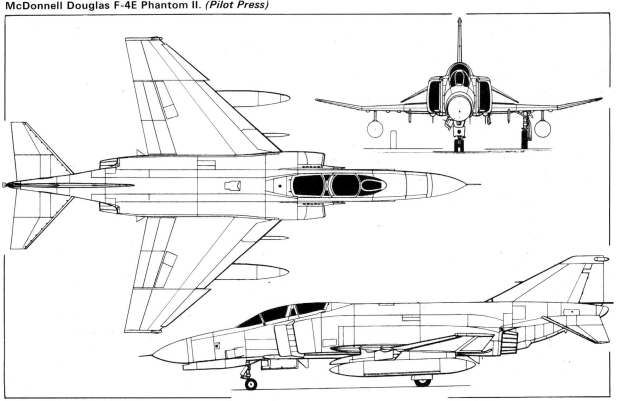

planar array antenna, a 16-bit (256 K) memory, and a radar data processor with advanced ECCM. Armament capability of the ICE Phantoms will be extended to include up to four Hughes AIM-120 (AMRAAM) air-to-air missiles. Other new avionics in the full ICE package are to include a new AEG radar control console, optimisation (by Hughes) of the cockpit display, installation of a new Litef digital fire control computer, Honeywell H-423 laser inertial platform, GEC Avionics CPU-143/A digital air data computer, new IFF system, a new guided missile launcher, a MIL-1553B digital data bus with advanced operational software, and improved resistance to electronic jamming and other countermeasures.

About 75 other Luftwaffe F-4Fs, serving in the fighter-bomber role with JaboG 35 and 36, are expected to undergo partial update (databus INS and ADC only, initially), with the option of a full ICE installation later.

Boeing. The company has a $22.6 million 1986 contract from the Ogden Air Logistics Center at Hill AFB, Utah, to modify the navigation and weapons delivery system on up to 600 F-4s of the USAF and Air National Guard. It includes production options extending up to 1990. Flight testing was to begin in mid-1987, with production of conversion kits starting in early 1988.

McDonnell Douglas. To reduce injuries to aircrew of F-4s, and loss of aircraft, due to bird strikes during low-level missions, McDonnell Douglas and Goodyear Aerospace have developed an improved, one-piece, bird-resistant windscreen. The first two F-4Es fitted retrospectively with the new windscreen successfully completed a one-year test and evaluation programme with the Missouri Air National Guard in 1986. Made from two layers of polycarbonate between two layers of acrylic plastics, the 2.5 cm (1 in) thick windscreen is designed to withstand impact by a 1.8 kg (4 lb) bird at an aircraft speed of 500 knots (925 km/h; 575 mph). Elimination of the former windscreen frame also improves the pilot's field of view.

The following details apply to the F-4E:

TYPE: Twin-engined two-seat all-weather fighter.

WINGS: Cantilever low-wing monoplane. Wing section NACA 0006.4-64 (mod) at root, NACA 0004-64 (mod) at wing fold line, NACA 0003-64 (mod) at tip. Average thickness/chord ratio 5.1%. Incidence 1°. Dihedral, inner panels 0°, outer panels 12°. Sweepback 45° on leading edges. Outer panels have extended chord and dihedral of 12°. Inset ailerons limited to down movement only, the 'up' function being supplied by spoilers on upper surface of each wing. Trailing-edge flaps and leading-edge manoeuvring slats. Airbrake under each wing aft of wheel well. Outer wing panels fold upward for stowage.

FUSELAGE: Semi-monocoque structure, built in forward, centre and rear sections. Double-wall construction under fuel tanks and for lower section of rear fuselage, with ram-air cooling.

TAIL UNIT: Cantilever structure, with 23° of anhedral on one-piece all-moving tailplane which has slotted leading edges. Rudder interconnected with ailerons at low speeds.

LANDING GEAR: Retractable tricycle type. Single wheel on each main unit, with tyres size 30 × 11.5 Type VIII; twin wheels on nose unit, which is steerable and self-centering and can be lengthened pneumatically to increase the aircraft's angle of attack for take-off. Brake-chute housed in fuselage tailcone. Mk II anti-skid system.

POWERPLANT: Two General Electric J79-GE-17A turbojet engines (each 79.6 kN; 17,900 lb st with afterburning). Variable-area inlet ducts monitored by air data computer. Integral fuel tankage in wings, between front and main spars, and in seven fuselage tanks, with total capacity of 7,022 litres (1,855 US gallons; 1,545 Imp gallons). Provision for one 2,270 litre (600 US gallon; 500 Imp gallon) external tank under fuselage and two 1,400 litre (370 US gallon; 308 Imp gallon) underwing tanks. Equipment for probe-and-drogue and 'buddy tank' flight refuelling, with retractable probe in starboard side of fuselage.

ACCOMMODATION: Crew of two in tandem on Martin-Baker Mk H7 ejection seats, under individual rearward-hinged canopies. Optional dual controls.

AVIONICS AND EQUIPMENT: Built with, or modified to have, digital intercept computer; AN/ASQ-19(B) com-nav-ident; MS25447/MS25448 counting accelerometer; AN/APN-155 radar altimeter; AN/AJB-7 all-altitude bomb system; AN/ASN-46A navigational computer; AN/ASN-63 INS; AN/ASQ-91 (MOD) weapons release system; AN/ASG-26 (MOD) lead computing optical sight; AN/APR-36, -37 RHAWS; AN/ASA-32 AFCS; AN/APQ-120 fire control system radar; AN/ARW-77 AGM-12 control system; some fitted with Northrop Tiseo (target identification system electro-optical); Pave Tack infra-red pod; Pave Spike day tracking/laser weapon designator pod; TD-709/AJB-7 sequential timer; ID-1755/A standby attitude reference system; and KB-25A gunsight camera. (See also model listing.)

ARMAMENT: Four AIM-7E Sparrow, Sidewinder (F-4Ds and Es in ANG use being modified to carry AIM-9L/M versions), AGM-45A Shrike or AGM-88A HARM missiles, on four semi-submerged mountings under fuselage and four underwing mountings. Provision for carrying alternative loads of up to about 7,250 kg (16,000 lb) on seven attachments under wings and fuselage. Stores which can be carried include bombs; land mine; fire bombs; cluster bombs; practice bombs; flares; rocket packs; ECM pods; gun pods; spray tanks; tow targets; and camera pod. One 20 mm M61A-1 Vulcan six-barrel cannon (1,020 rounds of ammunition).

DIMENSIONS, EXTERNAL:

Wing span	11.77 m (38 ft 7½ in)
Width, wings folded	8.41 m (27 ft 7 in)
Length overall	19.20 m (63 ft 0 in)
Height overall	5.02 m (16 ft 5½ in)
Wheel track	5.45 m (17 ft 10½ in)

AREA:

Wings, gross	49.2 m² (530 sq ft)

WEIGHTS:

Weight empty	13,757 kg (30,328 lb)
Weight empty, basic mission	14,448 kg (31,853 lb)
Combat T-O weight	18,818 kg (41,487 lb)
Design T-O weight	26,308 kg (58,000 lb)
Max T-O weight	28,030 kg (61,795 lb)

PERFORMANCE (A at 24,410 kg; 53,814 lb, B at 24,572 kg; 54,171 lb, C at 25,397 kg; 55,991 lb, D at 27,954 kg; 61,629 lb, and E at 28,030 kg; 61,795 lb T-O weight, except where indicated):

Max level speed with external stores	over Mach 2

Average speed:

A, B	504 knots (934 km/h; 580 mph)
C	506 knots (938 km/h; 583 mph)
D	502 knots (930 km/h; 578 mph)
E	496 knots (919 km/h; 571 mph)

Stalling speed, approach power with BLC:		Landing run (A at landing weight of 16,706 kg; 36,831 lb, B and	
A	148 knots (273.5 km/h; 170 mph)	C at 15,937 kg; 35,134 lb, D at 17,155 kg; 37,821 lb, and E at	
B	148.5 knots (275 km/h; 171 mph)	17,211 kg; 37,944 lb);	
C	151 knots (280 km/h; 174 mph)	A	1,122 m (3,680 ft)
D	158.4 knots (294 km/h; 182.5 mph)	B, C	1,073 m (3,520 ft)
E	158.6 knots (294.5 km/h; 183 mph)	D	1,146 m (3,760 ft)
Max rate of climb at S/L: A	2,847 m (9,340 ft)/min	E	1,152 m (3,780 ft)
B	2,816 m (9,240 ft)/min	Landing run, with parabrake: A	927 m (3,040 ft)
C	2,621 m (8,600 ft)/min	B, C	887 m (2,910 ft)
D	2,003 m (6,570 ft)/min	D	948 m (3,110 ft)
E	1,881 m (6,170 ft)/min	E	951 m (3,120 ft)
Service ceiling (supersonic)	16,580 m (54,400 ft)	Combat radius:	
T-O run: A	969 m (3,180 ft)	Area intercept	683 nm (1,266 km; 786 miles)
B	985 m (3,230 ft)	Defensive counter-air	429 nm (795 km; 494 miles)
C	1,064 m (3,490 ft)	Interdiction	618 nm (1,145 km; 712 miles)
D	1,329 m (4,360 ft)	Ferry range	1,718 nm (3,184 km; 1,978 miles)
E	1,338 m (4,390 ft)		

McDonnell Douglas F-15 Eagle

The US Air Force requested development funding for a new air superiority fighter in 1965, and in due course design proposals were sought from three airframe manufacturers: Fairchild Hiller Corporation, McDonnell Douglas Corporation, and North American Rockwell Corporation. On 23 December 1969 it was announced that McDonnell Douglas had been selected as airframe prime contractor. The resulting contract called for the design and manufacture of 20 aircraft for development testing, these to comprise 18 single-seat **F-15As** and two TF-15A two-seat trainers. First flight of the F-15A was made on 27 July 1972, and the first flight of a two-seat TF-15A trainer (subsequently redesignated **F-15B**) on 7 July 1973.

A production go-ahead for the first 30 operational aircraft (FY 1973 funds) was announced on 1 March 1973. The FY 1974 Defense Procurement Bill authorised production of 62 aircraft, and subsequent Procurement Bills authorised production of a further 622 aircraft through FY 1982. Under the multi-year plans proposed in early 1983, eventual procurement for the US Air Force is expected to total 1,266,

excluding the 20 development aircraft, by the early 1990s. An F-15B (the 21st Eagle built) was the first Eagle delivered to the US Air Force, on 14 November 1974. Structural weight of the F-15B is approx 363 kg (800 lb) more than that of the F-15A. Production of the F-15A and B totalled 361 and 58 respectively.

Eagles produced since June 1979 are to **F-15C** and **F-15D** standard, which provides for 6,103 kg (13,455 lb) of internal fuel, and the ability to carry two low-drag conformal fuel tanks (CFT) developed specially for the F-15 by McDonnell Aircraft Company. Each CFT contains approximately 3,228 litres (114 cu ft) of usable volume, which can accommodate 2,211 kg (4,875 lb) of JP-4 fuel. It attaches to the side of either the port or starboard engine air intake trunk (being made in handed pairs), is designed to the same load factors as the basic aircraft, and can be removed in 15 minutes. CFTs could be configured to accommodate avionics such as reconnaissance sensors, radar detection and jamming equipment, a laser designator, low-light-level TV system, and reconnaissance cameras, in addition to fuel. All external stores stations remain available with the CFTs in use, and McDonnell Douglas has developed for the F-15 a new

McDonnell Douglas F-15C Eagle of the USAFE's 36th Tactical Fighter Wing. (Mike Jerram)

Conformal reconnaissance pod under private-venture development for two-seat F-15s.

weapon attachment system which can extend the operating radius with large external loads by up to 40 per cent. Known as tangential carriage, it involves the installation of rows of stub pylons on the lower corner and bottom of each of the CFTs. Up to twelve 1,000 lb-class or four 2,000 lb-class weapons can be carried on these pylons, instead of on the normal multiple racks which cause more drag and occupy external fuel stations, so limiting the aircraft's range. AIM-7F missiles can also be attached directly to the CFTs.

Evaluation of the tangential carriage concept was undertaken by the US Air Force at Edwards AFB, California, between 18 and 31 August 1983, using the first-built F-15C. In-service F-15Cs and F-15Ds will be able to employ tangential-carriage CFTs after completion of the multi-staged improvement programme (MSIP) described in a later paragraph.

The first F-15C (78-468) flew for the first time on 26 February 1979, and the first F-15D on 19 June of that year. Since 1980 the APG-63 radar of F-15C/D aircraft has been equipped with a Hughes Aircraft programmable signal processor, which enables changes to be incorporated in the radar earlier and more cheaply. An updated radar data processor increases memory capability from 24K to 96K. These added features enable the radar to operate in a high-resolution raid assessment mode which can identify clustered targets individually. F-15C and F-15D aircraft delivered before the availability of the programmable signal processor and expanded computer will be retrofitted to bring them up to standard. Minor changes have been made to tyres, wheels and brakes to allow for an increased maximum T-O weight, which can be as high as 30,845 kg (68,000 lb) with full internal fuel, CFTs and external tanks. Landing gear and fuel system changes have added about 272 kg (600 lb) to the aircraft's dry weight.

An overload warning system is now being installed in F-15C/D aircraft which permits the pilot to manoeuvre safely to 9g throughout most of the flight envelope at flight design gross weights. It will be retrofitted to all F-15s delivered earlier.

In February 1983 the US Air Force awarded McDonnell Aircraft Co an $86.7 million contract for an initial F-15 multi-staged improvement programme (MSIP). This covers introduction of a Hughes APG-70 radar with memory increase to 1,000K and trebled processing speed; upgrading the aircraft's central computer to store four times as much data and process it three times as quickly; and replacing the current cockpit control panel for the armament control system by a single multi-purpose Sperry colour video screen. Linked to a computer, the Dynamics Control armament control system will be programmable, allowing for the addition of future weapons such as advanced versions of the AIM-7 and AIM-9 and AMRAAM. Other MSIP improvements include a tactical electronic system consisting of a Northrop Enhanced ALQ-135 internal countermeasures system, Loral ALR-56C radar warning receiver, Tracor ALE-45 chaff dispenser, and Magnavox electronic warfare warning system. A further $274.4 million contract was received in December 1983. Flight testing of the new system began in December 1984. The first production F-15C built under MSIP was unveiled at McDonnell Douglas' St Louis plant on 20 June 1985.

By June 1987 a total of 1,060 Eagles had been delivered, including 850 to the USAF. The 48th Fighter-Interceptor Squadron at Langley AFB, Virginia, was the first US air defence squadron to receive the Eagle, as opposed to earlier tactical fighter units.

On 15 September 1985 an F-15 from the 6512th TS at Edwards AFB, operating from Vandenburg AFB, California, carried out the successful destruction of an orbiting satellite (Solwind P78-1) with an air-launched LTV anti-satellite (ASAT) weapon. F-15s of the 48th FIS at Langley AFB, Virginia, and 318th FIS at McChord AFB, Washington, are expected to operate in anti-satellite roles as part of ADTAC if the ASAT programme leads to operational deployment of such a weapon.

Equipment of Air National Guard units with F-15A and F-15B aircraft began on 29 June 1985 with the 122nd TFS, at New Orleans, Louisiana, and has been followed by delivery of F-15As and F-15Bs to the 116th TFW, 159th TFG, Georgia ANG, at Dobbins AFB in 1986 and the 199th TFS, 154th Composite Group, Hawaii ANG, at Hickam AFB, starting in March 1987. The 102nd Fighter Interceptor Wing, based at Otis ANG Base, Massachusetts, is expected to receive its first F-15As and F-15Bs in early 1988, replacing F-106 Delta Darts.

The F-15 has also been selected by the US Air Force for assignment to the Central Command Rapid Deployment Force. To ensure optimum effectiveness for the aircraft allocated to this mission, the US Air Force has procured 325 sets of conformal fuel tanks and 150 BRU-26A/A six-station multiple bomb racks.

Export deliveries include 51 Eagles for Israel and 62 for Saudi Arabia. The JASDF plans to purchase a total of 187 **F-15Js** and **F-15DJs**, of which 173 are being licence-built in Japan, with Mitsubishi as the prime contractor. The first of the 14 US-built aircraft was handed over on 15 July 1980, and the first two were flown to Japan in March 1981.

McDonnell Douglas has developed an air-to-ground attack version of the Eagle, known as the **F-15E** dual-role fighter; this is described separately. Also described separately is an advanced STOL version of the Eagle which McDonnell Douglas will develop and flight test for the US Air Force.

McDonnell Douglas has proposed a version of the F-15 Eagle for the USAF's Follow-on Weasel defence suppression aircraft requirement to replace F-4G Wild Weasels in the USAF inventory. As a private venture the company is also developing a conformal reconnaissance pod designed to be

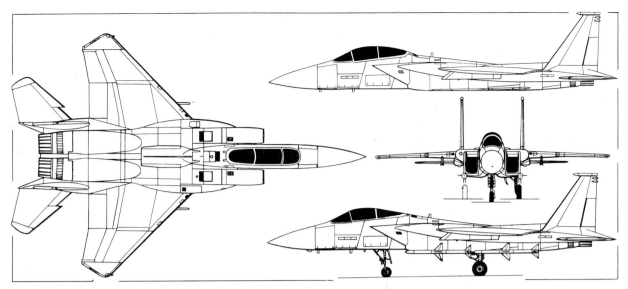

JASDF F-15J fighters, licence-built by Mitsubishi.

carried on the centreline stores station of two-seat F-15s. The pod, which was being flight tested in the Summer of 1987, transmits imagery to ground stations via a data link, but recording equipment could be housed in the aircraft's ammunition bay.

The following description applies to the standard F-15C:

TYPE: Single-seat twin-turbofan air superiority fighter, with secondary attack role.

WINGS: Cantilever shoulder-wing monoplane. Wing uses NACA 64A aerofoil section with varying thickness/chord ratios, ranging from 6.6% at the root to 3% at the tip. Leading edges modified with conical camber. Anhedral 1°. Incidence 0°. Sweepback at quarter-chord 38° 42′. Plain ailerons and plain trailing-edge flaps. No spoilers or trim tabs. No anti-icing system.

FUSELAGE: Semi-monocoque structure. Speedbrake on upper centre fuselage, constructed of graphite/epoxy, aluminium honeycomb and titanium.

TAIL UNIT: Cantilever structure with twin fins and rudders. All-moving horizontal tail surfaces outboard of fins, with extended chord on outer leading edges.

LANDING GEAR: Retractable tricycle type, with single wheel on each unit. Nosewheel and tyre by Goodyear, size 22 × 6.6-10. Mainwheels by Bendix, with Goodyear tyres size 34.5 × 9.75-18. Bendix carbon heat-sink brakes. Wheel braking skid control system.

POWERPLANT: Two Pratt & Whitney F100-PW-100 turbofan engines, each rated at approx 106.0 kN (23,830 lb st) with afterburning for take-off. Internal fuel in eight Goodyear fuselage tanks, total capacity 7,836 litres (2,070 US gallons; 1,724 Imp gallons). Fuel gauge system by Simmonds Precision Products Inc. Optional conformal fuel tanks attached to side of engine air intakes, beneath wing, each containing 2,839 litres (750 US gallons; 624 Imp gallons). Provision for up to three additional 2,309 litre (610 US gallon; 508 Imp gallon) external fuel tanks. Max total internal and external fuel capacity 20,441 litres (5,400 US gallons; 4,496 Imp gallons).

ENGINE INTAKES: Straight two-dimensional external compression inlet, on each side of the fuselage.

ACCOMMODATION: Pilot only, on ACES II ejection seat developed by McDonnell Douglas. Stretched acrylic canopy and windscreen.

AVIONICS: General Electric automatic analog flight control system standard. Hughes Aircraft APG-63 X-band pulse-Doppler radar (being upgraded to APG-70 by MSIP modification) provides long-range detection and tracking of small high-speed targets operating at all altitudes down to treetop level, and feeds accurate tracking information to the airborne central computer to ensure effective launch of the aircraft's missiles or the firing of its internal gun. For close-in dogfights, the radar acquires the target automatically and the steering/weapon system information is displayed on a head-up display. IBM is subcontractor for the central computer, and McDonnell Douglas Electronics Company for the head-up display. This latter unit projects all essential flight information in the form of symbols on to a combining glass positioned above the instrument panel at pilot's eye level. The display presents the pilot with all the information required to intercept and destroy an enemy aircraft without need for him to remove his eyes from the target. The display also provides navigation and other steering control information under all flight conditions. A transponder for the IFF system, developed by Teledyne Electronics Company, informs ground stations and other suitably equipped aircraft that the F-15 is a friendly aircraft. It also supplies data on the F-15's range, azimuth, altitude and identification to air traffic controllers. The F-15 carries a Hazeltine AN/APX-76 interrogator receiver-transmitter, to inform the pilot if an aircraft seen visually or on radar is friendly. A reply evaluator for the IFF system, which operates with the AN/APX-76, was developed by Litton Systems Inc. A Sperry Flight Systems vertical situation display set, using a cathode ray tube to present radar, electro-optical identification and attitude director indicator formats to

357

the pilot, permits inputs received from the aircraft's sensors and the central computer to be visible to the pilot under any light conditions. Sperry also developed the air data computer for the F-15, as well as an attitude and heading reference set to provide information on the aircraft's pitch, roll and magnetic heading that is fed to cockpit displays. This latter unit also serves as a backup to the Litton inertial navigation set which provides the basic navigation data and is the aircraft's primary attitude reference, enabling the F-15 to navigate anywhere in the world. In addition to giving the aircraft's position at all times, the inertial navigation system provides pitch, roll, heading, acceleration and speed information.

Other specialised equipment for flight control, navigation and communications includes a Collins micro-miniaturised Tacan system; Collins horizontal situation indicator to present aircraft navigation information on a symbolic pictorial display; Collins ADF and ILS receivers; Magnavox UHF transceiver and UHF auxiliary transceiver. The communications sets have cryptographic capability. Dorne and Margolin glideslope localiser antenna, and Teledyne Avionics angle-of-attack sensors. Northrop (Defense Systems Division) Enhanced AN/ALQ-135(V) internal countermeasures set provides automatic jamming of enemy radar signals; Loral ALR-56C radar warning systems; Magnavox electronic warfare warning set; and Tracor AN/ALE-45 chaff dispenser.

ARMAMENT: Provision for carriage and launch of a variety of air-to-air weapons over short and medium ranges, including four AIM-9L/M Sidewinders, four AIM-7F/M Sparrows or eight AMRAAM, and a 20 mm M61A1 six-barrel gun with 940 rounds of ammunition. General Electric lead-computing gyro. To keep the pilot informed of the status of his weapons and provide for their management, an armament control set has been developed by Dynamic Controls Corporation. Three air-to-surface weapon stations (five if configured with conformal fuel tanks) allow for the carriage of up to 10,705 kg (23,600 lb) of bombs, rockets or additional ECM equipment.

DIMENSIONS, EXTERNAL:

Wing span	13.05 m (42 ft 9¾ in)
Length overall	19.43 m (63 ft 9 in)
Height overall	5.63 m (18 ft 5½ in)
Wheel track	2.75 m (9 ft 0¼ in)
Wheelbase	5.42 m (17 ft 9½ in)

AREA:

Wings, gross	56.5 m² (608 sq ft)

WEIGHTS:

Weight empty, equipped (no fuel, ammunition, pylons or external stores)	12,973 kg (28,600 lb)
T-O weight (interceptor, full internal fuel and 4 Sparrows)	20,244 kg (44,630 lb)
T-O weight (incl three 2,309 litre; 610 US gallon; 508 Imp gallon drop-tanks)	26,521 kg (58,470 lb)

Max T-O weight: with CFTs	30,845 kg (68,000 lb)

PERFORMANCE:

Max level speed	more than Mach 2.5 (800 knots; 1,482 km/h; 921 mph CAS)
T-O run (interceptor)	274 m (900 ft)
Landing run (interceptor), without braking parachute	1,067 m (3,500 ft)
Service ceiling	18,300 m (60,000 ft)
Ferry range: with external tanks, without CFTs	more than 2,500 nm (4,631 km; 2,878 miles)
with CFTs	3,100 nm (5,745 km; 3,570 miles)

Max endurance:

with in-flight refuelling	15 h 0 min
unrefuelled, with CFTs	5 h 15 min
Design g limits	+9/−3

McDonnell Douglas F-15E Eagle

The F-15E is a two-seat dual-role version of the Eagle capable of performing long-range, deep interdiction, high-ordnance-payload air-to-ground missions by day or night, and in adverse weather, while retaining its proven air-to-air capabilities. The prototype, known initially as the Strike Eagle, was developed with industry funds as a modification of a two-seat F-15B. The rear cockpit was upgraded with four multi-purpose CRT displays for radar, weapon selection, and monitoring of enemy tracking systems. Production F-15Es will also have front cockpit modifications that include redesigned controls, a wide field-of-view head-up display, and three CRTs providing multi-purpose displays for improved navigation, weapons delivery and systems operation, including moving map displays, weapons options, precision radar mapping, and terrain following.

For tactical target missions at night and in all weather conditions, the F-15E has advanced radar and infra-red systems. A new high-resolution Hughes APG-70 radar, wide-field forward looking infra-red (FLIR) and Martin Marietta LANTIRN navigation and targeting pods will ensure target detection/identification and improve the accuracy of weapons delivery. Successful integration of these systems was demonstrated during 1982 in flight tests at Edwards AFB, California, and Eglin AFB, Florida, resulting in accurate 'blind' weapons delivery.

Some 60 per cent of the F-15's structure was redesigned to create the F-15E, the airframe of which is expected to have a fatigue life of 16,000 flying hours. To accommodate the new avionics, internal fuel capacity has been reduced slightly, to 7,643 litres (2,019 US gallons; 1,681 Imp gallons), by reducing the capacity of one fuselage tank, but for increased payload/range capability the F-15E can utilise standard F-15 conformal fuel tanks with a full complement of bombs carried on integral, tangential bomb racks. The conformal tanks add 5,678 litres (1,500 US gallons; 1,249 Imp gallons) of fuel for increased range, and can be used in conjunction with up to three 2,309 litre (610 US gallon; 508 Imp gallon) external fuel tanks. In addition to carrying a variety of guided and unguided bombs and other air-to-ground weapons, the F-15E retains its air-superiority performance and weapons (AIM-7 Sparrow, AIM-9 Sidewinder and AIM-120 AMRAAM). Built-in flexibility will allow for growth and increased variety in weapons carriage.

A digital, triple-redundant Lear Siegler Astronautics flight control system is installed in the F-15E, permitting coupled automatic terrain following, and a Honeywell ring laser gyro inertial navigation system provides quick reaction alignment

First prototype McDonnell Douglas F-15E Eagle dual-role fighter.

and improved navigational accuracy. A new engine bay developed by McDonnell Douglas enables the F-15E to be powered by either General Electric F110 or Pratt & Whitney F100 engines. The engine bay structure consists of large titanium sections manufactured with superplastic forming and diffusion bonding processes, and will permit future installation of growth versions of these engines, providing a total of up to 266.9 kN (60,000 lb st) on the aircraft's two-engine installation. An F-15 powered by Pratt & Whitney's improved F100-PW-220 engine was delivered to the 33rd TFW at Eglin AFB, Florida, in August 1986 for in-service evaluation. The F-15E incorporates digital electronic engine control, engine trimming and monitoring systems. Other improvements include foam filled fuel tanks for greater survivability, higher rated generators and an improved environmental control system.

US Air Force and McDonnell Douglas pilots began flight testing product improvements for the F-15E on four Eagles, including an F-15C, an F-15D and the prototype Strike Eagle, at Edwards AFB in November 1982. The programme was completed successfully on schedule on 30 April 1983, after more than 200 flights. During the tests, an F-15 took off

McDonnell Douglas F-15E Eagle. *(Pilot Press)*

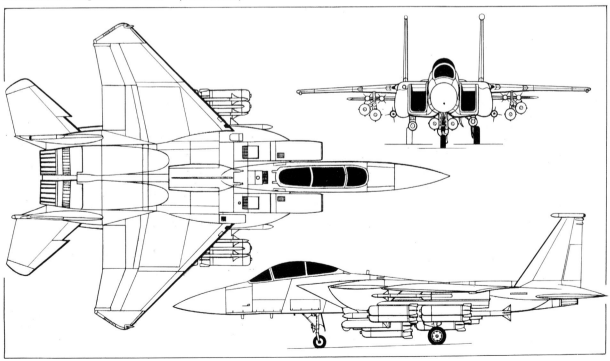

for the first time at a gross weight of 34,019 kg (75,000 lb), ie 3,175 kg (7,000 lb) more than the standard max T-O weight of the F-15C with conformal fuel tanks. On this occasion the aircraft was equipped with two CFTs, three other external tanks, and eight 500 lb Mk 82 bombs. In the overall programme 16 different stores loads configurations were tested, including the carriage of 2,000 lb Mk 84 bombs and BDU-38 and CBU-58 weapons, delivered both by visual and radar means.

After evaluating the potential of the dual-role Eagle against that of the General Dynamics F-16XL, the USAF announced on 24 February 1984 that it had selected the F-15E for development. Design work began in April 1984 under an initial increment of a $359.4 million fixed-price incentive contract. Construction of the first of three F-15E prototypes began in July 1985. This aircraft made its first flight on 11 December 1986, and took part in an official rollout ceremony at McDonnell Douglas's St Louis, Missouri, plant one week later. The first production F-15E was expected to fly in December 1987, for delivery to the USAF's 405th Tactical Training Wing at Luke AFB, Arizona, in January 1988. The US Air Force plans to procure 392 dual-role Eagles. IOC is expected in late 1988.

The description of the F-15C applies also to the F-15E except:

TYPE: Two-seat dual-role attack/air superiority fighter.

FUSELAGE: Upper rear fuselage, rear fuselage keel structure, main landing gear doors and some rear fuselage fairings incorporate superplastic-formed/diffusion bonded (SPF/DB) titanium structure, providing additional engine bay volume to permit compatibility with alternative engines.

LANDING GEAR: As for F-15C, but with Bendix wheels and Michelin tyres on all units. Nosewheel tyre size 22 × 7.75-9, mainwheel tyres size 36 × 11-18. Bendix five-rotor carbon disc brakes.

ACCOMMODATION: Two crew, pilot and weapon systems officer, in tandem on McDonnell Douglas ACES II ejection seats. Single-piece, upward-hinged canopy.

ARMAMENT: 20 mm M61A1 six-barrel gun in starboard wing root, with 512 rds. General Electric lead computing gyro. Provision on underwing (one per wing) and centreline pylons for air-to-air and air-to-ground weapons and external fuel tanks. Wing pylons use standard rail and ejection launchers for AIM-9 Sidewinder and AIM-120 AMRAAM air-to-air missiles; AIM-7 Sparrow and AIM-120 AMRAAM can be carried on launchers on centreline station or on tangential stores carriers on conformal fuel tanks (maximum total load four each AIM-7 or AIM-9, up to eight AIM-120). Single- or triple-rail launchers for AGM-65 Maverick air-to-ground missiles can be fitted to wing stations only. Tangential carriage on CFTs provides for up to six bomb racks on each tank, with provision for triple ejector racks on wing and centreline stations. The F-15E can carry a wide variety and quantity of guided and unguided air-to-ground weapons, including Mk 20 Rockeye (26), Mk 82 (26), Mk 83 (15), Ml 84 (seven), BSU-49 (26), BSU-50 (seven), GBU-8 (five), GBU-10 (seven), GBU-12 (15), GBU-15 (two), GBU-22 (15), GBU-24 (five), CBU-52 (25), CBU-58 (25), CBU-71 (25), CBU-87 (25), CBU-89 (25), CBU-90 (25), CBU-92 (25), CBU-93 (25) bombs; LAU-3A rockets (nine), SUU-20 training weapons (five), A/A-37 U-33 tow target (one), B-57 and B-61 series nuclear weapons (five), and AGM-65 Maverick (six). An AXQ-14 data link pod is used in conjunction with the GBU-15; LANTIRN pod illumination is used to designate targets for the GBU-12, -22 and -24 laser guided bombs.

WEIGHTS:

Basic operating weight empty	14,379 kg (31,700 lb)
Max weapon load	10,659 kg (23,500 lb)
Max T-O weight	36,741 kg (81,000 lb)

McDonnell Douglas F-15 STOL Manoeuvring Technology Demonstrator

In October 1984 McDonnell Douglas was awarded a $117.8 million cost-sharing contract to develop and flight test for the US Air Force Wright Aeronautical Laboratories an advanced-technology version of the F-15 with short take-off and landing (STOL) and new manoeuvring capabilities, designated **F-15S/MTD** (STOL/Manoeuvring Technology Demonstrator). The programme will investigate four specific technologies: two-dimensional (2-D) thrust-vectoring/reversing jet nozzles; integrated flight/propulsion control; rough/soft-field STOL landing gear; and advanced pilot/vehicle interfaces.

McDonnell Douglas is modifying its No. 1 F-15B flight test aircraft for the programme. Controllable foreplanes, adapted from the tailplanes of the F/A-18A Hornet, will be installed above the F-15B's engine air intake trunks, forward of the wings. Mounted at a dihedral angle of 20°, the foreplanes will operate symmetrically or asymmetrically to provide pitch and roll moments, and will be used as stability maintaining surfaces rather than for primary flight control. They will permit the F-15's maximum allowable load factor to be increased from 7.33g to 9g without additional structural strengthening. Rectangular, two-dimensional vectoring nozzles manufactured from carbonfibre will be

Artist's impression of the advanced technology S/MTD version of the F-15 Eagle.

installed at the rear of the aircraft's F100 engines, replacing the F-15B's standard afterburner ducts. The nozzles will vector engine thrust by up to 20° upwards or downwards from the longitudinal axis to enhance take-off performance and flight manoeuvring. Thrust reverser vanes in the nozzles will be flight-deployable for rapid deceleration, in addition to their short-landing-roll function.

A digital fly-by-wire system will integrate with the flight control system all functions of foreplanes, flaperons, horizontal tail surfaces and vectoring nozzles to provide high precision control of the aircraft's flightpath for landing approach. Structurally reinforced landing gear will permit 3.66 m (12 ft)/s landing impact loads. The F-15S/MTD will employ F-15E avionics and cockpit displays.

The F-15S/MTD incorporates new aluminium-lithium alloys, and an F-15 with major wing skin panels of this material, made by Alcan Ltd (UK), began flight testing in the Summer of 1986. The new skins are 5 per cent stronger and 9 per cent lighter than the conventional aluminium parts they replace. Aluminium accounts for about 2,948 kg (6,500 lb), or 51 per cent, of the current F-15's empty weight.

Performance parameters specified for the F-15S/MTD demonstrator include take-off and landing runs of 457 m (1,500 ft) on a 15 m (50 ft) wide, hard, wet, rough surface runway, at night and in adverse weather, with fuel, gun, ammunition and a 2,721 kg (6,000 lb) external payload. McDonnell Douglas is said to be aiming for take-off and landing runs of 305 m (1,000 ft) and 381 m (1,250 ft) respectively. A 6 to 7 per cent increase in manoeuvring performance over the standard F-15 is anticipated, with a 4,536 kg (10,000 lb) increase in payload when operating from a 457 m (1,500 ft) runway, a 27 per cent reduction in take-off run, 13 per cent improvement in cruise range, 24 per cent better roll rate and up to 100 per cent improvement in pitch rate.

The F-15S/MTD is scheduled to make its first flight in March 1988. The initial test programme will include some 150 hours of flight testing. For the initial flights, the 2-D nozzles will not be fitted; flights with the new nozzles are expected to begin in September 1988. Major subcontractors in the programme are Pratt & Whitney, General Electric's Flight Control Division, and the National Water Lift Division of Pneumo Corporation.

McDonnell Douglas/BAe AV-8B Harrier II

Details of the AV-8B Harrier II can be found in the International section.

McDonnell Douglas F/A-18A Hornet

Canadian AF designations: CF-18A/B
Spanish Air Force designations: C.15 and CE.15

In the spring of 1974 the US Department of Defense accepted a proposal from the US Navy to study a low-cost lightweight multi-mission fighter, then identified as the VFAX. In August of that year Congress terminated the VFAX concept, directing instead that the Navy should investigate versions of the General Dynamics YF-16 and Northrop YF-17 lightweight fighter prototypes then under evaluation for the USAF.

McDonnell Douglas concluded that Northrop's contender could be redesigned at minimum cost to meet the Navy's requirements. It then teamed with Northrop to propose a derivative of the YF-17 to meet the Navy's requirement, with McDonnell Douglas as the prime contractor. Identified as the Navy Air Combat Fighter (NACF), this received the name Hornet when selected for further development. Two single-seat versions were proposed originally, of which the F-18A was intended for fighter duties and the A-18 for attack missions. Except for a small amount of operational equipment and missile armament, the two proved so similar that a single configuration, known as the F/A-18, was able eventually to undertake both missions. Under the terms of an April 1985 agreement, McDonnell Douglas became prime contractor for all existing and future versions of the aircraft, and Northrop is principal subcontractor. Northrop builds the centre and rear fuselage, which is delivered totally assembled to McDonnell Douglas. Assembly is completed at St Louis. The following versions have been announced:

F/A-18A. Single-seat escort fighter/interdictor to replace F-4, armed with fuselage-mounted Sparrows; also a single-seat attack aircraft to replace A-7, with FLIR and a laser tracker, developed as part of the Hornet programme, replacing the Sparrow missiles.

F/A-18B. Tandem two-seat version of F/A-18A for

McDonnell Douglas F/A-18As of USMC Squadron VMFA-323. *(Brian M. Service)*

First production McDonnell Douglas F/A-18C strike fighter.

training, with combat capability, formerly known as TF/A-18A. Fuel capacity reduced by less than 6 per cent.

F/A-18C and F/A-18D. Single- and two-seat aircraft purchased from FY 1986 onwards. Similar to F/A-18A/B, but with provision for carriage of up to six AMRAAM weapons, two fuselage mounted and two on each outboard wing stores station; up to four imaging infra-red Maverick missiles, one on each wing station; provisions for AN/ALQ-165 airborne self-protection jammer (ASPJ), permitting interchangeability with AN/ALQ-126B; reconnaissance equipment; upgraded stores management set with 128K memory, Intel 8086 processor, upgraded armament multiplex bus to meet MIL-STD 1553B and MIL-STD 1760 weapons interface capability; flight incident recorder and monitoring set (FIRAMS) which incorporates an integrated fuel/engine indicator, data storage set for recording maintenance and flight incidence data, a signal data processor interfacing with the fuel system to provide overall system control, enhanced built-in test capability and automatic adjustment of aircraft centre of gravity as fuel is consumed in flight; a maintenance status panel enabling avionics faults to be isolated at circuit card level, new XN-6 mission computer with higher processing speed and double memory of the F/A-18A/B's XN-5; and Martin-Baker Naval Aircrew Common Escape System (NACES) ejection seat.

The first F/A-18C flew on 3 September 1986 and was delivered to NATC Patuxent River on 21 September. Flight testing was due to begin in late 1987 of all-weather night attack capability for the F/A-18, to include provision for pilot's night vision goggles, a FLIR navigation pod, raster head-up display, multi-function colour displays and a digital mapping system. The F/A-18D will also incorporate a fully mission-capable rear cockpit featuring independent display selection. F/A-18s delivered from October 1989 will incorporate night-attack capability as standard.

F/A-18(R). The US Navy began evaluation of a simple reconnaissance conversion of the standard F/A-18A in the autumn of 1982. This involves removal of the gun from the aircraft's nose, and its replacement by a twin-sensor package with two windows in a slightly bulged underfairing. Sensors can include a Fairchild-Weston KA-99 low/medium-altitude panoramic camera and/or Honeywell AAD-5 IR linescan. Additional sensors, including a low-altitude camera, are

being studied. The F/A-18(R) can be converted overnight to the fighter/attack configuration within the operational squadron. Flight testing of the first F/A-18 fitted with reconnaissance equipment began on 15 August 1984.

CF-18A. Version for Canadian Armed Forces, which plan to purchase 138, including 40 **CF-18B** two-seaters. Selection announced on 10 April 1980. First example made its initial flight on 29 July 1982. Deliveries began with CAF901 and CAF902 on 25 October 1982 and are scheduled to continue at the rate of two per month until 1988. By Summer 1987 a total of 110 CF-18s had been delivered. First CAF unit was No. 410 Squadron, based at CFB Cold Lake, Alberta. CF-18s are replacing CF-101s, CF-104s and CF-5s. By comparison with US Navy version, CF-18 has different ILS and added spotlight on port side of fuselage for night identification of other aircraft in flight.

Australian F/A-18A/B. Versions for the Royal

Canadian Armed Forces CF-18B two-seater. *(Erik Simonsen)*

McDonnell Douglas F/A-18B of the Royal Australian Air Force. *(The Age, Melbourne)*

Australian Air Force. The intention to procure 75 Hornets was announced on 20 October 1981. Two of the RAAF F/A-18Bs were manufactured by McDonnell Douglas, and delivered by air from NAS Lemoore, California, to RAAF Williamtown, near Sydney, on 17 May 1985. The first F/A-18B assembled in Australia by Aerospace Technologies of Australia made its first flight on 26 February 1985 and was handed over to the RAAF's No. 2 Operational Conversion Unit in the following month. The first Australian manufactured aircraft (F/A-18B A21-104) made its first flight on 3 June 1985. The RAAF's F/A-18s (57 single-seat F/A-18As and 18 two-seat F/A-18Bs) are now replacing Mirage III-Os. Three operational squadrons will be formed, with deliveries scheduled for completion in 1990.

EF-18. Version for Spanish Air Force, which has ordered 72 for delivery from 1986, with an option on 12 more. Contract signed in May 1983. First aircraft rolled out 22 November 1985 and delivered to Spain in 1986, with IOC in 1987. In Spanish Air Force service, aircraft is designated **C.15** (single-seat) and **CE.15** (two-seat).

RF-18D. Reconnaissance version of F/A-18D for US Marine Corps incorporating an all-weather reconnaissance pod on the centreline stores station. The pod, under development by Loral, houses a version of the UPD-4 SLAR high resolution synthetic aperture side-looking radar to supplement the F/A-18's nose mounted optical and infra-red sensors. Imagery is transmitted in real time via a datalink but could be displayed in the rear cockpit of the RF-18D, with growth potential within the pod for installation of an electro-optical camera. The pod, datalink and digital processing equipment has been successfully tested on a US Marine Corps RF-4B. A configuration definition study was under way in mid-1987, aimed at service entry of the RF-18D in late 1990.

A total of 1,157 Hornets, including the 11 development aircraft, is planned for construction into the 1990s, for the US Navy and Marine Corps. More than 150 of those built will be two-seat trainers. Deliveries to the US Navy totalled 415 by September 1987.

The first Hornet (160775) made its first flight on 18 November 1978; the second flew on 12 March 1979, and all 11 development aircraft were flying by March 1980, including two F/A-18B two-seat combat-capable trainers. In the fourth quarter of 1979, a Hornet became the first modern jet aircraft to complete initial sea trials within one year of its first flight, and the first production aircraft was delivered to the US Navy for operational evaluation in May 1980.

The first development squadron (VFA-125) was formed at NAS Lemoore, California, in November 1980. Operational evaluation and Navy BIS (Bureau of Inspection and Survey) trials began in early 1982. Fleet training began in mid-1982

McDonnell Douglas F/A-18A Hornet. *(Pilot Press)*

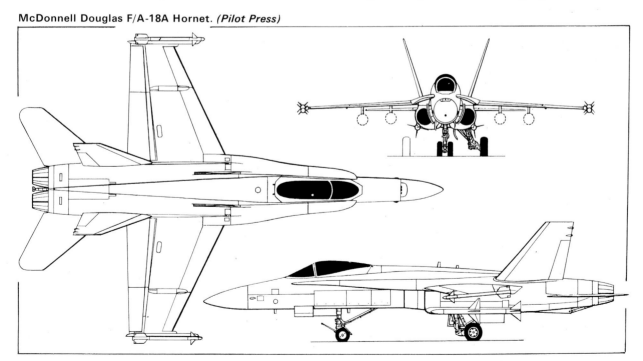

and the Hornet officially entered operational service on 7 January 1983, with Marine Fighter/Attack Squadron 314 at MCAS El Toro, California, and later with VMFA-531 and VMFA-323. On 1 February 1985 the first Atlantic Fleet F/A-18A operational squadrons began forming at Cecil Field NAS, Florida, after training at NAS Lemoore, California. Also in February, two F/A-18A squadrons, VFA-113 'Stingers' and VFA-25 'Fist of the Fleet' embarked in the aircraft carrier USS *Constellation* for the aircraft's first extended deployment at sea.

In February 1986 the F/A-18A was selected to replace the US Navy Blue Angels Flight Demonstration Squadron's A-4F Skyhawks from 1987. Eight early production aircraft, not suitable for shipboard operation, have been fitted with smoke-generating systems and special seat harnesses. The Blue Angels began training on the F/A-18A at El Centro NAS, California, in January 1987.

The following information applies specifically to the single-seat US Navy F/A-18C:

TYPE: Single-seat naval strike fighter.

WINGS: Cantilever mid-wing monoplane. Anhedral 3°. Sweepback 20° at quarter-chord. Multi-spar structure, primarily of light alloy and graphite/epoxy. Boundary layer control achieved by wing-root slots. Full-span leading-edge manoeuvring flaps have a maximum extension angle of 30°. Single-slotted trailing-edge flaps deploy to a maximum of 45°. Ailerons can be drooped to 45°, providing the advantages of full-span flaps for low approach speeds. Leading- and trailing-edge flaps are computer programmed to deflect for optimum lift and drag in both manoeuvring and cruise conditions, and ailerons and flaps are also deflected differentially for roll. Wing-root leading-edge extensions (LEX) permit flight at angles of attack exceeding 60°. Wings fold at the inboard end of each aileron.

FUSELAGE: Conventional semi-monocoque basic structure, with graphite/epoxy used for access doors/panels. Air-brake in upper surface of fuselage between tail fins. Pressurised cockpit section of fail-safe construction.

TAIL UNIT: Cantilever structure with swept vertical and horizontal surfaces. Twin 20° outward-canted fins and rudders, mounted forward of all-moving horizontal surfaces (stabilators) with 2° anhedral, actuated collectively and differentially for pitch and roll control.

LANDING GEAR: Retractable tricycle type, with twin-wheel nose and single-wheel main units. Bendix wheels and brakes. Nosewheel tyres size 22 × 6.6-10, 20 ply. Mainwheel tyres size 30 × 11.5-14.5, 24 ply. Ozone nosewheel steering unit. Nose unit towbar for catapult launch. Arrester hook, for carrier landings, under rear fuselage.

POWERPLANT: Two General Electric F404-GE-400 low-bypass turbofan engines, each producing approx 71.2 kN (16,000 lb thrust). Self-sealing fuel tanks and fuel lines; foam in wing tanks and fuselage voids. Internal fuel load approx 6,435 litres (1,700 US gallons; 1,415 Imp gallons); provision for up to three 1,250 litre (330 US gallon; 275 Imp gallon) external tanks. Flight refuelling probe retracts into upper starboard side of nose. Fixed-ramp air intakes.

ACCOMMODATION: Pilot only, on Martin-Baker Navy Aircrew Common Ejection Seat in pressurised, heated and air-conditioned cockpit.

SYSTEMS: Include quadruplex digital fly-by-wire flight control system, with direct electrical backup to all surfaces, and direct mechanical backup to stabilators.

AVIONICS AND EQUIPMENT: Include an automatic carrier landing system (ACLS) for all-weather carrier operations; a Hughes Aircraft AN/APG-65 multi-mode digital air-to-air and air-to-ground tracking radar, with air-to-air modes which include velocity search (VS), range-while-search (RWS), track-while-scan (TWS), which can track ten targets and display eight to the pilot, and raid assessment mode (RAM). Itek ALR-67 radar warning receiver; airborne self-protection jammer (ASPJ); General Electric quadruple-redundant flight control system; two AYK-14 digital computers; Litton AN/ASN-130A inertial navigation system; two Kaiser multi-function CRTs, central Ferranti/Bendix CRT and head-up display; Conrac communications system control; Normalair-Garrett digital data recorder for Bendix maintenance recording system; flight incident recording and monitoring system (FIRAMS); Smiths standby altimeter; and Kearflex standby airspeed indicator, standby vertical speed indicator, and cockpit pressure altimeter. Garrett APU for engine starting and ground pneumatic, electric and hydraulic power.

ARMAMENT: Nine external weapon stations with a combined capacity of 7,710 kg (17,000 lb) of mixed ordnance at high g. These comprise two wingtip stations for AIM-9 Sidewinder air-to-air missiles; two outboard wing stations for an assortment of air-to-ground or air-to-air weapons, including AIM-7 Sparrows, AIM-9 Sidewinders AIM-120 AMRAAMS and AGM-65 Maverick missiles; two inboard wing stations for external fuel tanks or air-to-ground weapons, including AGM-84 Harpoon missiles; two nacelle fuselage stations for Sparrows or Martin Marietta AN/ASQ-173 laser spot tracker/strike camera (LST/SCAM) and Ford AN/AAS-38 FLIR pods; and a centreline fuselage station for external fuel or weapons. Air-to-ground weapons include GBU-10 and -12 laser guided bombs, Mk 82 and Mk 84 general purpose bombs, and CBU-59 cluster bombs. An M61 20 mm six-barrel gun, with 570 rounds, is mounted in the nose and has a McDonnell Douglas director gunsight, with a conventional sight as backup.

DIMENSIONS, EXTERNAL:	
Wing span	11.43 m (37 ft 6 in)
Wing span over missiles	12.31 m (40 ft 4¾ in)
Width, wings folded	8.38 m (27 ft 6 in)
Length overall	17.07 m (56 ft 0 in)
Height overall	4.66 m (15 ft 3½ in)
Wheel track	3.11 m (10 ft 2½ in)
Wheelbase	5.42 m (17 ft 9½ in)
AREA:	
Wings, gross	37.16 m² (400.0 sq ft)
WEIGHTS:	
Weight empty	10,455 kg (23,050 lb)
Fighter mission T-O weight	16,651 kg (36,710 lb)
Attack mission T-O weight	22,328 kg (49,224 lb)
PERFORMANCE:	
Max level speed	more than Mach 1.8
Max speed, intermediate power	more than Mach 1.0
Combat ceiling	approx 15,240 m (50,000 ft)
T-O run	less than 427 m (1,400 ft)
Combat radius, fighter mission	more than 400 nm (740 km; 460 miles)
Combat radius, attack mission	575 nm (1,065 km; 662 miles)
Ferry range, unrefuelled	more than 2,000 nm (3,706 km; 2,303 miles)

McDonnell Douglas Hornet 2000

McDonnell Douglas has proposed an upgraded development of the F/A-18, known as the Hornet 2000, as a possible alternative to the European Fighter Aircraft (EFA) for the Royal Air Force and West German Air Force and also for future US use. Together with the Naval Air Systems Command and the Center for Naval Analysis, McDonnell Douglas is examining five possible configurations for an upgraded Hornet, one with new wings of 'cranked arrow' planform, new vertical and horizontal tail surfaces, canard foreplanes, uprated General Electric F404 engines and increased use of composite materials and control-configured-vehicle technology.

McDonnell Douglas/Northrop ATF

McDonnell Douglas and Northrop signed a teaming agreement covering their individual proposals for the US Air Force's Advanced Tactical Fighter. Submission of formal proposals began on 28 July 1986, and Northrop's design was one of two selected by the USAF on 31 October 1986. Northrop is prime contractor for all phases of the programme, and McDonnell Douglas is principal subcontractor. (See USAF Systems Command.)

Douglas Aircraft Company (Division of McDonnell Douglas Corporation)

The Douglas Aircraft Company operates plants at Long Beach and Torrance, California. The DC (Douglas Commercial) series of designations which had identified the company's civil designs ever since the DC-1 of 1933 was superseded in 1983 by a new system using the McDonnell Douglas initials MD. First to bear an MD designation was the Super 80 series of DC-9 airliner derivatives, now known as the MD-80. Existing DC-8, DC-9 and DC-10 designations were unchanged. Current military programmes include work on the C-17A long-range heavy-lift cargo transport and the T-45 Goshawk (Hawk) trainer. The Skyhawk and Skywarrior, detailed below, were Douglas products well before merger with McDonnell.

McDonnell Douglas Skyhawk

US Navy Designation: A-4
The Skyhawk is a single-seat lightweight attack bomber which was produced at the Douglas Long Beach works.

Designed originally to provide the US Navy and Marine Corps with a simple low-cost lightweight attack and ground-support aircraft, the Skyhawk was based on experience gained during the Korean War. Since the initial requirement called for operation by the US Navy, special design consideration was given to providing low-speed control and stability during take-off and landing, added strength for catapult launch and arrested landings, and dimensions that would permit it to negotiate standard aircraft carrier lifts without the complexity of folding wings.

Production of the Skyhawk began in September 1953 and the first flight of the XA-4A prototype, powered by a 32 kN (7,200 lb st) Wright J65-W-2 engine, took place on 22 June 1954.

The following versions are in service:

A-4E (formerly A4D-5). Improved version, with increased payload and 25% greater range. Powered by a Pratt & Whitney J52-P-6A turbojet (37.81 kN; 8,500 lb st). Douglas Escapac zero-height 90-knot rocket ejection seat. Four underwing and one underfuselage bomb racks able to carry as many as 20 separate items weighing up to 3,720 kg (8,200 lb). First flight 12 July 1961. Deliveries to US Navy began in November 1962. In 1980 Indonesian Air Force began to receive first of 14 A-4Es from Israel. Other operators remain Israel and US Navy/Marine Corps.

A-4F. Attack bomber with J52-P-8A turbojet (41.37 kN; 9,300 lb st), new lift-spoilers on wings to shorten landing run by up to 305 m (1,000 ft), nosewheel steering, low-pressure tyres, zero-height zero-speed ejection seat, additional bullet-and flak-resistant materials to protect pilot, updated electronics contained in fairing 'hump' aft of cockpit. Prototype flew for first time on 31 August 1966. Deliveries to US Navy began on 20 June 1967, and were completed in 1968.

TA-4F. Tandem two-seat dual-control trainer version of A-4F for US Navy. Fuselage extended 0.76 m (2 ft 6 in); fuselage fuel tankage reduced to 379 litres (100 US gallons; 83.3 Imp gallons). Douglas zero-zero ejection seats. Provision to carry full range of weapons available for A-4F. Reduced avionics. First prototype flew on 30 June 1965. Deliveries began to the US Navy in May 1966.

A-4G/TA-4G. Ten ex-Royal Australian Navy Skyhawks purchased by the Royal New Zealand Air Force in 1984, forming No. 2 Squadron at Ohakea. Upgraded with new radar and nav/attack system, plus structural work.

TA-4H. Tandem two-seat trainer version of the A-4H for Israel. Two purchased from Israel by the Indonesian Air Force. J52-P-6A engine.

TA-4J. Tandem two-seat trainer, basically a simplified version of the TA-4F. Ordered for US Naval Air Advanced Training Command, under $26,834,000 contract, followed by further contract in mid-1971. Deletion of the following equipment, although provisions retained: radar, dead-reckoning navigation system, low-altitude bombing system, air-to-ground missile systems, weapons delivery computer and automatic release, intervalometer, gun pod, standard stores pylons, in-flight refuelling system and spray tank provisions. Addition and relocation of certain instruments. J52-P-6 engine standard. Provision for J52-P-8A engine and combat electronics. Prototype flew in May 1969 and the first four were delivered to the US Navy on 6 June 1969. Currently used also by Israel.

A-4K. Similar to A-4F, for Royal New Zealand Air Force. Different radio, and braking parachute. First of ten handed over to the RNZAF on 16 January 1970. Similar upgrades to A-4G.

A-4KU. Designation of 30 aircraft similar to A-4M for Kuwait Air Force. Deliveries began in Spring 1977.

TA-4K. Similar to TA-4F, for Royal New Zealand Air Force. The first of four was handed over to the RNZAF on 16 January 1970.

TA-4KU. Designation of six aircraft, similar to the TA-4F, for Kuwait Air Force.

A-4M Skyhawk II. Similar to A-4F, but with J52-P-408A turbojet (50 kN; 11,200 lb st) and braking parachute standard, making possible combat operation from 1,220 m (4,000 ft) fields and claimed to increase combat effectiveness

McDonnell Douglas A-4M Skyhawk II operated by US Marine Corps Squadron VMA-211. *(K. Hinata)*

by 30%. Larger windscreen and canopy; windscreen bullet-resistant. Square-topped fin and rudder. Increased ammunition capacity for 20 mm cannon. More powerful generator, provision of wind-driven backup generator and self-contained engine starter. First of two prototypes flew for the first time on 10 April 1970. Ordered for US Marine Corps, the first being delivered on 3 November 1970. Funds subsequently allocated for the installation of improved electronic warfare equipment in service aircraft.

OA-4M. Forward-air-control version for US Marine Corps, converted from TA-4F. Converted by Naval Air Rework Facility at Pensacola, Florida. Avionics and weapons capability similar to those of A-4M. First OA-4M began flight testing at NATC Patuxent River in July 1978, before entry into service with H & MS 32 at Cherry Point, North Carolina, in late 1979.

A-4N Skyhawk II. Light attack version ordered by US Navy for export to Israel. Basically similar to A-4M, with new nav/attack system. Two 30 mm DEFA cannon. First flown on 8 June 1972.

A-4P. Revised A-4B and C for Argentine Air Force.

A-4PTM and TA-4PTM. Under a $12 million contract awarded in 1982, Grumman's St Augustine Division remanufactured a total of 40 McDonnell Douglas A-4 Skyhawk aircraft for the Royal Malaysian Air Force. The Skyhawks, 34 single-seat A-4PTM (Peculiar to Malaysia) and six two-seat TA-4PTM, received new wiring, updated avionics, two additional wing stores stations and refurbished engines. The TA-4PTMs were created by Grumman by a 0.71 m (2 ft 4 in) fuselage 'stretch' to accommodate tandem cockpits and dual controls. Delivery of the aircraft to the RMAF, with which they equip two squadrons based at

OA-4M Skyhawk FAC aircraft, photographed at El Toro US Marine Corps base. *(Erik Simonsen)*

366

Republic of Singapore Air Force TA-4S two-seat trainer. *(Mark Wagner)*

Kuantan, was completed in February 1986. These began as ex-US Navy A-4Cs, Ls, and trainers.

A-4Q. Revised A-4B for Argentine Navy.

A-4S. Designation of 40 Skyhawks for service with Singapore Air Defence Command. Conversion from ex-USN A-4Bs carried out by Lockheed Aircraft Services Company. First flown 14 July 1973. Primary changes included the addition of split wing spoilers above the flaps, a braking parachute canister beneath the aft fuselage, a longer nose to house advanced electronics equipment, flight refuelling probe, and replacement of the 20 mm guns in the wing roots by 30 mm Aden cannon. Newly installed equipment included a Ferranti lightweight lead-computing gunsight, and solid-state electronics packages for the communications, radio and navigation systems. The cockpit was completely redesigned to accommodate the new instrumentation and control boxes. The 34.25 kN (7,700 lb st) J65-W-16A turbojet was upgraded to 37.4 kN (8,400 lb st). Fifty Singapore A-4S/S-1s are being upgraded further with General Electric F404-GE-100 engines, Ferranti head-up displays and new weapon aiming computers.

A-4S-1. Refurbished (new avionics and weapon pylons) A-4Cs, used by Singapore Air Force.

TA-4S. Three two-seat A-4B conversions for Singapore, by LAS, with individual cockpits, steerable nosewheel and new braking system. Armour plate removed. Revised fuel system. First flown 1975.

TA-4S-1. Singapore Air Force two-seat trainer, based on TA-4B.

New production of the A-4 ended on 27 February 1979,

McDonnell Douglas A-4M Skyhawk II. *(Pilot Press)*

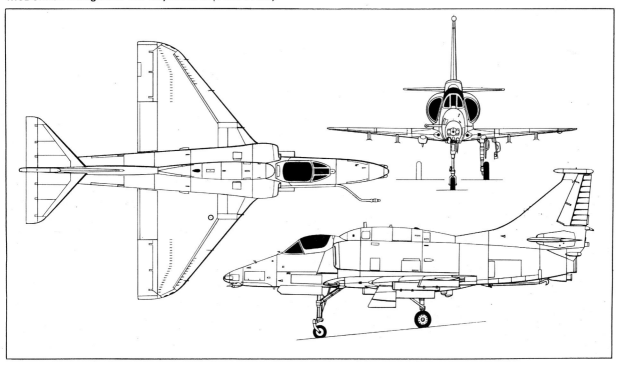

when the US Navy took delivery of the final aircraft off the assembly line, an A-4M for the US Marine Corps. Delivered to Marine Attack Squadron VMA-331, it was the 2,960th Skyhawk manufactured by McDonnell Douglas in 26 years of continuous production. The total was made up of 2,405 attack aircraft and 555 trainers, as follows:

XA4D-1	1	TA-4G	2
YA4D-1	19	A-4H	90
A4D-1 (A-4A)	146	TA-4H	10
A4D-2 (A-4B)	542	TA-4J	291
A4D-2N (A-4C)	638	A-4K	10
YA4D-5 (YA-4E)	2	TA-4K	4
A4D-5 (A-4E)	494	A-4KU	30
A-4F	146	TA-4KU	6
TA-4F	242	A-4M	162
A-4G	8	A-4N	117

Various modification programmes to upgrade the Skyhawk have been, and are being, offered. Some are detailed in the model listings. A current programme of modifications is offered by Israel Aircraft Industries and Singapore Aircraft Industries (which see).

The following structural description refers specifically to the A-4M:

TYPE: Single-seat attack bomber.

WINGS: Cantilever low-wing monoplane. Sweepback 33° at quarter-chord. Ailerons, with servo trim tab in port aileron. Split flaps. Automatic leading-edge slats with fences. Lift spoilers above flaps.

FUSELAGE: Semi-monocoque structure in two sections. Rear section removable for engine servicing. Outward-hinged airbrake on each side of rear fuselage. Detachable nose over communications and navigation equipment. Integral flak-resistant armour in cockpit area, with internal armour plate below and forward of cockpit.

TAIL UNIT: Cantilever structure. Variable-incidence tailplane. Elevators. Powered rudder with unique central skin and external stiffeners.

LANDING GEAR: Retractable tricycle type, with single wheel on each unit. Nosewheel steering. Ribbon-type braking parachute of 4.88 m (16 ft) diameter contained in canister secured in rear fuselage below engine exhaust. Arrester hook.

POWERPLANT: One 50 kN (11,200 lb st) Pratt & Whitney J52-P-408A turbojet engine. Fuel in integral wing tanks and self-sealing fuselage tank aft of cockpit, total capacity 3,028 litres (800 US gallons; 666 Imp gallons). One 568, 1,136 or 1,514 litre (150, 300 or 400 US gallon; 125, 250 or 333 Imp gallon) auxiliary tank can be carried on the underfuselage bomb-rack, and one 150 or 300 US gallon auxiliary tank on each of the inboard underwing racks. Maximum fuel capacity, internal plus auxiliary tanks, 6,814 litres (1,800 US gallons; 1,499 Imp gallons). Large flight refuelling probe on starboard side of nose. Douglas-developed self-contained flight refuelling unit can be carried on the underfuselage standard bomb shackles. Provisions for JATO.

ACCOMMODATION: Pilot on Douglas Escapac 1-G3 zero-zero lightweight ejection seat. Enlarged cockpit enclosure to improve pilot's view, with rectangular bullet-resistant windscreen.

AVIONICS: Include Bendix Automatic Flight Control, ARC-159 UHF radio transceiver, ARA-50 UHF direction finder, APX-72 IFF, Marconi Avionics AVQ-24 head-up display system, Douglas angle-of-attack indicator, electronic countermeasures, ASN-41 nav computer, APN-153(V) radar nav, ARC-114 VHF/FM radio transceiver, ARR-69 auxiliary radio receiver, ARN-84 Tacan and APN-194 radar altimeter.

ARMAMENT: Provision for several hundred variations of military load, carried externally on one underfuselage rack, capacity 1,588 kg (3,500 lb); two inboard underwing racks, capacity of each 1,020 kg (2,250 lb); and two outboard underwing racks, capacity of each 450 kg (1,000 lb). Weapons that can be deployed include nuclear or HE bombs, air-to-surface and air-to-air rockets, Sidewinder missiles, air-to-surface missiles, ground-attack gun pods, torpedoes, countermeasures equipment, etc. Two 20 mm Mk 12 cannon in wing roots standard.

DIMENSIONS, EXTERNAL:
Wing span	8.38 m (27 ft 6 in)
Length overall (excl flight refuelling probe)	
	12.29 m (40 ft 4 in)
Height overall	4.57 m (15 ft 0 in)
Wheel track	2.37 m (7 ft 9½ in)

AREA:
Wings, gross	24.16 m² (260.0 sq ft)

WEIGHTS:
Weight empty	4,899 kg (10,800 lb)
Normal T-O weight	11,113 kg (24,500 lb)

PERFORMANCE (at combat weight):
Max level speed (with 1,814 kg; 4,000 lb bomb load)
561 knots (1,040 km/h; 646 mph)
Max rate of climb (ISA at S/L)   3,140 m (10,300 ft)/min
Rate of climb (ISA at 7,620 m; 25,000 ft)
1,463 m (4,800 ft)/min
T-O run (at 10,433 kg; 23,000 lb T-O weight)
832 m (2,730 ft)
Max ferry range at 11,113 kg (24,500 lb) T-O weight with max fuel, standard reserves   1,740 nm (3,225 km; 2,000 miles)

Douglas AC-47 Spooky

Gunship conversions of the Douglas C-47 transport (DC-3) are still in use, current operators including El Salvador. It no longer holds a position within US active or reserve forces. Details of this aircraft will appear in a future publication on military transports and their derivatives.

Douglas Skywarrior

US Navy designation: EA-3B and KA-3B

First flown as the XA3D-1 prototype twin-jet carrier based attack bomber on 28 October 1952, the Skywarrior was then the most powerful aircraft ever designed for shipborne operations. The initial A3D-1 production version entered US Navy service in 1956, followed by other bomber,

US Navy Douglas EA-3B Skywarrior.

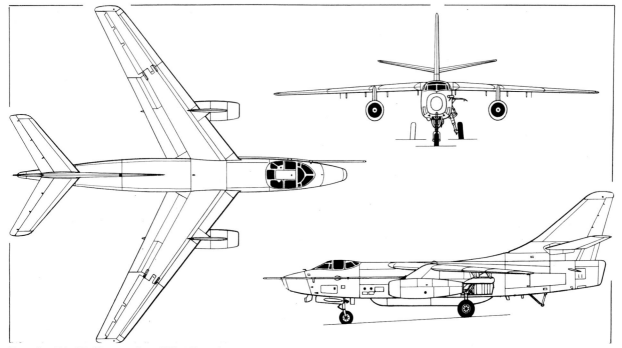

Douglas EA-3B Skywarrior. *(Pilot Press)*

photographic-reconnaissance, radar countermeasures and training versions.

Today the US Navy operates only two versions of Skywarrior, both conversions of earlier types. They are:

EA-3B. Specialised electronic countermeasures conversion of earlier aircraft. Some 21 remained with US Navy as part of the equipment of two elint squadrons in 1987. Flight crew of three plus four systems operators in weapons bay compartment. ECM equipment and forward- and side-looking radars.

KA-3B. US Navy Reserve flight refuelling tanker. Uses AN/APS-130 mapping radar. Fuel capacity 19,025 litres (5,026 US gallons; 4,185 Imp gallons).

TYPE (EA-3B): Seven-seat ECM aircraft.

WINGS: Cantilever shoulder-wing monoplane. 36° sweepback at quarter chord. Taper ratio 6% at root, 8.25% at tip. Slotted flaps inboard of wing fold. Ailerons and spoilers on outer panels. Leading-edge slats outboard of engine pylons.

FUSELAGE: Conventional structure in three sections. Airbrakes on rear of fuselage sides.

TAIL UNIT: Conventional type with dihedral all-moving tailplane. All surfaces swept.

LANDING GEAR: Retractable tricycle type, with single wheel on each unit.

POWERPLANT: Two 46.7 kN (10,500 lb st) Pratt & Whitney J57-P-10 turbojet engines.

ARMAMENT: Tail cannon removed and faired over.

DIMENSIONS, EXTERNAL:	
Wing span	22.10 m (72 ft 6 in)
Length overall	23.27 m (76 ft 4 in)
Height overall	6.93 m (22 ft 9 in)
AREA:	
Wings, gross	67.84 m² (730.0 sq ft)
WEIGHTS:	
Weight empty, approx	17,236 kg (38,000 lb)
Max T-O weight	33,110 kg (73,000 lb)
PERFORMANCE:	
Max level speed at 3,050 m (10,000 ft)	
	530 knots (982 km/h; 610 mph)
Service ceiling	13,715 m (45,000 ft)
Range	more than 2,520 nm (4,665 km; 2,900 miles)

McDonnell Douglas Helicopter Company (Subsidiary of McDonnell Douglas Corporation)

On 6 January 1984, Hughes Helicopters Inc, with more than 7,000 employees in California and Arizona, became a subsidiary of the McDonnell Douglas Corporation; on 27 August 1985 the company name was changed to McDonnell Douglas Helicopter Company. At that time more than 4,000 of the 6,400 helicopters that it had produced were still in operation by civil and military users in nearly 100 countries worldwide, with production of a series of advanced models continuing. Research activities included work on composites

rotor blades, hubs and tailbooms, metal insulation and IR suppression systems, the US Army's LHX programme, and Chain Gun ordnance systems for air and ground applications. The company was also designing and fabricating a crashworthy all-composites helicopter fuselage, based on the shape of its Model 500E.

In July 1981 Mesa, Arizona, was selected as the site for the company's AH-64A production and flight test facility. This now comprises a 52,955 m² (570,000 sq ft) Apache assembly, flight test and delivery centre, to which were added a further 123,980 m² (1,334,500 sq ft) complex of office, engineering and other buildings completed in 1986. In mid-1986 Mesa became the new official headquarters of the company, with a workforce of 5,000. The Arizona plant has a production capacity of 73 helicopters per month, although the combined production rate of MD 500/Apaches is about 20 per month. An 83,613 m² (900,000 sq ft) fabrication and ordnance centre is being developed at Culver City. When completed in 1998, the California facility will provide nearly 92,903 m² (1 million sq ft) of manufacturing, assembly and office space.

Manufacture of the former Hughes Model 300M is now undertaken by Schweizer Aircraft Corporation in Elmira, New York. Foreign licensees are RACA in Argentina (500D and 500E civil variants); Kawasaki in Japan (500D civil and military variants); Korean Air in the Republic of Korea (500D and 500E civil and military, excluding TOW variants); and BredaNardi in Italy (300C, 500D, 500E and 530F civil variants).

McDonnell Douglas Model 500/530 Defender
The Model 500 helicopter, which entered full-scale production in November 1968, originated as a civil development of the OH-6A Cayuse light observation helicopter used by the US Army; the first prototype Cayuse flew for the first time on 27 February 1963.

Military versions of the MD 500/530, of which more than 1,000 are in use worldwide, are as follows:

Model 500M. Initial uprated version of OH-6A, developed from civil MD 500.

Model 500MD Defender. Multi-role military version. Airframe and engine (derated Allison 250-C20B) as civil MD 500D, from which it differs in having self-sealing fuel cells, engine-inlet particle separator, optional armour protection, 'Black Hole' infra-red suppressor, and provision for the carriage and deployment of a variety of weapons, including TOW missiles. Its diverse capabilities include training, command and control, scout, light attack, ASW, troop lift and logistical support duties. It can carry up to seven people, including the pilot; or, in ambulance configuration, two stretcher patients with attendants in addition to a flight crew of two. Licence-assembly manufacture undertaken by Korean Air in Republic of Korea.

The versions available from US production in 1988 were as follows:

500MD Scout Defender. Basic military version, able to carry a variety of alternative weapons, including fourteen 2.75 in rockets and either a 7.62 mm Minigun with 2,000 rounds of ammunition, a 40 mm grenade launcher, or a 7.62 mm EX-34 Chain Gun machine-gun with 2,000 rounds of ammunition. Operators include Kenyan Army (15) and Republic of Korea Air Force (144).

500MD/TOW Defender. Anti-tank version armed with four TOW air-to-ground missiles. The TOW installation comprises four weapon pods, mounted two each side on a tubular mount carried through the lower aft fuselage, a stabilised telescopic sight mounted on the port side of the nose, sight control and armrest for the gunner, and a steering indicator for the pilot. In service with air forces of Israel (30), Kenya (15) and Republic of Korea (50). Available also in **500MD/MMS-TOW** version, with Hughes Aircraft mast mounted sight.

500MD/ASW Defender. Version for anti-submarine warfare and surface search missions, with two crew, search radar on nose, AN/ASQ-81 towed MAD, smoke marker launchers, hauldown gear, emergency 'popout' floats and armament of two Mk 44 or Mk 46 homing torpedoes. Max T-O weight 1,610 kg (3,550 lb). Can remain on station for 1 h 48 min when operated at a typical ASW mission radius of 22–87 nm (40–160 km; 25–100 miles) from ship or shore base.

McDonnell Douglas 500MD/TOW Defender of the Israeli Air Force.

Using its radar, 500MD/ASW could locate enemy destroyers and gunboats up to 150 nm (275 km; 172 miles) from its base ship during a two-hour patrol. Twelve delivered to Taiwanese Navy.

500MD Defender II. Multi-mission version, introduced in Summer of 1980. Five-blade main rotor standard; four-blade 'quiet' tail rotor optional: this turns at a rate 25 per cent slower than the standard two-blade rotor and is reported to be 47 per cent quieter in operation. Other options include Hughes Aircraft mast mounted sight (MMS), two twin-round pods for four TOW anti-tank missiles, 'Black Hole' infra-red suppression system, pod containing two Stinger or other air-to-air missiles, pilot's FLIR night vision system, AN/APR-39 (V-1) equipment to give warning that the helicopter is being tracked by hostile radar-directed weapon systems, self-sealing fuel tanks, auxiliary fuel tanks, and an advanced avionics/mission equipment package. The MMS uses a video link to TV displays for the crew, and includes laser rangefinder. Use of the MMS enables the Defender II to hover virtually out of sight behind trees or natural terrain, while the crew surveys the battlefield over extended ranges.

Standard lightweight avionics equipment (SLAE) as developed for the OH-6A has been adapted for the 500MD with minimal changes. This equipment comprises AN/ARC-164 UHF/AM, AN/ARC-115 UHF/AM, AN/ARC-114 VHF/FM, ARN-89 ADF, APX-72 IFF transponder, AN/ASN-43 directional gyro, ID-1351 heading and bearing indicator, and C-6533/ARC intercom.

500MG Defender. As 530MG, but with 313 kW (420 shp) Allison 250-C20B turboshaft engine and MD 500E rotor system. In July 1985 a **Paramilitary MG Defender** version was introduced which is intended as a low-cost helicopter suitable for use by police, border patrol, rescue, narcotics control and internal-security authorities. It is offered in both 500E and 530F configurations. In February 1986 McDonnell Douglas Helicopter completed delivery of six 500MG Defenders to the Colombian Air Force, which also received two commercial MD 500Es to serve as trainers.

Nightfox. Introduced in January 1986 as a low-cost

McDonnell Douglas 530MG Nightfox helicopter with FLIR thermal imaging system and EX-34 Chain Gun installation.

helicopter for night surveillance and military operations. Equipment includes FLIR thermal imaging and night-vision goggles, with weapons as for 530MG. Available in both 500MG and 530MG configurations.

530MG Defender. In late 1982 Hughes Helicopters began development of the 530MG Defender, based on the airframe and powerplant of the commercial MD 530F Lifter. The integrated crew station developed for the 530MG makes use of recent developments in control and display systems technology to provide a compact multi-function display which enhances cockpit field of view and enables hands-on control of the helicopter at all times, with all weapons delivery, communications management, and flight control conducted via the collective and cyclic sticks. It reflects many of the technologies expected to be standard for the US Army's LHX advanced helicopter series.

Design of the Model 530MG was finalised between

McDonnell Douglas 530MG Defender with Hughes Aircraft mast-mounted sight.

September and November 1983. The first demonstration aircraft made its first flight on 4 May 1984, and its first public appearance at the Farnborough Air Show in September of that year. A 79.5 litre (21 US gallon; 17.5 Imp gallon) internal auxiliary fuel tank is optional.

The 530MG Defender is designed primarily for point attack and anti-armour missions, but is equally suitable for scout, day and night surveillance, utility, cargo lift, and light attack duties. A programme is under way to develop an over-the-horizon capability for naval applications.

Equipment includes Racal Avionics RAMS 3000 integrated control and display system for all-weather and nap-of-the-earth flight, designed to operate with a MIL-STD-1553B interface and comprising a processor interface unit (PIU), a control display unit (CDU), and a data transfer device (DTD) linked by a dual 1553B databus. A multi-function display incorporates a high-resolution monochrome CRT with alpha-numeric and symbolic data overlay capability. The CDU incorporates a monochrome CRT with line keys and keyboard and can be used to conduct all normal flight planning, navigational, frequency selection, and subsystem management functions by use of dedicated keys on the CDU keyboard. Data are transferred to the DTD from a ground loader unit via an RS-232C serial data link which is placed in a cockpit receptacle for update transfer to the data base of the PIU. Other equipment includes Astronautics Corpn autopilot; Decca Doppler navigation system integrated with Racal Doppler velocity sensor; Ferranti FIN 1110 AHRS; twin Collins VHF/UHF AM/FM radios; King HF radio, ADF/VOR, radar altimeter and transponder; Telephonics intercom; and SFENA attitude indicator. Optional avionics include Hughes Aircraft TOW mast mounted sight system, FLIR, radar warning receiver,

IFF, GPWS and laser rangefinder.

Standard 14 in NATO racks are provided for external stores. Weapons qualified or tested include TOW anti-armour missiles, FN pods containing two 7.62 mm or one 0.50 in machine-gun, and 2.75 in rockets in 7-tube or 12-tube launchers. Additional weapons are planned to include four General Dynamics Stinger air-to-air missiles and a 7.62 mm McDonnell Douglas Chain Gun automatic machine-gun. Chaff and infra-red decoy flares can be carried, with automatic chaff ejection on threat detection facility. Both cyclic sticks have triggers for gun or rocket firing; the co-pilot/gunner's visual image display has two handgrips for TOW/FLIR operation.

TYPE: Multi-role helicopter.

ROTOR SYSTEM: Five-blade fully articulated main rotor. Trim tab outboard on each blade. Main rotor blades can be folded. Four-blade 'quiet' tail rotor optional to standard two-blade tail rotor (see 500MD Defender II).

FUSELAGE: Semi-monocoque structure of pod-and-boom type. Clamshell doors at rear of pod give access to engine and accessories.

TAIL UNIT: T tail with horizontal stabiliser at tip of narrow-chord sweptback fin; small auxiliary fin at tip of tailplane on each side; narrow-chord sweptback ventral fin with integral tailskid to protect tail rotor in tail-down attitude near ground.

LANDING GEAR: Tubular skids. Utility floats, snow skis and emergency inflatable floats optional.

POWERPLANT: One Allison 250-C20B turboshaft engine, which is derated to 280 kW (375 shp) for T-O and has a max continuous rating of 261 kW (350 shp). 530 MG Defender has a 485 kW (650 shp) Allison 250-C30 turboshaft engine, derated to 317 kW (425 shp) for take-

McDonnell Douglas 500MD Defender. *(Pilot Press)*

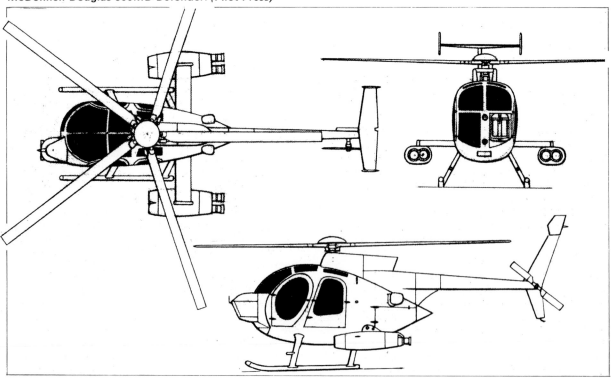

off and 261 kW (350 shp) max continuous. Two fuel tanks with combined usable capacity of 240 litres (63.4 US gallons; 52.8 Imp gallons). Auxiliary fuel system, with 79.5 litre (21 US gallon; 17.5 Imp gallon) internal tank, available optionally.

ACCOMMODATION: See model listing.

DIMENSIONS, EXTERNAL (A: 500MD/TOW, B: 530MG):

Main rotor diameter:	
A	8.03 m (26 ft 4 in)
B	8.33 m (27 ft 4 in)
Length of fuselage: A	7.62 m (25 ft 0 in)
B	7.29 m (23 ft 11 in)
Height of top of rotor head with MMS	
B	3.41 m (11 ft 2½ in)
Height over tail (endplate fins):	
A, B	2.71 m (8 ft 10¾ in)
Width over skids: A	1.95 m (6 ft 4¾ in)
B	1.96 m (6 ft 5 in)
Width over TOW pods: A	3.23 m (10 ft 7¼ in)

WEIGHTS:

Weight empty, equipped: A	896 kg (1,976 lb)
Max T-O weight: A	1,361 kg (3,000 lb)
B, normal	1,406 kg (3,100 lb)
B, max overload	1,610 kg (3,550 lb)

PERFORMANCE (at max normal T-O weight, ISA, except where indicated):

Never-exceed speed at S/L:	
A	130 knots (241 km/h; 150 mph)
Max cruising speed at S/L:	
A, B	119 knots (221 km/h; 137 mph)
Max cruising speed at 1,525 m (5,000 ft):	
A	115 knots (213 km/h; 132 mph)
B	122 knots (226 km/h; 140 mph)
Max rate of climb at S/L:	
A, ISA	503 m (1,650 ft)/min
B, up to ISA + 20°C	631 m (2,070 ft)/min
Vertical rate of climb at S/L:	
B, ISA	606 m (1,990 ft)/min
B, ISA + 20°C	558 m (1,830 ft)/min
Service ceiling: A	4,205 m (13,800 ft)
B	over 4,880 m (16,000 ft)
Hovering ceiling IGE: A, ISA	2,315 m (7,600 ft)
B, ISA	5,060 m (16,600 ft)
A, ISA + 20°C	1,525 m (5,000 ft)
B, ISA + 20°C	4,270 m (14,000 ft)
A, 35°C	1,100 m (3,600 ft)
B, 35°C	2,680 m (8,800 ft)
Hovering ceiling OGE: A, ISA	1,770 m (5,800 ft)
B, ISA	4,300 m (14,100 ft)
A, ISA + 20°C	915 m (3,000 ft)
B, ISA+ 20°C	3,475 m (11,400 ft)
A, 35°C	640 m (2,100 ft)
B, 35°C	2,135 m (7,000 ft)

Range with standard fuel, 2 min warmup, no reserves:

A at S/L	210 nm (389 km; 242 miles)
B at S/L	180 nm (333 km; 207 miles)
A at 1,525 m (5,000 ft)	231 nm (428 km; 266 miles)
B at 1,525 m (5,000 ft)	203 nm (376 km; 233 miles)

Endurance with standard fuel, 2 min warmup, no reserves:

A at S/L	2 h 34 min
B at S/L	2 h 6 min
A at 1,525 m (5,000 ft)	2 h 47 min
B at 1,525 m (5,000 ft)	2 h 18 min

McDonnell Douglas Apache

US Army designation: AH-64A

The Hughes Model 77 was designed to meet the US Army's requirement for an advanced attack helicopter (AAH) capable of undertaking a full day/night/adverse-weather anti-armour mission, and of fighting, surviving and 'living with' troops in a front-line environment. Two YAH-64 flight test prototypes were built for competitive evaluation against Bell's YAH-63, and these made their initial flights on 30 September and 22 November 1975 respectively. A ground test vehicle was also completed. The original contract covered, in addition, development of the M230 Chain Gun helicopter weapon for installation in the prototypes. In February 1976 Rockwell's Hellfire missile was chosen to replace the Hughes TOW as the primary anti-tank weapon. By January 1985, YAH-64 prototypes had fired more than 75 Hellfire missiles, nearly 5,600 2.75 in rockets, and more than 65,000 rounds of 30 mm ammunition. Selection of the YAH-64 was announced on 10 December 1976. The name Apache was adopted for the AH-64 in late 1981.

Teledyne Ryan is responsible for building the AH-64 fuselage, wings, engine nacelles, avionics bays, canopy and tail unit. A key subsystem is the Martin Marietta target acquisition and designation sight/pilot's night vision sensor (TADS/PNVS), for which an initial production contract (for 13 systems) was awarded on 30 April 1982; the first production TADS/PNVS was delivered in July 1983.

Self-deployment capability was demonstrated on 4 April 1985, when the 14th production Apache, with four 871 litre (230 US gallon; 191.5 Imp gallon) external fuel tanks, made a 1,020 nm (1,891 km; 1,175 mile) nonstop flight from Mesa to Santa Barbara, landing with 30 minutes' fuel remaining. Such ferry range permits deployment from the USA to Europe via a northern Atlantic route, with stops at Goose Bay, Frobisher Bay, Søndrestrøm, Reykjavik and Prestwick. If the required deployment is farther than ferry range the Apache can be carried in C-141B StarLifter and C-5 Galaxy transports (two and six Apaches respectively). Loading trials have also been conducted with a mockup of the McDonnell Douglas C-17A, which could accommodate up to three Apaches.

On 26 March 1982 the Defense Systems Acquisition Review Council gave approval for the production programme to be initiated. This resulted, on 15 April 1982, in a Lot 1 production contract for 11 Apaches, the first of which was delivered on 26 January 1984. The US Army's original requirement for 472 AH-64As was subsequently raised to 536, then cut to 446, increased again to 515 in late 1982 and to 675 in 1984, and reduced again to 593 in 1986. By 1988 Congress had agreed to procure 603 up to that fiscal year, with a further 72 wanted by the Army for FY1989. In the long term production could exceed 1,000 up to 1996. Currently, deliveries are scheduled for completion by December 1989. On 25 June 1986 the 100th production Apache was delivered, by which time production had

McDonnell Douglas AH-64A Apache with 230 US gal external fuel tanks.

reached 12 per month. On 30 January 1985 the first Apache for the US Army's Training and Doctrine Command (TRADOC) was delivered to the Army Transportation and Logistics School (ATALS) at Fort Eustis, Virginia. Later that month an Apache was delivered to the Army Aviation School at Fort Rucker, Alabama, where all maintenance and maintenance test pilot courses are conducted.

Initial operational capability was achieved in July 1986 by the 6th Cavalry Regiment's 3rd Squadron, the first unit to undergo the 90-day Apache Unit Training Programme at Fort Hood, Texas. The 1st Squadron, 6th Cavalry Regiment,

achieved combat ready status in November 1986.

In 1987 the North Carolina Army National Guard's 28th Aviation Battalion became the first Guard or Reserve unit to operate the type. The NCARNG's Apaches are based at a new Army Aviation support facility at Raleigh-Durham Airport.

McDonnell Douglas Helicopter Company has received contracts from the US Army Aviation Applied Directorate to develop an advanced composite main rotor hub and fibre-reinforced thermoplastic secondary structures for the AH-64A, and to develop artificial intelligence applications for

McDonnell Douglas AH-64A Apache. *(Pilot Press)*

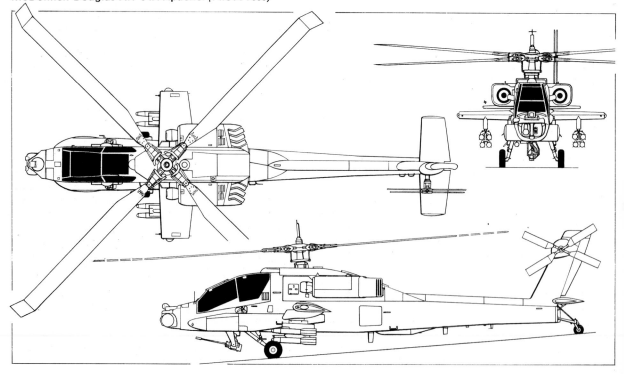

fault isolation and diagnosis of the helicopter's systems. A production AH-64A will be used for a five-year vibration analysis study funded by NASA's Langley Research Center.

In April 1987 McDonnell Douglas Helicopter Company announced preliminary details of a proposed **AH-64B/G Advanced Apache**, based on studies for an advanced development for the US Army which had been under way for 18 months. The AH-64B/G has been proposed for the West German Army's anti-tank helicopter requirement, and would include advanced avionics and flight controls, a data transfer system permitting cassette loading of mission data, more powerful engines with digital control, improved cockpit fields of view, provision for air-to-air Stinger missiles slaved to the gunner's helmet for off-axis aiming, rearward looking TV with a fin mounted video camera, and a gun with longer barrel, active recoil and digital turret control. The AH-64B would have 75 per cent commonality with the AH-64A, and the AH-64B/G would be 95 per cent common with the AH-64B. A licensing agreement has been signed with the German company Siemens for manufacture of the Advanced Apache in Germany if the AH-64B/G is selected.

Navalised versions of the Apache have been projected, and are described separately. The following description applies to the standard production AH-64A for the US Army:

TYPE: Twin-engined attack helicopter.

ROTOR SYSTEM: Four-blade fully articulated main rotor and four-blade tail rotor. Main rotor blades are of high-camber aerofoil section and broad chord, with sweptback tips, and can be folded or removed for air transportation. Each blade has five stainless steel spars lined with structural glassfibre tubes, a laminated stainless steel skin and a composite rear section, bonded together. Blades are fitted with elastomeric lead/lag dampers and offset flapping hinges. Tail rotor comprises two pairs of blades, mounted on port side of pylon/fin support structure at optimum quiet setting of approx 55°/125° to each other. Entire system is capable of flight in negative g conditions.

WINGS: Cantilever mid-mounted wings of low aspect ratio, located aft of the cockpit. Wings are removable, and attach to sides of fuselage for transport and storage. Two hardpoints beneath each wing for the carriage of fixed ordnance or ferry tanks.

FUSELAGE: Conventional semi-monocoque structure. Designed to survive hits by 12.7 mm and 23 mm ammunition.

TAIL UNIT: Bolted pylon structure, with tail rotor mounted on port side. Low-mounted all-moving tailplane.

LANDING GEAR: Trailing-arm type, with single mainwheels and fully castoring, self-centring and lockable tailwheel. Mainwheel tyres size 8.50-10, tailwheel tyre size 5.00-4. Hydraulic brakes on main units. Main gear is non-retractable, but legs fold rearward to reduce overall height for storage and transportation. Energy absorbing main and tail gears are designed for normal descent rates of up to 3.05 m (10 ft)/s and heavy landings at up to 12.8 m (42 ft)/s. Take-offs and landings can be made at structural design gross weight on terrain slopes of up to 12° (head-on) and 10° (side-on).

POWERPLANT: Two 1,265 kW (1,696 shp) General Electric T700-GE-701 turboshaft engines, derated for normal operations to provide reserve power for combat emergencies, and with automatic one-engine-out rating of 1,285 kW (1,723 shp). Engines mounted one on each side of fuselage, above wings, with key components armour-protected. Upper cowlings let down to serve as

maintenance platforms. Two crash-resistant fuel cells in fuselage, combined capacity 1,422 litres (376 US gallons; 313 Imp gallons).

ACCOMMODATION: Crew of two in tandem: co-pilot/gunner in front, pilot behind on 48 cm (19 in) elevated seat. Crew seats are of lightweight Kevlar. Teledyne Ryan canopy, with PPG transparencies and transparent acrylic blast barrier between cockpits, is designed to provide optimum field of view. Crew stations are protected by Ceradyne Inc lightweight boron armour shields in cockpit floor and sides, and between cockpits, offering protection against 23 mm high explosive and armour piercing rounds. Seats and structure designed to give crew a 95 per cent chance of surviving ground impacts of up to 12.8 m (42 ft)/s.

SYSTEMS: Redundant flight contol system for both rotors. In the event of a dual hydraulic system failure, the system reverts to Sperry Flight Systems secondary fly-by-wire control.

AVIONICS AND EQUIPMENT: Main avionics bays are adjacent to co-pilot/gunner's position, in large fairings on sides of fuselage. Tempest Enhanced C-10414 secure UHF, VHF, AM and FM com. Singer-Kearfott AN/ASN-128 light-weight Doppler navigation system, with Litton LR-80 (AN/ASN-143) strapdown attitude and heading reference system (AHRS). Doppler system, with AHRS, permits nap-of-the-earth navigation and provides for storing target locations. Avionics fit includes an ADF and an IFF transponder with secure encoding. Sperry Flight Systems digital automatic stabilisation equipment (DASE). Aircraft survivability equipment (ASE) consists of an Aerospace Avionics passive radar warning receiver, a Sanders infra-red jammer, chaff dispensers, and a radar jammer. Other avionics include Astronautics Corpn HSI, video display unit, remote magnetic indicator, and Pacer Systems omnidirectional air data system. A Sperry Flight Systems all-raster symbology generator processes TV data from IR and other sensors, superimposes symbology, and distributes the combination to CRT and helmet mounted displays in the aircraft. 'Black Hole' IR suppression system protects aircraft from heat-seeking missiles: this eliminates an engine-bay cooling fan by operating from engine exhaust gas through ejector nozzles to lower the gas plume and metal temperatures. BITE fault detection/location system.

ARMAMENT AND OPERATIONAL EQUIPMENT: Armament consists of a McDonnell Douglas M230 Chain Gun 30 mm automatic cannon, located between the mainwheel legs in an underfuselage mounting with Lear Siegler electronic controls. Normal rate of fire is 625 rds/min of Honeywell TP (target practice), HE or HEDP (high explosive dual purpose) ammunition, which is interoperable with NATO Aden/DEFA 30 mm ammunition. Max ammunition load is 1,200 rds. Gun mounting is designed to collapse into fuselage between pilots in the event of a crash landing. Four underwing hardpoints, with Aircraft Hydro-Forming pylons and ejector units, on which can be carried up to sixteen Rockwell Hellfire anti-tank missiles; or up to seventy-six 2.75 in FFAR (folding-fin aerial rockets) in their launchers; or a combination of Hellfires and FFAR. Hellfire remote electronics by Rockwell; Bendix aerial rocket control system; multiplex (MUX) system units by Sperry Flight Systems. Co-pilot/gunner (CPG) has primary responsibility for firing gun and missiles, but pilot can override his controls to fire gun or launch missiles.

Martin Marietta target-acquisition and designation sight and pilot's night vision sensor (TADS/PNVS) comprises two independently functioning systems mounted on the nose. The TADS consists of a rotating turret ($\pm$ 120° in azimuth, + 30/−60° in elevation) that houses the sensor subsystems, an optical relay tube in the CPG's cockpit, three electronic units in the avionics bay, and cockpit-mounted controls and displays. It is used principally for target search, detection and laser designation, with the CPG as primary operator (though it can also provide backup night vision to the pilot in the event of a PNVS failure). Once acquired by the TADS, targets can be tracked manually or automatically for autonomous attack with gun, rockets or Hellfire missiles. The TADS daylight sensor consists of a TV camera with narrow (0.9°) and wide-angle (4.0°) fields of view; direct-view optics (4° narrow and 18° wide angle); a laser spot tracker; and a International Laser Systems laser rangefinder/designator.

The night sensor, in the starboard half of the turret, incorporates a FLIR sight with narrow, medium and wide angle (3.1, 10.1 and 50.0°) fields of view. The PNVS consists of a FLIR sensor (30° × 40° field of view) in a rotating turret ($\pm$ 90° in azimuth, + 20/ − 45° in elevation) mounted above the TADS; an electronics unit in the avionics bay; and the pilot's display and controls. It provides the pilot with thermal imaging that permits nap-of-the-earth flight to, from and within the battle area at night or in adverse daytime weather, at altitudes low enough to avoid detection by the enemy. PNVS imagery is displayed on a single monocle in front of one of the pilot's eyes; flight information such as airspeed, altitude and heading is superimposed on this imagery to simplify the piloting task. The monocle is a part of the Honeywell Avionics integrated helmet and display sighting system (IHADSS) worn by both crew members.

DIMENSIONS, EXTERNAL:

Main rotor diameter	14.63 m (48 ft 0 in)
Length overall: tail rotor turning	14.68 m (48 ft 2 in)
both rotors turning	17.76 m (58 ft 3⅛ in)
Wing span	5.23 m (17 ft 2 in)
Height over tail rotor	4.30 m (14 ft 1¼ in)
overall (top of air data sensor)	4.66 m (15 ft 3½ in)
Wheel track	2.03 m (6 ft 8 in)
Wheelbase	10.59 m (34 ft 9 in)

AREA:

Main rotor disc	168.11 m² (1,809.5 sq ft)

WEIGHTS:

Weight empty	4,881 kg (10,760 lb)
Max external stores weight	771 kg (1,700 lb)
Structural design gross weight	6,650 kg (14,660 lb)
Primary mission gross weight	6,552 kg (14,445 lb)
Max T-O weight	9,525 kg (21,000 lb)

GENERAL PERFORMANCE (at 6,552 kg; 14,445 lb AUW, ISA except where indicated):

Never-exceed speed	197 knots (365 km/h; 227 mph)
Max level and max cruising speed	160 knots (296 km/h; 184 mph)
Max vertical rate of climb at S/L	762 m (2,500 ft)/min
Service ceiling	6,400 m (21,000 ft)
Hovering ceiling: IGE	4,570 m (15,000 ft)
OGE	3,505 m (11,500 ft)
Max range, internal fuel	260 nm (482 km; 300 miles)
Ferry range, max internal and external fuel, still air	918 nm (1,701 km; 1,057 miles)
Endurance at 1,220 m (4,000 ft) at 35°C	1 h 50 min
Max endurance, internal fuel	3 h 9 min
g limits at low altitude and airspeeds up to 164 knots (304 km/h; 189 mph)	+ 3.5/ − 0.5

WEIGHTS FOR TYPICAL MISSION PERFORMANCE (A: anti-armour at 1,220 m/4,000 ft and 35°C, 4 Hellfire and 320 rds of 30 mm ammunition; B: as A, but with 1,200 rds; C: as A, but with 6 Hellfire and 540 rds; D: anti-armour at 610 m/2,000 ft and 21°C, 8 Hellfire and 1,200 rds; E: air cover at 1,220 m/4,000 ft and 35°C, 4 Hellfire and 1,200 rds; F: as E but at 610 m/2,000 ft and 21°C, 4 Hellfire, 19 rockets, 1,200 rds; G: escort at 1,220 m/4,000 ft and 35°C, 19 rockets and 1,200 rds; H: escort at 610 m/2,000 ft and 21°C, 38 rockets and 1,200 rds):

Mission fuel:	A	727 kg (1,602 lb)
	G	741 kg (1,633 lb)
	E	745 kg (1,643 lb)
	C	902 kg (1,989 lb)
	B	1,029 kg (2,269 lb)
	D	1,063 kg (2,344 lb)
	H	1,077 kg (2,374 lb)
	F	1,086 kg (2,394 lb)
Mission gross weight:	A	6,552 kg (14,445 lb)
	E	6,874 kg (15,154 lb)
	G	6,932 kg (15,282 lb)
	B, C	7,158 kg (15,780 lb)
	D	7,728 kg (17,038 lb)
	F	7,813 kg (17,225 lb)
	H	7,867 kg (17,343 lb)

TYPICAL MISSION PERFORMANCE (A-H as above);

Cruising speed at intermediate rated power:

C	147 knots (272 km/h; 169 mph)
D	148 knots (274 km/h; 170 mph)
F	150 knots (278 km/h; 173 mph)
B	151 knots (280 km/h; 174 mph)
E, H	153 knots (283 km/h; 176 mph)
A	154 knots (285 km/h; 177 mph)
G	155 knots (287 km/h; 178 mph)

Max vertical rate of climb at intermediate rated power:

B, C	137 m (450 ft)/min
H	238 m (780 ft)/min
F, G	262 m (860 ft)/min
E	293 m (960 ft)/min
D	301 m (990 ft)/min
A	448 m (1,470 ft)/min

Mission endurance:

A, E, G	1 h 50 min
C	1 h 17 min
D, F, H	2 hr 30 min
B	2 h 40 min

McDonnell Douglas Sea-Going Apache

Under a company initiated programme, McDonnell Douglas is evaluating the concept of a sea-going Apache for attack and reconnaissance missions, operating in outer air battle regions from small US Navy warships. The sea-going Apache would have high capacity retractable landing gear, a folding main rotor and tail section, APG-65 search and track radar and provision for Sidewinder and AMRAAM air-to-air missiles and Penguin and Harpoon anti-shipping missiles. Integration of existing US Navy mission electronics, avionics and weapons would simplify and reduce the cost of logistical

Navalised McDonnell Douglas Sea-Going Apache. Weapon fit includes AIM-9L Sidewinder air-to-air missiles.

support. McDonnell Douglas Helicopter Company estimates that a sea-going Apache with retractable landing gear and a streamlined nose section would have cruising speed of 160–170 knots (296–315 km/h; 184–196 mph). Follow-on studies to refine naval applications will include avionics changes, integration of Advanced Apache computer and electrical bus systems, landing gear dynamic analyses and helicopter/ship dynamic interface analyses.

McDonnell Douglas/Bell LHX

In October 1983 the US Army Applied Technology Laboratory awarded Hughes Helicopters two research and development contracts valued at nearly $2 million for work on the LHX programme for a family of light scout/attack and utility helicopters which could replace Bell UH-1, AH-1 and OH-58, and Hughes OH-6A helicopters in the US Army

One of several McDonnell Douglas Helicopter Company configurations for the US Army LHX programme.

inventory. The contracts were for a two-year preliminary study to determine the best technical approach to an LHX production programme, and a one-year study for the application of the company's energy absorbing retractable landing gear to LHX utility helicopters.

Two industry teams are competing for the LHX development and production contracts. The development contract was expected to be awarded in early 1988, and the programme could involve more than 5,000 production helicopters. On 9 April 1986 McDonnell Douglas Helicopter announced that it was joining with Bell Helicopter Textron (which see) to develop its LHX submission. Other partners in the project are Eaton Corporation, Honeywell Inc, Litton Industries, Hughes Aircraft Company and Texas Instruments Inc. One proposal features McDonnell Douglas Helicopter's NOTAR system. This system is likely to be utilised only if speeds higher than 200 knots (370 km/h; 230 mph) are not required. McDonnell Douglas is also developing an integrated, automated ARTI one-man cockpit (the so-called 'glass cockpit') for the LHX. It has adapted the front cockit of an AH-64 (82-8258) with a fly-by-wire digital flight control system, and flew this helicopter for the first time on 12 October 1985. The rear cockpit remains standard, for a safety pilot.

In early 1985 McDonnell Douglas began ground tests of an MD 500E helicopter equipped with a hingeless and bearingless main rotor with composite blades of graphite and Kevlar 29 as part of its LHX technology advanced-rotor programme. Flight testing began in April 1985 at the company's Mesa, Arizona, facility. McDonnell Douglas is also building an all-composites rotor hub for the AH-64A as part of the LHX programme. This is expected to fly in 1988.

Allison and Garrett have jointly entered the ATE-109 turboshaft for the US Army's competition for an LHX powerplant. The only other known entry is the T800 free power turbine unit proposed jointly by Avco Lycoming and Pratt & Whitney. Both engines are in the 895 kW (1,200 shp) class.

Northrop
NORTHROP CORPORATION

This company was formed in 1939 by John K. Northrop and others to undertake the design and manufacture of military aircraft. Although continuing its activities in the design, development and production of aircraft, missiles and target drone systems, Northrop has broadened its scope of operation to include electronics, space technology, communications, support services and commercial products. To reflect this changing character of its business, the company changed its name from Northrop Aircraft Inc to Northrop Corporation in 1959. Since January 1982 its operations have been handled by an Aircraft Group, an Electronics Systems Group, and a Services Group.

Aircraft Group consists of four divisions and a wholly-owned subsidiary. The Aircraft Division is responsible for the design and manufacture of fighter aircraft and the manufacture of commercial aircraft major assemblies. Advanced Systems Division manages a number of aerospace programmes and is prime contractor to the USAF for research and development of the Advanced Technology Bomber. The former Ventura Division (working on pilotless target aircraft) became a unit of Aircraft Division in 1987. Aircraft Services Division provides technical and support services, as does subsidiary Northrop Worldwide Aircraft Services Inc, of Lawton, Oklahoma. Electronics Systems Group comprises an Electronics Division; Electro-Mechanical Division, which handles advanced missile programmes, electro-optical systems for target identification and target designation; Defense Systems Division, designer and manufacturer of electronics countermeasures systems, including the internal countermeasures set (ICS) for the US Air Force's F-15 Eagle; Precision Products Division; and Wilcox Electric Inc of Kansas City, Missouri. Services Group comprises an Aircraft Services Division; Northrop Services Inc, which provides technical support to NASA at Johnson Space Center in Houston, Texas, the Environmental Protection Agency, the National Institute of Health and the National Cancer Institute; and Northrop Worldwide Aircraft Services, Inc, of Lawton, Oklahoma.

Northrop Corporation Aircraft Group

Current production at Northrop's Aircraft Division, which has about 16,300 employees, is centred on the F/A-18 Hornet multi-mission fighter, and major Boeing 747 subcontract work, which includes manufacture of the main fuselage section, the extra-large side loading cargo door, passenger doors and the stretched upper deck of the 747-300.

Northrop is principal subcontractor for the McDonnell Douglas F/A-18A Hornet multi-mission fighter (which see). The company has design and production responsibility for the centre and rear fuselage and the twin vertical tails, including internal systems such as fuel, the environmental control system and auxiliary power system. The 600th shipset of these components was delivered in May 1987.

Northrop has been selected as prime contractor to proceed with research and development of US Air Force advanced technology bomber (ATB), the B-2. Key members of the team include Boeing, LTV and General Electric Company Aircraft Engine Group.

The company is also engaged in research projects involving advanced simulators and composite materials, and is teamed with McDonnell Douglas Corporation in USAF's advanced tactical fighter (ATF) programme.

The Aircraft Services Division is working with the Royal Saudi Air Force to provide support for RSAF technical resources, and also provides contracted maintenance and technical training programmes to international military and commercial operators.

Of major importance has been the end of all F-5 production in early 1987, together with the termination of further development of the F-20 Tigershark. Total pro-

Royal Norwegian Air Force Northrop F-5A tactical fighter. *(Aviation Picture Library)*

duction of the F-5A, F-5B, F-5C, F-5E, RF-5E and F-5F was 2,610 aircraft, including 'Es' and 'Fs' assembled by the Swiss Federal Aircraft Factory and manufactured under licence by KA in Korea and AIDC in Taiwan.

Northrop F-5

CAF designations: CF-5A/D
R Netherlands AF designations: NF-5A/B
R Norwegian AF designations: F-5G/RF-5G
Spanish AF designations: C-9/CE-9/CR-9
Design of this light tactical fighter started in 1955, and construction of the prototype of the single-seat version (then designated N-156C) began in 1958. It flew for the first time on 30 July 1959, exceeding Mach 1 on its maiden flight. Two more prototypes were built, followed by several production versions:

F-5A. Basic single-seat fighter. Two General Electric J85-GE-13 afterburning turbojets. First production F-5A flew in October 1963. Norwegian version has ATO and arrester hook for short-field operation.

F-5B. Generally similar to F-5A, but with two seats in tandem for dual fighter/trainer duties. First F-5B flew on 24 February 1964. Production was terminated during 1976.

CF-5A/D. These are the designations of the versions of the F-5A/B that were produced for the Canadian Armed Forces, the first of them entering service in 1968. Several improvements were incorporated in the CF series, including higher-thrust engines (two 19.1 kN; 4,300 lb st with afterburning Orenda J85-CAN-15s), and flight refuelling capability. 115 built under licence by Canadair, comprising 89 single-seat CF-5As and 26 two-seat CF-5Ds. Being replaced by CF-18A/B Hornets.

NF-5A/B. Versions of the F-5 produced for the Royal Netherlands Air Force with a Doppler navigation system, two-position nosewheel on single-seater, jettisonable pylons, inlet anti-icing, arrester hook, 1,040 litre (275 US gallon; 229 Imp gallon) fuel tanks and manoeuvring flaps. Manufacture and assembly of the 105 aircraft ordered were integrated with CF-5 production by Canadair Ltd, with the same engines as CF-5s.

RF-5A. Reconnaissance version of the F-5; initial

deliveries were made in mid-1968. Its four KS-92 cameras, each with a 100 ft film magazine, can provide forward oblique, trimetrogon and split vertical coverage, including horizon-to-horizon with overlap. Associated equipment includes four light sensors, defogging and cooling systems, a pitot-static nose boom and a computer/'J' box, all housed in a nose compartment with forward-hinged clamshell top cover. Operated currently by Greece, South Korea, Norway, Spain and Thailand.

SF-5A/B (C-9/CE-9). Under a 1966 contract, CASA built 36 single-seat SF-5As (C-9s) and 34 two-seat SF-5Bs (CE-9s) for the Spanish Air Force.

F-5E. Advanced version of F-5A. Described separately.

F-5F. Two-seat tactical fighter/trainer version of the F-5E. Described separately under F-5E Tiger II entry.

F-5G. Royal Norwegian Air Force designation for its 78 F-5As.

RF-5G. Royal Norwegian Air Force designation for its 16 RF-5As.

SRF-5A. Spanish built RF-5A, with local military designation CR-9.

The F-5 was first ordered into production by the US government, through the USAF, in October 1962, to meet the defence requirements of allied and friendly nations. Initial deliveries, beginning April 1964, were made to Williams AFB, Chandler, Arizona, where the USAF Tactical Air Command trained pilots and maintenance personnel of countries receiving F-5s. The first to receive F-5s was Iran, which put into service its initial squadron of 13 aircraft on 1 February 1965. Greece (F-5A and B), South Korea (F-5A and B), the Philippines (F-5A and B) and Turkey (F-5A and B) received F-5s in 1965. Morocco (F-5A and B), Norway (F-5G and F-5B) and Thailand (F-5A and B) first received F-5s in 1966. Current users also include Brazil (F-5B), Venezuela (F-5A and F-5D) and North Yemen (F-5B). The nations that received F-5A/Bs but are no longer users are Ethiopia, Libya, Taiwan and Viet-Nam, though Ethiopia and Taiwan operate the more advanced Tiger II.

TYPE: Light tactical fighter and reconnaissance aircraft.
WINGS: Cantilever low-wing monoplane. Wing section NACA 65A004.8 (modified). No dihedral or incidence.

Royal Netherlands Air Force Northrop NF-5B two-seat training fighter. *(Aviation Picture Library)*

Sweepback at quarter-chord 24°. Ailerons at approximately mid-span with single-slotted flaps inboard. Continuous-hinge leading-edge flaps. No trim tabs. No de-icing system.

FUSELAGE: Semi-monocoque basic structure. 'Waisted' area-rule lines. Two airbrakes on underside of fuselage forward of wheel wells.

TAIL UNIT: Cantilever structure, with rudder and one-piece all-moving tailplane. No trim tabs. Longitudinal and directional stability augmentors installed in series with control system.

LANDING GEAR: Retractable tricycle type with steerable nosewheel. Emergency gravity extension. Main wheels fitted with tubeless tyres size 22 × 8.5. Nosewheel fitted with tubeless tyre size 18 × 6.5. Multiple-disc hydraulic brakes.

POWERPLANT: Two General Electric J85-GE-13 turbojets (each with max rating of 18.15 kN; 4,080 lb st with afterburning). Two internal fuel tanks composed of integral cells with total usable capacity of 2,207 litres (583 US gallons; 485.5 Imp gallons). Provision for one 568 litre (150 US gallon; 125 Imp gallon) jettisonable tank on fuselage centreline pylon, two 568 litre (150 US gallon; 125 Imp gallon) jettisonable tanks on underwing pylons and two 189 litre (50 US gallon; 41.6 Imp gallon) wingtip tanks. Total fuel, with external tanks, 4,289 litres (1,133 US gallons; 943 Imp gallons).

ACCOMMODATION (F-5A): Pilot only, on rocket-powered ejection seat in pressurised cockpit. (F-5B): Pupil and instructor in tandem on rocket-powered ejection seats in pressurised cockpits separated by windscreen. Instructor's seat at rear raised 0.25 m (10 in) higher than that of pupil to give improved forward view.

AVIONICS AND EQUIPMENT: Standard equipment includes AN/ARC-34C UHF radio, PP-2024 SWIA-Missile AVX, AN/AIC-18 interphone, J-4 compass, Norsight optical sight, AN/APX-46 IFF, and AN/ARN-65 Tacan. Space provision for AN/ARW-77 Bullpup AUX. Blind-flying instrumentation not standard.

ARMAMENT: Basic interception weapons are two Sidewinder missiles on wingtip launchers and two 20 mm guns in fuselage nose. Five pylons, one under the fuselage and two under each wing, permit the carriage of a wide variety of other operational loads. A bomb of more than 907 kg (2,000 lb) or high-rate-of-fire gun pack can be suspended from the centre pylon. Underwing loads can include four air-to-air missiles, air-to-surface missiles, bombs, up to 20 air-to-surface rockets, gun packs or external fuel tanks. The reconnaissance nose does not eliminate the 20 mm nose gun capability.

DIMENSIONS, EXTERNAL:

Wing span	7.70 m (25 ft 3 in)
Wing span over tip-tanks	7.87 m (25 ft 10 in)
Length overall:	
F-5A	14.38 m (47 ft 2 in)
F-5B	14.12 m (46 ft 4 in)
Height overall:	
F-5A	4.01 m (13 ft 2 in)
F-5B	3.99 m (13 ft 1 in)
Wheel track	3.35 m (11 ft 0 in)
Wheelbase:	
F-5A	4.67 m (15 ft 4 in)
F-5B	5.94 m (19 ft 6 in)

AREA:

Wings, gross	15.79 m² (170.0 sq ft)

WEIGHTS:

Weight empty, equipped:	
F-5A	3,667 kg (8,085 lb)
F-5B	3,792 kg (8,361 lb)
Max military load	2,812 kg (6,200 lb)
Max T-O weight:	
F-5A	9,379 kg (20,677 lb)
F-5B	9,298 kg (20,500 lb)

PERFORMANCE (F-5A at AUW of 5,193 kg; 11,450 lb; F-5B at AUW of 4,916 kg; 10,840 lb, unless indicated otherwise):

Never-exceed speed	
	710 knots (1,315 km/h; 818 mph) IAS
Max level speed at 11,000 m (36,000 ft):	
F-5A	Mach 1.4
F-5B	Mach 1.34

Max cruising speed without afterburning, at 11,000 m (36,000 ft)   Mach 0.97
Econ cruising speed   Mach 0.87
Stalling speed, 50% fuel, flaps extended:
  F-5A   128 knots (237 km/h; 147 mph)
  F-5B   120 knots (223 km/h; 138 mph)
Max rate of climb at S/L:
  F-5A   8,750 m (28,700 ft)/min
  F-5B   9,265 m (30,400 ft)/min
Service ceiling:
  F-5A   15,390 m (50,500 ft)
  F-5B   15,850 m (52,000 ft)
T-O run (with two Sidewinder missiles):
  F-5A at AUW of 6,203 kg (13,677 lb)
    808 m (2,650 ft)
  F-5B at AUW of 5,924 kg (13,061 lb)
    671 m (2,200 ft)
T-O to 15 m (50 ft) with two Sidewinders:
  F-5A at AUW of 6,203 kg (13,677 lb)
    1,113 m (3,650 ft)
  F-5B at AUW of 5,924 kg (13,061 lb)
    960 m (3,150 ft)
Landing run, with brake-chute:
  F-5A at AUW of 4,504 kg (9,931 lb)
    701 m (2,300 ft)

F-5B at AUW of 4,363 kg (9,619 lb)
    671 m (2,200 ft)
Range with max fuel, with reserve fuel for 20 min max endurance at S/L:
  F-5A, tanks retained
    1,205 nm (2,232 km; 1,387 miles)
  F-5B, tanks retained
    1,210 nm (2,241 km; 1,393 miles)
  F-5A, tanks dropped
    1,400 nm (2,594 km; 1,612 miles)
  F-5B, tanks dropped
    1,405 nm (2,602 km; 1,617 miles)
Combat radius with max payload, allowances as above and 5 min combat at S/L:
  F-5A   170 nm (314 km; 195 miles)
  F-5B   175 nm (323 km; 201 miles)
Combat radius with max fuel, two 530 lb bombs, allowances as above and 5 min combat at S/L:
  F-5A   485 nm (898 km; 558 miles)
  F-5B   495 nm (917 km; 570 miles)
Operational hi-lo-lo-hi reconnaissance radius with max fuel, 50 nm (93 km; 58 mile) S/L dash to and from target and allowances as for combat radius with max fuel:
  RF-5A   560 nm (1,036 km; 644 miles)

Northrop Tiger II

USAF designations: F-5E and F-5F

Production of the Tiger II series ended in early 1987 with the delivery of two F-5Es to the Bahrain Air Force.

The F-5E was selected in November 1970 by the US government as the winner of a competition to determine the single-seat International Fighter Aircraft (IFA) which was to succeed Northrop's F-5A. The two-seat F-5F was developed subsequently.

The F-5E design places particular emphasis on manoeuvrability by the incorporation of auto-manoeuvring flaps. Full-span leading-edge flaps work in conjunction with conventional trailing-edge flaps, and are operated automatically in response to airspeed and angle of attack. The flaps may also be pilot controlled to full-down and full-up positions. Wing loading is maintained at approximately the same value as on the F-5A, as the result of an increase in area

due principally to the widened fuselage, which also increases wing span. The tapered wing leading-edge extension, between the inboard leading edge and fuselage, was refined to increase the wing area and maximise the lift coefficient of the wing.

The F-5E incorporates other features developed for the Canadian, Dutch and Norwegian F-5s, including two-position nosewheel gear, which increases wing angle of attack on the ground by 3° 22′. In conjunction with the more powerful engines, this improves F-5E take-off performance by some 30 per cent compared with earlier F-5s.

The first F-5E made its first flight on 11 August 1972. USAF Tactical Air Command, with assistance from Air Training Command, was assigned responsibility for training pilots and technicians of user countries. First deliveries, to the US Air Force's 425th Tactical Fighter Squadron, were

US Air Force Northrop F-5E Tiger II. *(Dr Alan Beaumont)*

made in the spring of 1973, and deliveries to foreign countries began in early 1974. In addition to their use as tactical fighters, F-5Es are operated by the US Air Force, US Navy and US Marine Corps in the 'aggressor' role, to simulate enemy aircraft at major air combat training schools in the USA, England and the Philippines.

In March 1985 the USAF announced plans to upgrade its fleet of 74 F-5Es and F-5Fs. The programme includes new Emerson AN/APQ-159(V)5 radar in the F-5Es and AN/APQ-159(V)6 in F-5Fs, replacing the earlier APQ-153 radar. The new radars double detection range and incorporate off-boresight target acquisition and track-while-scan. A new radar warning receiver and radar jammer are also installed. Northrop modified the control column grips on the USAF's F-5Es to standardise them with those on the F-5F, and transferred radar control switches from panel mounts to the control column hand grip.

Total production figures for the F-5E and F are included in those given in the company introduction. Customers for the F-5E and F-5F have included Bahrain, Brazil, Chile, Ecuador, Ethiopia, Honduras, Indonesia, Iran, Jordan, Kenya, South Korea, Malaysia, Mexico, Morocco, Philippines, Saudi Arabia, Singapore, Sudan, Switzerland, Taiwan, Thailand, Tunisia, USA and North Yemen.

Versions of the Tiger II are as follows:

F-5E. Standard production version, to which the detailed description applies. Produced, also, under licence, by AIDC in Taiwan and by KA in Korea. Assembly of F-5Es and F-5Fs by the Swiss Federal Aircraft Factory was completed in March 1985. The final Northrop production version has handling quality improvements resulting from installation of a shark-nose radome, automatic leading-edge and trailing-edge manoeuvring flaps, and a larger leading-edge extension.

To extend the range of armament options, certification was completed for a centreline mounted General Electric 30 mm gun pod firing GAU-8 ammunition.

The F-5Es for seven customer countries have a Litton LN-33 inertial navigation system, capable of accuracy exceeding 1.5 nm (2.7 km; 1.7 miles) CEP per flight hour, which provides attitude reference, range and bearing to preset destinations, as well as true ground track steering. The system is self aligning in 10 min in the gyro compass mode,

and can be aligned in 3 min to a stored heading.

F-5F. Tandem two-seat version of F-5E, with fuselage lengthened by 1.22 m (4 ft 0 in). Fire control system and one M39 cannon retained, enabling aircraft to be used both for training and combat duties. First flight was made on 25 September 1974. Two F-5Fs completed flight test and qualification in early 1976. Deliveries began in the Summer of 1976.

RF-5E TigerEye. Reconnaissance version, described separately.

The following details refer to the F-5E, but are generally applicable to the F-5F also, except for details noted under model listings:

TYPE: Single-seat light tactical fighter.

WINGS: Cantilever low-wing monoplane. Wing section NACA 65A004.8 (modified). No dihedral. No incidence. Sweepback at quarter-chord 24°. Ailerons at approximately mid span. Single-slotted trailing-edge flaps inboard of ailerons. Electrically operated leading-edge flaps. No de-icing system.

FUSELAGE: Semi-monocoque basic structure. Two airbrakes mounted on underside of fuselage forward of mainwheel wells. Rear avionics bay and cockpit pressurised; fail-safe structure in pressurised sections.

TAIL UNIT: Cantilever structure, with rudder and one-piece all-moving tailplane. No trim tabs. Dual hydraulic actuators of Northrop design for control of rudder and tailplane.

LANDING GEAR: Retractable tricycle type. Two-position extending nose unit increases static angle of attack by 3° 22′ to reduce T-O distance, and is shortened automatically during the retraction cycle. Gravity operated emergency extension. Mainwheels and tyres size 24 × 8.00-13. Steerable nose unit with wheel and tyre size 18 × 6.50-8. All-metal multiple-disc brakes of Northrop design.

POWERPLANT: Two General Electric J85-GE-21B turbojet engines, each rated at 22.24 kN (5,000 lb st) with afterburning. Two independent fuel systems, one for each engine. Fuel for starboard engine supplied from two rubber impregnated nylon fabric bladder cells, comprising a centre fuselage cell of 803 litre (212 US gallon; 176.5 Imp gallon) capacity, and a rear fuselage cell of 640 litre (169

Northrop F-5E Tiger II. *(Pilot Press)*

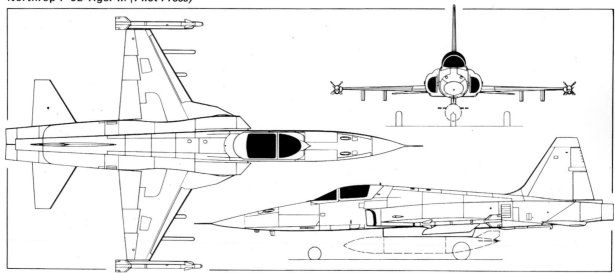

382

US gallon; 141 Imp gallon) capacity. Port engine supplied from a forward fuselage cell of 1,120 litre (296 US gallon; 246.5 Imp gallon) capacity. Total internal fuel capacity 2,563 litres (677 US gallons; 564 Imp gallons) in F-5E, 2,555 litres (675 US gallons; 562 Imp gallons) in F-5F. No fuel is carried in the wings. Fuel crossfeed system allows fuel from either or both cell systems to be fed to either or both engines. Auxiliary jettisonable fuel tanks or 568 or 1,041 litres (150 or 275 US gallons; 125 or 229 Imp gallons) can be carried on the fuselage centreline pylon and the inboard underwing pylons.

ENGINE INTAKES: Intakes are supplemented by auxiliary air inlet doors for use during T-O and low-speed flight, to improve compressor face pressure recovery and to decrease distortion. Each door consists of a set of six pivot mounted louvres in removable panels on each side of the fuselage. The doors are actuated by the pilot at T-O and controlled automatically in flight by Mach sensor switches, and are maintained in the open position at airspeeds below Mach 0.35–0.4.

ACCOMMODATION: Pilot only, in pressurised cockpit, on rocket powered ejection seat.

AVIONICS AND EQUIPMENT (F-5E): AN/ARC-164 UHF command radio, 7,000-channel with 25kHz spacing. Emerson Electric AN/APQ-159 lightweight micro-miniature pulse radar for air-to-air search for target detection with range and angle tracking; target information, at a range of up to 20 nm (37 km; 23 miles), is displayed on a 0.13 m (5 in) DVST (direct view storage tube) in cockpit. AN/ASG-31 lead computing optical sight; AN/ARA-50 UHF ADF; AN/AIC-25 intercom; AN/APX-101 IFF; AN/ARN-118 Tacan; attitude and heading reference system; angle-of-attack system; and central air data computer. Full blind-flying instrumentation. Optional avionics include Litton LN-33

inertial navigation system; AN/ARN-108 instrument landing system; CPU-129/A flight director computer; VHF; VOR/ILS with DME; LF ADF; CRT with scan converter for radar or electro-optical weapon (AGM-65 Maverick); AN/ALE-40 countermeasures dispenser system; and Itek AN/ALR-46 digital or analog radar warning receiver.

AVIONICS AND EQUIPMENT (F-5F): As detailed for F-5E. Optional equipment includes the Northrop AN/AVQ-27 laser target designation set.

ARMAMENT (F-5E): Two AIM-9 Sidewinder missiles on wingtip launchers. Two M39A2 20 mm cannon in fuselage nose, with 280 rds/gun. Up to 3,175 kg (7,000 lb) of mixed ordnance can be carried on one underfuselage and four underwing stations, including M129 leaflet bombs; up to nine Mk 82 GP and Snakeye 500 lb bombs; Mk 36 destructors; Mk 84 2,000 lb bomb; Matra Durandal air-to-surface missiles; LAU-68 (7) 2.75 in rockets; LAU-3 (19) 2.75 in rockets; CBU-24, -49, -52 or -58 cluster bomb units; SUU-20 bomb and rocket packs; SUU-25 flare dispensers; TDU-10 tow targets (Dart); and RMU-10 reel (Dart). Lead computing optical gunsight uses inputs from airborne radar for air-to-air missiles and cannon, and provides a roll stabilised manually depressible reticle aiming reference for air-to-ground delivery. A 'snapshoot' capability is included for attack on violently manoeuvring and fleeting targets. The gunsight incorporates also a detachable 16 mm reticle camera with 15 m (50 ft) film magazine. Optional ordnance capability includes the AGM-65 Maverick; centreline multiple ejector rack; and laser guided bombs.

ARMAMENT (F-5F): Two AIM-9 Sidewinder missiles on wingtip launchers. One M39 20 mm cannon in port side of nose with 140 rounds. Underfuselage and underwing stores as detailed for the F-5E.

DIMENSIONS, EXTERNAL:

Wing span	8.13 m (26 ft 8 in)
Wing span over missiles	8.53 m (27 ft 11$\frac{7}{8}$ in)
Length overall (incl nose probe):	
F-5E	14.45 m (47 ft 4$\frac{3}{4}$ in)
F-5F	15.65 m (51 ft 4 in)
Height overall: F-5E	4.07 m (13 ft 4$\frac{1}{4}$ in)
F-5F	4.13 m (13 ft 2 in)
Wheel track	3.80 m (12 ft 5$\frac{1}{2}$ in)
Wheelbase: F-5E	5.17 m (16 ft 11$\frac{1}{2}$ in)
F-5F	6.52 m (21 ft 1$\frac{1}{2}$ in)

AREA:

Wings, basic	17.3 m² (186.0 sq ft)

WEIGHT:

Weight empty: F-5E	4,410 kg (9,723 lb)
F-5F	4,797 kg (10,576 lb)
Max external fuel weight:	
F-5E/F-5F	2,415 kg (5,324 kg)
Max T-O weight: F-5E	11,214 kg (24,722 lb)
F-5F	11,409 kg (25,152 lb)

PERFORMANCE (F-5E at combat weight of 6,055 kg; 13,350 lb, F-5F at combat weight of 6,375 kg; 14,055 lb, unless stated otherwise):

Never-exceed speed	
	710 knots (1,314 km/h; 817 mph) EAS
Max level speed at 10,975 m (36,000 ft):	
F-5E	Mach 1.64
F-5F	Mach 1.56
Max cruising speed:	
F-5E at 10,975 m (36,000 ft)	Mach 0.98

Econ cruising speed	Mach 0.80
Stalling speed, flaps down, power off:	
F-5E	124 knots (230 km/h; 143 mph)
F-5F	136 knots (253 km/h; 157 mph)
Max rate of climb at S/L:	
F-5E	10,516 m (34,500 ft)/min
F-5F	10,030 m (32,900 ft)/min
Service ceiling: F-5E	15,790 m (51,800 ft)
F-5F	15,485 m (50,800 ft)
T-O run:	
F-5E at 7,053 kg (15,550 lb)	
	610 m (2,000 ft)
F-5F at 7,371 kg (16,250 lb)	
	701 m (2,300 ft)
T-O run at max T-O weight:	
F-5E	1,737 m (5,700 ft)
F-5F	1,829 m (6,000 ft)
T-O to 15 m (50 ft):	
F-5E at 7,053 kg (15,550 lb)	884 m (2,900 ft)
F-5F at 7,371 kg (16,250 lb)	975 m (3,200 ft)
Landing from 15 m (50 ft):	
F-5E at 5,230 kg (11,530 lb), without brake-chute	
	1,417 m (4,650 ft)
F-5F at 5,554 kg (12,245 lb), without brake-chute	
	1,524 m (5,000 ft)
Landing run with brake-chute:	
F-5E at 5,230 kg (11,530 lb)	762 m (2,500 ft)
F-5F at 5,554 kg (12,245 lb)	792 m (2,600 ft)

Combat radius, F-5E:
with max fuel, two Sidewinder missiles, reserves for 20 min max endurance at S/L and 5 min combat with max afterburning power at 4,575 m (15,000 ft)

570 nm (1,056 km; 656 miles)

with 2,358 kg (5,200 lb) ordnance load, two Sidewinder missiles, max fuel, allowances as above and 5 min combat at military power at S/L, lo-lo-lo mission

120 nm (222 km; 138 miles)

with max fuel, two Sidewinder missiles and two 530 lb bombs, allowances as above, and 5 min combat at military power at S/L, hi-lo-hi mission

480 nm (890 km; 553 miles)

Combat radius, F-5F:
with max internal fuel, and allowances comprising 2 min at normal thrust, 1 min at max thrust, 5 min max thrust for

combat at 4,575 m (15,000 ft), 20 min loiter at S/L, plus reserve of 5% of initial fuel

520 nm (964 km; 599 miles)

with max fuel, two Sidewinder missiles and two 530 lb bombs, allowances as above, and 5 min combat at military power at S/L, hi-lo-hi mission

450 nm (834 km; 518 miles)

Range, F-5E:
with max fuel and reserves for 20 min max endurance at S/L:
tanks retained   1,340 nm (2,483 km; 1,543 miles)
tanks dropped   1,545 nm (2,863 km; 1,779 miles)

Range, F-5F:
ferry range with max fuel, allowances comprising 5 min at normal thrust, 1 min at max thrust, 20 min loiter at S/L, plus reserve of 5% of initial fuel:
crew of two   1,270 nm (2,353 km; 1,462 miles)

Northrop RF-5E TigerEye

In March 1978 Northrop announced receipt of US government approval for a company funded development and flight demonstration programme of an RF-5E having a modified forward fuselage with quick-change capabilities to accommodate a wide variety of reconnaissance equipment. Both day and night photo missions were demonstrated during the subsequent test programme. Modification of a production F-5E made possible the first flight of the RF-5E prototype in January 1979, and this aircraft made its international debut at the 1979 Paris Air Show. The first production RF-5E, one of two delivered to the Royal Malaysian Air Force in 1983, made its first flight on 15 December 1982. Saudi Arabia ordered ten, the first of which were delivered in 1985.

Basically similar to the F-5E Tiger II, the RF-5E TigerEye differs in having a modified forward fuselage, and specialised equipment to enable it to fulfil a highly efficient reconnaissance role. The modified forward fuselage extends the overall length by 0.20 m (8 in), and provides 0.74 m³ (26 cu ft) of space to accommodate reconnaissance equipment. To allow maximum flexibility for differing reconnaissance

roles, Northrop decided to group the various combinations of proposed cameras/sensors on portable pallets, any one of which could be loaded easily and quickly into this forward fuselage compartment. In addition to the selected pallet, a KS-87D1 oblique frame camera is mounted in a forward nose compartment and provided with lenses of 6 in and 12 in focal length.

Two pallets were developed for the RF-5E, the first comprising a KA-95B medium-altitude panoramic camera, KA-56E low-altitude panoramic camera, and an RS-710E infra-red linescanner. Pallet 2 also has the KA-56E panoramic camera, with a KA-93B6 panoramic camera with a 145° scan angle for heights of 3,050–15,240 m (10,000–50,000 ft).

The pilot has available advanced nav/com systems to complement the reconnaissance equipment, plus a video viewfinder system which enables him to view the terrain below the aircraft on a cathode-ray-tube display in the cockpit. Using this system, the pilot can monitor and correct his line of flight during mapping runs, and can also update the INS when passing over recognisable terrain features. In

First production example of the RF-5E TigerEye, showing clearly the undernose windows for the installation of cameras and infra-red equipment.

addition, there is a photographic sensor control system (PSCS) which handles many operations automatically.

The RF-5E TigerEye retains the external stores stations of the F-5E, permitting the carriage of up to three external fuel tanks (each 1,041 litres; 275 US gallons; 229 Imp gallons) for maximum range performance. It has essentially the same weights, performance and armament capabilities as the F-5E tactical fighter, and on all missions is able to carry one M39 20 mm gun with 280 rounds, plus two AIM-9 Sidewinder missiles.

PERFORMANCE: As for F-5E except:
Mission radius (A, with one drop-tank and two AIM-9s; B, with three drop-tanks and two AIM-9s):
low altitude throughout:

A	245 nm (454 km; 282 miles)
B	350 nm (648 km; 403 miles)
hi-lo-hi: A	390 nm (723 km; 449 miles)
B	530 nm (982 km; 610 miles)
hi-lo-lo-hi: A	345 nm (639 km; 397 miles)
B	485 nm (898 km; 558 miles)
high altitude throughout:	
A	475 nm (830 km; 547 miles)
B	595 nm (1,102 km; 685 miles)

Northrop F-20 Tigershark

Following the October 1986 announcement that the USAF had selected an upgraded General Dynamics F-16A to replace F-4s and F-106s in the air defence fighter (ADF) role, Northrop terminated further development of the F-20 Tigershark and ceased its marketing efforts. In the Summer

Northrop F-20 Tigershark.

of 1987 the company was reported to be offering an F-20 'package', comprising the third prototype aircraft, the part-completed fourth prototype and blueprints for the aircraft to countries interested in taking over development and production.

Northrop B-2 (ATB)

During October 1981 it was reported that contracts totalling $7,300 million had been awarded to Northrop, to develop and build prototypes of an advanced technology ('stealth') bomber (ATB) to take over the B-1B's penetration role during the final years of this century. Northrop, as prime contractor, is being assisted by Boeing Aerospace, LTV (Vought) and General Electric Engine Group. However, the B-2 has a flying-wing configuration, is expected to be smaller than the B-1B, and is scheduled to make its first flight in 1988. Indications in mid-1987 were that the B-2 would have four (F101?) engines, and a gross weight in the region of 158,760–170,100 kg (350,000–375,000 lb). In early 1986 Northrop's Advanced Systems Division at Pico Rivera, California, had completed a full-scale engineering mockup of the B-2, which was generally similar in shape to the Northrop YB-49 'flying wing' jet bomber. A scaled proof-of-concept vehicle is believed to have been flying since 1982. Subject to satisfactory flight testing, the USAF plans to acquire 132 B-2s in a $36,000 million programme, with first deliveries to Whiteman AFB, Missouri, in the early 1990s.

Northrop YF-23A (ATF)

Northrop is contracted to build two YF-23A prototypes of the advanced tactical fighter for the USAF, in partnership with McDonnell Douglas.

Rockwell International
ROCKWELL INTERNATIONAL CORPORATION

North American Aviation Inc, incorporated in Delaware in 1928 and a manufacturer of aircraft of various kinds from 1934, and Rockwell-Standard Corporation of Pittsburgh, Pennsylvania, a manufacturer of automotive components and builder of the Aero Commander line of civilian aircraft, merged on 22 September 1967 to form North American Rockwell Corporation.

During 1973 the Corporation adopted its present name, Rockwell International, to reflect its expanding international business. The corporation applies advanced technology to a wide range of products in its four major businesses: **Aerospace**, which is engaged in the research, development and manufacture of military aircraft, manned and unmanned space systems and rocket engines, advanced space-based surveillance systems and high-energy laser and other directed-energy programmes; **Automotive**, which develops, manufactures and markets components for heavy and medium-duty trucks, buses, trailers and heavy-duty off-road vehicles, light trucks and cars; **Electronics**, engaged in research, development, manufacture and marketing of a broad range of defence and commercial electronics systems and products for precision guidance and control, tactical weapons command, control, communications and intelligence, precision navigation, avionics, telecommunications and semiconductor applications; and **General Industries**, which develops, manufactures and markets high-speed printing presses and related graphic arts equipment, flow control and measurement equipment, components for energy markets including oil, utility, gas and nuclear industries, and industrial sewing machines.

North American Aircraft Operations

Rockwell International Bronco

US military designation: OV-10

This aircraft was North American's entry for the US Navy's design competition for a light armed reconnaissance aeroplane (LARA) specifically suited for counter-insurgency missions. Nine US airframe manufacturers entered for the competition and the NA-300 was declared the winning design in August 1964. Seven prototypes were built by the company's Columbus Division, under the designation YOV-10A Bronco. The first of these flew on 16 July 1965, followed by the second in December 1965.

A number of modifications were made as a result of flight experience with the prototypes. In particular, the wing span was increased by 3.05 m (10 ft 0 in), T76 turboprop engines were uprated from 492 kW (660 shp) to 534 kW (716 shp), and the engine nacelles were moved outboard approximately 0.15 m (6 in) to reduce noise in the cockpit.

A prototype with increased span flew for the first time on 15 August 1966. The seventh prototype had T74 (PT6A) turboprops for comparative testing.

The following versions were built:

OV-10A. Initial production version ordered in October 1966 and first flown on 6 August 1967. US Marine Corps had 114 in service in September 1969, of which 18 were on loan to the USN; used for light armed reconnaissance, helicopter escort and forward-air-control duties. At the same date the USAF had 157 OV-10As for use in the forward-air-control role, as well as for limited quick-response ground support pending the arrival of tactical fighters. Some used to replace O-2As. 533 kW (715 hp) Garrett T76-G-416/417 turboprops.

Production of the OV-10A for the US services ended in April 1969, but 15 aircraft were modified by LTV Electrosystems Inc, under the USAF Pave Nail programme, to permit their use in a night forward-air-control and strike-designation role in 1971.

Equipment installed by LTV included a stabilised night periscopic sight, a combination laser rangefinder and target illuminator, a Loran receiver and a Lear Siegler Loran co-ordinate converter. This combination of equipment generated an offset vector to enable an accompanying strike aircraft to attack the target or, alternatively, illuminate the target, enabling a laser-seeking missile to home on to it. These specially configured aircraft reverted to the OV-10A configuration in 1974 by removal of the LTV-installed equipment. Production totalled 271 aircraft.

OV-10B. Generally similar to the OV-10A; six supplied to the Federal German government for target-towing duties.

OV-10B(Z). Structurally similar to the OV-10B, except that a General Electric J85-GE-4 turbojet engine of 13.12 kN (2,950 lb st) is mounted above the wing, on a pylon attached to existing hoisting points, to increase performance for target-towing duties. First flown on 21 September 1970. Delivery of 12 OV-10B(Z) aircraft to the Federal German government was completed in November 1970. The jet pods were fitted by RFB, in Germany, following the prototype installation by Rockwell.

OV-10C. Version of the OV-10A for the Royal Thai Air Force. Deliveries of 40 completed in 1973.

OV-10D. Designation of 17 US Marine Corps OV-10As converted for Night Observation Surveillance (NOS) role. In addition to NOS systems and the basic OV-10A fuselage stores and external fuel capability, the OV-10D NOS has uprated engines, and wing pylons for additional weapons (or external fuel tanks when extended radius/loiter time is required). A Texas Instruments AN/AAS-37 FLIR sensor and laser target designator is installed in a rotating ball turret in the nose. This can be linked to a turret-mounted General

US Marine Corps OV-10D Bronco with Night Observation System.

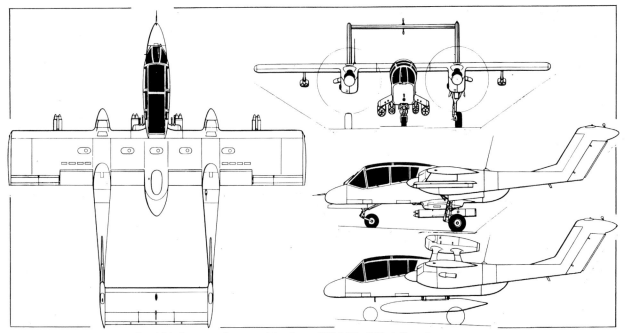

Rockwell International OV-10A Bronco. Lower side view: OV-10B. *(Pilot Press)*

Electric M97 20mm cannon, installed beneath the fuselage, in lieu of normal operation with standard OV-10A armament sponsons and centreline station. Equipment includes optional APR-39 radar homing and warning system, ALE-39 chaff/flare dispensers and IR-suppressant engine exhaust system. Deliveries were completed in 1980.

In the spring of 1985 it was reported that the government of South Korea had set aside $240 million in its defence budget for the acquisition of 24 OV-10Ds equipped with 20 mm gun turrets, FLIR systems and laser rangefinder/target designators. These are not believed to have been built (see OV-10G).

OV-10E. Version of the OV-10A for the Fuerzas Aéreas Venezolanas. Sixteen ordered through the US Department of Defense foreign military sales programme. The first of these was delivered in March 1973.

OV-10F. Version of the OV-10A for the government of Indonesia. Sixteen aircraft ordered through the US Department of Defense foreign military sales programme. Delivery of the first of these aircraft was made in 1976.

OV-10G. Designation of 24 Broncos believed to have been acquired by South Korea in a 1976 Department of Defense foreign military sales programme, costing over $58 million.

The following description applies to the OV-10D, except where indicated:

TYPE: Two-seat multi-purpose counter-insurgency and night surveillance aircraft.

WINGS: Cantilever shoulder-wing monoplane. Constant-chord wing without dihedral or sweep. Conventional structure. Ailerons, supplemented by four small spoilers forward of outer flap on each wing. Two-section double-slotted flaps on each wing, separated by tailbooms. Trim tab on each aileron (one spring, one geared, on each wing).

FUSELAGE: Short pod-type fuselage of conventional semi-monocoque construction, suspended from wing. Glass-fibre nosecone.

TAIL UNIT: Cantilever structure carried on twin booms of semi-monocoque construction. Fixed-incidence tailplane mounted near tips of fins. Trim tabs in rudders and elevator.

LANDING GEAR: Retractable tricycle type, with single wheel on each unit. Forged aluminium wheels. Mainwheel tyres size 29 × 11-10. Steerable nosewheel with tyre size 7.50-10. Cleveland disc brakes.

POWERPLANT: Two 775.5 kW (1,040 ehp) Garrett T76-G-420/421 turboprop engines, each driving a Hamilton Standard three-blade constant-speed reversible-pitch fully-feathering metal propeller with glassfibre blades. Five self-sealing bladder fuel tanks in wings, with combined capacity of 954 litres (252 US gallons; 210 Imp gallons). Provision for carrying one 568 litre (150 US gallon; 125 Imp gallon) drop-tank on underfuselage pylon, and one 378 litre (100 US gallon; 83 Imp gallon) drop-tank on each wing pylon.

ACCOMMODATION: Crew of two in tandem, on LW-3B zero/zero ejection seats, under canopy with two large upward opening transparent door panels on each side. Dual controls optional. Cargo compartment aft of rear seat, with rear loading door at end of fuselage pod. Rear seat removable to provide increased space for additional personnel or up to 1,452 kg (3,200 lb) of freight.

AVIONICS: US Air Force OV-10As are equipped with AN/AIC-18 intercom; AN/ARC-51BX UHF, Wilcox 807A VHF, dual FM-622A VHF, and HF-103 HF com radios; nav system includes AN/ASN-75 compass, AN/ARN-52(V) Tacan, AN/ARA-50 UHF-ADF, AN/ARN-83 LF-ADF, 51R-6 VOR, and 51V-4A ILS glideslope; identification system includes AN/APX-64(V) IFF/SIF, and SST-181-X radar beacon. US Marine Corps aircraft are equipped with AN/AIC-18 intercom; AN/ARC-51AX UHF, AN/ARC-54 VHF, and AN/ARC-120 HF com radios; nav system includes AN/ASN-75 compass, AN/APN-171 radar altimeter,

AN/ARN-52(V) Tacan, and AN/ARA-50 UHF-ADF; AN/APX-64(V) IFF/SIF for identification. OV-10D NOS aircraft have an AN/AAS-37 FLIR sensor system package, comprising FLIR, a laser target designator, and an automatic video tracker installed in a rotating ball turret in nose. Optional APR-39 radar homing and warning system, ALE-39 chaff/flare dispensers and IR-suppressant engine exhaust system.

ARMAMENT: Four weapon attachment points, each with capacity of 272 kg (600 lb), under short sponsons extending from bottom of fuselage on each side, under wings. Fifth attachment point, capacity 544 kg (1,200 lb) under centre fuselage. Two 7.62 mm M60C machine-guns, each with 500 rounds of ammunition, carried in each sponson. USMC OV-10A has provision also for carrying one AIM-9 Sidewinder missile under each wing. Stores which can be carried on the underfuselage and sponson stations include Mk 81, 82 and 83 GP bombs, Mk 81 and 82 GP (Snakeye) bombs; Mk 77 Mod 2 and Mod 4 fire bombs; LAU-3/A, LAU-10/A, LAU-32/A, LAU-59/A, LAU-60/A, LAU-61/A, LAU-68/A and LAU-69/A rocket packages: SUU-11A/A (7.62 mm Minigun), Mk 4 Mod 0 (20 mm), and GPU-2/A (20 mm) gun pods; SUU-40/A and SUU-44/A with Mk 24 and Mk 45 flares; Mk 12 Mod 0 (Podeye) smoke tank; Mk 86A/A37B-3 MBR with Mk 76 and Mk 106 practice bombs; CBU-55/B cluster bomb. Max weapon load on fuselage stations 1,633 kg (3,600 lb). OV-10D has, in addition, wing pylons with stores capacity of 272 kg (600 lb) each, which can carry CBU-55/B cluster bombs; 250 lb laser guided bombs; LAU-10/A, LAU-68/A and LAU-69/A rocket packages; SUU-40/A and SUU-44/A with Mk 24 and Mk 45 flares. In lieu of sponsons and fuselage centreline load, the OV-10D can carry a General Electric M97 20 mm gun turret, with 1,500 rds, on centreline station hardpoint.

DIMENSIONS, EXTERNAL:	
Wing span	12.19 m (40 ft 0 in)
Length overall	13.41 m (44 ft 0 in)
Height overall	4.62 m (15 ft 2 in)
Wheel track	4.52 m (14 ft 10 in)
Wheelbase	3.56 m (11 ft 8 in)
Propeller diameter	2.59 m (8 ft 6 in)
AREA:	
Wings, gross	27.03 m² (291.0 sq ft)
WEIGHTS:	
Weight empty	3,127 kg (6,893 lb)
Normal T-O weight	4,494 kg (9,908 lb)
Overload T-O weight	6,552 kg (14,444 lb)
PERFORMANCE:	
Max level speed at S/L, without weapons	250 knots (463 km/h; 288 mph)
Max rate of climb at S/L at normal T-O weight	920 m (3,020 ft)/min
Service ceiling at normal T-O weight	9,150 m (30,000 ft)
T-O run at normal T-O weight	226 m (740 ft)
T-O to 15 m (50 ft):	
at normal T-O weight	341 m (1,120 ft)
at max T-O weight	853 m (2,800 ft)
Landing from 15 m (50 ft) at normal T-O weight	372 m (1,220 ft)
Landing run: at normal T-O weight	226 m (740 ft)
at max T-O weight	381 m (1,250 ft)
Combat radius with max weapon load, no loiter	198 nm (367 km; 228 miles)
Ferry range with auxiliary fuel	1,200 nm (2,224 km; 1,382 miles)

Rockwell International B-1B

The original B-1 was the outcome of a succession of defence studies, begun in 1962 and leading to the AMSA (Advanced Manned Strategic Aircraft) requirement of 1965, for a low-altitude penetration bomber to replace the Boeing B-52s of USAF Strategic Air Command by 1980. It was intended as the third and most flexible component of the US Triad defence system, which comprises also land-based and submarine-launched ballistic missiles.

To meet the B-1 requirement, the Department of Defense issued RFPs (requests for proposals) to the US aerospace industry on 3 November 1969, and from three airframe and two engine finalists it awarded research, development, test and evaluation contracts on 5 June 1970 to North American Rockwell's Los Angeles Division (now Rockwell International's North American Aircraft Operations) for the airframe, and to the General Electric Company for the F101

Rockwell International B-1B strategic bomber with wings fully swept.

turbofan engine. The original cost-plus-incentive contracts were for five flying prototypes, two structural test airframes and 40 engines. In January 1971, in which month the essential design of the B-1 was frozen, these quantities were reduced to three flight-test aircraft, one ground-test aircraft and 27 engines. Procurement of a fourth flight-test aircraft, as a pre-production prototype, was approved under the FY 1976 budget. The US Air Force planned originally to order 244 B-1s, including the four prototypes, to replace in-service B-52s; if this programme had proceeded on schedule, all 244 would have been delivered by 1981.

Assembly of the first B-1 began on 15 March 1972; this aircraft (USAF serial number 74-158) made its first flight, at Palmdale, California, on 23 December 1974. This occasion was also the first flight of the YF101 engine. The third B-1 (74-160), used as a testbed for the avionics systems, made its first flight on 26 March 1976, and was followed by the first flight of the second B-1 (74-159) on 14 June 1976. The fourth B-1 (76-174), flown for the first time on 14 February 1979, represented an operational configuration, with both defensive and offensive avionics systems installed.

The first prototype, used to evaluate flying qualities, completed a test programme of 79 flights totalling 405 h 18 min before being placed in storage. The second aircraft, used for structural load testing, completed 60 flights totalling 282 h 30 min before being stored in flyable condition. The third prototype had an advanced ECM system and a Doppler beam-sharpening modification to the forward-looking attack radar. Continued testing of the third and fourth B-1s concentrated on offensive system performance and advanced ECM development. Testing was carried out against simulated enemy threats, defence systems, and against US surrogate threats. By 30 April 1981, when the originally authorised test programme ended, the third prototype had made 138 flights totalling 829 h 24 min; the fourth B-1 had accumulated 378 h during 70 flights. During this programme the second B-1 attained the highest speed, Mach 2.22, on 5 October 1978.

Phase I flight testing was completed on schedule by 30 September 1976, and the DoD and USAF announced on 2 December 1976 that production contracts had been placed for construction of the first three operational aircraft and for the purchase of long-lead items for the second lot of eight operational aircraft. In addition, funds were authorised for the purchase and fabrication of production tooling for the operational aircraft. The production funds were included in the US FY 1978 budget by the outgoing Ford administration. However, on 30 June 1977 President Carter announced that production of the B-1 would be cancelled and priority given instead to the cruise missile development programme. This led, in 1978, to B-1 derivative designs being included in DoD studies to evaluate various types of aircraft as cruise missile carriers. In November 1979, as a result of these studies, Rockwell was requested by the USAF to submit a proposal for the initial planning and design effort associated with flight demonstration of a prototype B-1 derivative aircraft. Identified then as a strategic ALCM launcher (SAL), it would have been produced by modification of the third B-1 prototype.

In addition to developing this proposal for the Air Force, Rockwell began an in-house examination of various derivative designs of the B-1, with reduced cost and expanded mission roles as priorities. Simultaneously, the DoD initiated a study through the Air Force Scientific Advisory Board to determine the direction that future strategic bomber development should take. The conclusion of this last study was that the nation's next strategic bomber should have multi-mission capability, rather than a single

Rockwell International B-1B photographed at the 1987 Paris Salon. *(Brian M. Service)*

dedicated role, and that a B-1 derivative was the best candidate to fulfil the requirement and provide initial operational capability (IOC) in 1987. This led to selection of the derivative B-1B as the next strategic bomber, and in October 1981 President Reagan announced that the USAF was to receive 100 of these aircraft.

On 20 January 1982 Rockwell signed two contracts. The first was a $1,317 million full-scale development contract which required the company to finalise the B-1B design, modify two of the original B-1 prototypes (the second and fourth) and carry out a further flight test programme; the second was an $886 million production contract, which covered construction of the first B-1B and procurement of long-lead items for early production lots. Under this programme the first aircraft to fly, on 23 March 1983, was the modified No. 2 prototype, which was used to evaluate many of the new features and for stability and control, flutter and weapons systems tests until it was lost on 29 August 1984. Thereafter contributing to B-1B development was the No. 4 prototype, which incorporated the remainder of the B-1B improvements and was used for verification testing of the defensive and offensive avionics systems. The first production B-1B flew for the first time on 18 October 1984. The next seven production aircraft were ordered under the FY 1983 defence budget, followed by 10 more in FY 1984, 34 in FY 1985 and the remaining 48 requested in FY 1986 budget proposals. Initial delivery, of the second production aircraft (first flown 4 May 1985), to the 96th Bomb Wing at Dyess AFB, Texas, took place on 7 July 1985, and this base achieved IOC in September 1986 and had received all 29 of its aircraft by the end of the year. Deliveries were continuing in the summer of 1987 at a rate of approximately four aircraft per month to the 28th Bomb Wing at Ellsworth AFB, South Dakota (35 aircraft), the 319th Bomb Wing at Grand Forks AFB, North Dakota (17 aircraft starting September 1987), and the 384th Bomb Wing at McConnell AFB, Kansas (17 aircraft starting January 1988). Each base also deploys supporting tankers. Deliveries were to be completed by June 1988, with three B-1Bs allocated for test and development flying. On 28 September 1987, an operational B-1B crashed in Colorado, with the loss of three crew members. Investigations as to the cause were then centring on birdstrikes.

Operational B-1Bs are able to carry, in three weapons bays, varying combinations of nuclear air-to-ground missiles, conventional or nuclear free-fall bombs, and auxiliary fuel. Using electronic jamming equipment, infra-red countermeasures, radar location and warning systems, other advanced avionics and 'low observable' technology to defeat hostile defensive systems, the B-1B will be able to penetrate present and predicted sophisticated enemy defences well into the 1990s and to operate within less heavily defended areas into the next century. It will also be suitable for deployment in a variety of roles now flown by the Boeing B-52, including anti-submarine patrol or maritime surveillance at long ranges, and aerial minelaying.

The first launch of an AGM-69 short range attack missile (SRAM) from a B-1B was made successfully on 16 January 1987, while the bomber was flying at Mach 0.9 at a height of 150 m (500 ft).

Outwardly the B-1B is generally similar to the B-1 prototype No. 4, but has structural strengthening for operation at a gross weight that is increased from 179,170 kg (395,000 lb) to 216,365 kg (477,000 lb). Major airframe

Rare photograph of the B-1B with weapons-bay doors open and showing mounts for cruise missiles.

improvements include a strengthened landing gear; a movable bulkhead in the forward weapons bay to allow for the carriage of a wide range of different sized weapons, including the ALCM, which was incorporated from the ninth production airframe onwards and retrofitted to earlier aircraft; optional weapons bay fuel tanks to give extended range; and external stores stations beneath the fuselage to accommodate additional fuel or weapons. The variable engine inlets of the original B-1 are replaced by fixed inlets, and new engine nacelles and simplified overwing fairing have been introduced. These modifications are designed to provide optimum performance for the new high-subsonic low-altitude penetration role. The new bomber retains the variable-geometry wing of the B-1, its unswept setting allowing rapid take-off from a base threatened by imminent attack, or operation from shorter runways and less sophisticated airfields; the fully swept position is used in supersonic flight and for the primary role of high-subsonic low-level penetration. It also retains the crew ejection seats which, in the fourth B-1, replaced the crew escape capsule of the first three prototypes.

It is, however, the high-technology avionics that make the major difference between the original B-1 and the B-1B. Although externally similar to the B-1, the B-1B incorporates technological advances that considerably reduce its radar observability and increase its ability to penetrate hostile airspace. The B-1B has a low radar cross-section, and through the application of 'low observable' technology has a radar signature only one per cent that of a B-52. It uses advanced radar and navigation equipment in the category of that developed for the latest generation of fighter aircraft, such as the General Dynamics F-16, as well as avionics technology from both the B-52's offensive system and that of the original B-1. Thus, offensive avionics of the B-1B include advanced forward-looking and terrain following radars, an extremely accurate inertial navigation system, a link to the Air Force Satellite Communications (AFSAT-COM) system, and a strategic Doppler radar altimeter. The defensive avionics are built around the AN/ALQ-161 ECM system, with extended frequency coverage, and include tail warning radar and expendable decoys such as chaff and flares. Development of the full potential of this system will not be achieved for several years.

The structure of the B-1B is made principally of

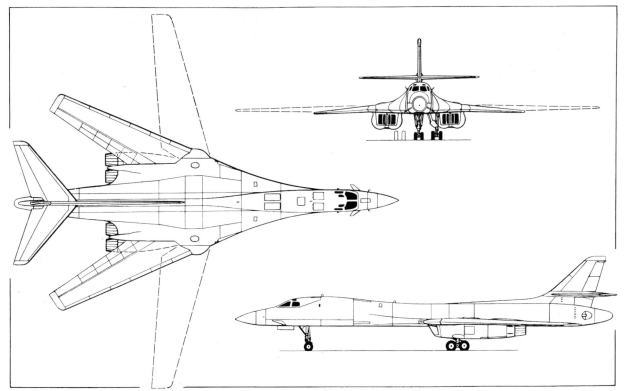

Rockwell International B-1B. *(Pilot Press)*

aluminium alloys and titanium, and is hardened to withstand nuclear blast and overpressure. More than 60 per cent of the structure and equipment is subcontracted, with some 3,000 subcontractors and suppliers being involved in the programme in addition to AIL/Eaton (defensive avionics), Boeing (offensive avionics) and General Electric (powerplant).

TYPE: Long-range multi-role strategic bomber.

WINGS: Cantilever low-wing fail-safe blended wing/body structure, with variable geometry on outer panels. The wing carry-through structure, which is sealed as an integral fuel tank, is mainly of diffusion bonded 6AL-4V titanium. Sweep actuators are covered by a leading-edge 'knuckle' fairing which prevents a gap from opening when the outer panels are swept back. Aft of the wing pivot on each side are overwing fairings which blend the wing trailing edges and engine nacelles. Each of the outer wing panels has 15° of leading-edge sweep when fully forward and 67° 30′ when fully swept. Wingtips, wing/body fairings, and some outer wing skin panels, are of GRP. Full span seven-segment leading-edge slats on each outer panel can be drooped 20° for take-off and landing. Six-segment single-slotted trailing-edge flaps on each outer panel, with maximum downward deflection of 40°. There are no ailerons; instead, lateral control is provided by four-segment airbrake/spoilers on each outer wing, forward of the outer four flap segments, with a maximum upward deflection of 70°. Two outboard spoilers on each wing are controlled by a fly-by-wire system, all other control surfaces are operated electro-hydraulically.

FUSELAGE: Conventional area-ruled fail-safe structure. Built in five main sections comprising forward, forward intermediate, wing carry-through, rear intermediate and rear fuselage. Nose radome of polyimide quartz; dielectric panels of GRP. Nose radome of polyimide quartz; dielectric panels of GRP. Small sweptback movable vane of composite material, with 30° anhedral, on each side of nose, actuated by structural mode control system (SMCS) accelerometers in the fuselage. These sense lateral and vertical motion of the forward fuselage in turbulent conditions and compensate for it by relaying electrical signals to the vanes, providing both yaw and pitch damping.

TAIL UNIT: Cantilever fail-safe structure with sweepback on all surfaces. Rudder is in three sections, all of which have 25° of travel each side. Two-section all-moving tailplane is operated collectively for control in pitch (between 10° up and 25° down) and differentially ($\pm$ 20°) for roll, the two halves moving independently on the spindle. Rudder and tailplane actuated hydraulically, with fly-by-wire backup system for use in the event of a mechanical system failure.

LANDING GEAR: Retractable tricycle type. Each main unit has two pairs of wheels in tandem. Steerable nose unit has twin wheels. Goodyear wheels and carbon brakes. Goodrich tyres. Mainwheel diameter 60 cm ($23\frac{1}{2}$ in), tyre size 46 × 16-325, 30-ply rating. Nosewheel diameter 41 cm (16 in), tyre size 35 × 11.5-16, 22-ply rating.

POWERPLANT: Four General Electric F101-GE-102 augmented turbofan engines, each rated in 136.9 kN (30,780 lb st) class, mounted in pairs beneath the fixed centre-section of the wing, close to the CG, to provide optimum stability in low-altitude turbulence conditions. Fixed-geometry inlets. Integral fuel tanks in the fuselage and outer wings; provision for auxiliary fuel tanks to be carried in the two forward weapons bays and beneath the fuselage. Fuel capacity increased considerably over that of the original

B-1. Receptacle in upper nose section, forward of windscreen, for in-flight refuelling; aircraft is compatible with KC-10 and KC-135 tankers.

ACCOMMODATION: Four-man operational crew comprising pilot, co-pilot and two systems operators (defensive and offensive) on Weber ACES II ejection seats in a pressurised crew compartment.

AVIONICS: The B-1B uses radar and navigation equipment technology developed for the latest generation of fighter aircraft such as the F-16, as well as avionics technology from the B-52 bomber's updated offensive avionics system. Standard GFE (government furnished equipment) includes communications, IFF, ILS, intercom, some navigation equipment, Honeywell ASN-131 SPN/GEANS radar altimeter (similar to that in B-52) and altimeter indicator, rescue beacon and transponder. Boeing Military Airplane Company is responsible for the B-1B's offensive avionics system (OAS). This includes a Singer Kearfott high-accuracy inertial navigation system (developed from that used in the F-16); a Teledyne Ryan AN/APN-218 Doppler velocity sensor, comprising a single antenna/receiver/transmitter unit; Westinghouse AN/APQ-164 multi-mode offensive radar system (ORS), derived from the AN/APG-66 in the F-16, which includes a low-observable phased-array antenna to provide low-altitude terrain following and precise navigational functions; IBM avionics control units (ACUs), including two for terrain following based on those used in the B-52 plus a mass storage device (MSD), using AP-101C computers initially (1750As later) to provide programme instructions for navigation, weapons delivery, bomb damage assessment, defensive system computation, and central integrated test; Sperry Flight Systems offensive display sets, similar to those in the B-52, comprising three multi-function displays (two at the offensive systems operator's station and one for the defensive systems operator), an electronics display unit, and a video recorder similar to that used in the B-52; Sanders Associates electronic CRT display units, modified from those developed for the original B-1, to allow the defensive systems operator to analyse threat situations and assign appropriate countermeasures; and Sundstrand data transfer units (similar to those in the B-52) to gather and store mission and flight data.

The defensive avionics system, which is the responsibility of Eaton Corporation's AIL Division, is based on that company's AN/ALQ-161 system, which comprises an AN/ALQ-161A radio frequency surveillance/ECM system (RFS/ECMS), tail warning function (TWF), AN/ASQ-184 defensive management system and an expendable countermeasures system, totalling 108 separate elements. Developed to support the original B-1 over a broad spectrum of missions, including deep solo penetration of hostile airspace, the system was extensively flight tested over a two-year period and a number of additions have extended both the frequency coverage and the repertoire of electronic jamming techniques of the original design. The current AN/ALQ-161 will enable the B-1B to penetrate present and predicted enemy defences well into the 1990s. The system is controlled by a network of digital computers which can be reprogrammed easily; in addition, all electronic systems boxes 'plug in' to a dedicated data bus network, enabling the system to be upgraded continuously to adapt to future threats until well into the next century. To protect the B-1B, the system must counter a very dense environment of signals from increasingly sophisticated hostile radar networks. These radars, if not effectively jammed, would vector fighter aircraft to, or guide missiles and anti-aircraft gunfire against, the B-1B. A single AN/ALQ-161 system contains and controls a large number of Northrop (Defense Systems Division) jamming transmitters and Raytheon phased-array antennae. In addition to the jamming hardware, a sophisticated control system, managed by a network of special digital computers, is employed. This network can control the jamming chains so rapidly that each can jam signals from many radars simultaneously. The numerous jamming chains are deployed around the periphery of the B-1B to jam signals in any frequency band coming from any direction. Integrated with the jamming control subsystem is an equally sophisticated network of separate receiving antennae, receivers and processors which act as the 'ears' of the system. By means of this receiving subsystem new signals can be picked up, identified and then jammed, with optimised jamming techniques, in a fraction of a second. One of the advantages of having the receiving function completely integrated with the jamming function, which was unique to the AN/ALQ-161 when it was first designed, is that it allows the receiving system to detect new signals and continue to monitor old signals while jamming in the same frequency band. A special subsystem allows this to be accomplished by monitoring the output of the jamming transmitters and adjusting the receivers continuously. All main systems computers on the B-1B, including the AN/ALQ-161's main computer, are identical, and communicate over a time multiplexing military standard databus designated 1553. Via this bus, the AN/ALQ-161 communicates with a set of controls and displays used by the defensive systems operator. It also uses this bus to send status reports to a central integrated test system (CITS), which records all in-flight failures and battle damage for later diagnosis and repair. Within the AN/ALQ-161 itself there is also a local status monitoring network called SEAT (status evaluation and test), which reports to CITS and allows the system automatically to route electronic signals around failed components and maintain full jamming response against the highest priority threat signals. Other defensive equipment of the B-1B includes expendable decoys such as chaff and flares.

ARMAMENT: Three internal weapons bays, comprising 9.53 m (31 ft 3 in) double bay forward of the wing carry-through structure and a single 4.57 m (15 ft) long bay aft. Forward bay incorporates a movable bulkhead permitting the accommodation of a wide variety of weapons, of various sizes, and mixed loads. Internal capacity in a nuclear role for up to eight AGM-86B air-launched cruise missiles (ALCMs), twenty-four AGM-69 short-range attack missiles (SRAMs), twelve B-28 or twenty-four B-61 or B-83 free-fall nuclear bombs; or, in a non-nuclear role, for up to eighty-four 500 lb Mk 82 or twenty-four 2,000 lb Mk 84 bombs. Eight external stores stations beneath the fuselage, on which can be carried an additional fourteen ALCMs or SRAMs, eight B-28s, fourteen B-43/B-61/B-83s, fourteen Mk 84s, or forty-four Mk 82s. Provision for carrying auxiliary fuel tank(s) in weapons bay.

DIMENSIONS, EXTERNAL:		Max weapons load:	
Wing span: fully spread	41.67 m (136 ft 8½ in)	internal	34,019 kg (75,000 lb)
fully swept	23.84 m (78 ft 2½ in)	external	26,762 kg (59,000 lb)
Length overall	44.81 m (147 ft 0 in)	Typical conventional weapon load	29,030 kg (64,000 lb)
Height overall	10.36 m (34 ft 0 in)	Max T-O weight	216,365 kg (477,000 lb)
Wheel track (c/l of shock absorbers)	4.42 m (14 ft 6 in)	PERFORMANCE (design):	
Wheelbase	17.53 m (57 ft 6 in)	Max level speed	approx Mach 1.25
AREA:		Low-level penetration speed at approx 61 m (200 ft)	
Wings, gross	approx 181.2 m² (1,950 sq ft)	more than 521 knots (965 km/h; 600 mph)	
WEIGHTS:		Max unrefuelled range	
Weight empty, equipped	87,090 kg (192,000 lb)	approx 6,475 nm (12,000 km; 7,455 miles)	

Sikorsky
SIKORSKY AIRCRAFT, DIVISION OF UNITED TECHNOLOGIES CORPORATION

Founded on 5 March 1923 by the late Igor I. Sikorsky as the Sikorsky Aero Engineering Corporation, this company has been a division of United Technologies since 1929. It became involved in helicopter production in the 1940s, since which time it has produced more than 6,000 rotating-wing aircraft.

Sikorsky's company headquarters and main plant are at Stratford, Connecticut, with a secondary facility nearby at Bridgeport. Development flight test, commercial service and training centres are at West Palm Beach, Florida, where UTC subsidiary Pratt & Whitney has its military engine operation. Sikorsky's laboratories, test stands and data processing facilities are located at Stratford. Employment at all Sikorsky facilities totalled more than 14,000 in 1987, making the company the largest helicopter manufacturer outside the Soviet Union.

Current production is centred on the UH-60A Black Hawk and its derivatives, the CH-53E Super Stallion heavy lift helicopter and its derivatives, and the S-76 series. The company's main research programmes concern the US Army's Advanced Rotorcraft Technology Integration (ARTI) programme; and the DARPA/NASA X-Wing Rotor Systems Research Aircraft (RSRA) programme.

On 3 June 1985 Sikorsky signed a memorandum of understanding with Boeing Helicopter Company to bid jointly for development of the US Army's LHX helicopter.

Sikorsky licensees include Westland of Great Britain, Agusta of Italy, Aérospatiale of France, MBB in West Germany, Mitsubishi of Japan, and Pratt & Whitney Canada Ltd. In the Summer of 1983 Sikorsky and Brazilian manufacturer Embraer signed an agreement for the transfer of technology involved in the design and manufacture of components made from composites materials. In June 1984 Sikorsky and Construcciones Aeronauticas SA (CASA) signed a memorandum of understanding to establish a long-term helicopter industrial co-operation programme in Spain. CASA builds tail rotor pylon, tailcone and stabiliser components for the H-60 and S-70 helicopters, and has responsibility for final assembly and test flying of Sikorsky helicopters supplied to Spain, which has ordered six S-70Bs for delivery in 1987–88. The first CASA-manufactured S-70 components were delivered to Sikorsky in early January 1986. S-70s have also been ordered for the Royal Australian Navy and Air Force, and Sikorsky has signed contracts with Australian manufacturers for helicopter components.

On 12 February 1986 shareholders of Westland PLC approved a joint Sikorsky/Fiat plan involving financial and technical support and minor equity participation in the British company. Under the terms of the agreement Westland will be licensed to manufacture the S-70 series of helicopters.

Sikorsky S-61/SH-3 Sea King

US military designation: SH-3 Sea King
CAF designation: CH-124

Manufacture of the S-61 series by Sikorsky has ended, but various military and commercial models remain in production by Agusta in Italy, Mitsubishi in Japan, and Westland in the UK (which see). The S-61 series included civil and military transports, assault and rescue helicopters, the details of some of which will be available in an accompanying publication.

The first version of the S-61 ordered into production was the **SH-3A** (originally HSS-2) Sea King amphibious anti-submarine helicopter, of which the prototype flew for the first time on 11 March 1959. Deliveries to the US Navy began in September 1961. Powered by 932 kW (1,250 shp) T58-GE-8B turboshafts, some remain in use with Japan. Canadian **CH-124s** are similar. Many other versions followed, and those in prominent current use for an ASW role are detailed below, together with the SH-3G conversion.

SH-3D Sea King. Standard anti-submarine helicopter of the US Navy, with T58-GE-10 engines and more fuel than SH-3A. First SH-3D, delivered in June 1966, was one of 22 for the Spanish Navy. Four were delivered to the Brazilian Navy and 72 to the US Navy. Versions with Rolls-Royce Gnome turboshaft engines and British anti-submarine equipment are manufactured by Westland Helicopters Ltd (which see). SH-3Ds have also been manufactured under licence by Agusta in Italy. Argentina received similar **S-61 D4s**.

SH-3G. US Navy conversion of 105 SH-3As into utility helicopters, by removing anti-submarine warfare equipment. Six equipped with Minigun pods for search and rescue missions in combat conditions.

SH-3H. Multi-purpose version of SH-3A and SH-3G with T58-GE-10 engines. US Navy contracts, awarded from 1971, called for conversion to increase fleet helicopter capability against submarines and low-flying enemy missiles.

Sikorsky SH-3H Sea King helicopters. *(Brian M. Service)*

New ASW equipment included lightweight sonar, active and passive sonobuoys, and magnetic anomaly detection equipment. Electronic surveillance measurement (ESM) equipment enables the SH-3H to make an important contribution to the missile defence of the fleet. Also built under licence by Agusta in Italy.

By early 1982 more than 750 examples of the S-61 (all models) had been built by Sikorsky, and more than 350 by the company's foreign licensees.

Sikorsky was awarded an initial $14.7 million US Navy contract in early 1983 to develop a service life extension programme (SLEP) for the SH-3. The contract called for the

company to design and manufacture two SLEP kits containing hardware to upgrade and modernise the integral parts of the SH-3, including structural members and dynamic components. Options called for Sikorsky to install one kit on an in-service SH-3H, and to flight-test the rebuilt aircraft in FY 1985. The US Navy then planned to acquire 129 kits to enable its SH-3s to remain effective in an anti-submarine role into the 1990s.

The following details apply to the SH-3D Sea King, but are generally applicable to other versions except for accommodation and equipment:

TYPE: Twin-engined amphibious all-weather anti-submarine

Sikorsky SH-3H Sea King. *(Pilot Press)*

helicopter.

ROTOR SYSTEM: Five-blade main and tail rotors. Main rotor blades are interchangeable and are provided with an automatic powered folding system. Rotor brake standard.

FUSELAGE: Boat hull of semi-monocoque construction. Single step. Tail section folds to reduce stowage requirements.

TAIL SURFACE: Fixed stabiliser on starboard side of tail section.

LANDING GEAR: Amphibious. Land gear consists of two twin-wheel main units, which are retracted rearward into stabilising floats, and non-retractable tailwheel. Goodyear mainwheels and tubeless tyres size 6.50-10 type III. Goodyear tailwheel and tyre size 6.00-6. Goodyear disc brakes. Boat hull and pop-out flotation bags in stabilising floats permit emergency operation from water.

POWERPLANT: Two 1,044 kW (1,400 shp) General Electric T58-GE-10 turboshaft engines. Three bladder-type fuel tanks in hull; forward tank 1,314 litres (347 US gallons; 289 Imp gallons), centre tank 530 litres (140 US gallons; 116.5 Imp gallons), rear tank 1,336 litres (353 US gallons; 294 Imp gallons). Total fuel capacity 3,180 litres (840 US gallons; 699.5 Imp gallons).

ACCOMMODATION: Pilot and co-pilot on flightdeck, two sonar operators in main cabin. Dual controls. Large loading door at rear of cabin on starboard side.

AVIONICS AND EQUIPMENT: Bendix AQS-13 sonar with 180° search beam width. Hamilton Standard autostabilisation equipment. Automatic transition into hover. Sonar coupler holds altitude automatically in conjunction with Teledyne APN-130 Doppler radar (Litton AN/APS-503 in CH-124) and radar altimeter. Provision for 272 kg (600 lb)

capacity rescue hoist and 3,630 kg (8,000 lb) capacity automatic touchdown-release low-response cargo sling for external loads.

ARMAMENT: Provision for 381 kg (840 lb) of weapons, including homing torpedoes.

DIMENSIONS, EXTERNAL:	
Diameter of main rotor	18.90 m (62 ft 0 in)
Length overall	22.15 m (72 ft 8 in)
Length of fuselage	16.69 m (54 ft 9 in)
Length, tail pylon folded	14.40 m (47 ft 3 in)
Width, rotors folded	4.98 m (16 ft 4 in)
Height overall	5.13 m (16 ft 10 in)
Wheel track	3.96 m (13 ft 0 in)
Wheelbase	7.18 m (23 ft 6½ in)
AREA:	
Main rotor blades (each)	4.14 m² (44.54 sq ft)
WEIGHTS:	
Normal T-O weight:	
SH-3D (ASW)	8,449 kg (18,626 lb)
Max T-O weight, SH-3H	9,525 kg (21,000 lb)
PERFORMANCE (at 9,300 kg; 20,500 lb AUW):	
Max level speed	144 knots (267 km/h; 166 mph)
Cruising speed for max range	
	118 knots (219 km/h; 136 mph)
Max rate of climb at S/L	670 m (2,200 ft)/min
Service ceiling	4,480 m (14,700 ft)
Hovering ceiling IGE	3,200 m (10,500 ft)
Hovering ceiling OGE	2,500 m (8,200 ft)
Range with max fuel, 10% reserves	
	542 nm (1,005 km; 625 miles)

Sikorsky MH-53E Sea Dragon

In 1982, Sikorsky received $39 million to develop the MH-53E Sea Dragon, an airborne mine countermeasures (AMCM) version of the Super Stallion heavy-duty multi-purpose helicopter. It has enlarged sponsons to carry nearly 3,785 litres (1,000 US gallons; 833 Imp gallons) more fuel, improved hydraulic and electrical systems, and minefield, navigational and AFC systems, including automatic tow couplers and automatic approach to/depart from hover features to enhance its AMCM capabilities. During 1982 a prototype, converted from one of the production prototype CH-53Es, completed a test programme, including a 20 h flight. The first pre-production MH-53E made its initial

First Sikorsky MH-53E Sea Dragon airborne mine countermeasures helicopter to be delivered to the US Navy.

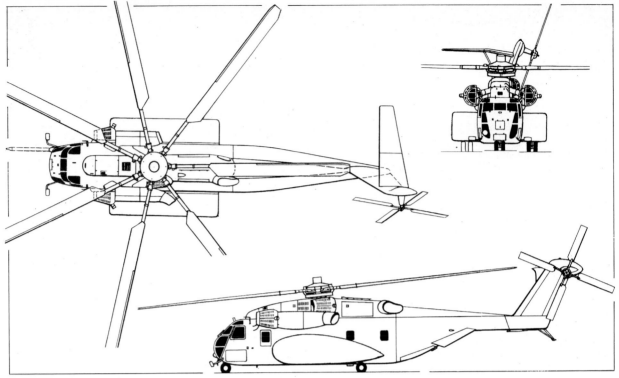

Sikorsky MH-53E Sea Dragon. *(Pilot Press)*

flight on 1 September 1983. The first of 32 required by the US Navy was delivered on 26 June 1986 and entered operational service with HM-12 on 1 April 1987. Japan authorised funding for two MH-53E type minesweeping helicopters in 1986.

The following brief details are complementary to the full description of the H-53 Super Stallion that will appear in an accompanying publication.

POWERPLANT: Three General Electric T64-GE-416 turboshaft engines, each with a max rating of 3,266 kW (4,380 shp) for 10 min, intermediate rating of 3,091 kW (4,145 shp) for 30 min and max continuous power rating of 2,756 kW (3,696 shp). Total internal fuel capacity of MH-53E is 12,113 litres (3,200 US gallons; 2,664 Imp gallons).

DIMENSIONS, EXTERNAL:

Main rotor diameter	24.08 m (79 ft 0 in)
Length overall, rotors turning	30.19 m (99 ft 0½ in)
Length of fuselage	22.35 m (73 ft 4 in)
Width of fuselage	2.69 m (8 ft 10 in)
Width, rotor and tail pylon folded	
	8.41 m (27 ft 7 in)
Height overall, tail rotor turning	8.97 m (29 ft 5 in)
Wheel track (c/l of shock struts)	
	3.96 m (13 ft 0 in)
Wheelbase	8.31 m (27 ft 3 in)

AREA:

Main rotor disc	455.38 m² (4,901.7 sq ft)

WEIGHTS:

Weight empty	16,482 kg (36,336 lb)
Useful load, influence sweep mission	11,793 kg (26,000 lb)
Max T-O weight	33,340 kg (73,500 lb)

PERFORMANCE (ISA, at T-O weight of 25,400 kg; 56,000 lb):

Max level speed at S/L	170 knots (315 km/h; 196 mph)
Cruising speed at S/L	150 knots (278 km/h; 173 mph)
Max rate of climb at S/L, with 11,340 kg (25,000 lb) payload	
	762 m (2,500 ft)/min
Service ceiling at max continuous power	5,640 m (18,500 ft)
Hovering ceiling at max power:	
IGE	3,520 m (11,550 ft)
OGE	2,895 m (9,500 ft)

Sikorsky S-70B

US Navy designations: SH-60B and SH-60F Seahawk

The US Navy's LAMPS (light airborne multi-purpose system) programme was initiated in 1970, when the Kaman SH-2D Seasprite won the contract for the LAMPS Mk I aircraft. The Mk II mission was considered beyond the capabilities of the Seasprite; so this phase of the programme was cancelled and the US Navy turned to planning a Mk III version. In 1974 IBM Federal Systems Division was selected as prime contractor for LAMPS Mk III, reflecting the relative importance of the avionics fit compared with the airframe. Fly-off tests of competitive airframes from Boeing

Sikorsky SH-60B Seahawk LAMPS Mk III helicopter operating from USS _Crommelin_.

Vertol and Sikorsky were conducted in 1977, each manufacturer submitting a developed version of the aircraft built for the US Army's UTTAS competition. Sikorsky was selected to supply the LAMPS Mk III airframe, and General Electric to supply a navalised version of the T700 engine.

A key factor in the selection of the Sikorsky S-70B airframe was its promise of reduced development costs, due to the high degree of commonality with the Army's UH-60A Black Hawk assault transport helicopter. The designation **SH-60B** and name Seahawk were allocated to the Navy model, which embodies changes to integrate the mission equipment and to provide shipboard compatibility. These changes include the addition of chin mounted pods for ESM equipment, pylons for two torpedoes or auxiliary fuel tanks, a pylon for MAD equipment on the starboard side, installation of more powerful navalised engines; addition of a sensor operator's station and port side launcher for 25 sonobuoys in the cabin; increased fuel capacity; rescue hoist; automatic main rotor folding system; main rotor brake; tail pylon folding; modified landing gear; a DAF Indal RAST (recovery assist, secure and traversing) device to haul down the helicopter in rough seas on to a small deck, and stow it in the ship's hangar; a sliding cabin door; hover in-flight refuelling system; and buoyancy features. The pilot's and co-pilot's seats are not armoured.

The first of five prototypes flew on 12 December 1979. Production of a first batch of 18 SH-60Bs was authorised in FY 1982, followed by 27 more in FY 1983. Total planned requirement by the US Navy is 204 aircraft. The first production Seahawk flew on 11 February 1983, and deliveries to the Navy continue at the rate of two per month, with a total of 85 delivered by June 1987. First USN squadron was HSL-41, at North Island, San Diego, California. Operational deployment began in 1984, and by the summer of 1987 six US Navy squadrons were operational, with four SH-60B detachments operating with the Atlantic Fleet and three with the Pacific Fleet. Mission capability of 97% has been recorded by the USN.

Under a US Navy contract with Sikorsky and Rolls-Royce Turboméca, an SH-60B underwent engine tests in 1987 with a 1,566 kW (2,100 shp) RTM 322 turboshaft powerplant. A US Navy flight evaluation involving some 60 hours of flight

testing was scheduled to follow at Sikorsky's West Palm Beach facility and at the Naval Air Test Center, NAS Patuxent River.

Japan has selected the SH-60B to replace the SH-3A/Bs of the JMSDF. Two Sikorsky-built Seahawk airframes, designated **XSH-60J**, have been delivered to Mitsubishi at Nagoya for installation of Japanese electronics and mission equipment under a $27 million contract from the Japan Defence Agency's Technical Research and Development Institute. The first of these helicopters flew in 1987. The SH-60J Seahawk will be built by Mitsubishi, and is scheduled to enter service with the JMSDF in the early 1990s, with replacement of SH-3s completed by the middle of the decade.

On 9 October 1984 the Royal Australian Navy confirmed an initial order for eight Seahawks for its full-spectrum ASW requirement, and ordered a further eight in May 1986. The Seahawks, designated **S-70B-2** RAWS (role adaptable weapon system), will operate from the RAN's 'Adelaide' (FFG-7) class guided missile frigates. Fifteen of the S-70B-2 RAWS will be assembled in Australia by Hawker de Havilland. The RAN helicopters will be equipped with MEL Super Searcher radar and Collins advanced integrated avionics including cockpit controls and displays, navigation receivers and communications transceivers, an airborne target off-hand data link and a tactical data system (TDS). The first Australian Seahawk flew at West Palm Beach in early 1988. The Spanish Navy has ordered six S-70Bs for 1988 delivery.

US Navy SH-60Bs will be deployed on a total of 106 'Oliver Hazard Perry' class frigates, and 'Spruance' class and Aegis equipped destroyers and 'Ticonderoga' class guided missile cruisers. They will provide all-weather capability for detection, classification, localisation and interdiction of surface vessels and submarines. Compared with the LAMPS Mk I, range, loiter time and endurance are increased significantly. ASW listening time is increased by 57 min, ASST (anti-ship surveillance and targeting) loiter time by 45 min. The helicopter interfaces with its mother ship via a data link, but can also operate independently. Secondary missions include search and rescue (SAR), vertical replenishment (vertrep), medical evacuation (medevac), fleet support and communications relay.

On 6 March 1985 Sikorsky received a $50.9 million contract for full-scale development and production options for a 'CV-Helo' version of the Seahawk designated **SH-60F** and known officially as the CV Inner Zone ASW helicopter. Intended as a replacement for the SH-3H Sea King, this helicopter will operate from aircraft carriers to protect the inner zone of a carrier battle group from submarine attack. The SH-60F differs from the SH-60B in having all LAMPS Mk III avionics, sensors and pneumatic sonobuoy launcher equipment removed, together with the cargo hook, recovery assist secure and transverse system main probe, tail probe and control panel, although installation provisions will be retained. An integrated ASW mission avionics suite will be installed, comprising a MIL-STD-1553B tactical data system with dual Teledyne Systems AN/ASN-123 tactical navigation computers, a redundant digital databus, a tactical data link to other aircraft, a communications control system, and multi-function keypads and display units for each of the four crew members.

Additional equipment planned for the SH-60F includes an Allied Bendix Oceanics AN/AQS-13F dipping sonar system; internal/external auxiliary fuel system and an additional weapons station on an extended pylon on the port side of the fuselage. Armament includes Mk50 acoustic homing torpedoes. Modifications include rearrangement of the cabin interior, removal of external sensor fairings, and improvements to the automatic flight control system to permit increased rates of deceleration on automatic approaches, in addition to automatic coupled sonar cable angle hover or coupled Doppler hover. Provision is made for a chaff/sonobuoy launcher system, an attitude/heading referencing system and global positioning system, with future growth potential for a fatigue monitoring system, surface search radar, FLIR, night vision equipment, passive ESM,

MAD, air-to-surface missile capability, a sonobuoy data link, and an increase in max T-O weight to 10,659 kg (23,500 lb). Secondary missions will include SAR and standby during launch and recovery of the carriers' fixed-wing aircraft to provide a rescue service in case of ditching. The US Navy requirement is for 175 SH-60Fs. The initial contract provides production options on 76 helicopters in five lots. In January 1986 Sikorsky received a contract for the first seven SH-60Fs. The first SH-60F flew on 19 March 1987. Production deliveries are scheduled to begin in spring 1989.

In September 1986 the US Navy awarded Sikorsky a contract for an initial production increment of five combat search-and-rescue/special-warfare-support (HCS) helicopters for the Navy, designated **HH-60H**, and two medium-range recovery (MRR) helicopters for the Coast Guard, designated **HH-60J**. This order was subsequently increased to nine HH-60Hs and five HH-60Js in a contract valued at $135.2 million. The HH-60H/J 'Rescue Hawks' are close derivatives of the SH-60F. It is expected that 18 will eventually serve with the Navy and 35 with the Coast Guard, with deliveries starting in 1989 and 1990 respectively.

The following description applies to the SH-60B:

TYPE: Twin-turbine ASW/ASST helicopter.

ROTOR SYSTEM: Four-blade main rotor. Sikorsky SC-1095 blade section, with thickness/chord ratio of 9.5%. Middle section has leading-edge droop and trailing-edge tab to overcome vortex impingement from preceding blade in cruising flight. Blade twist 18°. Blade tips swept back 20°. Each blade has a hollow oval titanium spar, Nomex honeycomb core, graphite trailing edge and root, covered with glassfibre/epoxy, with glassfibre leading-edge counterweight, titanium leading-edge sheath and Kevlar tip. Blades are tolerant to 23 mm gunfire damage, and are pressurised and equipped with gauges providing fail-safe

Sikorsky SH-60B Seahawk. *(Pilot Press)*

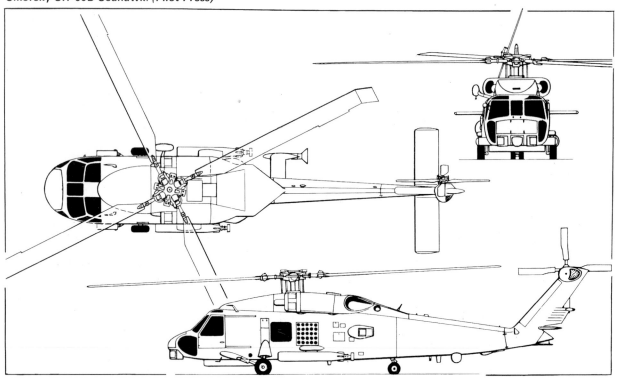

confirmation of blade structural integrity. Electrically heated de-icing mat in leading edge of each blade of both main and tail rotors. Electrically folding blades. Canting of tail rotor (20° to port) increases vertical lift and allows greater CG travel. 'Cross beam' four-blade tail rotor of composite materials, eliminating all rotor head bearings. Rotor brake.

FUSELAGE: Conventional semi-monocoque structure. Composite materials including glassfibre and Kevlar are used for the cockpit doors, canopy, fairings and engine cowlings. Glassfibre/Nomex floors.

TAIL UNIT: Pylon structure with port-canted tail rotor mounted on starboard side. Tail pylon design permits normal forward flight and roll-on landing if tail rotor is destroyed. Large variable-incidence tailplane has a control system which senses airspeed, collective lever position, pitch attitude rate and lateral acceleration. Tailplane is set at about +34° incidence in the hover, and −6° for autorotation. Tailboom folds (to starboard) immediately forward of tail pylon for transport and storage.

LANDING GEAR: Non-retractable tailwheel type with single wheel on each unit. Energy absorbing main gear with tailwheels which give protection for the tail rotor in taxying over rough terrain or during a high-flare landing. Wheelbase is shortened by 46.6 per cent compared with UH-60A, with twin wheels on tail unit, tyre size 17.5 × 6.006. Multiple disc brakes on mainwheels. Landing gear structure is less complex because the SH-60B's vertical impact requirement is 71.5 per cent below that of the UH-60A.

POWERPLANT: Two 1,260 kW (1,690 shp) General Electric T700-GE-401 turboshaft engines. Internal fuel with usable capacity of 1,361 litres (359.7 US gallons; 299.5 Imp gallons). Hovering in-flight refuelling capability. Two auxiliary fuel tanks on fuselage pylons optional.

ACCOMMODATION: Pilot and airborne tactical officer/backup pilot in cockpit, sensor operator in specially equipped station in cabin. Dual controls standard.

AVIONICS AND EQUIPMENT: Com equipment comprises Collins AN/ARC-159(V)2 UHF and AN/ARC-174(V)2 HF, Hazeltine AN/APX-76A(V) and Bendix AN/APX-100(V)1 IFF transponders, TSEC/KY-75 voice security set, TSEC/KG-45(E-1) com security, Telephonics OK-374/ASC com system control group and Sierra Research AN/ARQ-44 data link and telemetry. Nav equipment comprises Collins AN/ARN-118(V) Tacan, Honeywell AN/APN-194(V) radar altimeter, Teledyne Ryan AN/APN-217 Doppler, and Collins AN/ARA-50 UHF DF. Mission equipment includes Sikorsky sonobuoy launcher, Edmac AN/ARR-75 and R-1651/ARA sonobuoy receiving sets, Texas Instruments AN/ASQ-81(V)2 MAD, Raymond MU-670/ASQ magnetic tape memory units, Astronautics IO-2177/ASQ altitude indicator, Fairchild AN/ASQ-164 control indicator set and AN/ASQ-165 armament control indicator set, Texas Instruments AN/APS-124 search radar (under front fuselage), IBM AN/UYS-1(V)2 Proteus acoustic processor and CV-3252/A converter display, Control Data AN/AYK-14 (XN-1A) digital computer, and Raytheon AN/ALQ-142 ESM (in chin mounted pods). External cargo hook and rescue hoist standard.

ARMAMENT: Includes two Mk 46 torpedoes.

DIMENSIONS, EXTERNAL:	
Main rotor diameter	16.36 m (53 ft 8 in)
Length overall (rotors and tail pylon folded)	
	12.47 m (40 ft 11 in)
Width (rotors folded)	3.26 m (10 ft 8½ in)
Height overall, tail rotor turning	5.18 m (17 ft 0 in)
Height overall (pylon folded)	4.04 m (13 ft 3¼ in)
Wheel track	2.79 m (9 ft 2 in)
Wheelbase	4.83 m (15 ft 10 in)
AREAS:	
Main rotor blades (each)	4.34 m² (46.70 sq ft)
Main rotor disc	210.05 m² (2,261 sq ft)
WEIGHTS (estimated. A, ASW mission; B, ASST mission; C, Utility role):	
Weight empty: A	6,191 kg (13,648 lb)
Mission gross weight: A	9,182 kg (20,244 lb)
B	8,334 kg (18,373 lb)
Max gross weight: C	9,926 kg (21,884 lb)
PERFORMANCE:	
Dash speed at 1,525 m (5,000 ft), tropical day	
	126 knots (234 km/h; 145 mph)
Vertical rate of climb at S/L, 32.2°C (90°F)	
	213 m (700 ft)/min
Vertical rate of climb at S/L, 32.2°C (90°F), one engine out	
	137 m (450 ft)/min

Sikorsky H-76 Eagle

The Sikorsky H-76 Eagle is a military development of the S-76B general-purpose helicopter. The prototype made its first flight in February 1985 and was introduced at the Paris Air Show in May 1985. It incorporates the optional armoured crew seats, sliding cabin doors and heavy-duty floor of that version, and introduces a wide range of optional items that include weapon pylons, an optical sight mounted above the instrument panel, self-sealing high-strength fuel tanks, and provisions for door mounted weapons. The main transmission has been upgraded, as have the intermediate and tail rotor gearboxes. The main rotor hub and shaft have been strengthened, chord of the horizontal tail surface increased, dual spars employed in the vertical fin, and tail-rotor blade chord increased. Fuselage skin thickness has been increased to withstand the blast of weapons launch. The H-76 can be equipped for troop transport/logistic support, as a gunship, and for roles including airborne assault, air observation post, combat SAR, evacuation, ambulance, and conventional SAR.

The H-76 Eagle can be equipped with either a mast mounted sight (MMS) or roof mounted sight (RMS). Further developments planned for the H-76 include a version armed with air-to-air missiles, of which the helicopter could carry up to 16, although a more likely weapons load would be eight AAMs and two cannon pods; head-up display; laser rangefinder; integrated armament management system; self-protection systems including a radar warning receiver, infrared jammer and chaff/flare dispensers; high-clearance landing gear; and a Sperry SPZ-7000 automatic flight control system.

In early 1987 the H-76 prototype successfully completed weapons firing tests on a four-station pitch-compensated

Sikorsky H-76 Eagle military utility helicopter.

armament pylon (PCAP) at Mojave, California. The PCAP permits a speed increase of 3–4 knots over previously installed pylons and was tested with a GIAT M261 20 mm cannon pod, 7.62 mm and 12.7 mm machine-gun pods, the VS-MD-H mine dispenser and 70 mm rockets. The pod is one of several integrated improvements to the H-76's weapons systems, which include operation of the integrated armament management system (IAMS) from the collective pitch lever as well as from the panel, and provision of system-ready signals and a sideslip trim ball on the head-up display.

TYPE: Twin-turbine armed utility helicopter.

ROTOR SYSTEM, FUSELAGE, TAIL UNIT and LANDING GEAR: Generally as for SH-60B. Strobex rotor blade tracker optional.

POWERPLANT: Two 716 kW (960 shp) Pratt & Whitney Canada PT6B-36 turboshaft engines, maximum continuous power rating 649 kW (870 shp). Fuel is contained in two high-strength, optionally self-sealing, tanks located below the rear cabin, with a total capacity of 993 litres (262.4 US gallons; 218.4 Imp gallons). Engine air particle separator optional.

ACCOMMODATION: Pilot and co-pilot, plus varying troop/passenger loads according to role. Armoured pilot seats optional. Ten fully armed troops can be transported, or seven troops when configured as an airborne assault vehicle with multi-purpose pylon system (MPPS) and one 7.62 mm door gun installed. For evacuation use the cabin can be equipped with 12 seats or, in emergency, all seats can be removed and 16 persons can be airlifted sitting on the cabin floor. For SAR use the cabin will accommodate three patients on litters, or six persons lying prone on the floor and on the rear cabin raised deck. The standard medevac layout provides for three litters and a bench seat for two medical attendants.

AVIONICS AND EQUIPMENT: Typical avionics include VHF-20A VHF transceiver, AN/ARC-186 VHF-AM/FM com, 719A UHF com, ADF-60A ADF, DF-301E UHF DF, VIR-30A VOR with ILS, glideslope and marker beacon receivers, DME-40 DME, TDR-90 transponder and dual RMI-36 RMI, all by Collins, course deviation indicators, ELT, Andrea A301-61A intercom, cabin speaker system and loudhailer. Typical equipment includes dual controls and instrumentation, stability augmentation system, dual 5 in VGIs, Allen RCA-26 standby self-contained attitude indicator. Collins ALT-50A radio altimeter, soundproofing, provisions for optional emergency flotation system, and provisions for installation of cargo hook with certificated capacity of 1,497 kg (3,300 lb), and rescue hoist of 272 kg (600 lb) capacity.

ARMAMENT: One 7.62 mm machine-gun can be pintle mounted in each doorway and fired with or without the MPPS system installed. Pintles incorporate field-of-fire limiters and will accept Fabrique National or Maramount M60D machine-guns. The MPPS can be installed on the cabin floor, providing the capability to carry and deploy pods containing single or twin 7.62 mm machine-guns, 0.50-in machine-guns, 2.75 in and 5 in rocket pods, Mk 66 2.75 in rockets, Oerlikon 68 mm rockets, Hellfire, TOW, Sea Skua and Stinger missiles, and Mk 46 torpedoes. Targeting equipment can include FLIR, Saab-Scania reticle sight, TOW roof sight or TOW mast mounted sight and laser rangefinder.

DIMENSIONS, EXTERNAL:	
Main rotor diameter	13.41 m (44 ft 0 in)
Length overall, rotors turning	16.00 m (52 ft 6 in)
AREA:	
Main rotor disc	141. 21 m² (1,520 sq ft)
WEIGHTS:	
Weight empty	2,545 kg (5,610 lb)
Weight empty, equipped (typical)	3,030 kg (6,680 lb)
Max fuel weight	792 kg (1,745 lb)
Max T-O weight	5,171 kg (11,400 kg)
PERFORMANCE:	
Similar to S-76B, but range highly variable according to loading and mission	

Sikorsky H-76N

In February 1984 Sikorsky announced development of an H-76N naval version of the H-76, designed for anti-ship surveillance and targeting, anti-submarine warfare, surface attack, search and rescue, and utility missions, operating from frigate sized ships. Over-the-horizon targeting (OTHT) and anti-ship (ASV) variants will be available with Ferranti Seaspray 3 and MEL Super Searcher radars in mounted pods. The ASV H-76N will be armed with two British Aerospace Sea Skua air-to-surface missiles. The anti-submarine warfare version will have a dipping sonar, processing suite and two Gould Mark 46 or Marconi Underwater Systems Sting Ray torpedoes. Other developments planned for the naval version of the helicopter include a dual digital AFCS-coupled hover capability, target information data link, a tactical navigation system, hover in-flight refuelling system, roof- or mast-mounted FLIR system, ECM pod, chaff/flare dispensers on the tailboom, strengthened landing gear providing greater ground/deck clearance, folding main rotor blades, and provision for deck securing.

The H-76N will be offered with a choice of Allison 250-C34S or Pratt & Whitney Canada PT6B-36 engines.

Artist's impression of Sikorsky H-76N naval helicopter with MEL Super Searcher radar and torpedoes.

Provisional specifications include an estimated empty weight (all versions) of 2,812 kg (6,200 lb) and max T-O weights of 4,473 kg (9,861 lb) for the OTHT variant, 4,968 kg (10,953 lb) for the ASV version and 4,754 kg (10,481 lb) for an H-76N equipped with a 136 kg (300 lb) ECM pod for secondary role jamming. Total fuel capacity for all proposed variants is 999 litres (264 US gallons; 210 Imp gallons).

Summit
Summit Aviation Inc

Summit Sentry O2-337

Summit Aviation developed this version of the Cessna Model T337 for a wide range of military missions. These include forward air control, helicopter escort, light air-to-ground attack, convoy protection, maritime patrol, six-seat personnel carrier, light cargo transport, aerial photography, psychological warfare and airborne discharge. Special configurations are available for VIP transport, medevac and high-altitude missions. In all configurations day or night capability can be provided.

Summit's modifications begin with the purchase of a Model T337. Powerplant comprises two 168 kW (225 hp) Continental TSIO-360 turbocharged flat-six engines. For orders of fewer than 20 aircraft, Summit rebuilds Cessna

T337 airframes to zero-time status. For larger orders the Cessna factory was originally expected to supply new airframes, as required, for Summit to outfit according to customer specification.

With four standard NATO MALL-4A pylons mounted beneath the wings, each able to carry a max load of 159 kg (350 lb), the Summit Sentry can carry weapons which include SUU-11A/A 7.62 mm gun pods; FFV UNI 12.75 mm gun pods; LAU-32A/A, 32B/A, 59A, 68A and 68B/A rocket launchers; CBU-14, SUU/14/A containers and bombs, LUU-1B, 5B, and Mod 6 Mk 3 markets; Mk 24 flares; ADSID; and a combined search radar and speaker system.

Summit supplied six Sentry O2-337s to the Royal Thai

Summit O2-337s for the Royal Thai Navy air arm.

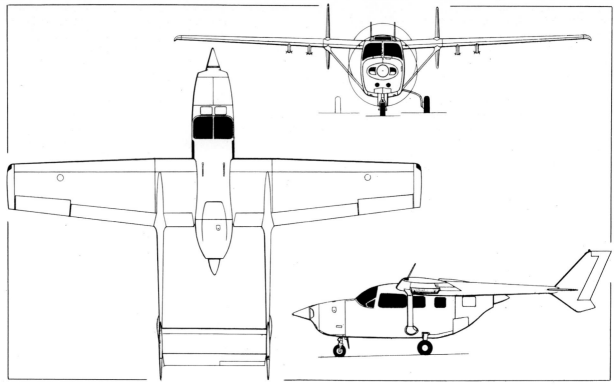

Summit Sentry O2-337. *(Pilot Press)*

Navy air arm in 1980 and a further four in 1983. Other reported operators include the air forces of Haiti, Honduras, Nicaragua and Senegal. According to the *Washington Post* newspaper, at least three were supplied to the Nicaraguan *contras*, via the CIA, under Operation Elephant Herd in 1984.

Available specification and performance details are as follows:

DIMENSIONS, EXTERNAL (based on Cessna T337):

Wing span	11.63 m (38 ft 2 in)
Length overall	9.07 m (29 ft 9 in)
Height overall	2.79 m (9 ft 2 in)
Wheel track	2.49 m (8 ft 2 in)
Wheelbase	2.39 m (7 ft 10 in)

WEIGHTS:

Weight empty, approx	1,433 kg (3,160 lb)
Max T-O weight	2,359 kg (5,200 lb)

PERFORMANCE (at max T-O weight):

Max level speed:	
ay S/L	163 knots (302 km/h; 188 mph)
at 3,050 m (10,000 ft)	179 knots (332 km/h; 206 mph)
Max cruising speed:	
at S/L	150 knots (278 km/h; 173 mph)
at 1,525 m (5,000 ft)	155 knots (287 km/h; 178 mph)
at 3,050 m (10,000 ft)	165 knots (306 km/h; 190 mph)
Max rate of climb at S/L	335 m (1,100 ft)/min
Service ceiling	8,690 m (28,500 ft)
T-O run	164 m (538 ft)
Landing run	137 m (449 ft)
Range at 75% power with 560 litres (148 US gallons) usable	
fuel	955 nm (1,770 km; 1,100 miles)
Max range, long-range cruise power, fuel as above	
	1,175 nm (2,177 km; 1,353 miles)

USAF
UNITED STATES AIR FORCE SYSTEMS COMMAND

USAF Advanced Tactical Fighter (ATF)

US Air Force designations: YF-22A and YF-23A

The Advanced Tactical Fighter (ATF) represents a United States Air Force requirement for a new air-superiority fighter to replace the McDonnell Douglas F-15 Eagle. The ATF programme also includes development of an advanced technology engine for the aircraft. Concept definition study contracts were awarded in September 1983 to Boeing, General Dynamics, Grumman, Lockheed, McDonnell Douglas, Northrop and Rockwell. These companies submitted their prototype design proposals to the USAF on 28 July 1986.

On 31 October 1986 the USAF announced the selection of Lockheed and Northrop to begin the prototype phase of the

402

ATF programme. Under respective designations **YF-22A** and **YF-23A**, each contractor will build two flying prototypes for demonstration and validation purposes, leading to selection of the successful ATF contender in 1991 when the full-scale development phase will begin. The prototypes are expected to fly in late 1989. Engines for the ATF will be developed from ground demonstrator power-plants which were being tested in early 1987. Pratt & Whitney's prototype engine is designated YF119 and General Electric's YF120. Each of the prototype aircraft will be required to fly with GE and P&W engines.

The ATF will combine a highly manoeuvrable airframe with low-observable 'stealth' technologies, sustained super-sonic cruise capability and advanced avionics and weapons systems permitting simultaneous engagement of multiple targets. A 'flat panel' colour CRT display cockpit with six screens, three providing a single tactical panoramic display, an extra-wide HUD and articulating pilot's seat to enhance tolerance of g loads will form part of the aircraft's advanced cockpit concept.

The USAF has a requirement for up to 750 ATFs, with IOC anticipated in the mid-1990s. The US Navy is also evaluating the ATF as a possible replacement for the Grumman F-14 Tomcat as a fleet air defence interceptor at the end of this century. Up to 550 'navalised' ATFs could be required.

Yugoslavia

SOKO
SOKO VAZDUHOPLOVNA INDUSTRIJA, RO VAZDUHOPLOVSTVO

Founded in 1951, this company manufactures aircraft of its own design and is participating, with Romania, in developing and producing the Orao/IAR-93 strike aircraft described in the International section.

SOKO also continues to build under licence the Aérospatiale SA 342L Gazelle helicopter, on behalf of the Yugoslav government.

SOKO G2-A Galeb (Seagull)

Design of the Galeb jet trainer was started in 1957. Construction of two prototypes began in 1959, and the first of these flew for the first time in May 1961. Production began in 1963 and continued to fulfil Yugoslav and export orders. First overseas operator was the Zambian Air Force, in early 1971.

The two production versions of the Galeb were:

G2-A. Standard version for Yugoslav Air Force. Progressive design improvements included optional cockpit air-conditioning system. About 150 are in use, a number for light-attack missions. Two with Zambia.

G-2A-E. Official export version, with updated equipment. First flown in late 1974. Series production began in 1975, and Libya became the only receiver.

TYPE: Two-seat armed jet basic trainer and light-attack aircraft.

WINGS: Cantilever low-wing monoplane. Wing section NACA 64A213.5 at root, NACA 64A212.0 at tip. Dihedral 1° 30′. No incidence. Sweepback at quarter-chord 4° 19′. Conventional structure. Ailerons. Trim tab on port aileron. Fowler flaps. No de-icing system.

FUSELAGE: Semi-monocoque structure in two portions. Rear portion removable for engine servicing. Two door-type air-brakes under centre-fuselage.

TAIL UNIT: Cantilever structure. Fixed-incidence tailplane. Rudder and elevators statically and dynamically balanced. Trim tab in each elevator. VHF radio aerial forms tip of fin.

LANDING GEAR: Retractable tricycle type, with single wheel on each unit. Dunlop mainwheels and tyres size 23 × 7.25-10. Dunlop nosewheel and tyre size 6.50-5.5 TC. Prva Petoletka hydraulic differential disc brakes, toe-operated from both cockpits.

POWERPLANT: One Rolls-Royce Viper 11 Mk 22-6 turbojet engine, rated at 11.12 kN (2,500 lb st). Two flexible fuel tanks aft of cockpits, with total capacity of 780 kg (1,720 lb). Two jettisonable wingtip tanks, each with capacity of 170 kg (375 lb). Refuelling point on upper part of fuselage aft of cockpits. Fuel system designed to permit up to 15 s of inverted flight.

ACCOMMODATION: Crew of two in tandem on BAe (Folland) Type 1-B fully-automatic lightweight ejection seats.

AVIONICS AND EQUIPMENT (G2-A): Blind-flying instrumentation. Marconi radio compass (licence-built by Rudi Cajavec), intercom and STR-9Z1 VHF radio transceiver standard. Standard electrical equipment includes navigation lights. 250W landing light in nose, and 50W taxying light on nose landing gear. Camera, with

SOKO G2-A Galeb armed trainer. *(Aviation Picture Library)*

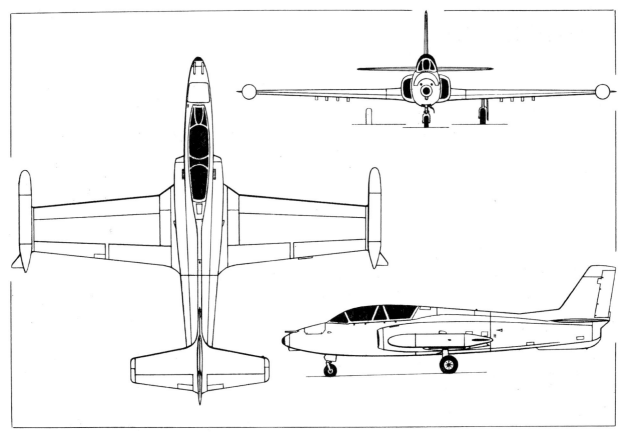

SOKO G2-A Galeb. *(Pilot Press)*

focal length of 178 mm (7 in) and 125-exposure magazine, can be fitted in fuselage, under rear cockpit floor. Flares can be carried on the underwing bomb racks for night photography. Target towing hook under centre fuselage.

AVIONICS AND EQUIPMENT (G-2A-E): Full IFR instrumentation. Electronique Aérospatiale (EAS) Type TVU-740 VHF/UHF com radio transceiver. Marconi AD 370B radio compass, EAS RNA-720 VOR/LOC and ILS, Iskra 75R4 marker beacon receiver, and intercom. Vinten

Type 360/140A camera with 3 in automatic exposure-control lens. Otherwise as G2-A.

ARMAMENT: All production aircraft have two 0.50 in machine-guns in nose (with 80 rds/gun); and underwing pylons for two 50 kg or 100 kg bombs and four 57 mm rockets or two 127 mm rockets; or clusters of small bombs and expendable bomblet containers of up to 150 kg (330 lb) weight (300 kg; 660 lb total).

DIMENSIONS, EXTERNAL:	
Wing span	10.47 m (34 ft 4½ in)
Wing span over tip-tanks	11.62 m (38 ft 1½ in)
Length overall	10.34 m (33 ft 11 in)
Height overall	3.28 m (10 ft 9 in)
Wheel track	3.89 m (12 ft 9 in)
Wheelbase	3.59 m (11 ft 9½ in)
AREA:	
Wings, gross	19.43 m² (209.14 sq ft)
WEIGHTS:	
Weight empty, equipped	2,620 kg (5,775 lb)
Max T-O weight, strike version	4,300 kg (9,480 lb)
PERFORMANCE (at normal T-O weight):	
Max level speed at S/L	408 knots (756 km/h; 470 mph)
Max level speed at 6,200 m (20,350 ft)	438 knots (812 km/h; 505 mph)
Max cruising speed at 6,000 m (19,685 ft)	394 knots (730 km/h; 453 mph)

Stalling speed:	
flaps and airbrakes down	85 knots (158 km/h; 98 mph)
flaps and airbrakes up	97 knots (180 km/h; 112 mph)
Max rate of climb at S/L	1,370 m (4,500 ft)/min
Time to 3,000 m (9,840 ft)	2 min 24 s
Time to 6,000 m (19,685 ft)	5 min 30 s
Time to 9,000 m (29,520 ft)	10 min 12 s
Service ceiling	12,000 m (39,375 ft)
T-O run on grass	490 m (1,610 ft)
T-O to 15 m (50 ft)	640 m (2,100 ft)
Landing from 15 m (50 ft)	710 m (2,330 ft)
Landing run on grass	400 m (1,310 ft)
Max range at 9,000 m (29,520 ft), with tip-tanks full	669 nm (1,240 km; 770 miles)
Max endurance at 7,000 m (23,000 ft)	2 h 30 min
Design g limits	+ 8/ − 4

SOKO G-4 Super Galeb jet training and light attack aircraft.

SOKO G-4 Super Galeb (Seagull)

This light strike and training aircraft was designed to replace the earlier G2-A Galeb and Lockheed T-33 in basic and advanced training units of the Yugoslav Air Force. It is a completely new design, inheriting little but its name and role from the original Galeb. It is, however, powered by a higher-rated version of the latter's Rolls-Royce Viper turbojet.

The first of two Super Galeb prototypes flew for the first time on 17 July 1978. The second was flown on 18 December 1979, followed by the first of several pre-production aircraft on 17 December 1980. The production Super Galeb, for which the Yugoslav Air Force has placed a substantial order, differs from the pre-production model in having an all-moving tailplane with considerable anhedral, instead of the original conventional horizontal tail surfaces with elevators and no anhedral. A substantial proportion of the quantity ordered initially had been delivered by 1987.

TYPE: Two-seat basic trainer and light strike aircraft.

WINGS: Cantilever low-wing monoplane. No dihedral. Sweepback at quarter-chord 22°; leading-edge sweep increased near wing roots. Shallow boundary layer fence on upper surface of each wing, forward of inboard end of aileron. Entire trailing edge made up of conventional ailerons and flaps. Ailerons have artificial feel. No slats or tabs.

FUSELAGE: Semi-monocoque structure, with air intake trunk blended into each side. Rear portion, complete with tail surfaces, detachable for access to engine. Door-type airbrake under rear fuselage.

TAIL UNIT: Conventional cantilever structure, with all surfaces sweptback. All-moving horizontal surfaces have 10° anhedral, and artificial feel. Dorsal fin. Ground-adjustable tab on rudder. Two ventral strakes under jetpipe.

LANDING GEAR: Retractable tricycle type, with single wheel on each unit. Steerable nose unit optional. Mainwheels fitted with Dunlop tyres size 615 × 225-10 and hydraulic brakes. Nosewheel has Dunlop tyre size 6.50-5.5 TC.

Brake parachute container at base of rudder. Provision for attaching two assisted take-off rockets under centre-fuselage.

SOKO G-4 Super Galeb. *(Pilot Press)*

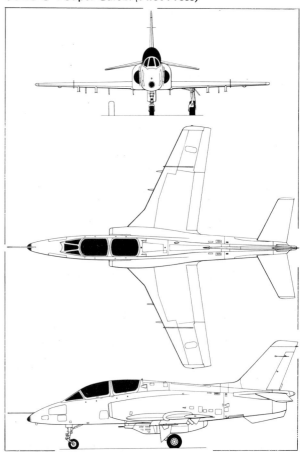

POWERPLANT: One Rolls-Royce Viper Mk 632 turbojet engine, rated at 17.8 kN (4,000 lb st). Fuel in three flexible bag tanks in centre fuselage and an integral tank between the spars of each inner wing. Total internal fuel capacity 1,720 litres (454.5 US gallons; 378.5 Imp gallons). Provision for two underwing auxiliary tanks, on inboard pylons, total capacity 625 litres (165 US gallons; 137.5 Imp gallons). Max fuel capacity 2,345 litres (620 US gallons; 516 Imp gallons).

ACCOMMODATION: Crew of two in tandem on Martin-Baker zero-height/90 knot Mk J8 or zero/zero Mk J10 ejection seats. Rear seat raised by 25 cm (10 in) to give occupant forward view over front seat occupant. Cockpit pressurised.

AVIONICS AND EQUIPMENT: Dual controls and full blind-flying instrumentation in each cockpit. Standard nav/com equipment comprises EAS type ER4.671D or VHF RC E163 Kondor VHF com radio, GEC Avionics AD 370B or Iskra VARK-1 radio compass, Collins VIR-30 VOR/ILS, Iskra 75R4 VOR marker beacon receiver, Collins DME 40 and TRT AHV-6 radio altimeter. Optional UHF and V/UHF com, gyro platform and other equipment to customer's specification.

ARMAMENT AND OPERATIONAL EQUIPMENT: Removable ventral gun pod containing 23 mm GSh-23L twin-barrel rapid-fire cannon with 200 rds. Two attachments under each wing, with capacity of 500 kg inboard and 350 kg outboard. Total weapon load capacity, with centreline gun pod, 1,950 kg (4,300 lb). In addition to standard high-explosive bombs and napalm pods, typical Yugoslav stores include S-8-16 cluster bombs, each with eight 16 kg fragmentation munitions; KPT-150 expendable containers, each with up to 40 anti-personnel or 54 anti-tank bomblets; L-57-16MD pods, each with sixteen 57 mm rockets; L-128-04 pods, each with four 128 mm rockets; adaptors for twin 5 in HVAR rockets, single 57 mm VRZ-57 training rockets; SN-3-050 triple carriers for 50 kg bombs; SN-3-100 triple carriers for 100 kg bombs; SAM Z-80 towed target system; and auxiliary fuel tanks on the inboard attachments. Ferranti D282 gyro gunsight standard. Other types of fire control system optional. A photo reconnaissance/infra-red linescan pod and night illumination system have been under development.

DIMENSIONS, EXTERNAL:

Wing span	9.88 m (32 ft 5 in)
Length overall	11.86 m (38 ft 11 in)
Height overall	4.28 m (14 ft 0½ in)
Wheel track	3.49 m (11 ft 5½ in)
Wheelbase	4.15 m (13 ft 7½ in)

AREA:

Wings, gross	19.5 m² (209.9 sq ft)

WEIGHTS:

Weight empty, equipped	3,250 kg (7,165 lb)
T-O weight, training mission	4,760 kg (10,495 lb)
T-O weight, normal combat mission, with 1,350 kg (2,975 lb) of weapons	6,110 kg (13,470 lb)
Max T-O weight, combat overload	6,330 kg (13,955 lb)

PERFORMANCE (at AUW of 4,760 kg; 10,495 lb, except where indicated):

Never-exceed speed	Mach 0.866
Max level speed at 6,000 m (19,680 ft)	491 knots (910 km/h; 565 mph)
Max rate of climb at S/L	1,800 m (5,905 ft)/min
Time to 8,000 m (26,240 ft)	6 min
Absolute ceiling	15,000 m (49,200 ft)
T-O run	532 m (1,745 ft)
T-O to 15 m (50 ft)	850 m (2,790 ft)
Landing from 15 m (50 ft) at landing weight of 3,800 kg (8,375 lb)	750 m (2,460 ft)
Landing run at above landing weight	550 m (1,805 ft)

Combat radius, with gun pack and full internal fuel, 10% reserves:
with four BL755 cluster bombs:

lo-lo-lo	208 nm (386 km; 240 miles)
hi-lo-hi	260 nm (483 km; 300 miles)

with two BL755 and two aux fuel tanks:

lo-lo-lo	321 nm (595 km; 370 miles)
hi-lo-hi	438 nm (812 km; 504 miles)
Range at 11,000 m (36,000 ft), with two aux fuel tanks, 10% reserves	1,420 nm (2,630 km; 1,635 miles)
Endurance at 11,000 m (36,000 ft), with two aux fuel tanks	4 h 20 min
g limits	+ 8/ − 4.2

SOKO J-1/RJ-1 Jastreb (Hawk)

The basic J-1 Jastreb is a single-seat light-attack version of the G2-A Galeb, developed and produced for service with the Yugoslav Air Force. An export version was made available, but the only certain overseas operator is the Zambian Air Force, which received four Jastrebs in early 1971.

In the J-1 Jastreb, the front cockpit of the G2-A Galeb trainer was retained, a metal fairing replacing the rear canopy. The engine is the more powerful Rolls-Royce Bristol Viper 531. Other changes included installation of improved day and night reconnaissance equipment, navigation and communications equipment, and self-contained engine starting. In other respects the airframe and powerplant remained essentially unchanged except for some local strengthening and the provision of strongpoints for heavier underwing stores.

Versions built were:

J-1. Standard attack version for Yugoslav Air Force.

J-1-E. Export attack version with updated equipment. Used by Zambia. Reports have suggested that Libya may operate this model also.

RJ-1. Tactical reconnaissance version for Yugoslav Air Force. Armament optional.

RJ-1-E. Export reconnaissance version with updated equipment. Used by Zambia.

The details given for the G2-A Galeb apply equally to the J-1, J-1-E, RJ-1 and RJ-1-E Jastreb, with the following exceptions:

TYPE: Single-seat light-attack and tactical reconnaissance aircraft.

POWERPLANT: One Rolls-Royce Viper 531 turbojet engine, rated at 13.32 kN (3,000 lb st). Capacity of each wingtip tank 220 kg (485 lb). Provision for attaching two 4.44 kN (1,000 lb st) JATO rockets under fuselage for use at take-off or in flight.

ACCOMMODATION: Pilot only, on HSA (Folland) Type 1-B fully-automatic lightweight ejection seat.

SOKO J-1 Jastreb, seen at the Paris Salon with dummy rocket launchers and other weapons. *(Aviation Picture Library)*

AVIONICS AND EQUIPMENT (J-1 and RJ-1): Full IFR instrumentation. Standard Telephones & Cables STR-9Z1 VHF com transceiver and Marconi AD 370B radio compass. The fuselage camera of the RJ-1 is supplemented by two further cameras in nose of tip-tanks, which are also available for the J-1 and J-1-E attack versions. An aerial target can be towed from a hook under the centre fuselage. Brake parachute housed in fairing above jet nozzle.

AVIONICS AND EQUIPMENT (J-1-E and RJ-1-E): Nav/com equipment same as for G-2A-E Galeb export version. Photo-reconnaissance equipment of RJ-1-E consists of a daylight reconnaissance system comprising two Vinten 360/140A cameras with 3 in AEC lenses in nose of tip-tanks (also available on J-1-E attack version), and a third camera of the same type in the fuselage, with interchangeable lens units; and a night-reconnaissance system comprising one Vinten 1025/527 camera at the fuselage station.

ARMAMENT (J-1 and J-1-E): Three 0.50 in Colt-Browning machine-guns in nose (with 135 rds/gun). Total of eight underwing weapon attachments. Two inboard attachments can carry two bombs of up to 250 kg each, two clusters of small bombs, two 200 litre napalm tanks, two pods each with twelve or sixteen 57 mm or four 128 mm rockets, two multiple carriers each with three 50 kg bombs, two bomblet containers, or two 45 kg photo flares. Other attachments can each carry a 127 mm rocket. Semi-automatic gyro gunsight and camera gun standard.

ARMAMENT (RJ-1 and RJ-1-E): Four underwing attachments, intended basically for carrying flash bombs for night photography, can be used also for carrying high-explosive or other types of bombs. The inboard pylons can each carry a single bomb of up to 250 kg, the outboard pylons up to 150 kg. No rocket armament. Otherwise same as for J-1 and J-1-E.

DIMENSIONS, EXTERNAL: As for Galeb, except:	
Wing span over tip-tanks	11.68 m (38 ft 4 in)
Length overall	10.88 m (35 ft 8½ in)
Height overall	3.64 m (11 ft 11½ in)
Wheelbase	3.61 m (11 ft 10 in)
AREA: As for Galeb	
WEIGHTS:	
Weight empty, equipped	2,820 kg (6,217 lb)
Max T-O weight	5,100 kg (11,243 lb)
PERFORMANCE (T-O and landing runs on concrete):	
Max level speed at 6,000 m (19,680 ft) at AUW of 3,968 kg (8,748 lb)	442 knots (820 km/h; 510 mph)
Max cruising speed at 5,000 m (16,400 ft), at AUW of 3,968 kg (8,748 lb)	399 knots (740 km/h; 460 mph)
Stalling speed, wheels down:	
flaps and airbrakes down	82 knots (152 km/h; 95 mph)
flaps and airbrakes up	94 knots (174 km/h; 108 mph)
Max rate of climb at S/L, at AUW of 3,968 kg (8,748 lb)	1,260 m (4,135 ft)/min
Service ceiling at AUW of 3,968 kg (8,748 lb)	12,000 m (39,375 ft)
T-O run at AUW of 3,968 kg (8,748 lb)	700 m (2,300 ft)
T-O run, rocket-assisted, at max T-O weight	404 m (1,325 ft)
T-O to 15 m (50 ft) at AUW of 3,968 kg (8,748 lb)	960 m (3,150 ft)
T-O to 15 m (50 ft), rocket-assisted, at max T-O weight	593 m (1,945 ft)
Landing from 15 m (50 ft)	1,100 m (3,610 ft)
Landing run	600 m (1,970 ft)
Max range at 9,000 m (29,520 ft), with tip-tanks full	820 nm (1,520 km; 945 miles)

NOVI AVION

Known as the Novi Avion at this stage, a multi-role fighter to replace the MiG-21 in the Yugoslav Air Force has been under development for several years. No details are available, but it can be assumed that the development programme is directed by the Vazduhoplovno Tehnicki Institut in Zarkovo, near Belgrade, which was responsible for the Yugoslav input to the international J-22 Orao attack aircraft programme. Production will almost certainly be undertaken by Soko.

It is understood that discussions concerning collaborative airframe development have taken place with various European and US manufacturers, and that engine proposals from Rolls-Royce, General Electric and Pratt & Whitney are being studied.

INDEX

Numerals in *italics* refer to captions